ENZYMES

ENZYMES

by

MALCOLM DIXON

Sc.D., F.R.S.

Reader in Enzyme Biochemistry in the University of Cambridge
Fellow of King's College, Cambridge

and

EDWIN C. WEBB

M.A., Ph.D.

Professor of Biochemistry in the University of Queensland

SECOND EDITION

LONGMAN

LONGMAN GROUP LIMITED
London
*Associated companies, branches and representatives
throughout the world*

First edition 1958
Seventh impression 1962
Second edition (*completely revised*) 1964
New impression 1971

ISBN 0 582 46214 2

PRINTED IN GREAT BRITAIN BY
WILLIAM CLOWES AND SONS, LIMITED
LONDON, BECCLES AND COLCHESTER

'It is, I think, difficult to exaggerate the importance to biology, and I venture to say to chemistry no less, of extended studies of enzymes and their action'—F. G. HOPKINS (Presidential Address to the Royal Society, 1932).

PREFACE

IN THE FIVE years since the first edition of this book was written a good deal has happened in the field of enzymology. Over 170 new enzymes have been recognized, and there have been considerable advances in many parts of the subject in other ways. Perhaps the major event has been the publication of the Report of the Commission on Enzymes of the International Union of Biochemistry, which has done much to bring order into a previously confused nomenclature. We have followed the Commission's recommendations throughout this edition, and this alone has involved a considerable amount of revision.

Although a great deal of new material has been incorporated, we have endeavoured to retain the character of the book and to avoid any great increase in size. We still feel that a book of this size, dealing with the general principles of the subject at the research level, meets a real need. We are grateful to those who have reviewed the first edition for their kind remarks, and also for a number of valuable suggestions, which we have adopted as far as possible in this edition. It is interesting that the reviewers, almost without exception, have felt that our treatment of their own specialized branches of the subject has been insufficient, which encourages us to think that we have maintained a proper balance between the various aspects of enzymology. To treat all aspects adequately would require a many-volumed work. For those who seek such a detailed treatment, the volumes of the second edition of *The Enzymes*, now in course of publication under the editorship of Drs. Boyer, Lardy and Myrbäck, will be available.

As before, we are grateful to all those who have helped us by making available reprints, journals, photographs and manuscripts in advance of publication, as well as to authors, editors and publishers of journals for permission to reproduce figures. We are again indebted to the staff of our publishers and printers for their care and helpfulness. Various members of the Webb family have once more assisted with the routine work involved, and Miss Miriam Armstrong gave invaluable help with the preparation of the references for the printer.

We hope that many research workers and other biochemists will find this new edition helpful.

Sub-Department of Enzyme Biochemistry,   MALCOLM DIXON
Department of Biochemistry,   EDWIN C. WEBB
University of Cambridge.

16 *August* 1962.

CONTENTS

DETAILED LIST OF CONTENTS

I

INTRODUCTION

THE STUDY OF enzymes is a subject which has a special interest, because it lies just on the borderline where the biological and the physical sciences meet. On the one hand, enzymes are of supreme importance in biology. Life depends on a complex network of chemical reactions brought about by specific enzymes, and any modification of the enzyme pattern may have far-reaching consequences for the living organism. On the other hand, enzymes, as catalysts, are receiving increasing attention from physical chemists. The mechanism of action of enzymes is in itself one of the most fascinating fields of scientific investigation being pursued at the present time.

Enzymology has become a large and rapidly developing subject, with ramifications in many directions and close connections with many sciences, especially biochemistry, physical chemistry, bacteriology and microbiology, genetics, botany and agriculture, pharmacology and toxicology, pathology, physiology, medicine, and chemical engineering. It has in addition important practical applications to activities as diverse as brewing and industrial fermentations, pest control, and chemical warfare.

Many research workers in various parts of the world are now devoting their attention to such problems, institutes specifically for enzyme studies have been established, several journals of enzymology exist and the literature of the subject has now become very large.

It is sometimes difficult to realize that enzymology is a subject of comparatively recent growth; the beginnings of the subject can be traced back to the early nineteenth century, but the great developments have come during the last forty years. Although the phenomena of fermentation and digestion had long been known, what was probably the first clear recognition of an enzyme was made by PAYEN and PERSOZ (2060) in 1833, when they found that an alcohol precipitate of malt extract contained a thermolabile substance which converted starch into sugar. This substance, which we should now call amylase, was named by them 'diastase', from διάστασις (separation), because of its power of separating soluble dextrin from the insoluble envelopes of the starch grains. The name diastase later came to be used as a general term for enzymes. Ultimately DUCLAUX proposed in 1898 the use of the last three letters of this name as a suffix '-ase' to be attached to a root indicating the nature of the substance on which the enzyme acts. This provided a basis for a systematic nomenclature of enzymes, which is still in use; a few names ending in '-in' had meanwhile been given to digestive enzymes, and these have persisted. As the number of known enzymes has increased, it has become necessary to indicate in the name not only the nature of the substance acted on, but also the nature of the reaction, although the suffix '-ase' has been retained, e.g. lactate dehydrogenase. The question of systematic nomenclature is discussed further in Chapter V.

During the early days of the discovery of enzymes, many workers had seen a parallelism between their action and that of yeast in fermentation. The name 'ferment' was consequently used for enzymes. During the second half of the nineteenth century, much controversy took place around the views of LIEBIG, who held that fermentation and similar processes were due to the action of chemical substances, and of PASTEUR, who held that fermentation was inseparable from living cells. The names 'unorganized ferments' and 'organized ferments' were used to denote what we should now call extracted enzymes and micro-organisms respectively. In order to avoid these unsatisfactory names, W. KÜHNE (1485) introduced the name 'enzyme' in 1878. As there have been some misconceptions as to the reasons for suggesting this name, we quote Kühne's statement (Bayliss's translation): 'This is not intended to imply any particular hypothesis, but it merely states that ἐν ζύμῃ (in yeast) something occurs that exerts this or that activity, which is considered to belong to the class called fermentative. The name is not, however, intended to be limited to the invertin of yeast, but it is intended to imply that more complex organisms, from which the enzymes pepsin, trypsin, etc., can be obtained, are not so fundamentally different from the unicellular organisms as some people would have us believe.' Kühne's intention was to denote something which was in yeast, in contrast to the yeast itself.

The Pasteur–Liebig controversy came to an end when BUCHNER succeeded in obtaining the fermentation system from yeast in a cell-free extract, but the name 'ferment' for enzymes has persisted in Germany almost up to the present time.

Towards the end of the nineteenth century, increasing knowledge of the structural organic chemistry of substances of biological interest made it possible to study the range of action or 'specificity' of enzymes. It is to EMIL FISCHER (733) that we owe the idea of enzyme specificity and of the close steric relationship between enzyme and substrate. On the basis of his observations with substrates of known structure, Fischer developed his famous 'lock and key' analogy for enzyme–substrate interaction. Specificity has become a very important branch of enzyme studies and Chapter VI is devoted to it. A necessary consequence of the close fit between enzyme and substrate is that each enzyme acts on a very limited range of substrates; this in turn implies the existence of a large number of different enzymes. Adequate studies of enzyme specificity are dependent on the separation of the individual enzymes.

The serious purification of enzymes did not begin until after 1920. Most of the early purifications were carried out by WILLSTÄTTER and his colleagues between 1922 and 1928 (see Table XX of *979*). A few purifications were carried out by other workers during this period, e.g. of xanthine oxidase by DIXON and KODAMA (*627*), but in no case was complete purity attained. The next important development was the preparation of an enzyme in crystalline form. The first enzyme to be crystallized was urease (SUMNER, 1926, *2564*), although these first crystals were very far from pure. This work was soon followed by the classical isolation of crystalline proteolytic enzymes by NORTHROP and his colleagues (*1996*). Even twenty-five years ago, however, the number of purified enzymes was very small, whereas now the number obtained pure and crystalline exceeds one hundred and upwards of six hundred have been purified to a greater or less extent.

The early work on enzyme purification met with a good deal of criticism on the ground that it was 'unphysiological' to separate enzymes from cells and that only work on undamaged cells was valuable. Later, when the first protein crystals of high enzymatic activity had been obtained there was considerable scepticism towards the claim that the enzymes themselves had been crystallized; it was suggested that the enzyme was present as a mere impurity, adsorbed on crystals of an inert protein. Northrop, however, produced conclusive evidence that his crystals were crystals of the enzymes themselves, and all the enzymes which have since been isolated in the pure state have proved to be proteins. Thus the conception of an enzyme has undergone a development, first from a vague influence or property in certain preparations to definite chemical substances, and finally to specific proteins.

The main interest during the early days of the subject was centred on the enzymes of digestion and fermentation; it was only much later that the importance of the intracellular enzymes was recognized. In fact the serious purification of intracellular enzymes did not begin until 1937, despite the fact that comparatively few enzymes occur naturally outside living cells. Since that date the emphasis has entirely changed, and the enormous increase in the number of known enzymes has been largely due to the discovery of new intracellular enzymes. This great increase in the knowledge of the enzymes of living matter has brought in its train a greatly increased understanding of the mechanism of many of the most fundamental vital processes, especially of the metabolic processes which lead to the production and utilization of energy, on which life depends. Photosynthesis, respiration and biological oxidations, fermentations, the synthesis of the many organic compounds required for growth, the performance of mechanical or osmotic work, are among the processes on which a flood of light has been thrown by the isolation and study of the enzymes responsible.

The availability of enzymes in the pure state has in recent years made possible the study of their molecular size and shape by physical methods, and also of the chemical structure of the enzyme protein. The recent development of methods for determining the arrangement of the amino-acids in a peptide chain has given important results in the enzyme field, and special methods have been developed for the study of the chemical structure of the active centres of enzymes. These structural studies are discussed in Chapter X.

Recent work has thrown a flood of light on the mechanism of the biosynthesis of enzymes and the means by which their chemical structure is determined by the genetic material of the chromosomes, and has brought out the importance of biological control through these mechanisms. This subject is dealt with in Chapter XI.

Enzyme kinetics, which has undergone great development since the classical work of HENRI and MICHAELIS early in the century, has now reached an advanced stage (as will be seen from the length of Chapter IV) and is being actively pursued, with the object of elucidating the mode of catalysis by enzymes. The mechanism of enzyme catalysis is also being studied by more direct methods, including especially the use of isotopes, and is discussed in Chapter VII.

The purification of enzymes also led to a greatly increased realization of their high specificity, which is quite unparalleled in other catalysts, and is one of the most fundamental and important properties of enzymes. This property makes possible the existence of systems composed of many enzymes, which bring about chains of reactions forming the various lines of metabolism; a number of these systems are set out in tables in Chapter XII, with details of the enzymes involved.

Considerable progress has been made in the study of the properties and functions of enzymes. However, an enormous amount of work remains to be done; many important enzymes remain to be discovered, and many of whose existence we already have indications have hardly been studied at all as such. In addition, we have drawn attention at various points in the book to a number of promising fields which are almost untouched.

We believe that the subject has now reached a very interesting stage, when a rich harvest may be expected in the near future from the very large amount of patient investigation which has been done over the past years. In particular, many different lines of study are converging to give the beginnings of a picture of the intimate mechanism of enzyme action, which is one of the most fascinating problems of the present time.

A number of special terms have come into general use by enzymologists, and as they will be used frequently throughout the book it may be useful if we explain here the meaning which we attach to them. Such terms are 'enzyme', 'substrate', 'activation', 'active centre', 'coenzyme', 'inhibitor'.

We have already mentioned the historical origin of the term 'enzyme'. Since the introduction of the name, there has developed a clearer idea of what it denotes, although an exact definition is not altogether an easy matter. Various forms of words have been proposed, and perhaps the most satisfactory definition is as follows: 'A protein with catalytic properties due to its power of specific activation'. This description raises a number of debatable points, which we will now briefly discuss. The inclusion of the word 'protein' in the definition, which rules out such non-enzymatic catalysts as glutathione and other coenzymes, is a generalization from the fact that all the enzymes which have been obtained in the pure state have proved to be proteins, and enzymes generally, whether isolated or not, possess properties characteristic of proteins, e.g. thermolability. Various unfounded claims have been made in the past from time to time that protein-free enzymes had been prepared, but these were in fact due to the use of very dilute solutions of highly active enzymes, which on concentration and isolation were found to be proteins. The generally accepted concept of an enzyme is now so intimately connected with its protein nature that, even if a non-protein macromolecular biological catalyst were to be discovered, there would be much to be said for not applying the name 'enzyme' to it. The existence of such catalysts is in any case now most unlikely, since all the enzymes so far purified have been isolated by following up catalytic activities through a series of fractionations, without any prior knowledge of the chemical nature of the substances responsible.

The second half of the definition rules out such non-enzymatic proteins as cytochrome c, which indeed is a catalytic protein, but by virtue of its action as a carrier and not by activating any other substance. Such proteins may be compared with other coenzymes which function as biological catalysts only when themselves activated by specific enzymes.

The substance on which an enzyme acts, and which is activated by the enzyme, is termed the 'substrate' of the enzyme. This term, originally introduced by German workers, has been in common use for over fifty years, and is to be preferred to the more general word 'reactant' when enzymatic reactions are concerned.

'Activation' is a concept not restricted to enzymology. It is frequently used without any precise implication as to mechanism, merely to denote that the reactant molecule is made more reactive. The term is used by physical chemists in two rather different senses. In terms of the Arrhenius theory of reaction rates, molecules possessing more than a certain amount of kinetic energy are said to be activated, whereas in terms of the more modern theory of absolute reaction rates, discussed in Chapter IV, section (D), activation takes place by the formation of a specific 'activated complex' which involves changes of both kinetic and potential energy. In enzyme reactions, activation of the substrate occurs by the formation of an 'enzyme–substrate complex', and the process has much in common with the formation of the activated complex of the absolute rate theory. The analogy must not be pressed too far; the enzyme–substrate complex is a less transient entity than the activated complex, and in fact it goes through the form of activated complexes in its formation and breakdown. The question is discussed in more detail later.

The facts of specificity (see Chapter VI) show that the substrate combines with a particular part or site in the enzyme, and this is known as the 'active centre'. This active centre, at which the whole process of activation and reaction occurs, is closely adapted to fit the particular substrate of the enzyme. It was first thought that there were many active centres in each molecule of enzyme, but it has now become clear that in the majority of cases only one or two active centres per molecule are present. The structure of enzymes is discussed in Chapter X.

In many cases, but by no means all, an additional substance besides the enzyme and substrate is required in order that the reaction may proceed. Such 'coenzymes' are a part of the catalytic mechanism, and are found unchanged at the end of the reaction. They are thus distinguished from substrates. It should be noted, however, that a substance may behave as a coenzyme for a system of two enzymes, but as a substrate for each of the component enzymes. Thus the substances known as NAD and NADP act as coenzymes in linked-dehydrogenase systems and as true substrates for the individual dehydrogenases. It has often happened that a substance which appeared to be a coenzyme for a reaction catalysed by a crude enzyme preparation is seen on resolution of the system into two component enzymes to be a substrate of each. Several examples are given in Chapter IX.

It is frequently found that the addition of substances which do not take part in the reaction diminishes its velocity. These substances are usually known as 'inhibitors', though the term is not usually applied to substances like strong acids which merely destroy the enzyme protein. Many of these inhibitors act specifically as poisons of particular enzymes, and in some cases in extremely small concentrations. The study of such inhibitors has contributed materially to our knowledge of enzymes, as well as being of importance in toxicology and pharmacology. They are discussed at length in Chapter VIII.

Finally, it must never be forgotten that enzymes derive their greatest importance from the fact that life itself is intimately bound up with enzyme catalysis. Of necessity, during the development of the subject attention has hitherto been focused on the study of isolated enzymes. Only comparatively recently has it been possible to develop the biological side of the subject, namely the study of enzymes and enzyme systems in relation to the living cell. We conclude the book with a chapter on a number of biological aspects of enzymology, an increasingly important part of the subject.

II

ENZYME TECHNIQUES

THE SPECIAL TECHNIQUES used in the isolation of enzymes are dealt with in the following chapter; here we are concerned with those used in the study of enzymes and enzyme action.

The characteristic property of enzymes is their power of catalysing certain definite chemical reactions. Except for a few enzymes which can be detected by direct spectroscopic or other observations, the presence of enzymes is detected by the occurrence of the specific reactions which they catalyse, and the amount present is estimated from the reaction velocity. The measurement of the reaction velocity is therefore the most essential part of the technique of investigations on enzymes.

MEASUREMENT OF VELOCITY

The progress curves of most enzyme reactions are of the general form shown in Fig. II.1, in which the velocity falls with time. Various causes may contribute to this falling off. For instance, the products of the reaction may inhibit the enzyme, the degree of saturation of the enzyme with substrate may fall because of the fall in substrate concentration as the reaction proceeds, the reverse reaction may become more important as the concentration of products increases, the enzyme (or a coenzyme) may undergo some inactivation at the temperature or pH of the reaction owing to instability, and several of these causes may operate at the same time. For this reason the progress curves of enzyme reactions commonly do not fit the standard equations of homogeneous chemical reactions and indeed it may be a very difficult matter to derive an equation to fit the curve (see Chapter IV).

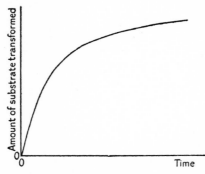

Fig. II.1. *A typical progress curve.*

A different approach is therefore usually adopted in the study of enzyme action, depending on the measurement of the *initial* velocity.

It is only at the initial point, when the various causes just mentioned have not yet had time to operate, that the conditions are accurately

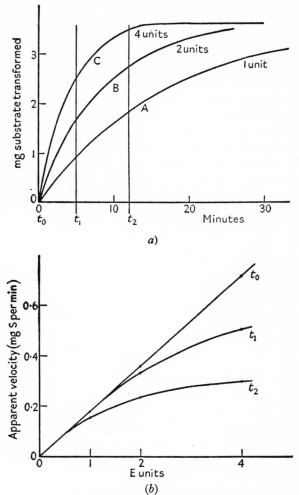

Fig. II.2. *Importance of taking initial velocities.*
(a) Progress curves with three different amounts of enzyme.
(b) Apparent velocity, derived from points on (a) at three different times, plotted against amount of enzyme.

known, and it is a sound principle in enzyme work to determine the effect on the initial velocity of varying only one factor at a time while all the others are held constant.

To obtain the initial velocity it is only necessary to determine the first part of the progress curve and to draw a tangent at the origin. The curves are usually practically straight lines as long as the amount of change does not exceed 20 per cent of the total.

The amount of substrate which has reacted in a given period of time from the start of the reaction is only a measure of the velocity so long as this limit is not exceeded. All too often in the past this limitation has been neglected and figures have been published showing merely the amount of change after a certain time. The following simple example shows that such results do not give a true picture. The progress curves in Fig. II.2 (a) might represent experiments at three different pHs, or with three different substrates, or with three different amounts of enzyme or of coenzyme; for simplicity we will suppose that they represent curves obtained with different amounts of enzyme, and that curves A, B and C were obtained with 1, 2 and 4 units of enzyme respectively. If the initial velocities at t_0 are plotted against the amount of enzyme, as in Fig. II.2 (b), a straight line is obtained, showing that the velocity is proportional to the amount of enzyme. The amount of substrate changed at time t_2, however, is far from being proportional to the amount of enzyme, and the apparent velocities, obtained by dividing these values by the time t_2, give quite a misleading result, as shown in Fig. II.2 (b).

In what follows, and in the chapter on kinetics, when velocity is mentioned, initial velocity is to be understood, unless otherwise stated.

CLASSES OF METHODS

Methods of following enzyme reactions are of two types: sampling methods and continuous methods. In the sampling methods the observations are not made on the reacting mixture itself, but on samples withdrawn at various times, so that the methods are essentially discontinuous and give a number of separate points on the progress curves. In the continuous methods observations are made on the mixture while it is reacting, and by making a large number of readings, or by automatic recording, continuous curves may be drawn.

Sampling methods usually consist of chemical estimations, either of the substrate or of the product of the reaction. If the reaction is a simple one, either of these can be used as a measure of enzyme activity; but for a two-stage reaction, in which an intermediate between substrate and product may accumulate, results from the two methods may not agree. In this case only the disappearance of substrate gives a correct measure of the first reaction.

In the special cases of hydrolysis of proteins and polysaccharides, where the substrate molecule contains many bonds of the same type which are attacked by the same enzyme, it is more usual to take the number of bonds hydrolysed as a measure of the reaction, and to use methods such as formol titration or measurement of reducing power which estimate the amount of hydrolysis in this sense.

In a sampling method at least three points are usually necessary for each determination of velocity, one at zero time, the second after a suitable time interval and the third after about twice this time. This gives a check on the linearity of the curve over the time interval chosen. It is necessary to run each sample, immediately after withdrawal, into some reagent which instantaneously stops the enzyme reaction, so that it may accurately represent the composition of the reacting mixture at the time of withdrawal. As the reagent will be highly toxic to the enzyme, great care must be taken that no traces are transferred back into the reacting mixture, for example on the tips of pipettes.

The majority of the methods used for following enzyme reactions are of the continuous type and these are usually preferred when practicable. With these methods all that is necessary is to take a sufficient number of readings to make sure that a straight line has been obtained, unless a continuously recording instrument is used, in which case the velocity is given by the slope of the tracing. In special cases an instrument may give readings of the velocity directly, as in the case of luciferase, where the intensity of the luminescence is directly proportional to the velocity of the enzyme reaction (*438*).

SOME PRACTICAL POINTS

A number of fairly obvious points of practical technique in work with enzymes may be mentioned here. In the interests of linearity, the conditions in the reacting mixture must be maintained as constant as possible during the observations. The reaction must be carried out in a thermostat and all the reagents must be brought to the correct temperature before the reaction is started by mixing them. Adequate buffering must be provided to prevent the pH from changing appreciably in cases where acid is produced by the reaction. If possible, it is desirable to choose conditions under which the enzyme is reasonably stable; the temperature should not be too high and the pH should be within the zone of stability of the enzyme. This may not always be possible when studying the enzyme under a wide range of conditions.

Owing to the high catalytic activity of enzymes, scrupulous care must be taken that no traces are introduced into vessels inadvertently, for example on the tips of pipettes, or as dust from dry enzyme preparations, or in traces of saliva in pipettes. In working with amylases, pipettes plugged with cotton wool at the top are essential.

The reaction rate should always be adjusted to a convenient value by altering the amount of enzyme taken, so that the readings may be properly made.

THE GENERAL HANDLING OF ENZYMES

Enzymes are relatively fragile substances, with a tendency to undergo denaturation and inactivation under unsuitable conditions. In the handling of enzymes, the first consideration must always be to avoid inactivation. The comparatively violent treatments (strong acids, high temperatures, powerful reagents, etc.) frequently used in organic chemistry are instantly fatal to enzymes, and the treatments to which they can be subjected are severely limited by their instability.

Success in dealing with enzymes depends upon the avoidance of conditions in which they are unstable. These conditions vary with different enzymes, but in general high temperatures and acid or alkaline solutions are to be avoided. It is advisable as far as possible not to expose enzymes to temperatures above body temperature, and many enzyme purifications are now carried out entirely at 0° as a matter of course. For this purpose a refrigerated bath containing dilute alcohol is much better than a cold room, not only for the comfort of the worker, but also because a vessel of liquid placed in such a bath is cooled very rapidly, since it is in direct contact with the cooling liquid, while in the cold room, being surrounded by poorly conducting air, it cools relatively slowly. For work at 0° stainless steel vessels are preferable to glass because of their high heat conductivity.

The majority of enzymes are inactivated in solutions of pH less than 5 or greater than 9, though there are exceptions to this rule. In adjusting the pH of an enzyme solution by adding acid or alkali, it is therefore important that there should not be a zone of destruction round each drop of the reagent as it goes into the solution. The reagent should be run in slowly down the side of the vessel while the solution is well stirred, preferably by a mechanical stirrer, and the addition should be made at 0° if possible.

Many enzymes are denatured at surfaces. It is therefore important to avoid the formation of froth; when transferring an enzyme solution from one vessel to another it should be poured down the side of the vessel. For the same reason stirrers which whip up the surface should not be used; the blades of the stirrer should be deeply immersed and the stem should run true. Occasionally fractionations by ammonium sulphate cause difficulties if the salt is added in the solid form, as it 'salts out' dissolved air from the solution as fine air bubbles which denature the enzyme. This difficulty is not often met with, but where it occurs it can be largely overcome by adding the salt as saturated solution.

Organic solvents, e.g. alcohol, inactivate most enzymes at room temperature, except at low concentrations. Enzyme fractionations by alcohol or acetone must therefore be done at the lowest possible temperature and care taken that the solution is not warmed by the heat produced on mixing the solvent with water. No fraction must be allowed to warm up, even by a few degrees, until the solvent is either removed or diluted to harmless concentrations.

The separation of precipitates by centrifuging has usually been found to be preferable to filtration and a refrigerated centrifuge is a highly desirable piece of equipment. In certain cases, however (e.g. with precipitates at high ammonium sulphate concentrations, where the density difference between solid and liquid phases may be too small to allow efficient centrifugation), filtration with the use of filter aids, such as paper pulp, Celite, Hyflo Supercel, etc., is to be preferred.

In many cases there is a slow inactivation of enzyme on standing, even under the most favourable conditions. It is therefore advisable when possible to carry out enzyme purifications without undue loss of time, and the whole preparation should be carried through in two or three days unless the enzyme is quite stable.

The storing of enzymes without loss of activity is sometimes a problem. When an enzyme solution can be frozen and thawed without loss of activity, it is most convenient simply to keep it in the deep-freeze, where it is usually stable for many months. Some enzymes are stabilized by high concentrations of salts and can be kept without loss for long periods as precipitated suspensions in saturated ammonium sulphate. When required, they can be centrifuged down and dissolved in water.

Drying an enzyme solution at room temperature usually causes complete inactivation, but drying in high vacuum at low temperatures from the frozen state is a valuable method, often giving an active and soluble powder which can be stored at room temperature.

Bacterial contamination of enzyme solutions usually gives no trouble while fractionations are actually proceeding, but if the solution has to be left to stand for a long time at any stage, it is necessary to take suitable precautions.

THE STUDY OF AN ENZYME

The thorough study of an enzyme involves the investigation of a number of characteristic properties. The following summary may give some idea of what is involved, but it should be understood that it is very rare indeed to find an enzyme on which more than a small part of this programme has been carried out.

Protein properties: sedimentation and diffusion constants; molecular weight; shape (axial ratio) of the molecule; titration curve; isoelectric point; electrophoretic mobility; degree of hydration; stability towards pH, heat, oxidation and radiations; dissociation into smaller units; absorption spectrum, etc.

Structure: aminoacid composition; number of peptide chains; aminoacid sequence; presence of a prosthetic group or special group or metal atom; number of prosthetic groups per molecule, their nature and mode of attachment; number of –SH groups and whether essential for activity; effect of chemical reagents.

Enzyme properties: nature of the reaction; whether a coenzyme is involved, its nature and mode of action; specificity for substrate; nature of chemical structure required in the substrate in order to combine with the enzyme and in order to react; stereochemical specificity; if the reaction is reversible, specificity in the reverse reaction; specificity towards inhibitors.

Active centre: how many per molecule; their chemical structure; effect on substrate of combination with active centre; mechanism of reaction, studied by isotopic and other methods; mode of action of prosthetic group, if any.

Thermodynamics: reversibility and equilibrium constant of the enzyme reaction; temperature coefficient; heats, free energies and entropies of enzyme–substrate combination, of activation of enzyme–substrate complex, of conversion of this into enzyme–product complex, and of dissociation of this into free enzyme and product; balance sheet by comparison of these with the corresponding quantities of the overall reaction; affinity of the enzyme for its substrate; the Michaelis constant; effect of pH on affinity (which may give information about the nature of the substrate-binding groups); affinities for inhibitors, inhibitor constants and the effect of pH on them; competition of inhibitors with substrate.

Kinetics: the specific activity; the molecular activity; absolute activities per active centre; measurement of the velocity constants of combination with substrate, of dissociation of the substrate from the complex, of dissociation of the product, and of the reaction; effect of any activators; effect of various ions at different pHs.

Biological properties: significance of the enzyme in metabolic reactions; coupling with other enzymes to produce biological reactions; occurrence and distribution among different species and different tissues; intracellular localization; formation of the enzyme from precursors; adaptive formation; genetics of the enzyme, effects of gene mutations; existence of isoenzymes; effects of deficiency of the enzyme; biological effects of specific poisoning of the enzyme; immunological behaviour; anti-enzymes.

Most of the above-mentioned enzyme properties are dealt with separately in later chapters, but it may be useful here to make some comments on the technique of determination of two kinds of basic quantities, related respectively to enzyme velocity and enzyme affinity.

THE SPECIFIC AND MOLECULAR ACTIVITIES

It is convenient to define some quantity which expresses the rate of reaction which can be produced by a given amount of an enzyme preparation. This has been done in a great many different ways in the past. In other fields it is usual to denote the amount of a quantity per unit weight by the adjective 'specific' and the amount per molecule by the adjective 'molecular'. This principle can be applied to enzyme activity.

The specific activity has been expressed in various ways. It has been given (a) in arbitrarily defined enzyme units per mg (the enzyme unit being related to the decomposition of a certain amount of substrate, or formation of a certain amount of product, in a certain time), or (b) in Q notation (see below), or (c) in terms of the velocity constant of the reaction per mg of enzyme, or (d) as μmoles of substrate reacting per min per mg of enzyme, or (e) as μmoles of substrate reacting per min per 100,000 g of enzyme.

(a) Units/mg' is the simplest and also the least informative method; the units are usually quite arbitrary and different for each enzyme, so that it is difficult to get an idea of the activity of the enzyme in relation to other enzymes. It is not uncommon for several different units to be in use for the same enzyme by different workers. In a few cases special names have been used for the specific activity, e.g. the P.Z. (Purpurogallinzahl) for peroxidases. This represents the number of units per mg, where the unit is the amount of enzyme which forms 1 mg of purpurogallin from pyrogallol in 5 min at 20° under certain conditions.

(b) The Q notation derives from manometric technique. $-Q_s$ is defined as the number of μl (at N.T.P.) of the substrate S used up per hr per mg of enzyme. Strictly speaking, the Q_s values of enzyme reactions are negative, since the substrate is always used up in the reaction, but the minus sign is often omitted. Originally the Q notation was used for gaseous substances (e.g. O_2 or CO_2) and has therefore been much used in work on the respiratory enzymes. Later, however, it was extended to other substrates by assuming that 1 μmole of the substance is equivalent to 22·4 μl. For enzyme reactions involving phosphate, Q_P has been much used to denote 'μl of phosphate' per hr per mg of enzyme (e.g. *135*).

(c) Occasionally the velocity constant of the reaction has been used as a measure of the specific activity. The activity of catalase (1.11.1.6), the 'kat.f.' (Katalasefähigkeit), is the velocity constant (calculated from the standard unimolecular equation) per min under certain conditions divided by the number of grams (not mg) of enzyme in the total test volume of 51 ml. Since the reaction does not in fact follow unimolecular kinetics, the method is not very satisfactory; moreover confusion has been caused by the fact that some workers have used common logarithms and others natural logarithms in calculating the velocity constants. For peptidases, the 'proteolytic coefficient' has been much used (*1215*). At low substrate concentrations the reaction follows a unimolecular course, and the proteolytic coefficient with a particular substrate is the unimolecular velocity constant under specified conditions divided by the enzyme concentration. The 'proteolytic quotient', which is the ratio of the proteolytic coefficients obtained with two different substrates, has been used as an indication of enzymatic homogeneity.

(d) 'μmoles per min per mg' is the basis of the definition of specific activity now adopted by international agreement (*2212*).

(e) This is a rather unsatisfactory attempt to give some estimate of the molecular activity when the molecular weight is unknown, by taking 100,000 as an average molecular weight of an enzyme. When the molecular weight is unknown it is better to use specific activity, and where it is known, the correct molecular activity.

The molecular activity has been expressed as (a) molecules of substrate reacting per min per molecule of enzyme, or (b) molecules of substrate reacting per min per active centre (which implies some method of determining the number of active centres present). The term 'turnover number' has in the past been used for both these quantities. Since this has led to some confusion it has been decided by international agreement to recommend the discontinuance of this term, and to restrict the term 'molecular activity' to (a) and to call (b) 'the catalytic centre activity'. (*2212*).

The three quantities defined by the Commission on Enzymes of the International Union of Biochemistry are all based on the idea of a standard enzyme unit; we quote from the report of the Commission (*2212*):

'One *unit* (U) of any enzyme is defined as that amount which will catalyse the transformation of 1 micromole of substrate per minute, or, where more than one bond of each substrate molecule is attacked, 1 ` micro-equivalent of the group concerned per minute, under defined conditions. The temperature should be stated, and it is suggested that where practicable it should be 25°. The other conditions, including pH and substrate concentration, should, where practicable, be optimal. Where inconvenient numbers would otherwise be involved, terms such as milli-unit (mU), kilo-unit (kU), etc., may be used.

'*Specific activity* is expressed as units of enzyme per milligram of · protein.

'*Molecular activity* is defined as units per micromole of enzyme at optimal substrate concentration, that is, as the number of molecules of substrate transformed per minute per molecule of enzyme.

'When the enzyme has a prosthetic group or catalytic centre whose concentration can be measured, the catalytic power can be expressed as *catalytic centre activity*, i.e. the number of molecules of substrate transformed per minute per catalytic centre.

'It is recommended that enzyme assays be based whenever possible upon measurements of initial rates of reaction in order to avoid complications due, for instance, to reversibility of reactions or to formation of inhibitory products. The substrate concentration should be, whenever possible, sufficient for saturation of the enzyme, so that the kinetics in the standard assay approach zero order. Where a sub-optimal concentration of substrate must be used, it is recommended that the Michaelis constant be determined so that the observed rate may be converted into that which would be obtained on saturation with substrate.

'Where two identical molecules react together, the unit will be the amount of enzyme which catalyses the transformation of 2 micromoles of substrate per minute.'

It will be noted that the unit defined above, unlike many of the earlier units, is an absolute one, by which the activities of different enzymes may be compared. It can be applied to all enzymes for which the catalysed reaction is clearly known.

The determination of the specific activity of a pure enzyme involves a measurement of the velocity of the reaction and an estimation of the amount of enzyme which produces this reaction velocity. Estimation of the amount of enzyme presents no difficulty, provided either that the enzyme is available in the pure state, so that a solution of known strength can be prepared, or that it can be estimated by spectroscopic or chemical means. If this is not possible, obviously the specific activity of the enzyme cannot be determined, though it is possible to determine the specific activity of the *preparation* as distinct from that of the pure enzyme itself. If the specific activity of the pure enzyme is known, a determination of the specific activity of the preparation, namely, the activity per unit weight of total solids, will give the purity of the preparation.

Enzyme-catalysed reactions take place in complexes of the enzyme with the reactants. The concentrations of such complexes at any moment are determined by the concentrations of the enzyme and the reactants and the affinities of the enzyme for the different reactants. The determination of enzyme affinities is therefore of fundamental importance for the study of enzyme reactions.

The equilibria between the complex and its free components could be expressed in terms of either association or dissociation constants, but it has long been the practice in enzyme kinetics to use only dissociation constants; we shall follow this practice, which has been endorsed by the Enzyme Commission.

An enzyme may combine with substances of two classes, namely those which take part in the reaction (substrates) and those which do not. Of the latter, some may be inhibitors and some may be activators. The enzyme-substrate affinity constant is obviously of special importance.

The dependence of velocity on substrate concentration is an important part of enzyme kinetics, and is dealt with at length in Chapter IV. In the great majority of cases the relationship is of the form

II.1
$$v = \frac{V}{1 + \dfrac{K_m}{s}}$$

where v is the velocity when the substrate concentration is s, V is the maximum velocity obtained when the substrate concentration is high enough to saturate the enzyme, and K_m is a constant known as the Michaelis constant of the enzyme for this substrate. K_m can be determined by a number of graphical methods which will be found set out in Chapter IV (p. 67). It is equal to the substrate concentration giving half-maximal velocity. It was long believed to be the same as the dissociation constant of the enzyme-substrate complex, but it is now clear that this is not always the case. It is therefore necessary to distinguish carefully between the two quantities, and the international recommendation is to restrict the name 'Michaelis constant' and the symbol K_m to the substrate concentration at which $v = V/2$, and to use the name 'substrate constant' and the symbol K_s for the equilibrium (dissociation) constant of the reaction $E + S = ES$. Methods for obtaining the true K_s are given in Chapter IV.

By analogy with the substrate constant, the 'inhibitor constant' K_i and the 'activator constant' K_A are the equilibrium (dissociation) constants of the reactions $E+I = EI$ and $E+A = EA$ respectively, where I and A represent an inhibitor and an activator. Methods for obtaining K_i and K_A are discussed in Chapters VIII and IX.

METHODS OF QUANTITATIVELY FOLLOWING ENZYME REACTIONS

(a) *Spectrophotometric methods*

Many substrates and products of enzyme reactions absorb light, if not in the visible region of the spectrum, in the ultraviolet region. The presence of a double bond or a ring system in the molecule usually gives rise to an absorption spectrum. Since it is unlikely that the substrate and the product of a given enzyme reaction will have identical spectra, it frequently happens that a wavelength can be found at which the conversion of one into the other is attended by a considerable change of absorption, and by measuring this change the progress of the reaction can be followed quantitatively. The advent of the Beckman spectrophotometer and similar instruments has provided what is probably the most convenient and widely applicable of all the methods of following enzyme reactions. Where it can be used, the spectrophotometric method is usually preferred to any other on account of its ease, simplicity, and sensitivity. No sampling is required, no reagents are necessary apart from the actual reactants, and the whole progress curve can be obtained with one small sample.

Frequently, where only comparative measurements are necessary, the readings of optical density changes themselves are taken as a measure of the reaction, and the enzyme unit is defined in terms of the change of optical density in a certain time. Where absolute measurements are desired, the absorption of the substrate and the product must first be determined separately at the wavelength used, and then the linear relationship between optical density and concentration readily allows the readings to be converted into amounts of substrate reacting.

In studying enzyme reactions by this method it is absolutely essential to have the cell containing the reacting mixture thermostatically controlled while in the instrument. The instruments are usually not built with such a device and it is necessary to have a jacketed cell-holder through which water can be circulated from an external thermostat.

Several instruments are now available which will record the optical density at any chosen wavelength continuously as a function of time. This not only saves trouble, but by presenting the results as a continuous progress curve rather than as a series of points it makes possible the accurate determination of initial velocity in a much shorter time. This has now become one of the most widely used methods for following enzyme reactions.

It may be useful to mention a few typical enzyme systems which have been studied by spectrophotometric methods, though in fact the number of cases in which they have been used is very large. First there are the cases in which the product absorbs but not the substrate. This will include, among others, the enzymes which catalyse the addition of groups to double bonds or the reverse reaction, e.g. phosphopyruvate hydratase (4.2.1.11) (2788), fumarate hydratase (4.2.1.2) (1743, 2148). In the case of fumarate hydratase, for example, the fumarate absorbs rather strongly at 300 mμ, owing to its double bond, but malate does not absorb at this wavelength. Xanthine oxidase (1.2.3.2) is an example of a change in a ring system; the oxidation of hypoxanthine to urate is accompanied by a large increase of absorption at 290 mμ (1284).

Next we have the large class of oxidizing enzymes in which the second reactant (hydrogen acceptor) undergoes a change in absorption on reduction by the substrate. The fact that the coenzymes NAD and NADP have an absorption band at 340 mμ in the reduced state but not in the oxidized state makes a large number of dehydrogenases accessible to the method and numerous references could be quoted. The flavoprotein enzymes in their oxidized forms absorb at 450 mμ, while the reduced forms absorb very much less at this wavelength. The very sharp bands of the reduced forms of the cytochromes in the visible region make the spectroscopic method the ideal one for studying their oxidation and reduction. Finally, the reduction of ferricyanide, or of dyes like methylene blue and indophenol blue, by oxidizing enzymes can be accurately followed by this method.

Thus practically all oxidizing enzymes can be followed very conveniently in the spectrophotometer. Unfortunately such reactions as the transfer of phosphate groups or of glycosyl groups are not usually accompanied by absorption changes and these enzymes must be studied by other methods.

Even when there is no absorption change with the normal substrates, it is sometimes possible to find an artificial substrate which gives absorption changes at a suitable wavelength. For hydrolysing enzymes, nitrophenyl derivatives have been widely employed; for example, on hydrolysis of p-nitrophenylsulphate the wavelength of the absorption maximum shifts from 278 mμ to 318 mμ, and the arylsulphatase (3.1.6.1) reaction can be followed by the large increase of absorption at 330 mμ (2809). Similarly, the formation of a thiolester bond by acyl-CoA synthetase (6.2.1.2) can be followed by using an acid with a conjugated double bond system, such as sorbic acid, with which a new band at about 300 mμ appears on formation of the ester (2756).

When the enzyme reaction being studied cannot be made to give an appreciable absorption change, the spectrophotometric method may often still be used by adding another enzyme which acts on the product of the reaction in such a way as to cause such a change. For instance, the product of an enzyme reaction is itself a substrate for one of the dehydrogenases in many cases. In such a case the addition of an excess of the (purified) dehydrogenase, together with the appropriate coenzyme will enable the first reaction to be followed by the reduction of the coenzyme, as shown by the increase of absorption at 340 mμ. The production of isocitrate from aconitate by aconitate hydratase (4.2.1.3) can be followed by adding isocitrate dehydrogenase (1.1.1.42) and NADP (2006). The dehydrogenase must be added in excess (or the amount of the enzyme under study sufficiently reduced), so that the rate of the overall process is in no way limited by the dehydrogenase reaction and the reduction of the coenzyme accurately follows the primary enzyme reaction. A somewhat similar case is the conversion of NADP into NAD by purified phosphatase (3.1.3.1) (1876), which can be followed in the presence of alcohol dehydrogenase (1.1.1.b) and alcohol. This dehydrogenase does not react with NADP, but any NAD formed is immediately reduced by it.

Yet another type of system is that in which the product of the primary reaction is also the oxidation product of a dehydrogenase; here the reaction can often be followed by adding the dehydrogenase and the reduced form of the coenzyme, so that the decrease in absorption measures the oxidation of the coenzyme by the reversed dehydrogenase reaction. An example of this is RACKER's (2146) method for measuring phosphofructokinase (2.7.1.11) activity. This enzyme phosphorylates fructose 6-phosphate to give fructose 1,6-diphosphate. By adding excess of aldolase (4.1.2.b) (which converts the diphosphate into a mixture of glyceraldehyde phosphate and dihydroxyacetone phosphate) and of glycerolphosphate dehydrogenase (1.1.1.8) (which causes the reduction of dihydroxyacetone phosphate by NADH$_2$), together with the reduced coenzyme, the kinase reaction can be followed by the oxidation of the coenzyme. Numerous systems of a similar kind can be devised and the method is not restricted to the use of dehydrogenases.

Most spectrophotometers can be used for measurements of fluorescence and in some cases these may be even more sensitive than absorption measurements. Flavin compounds, which fluoresce strongly in the oxidized form, lose their fluorescence on reduction. NAD and NADP do not fluoresce in their oxidized forms, but the reduced forms have a blue fluorescence and this can be used as a sensitive method for following dehydrogenase reactions (*2638*). Fluorescence, however, is more affected than is absorption by the presence of other substances, which may act as quenchers.

(b) *Manometric methods*

These are convenient and accurate methods for following reactions in which one of the components is a gas. They are therefore well adapted for the study of oxidases (O_2 uptake) or decarboxylases (CO_2 output), as well as such enzymes as hydrogenase, urease or carbonic anhydrase.

Their use, however, is by no means restricted to such reactions. Any of the numerous reactions which involve the production or consumption of acid or alkaline substances can be followed, if they are carried out in the presence of bicarbonate in equilibrium with a gas mixture containing a definite percentage of CO_2. Any acid produced will liberate a corresponding amount of CO_2 from the bicarbonate and this can be measured on the manometer.

An obvious case is the oxidation of an aldehyde group to a carboxyl group, e.g. in the glycolysis system by glyceraldehydephosphate dehydrogenase (1.2.1.12). As with the spectrophotometric methods, it is possible to extend the method to other enzymes by linking them with this dehydrogenase and many coenzyme-linked dehydrogenase reactions have been studied manometrically (*904*). Carboxyl groups may also arise by hydrolysis, e.g. of a peptide bond or an ester, and protein hydrolysis has been followed manometrically (*1462*) as well as the action of esterases, especially cholinesterase (3.1.1.8) (*64*). Some phosphate-transfer reactions which cause a change of ionization have also been studied (*480*). Ferricyanide is reduced by many oxidizing enzymes and as its reduction is accompanied by the production of a hydrogen ion it can be measured manometrically in bicarbonate (*2132*).

Manometric methods have been dealt with in considerable detail elsewhere (*619, 2696*).

(c) *The Thunberg method*

A considerable amount of the work on dehydrogenases in the past has been carried out by this method, which depends on visual observation of the time taken to reduce (decolorize) a definite amount of methylene blue or some similar dye. To prevent reoxidation of the dye by atmospheric O_2 it is essential to carry out the test in special test-tubes which can be evacuated (Thunberg tubes). The amount of dye added is extremely small, so that the substrate concentration remains practically constant during the reaction. Normally only the reduction time is measured and the course of the reaction is not followed. In a few cases in which the time curve has been determined it was found that the reaction was fairly linear, slowing only at the end, so that the reciprocal of the reduction time gives the reaction velocity. The usefulness of the method, however, does not depend on this, for it is more used for the determination of relative than of absolute velocities and the reciprocal of the reduction time will be proportional to the velocity even when the curve is not linear.

The method is simple and requires no expensive apparatus; when due precautions are taken it is fairly accurate. In the case of the NAD-dependent dehydrogenases, however, it is necessary to add an excess of a flavoprotein such as 1.6.4.3 to catalyse the reaction between the coenzyme and the dye, and this somewhat limits its usefulness with such enzymes.

A modification of the method is to follow the decolorization of 2,6-dichlorophenol-indophenol in the spectrophotometer. The reduced form of this dye reacts with O_2 very much more slowly than that of methylene blue and it is possible to carry out the tests in ordinary open spectrophotometer cells, though Thunberg tubes with optical faces have been manufactured.

(d) *Electrode methods*

The use of the glass electrode gives another method of following reactions which involve the production of acid. The simplest method is merely to follow the pH changes as the reaction proceeds, but there are two objections to this. The first is that the change of pH during the reaction will probably cause complications by altering the activity of the enzyme. The second objection is that the rate of change of pH depends not only on the rate of the reaction but also on the buffering power of the solution. This is a serious objection because proteins have a high buffering power and a crude enzyme preparation will contain a large amount of inactive protein which is removed during the purification, so that it is difficult to keep the buffering power constant.

A much better method is that of continuous titration, in which the pH is kept approximately constant by frequent additions of alkali; the rate of addition of alkali then gives the reaction velocity and is independent of the amount of buffer. The amount of buffer, however, does affect the accuracy of the method; if too little is used it is difficult to keep the pH sufficiently constant, while too much makes the method insensitive.

A very convenient automatic apparatus (the Radiometer pH-stat) is available commercially which keeps the pH constant by continuous additions of acid or alkali, and at the same time plots a curve of amount added against time. With this apparatus progress curves of many enzyme reactions can be obtained automatically. An excellent review of the use of the pH-stat is given in *1228*.

Electrode methods can also be used for oxidizing enzymes, by measuring the redox potential. A plain platinum electrode in a solution containing a mixture of the reduced and oxidized forms of a dye or similar hydrogen acceptor, gives a potential which depends on the ratio of the concentrations of the two forms. The reduction of the dye can therefore be followed by the change of potential of the electrode. Ferricyanide is usually more convenient than a dye, partly because it reacts directly with the coenzymes and does not require the addition of a flavoprotein, and partly because O_2 does not interfere and the reaction can be done in open test-tubes. In the interests of linearity, it is advisable to start with a mixture of equal amounts of ferri- and ferro-cyanide, then over a certain range the change of potential is approximately proportional to the amount of ferricyanide reduced (*625*). The method has been found very convenient.

Reactions involving O_2 may conveniently be studied by a polarographic method. The current through a polarized platinum electrode depends on the concentration of O_2 in the solution in which it is immersed, and by continuously recording the current progress curves showing changes in O_2 concentration can be obtained. Two kinds of O_2 electrode are in use for this purpose. CHANCE (*428*) has used a vibrating platinum electrode directly immersed in the reaction mixture in much of his work on oxidative phosphorylation. The Clark electrode† is separated from the reaction mixture by a polyethylene membrane, through which molecular O_2 can diffuse. This electrode is being increasingly used for the study of oxidation by mitochondrial suspensions and similar systems; a description of its use is given by CHAPPELL (*430*). This method differs from the manometric method in that a closed liquid system without a gas phase is used.

(e) *Polarimetric methods*

Many enzymes act only on one optical isomer of their substrate. If, as often happens, the product is optically inactive, the reaction can be followed by the change of rotation. This is also the case where the substrate is optically inactive, but an optically active product is formed, or where the substrate and product are both optically active but differ sufficiently in their specific rotations. This method, while not quite so convenient as some of the other methods, can be used for a number of enzymes to which they are inapplicable, especially for enzymes acting

† Obtainable from The Yellow Springs Instrument Co., Inc., Ohio; another form is described in *2200*.

on carbohydrates. 'Sucrase' (3.2.1.26) is a classical example. A thermostated polarimeter tube is of course essential.

In some cases the substrate has too low a rotation to measure directly, but the rotation may be greatly increased by forming a complex. This is the case with the hydroxyacids, e.g. malic acid, which form complexes with molybdate which have high specific rotations. Fumarate hydratase was first studied in this way, but since the reaction will not proceed in the presence of the molybdate reagent, a sampling method is necessary and the method has now been superseded by the much more rapid spectrophotometric method.

(f) Chromatographic methods

Where other methods fail, it is sometimes necessary to detect the formation of a product by chromatography. This is essentially a sampling method; samples are withdrawn from the reacting mixture at intervals, placed on the chromatographic paper, dried and run as chromatograms in the usual way. The gradual appearance of a new spot gives a qualitative idea of the progress of the enzyme reaction. If quantitative results are desired, it is necessary to cut out the spots, extract the material from them and estimate it by some chemical or spectrophotometric method. This method has been applied, for example, to transglucosylation reactions with flavins (2853).

The great objection to the method is the time required, especially for running the chromatograms, which takes several hours. To purify an enzyme, using such a test method, would be an extremely slow and laborious procedure. For this reason chromatographic methods have not found much application in enzyme work, except where no other method is available.

(g) Chemical estimations

Many enzyme reactions are followed by withdrawing samples at intervals and estimating the substrate or product by chemical methods. There is little of a general nature to be said about these methods, since the different enzymes require different estimation methods, but there are a few methods of more general application which can be applied to whole classes of enzymes. The convenient colorimetric method of FISKE and SUBBAROW (745) for inorganic phosphate has wide application, since so many enzyme reactions are concerned with phosphate compounds of various kinds. Phosphatases, phosphorylases and nucleotidases can be followed directly by such estimations. In addition, pyrophosphate links are split by hydrolysis in N-HCl in 10 min at 100° and the phrase '10-minute P' has become common, denoting the inorganic phosphate produced by this treatment. This makes it possible to follow numerous enzyme reactions involving ATP or ADP, including some of the kinases and the synthetases, for ATP has two pyrophosphate links and ADP only one.

Since the breaking of a glycosidic link produces a reducing group, copper-reduction methods have been much used for the study of enzymes acting on carbohydrates. Formol titration methods have been much used in the study of peptidases.

As LIPMANN has shown, the addition of hydroxylamine to acyl-phosphates yields a hydroxamic acid which gives a purple colour with ferric salts. Acetyl-phosphate can be estimated in this way, and the addition of coenzyme A and excess of phosphate acetyltransferase (2.3.1.8) gives a means of following enzyme reactions in which acetyl-CoA is involved. For instance, the citrate synthase (4.1.3.7) forms citrate from oxaloacetate and acetyl-CoA, and if acetyl-phosphate, CoA and phosphate acetyltransferase are added instead of acetyl-CoA, the reaction can be followed by the disappearance of acetyl-phosphate (*2012*).

For further details of methods of studying particular enzymes, the volumes of *Methods in Enzymology* edited by COLOWICK and KAPLAN (*481*) should be consulted.

III

ENZYME ISOLATION

IMPORTANCE OF ENZYME PURIFICATION

ENZYMES ARE FOUND in nature in complex mixtures, usually in cells which perhaps contain a hundred or more different enzymes, and in order to study a given enzyme properly it must be purified. In some cases, it is true, it is possible by the use of sufficiently specific test methods to study enzymes while they are still in an impure state, and indeed the foundations of enzyme biochemistry were laid long before any pure enzymes had been obtained. But in most cases some of the other enzymes present will interfere, either by attacking the substrate so as to give side reactions, or by transforming the product into some other substance, or by attacking the coenzyme or even the enzyme itself. Indeed it is sometimes difficult, until the enzyme in question has been purified, to say exactly what reaction it catalyses.

Apparently simple metabolic reactions are often found, when the enzymes are purified, to take place in a series of steps, each catalysed by a separate enzyme. Again and again lines of metabolism have been put forward which have remained obscure and controversial until isolation of the enzymes concerned has cleared up the mechanism. A case in point is the citric cycle, the mechanism of which only became clear when the citrate-forming enzyme (4.1.3.7) was isolated. The present obscurities in the mechanisms of aerobic phosphorylation, on the other hand, are largely due to the difficulty of separating the various components of the mitochondrial system.

For studies of enzyme specificity in particular it is necessary to have the enzymes as pure as possible. If an additional reaction is found to be catalysed by an impure enzyme, there will always be some doubt whether it is not due to some other enzyme present in the preparation.

The serious purification of enzymes dates from about 1922; the first crystalline enzyme (urease (3.5.1.5)) was obtained by SUMNER (*2564*) in 1926; by 1940 about twenty highly purified enzymes had been obtained, and the process has continued since at an ever-increasing rate. At the present time a dozen or more enzyme purifications are announced each year and the total number purified is probably approaching two hundred. By no means all of these are crystalline, though probably some of the non-crystalline preparations are purer than the crystalline ones, for the crystallization of a protein gives no guarantee of its purity and it is not uncommon for the first crystals obtained to be only 50 per cent pure. The Table of Enzymes at the end of this book shows about seventy-five different enzymes as having been crystallized, though it is possible that there may be other cases of which we are not aware.

Now that the importance of working with purified enzymes is so generally recognized, it seems strange that the early attempts at isolation met with criticism on the ground that it was 'unphysiological' to separate enzymes from the living cells and that it was important to work with intact tissues as far as possible. The tendency now is quite the reverse, namely, to regard with some suspicion work done with enzymes which have not been purified.

METHODS OF PURIFICATION

A great deal of useful information on this subject has been collected in a review dated 1953 by SCHWIMMER and PARDEE (*2354*) to which the reader is referred for additional details.

For the purpose of discussion, let us assume that a new enzyme has been discovered and that it is desired to isolate it in the pure state.

(a) *Test*

The first requirement is a convenient quantitative test of activity by which the enzyme can be estimated. Since a large part of the time spent in an enzyme isolation is used up in testing the activity of the different fractions, it is most desirable that the test should be a rapid one. Speed here is more important than extreme accuracy; a method taking 5 min and giving an accuracy of 5 per cent is preferable to one taking 30 min and giving an accuracy of $0 \cdot 5$ per cent, as far as the actual fractionation processes are concerned.

The nature of the test method adopted will naturally depend on the type of reaction catalysed by the enzyme and a suitable method must be worked out for each case. Some remarks on the various methods available will be found in Chapter II.

One of the commonest causes of difficulty is that the system may be more complex than appears at first sight. For instance, if the substrate A is converted by the enzyme reaction into the product B, and the test is based on the estimation of B, it may be that in reality the conversion goes by way of an unsuspected intermediate form C, so that two enzymes are involved, one to convert A into C and one to convert C into B. In this case any purification step which separates the two enzymes will cause a total loss of activity as measured by the test. A clue to the cause of the trouble may be obtained if activity is once more found on mixing the inactive fractions. The test may then be altered to a test for C, so that the first enzyme can be purified without reference to the second, or if this is inconvenient a preparation of the second enzyme may be made and added in excess to all the tests as one of the reagents.

A somewhat similar case arises when an unsuspected coenzyme is involved in a reaction catalysed by a single enzyme. Again activity will be lost on purification. If the factor proves to be one of the known coenzymes, it may simply be added to the test; if it is of unknown nature, it may be possible to restore it by adding an extract of the tissue which has been boiled to remove enzymes and proteins (since many coenzymes are comparatively heat-stable), or a trichloroacetic acid extract (neutralized), or possibly a dialysate (since many coenzyme molecules are sufficiently small to pass through cellophane membranes).

(b) *General procedure*

Since we have assumed that the enzyme in question has not previously been purified, its specific activity and therefore the purity of the initial preparation will be unknown. The enzyme may form anything from one-tenth to one-ten-thousandth part of the total material. It is therefore usual to define an arbitrary *unit of enzyme*, in terms of which the purity and activity of the various fractions may be quantitatively expressed. In most cases this unit will be defined with reference to the estimation method used. If this is a spectrophotometric method, it may be the amount of enzyme which produces a certain change of optical density in a certain time under the test conditions; if some product is being estimated, it may be the amount of enzyme which produces a certain amount of the substance per min, and so on. It is desirable in the interests of consistency to make the new unit conform as far as possible to that internationally recommended and defined on p. 16. Other quantities may now be defined in terms of the unit. The *concentration* of the enzyme in solution is expressed as units per ml; the *specific activity*, which is a measure of the purity of the enzyme preparation, is expressed as units per mg of material.

In the past specific activities have been expressed in relation to a number of different quantities, such as total solids, total organic material, non-dialysable solids, or protein nitrogen. The recommendation of the Enzyme Commission is that specific activities should be given as units per mg protein. This is the most satisfactory basis, although it may be argued that it does not give a true measure of the purification achieved when much non-protein material (e.g. polysaccharides) is initially present. For example, yeast extracts contain large amounts of gums which precipitate with the proteins; yet their removal would not be shown as a purification by these methods.

Protein may be estimated by a number of methods. The classical method is the determination of total nitrogen by the KJELDAHL method (446). The amount of nitrogen, however, may not be an accurate measure of the amount of protein, since the nitrogen content of different proteins varies over an appreciable range (from 12 to 19 per cent); also nitrogenous substances other than protein may be included in the estimation. The latter point becomes particularly troublesome when ammonium sulphate fractionation is being employed; in this case it is' necessary either to dialyse exhaustively or to precipitate with trichloro- acetic acid and wash the precipitate until ammonia-free (1080). This makes the method a slow one, especially as the Kjeldahl incineration should be continued for at least 8 hr to give complete conversion of all the aminoacids.

Turbidimetric methods, using such precipitants as trichloroacetic acid and sulphosalicylic acid, have been successfully used; they are rapid, and would probably be generally satisfactory, provided that conditions are standardized to ensure complete precipitation and to avoid flocculation (see for example 354). It should be noted that trichloro- acetic acid sometimes gives very incomplete precipitation, even when heated; this is especially true when mucoproteins are present (1242).

Several colorimetric methods are available. A quantitative method depending on the biuret reaction has been developed (893, 2817) and since it depends on the peptide chain rather than the side chains, should be independent of the composition of the protein. According to KIRK (1388), 'The reaction would appear to be less subject to criticism as the basis for a colorimetric method for protein analysis than nearly any other such method'. Few of the non-protein materials likely to be present affect the estimation, and it is particularly useful because it is insensitive to ammonium salts. The FOLIN-CIOCALTEAU method which has been applied to protein estimation (1625) depends on the presence of tyrosine and tryptophan in the protein, consequently there will be wide variations with different proteins.

It is now quite common to rely on spectrophotometric measurements of the absorption at 280 mμ due to aromatic aminoacids. Different proteins contain different amounts of these aminoacids and therefore absorb to different extents, but it is convenient to remember that in a 1 cm cell a solution containing 1 mg of a fairly average protein per ml has an optical density of 1 at 280 mμ. Nucleic acid also absorbs strongly at this wavelength, but it is possible to make an approximate correction for this by taking measurements at both 260 and 280 mμ (*2788*).

The remarks made previously about the importance of speed in determining the activity also apply to the estimation of solids or protein. For this reason a convenient rapid method, such as the measurement of absorption at 280 mμ is to be preferred for use during the purification. The time factor is more important than possible errors due to the fact that the specific absorption of the protein being purified may be very different from the average absorption of the mixed proteins forming the starting material. But if this or any other method depending on one particular constituent of the protein is used, it is necessary to check from time to time that no appreciable changes in the mean content of this constituent in the protein material have been brought about by the purification. This can be done by estimations of protein at key points, using one of the more reliable methods, such as the biuret method or Kjeldahl nitrogen estimations.

When once the pure enzyme has been obtained and its specific activity determined, the purity of any fraction can be given in absolute values, usually in terms of the percentage of the pure enzyme which it contains. In describing an enzyme purification, however, the purities are usually left as enzyme units per mg of protein. A few years ago the practice was fairly common of arbitrarily assigning a purity of 1·0 to the purest fraction obtained, no matter whether it was actually pure or not, and of expressing the purity of all other fractions in terms of this figure. This was very misleading, as it gave the impression that the enzyme had actually been obtained in the pure state.

It is helpful, when publishing a description of an isolation procedure, to include a table by which it is possible to see the progress of the purification through the different stages, the efficiency of the different fractionations, the overall degree of purification and the yield. It is most desirable that the results should be presented in a standard form of table. A table of eight columns, headed as shown in Table III.1, is satisfactory and gives the required information. Column 1 gives a brief description of the fraction tested, column 2 its volume, column 3 the enzyme concentration, column 4 (= column 3 × column 2) the total enzyme units contained in it, column 5 the protein concentration, column 6 (= column 3 ÷ column 5) the specific activity, column 7 the yield (obtained from column 4 by taking the first figure in that column as 100 per cent), column 8 the degree of purification effected (obtained from column 6 by taking the first figure of that column as equivalent to 1).

Table III.1 will also serve to illustrate the course of a fairly typical enzyme purification. The number of separate steps required in enzyme

TABLE III.1

PURIFICATION OF ALKALINE PHOSPHATASE (3.1.3.1) FROM CALF INTESTINAL MUCOSA

(MORTON, 1874)

Procedure	Vol. (ml)	Concentration (units/ml)	Total units (×10³)	Protein (mg/ml)	Specific activity (units/mg)	Yield (%)	Purification
Initial extract	12,000	205	2,460	12·85	16	100	1
Ppt. pH 5	5,000	216	1,080	4·97	43	44	3
After butanol ..	4,450	166	739	0·18	920	30	57
60% acetone ppt. ..	55	12,360	680	12·42	995	28	62
35–48% acetone ppt. ..	20	26,250	525	11·88	2,210	21	138
40–50% acetone ppt. ..	20	18,900	378	5·70	3,320	15	207
After charcoal	32	7,340	235	0·67	11,000	10	688
40–48% acetone ppt. ..	10	14,200	142	1·03	13,800	6	861

(N.B.—This table is merely given as an illustration of the standard way of setting out the results of a purification, although it represents an actual case. It has been modified in a number of respects from Morton's table; the procedure in particular has been greatly abbreviated. If it is desired to repeat the preparation the original table should be consulted.)

purifications is frequently found to be about ten and each step may on the average increase the purity two or three times. The overall degree of purification may be up to several thousandfold and the total yield of pure enzyme only about 5 per cent. The low yield is not important, as the starting material is usually fairly plentiful.

(c) *Source of enzyme*

After a satisfactory test method has been devised, it is usually worth while to spend some time in searching for a rich source of the enzyme, unless there is some reason for preparing it from a particular source. The amount of a given enzyme may be very different in different tissues (see Table XIII.3) and by choosing a tissue which is rich in the enzyme not only is more enzyme obtained, but the degree of purification required to obtain the pure enzyme is much less, perhaps by a factor of 10 or even 100. In choosing a source due regard must be paid to its ready availability in quantity and also to its reproducibility.

In the case of bacteria, which are not usually available in large quantities, it is often possible to make use of the phenomenon of induction in order to obtain cultures which are greatly enriched with respect to the enzyme in question, by growing them in the presence of the substrate.

A number of enzymes are normally situated within the intracellular particles, for example in mitochondria. It is sometimes worth while in such cases to prepare the mitochondria first by high-speed centrifugation of tissue extracts and to use this preparation as the starting material. The enzymes and other constituents of the cytoplasm are thereby removed and a considerable degree of purification achieved before the ordinary fractionation methods are applied. To prepare mitochondria in large quantities, however, it is necessary to have reasonably large high-speed centrifuges and plenty of assistance.

(d) *Extraction*

When a suitable source has been found, it is necessary to bring the enzyme into solution. For this, rupture of the cell-membrane is usually necessary. Generally speaking, it is easier to extract enzymes from animal tissues than from micro-organisms, and in many cases simple extraction of minced muscle or liver with water is sufficient. With a strongly glycolysing tissue care must be taken that it does not become sufficiently acid to damage the enzyme and it is sometimes advisable to extract with a buffer solution. It may be necessary to bring the tissue into a finely divided state by the use of a high-speed homogenizer or a Waring blendor, though the latter should be used with some caution.

In many cases it will be necessary to take more energetic measures

c

to disrupt the cell membrane. Among the methods which have been used are mechanical breaking by grinding with sand or shaking at high speed with fine glass beads, ultrasonic or sonic oscillations, freezing and thawing, treatment with solvents such as acetone, autolysis (either alone or with toluene, ethyl acetate or sodium sulphide), or lysis with added enzymes. Generally speaking, autolysis or treatment with proteinases should be avoided if other methods will serve, as it will otherwise be necessary to isolate the enzyme from an extremely complex mixture of protein breakdown products produced by the digestion. Frequently, however, especially with yeast, autolysis is the only method which can be applied on a sufficiently large scale. Drying with acetone is not only a useful method of attacking the cell membrane, but it frequently gives an active dry powder which can be stored in bulk and forms a convenient starting material from which the enzyme can be extracted with water or buffer solution. The acetone treatment must always be carried out at a low temperature, and even then some enzymes are destroyed by it. A special case of enzymatic lysis is that of *Micrococcus lysodeikticus* by muramidase (3.2.1.17). Most forms of mechanical disintegration are difficult to carry out on a sufficiently large scale.

The extraction of enzymes from mitochondria is a special problem. Until recently mitochondrial enzymes were regarded as insoluble and inseparable from the mitochondrial particle. It is now clear that many mitochondrial enzymes pass freely into solution once the mitochondrial membrane has been ruptured or made permeable by bringing about swelling of the mitochondria. On the other hand some enzymes are more firmly bound to the structural framework of the mitochondria, probably as a lipoprotein complex, and require special methods for their extraction. These methods, which have been reviewed by Morton (*1877*), include drying with acetone, treatment with a butanol–water mixture, extraction of dried mitochondria with various organic solvents, extraction with aqueous solutions of detergents such as cholate, deoxycholate, Tween, Triton, Teepol, Emasol, etc., or treatment with hydrolytic enzymes such as lipases, nucleases or proteolytic enzymes.

The butanol procedure, which has been outstandingly successful with some enzymes, for instance alkaline phosphatase (3.1.3.1), appears to involve the disruption of the lipoprotein association so that the enzyme passes into the aqueous phase. The detergent procedure, which has been extensively used for the isolation of the components of the cytochrome system, sometimes results in true solubilization of the enzyme, which remains in clear solution after removal of the detergent; in other cases purification must be carried out in the presence of the detergent, otherwise the enzyme precipitates.

FRACTIONATION METHODS

The extract containing the enzyme will also contain numerous other substances, of both large and small molecular weight. The small molecules can be removed by dialysis, leaving the large molecules, which are predominantly proteins, though some polysaccharides may be present. The main part of the purification will consist of a series of fractionations by which the enzyme protein is separated from the other proteins present. In the past a number of different types of fractionation methods have been used, but now the majority of purifications are carried out with a relatively small number of standard procedures which have proved particularly effective and convenient.

The order in which these are used must be determined by trial, but it is generally true to say that more rapid purification is achieved by alternating the different fractionation methods than by repetition of fractionations of one type.

Fractionation must always be controlled by activity tests; it is not often possible to obtain good results by following a published description blindly.

For each stage a pilot fractionation on a small scale is carried out, before treating the main bulk of the solution. In the small-scale tests it is always necessary to keep in mind the practicability of carrying out the operation under the same conditions on a large scale. For instance, it is easy to heat a few ml of solution to 55° for exactly 5 min, but it is not possible to do this with 10 l. of solution, because of the time required for heating and cooling such a large volume of liquid. Since a purification of several thousand-fold is often required, it is generally necessary to handle large volumes of liquid in the first stages.

In all fractionations attention must be given to two factors which affect the results considerably, namely the pH and the electrolyte concentration, particularly the former. Most of the difficulties met with in repeating published preparation methods are due to failure to record these conditions. A good glass electrode outfit is an essential for successful work.

Each fractionation step consists in the separation of the total protein into a series of fractions (half a dozen to a dozen in the pilot stage) by gradually increasing the salt concentration, or the amount of adsorbent added, or the concentration of organic solvent, or the acidity, etc., in such a way that the greater part of the enzyme is found in one fraction if possible. Fractional denaturation by heating or by changing the pH is also sometimes used to remove unwanted proteins.

It is not correct to proceed by taking a series of portions of the enzyme solution and adding different amounts of the salt or other precipitating agent to the different portions. This is not a true fractionation, for any given precipitate will contain all the proteins brought down up to that salt concentration; in other words it will contain all the components of the previous fractions. The correct method is to take only one portion of the enzyme solution and to remove each fraction before the next is precipitated. In this way each fraction contains only those proteins which are brought down over a small range of salt concentration and a true fractionation is effected.

In the large-scale fractionation it is not usual to separate the protein into as many fractions as in the pilot tests. Usually only three fractions are obtained, two of which are discarded. Thus if for example the pilot fractionation shows that precipitation of the wanted enzyme begins when the ammonium sulphate concentration reaches 66 per cent of saturation and that the greater part has come down by 69 per cent of saturation, the main solution will be brought in one step to 65 per cent saturation, the precipitate discarded, the solution then brought to 70 per cent saturation, the enzyme-containing precipitate retained, and the remainder of the solution discarded. This, however, may not be safe without further tests, because the conditions of precipitation are not quite the same as in the pilot fractionation. For instance, the precipitation of the enzyme may be influenced by the presence of proteins which, in the pilot test, had been removed in the earliest fractions, but which in the main fractionation may cause the enzyme to precipitate at 62 per cent saturation. For this reason it may be advisable to do a second pilot separation into the three fractions only, before carrying out the main fractionation, in order to make sure that the concentration limits have been correctly determined.

(a) *Fractional precipitation by change of* pH

Although not one of the important fractionation methods, it is often very advantageous with extracts of animal tissues to adjust to pH 5, allow to stand for a few minutes and centrifuge, as the first step before the main purification begins. By removing much nucleoprotein and particulate material, this often converts a turbid extract into a perfectly clear solution. Occasionally an enzyme may be precipitated in this way.

(b) *Fractional denaturation by heating*

This is another treatment which, with a fairly stable enzyme, may be valuable as a preliminary step. The heat denaturation of proteins has a large temperature coefficient, consequently the destruction temperature is usually quite sharply defined and is different for each protein. By heating the solution for a definite time to a temperature just below that at which the enzyme is destroyed, it is sometimes possible to co-agulate much unwanted protein, which can then be centrifuged off and discarded. It is also possible to make use of the fact that the presence of the substrate frequently has a specific stabilizing effect on the enzyme; it may be possible to heat the solution 10° higher in the presence of the substrate than in its absence without loss of enzyme and thus get rid of much more of the other protein (*119*; cf. *367*).

In carrying out the heating, it is best to have three water baths, one at the desired temperature, one a few degrees hotter and one cold. The solution is placed in a round flask, which should not be more than half full; this is immersed in the hottest bath and the contents of the flask are kept rapidly swirling round so that no part becomes overheated. The rise of temperature is followed by a thermometer immersed in the solution and as soon as the desired temperature is reached the flask is transferred to the bath at that temperature, where it is left for a definite time while the next batch is heated. After the desired heating period the flask is transferred to the cold bath and the contents rapidly cooled a few degrees by swirling. It can then be left until cold. The time of heating is commonly 10 or 15 min.

(c) *Fractional precipitation with organic solvents*

This is one of the main fractionation methods. Ethanol has been used extensively for separating blood proteins by COHN and his group (*470*). The use of various solvents for separating the enzymes of muscle ex-tract was studied by ASKONAS (*92*) who came to the conclusion that acetone gave the sharpest separations and the lowest losses. To get good separations a low electrolyte concentration (less than M/30) is required, and this means that a preliminary dialysis is desirable, though the solution must not be completely free from electrolytes, or the precipitates will not centrifuge down. pH 6·5 was found to give the best results with muscle.

Since most enzymes are inactivated by solvents at room temperature, special precautions have to be taken to keep the temperature low through-out the procedure. For work on a 1-litre scale the method shown in Fig. III.1 (*92*) is satisfactory. The enzyme solution is in a metal (stain-less steel or aluminium) vessel immersed in a bath at about −5° and provided with an efficient stirrer. The acetone is contained in a gradu-ated cylinder also in the bath and is driven by gentle air pressure through a capillary jet touching the wall of the metal vessel. It then flows down the cold metal surface in a thin layer before mixing with the solution. The addition of the solvent begins as soon as the temperature of the solution has fallen to 0° (to prevent freezing) and is continued until the desired amount of precipitate for the first fraction (or the desired acetone concentration) is obtained. The solution is then centrifuged in a refrigerated centrifuge at the same temperature (a few minutes only

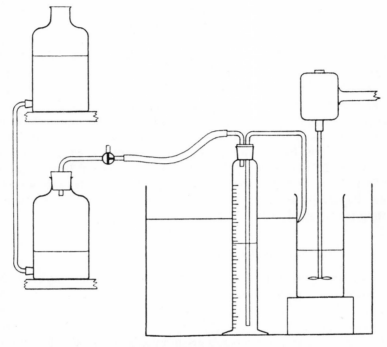

Fig. III.1. *Apparatus for fractionation with organic solvents.*

after Askonas *92*

should be adequate) and poured back into the metal vessel. The addition of acetone is then continued. The precipitate is either freeze-dried or immediately dissolved in a sufficient quantity of cold water or buffer solution to dilute the acetone in it to a harmless concentration, or it may be dialysed at the freezing point.

The enzyme activity tests are done on the dissolved fractions, not on the main solution, in which the increasing concentration of acetone may considerably affect the results.

A few enzymes are very stable to acetone. In these cases it is a positive advantage to allow the solution to stand at room temperature; this causes extensive denaturation and inactivation of other proteins and enzymes, which can then be removed.

(d) *Fractional precipitation by salts*

This is a very widely used method. The salt most employed is ammonium sulphate, on account of its large solubility in water and absence of harmful effects on most enzymes. It has in fact a stabilizing action on many enzymes and it is usually not necessary to carry out the fractionations at a low temperature. The total enzyme recovery in all fractions is often 100 per cent, but the separations are not always very sharp and it may be advisable to sacrifice a percentage of the enzyme in discarded fractions in the interests of greater purity.

It is advisable to use good quality ammonium sulphate in order to avoid toxic impurities or the free acid which some samples contain. Even pure preparations are slightly acid and due attention must be paid to the control of pH. It is usually necessary to add the solid and not a solution, in order to keep the volume down.

The pilot fractionation is conveniently done by having the enzyme solution in a centrifuge tube and the solid ammonium sulphate in a boiling-tube. The tube of ammonium sulphate is weighed, and enough of the salt is added to the enzyme solution to bring down an amount of precipitate suitable for one fraction, care being taken that all the crystals are dissolved. The boiling-tube is then weighed again, the difference giving the amount of salt added. There is a time factor in the precipitation of proteins by ammonium sulphate and it is advisable to wait for at least 15 min before centrifuging, and longer if possible, otherwise the fractions will not be cleanly separated. The precipitates do not always centrifuge very readily and it may be desirable to use a high-speed centrifuge (10,000 rpm). They usually filter well under gravity through fluted papers, but this is very time-consuming. Filtration under suction is usually unsatisfactory, unless some filter aid is used, which may adsorb some of the enzyme and is not very satisfactory for a small-scale fractionation, though it has been used successfully in large-scale work.

After centrifuging the first fraction, the solution is poured off into another centrifuge tube and the addition of salt continued. The precipitate is dissolved in a small volume of water or buffer solution.

The activity tests are carried out on the redissolved fractions rather than the solution, on account of the high salt concentrations in the latter.

There is usually no difficulty in repeating the pilot fractionation on the main bulk of the solution. Some time may be saved in weighing out the salt if it is remembered that the ordinary small crystals of ammonium sulphate, together with the air spaces between them, have a density of about 1, so that if packed down in a measuring cylinder the graduations read grams of ammonium sulphate ! This method is not sufficiently accurate to replace weighing, but it helps to measure out the approximate quantity rapidly.

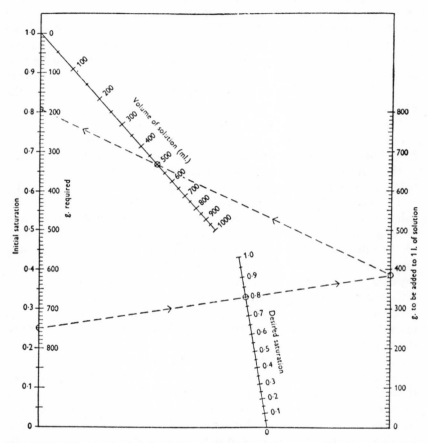

Fig. III.2. *Nomogram for obtaining amounts of ammonium sulphate to be added.*

from Dixon *620*

The published enzyme preparations usually express amounts of ammonium sulphate in terms of percentage saturation and often give such directions as 'Take the fraction precipitated between 55 and 60 per cent saturation'. The calculation of the correct amounts of the solid to be added to a given volume of solution to obtain these limits is by no means an easy matter. On account of the volume change which takes place on dissolving the salt, the amount of solid to be added to a given volume of liquid is not proportional to the percentage saturation required. For instance, the amount of solid required to give 50 per cent saturation is only 41 per cent and not 50 per cent of the amount required to give 100 per cent saturation. A nomogram giving the amount required in order to pass from any percentage saturation to any other has been published (620) and is reproduced in Fig. III.2. As is usual in fractionations with ammonium sulphate, 100 per cent saturation is taken as complete saturation at room temperature, not at 0°.

The theory of enzyme fractionation by salting out has been discussed by the authors elsewhere (631), starting from the well-known relationship

$$\log s = \beta' - K_S' \frac{\Gamma}{2},$$

where s is the solubility of the enzyme in grams per litre of solution, $\Gamma/2$ is the ionic strength in moles per litre of solution, and β' and K_S' are constants. As the salt concentration is increased, a point will be reached at which the solubility of the enzyme is equal to its concentration, and it will begin to precipitate. The greater part of the enzyme will then precipitate within a range of salt concentration above this point, this range being usually (in the case of ammonium sulphate) about 5 to 10 per cent of saturation. The actual position of the precipitation range is determined not only by the pH, temperature, and nature of the salt, but also by the concentration of the enzyme. Thus in order to repeat a published purification procedure successfully it is necessary to adjust the initial enzyme activity of the solution always to the same value.

It is usually not worth while to repeat an ammonium sulphate fractionation under the same conditions several times in succession. However, on varying the pH or temperature of the fractionation, the order in which the different proteins precipitate may become quite different, and successive fractionations under different conditions may be well worth while.

(e) *Fractional adsorption*

This is one of the most important and successful of the enzyme fractionation methods. It can be used in two distinct ways. If the enzyme becomes adsorbed, it may thus be removed and separated from other components of the solution and afterwards extracted or eluted from the adsorbent. If the enzyme is not adsorbed, treatment with the adsorbent may be used to remove much unwanted material from the enzyme solution.

The chief adsorbents now used are calcium phosphate gel and alumina Cγ gel, which have a very wide application.† Charcoal has been used for adsorbing unwanted components (627, 1874) and other adsorbents, e.g. $Zn(OH)_2$ gel, are occasionally used. It seems, however, that calcium phosphate gel will answer most requirements.

Adsorption usually occurs best in slightly acid solution, about pH 5 or 6, and at low electrolyte concentration. The presence of any considerable amount of salts generally interferes with the adsorption, that is to say a larger amount of adsorbent will be required to bring about a given result. In the interests of economy, therefore, a preliminary dialysis is beneficial. The method is a rapid one, for equilibrium between adsorbent and solution occurs very quickly and only a few minutes of centrifuging is needed to spin down the adsorbent.

The procedure is to add successive portions of the gel to the enzyme solution, mixing, spinning down and removing each portion before adding the next. In contrast to the other fractionation methods, the activity tests are carried out on small samples from the main solution, and the course of the enzyme removal so followed. Particularly with calcium phosphate, it is not uncommon to find that the first portions of adsorbent do not remove any of the enzyme while other proteins are being removed; then the enzyme is removed rather suddenly, perhaps on one or two fractions only, leaving an inactive solution which still contains much protein. The greatest degree of purification is usually obtained if the amounts of adsorbent are adjusted so that the first (discarded) fractions remove about 10 per cent of the enzyme, while 10 per cent is also left behind in the solution after the active fractions have been removed.

† *Preparation of calcium phosphate gel* (*1339*). 150 ml calcium chloride solution (132 g $CaCl_2.6H_2O$ per l.) is diluted to about 1,600 ml with tap water and shaken with 150 ml trisodium phosphate solution (152 g $Na_3PO_4.12H_2O$ per l.). The mixture is brought to pH 7·4 with dilute acetic acid and the precipitate washed three or four times by decantation with large volumes of water (15–20 l.). The precipitate is finally washed with distilled water in a centrifuge. (Yield 9·1 g dry weight.) We suspend it in distilled water and allow it to stand for about a month. After removing the clear water layer, the gel is well shaken and the dry weight per ml determined. It is then ready for use. It should be kept in the dark.

Preparation of alumina Cγ gel (*2875*). Dissolve 300 g $(NH_4)_2SO_4$ in 6·5 l. water, heat to 60° and add 420 ml of 20 per cent (w/w) NH_3 (i.e. 77·5 g NH_3 (theor. 76·6 g); the fluid must remain slightly alkaline during the subsequent precipitation). Into this pour a hot solution of 500 g $Al_2(SO_4)_3.18H_2O$ in 1 l. water, with vigorous stirring. Continue stirring 15 min after the addition, keeping the temperature at not less than 60°. Dilute to 40 l., allow the precipitate to settle (settling should be fairly rapid) and decant. Wash repeatedly by decantation, adding to the fourth wash-water 80 ml 20 per cent NH_3. After twelve to twenty washings the water remains opalescent; wash twice more after this point is reached. Allow to stand several weeks, to convert the Cα form into the Cγ form.

It is now necessary to recover the adsorbed enzyme from the active fractions by elution from the adsorbent. If the enzyme is not eluted by water, it is advantageous to wash the fraction by dispersing it in water and recentrifuging. For dispersing the gel in the washing fluids or eluents when working on a large scale, a high-speed stirrer is essential. Elution of the enzyme can often be accomplished by slightly alkaline buffer solutions, e.g. phosphate buffer pH 7·6. If this fails to elute the enzyme it is a very favourable circumstance, for by repeated elution with phosphate until no further protein is removed a considerable degree of further purification can be achieved. The elution of the greater part of the material remaining adsorbed can nearly always be brought about by phosphate containing about 10 per cent of ammonium sulphate (119). This method of elution has been successfully used with several different enzymes.

The volume of eluent used should not be too large and is commonly not greater than the volume of the centrifuged gel. It is better to elute several times in succession with small volumes than once with a large volume.

(f) Column chromatography

Since the appearance of the first edition of this book considerable improvements have been made in the separation of enzymes by chromatography on columns. The separations may depend in different cases on adsorption, ion exchange or molecular sieve effects, but in practice the technique is very much the same for all. The usual procedure is to add the enzyme preparation in solution in a dilute buffer with which the column has been equilibrated, to wash with the buffer, and to elute with a 'salt gradient', i.e. a gradually increasing concentration of the salt, using a fraction collector to separate the effluent into a large number of fractions. These are tested for enzyme activity and total protein. It may be desirable to use several successive salt gradients. Fig. III.3 illustrates the possibilities of the method.

Gels used for the adsorption fractionation methods described in section (e) are not suitable for use in columns, but special materials have been developed for this purpose. Certain forms of calcium phosphate may be used mixed with Super-Cel (2589) or cellulose (1748). Calcium phosphate can be converted into the micro-crystalline hydroxyapatite,†

† *Preparation of hydroxyapatite (1560).* 2 l. of 0·5 M Na_2HPO_4 and 2 l. of 0·5 M $CaCl_2$ are run at speeds of 15 ml/min each into a 5 l. vessel with mechanical stirring. The supernatant is sucked off and the precipitate washed four times with 3 l. of water. To the precipitate suspended in 3 l. of water are added 100 ml 40 per cent (w/w) NaOH, and the contents are boiled for 1 hr with stirring. After 5 min settling the supernatant is sucked off, the precipitate stirred with 4 l. of

which can be used in columns without the addition of any granular material. A description of its use is given in *2655*.

A number of ion-exchange resins, particularly Amberlite IRC-50 (or its finer form XE-64), have given successful results with a number of enzymes. The pH of the eluting buffer may be very critical, if considerable denaturation is to be avoided (*277*). Various derivatives of cellulose, in particular diethylaminoethyl-cellulose (DEAE-cellulose) and carboxymethyl-cellulose (CM-cellulose) are much used for the ion-exchange chromatography of enzymes (*2080*). One example is shown in Fig. III.3, and a thorough investigation of the enzymes of liver extract using DEAE-cellulose is described in *1853*.

Sephadex, which is a three-dimensional polysaccharide network, and similar materials act as molecular sieves and can be used to separate a mixture of proteins according to their molecular size. Excellent separations have been obtained in a few cases using such materials, which depend on the principle that the smaller molecules can penetrate into and be retained by the particles. Sephadex, in the forms available at the time of writing, is limited to proteins of molecular weights up to 100,000, but a cross-linked polyacrylamide suitable for molecular weights up to 300,000 has been described (*1113*).

Apart from the sephadex type, all columns need a salt-gradient for elution, and devices for generating gradients of various shapes have been described (*278*).

Two detailed reviews of recent developments in chromatographic methods of enzyme separation have been written by TURBA (*2686*) and PETERSON and SOBER (*2080*).

(g) *Crystallization*

When the enzyme has been brought to a reasonable degree of purity it may be possible to crystallize it. Crystallization, however, must not be regarded as evidence that the enzyme is pure. The first crystals of a protein or enzyme are sometimes not more than 50 per cent pure and they may contain a number of other enzymes. On recrystallization the specific activity of the crystals increases and it may be necessary to re-crystallize several times until the specific activity rises to a constant maximum value. For this reason it is best to regard crystallization as a specific method of fractionation, to be used in the final stages.

water for 5 min, and allowed to settle for 5 min. This is repeated three times. 4 l. of 0·01 M phosphate buffer pH 6·8 are added, and the mixture just brought to the boil with stirring. After 5 min settling the supernatant is sucked off and the operation repeated once with 0·01 M and twice with 0·001 M phosphate buffer, each time with 15 mins boiling. When stored in the 0·001 M phosphate, it is stable for at least a year.

The most usual method of crystallization is from ammonium sulphate solutions. It should be carried out slowly, perhaps over a period of days or weeks, if good crystals are to be obtained. The usual method is to

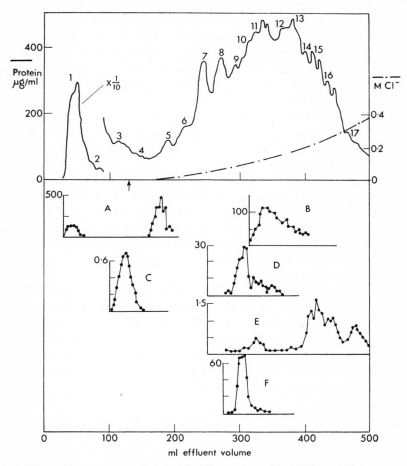

Fig. III.3. *Chromatography of soluble proteins of rat liver on DEAE-cellulose.*

The upper part of the figure shows the distribution of protein and the lower part of a number of different enzymes among the effluent fractions.

A. Aspartate aminotransferase (2.6.1.1)
B. Alanine aminotransferase (2.6.1.2)
C. An NADP-specific glycerol dehydrogenase
D. Isocitrate dehydrogenase (1.1.1.42)
E. Glucose-6-phosphate dehydrogenase (1.1.1.49)
F. Phosphogluconate dehydrogenase (1.1.1.44)

from *1354*

add the salt to a rather concentrated enzyme solution until a slight turbidity appears. It is then allowed to stand while the salt concentration is very slowly increased. This may be done by adding a strong solution of the salt drop by drop at long intervals, or through a fine capillary, or through a dialysing membrane, or the solution may simply be allowed to evaporate slowly. It may be necessary to try several pH values and temperatures before success is obtained. Alternatively, crystallization may be brought about at constant salt concentration by gradually changing the pH or the temperature. It is not possible to give general rules and the best conditions must be found in each case by experiment, but the review of Czok and Bücher (529) will be found useful. Crystallization seems to be facilitated if one of the previous stages has been a fractionation with organic solvent, perhaps owing to the removal of some interfering lipid material.

Enzymes have occasionally been crystallized in other ways, for example, from solutions of organic solvents. When other methods fail, it may even be possible to crystallize a heavy metal salt of the enzyme; phosphopyruvate hydratase (4.2.1.11) was crystallized as the inactive mercury salt, from which the active enzyme could be obtained on removal of the metal by dialysis against ammonium sulphate solution containing ammonia and cyanide (2788).

The mere appearance of active crystals provides no proof that the enzyme itself has been crystallized; there have been many disappointments when the crystals have been found to be either inorganic or of some other protein containing some of the enzyme. The best test is recrystallization; a fall in activity indicates that the enzyme is present as an impurity in the crystals, while a rise to a constant value indicates that they are crystals of the enzyme itself.

(h) *Sequence of fractionation methods*

In carrying out an enzyme purification, the order in which the different fractionations are to be applied has to be considered. Obviously crystallization comes last, and because heating has the object of removing large amounts of unwanted protein and does not require the addition of inconveniently large volumes of liquids, it is logical that it should come first. There are many cases in which this is not practicable, either because of the instability of the enzyme, or because of the presence of destructive enzymes (e.g. proteinases) which would do too much damage at the higher temperature, or simply because the degree of purification achieved is not worth while.

This leaves a choice between salts, organic solvents, adsorbents or columns. The best order must be determined by experiment, but a few points may be noted. In the early stages rather large volumes of enzyme solution have to be dealt with, and the use of organic solvents at this stage may well be limited by the size of refrigerated centrifuge available. This need not apply if the starting material is a stable powder, which can be worked up in portions of a convenient size. Ammonium sulphate precipitation can be used first, if the precipitates will centrifuge well, but if not, a limit may again be imposed by the size of high-speed centrifuge available. No preliminary dialysis is required for the ammonium sulphate fractionation. Adsorption, though otherwise very convenient as a first step, does usually require such a dialysis. At present no apparatus is available for the convenient and rapid dialysis of large volumes of liquid, and many yards of cellophane tubing are required to handle the usual 10 or 20 l. of enzyme solution by the ordinary method. Dialysis is the slowest process in enzyme purifications and such steps, though unavoidable, should be reduced to a minimum and restricted as far as possible to the later stages, where the volumes are smaller. Nevertheless, the dialysis before adsorption need not be exhaustive and adsorption methods are so convenient that they may be worth while at the beginning.

A loss of activity on dialysis may be found. This may be due to instability of the enzyme, or to the removal of some cofactor, but a common cause, unless very pure water is used, is the dialysing *in* of traces of inhibitory metals from the water, e.g. Cu. The enzyme usually has a very high affinity for these, and even though their concentration in the external water is very small, it may take up all the traces present in a very large volume of water. This is not usually so important with crude preparations as in the later stages.

If a preliminary dialysis is practicable, adsorption may well be found to be the best first step. Adsorbents usually settle quite rapidly, so that by waiting for a short time most of the liquid may be poured off and centrifugation of the large volume of liquid avoided.

The eluates obtained from an adsorption fractionation contain salts and it therefore seems logical to follow the adsorption with an ammonium sulphate fractionation, so that an intervening dialysis is avoided. Unless a second salt fractionation is to follow immediately, a dialysis will then be necessary, but by then the volume will have been considerably reduced. Sephadex columns provide a convenient alternative method of desalting.

If an elution which has been made with ammonium sulphate solution is to be followed immediately by a salt fractionation, the amount of ammonium sulphate in the eluate must be allowed for in calculating the percentage saturation. Similarly, if a second ammonium sulphate fractionation is to follow the first, it is necessary to allow for the salt contained in the redissolved precipitates from the first fractionation.

Since the dry weight of protein in such a precipitate is small in comparison with its volume, it is usually sufficient to estimate the volume of the precipitate as centrifuged, and to treat it as an equal volume of ammonium sulphate solution at the concentration used.

Methods using columns are not conveniently carried out on a large scale, and are hence more suitable for the later stages of a purification. In comparing them with other methods it should not be overlooked that the setting up, washing and elution of a column take a considerable time. Unless the enzyme elutes in a very narrow band, considerable dilution may occur.

(i) *Other methods*

A large part of the work on enzyme purification which has been carried out up to the present has been accomplished by the use of the four main methods above mentioned, namely, ammonium sulphate precipitation, adsorption on calcium phosphate (or alumina Cγ) gel, precipitation by acetone (or alcohol) and chromatography on a column such as one of DEAE-cellulose. It now seems rather probable that most enzymes could be purified by a combination of these four methods alone. A number of other methods, however, have been used in particular cases and may be tried if the above-mentioned methods should fail.

Other precipitants

In the early stages, much unwanted protein can sometimes be removed without loss of enzyme by the cautious addition of salts of heavy metals, e.g. lead (*167*). Too much will result in a loss of enzyme.

In the purification of glucose oxidase, the enzyme was precipitated with tannic acid (*508*) and the complex decomposed with acetone. In several cases, enzymes have been precipitated by adding nucleic acid (*2787*) and subsequent removal of the latter by precipitation with a protamine.

Denaturation with chloroform

Much inactive protein can often be removed initially by the TSUCHI-HASHI method (*2684*), that is by denaturation by shaking with a mixture of alcohol and chloroform. It is especially useful for removing all haemoglobin from extracts of animal tissues or erythrocytes (*288, 1078*).

Electrophoresis

Electrophoresis with the standard Tiselius apparatus is useful rather as a test of homogeneity than as a method of preparation on any considerable scale. It is very helpful for following the progress of the purification. There is one way in which it is especially valuable, namely, for obtaining small samples of the pure enzyme, so that its specific activity can be measured and used to determine the purity of the various fractions. Using the two-section cell, the current is passed until the peaks corresponding to the various components are fairly well separated. The current is then switched off and the liquid very carefully driven back until only the fastest-moving component remains in the upper half of the cell on the ascending side. In the other limb it will frequently be found that only the slowest-moving component is present in the upper part, so that by cutting off the upper halves of both limbs it is possible to obtain these two components separately in a state approximating to purity and to measure their specific activities. If either of them is the enzyme, its specific activity will be much higher than the mean specific activity of the original solution; if neither of them is the enzyme, both activities will be lower and it will then only be possible to obtain the enzyme mixed with one or more of the other components.

Of course, after the purification has been completed, the specific activity should be redetermined on the isolated enzyme, as the methods just mentioned are only approximate.

Special cells have been devised to facilitate the use of the Tiselius apparatus for preparative purposes.

Electrophoresis on paper has been shown to be capable of use for enzyme separations; the apparatus of GRASSMANN and HANNIG (887) now makes is possible to run the process continuously and so to use a reasonable amount of solution. In this method buffer solution flows continuously down a sheet of filter paper, dripping from serrations in the bottom edge into a series of tubes. The electric current is passed at right angles to this flow from the left edge of the paper to the right, and the enzyme solution is fed on to the paper at one point near the top. The components having different mobilities in the electric field, will flow down lines inclined at different angles to the vertical and will arrive at different points along the bottom edge. These methods have been reviewed by BIER (247).

Zone electrophoresis in starch gels (SMITHIES, 2457) has been successfully employed for the small-scale isolation of enzymes in the final stages of purification, although difficulty is sometimes experienced in eluting the enzyme from the gel. On a somewhat larger scale, the electrophoretic cellulose column of PORATH (2106) has also been successfully used.

Concentration

Normally a reduction in volume is effected as a matter of course by the fractionation methods which have been described, but occasionally it is necessary to concentrate an enzyme solution to a smaller bulk. This happens, for instance, when an adsorbent has a rather high affinity for the enzyme, so that the eluate only contains it in low concentration. Evaporation by distillation *in vacuo* is not desirable, as the frothing may denature the enzyme. One method which can be used is partially to freeze the solution and to remove the ice; another is to place the solution in dialysis tubing and expose it to a current of warm air. A commonly used method is freeze-drying (the so-called lyophilization). However, all these methods concentrate the salts as well as the enzyme and one may simply obtain a mass of salt containing a small quantity of protein, which must then be dialysed. A valuable method is to concentrate the solution on an ultrafilter, when the salts pass through with the water and it is even possible to wash the enzyme free from salts on the filter. A useful form† has been described by ARONSSON (*88*).

Another method of concentrating enzyme solutions is the addition of dry Sephadex, which takes up both water and salts, leaving the enzyme in more concentrated solution.

CRITERIA OF PURITY OF ENZYMES

Probably no single test by itself is sufficient to prove that the final product consists of only one protein, the enzyme itself. Each test establishes a certain degree of probability, but if the product appears homogeneous by several different tests the probability becomes very high indeed and the enzyme may be accepted as pure.

The tests of homogeneity employed for other proteins are available for enzymes also. These are tests based on physical properties, of which the chief are ultracentrifugation, electrophoresis and solubility tests. But in the case of enzymes, there are in addition tests based on the catalytic activity, which may powerfully confirm the physical tests.

As a matter of general experience, apparent homogeneity in the ultracentrifuge, i.e. sedimentation as a single component, is not such good evidence as homogeneity by electrophoresis. This is because the sedimentation constants of proteins are not uniformly distributed, but tend to lie close to certain probable values. Thus it is not very improbable that in a mixture of two proteins they might both have about the same sedimentation constant and sediment as a single protein, especially if they are sufficiently similar in properties to have come through a purification process together.

This does not apply to the electrophoretic mobilities of proteins, and with a given complex mixture of proteins, e.g. a muscle extract, one

† Available from LKB-Produkter AB, Stockholm.

usually observes more components in the Tiselius apparatus than in the ultracentrifuge. With rabbit muscle extract, for instance, the ultracentrifuge gives two peaks and electrophoresis gives eight. If the purified preparation gives only a single peak in the Tiselius apparatus, it is fair evidence of purity. But it is not unknown, even on electrophoresis, for a mixture of two proteins to give a single peak at one pH and it is necessary to carry out electrophoresis at more than one pH to obtain satisfactory evidence.

It should be noted that neither of these methods is very sensitive for the detection of components which are present only in small amount. It is quite possible that components which form less than 1 per cent of the total protein may be overlooked altogether. Muscle extract certainly contains many more than the eight proteins indicated by direct electrophoresis and it is quite common for peaks to appear in new positions as purification proceeds.

Thus if the product consisted of a single protein merely contaminated with the enzyme, it would appear to be a pure enzyme by these two tests.

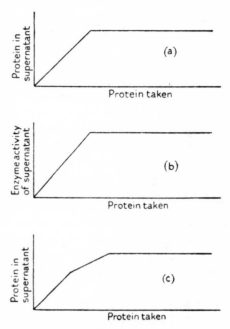

Fig. III.4. *Solubility criterion of purity.*

However, if the size of the peak remains proportional to the enzyme activity during the purification, it is very probable that it is due to the enzyme. By means of a fractionating electrophoresis cell it is possible to take 'cuts' at various points across the peak, and if they all have the same specific activity it is clear that the mobilities of enzyme and protein must be identical.

The solubility test is more sensitive for detecting minor components (see NORTHROP, *1996*). A series of different amounts of the enzyme are shaken, each with a given constant volume of solvent (water or a salt solution), then filtered or centrifuged and the protein in the resulting liquid estimated. This amount is then plotted against the amount taken, as shown in Fig. III.4.(*a*). At first all the protein added dissolves, so that the amount in solution is equal to the amount added and a straight line with unit slope is obtained. Ultimately the solution becomes saturated with the protein and (provided that we are dealing with a pure protein) after this point no matter how much is added no more will go into solution, so that a horizontal line is given. If a second protein is present, however, after the saturation point of the less soluble protein is reached the second protein will continue to dissolve until *its* saturation point is reached, when the plot will become horizontal. There will therefore be a second straight-line portion (see Fig. III.4(c)) of which the slope will be less, since the second protein forms only a portion of the protein taken. There will in fact be a separate straight-line portion for each component present.

It is just conceivable that the graph shown in (a) could be obtained with a mixture of proteins in which the amounts of the proteins present were proportional to their solubilities, so that the solution would become saturated with all the proteins at the same instant. This is unlikely and it is still more unlikely that the ratio of their solubilities would remain the same in different solvents. If (a) is obtained in a number of different salt solutions, the evidence is very strong that only one protein is present.

Since it is likely that a slope of 1 in 100 might be taken as horizontal, it is very possible that a protein impurity which forms only 1 per cent of the total may be missed, unless the observations are extended to a high excess of the solid phase.

A simplified form of the test has been proposed by Northrop, in which only two points are determined, namely, the point where the first bend occurs and a point far to the right on the graph. Two tubes of solvent are taken; to the first is added just enough of the protein to give a very faint turbidity, to the second ten times this amount, and both are centrifuged. If exactly the same amount of protein is found in both supernatants, it is clear that the complete graph would be of the form shown in (a); if on the other hand there is an increase, more than one protein must be present.

For enzymes, the evidential value of the solubility test is greatly strengthened by estimating the enzyme activity as well as the protein content of the supernatants. If the enzyme is present merely as an impurity in the protein, it is clear that more enzyme will continue to pass into solution (and therefore the activity to increase) long after the solution has become saturated with the protein. If the activity graph obtained is of the same form as the protein solubility graph, with a sharp bend at the same point, as shown in (b), it proves that the enzyme has the same solubility as the protein, and if the same result is obtained with several different solvent solutions the evidence becomes highly convincing.

Evidence depending on identical solubilities can also be obtained by recrystallizing. It is often observed that on repeated recrystallization the specific activity increases to a constant maximum value, which moreover is the same for a series of different preparations of the enzyme. This gives a strong indication that purity has been reached.

Even when an enzyme appears to be a single homogeneous protein in the ultracentrifuge and in the Tiselius apparatus, electrophoresis on starch gel (*2457*) or on agar gel (*2861*) may separate it into several 'isoenzymes', all possessing the enzyme activity. By revealing the existence of multiple forms of many enzymes, these methods have opened up an important section of enzyme biology, which is discussed in Chapter XIII.

PITFALLS IN WORKING WITH PURE ENZYMES

The availability of enzymes in the pure state makes it easily possible to take relatively enormous quantities when carrying out tests in the investigation of their action. The usual quantity of an enzyme required in an activity test is of the order of 1 μg. The fact that it is now possible to add quantities of up to 10 mg brings its own dangers.

While it is desirable to use pure enzymes for studies of specificity, it is also important not to take excessive quantities of the enzyme. If with a large amount of enzyme an additional reaction is found to be catalysed, there must always be a suspicion that it is due to another enzyme present in small amounts as an impurity. This is especially to be borne in mind in view of what has been said above about the difficulty of detecting other proteins present in amounts of less than 1 per cent. If only 1 mg of the enzyme were taken, this would mean that 10 μg of the contaminating enzyme would be present, which is far more than is usually necessary to catalyse an enzyme reaction efficiently. The danger is less with enzymes which have been recrystallized many times, but it is always present if large quantities are used.

A danger of a different kind is present when a two-enzyme system is under test, if one of them is added in large excess. If the two enzymes are linked by an intermediate coenzyme or carrier, for which the enzyme in question has an appreciable affinity, this enzyme may take up practically all the coenzyme present, so that none reaches the second enzyme. STRAUB (*2545*) has shown that with the lactate dehydrogenase (1.1.1.27) system the reaction will scarcely proceed at all if enough of the enzyme is added !

IV

ENZYME KINETICS

THE IMPORTANCE OF ENZYME KINETICS

THE CHARACTERISTIC PROPERTY and function of enzymes is the catalysis of chemical reactions. Any fundamental study of this catalytic function must be based on quantitative measurements of the rate of the catalysed reaction. From the effect of varying the conditions on the rate, inferences may be made about the mechanism of enzyme action. Ideally, such kinetic studies should be brought into relation with chemical and structural studies on the enzyme in order to get a definite picture of the process, but this is only possible if the enzyme has been obtained in a high degree of purity. Many enzymes have not been so purified and kinetic studies are the only approach possible at present.

In addition to the more fundamental aspects, the study of enzyme kinetics is important for practical reasons; the definition of satisfactory units, for example, requires some knowledge of the best conditions for the action of the enzyme and the effect of various factors on it. Such a preliminary study of the kinetics is usually essential before a purification can be effected, since this process must be followed quantitatively, as discussed in Chapter III.

It is well known that biological systems, particularly living cells, are more sensitive to changes of temperature, pH, etc., than most non-biological chemical reactions, and this is due largely to the properties of the enzymes on which these systems depend. A knowledge of enzyme kinetics thus helps in the understanding of many biological phenomena.

A proper understanding of biochemical systems depends on the realization that the ordinary kinetic equations of the physical chemist cannot be applied to such systems without modification. Enzyme kinetics is thus a study in its own right, and an important one.

FACTORS INFLUENCING ENZYME REACTION VELOCITY

The factors which determine the form of the progress curves of enzyme reactions are numerous and varied, as mentioned in Chapter II. It is therefore difficult to derive kinetic equations which will represent the. curves. In some cases the conditions are sufficiently simple to allow a reasonably close approximation to be made and these cases are dealt with in a later section. Normally the complications can be ignored altogether if the velocity is determined before any of these disturbing factors have begun to act, in other words at zero time. The method of determining initial velocities has been described in Chapter II, where

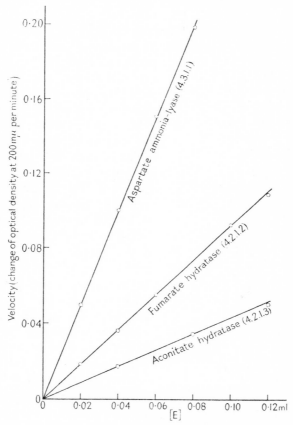

Fig. IV.1. *Typical effect of enzyme concentration on reaction velocity.*
from *2148*

it was pointed out that the best method of investigation is to vary one factor at a time, keeping the other conditions constant, and to determine the effect on the initial velocity of the enzyme reaction. The chief factors which determine the initial velocity of a particular reaction are enzyme concentration, substrate concentration, pH, temperature and the presence of activators or inhibitors. We will now consider each of these factors in turn.

(A) EFFECT OF ENZYME CONCENTRATION

Under given conditions, two molecules of enzyme acting independently in solution will transform twice as much substrate in a given time as one molecule; the velocity should therefore be proportional to the enzyme concentration

IV.1 $\qquad v = k[\mathrm{E}]$

This is what is actually found in the great majority of cases and indeed is the basis of nearly all methods of estimation of enzymes. Typical examples are shown in Fig. IV.1. This is the normal case; when deviations are found, they can usually be explained in one of the ways (a) to (g) given below.

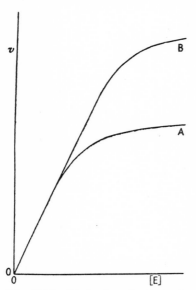

Fig. IV.2. *Limitation of velocity by test method.*

(a) It is sometimes found that if the enzyme concentration is greatly increased there is a falling off from the linear relationship, as shown in Fig. IV.2. This is usually due to a limitation in the capacity of the method of estimation and does not indicate a true decrease in the activity of the enzyme. It is common for instance in manometric work, where the limitation is due to the rate of diffusion of gas into the liquid, so that there is a definite limit to the velocities which can be measured in this way. The limitation can be clearly revealed by increasing the capacity of the method; if, for example, curve A in Fig. IV.2 represents the results obtained manometrically with a certain rate of shaking, curve B will be obtained when the rate of shaking (and therefore the rate of diffusion of gas) is increased, so that the velocity is proportional to enzyme concentration over a much wider range. Such methodological limitations may occur with other ways of estimating activity.

In cases where the test method depends on a second (added) enzyme, the activity of the latter will set a definite limit to the velocity which can be measured, so that a curve similar to curve A will be obtained, and an increase in the amount of the second enzyme added will raise the limit, as in curve B. The same consideration applies to a system of several enzymes in which the amount of one enzyme is varied and the amounts of the others kept constant. So long as the amount of the enzyme in question is sufficiently small, so that the other enzymes can be regarded as being in excess, the overall velocity will be proportional to its concentration; but when the amount becomes large, the other enzymes will begin to limit the velocity. Thus the catalytic efficiency of the enzyme (as measured for example by its molecular activity) will be constant as long as the other enzymes are in excess, but will fall off at higher concentrations and in the limit will vary inversely with its concentration.

(b) As already mentioned in Chapter III, when an enzyme is available in the pure state it becomes possible to add relatively enormous amounts. If it has an appreciable affinity for one of the components of the system, e.g. a coenzyme, practically the whole of this

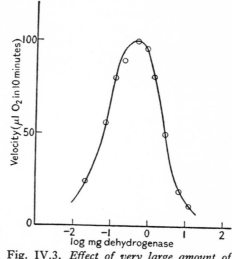

Fig. IV.3. *Effect of very large amount of enzyme in a complex system.*

Lactate + lactate dehydrogenase (1.1.1.27) + NAD + flavoprotein (1.6.4.3) + methylene blue + O_2.

after *2545*

component may be bound by the enzyme and thus will not be available to react with the other enzymes. In this case the velocity will fall as the amount of enzyme is increased. The lactic system just considered provides an example of this. It was shown by STRAUB (*2545*) that if the amount of lactate dehydrogenase (1.1.1.27) is greatly increased, with a constant small amount of NAD and a large amount of flavoprotein, the curve shown in Fig. IV.3 is obtained. In this figure the enzyme concentration is plotted on a logarithmic scale for convenience. Owing to the affinity of the dehydrogenase for the coenzyme, the higher the concentration of enzyme the lower is the concentration of free coenzyme.

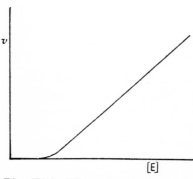

Fig. IV.4. *Effect of toxic impurities in reagents.*

This binding of the coenzyme by high concentrations of the dehydrogen-ase prevents it from reacting with the flavoprotein and produces a con-siderable inhibition of the overall reaction.

(*c*) A somewhat similar curve to that of Fig. IV.2 may be obtained if, instead of determining initial velocities, the amount of change in a fixed period of time is measured, as shown in Fig. II.2(*b*). This effect is due to exhaustion of substrate and does not indicate a lack of proportionality of initial velocity to enzyme concentration. An example of such an effect in the case of aldolase (4.1.2.b) has been reported (*1076*).

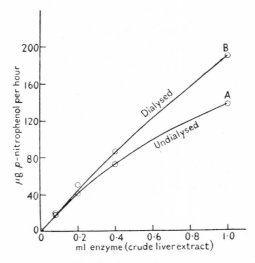

Fig. IV.5. *Effect of inhibitor in enzyme preparation.*
Arylsulphatase (3.1.6.1)

from *2808*

(*d*) Very rarely a curve as shown in Fig. IV.4 is obtained. This in-dicates the presence of small amounts of some highly toxic impurity in one of the components of the incubation mixture other than the enzyme solution itself. This will poison the first amounts of enzyme added, and it is only when enough of the enzyme (or other protein in the prepara-tion) is added to combine with the whole of the impurity that further amounts of enzyme will remain active. Thus the normal type of linear curve is obtained, but this is displaced from the origin by an amount which is proportional to the amount of the toxic impurity. For example, if an enzyme is sensitive to traces of heavy metal ions, as is often the case, the presence of minute amounts of copper in the buffer solution or the distilled water used may produce this effect.

(*e*) If the enzyme preparation contains a reversible inhibitor which combines with the enzyme to give an inactive complex EI, thus

IV.2 $\qquad$ $E + I \rightleftharpoons EI$

then the percentage of the enzyme which is in the inactive form increases as the concentration of inhibitor in the incubation mixture increases. But since the inhibitor is being added with the enzyme the inhibitor concentration increases with the enzyme concentration, so that the observed activity at higher enzyme concentrations falls below that which would be expected from a linear relationship. To put it another

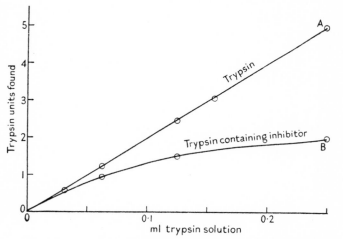

Fig. IV.6. *Effect of inhibitor added to enzyme preparation.*
Trypsin (3.4.4.4).

from *1996*

way, since there are two molecules on the left of equation IV.2 and only one on the right, increase of total concentration will favour combination, so that more of the enzyme is in the inactive form at higher concentrations.

Two examples of this are shown in Figs. IV.5-6. Fig. IV.5 curve A shows the rate of hydrolysis of *p*-nitrophenylsulphate by an undialysed extract of rat liver, plotted against enzyme concentration. Curve B is for the same preparation after thorough dialysis. The non-linearity in A is due to inhibition by traces of phosphate in the original extract, which have been removed by the dialysis before curve B was obtained (*2808*).

Fig. IV.6 shows a model system in which an inhibitor was deliberately added to the enzyme preparation (*1996*). Curve A was obtained with a solution of pure trypsin (3.4.4.4) and curve B with trypsin solution to which trypsin inhibitor had been added. Whenever a plot of velocity against enzyme concentration is found to curve downwards in this way, the presence of a dissociable inhibitor should be suspected and an effort made to remove it by dialysis or other means.

(*f*) Proteinases acting on proteins have been repeatedly shown to give non-linear enzyme concentration curves, usually showing a downward curvature. Various attempts have been made to fit empirical equations to such curves, some of which have been dignified with the title of 'laws', although they are of little general significance. The best known

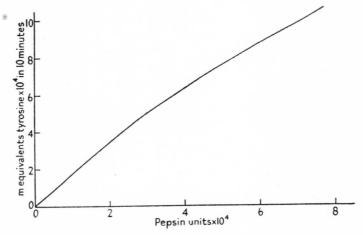

Fig. IV.7. *Non-linear proteinase concentration curve.*
Standard calibration curve for pepsin (3.4.4.1) acting on haemoglobin.
from *78*

is the so-called 'Schütz law' (E. SCHÜTZ (*2345*), developed by J. SCHÜTZ (*2346*)), according to which the velocity is proportional to the square root of the enzyme concentration

IV.3 $$v = k[E]^{\frac{1}{2}}$$

This was first developed for pepsin (3.4.4.1), although it only applies to the crude enzyme. Results approximating to this relation have been obtained under certain limited conditions with some other proteinases. Usually, however, the results fit no simple equation and proteolytic activities are read off empirically from experimental curves. A number of such curves have been given by ANSON (*78*), of which an example is given in Fig. IV.7.

Some possible explanations of the special effects obtained with proteinases are the following ((i)–(iv)).

(i) The enzyme preparations may contain inhibitors, in other words the effects are those discussed in section (e) above. For example, crude preparations of pepsin, such as were available to Schütz, must have contained appreciable amounts of the dissociable pepsin inhibitor liberated during the activation of pepsinogen (1081). This would explain why the curve shown in Fig. IV.7, obtained with pure pepsin, is much closer to equation IV.1 than to equation IV.3, but it is clearly not the whole explanation of the non-linearity.

(ii) Most of these anomalies are only found when the proteinases are acting on protein substrates. When simple peptides are used as substrates, the same enzymes give perfect straight lines. Many such results were obtained with synthetic peptides by BERGMANN and his collaborators (e.g. 1215). The hydrolysis of a protein involves the simultaneous or consecutive splitting of many different peptide bonds and the kinetics are extremely complicated. It has also been suggested that with a substrate of high molecular weight, such as a protein, the time required for the diffusion of the substrate to the enzyme molecules may complicate the picture.

(iii) The test method itself may introduce a non-linearity. Thus many accepted methods are based on the estimation of the total amount of all those derivatives of protein hydrolysis which are not precipitated by trichloroacetic acid or other such reagents. 'The assumption that the increase in non-protein nitrogen is proportional to the number of peptide bonds hydrolysed appears to have no sound basis. The amount of non-protein nitrogen liberated is determined by the position of the hydrolysed peptide bond within the protein molecule and also by the nature of the split-products' (1215).

(iv) If enzyme activities are measured by the amount of product produced in a given time, and the initial velocity is not measured, there is a possibility that inhibitory products may introduce a non-linearity, as shown for pepsin by NORTHROP (1989).

(g) If the enzyme preparation contains a dissociable activator or coenzyme, the reverse effect to that described under (e) will be obtained. As the concentration increases, an increasing proportion of the enzyme will be in the activated form and an upward curvature of the enzyme concentration curve will be obtained. At high dilution a velocity proportional to the square of the enzyme concentration would be expected, while at high concentrations the velocity will become proportional to the first power of the enzyme concentration, when the enzyme becomes saturated with activator. Such an effect is shown in Fig. IV.8. Curve A

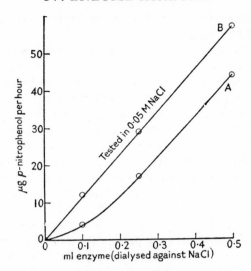

Fig. IV.8. *Effect of activator in enzyme preparation.*

Arylsulphatase (3.1.6.1).

from *2808*

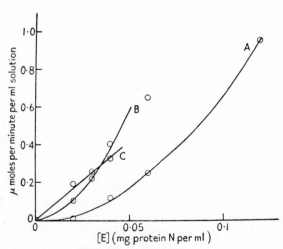

Fig. IV.9. *Effect of activator.*

Hydrolysis of benzoyl-arginineamide by ficin (3.4.4.12): A, no added activator; B, activated with cyanide; C, activated with thioglycollate.

plotted from data in *1215*

shows the activity of a partially purified arylsulphatase (3.1.6.1) which had been dialysed against sodium chloride. The enzyme is in fact activated by chloride, and if the activities are determined in constant and optimal chloride concentration a straight line is obtained, as shown in curve B (2808–9). Somewhat similar curves were obtained for certain proteinases which are known to need an activator (Fig. IV.9 (1215)) and a similar mechanism is probably operating. In the absence of added activator, or on activation with added cyanide, the activity depends upon sub-optimal amounts of thiol compounds in the enzyme preparation, and as would be expected, marked upward curvatures are observed. With thioglycollate as activator, on the other hand, the thiol concentration does not vary with the enzyme concentration and a more nearly linear relationship is obtained.

Despite these exceptions, which we have discussed at some length, in the vast majority of cases an exact proportionality between enzyme concentration and initial velocity is found. Indeed this is a basic assumption in most of the kinetic work which has been published.

(B) EFFECT OF SUBSTRATE CONCENTRATION

Michaelis theory

Substrate concentration is one of the most important factors which determine the velocity of enzyme reactions. In nearly all cases when initial velocity is plotted against substrate concentration a section of a rectangular hyperbola is obtained, as shown in Fig. IV.10. The equation of the curve is

IV.4 $$(a-v)(b+s) = \text{const.}$$

(In certain cases the velocity may fall again at high substrate concentrations, but this is a special effect which will be dealt with later in this section.)

Such a result is obtained whenever a process depends upon a simple dissociation; if, for a dissociation $XY \rightleftharpoons X+Y$, $[Y]$ is held constant, plotting $[XY]$ against $[X]$ will give a curve resembling Fig. IV.10.

A theory involving a dissociation of this type was put forward in 1913 by MICHAELIS and MENTEN (1815) and has been the foundation of the greater part of enzyme kinetics. It adopts the earlier suggestion of HENRI (1065) that the enzyme first forms a complex with its substrate and this subsequently breaks down giving the free enzyme and the products of the reaction. If we write the process in two stages as

IV.5 $$E+S \rightleftharpoons ES$$

IV.6 $$ES\ (+\text{any second reactant}) \rightarrow E+\text{products}$$

and write s for the concentration of free substrate (which can be taken as equal to the total substrate concentration if the amount of enzyme is small in comparison, as is usually the case), e for the *total* enzyme concentration and p for the concentration of the complex, then since the concentration of *free* enzyme is $e-p$,

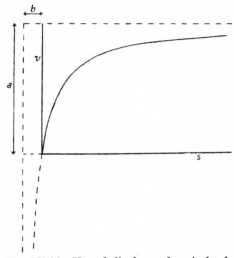

$$\text{IV.7} \qquad K_s = \frac{(e-p)s}{p}$$

where K_s is the equilibrium constant of the dissociation of ES into E and S, the 'substrate constant'. This equation applies to equilibrium conditions in which any effect of reaction IV.6 on the equilibrium is ignored.

Fig. IV.10. *Hyperbolic form of typical substrate concentration curve.*

If the equilibrium IV.5 is not attained so rapidly that ES remains always in equilibrium with E and S while the enzyme action is proceeding, the value of p will be less than that given by equation IV.7, but for the moment we shall assume with Michaelis that it is that given by rearranging the equation, namely

$$\text{IV.8} \qquad p = \frac{es}{K_s+s}$$

The rate of the enzyme reaction is determined by the rate of breakdown of the complex according to equation IV.6. This will be given by

$$\text{IV.9} \qquad v = kp$$

where k is the velocity constant of the breakdown of ES. If a second reactant is involved, its concentration will be included in k. Substituting the value of p from IV.8,

$$\text{IV.10} \qquad v = \frac{ke}{1+\dfrac{K_s}{s}}$$

When s becomes large in comparison with K_s, v will become equal to *ke*; we may write this maximum velocity, obtained when the enzyme is saturated with substrate, as V, so that

IV.11 $$v = \frac{V}{1 + \frac{K_s}{s}}$$

This is the well-known Michaelis equation. It can be rearranged as

IV.12 $$(V-v)(K_s+s) = VK_s$$

which is of the same form as equation IV.4. It may be noted that when s is equal to K_s, v will be equal to $V/2$; the value of s which is experimentally found to give half the maximum velocity (the Michaelis constant) is written K_m, so that under these conditions $K_m = K_s$. This equality depends on the truth of the assumption implicit in equation IV.8, that equilibrium is maintained between ES, E and S, which may not always obtain; the validity of this assumption in particular cases, and the significance of K_m in such cases, are considered later in this chapter (pp. 92 ff.).

Thus in the two extremes, when s is large, $v = V$, while when s is small, $v = \dfrac{V}{K_s} s$.

Although the assumptions made in this treatment lead to an equation which fits the experimental facts, this does not prove that the assumptions are correct, for a number of other assumptions also lead to the same form of equation. Among possible alternative mechanisms of which this is true are adsorption in accordance with the LANGMUIR isotherm (*1515*), and chain reaction mechanisms.

Whatever the theoretical interpretation, the equation of Michaelis and Menten does in fact hold in the vast majority of cases. In all such cases the response to changes in concentration of the substrate is of the same type, depending on the ratio of the substrate concentration to the Michaelis constant. If for convenience we term this the 'relative substrate concentration', denoted by σ,

IV.13 $$\sigma = \frac{s}{K_m}$$

and we also define 'relative velocity' by

IV.14 $$\phi = \frac{v}{V}$$

D

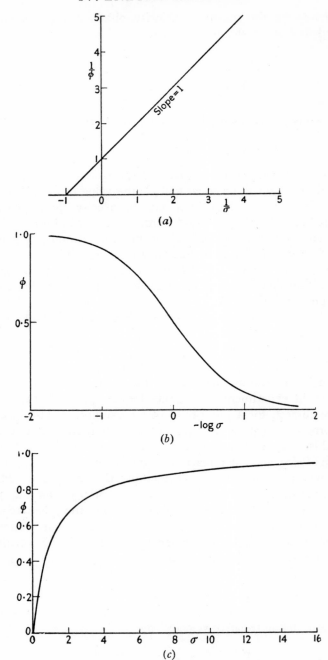

Fig. IV.11. *Normalized substrate concentration curves.*

then the Michaelis equation can be written as

IV.15 $$\phi = \frac{\sigma}{1+\sigma}$$

This gives the 'normalized curves' plotted in three forms in Fig. IV.11, which can be applied to any enzyme.

It follows from equation IV.15 that when the substrate concentration is high, $\phi = 1$, and when it is very low, $\phi = \sigma$.

The graph of velocity against substrate concentration for a given enzyme is defined by two quantities, namely V and K_m. From the simple derivation of the Michaelis equation given above it will be seen that, while K_m (here assumed to be equal to K_s) is the equilibrium constant of reaction IV.5, V is a measure of the velocity constant of breakdown of the complex. Thus these two quantities are related respectively to the two postulated stages of the overall reaction. It should be noted that under these conditions K_m is the reciprocal of the affinity of the enzyme for the substrate.

It is important to realize that factors which influence the velocity of enzyme reactions may produce their effects in two distinct ways, namely, by an effect either on the formation or on the breakdown of the enzyme-substrate complex (or on both). The determination of K_m and V enables these two effects to be studied separately; K_m depends on the formation of the complex, whereas V is a measure of the rate of its breakdown.

Determination of V and K_m

The Michaelis equation IV.11 may be plotted in several different ways for the determination of V and K_m from a set of measurements of velocity at different substrate concentrations.

(a) If v is plotted against s, as in Fig. IV.12 (a), the curve represents a section of a rectangular hyperbola. By substituting $v = V/2$, the equation becomes $s = K_m$, and K_m can thus be determined, being given by the 'half-way point' of the experimental curve. Different enzymes of course give different curves, depending on the values of V and K_m.

(b) Another method of plotting is shown in Fig. IV.12 (b), where v is plotted against pS ($= -\log s$), giving a curve of the familiar form met with in dissociations. This corresponds with the logarithmic form of the Michaelis equation

IV.16 $$pS = pK_m + \log \frac{V-v}{v}$$

Here a change of value of K_m does not affect the form of the curve, which depends only on the last term of the equation, but merely

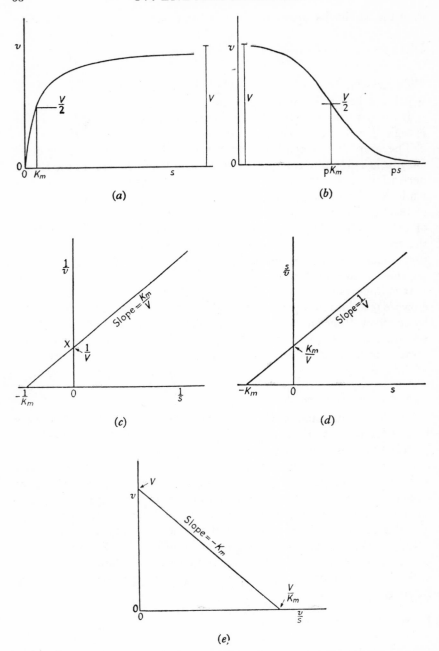

Fig. IV.12. *Five ways of plotting the effect of substrate concentration in order to determine K_m and V.*

displaces it along the horizontal axis by changing pK_m ($= -\log K_m$). If v is put equal to $V/2$, the last term becomes zero and the value of pS at the mid-point of the curve gives pK_m. In practice the main difficulty in obtaining K_m from either of these curves is to make sure of getting some experimental points at high enough substrate concentrations to reach the full value of V.

(c) A third method of plotting, usually ascribed to LINEWEAVER and BURK[†] (1596), avoids this difficulty. If $1/v$ is plotted against $1/s$, as shown in Fig. IV.12 (c), a straight line is obtained, corresponding to the reciprocal form of equation IV.11,

IV.17 $$\frac{1}{v} = \frac{K_m}{V} \cdot \frac{1}{s} + \frac{1}{V}$$

and this straight line cuts the base line at a point giving $-1/K_m$. This is easily shown by putting $1/v = 0$ in equation IV.17, which then gives $\frac{1}{s} = -\frac{1}{K_m}$. The graph cuts the vertical axis at a point which gives $1/V$ and has a slope of K_m/V.

(d) An alternative method, which gives a straight line apparently rather similar to the previous method, is to plot s/v against s, corresponding to the equation (given, but not plotted, by HANES, 996) obtained by multiplying IV.17 through by s

IV.18 $$\frac{s}{v} = \frac{K_m}{V} + \frac{1}{V} \cdot s$$

Here it is the slope which gives $1/V$ and the intercept on the vertical axis which gives K_m/V, as shown in Fig. IV.12(d). $-K_m$ is obtained by prolonging the graph to cut the base line.

(e) Another method of plotting, first put forward by WOOLF (2914) and strongly advocated by HOFSTEE (1125), is shown in Fig. IV.12 (e). Here v is plotted against v/s in accordance with the equation

IV.19 $$v = V - K_m \frac{v}{s}$$

which can be obtained by rearranging equation IV.11. K_m can be obtained by dividing the intercept on the vertical axis by the intercept on the horizontal axis.

The method of plotting which is most widely used is the double reciprocal plot (c). It has been argued, however, that method (e) is better.

[†] This method of plotting was originally suggested by WOOLF (2914) (quoted by Haldane and Stern in 1932, two years before Lineweaver and Burk's paper). Woolf also gave the values of the intercepts.

The arguments have been set out by HOFSTEE (*1125*), but have been answered by the authors (*633*). The main objection to (*c*) is that if a series of experimental points at equal increments of substrate concentration is plotted, they will tend to be concentrated near the left-hand side of the graph, whereas method (*e*) will give a more uniform distribution. We do not feel that there is much force in this argument because in any case it is best to take equal increments of pS (e.g. concentrations in the ratio 1, 2, 4, 8 . . .) rather than of s, and when this is done the reciprocal plot will give a more uniform distribution of points. In any case it is not clear that an equally spaced distribution is the best, since the position of a straight line is determined more precisely by points near its ends than by points near its centre. With the plot of v against v/s, there is no scale of substrate concentrations and it is difficult to identify the different points; moreover any error in v will cause an oblique displacement of the corresponding point. We prefer the reciprocal plot.

A statistical method for obtaining K_m and V from experimental results has been published (*2865*), but we feel that the above graphical methods are adequate for nearly all purposes.

Reactions involving two substrates

The great majority of enzyme reactions are of the type

IV.20 $A + B = C + D$

in which two substrate molecules react together. The classical theory developed in the previous section deals with the effect of only one substrate concentration and can be applied only to the comparatively uncommon cases where a single substrate molecule is involved. The theory has been extended by HALDANE (*979*, p. 83) to the case in which both A and B of equation IV.20 combine with the enzyme; see also *2466*.

Assuming the four equilibria

IV.21 $E + A \rightleftharpoons EA$

IV.22 $E + B \rightleftharpoons EB$

IV.23 $EA + B \rightleftharpoons EAB$

IV.24 $EB + A \rightleftharpoons EAB$

we have four corresponding equilibrium equations

IV.25 $(e - p_a - p_b - p)a = K_a p_a$

IV.26 $(e - p_a - p_b - p)b = K_b p_b$

IV.27 $p_a b = K_b' p$

IV.28 $p_b a = K_a' p$

where a, b, p, p_a, p_b are the concentrations of A, B, EAB, EA and EB respectively, and K_a, K_b, K'_b, K'_a are the respective dissociation constants of the four equilibria. The velocity will be proportional to the concentration of EAB, thus

IV.29 $\qquad v = kp$

Eliminating the p terms from these equations, we get

IV.30 $\qquad v = \dfrac{ke}{1 + \dfrac{K'_a}{a} + \dfrac{K'_b}{b} + \dfrac{K_a K'_b}{ab}}$

This equation contains only three of the four equilibrium constants; it can be expressed in terms of any three of the constants, since the fourth is redundant as it is related to the other three by the equation

IV.31 $\qquad K_a K'_b = K'_a K_b.$

In deriving equation IV.30, no assumptions have been made as to the effect which combination of the enzyme with one substrate may have on its combination with the other.

For any constant concentration of B, variation of the concentration of A thus gives a curve of the Michaelis type, represented by the equation

IV.32 $\qquad v = \dfrac{\dfrac{keb}{K'_b + b}}{1 + \dfrac{1}{a} \cdot \dfrac{K_a K'_b + K'_a b}{K'_b + b}}$

in which the apparent affinity for A is seen to be dependent on the concentration of B. This equation reduces to two simple approximations when the concentration of B is made very large or very small in relation to K'_b, namely

IV.33 $\qquad v = \dfrac{ke}{1 + \dfrac{K'_a}{a}}$

or

IV.34 $\qquad v = \dfrac{\dfrac{keb}{K'_b}}{1 + \dfrac{K_a}{a}}$

respectively. Thus in the first case $K_m = K_a'$ and in the second case $K_m = K_a$, so that these two constants can be measured. By keeping A constant and varying B, the other two constants may be determined.

K_a' and K_b' are readily obtained by the following graphical method (FLORINI and VESTLING, 753). A reciprocal plot of $1/v$ against $1/b$ at constant a gives a straight line cutting the vertical axis at $1/V_a = \{1+(K_a'/a)\}/ke$. A series of values of $1/V_a$ is obtained in this way, using different values of a, and these are plotted against $1/a$. A straight line is obtained, corresponding to the reciprocal of equation IV.33, and this cuts the base-line at $-1/K_a'$. A corresponding procedure, plotting $1/v$ against $1/a$ for various values of b, and replotting the intercepts against $1/b$, gives $-1/K_b'$. The original plots of $1/v$ against $1/b$ for various values of a intersect at a point situated at $1/b = -1/K_b$; similarly the plots of $1/v$ against $1/a$ for various values of b intersect at a point which gives $-1/K_a$. In this way all four constants can readily be obtained. This method has also been used by DALZIEL (534) (see Fig. IV.27).

If each substrate combines only with its own specific site and there is no effect of one substrate on the affinity for the other, then $K_a = K_a'$ and $K_b = K_b'$. Equation IV.30 then reduces to

$$\text{IV.35} \qquad v = \frac{ke\,\dfrac{ab}{K_a K_b}}{\left(1+\dfrac{a}{K_a}\right)\left(1+\dfrac{b}{K_b}\right)}$$

Making use of relative concentrations as previously defined (equation IV.13) and writing $\alpha = a/K_a$ and $\beta = b/K_b$, this equation becomes

$$\text{IV.36} \qquad \phi = \frac{\alpha}{1+\alpha}\cdot\frac{\beta}{1+\beta}$$

This will be seen by comparison with equation IV.15 to be the product of two Michaelis functions, one for each substrate. As the affinity of each substrate in this case is independent of combination of the enzyme with the other, the true Michaelis constants may be determined by variation of each substrate concentration at any fixed concentration of the other.

If an enzyme catalyses a reaction between two identical molecules combining with the same affinity, $\alpha = \beta = \sigma$ and

$$\text{IV.37} \qquad \phi = \frac{\sigma^2}{(1+\sigma)^2}$$

or in reciprocal form

IV.38 $$\frac{1}{\phi} = 1 + \frac{2}{\sigma} + \frac{1}{\sigma^2}$$

This will give non-linear reciprocal plots with an upward curvature, similar to those given by a substrate which is also an activator, shown in Fig. IV.20, curve B. A tangent drawn at the point where the curve cuts the vertical axis will cut the base-line at $-\frac{1}{2K_s}$, which means that the apparent Michaelis constant will be twice the constant for each site separately.

It is possible to think of reactions between two substances as occurring without a definite combination of one of them with the enzyme, the second reactant being involved in a bimolecular reaction with a complex of the first reactant with the enzyme, thus

IV.39 $\quad$ E+A = EA

IV.40 $\quad$ EA+B = E+C+D

In this case equation IV.9 must be replaced by

IV.41 $\quad v = k'bp_a$

where k' is now a bimolecular velocity constant and p_a is as before the concentration of EA. Equation IV.36 is then replaced by

IV.42 $$\phi = \frac{\alpha}{1+\alpha} \cdot b$$

It follows that as the concentration of A is increased, the velocity rises to a limit, but as the concentration of B is increased, it rises linearly. This, however, is only true if K_a is the actual dissociation constant of reaction IV.39. For cases in which K_a has a more complex kinetic meaning, see p. 94.

Many transferring enzymes, e.g. creatine kinase (2.7.3.2) (1480), are examples of the mechanism shown in equations IV.21–24; Michaelis constants have been obtained for both reactants. Peroxidase (1.11.1.7) (418) is an example of the mechanism shown in equations IV.39–40; a Michaelis constant has been obtained for hydrogen peroxide, but the velocity is proportional to the concentration of hydrogen donor.

The hydrolysing enzymes also involve a second reactant, namely, water. In the majority of cases it has not been possible to determine the effect of altering the water concentration appreciably, but in the case of yeast β-fructofuranosidase (3.2.1.26) the falling off in velocity in very high sucrose concentrations has been attributed to the reduction of the

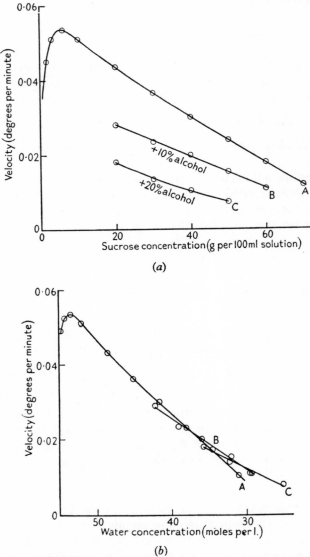

Fig. IV.13. *Hydrolysis of high concentrations of sucrose by yeast β-fructofuranosidase (3.2.1.26): effect of reducing water concentration.*

In A the water concentration was lowered by sucrose; in B and C by alcohol in addition.

The curves have been replotted in (*b*) in terms of water concentration.

from *1937*

water concentration (*1937*). It has been shown that over a wide range the velocity is a function of the concentration of water, and it is immaterial whether the reduction in water concentration is due to the addition of sucrose of alcohol (see Fig. IV.13). However, there are complications in these experiments, since in the presence of alcohol the enzyme catalyses transfructosylation to alcohol as well as the hydrolysis and this would produce an apparent decrease in the hydrolysis rate (*126*); but the inhibition by high sucrose concentration cannot be accounted for by fructosyl transfer to sucrose (*125*).

Inhibition by high substrate concentrations

It is not uncommon to find that, while the Michaelis law is obeyed at lower substrate concentrations, the velocity falls off again at high concentrations. This effect may be due to a number of different causes.

(*a*) Studies on the specificity of enzymes suggest that a great many enzymes have two or more groups, each combining with a particular part of the substrate molecule. In the effective enzyme–substrate complex one substrate molecule is combined with all these groups, but it is possible to imagine an ineffective complex in which a substrate molecule may combine with only one of these groups if the other groups are combined with other molecules. In high substrate concentrations, where the substrate molecules tend to crowd on to the enzyme, the chance of formation of ineffective complexes with two or more substrate molecules combined with the active centre increases. This possibility, which is really a case of competitive inhibition by the substrate itself (cf. p. 318), has been treated theoretically by HALDANE (*979*, p. 84).

The reactions may be written as

IV.43 $\qquad$ $E + S \rightleftharpoons ES$

IV.44 $\qquad$ $ES + S \rightleftharpoons ES_2$

IV.45 $\qquad$ $ES \rightarrow E + products$

The appropriate equilibrium equations are

IV.46 $\qquad$ $(e - p - q)s = K_s p$

IV.47 $\qquad$ $ps = K'_s q$

where q is the concentration of ES_2 and K'_s its dissociation constant, that is to say, the equilibrium constant of reaction IV.44. From these equations, assuming that the velocity is proportional to p,

IV.48 $\qquad$ $v = \dfrac{ke}{1 + \dfrac{K_s}{s} + \dfrac{s}{K'_s}}$

Once more using relative concentrations, and for convenience introducing a 'relative inhibition constant' r, defined by

IV.49
$$r = \frac{K_s'}{K_s}$$

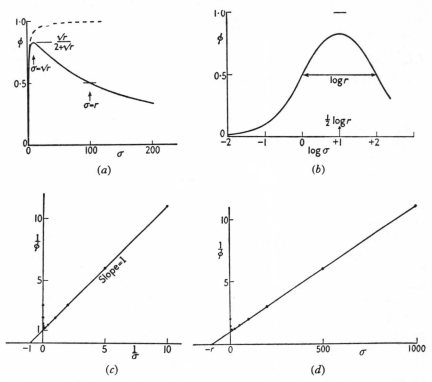

Fig. IV.14. *Inhibition by high substrate concentration: normalized curves, drawn for an arbitrary value of $r = K_s'/K_s = 100$ (cf. Fig. IV.11).*

(a) Direct plot of ϕ against σ: the dotted curve is the curve without excess substrate inhibition.

(b) Plot of ϕ against log σ: note that owing to change of sign the left-hand side of the curve corresponds with Fig. IV.11(b). The curve is symmetrical about the value $\sigma = \sqrt{r}$ and has a width of log r at $\phi = 0\cdot5$; consequently the point of inflexion of the left-hand side is at log $\sigma = 0$.

(c) Plot of $1/\phi$ against $1/\sigma$; the points shown are the calculated values which lie on the unit-slope line of Fig. IV.11(c) over most of the range. The upward deviation at low $1/\sigma$ values represents the high substrate inhibition.

(d) Plot of $1/\phi$ against σ; the points now lying on the straight line are those which represent the high substrate inhibition and those which lay on the straight line of (c) now appear as an upward deviation at low values of σ.

we get

IV.50
$$\phi = \frac{1}{1 + \frac{1}{\sigma} + \frac{\sigma}{r}}$$

In Fig. IV.14 this standard equation is plotted in various ways, taking an arbitrary value of $r = 100$, which corresponds with the value experimentally found for the action of liver carboxylesterase (3.1.1.1) on ethyl mandelate (150). It will be noticed that although the two Ks are well separated, the maximum value of ϕ obtained is considerably less than 1, or in other words v fails by an appreciable margin to reach V. Consequently, any attempt to calculate K_s from curves of the type (a) or (b) would give erroneous values if the maximum velocity is taken as V. The reciprocal plot (c) is not affected by this error, for this graph spreads out the data for the lower substrate concentrations so that the greater part of the curve represents the region where the Michaelis law is obeyed. The true value of $1/V$ can be obtained from the reciprocal plots of the experimental data, as shown by the fact that the standard graph cuts the vertical axis at $1/\phi = 1$. Using this value of V, r may be determined from either (a) or (b) as shown. The highest relative velocity, $\sqrt{r}/(2 + \sqrt{r})$ is obtained at an actual substrate concentration equal to $\sqrt{(K_s K_s')}$, corresponding to a relative concentration of $\sqrt{r}$. The logarithmic curve (b) is symmetrical about this value. r may be directly determined by plotting $1/\phi$ against σ, as shown in (d), and producing the straight line obtained at high values of σ to cut the base-line. This is because at high substrate concentration the term K_s/s in equation IV.48 becomes negligible and the inhibition term becomes dominant. The equation then becomes, writing $ke = V$,

IV.51
$$v = \frac{V K_s'}{s + K_s'}$$

or in reciprocal form

IV.52
$$\frac{1}{v} = \frac{1}{V} + \frac{s}{K_s' V}$$

Fig. IV. 15 shows a plot of $1/v$ against s for the case of liver carboxylesterase, calculated from the data of MURRAY (1902), for high substrate concentrations. The intercept on the base-line gives a value for K' of $0 \cdot 010$ M. The value obtained by Murray from the same data by a more laborious procedure was $0 \cdot 0097$ M. Where the enzyme reaction is a two-step one (see p. 290), for instance where an esterase is first acylated with release of the alcohol moiety of the substrate and later deacylated, the second substrate molecule may combine with the alcohol-binding site of the acylated enzyme, so retarding deacylation. Substrate inhibition of acetylcholinesterase appears to be due to such an effect (*1471*).

(*b*) Since all enzymes act in aqueous media, very high substrate concentrations will imply a reduction in the concentration of the water, which may lower the velocity, especially if water is one of the reactants. An example of this effect has already been given in the last section (Fig. IV.13).

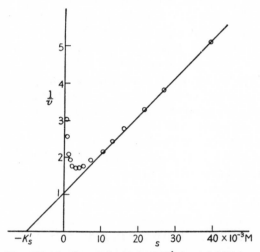

Fig. IV.15. *Determination of K'_s from inhibition by excess substrate.*

Hydrolysis of ethyl butyrate by sheep liver carboxylesterase (3.1.1.1).

plotted from data in *1902*

(*c*) Fig. IV.16 shows the rate of reduction of methylene blue by varying concentrations of hypoxanthine with xanthine oxidase (1.2.3.2)(*630*). The inhibition by substrate is due to a competition with the methylene blue, as shown by the fact that the effective affinity for the dye is reduced twentyfold on increasing the substrate concentration from A to B. This is a special case of competitive inhibition in which one substrate is a competitive inhibitor of the other. Another case of this kind is the L-aminoacid oxidase of snake venom (1.4.3.2) (*2411*), which has more recently been investigated in some detail, using leucine as substrate and methylene blue as hydrogen acceptor (*629*). In Fig. IV.17 $1/v$ has been plotted against leucine concentration for four different concentrations of methylene blue. On comparing this figure with Fig. VIII.2(*a*) (see also

Figs.IV.14(d) and IV.15), it will be evident that the leucine is acting as an inhibitor competing with the methylene blue. The curves cross at a point (corresponding to $-K_i$ in the case of an ordinary inhibitor) which gives the dissociation constant of the substrate when acting as an inhibitor.

(d) An apparent case of inhibition by high substrate concentration is that of inorganic pyrophosphatase (3.6.1.1)(*137*). Here there is an additional factor, as Mg functions as an essential activator (see Chapter IX).

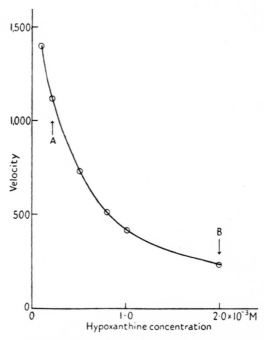

Fig. IV.16. *Inhibition with increase of substrate concentration.*

Xanthine oxidase (1.2.3.2).

from *630*

Fig. IV.18 shows the effect of varying the pyrophosphate concentration keeping the added Mg constant at $0 \cdot 004$ M. The concentrations of pyrophosphate required for inhibition are far higher than those needed to saturate the enzyme with substrate, so that the maximum velocity is obtained over a wide range.

Two different explanations have been given for the inhibition, both depending on the formation of a magnesium–pyrophosphate complex. The first explanation (*1068*) is that the excess of substrate binds magnesium and so lowers the effective concentration of the enzyme activator, so that the velocity falls and when the concentration of free Mg^{++} ions is reduced to zero the enzyme becomes inactive. The other explanation (*275*) depends on the assumption (for which there is some evidence) that the true substrate of the enzyme is the complex ion $(MgP_2O_7)^{--}$

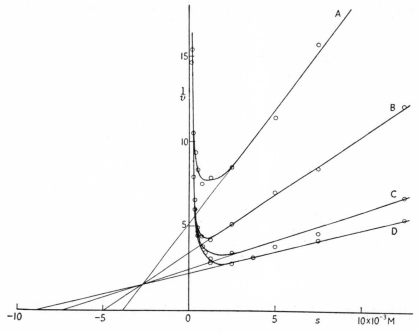

Fig. IV.17. *Competitive inhibition by excess substrate.*
Oxidation of leucine by methylene blue with snake venom L-aminoacid oxidase (1.4.3.2). s = leucine concentration.
Methylene blue concentrations: curve A, $0\cdot334 \times 10^{-4}$ M; curve B, $0\cdot67 \times 10^{-4}$ M; curve C, $1\cdot34 \times 10^{-4}$ M; curve D, $2\cdot67 \times 10^{-4}$ M.

from *629*

and not free pyrophosphate. The inhibition is assumed to be due to a competition of the pyrophosphate with the true substrate. In any case, the effect is not in fact due to a true inhibition by high substrate concentration, for if the Mg is varied in proportion to the added pyrophosphate, so as to keep the pyrophosphate in the form of the Mg complex, the inhibition largely disappears (Fig. IV.19).

With enzymes which depend on an activator, such as that just discussed, the possibility exists that the substrate will compete with the activator for the enzyme and thus inhibit in high concentration (BOTTS, *297*).

Substrate acting also as activator

In the previous section we have been dealing with cases in which the substrate also acts as an inhibitor. It is possible that in some cases the

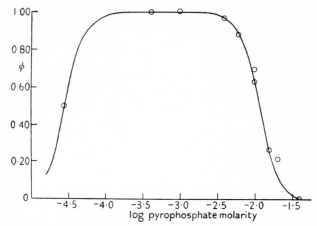

Fig. IV.18. *Substrate concentration curve of inorganic pyrophosphatase (3.6.1.1) in presence of 0·004 m MgCl₂.*
from *137*

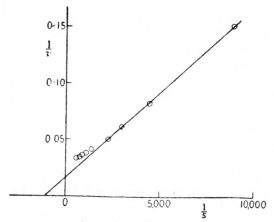

Fig. IV.19. *Lineweaver–Burk plot of inorganic pyrophosphatase (3.6.1.1) with constant MgCl₂/Na₂P₂O₇ molar ratio of 3·8.*
after *275*

substrate also functions as an activator of the enzyme. For instance, fumarate hydratase (4.2.1.2) is activated by anions (*1744*) and since the substrates are themselves anions it is probable that they may act in this capacity in addition to their normal functions as substrates. MASSEY (1746) has in fact suggested that substrate molecules may combine with fumarase at points other than the active centre.

The reactions involved can be represented as

IV.53 $\qquad$ $E+S \rightleftharpoons ES$

IV.54 $\qquad$ $E+S \rightleftharpoons ES_a$

IV.55 $\qquad$ $ES_a+S \rightleftharpoons ES_a S$

Here S_a represents the substrate combined as an activator, so that IV.54 represents the conversion of the free enzyme into the active form ES_a, while IV.53 and IV.55 represent the substration of the free enzyme and the activated enzyme respectively. The activating substrate molecule and the true substrate molecule are assumed to combine at different sites, so that they do not compete with each other.

The corresponding equilibrium equations are

IV.56 $\qquad$ $(e-p-q-r)s = K_s q$

IV.57 $\qquad$ $(e-p-q-r)s = K_{sa} r$

IV.58 $\qquad$ $rs = K'_s p$

where p, q and r are the concentrations of $ES_a S$, ES and ES_a respectively and K_s, K_{sa} and K'_s are the respective dissociation constants of the equilibria IV.53–55.

Assuming that ES is completely inactive (although perhaps in some cases it may break down at a slow rate) the velocity will be proportional to p, as in previous cases. This leads to

IV.59 $\qquad$ $$v = \frac{ke}{1+\dfrac{K'_s}{s}\left(1+\dfrac{K_{sa}}{K_s}+\dfrac{K_{sa}}{s}\right)}$$

or in the reciprocal form

IV.60 $\qquad$ $$\frac{1}{v} = \frac{1}{V} + \frac{K'_s}{V}\left(1+\frac{K_{sa}}{K_s}\right)\frac{1}{s} + \frac{K_{sa}K'_s}{V}\cdot\frac{1}{s^2}$$

This will in general give a curved reciprocal plot and not a straight line, owing to the term involving s^2 in the denominator, which arises from the fact that the active complex contains two substrate molecules. At high substrate concentrations the last term will become negligible, especially if K_{sa} is small in relation to K'_s, and under these conditions the curve will approximate to a straight line, which will give an apparent Michaelis constant of $K'_s\left(1+\dfrac{K_{sa}}{K_s}\right)$. This will differ from the true

Michaelis constant by the term in brackets, which is a correction term for the competitive effect of reaction IV.53, which we have assumed to give an inactive complex.

Fig. IV.20 shows some theoretical curves plotted from this equation; the true Michaelis constant K_s' is arbitrarily taken as $0 \cdot 01$ for all the curves and it will be seen that they diverge considerably from the dotted line, which is the line which would be obtained with this Michaelis

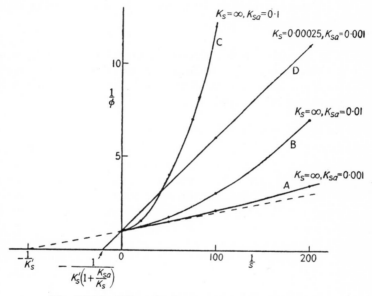

Fig. IV.20. *Effect of substrate acting also as activator.*

Theoretical substrate concentration curves, calculated from various combinations of constants.

For all curves $K_s' = 0 \cdot 01$.

constant in the absence of these special effects. In order to show the effect of the last term, the competitive effect has been eliminated in curves A, B and C by making K_s equal to infinity; this is equivalent to assuming that only the active centre of the form ES_a is capable of combining with substrate. It can be shown that all the curves have the same slope as the dotted line at $1/s = 0$, but diverge upwards to very different extents, depending on the value of K_{sa}. When K_{sa} is small in comparison with K_s' (curve A, where $K_{sa}/K_s' = 0 \cdot 1$), the departure from a straight line is comparatively small; when K_{sa} becomes larger (curves B and C, where K_{sa}/K_s' is $1 \cdot 0$ and 10 respectively), the curvature may become very large indeed, which makes it impossible to determine any Michaelis constant.

The effect of the competition term is shown by curve D, which has been plotted for the same value of K_{sa} as curve A, but now taking K_s as $0 \cdot 00025$. This produces a marked inhibition, increasing the slope of the curve, which however remains linear. Thus it is difficult to distinguish it from a normal reciprocal plot, but the apparent value of the Michaelis constant obtained from it differs greatly from the true value; in this case it gives five times the true value, since with the values chosen

$$1 + \frac{K_{sa}}{K_s} = 5.$$

The effects discussed in this section are probably not very common for only a few enzymes appear to be activated in this way; we have not in fact found any experimental data in the literature to which this quantitative theory can be applied.

Enzymes catalysing two reactions simultaneously

When an enzyme is not absolutely specific for one substrate only, the possibility arises that it may act on two different substrates present at the same time. This cannot be considered simply as a case of two independent parallel reactions, for the same active centres act on both substrates and therefore there will be competition between them. For an enzyme acting on two substrates A and B

IV.61 $E + A \rightleftharpoons EA$

IV.62 $EA \rightarrow E + \text{products}_A$

IV.63 $E + B \rightleftharpoons EB$

IV.64 $EB \rightarrow E + \text{products}_B$

So far as A is concerned, B behaves simply as a competitive inhibitor, and vice versa. The rate of breakdown of A will therefore be given, by analogy with equation VIII.16, by

IV.65 $$v_a = \frac{V_a}{1 + \dfrac{K_a}{a}\left(1 + \dfrac{b}{K_b}\right)}$$

and that of B by

IV.66 $$v_b = \frac{V_b}{1 + \dfrac{K_b}{b}\left(1 + \dfrac{a}{K_a}\right)}$$

If we write the sum of reactions IV.65 and IV.66 as v_t

IV.67
$$v_t = v_a + v_b = \frac{V_a \frac{a}{K_a} + V_b \frac{b}{K_b}}{1 + \frac{a}{K_a} + \frac{b}{K_b}}$$

In any mixture containing concentrations a and b of A and B respectively, the total velocity v_t must lie between the two velocities which would be obtained with these concentrations of A and B separately. If we assume for convenience that the velocity constant of reaction IV.62 is higher than that of reaction IV.64, the maximum velocity attainable with a mixture of A and B is V_a. We may therefore define a relative velocity ϕ_t as

IV.68
$$\phi_t = \frac{v_t}{V_a}$$

Expressing equation IV.67 in terms of relative concentrations, we get

IV.69
$$\phi_t = \frac{\alpha + R\beta}{1 + \alpha + \beta}$$

where R, which must be less than 1, is written for the ratio V_b/V_a.

Two special cases of interest arise when the two substrates are present in the same concentration, so that $a = b$. It may be possible either to measure each of the two reactions separately, or, alternatively, to measure the sum of the reactions, for instance, by measuring the total acid production of an esterase.

In the first case the ratio of the rates of breakdown of A and B in an equimolar mixture is obtained by dividing equation IV.65 by IV.66, which gives

IV.70
$$\frac{v_a}{v_b} = \frac{V_a K_b}{V_b K_a}$$

In the second case (*2646, 2857*) writing $a = b = s$ and putting v_M for the velocity in an equimolar mixture, equation IV.67 becomes

IV.71
$$v_M = \frac{\frac{V_a}{K_a} + \frac{V_b}{K_b}}{\frac{1}{s} + \frac{1}{K_a} + \frac{1}{K_b}}$$

The maximum velocity attainable in an equimolar mixture is

IV.72
$$V_M = \frac{\dfrac{V_a}{K_a} + \dfrac{V_b}{K_b}}{\dfrac{1}{K_a} + \dfrac{1}{K_b}}$$

which on rearrangement gives

IV.73
$$\frac{K_a}{K_b} = \frac{V_a - V_M}{V_M - V_b}$$

Thus the ratio of the affinities of an enzyme for two substrates can be determined from three measurements of velocity, namely, the maximum velocities with the two substrates separately and with an equimolar mixture of both. Thus in specificity studies it may only be necessary to determine one substrate concentration curve completely; having found one K_m, those for other substrates can be calculated by means of mixed substrate measurements, using equation IV.73. Cholinesterase (3.1.1.8) has been studied by this method (7). The method only gives accurate results if V_a differs considerably from V_b and K_a does not differ too much from K_b.

The mixed substrate method has been much used, often in a semi-qualitative way, to determine whether two reactions are due to the same enzyme. For example, with a preparation of horse serum cholinesterase the rate of hydrolysis of benzoyl choline was found (2562a) to be 440 µl per hour, that of isoamyl acetate was 131, while that of a mixture of the two was 314. Had the hydrolysis been due to two different enzymes it should have been the sum, namely 571. From such results it was concluded that the hydrolysis of a number of choline and non-choline esters was due to one and the same enzyme.

The method can be made quantitative if the relative concentrations α and β of the two substrates are known (i.e. if the Michaelis constants have been determined) (2809). If the two substrates are being attacked by the same enzyme, then from equation IV.67

IV.74
$$v_t = \frac{V_a \alpha + V_b \beta}{1 + \alpha + \beta}$$

When the two substrates are present separately

IV.75
$$v_a = \frac{V_a \alpha}{1 + \alpha}$$

IV.76
$$v_b = \frac{V_b \beta}{1 + \beta}$$

Substituting IV.75 and IV.76 into IV.74, we get

IV.77
$$v_t = \frac{v_a(1+\alpha)+v_b(1+\beta)}{1+\alpha+\beta}$$

If the substrates are used at equal *relative* concentrations, $\alpha = \beta = \sigma$ and

IV.78
$$v_t = (v_a+v_b) \cdot \frac{1+\sigma}{1+2\sigma}$$

Thus the 'mixed substrate' velocity falls from the sum of the separate velocities when σ is very low to $\frac{3}{4}$ of the sum when $\sigma = \frac{1}{2}$, $\frac{2}{3}$ when $\sigma = 1$, and $\frac{1}{2}$ when σ is very large.

An interesting mixed-substrate phenomenon is seen when the substrate contains, as an impurity, small amounts of another substrate which has a much higher affinity and at the same time a much lower maximum velocity than the substrate being tested. Such a case was found by WILLSTÄTTER (*2876*) when investigating the hydrolysis of redistilled ethyl mandelate by liver carboxylesterase (3.1.1.1). The substrate contained small amounts of the corresponding keto-ester, which had a very high affinity for the enzyme but broke down only slowly. On account of its high affinity it almost entirely displaced the mandelate from the enzyme, reducing the observed velocity almost to zero and acting as a competitive inhibitor. The keto-ester, however, underwent slow but steady hydrolysis by the enzyme, and when its hydrolysis was complete and the mandelate was able to obtain access to the enzyme there was a sudden great increase in velocity, as shown in Fig. IV.21. There was thus a long latent period, the duration of which was proportional to the amount of substrate taken (and hence to the amount of the impurity), after which the normal reaction started and proceeded linearly. When the mandelate was purified by recrystallization the lag period disappeared.

Two enzymes acting on one substrate

The disappearance of a substrate may be due to the simultaneous action of two or more enzymes. If we consider two enzymes, distinguished by the use of the subscripts 1 and 2, the total rate of disappearance will be the sum of the two separate reactions, so that we may write

IV.79
$$v_t = \frac{V_1}{1+\dfrac{K_1}{s}} + \frac{V_2}{1+\dfrac{K_2}{s}}$$

In reciprocal form this equation reduces to

IV.80
$$\frac{1}{v} = \frac{1 + \dfrac{K_1 + K_2}{s} + \dfrac{K_1 K_2}{s^2}}{V_1 + V_2 + \dfrac{V_1 K_2 + V_2 K_1}{s}}$$

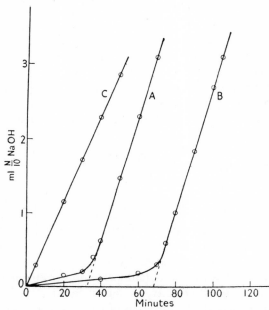

Fig. IV.21. *Lag period produced by impurity in substrate.*

Hydrolysis of ethyl mandelate by liver carboxyl-esterase.

A, 0·008 M redistilled substrate.
B, 0·016 M redistilled substrate.
C, 0·008 M recrystallized substrate.

after *2876*

The shape of the curve obtained will depend on the relative values of K_1 and K_2. If $K_1 = K_2$, a straight-line plot is obtained, as would be the case with a single enzyme (see Fig. IV.22(*a*), curve A). The intercepts then give $1/(V_1 + V_2)$ and $-1/K_1(= -1/K_2)$ respectively. If the constants differ, a straight line will not be obtained and the results will not be easy to interpret. A number of theoretical curves have been plotted from equation IV.80 in Fig. IV.22, (*a*) showing the effect of changing

K_2 while $V_1 = V_2 = 1$ and K_1 is kept constant at 10^{-3}, and (b) showing the effect of varying V_1 and V_2 while K_1 and K_2 are kept constant at 10^{-3} and 10^{-4} respectively. The curves are all hyperbolic in form, with two branches, of which one is completely, and the other partly,

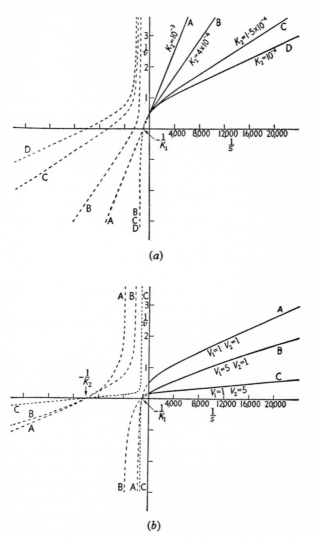

(a)

(b)

Fig. IV.22. *Hydrolysis of one substrate by two enzymes.*
Theoretical curves plotted from equation IV.80.
(a) for $V_1 = V_2 = 1$; $K_1 = 10^{-3}$ M.
(b) for $K_1 = 10^{-3}$ M, $K_2 = 10^{-4}$ M.

imaginary, corresponding to negative values of substrate concentration. These two branches cut the base line at $-1/K_2$ and $-1/K_1$ respectively, as can readily be seen from equation IV.80.

When the substrate concentration is sufficiently low, i.e. far to the right of the graphs shown, all of the curves approximate to straight lines, cutting the base line when produced at $-1/K_2$. This would be expected,

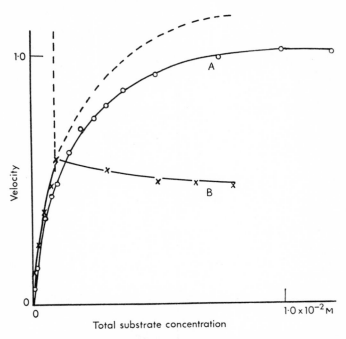

Fig. IV.23. *Substrate concentration curves of carboxylesterase with ethyl butyrate (curve A) and tributyrin (curve B).*

The vertical dotted line shows the limit of solubility for tributyrin.

from *2808*

since at very low substrate concentrations only the enzyme with the higher affinity will contribute appreciably to the observed velocity. In all the curves drawn, K_1 is assumed to be greater than K_2. As $1/s$ decreases, the curves bend downwards because their imaginary extensions must cut the base-line at $-1/K_1$. For certain conditions, e.g. those of curves (a) D and (b) C, this curvature might be overlooked in practice; if the system is then treated as a one-enzyme system and a straight line ruled through the points, a value of K_m intermediate between K_1 and K_2 will be obtained.

Insoluble substrates

Enzymes usually act on substrates in solution. If the amount of substrate added is increased beyond the solubility limit, the excess will no longer be available to the enzyme. If the solubility is not very great in comparison with the Michaelis constant the velocity will follow the Michaelis curve only up to the solubility limit, after which the velocity will not increase further. V in equation IV.11 will never be reached, since

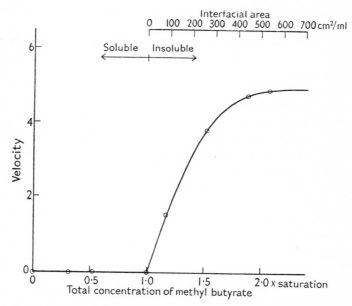

Fig. IV.24. *Substrate concentration curve of pancreatic lipase with methyl butyrate.*

The velocity is given in per cent of the maximal velocity with triolein, and the total ester concentration is expressed in relation to a saturated solution, taken as 1·0.

from *2302*

the concentration of substrate which saturates an aqueous solution is insufficient to saturate the enzyme. Fig. IV.23 shows a typical experiment with liver carboxylesterase (3.1.1.1) acting on ethyl butyrate and on tributyrin. The whole of the ethyl butyrate was in solution. The tributyrin, which is comparatively insoluble, was added in the form of a stock emulsion to give the total concentrations shown; to the left of the dotted line the tributyrin was all in water-clear solution, whereas to the right only part of the emulsion dissolved up in the reaction mixture, and in this region the actual concentration in solution was presumably constant.

SARDA and DESNUELLE (*2302*) have shown that pancreatic lipase (3.1.1.3) does not act on dissolved substrates, but is only active when adsorbed at an ester–water interface, apparently because the active centre of the enzyme is only then exposed. If a very insoluble substrate, such as triolein, is used as an emulsion, a typical Michaelis curve starting from the origin is obtained. On the other hand, with a more soluble substrate, such as methyl butyrate, no activity is shown on the left of the dotted line, but a Michaelis-type curve starts from the point at which the aqueous phase is saturated with ester (Fig. IV. 24), forming a complete contrast to Fig. IV.23.

As is to be expected if there is an equilibrium between free and adsorbed enzyme, a 'Michaelis constant' can be obtained from the curve, and this represents the dissociation constant of the enzyme-interface complex. The interfacial area takes the place of substrate concentration in the usual theory; this depends on the degree of emulsification as well as the amount of substrate present. Sarda and Desnuelle express their results in terms of a Michaelis constant given as the 'molar interfacial concentration' for half maximal velocity. The molar interfacial concentration is the area of interface in a litre of emulsion divided by the interfacial area occupied by one mole of substrate. Since the number of enzyme molecules that can combine with 1 cm^2 of interface will presumably be determined more by the area occupied by an enzyme molecule than by the area occupied by the much smaller substrate molecule, the actual interfacial area is probably more significant.

Steady-state theory

As pointed out on p. 65, it was assumed in working out the Michaelis theory that the equilibrium between enzyme and substrate (reaction IV.5) is attained so rapidly in comparison with the breakdown of ES (reaction IV.6) that ES remains always in equilibrium with E and S while the enzyme action is proceeding. In view of the very high catalytic activities shown by many enzymes it is probable that this may not always be the case, so that p will differ from its equilibrium value. An alternative treatment, applicable to such cases, was put forward by BRIGGS and HALDANE (*328*) in 1925. This is based on the postulate that at any moment the rates of formation and breakdown of the ES complex are essentially equal, so that its concentration p can be regarded as constant over the short period of time necessary for a velocity measurement. Over a longer period of course p will change as the reaction proceeds and the substrate concentration consequently falls, but the rate of change of p will always be much smaller than the rate of the enzyme reaction. In using this postulate to develop a theory of the relation between the velocity of the reaction and the substrate concentration, these long-term changes may be neglected and the system may be treated as being in a steady state.

In order to do this, velocity constants† must be introduced for the separate reactions as follows

IV.81 $$E + S \underset{k_{-1}}{\overset{k_{+1}}{\rightleftharpoons}} ES \overset{k_{+2}}{\longrightarrow} E + \text{products}$$

Then the rate of formation of ES will be $k_{+1}(e-p)s$ and the rate of breakdown will be the sum of the two rates of breakdown into E and S and into E and products, namely $k_{-1}p$ and $k_{+2}p$ respectively. Thus the net rate of change of p will be

IV.82 $$\frac{dp}{dt} = k_{+1}(e-p)s - (k_{-1} + k_{+2})p$$

For the steady state, when $dp/dt = 0$, it follows that

IV.83 $$p = \frac{es}{\dfrac{k_{-1} + k_{+2}}{k_{+1}} + s}$$

This value replaces the one obtained from simple equilibrium theory given in equation IV.8. The velocity of the enzyme reaction, as measured by the formation of products, will be

IV.84 $$v = k_{+2}p = \frac{k_{+2}\,es}{\dfrac{k_{-1} + k_{+2}}{k_{+1}} + s}$$

The maximum velocity is given by

IV.85 $$V = k_{+2}e$$

so that equation IV.84 can be written as

IV.86 $$v = \frac{V}{1 + \dfrac{K_m}{s}}$$

This is identical with the Michaelis equation IV.11, except that K_s is replaced by K_m, which is given by

IV.87 $$K_m = \frac{k_{-1} + k_{+2}}{k_{+1}} = K_s + \frac{k_{+2}}{k_{+1}}$$

† The numbering of the rate constants is in accordance with the Enzyme Commission's recommendations.

If k_{+2} is much smaller than k_{-1}, the last term can be neglected and K_m becomes k_{-1}/k_{+1} which, being the ratio of the velocity constants of reaction IV.5 in opposite directions, is equal to the equilibrium constant K_s.

Thus with the reaction system we have considered above, involving one substrate and one intermediate complex, the Briggs–Haldane treatment and the Michaelis treatment give identical results, provided that k_{+2} may be neglected in comparison with k_{-1}. With more complicated reaction systems, however, steady-state treatment gives more complicated expressions for V and K_m, or even rate equations which are not of the same form as the Michaelis equation. Some of these cases are considered in the succeeding sections.

General methods for writing steady-state equations

For any particular sequence of steps in an enzymatic reaction, it is possible to write down a set of simultaneous equations, one stating that the sum of the concentrations of all forms of the enzyme remains constant, and one for each enzyme complex, stating that its concentration remains constant in the steady state, expressed in terms of the rate constants involving that complex. It is possible by the usual methods to solve this set of equations, as was done in the simple case in the last section, to give expressions for the concentration of a chosen intermediate, analogous with equation IV.83; multiplication by the rate constant for the breakdown of this complex will give the rate of the overall reaction.

Equations for a number of special cases have been worked out in this way by direct calculation by several groups of workers; two of the earliest collections of results were given by SEGAL, KACHMAR and BOYER (*2363*) in 1952 and by INGRAHAM and MAKOWER (*1212*) in 1954, and other sets are given by DALZIEL (*534*) and ALBERTY (*33*).

KING and ALTMAN (*1383*) have made use of the determinant method for solving the above sets of simultaneous equations, and from the results have deduced a valuable set of schematic rules which enable the rate equation for any given reaction system to be written down without the tedium of expanding the individual determinants. The method is best explained by using a particular case as an example, and treating it in some detail. The example which we shall consider is that of an enzyme catalysing a reaction between two substrates A and B with the formation of a product Z; the reaction sequence involves the formation of a ternary complex (which we shall write as EXY), by combination of A and B successively in random order with the enzyme. The system of reactions, with the rate constants and substances involved, is shown in Fig. IV.25. This is one of several examples worked out by WONG and HANES (*2905*) using the King and Altman procedure.

This consists in setting out diagrammatically arrangements of arrows in accordance with certain rules; these arrangements define the terms in the overall rate equation. For the numerator one notes all the possible combinations of arrows which fulfil the following requirements: (a) one arrow (not more) starts from each enzyme-containing species (including the free enzyme itself), (b) the arrows must not form a closed ring, (c) not more than one direction of any step must be shown. It must be remembered that the first and last species in Fig. IV.25 are the same.

The possible combinations for Fig. IV.25, of which there are eight, are set out in Fig. IV.26 as 'numerator terms', each representing a product of the corresponding rate constants which forms one term in the

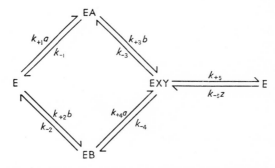

Fig. IV.25. *Reaction sequence for enzyme system dealt with in Fig. IV.26.*
Overall reaction: $A + B \rightleftharpoons Z$

numerator of the rate equation. Half of these terms are concerned with the forward reaction and half with the back reaction. The forward terms are positive and contain the concentration of substrate; the backward terms are negative and contain the concentration of product.

The denominator terms are obtained by setting out all the possible non-cyclic arrangements containing one arrow fewer than for the numerator terms; the same requirements must be fulfilled, except that there is always one form from which no arrow starts. These are also shown in Fig. IV.26. Each term in the rate equation is shown below the corresponding arrangement.

In this way one obtains the general rate equation for the reversible system shown in Fig. IV.25:

IV.88
$$v = \frac{(c_1 ab + c_2 a^2 b + c_3 ab^2 - c_4 z - c_5 az - c_6 bz)e}{\begin{array}{l} c_7 + c_8 a + c_9 b + c_{10} ab + c_{11} a^2 + c_{12} b^2 + c_{13} a^2 b + \\ + c_{14} ab^2 + c_{15} z + c_{16} az + c_{17} bz + c_{18} abz \end{array}}$$

8 numerator terms:

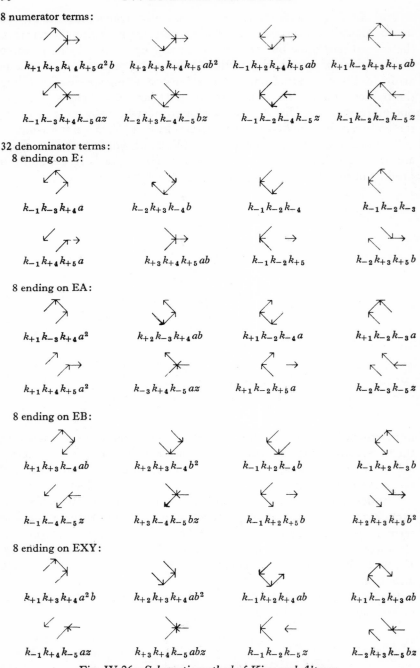

$$k_{+1}k_{+3}k_{+4}k_{+5}a^2b \quad k_{+2}k_{+3}k_{+4}k_{+5}ab^2 \quad k_{-1}k_{+2}k_{+4}k_{+5}ab \quad k_{+1}k_{-2}k_{+3}k_{+5}ab$$

$$k_{-1}k_{-3}k_{+4}k_{-5}az \quad k_{-2}k_{+3}k_{-4}k_{-5}bz \quad k_{-1}k_{-2}k_{-4}k_{-5}z \quad k_{-1}k_{-2}k_{-3}k_{-5}z$$

32 denominator terms:
  8 ending on E:

$$k_{-1}k_{-3}k_{+4}a \quad k_{-2}k_{+3}k_{-4}b \quad k_{-1}k_{-2}k_{-4} \quad k_{-1}k_{-2}k_{-3}$$

$$k_{-1}k_{+4}k_{+5}a \quad k_{+3}k_{+4}k_{+5}ab \quad k_{-1}k_{-2}k_{+5} \quad k_{-2}k_{+3}k_{+5}b$$

8 ending on EA:

$$k_{+1}k_{-3}k_{+4}a^2 \quad k_{+2}k_{-3}k_{+4}ab \quad k_{+1}k_{-2}k_{-4}a \quad k_{+1}k_{-2}k_{-3}a$$

$$k_{+1}k_{+4}k_{+5}a^2 \quad k_{-3}k_{+4}k_{-5}az \quad k_{+1}k_{-2}k_{+5}a \quad k_{-2}k_{-3}k_{-5}z$$

8 ending on EB:

$$k_{+1}k_{+3}k_{-4}ab \quad k_{+2}k_{+3}k_{-4}b^2 \quad k_{-1}k_{+2}k_{-4}b \quad k_{-1}k_{+2}k_{-3}b$$

$$k_{-1}k_{-4}k_{-5}z \quad k_{+3}k_{-4}k_{-5}bz \quad k_{-1}k_{+2}k_{+5}b \quad k_{+2}k_{+3}k_{+5}b^2$$

8 ending on EXY:

$$k_{+1}k_{+3}k_{+4}a^2b \quad k_{+2}k_{+3}k_{+4}ab^2 \quad k_{-1}k_{+2}k_{+4}ab \quad k_{+1}k_{-2}k_{+3}ab$$

$$k_{-1}k_{+4}k_{-5}az \quad k_{+3}k_{+4}k_{-5}abz \quad k_{-1}k_{-2}k_{-5}z \quad k_{-2}k_{+3}k_{-5}bz$$

Fig. IV.26. *Schematic method of King and Altman.*

where

$$c_1 = k_{+1}k_{-2}k_{+3}k_{+5}+k_{-1}k_{+2}k_{+4}k_{+5}$$
$$c_2 = k_{+1}k_{+3}k_{+4}k_{+5}$$
$$c_3 = k_{+2}k_{+3}k_{+4}k_{+5}$$
$$c_4 = k_{-1}k_{-2}k_{-3}k_{-5}+k_{-1}k_{-2}k_{-4}k_{-5}$$
$$c_5 = k_{-1}k_{-3}k_{+4}k_{-5}$$
$$c_6 = k_{-2}k_{+3}k_{-4}k_{-5}$$
$$c_7 = k_{-1}k_{-2}k_{-3}+k_{-1}k_{-2}k_{-4}+k_{-1}k_{-2}k_{+5}$$
$$c_8 = k_{+1}k_{-2}k_{-3}+k_{+1}k_{-2}k_{-4}+k_{+1}k_{-2}k_{+5}+k_{-1}k_{-3}k_{+4}+k_{-1}k_{+4}k_{+5}$$
$$c_9 = k_{-1}k_{+2}k_{-3}+k_{-1}k_{+2}k_{-4}+k_{-1}k_{+2}k_{+5}+k_{-2}k_{+3}k_{-4}+k_{-2}k_{+3}k_{+5}$$
$$c_{10} = k_{+1}k_{-2}k_{+3}+k_{-1}k_{+2}k_{+4}+k_{+1}k_{+3}k_{-4}+k_{+2}k_{-3}k_{+4}+k_{+3}k_{+4}k_{+5}$$
$$c_{11} = k_{+1}k_{-3}k_{+4}+k_{+1}k_{+4}k_{+5}$$
$$c_{12} = k_{+2}k_{+3}k_{-4}+k_{+2}k_{+3}k_{+5}$$
$$c_{13} = k_{+1}k_{+3}k_{+4}$$
$$c_{14} = k_{+2}k_{+3}k_{+4}$$
$$c_{15} = k_{-1}k_{-2}k_{-5}+k_{-1}k_{-4}k_{-5}+k_{-2}k_{-3}k_{-5}$$
$$c_{16} = k_{-1}k_{+4}k_{-5}+k_{-3}k_{+4}k_{-5}$$
$$c_{17} = k_{-2}k_{+3}k_{-5}+k_{+3}k_{-4}k_{-5}$$
$$c_{18} = k_{+3}k_{+4}k_{-5}$$

Equation IV.88 contains terms in the concentrations of the two substrates and the product. v represents the velocity generally, taken as positive in the forward direction. It can be simplified to the expressions for the initial velocities in either direction by putting either $z=0$ or $a=b=0$. In the first case

IV.89
$$v_f = \frac{(c_1 ab+c_2 a^2 b+c_3 ab^2)e}{c_7+c_8 a+c_9 b+c_{10} ab+c_{11} a^2+c_{12} b^2+c_{13} a^2 b+c_{14} ab^2}$$

and in the second case

IV.90
$$v_b = \frac{c_4 ze}{c_7+c_{15} z}$$

The latter equation is of the same form as the Briggs–Haldane equation IV.84, but with more complex expressions for V and K_m, namely

IV.91
$$V = \frac{c_4 e}{c_{15}} = \frac{(k_{-1}k_{-2}k_{-3}k_{-5}+k_{-1}k_{-2}k_{-4}k_{-5})e}{k_{-1}k_{-2}k_{-5}+k_{-1}k_{-4}k_{-5}+k_{-2}k_{-3}k_{-5}}$$

and

IV.92
$$K_m = \frac{c_7}{c_{15}} = \frac{k_{-1}k_{-2}k_{-3}+k_{-1}k_{-2}k_{-4}+k_{-1}k_{-2}k_{+5}}{k_{-1}k_{-2}k_{-5}+k_{-1}k_{-4}k_{-5}+k_{-2}k_{-3}k_{-5}}$$

On the other hand equation IV.89, which applies to the forward reaction, cannot be reduced to the form of equation IV.84 for either

E

substrate, since if a or b is held constant one still has terms involving b^2 or a^2.

If b is held constant, we get

IV.93 $$v_f = \frac{(ia^2+ja)e}{k+la^2+ma}$$

where

$$i = c_2 b$$

$$j = c_1 b + c_3 b^2$$

$$k = c_7 + c_9 b + c_{12} b^2$$

$$l = c_{11} + c_{13} b$$

$$m = c_8 + c_{10} b + c_{14} b^2$$

This system is said by Wong and Hanes to be of the second degree in a. This arises from the fact that A combines with two different enzyme-containing species. Wherever this occurs, the system cannot be treated in terms of a 'Michaelis constant' and the reciprocal plots are non-linear. There are two main possible causes of such anomalous behaviour. The first is, as here, the occurrence of parallel pathways by which the substrate reacts, due to the formation of the enzyme-substrate complex by combination in random order; for instance in the present case the substrate A combines both with E and with EB. If one of these paths is eliminated, e.g. by putting $k_{+4}=0$, the coefficients involving the a^2 terms become zero and a normal Michaelis-type equation results. The second possible cause is that the enzyme catalyses a reaction involving two identical substrate molecules, which are both involved in a ternary complex.

Systems with several successive steps

Even if only one substrate is involved, the reaction mechanism may well contain more than one intermediate complex. This will mean that the rate equation will contain more velocity constants than the simple Briggs–Haldane equation, although the form of the equation will not be affected. The appropriate rate equation, and hence the expressions for V and K_m, for any number of intermediates can be obtained either by direct algebra or by using the schematic method described in the last section. In order to illustrate the effect we give the results for one, two and three intermediate complexes.

IV.94 $$E \underset{k_{-1}}{\overset{k_{+1}s}{\rightleftharpoons}} ES \underset{k_{-2}z}{\overset{k_{+2}}{\rightleftharpoons}} E$$

IV.95 $\qquad V = k_{+2}e$

IV.96 $\qquad K_m = \dfrac{k_{-1}+k_{+2}}{k_{+1}}$

For two complexes

IV.97 $\qquad E \underset{k_{-1}}{\overset{k_{+1}s}{\rightleftharpoons}} ES \underset{k_{-2}}{\overset{k_{+2}}{\rightleftharpoons}} EZ \underset{k_{-3}z}{\overset{k_{+3}}{\rightleftharpoons}} E$

IV.98 $\qquad V = \dfrac{k_{+2}k_{+3}e}{k_{+2}+k_{-2}+k_{+3}}$

IV.99 $\qquad K_m = \dfrac{k_{-1}k_{-2}+k_{-1}k_{+3}+k_{+2}k_{+3}}{k_{+1}(k_{+2}+k_{-2}+k_{+3})}$

For three complexes

IV.100 $\qquad E \underset{k_{-1}}{\overset{k_{+1}s}{\rightleftharpoons}} ES \underset{k_{-2}}{\overset{k_{+2}}{\rightleftharpoons}} EX \underset{k_{-3}}{\overset{k_{+3}}{\rightleftharpoons}} EZ \underset{k_{-4}z}{\overset{k_{+4}}{\rightleftharpoons}} E$

IV.101 $\qquad V = \dfrac{k_{+2}k_{+3}k_{+4}e}{k_{+2}k_{+3}+k_{+2}k_{-3}+k_{-2}k_{-3}+k_{+2}k_{+4}+k_{-2}k_{+4}+k_{+3}k_{+4}}$

IV.102 $\quad K_m = \dfrac{k_{-1}k_{-2}k_{-3}+k_{-1}k_{-2}k_{+4}+k_{-1}k_{+3}k_{+4}+k_{+2}k_{+3}k_{+4}}{k_{+1}(k_{+2}k_{+3}+k_{+2}k_{-3}+k_{-2}k_{-3}+k_{+2}k_{+4}+k_{-2}k_{+4}+k_{+3}k_{+4})}$

Although these expressions are complex, the various velocity constants will probably be of very different magnitudes; some of the forward constants will be so large and some of the backward constants so small that the kinetics will be mainly determined by the other constants. It will frequently happen that one stage will have a forward velocity constant so small that it controls the whole kinetics of the system. For instance, let us assume that the back reactions in IV.100 are negligible, so that all terms involving negative constants can be neglected in comparison with the others. Let us further assume that k_{+3} is much smaller than the other forward constants. Then the expressions reduce to

IV.103 $\qquad K_m = \dfrac{k_{+2}k_{+3}k_{+4}}{k_{+1}k_{+2}k_{+4}} = \dfrac{k_{+3}}{k_{+1}}$

IV.104 $\qquad V = \dfrac{k_{+2}k_{+3}k_{+4}e}{k_{+2}k_{+4}} = k_{+3}e$

In general terms, if the back reactions can be neglected, and the transformation of the mth complex into the $(m+1)$th complex is much the slowest forward reaction, V/e will be given by the constant of this transformation and K_m by this constant divided by k_{+1}. As we have assumed that $k_{-1} = 0$, this naturally represents the extreme Briggs–Haldane case, but with their constant k_{+2} now replaced by the constant of the slowest of the reactions involved in the breakdown of ES. This case could not be distinguished from the case in which k_{+2} is limiting unless the concentrations of the complexes could be separately measured and the appropriate kinetic constants determined; methods for doing this are discussed in a later section. In cases where the enzyme has a high affinity for the product, the rate of dissociation of EZ into E and Z may well be slow and in such a case this process might be the limiting step which mainly determines the magnitude of V and K_m.

Reactions involving two substrates

On p. 70 we considered two-substrate systems from the point of view of Michaelis kinetics (i.e. assuming that equilibrium between the complex EAB and its free components is rapidly set up), and showed that a Michaelis-type equation is obtained for each substrate, giving linear reciprocal plots. This is true even when the two substrates combine in random order. On the other hand it was shown on pp. 94–8 that steady-state treatment of such systems does not give Michaelis-type equations for random order of combination, and non-linear plots are obtained.

There are three conditions which may lead to linear plots in two-substrate systems. Firstly, no ternary complex may be formed; the binary complex formed with one substrate reacts with the other substrate to form the product and free enzyme, as in the case of peroxidase discussed below. Secondly, one of the substrates may combine with the free enzyme so much more rapidly than the other that effectively there is only one path to the ternary complex, i.e. there is an obligatory order of combination. This has already been discussed on p. 98. Thirdly, the breakdown of the ternary complex in the forward direction may be sufficiently slow to ensure that it remains in equilibrium with the substrates, i.e. Michaelis conditions prevail, so that equation IV.30 applies. DALZIEL (534) has stated that yeast alcohol dehydrogenase (1.1.1.1) belongs to this category.

For these cases, in which the equations contain no squared terms, the only terms remaining are those in a, b and ab, and a constant term. The general rate equation can then be rearranged into the form

IV.105
$$v = \frac{V}{1 + \dfrac{c_A}{a} + \dfrac{c_B}{b} + \dfrac{c_{AB}}{ab}}$$

A method for graphical determination of the constants, similar to that of Florini and Vestling (see p. 72), has been given by DALZIEL (*534*), who writes the equation in the form

IV.106 $$\frac{e}{v} = \phi_0 + \frac{\phi_a}{a} + \frac{\phi_b}{b} + \frac{\phi_{ab}}{ab}$$

if e/v is plotted against $1/a$, with a constant concentration of B, a straight line is obtained with a slope of $\phi_A + \dfrac{\phi_{AB}}{b}$ and an intercept on the vertical axis of $\phi_0 + \dfrac{\phi_B}{b}$, as shown in Fig. IV.27(a). A series of such primary plots

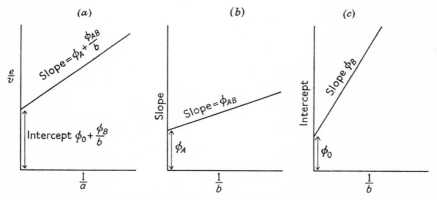

Fig. IV.27. *Dalziel's graphical method for determining ϕ constants.*

after *534*

are carried out with different concentrations of B. Two secondary plots are then constructed, giving the slopes and intercepts of the primary plots against $1/b$. The former gives a straight line (Fig. IV.27(b)) with slope ϕ_{AB} and intercept ϕ_A; the latter (Fig. IV.27(c)) has a slope ϕ_B and an intercept ϕ_0. All the four constants are thus determined, and the values can be checked by reversing the procedure, replacing $1/a$ by $1/b$. The four ϕs are functions of the velocity constants of the reaction system, and Dalziel has given a table setting out the meaning of these functions for various reaction systems.

FRIEDEN (*779*) has shown that for systems which obey equation IV.105 the primary plots all meet at a point (which may be above, on, or below the base-line) which corresponds to a concentration of $-c_{AB}/c_B$ if $1/a$ is being plotted, or $-c_{AB}/c_A$ if the plot is in terms of $1/b$. For the reactant which combines first in an obligatory order mechanism, i.e. the reactant which combines with the free enzyme, Frieden has shown that c_{AB}/c_B is equal to K_s for A. This gives a method for determining the true affinity of the enzyme for A. In order to apply this method, however, one must know which of the two substrates is A; in other words one must have an independent method for demonstrating the combination of one of the substrates with the free enzyme. Fig. IV.28 shows three actual cases; these are all dehydrogenases which can be shown to combine with $NADH_2$ in the absence of the other substrates. The K_s values for $NADH_2$ obtained from these plots agree reasonably well with the dissociation constants determined by physical methods.

When the substrates combine in random order the method can only be used when Michaelis conditions prevail; in other cases non-linear plots are obtained.

The method has been extended by FRIEDEN (781) to a three-substrate obligatory-order system obeying the equation

IV.107 $$v = 1 + \cfrac{V}{\dfrac{c_A}{a} + \dfrac{c_B}{b} + \dfrac{c_C}{c} + \dfrac{c_{AB}}{ab} + \dfrac{c_{BC}}{bc} + \dfrac{c_{ABC}}{abc}}$$

Measurement of the velocity constants

In a few cases it is possible to determine the concentration of the complex ES directly, especially by spectrophotometric means, and this makes it possible to measure the separate kinetic constants. The first application was to peroxidase (1.11.1.7) (CHANCE, 418), a haematin enzyme which had been shown by KEILIN and MANN (1347) to change its absorption spectrum when combined with H_2O_2. This enzyme has the additional advantage that the ES complex can be formed without the occurrence of any overall reaction when the hydrogen donor is omitted; it can thus be studied under either equilibrium or kinetic conditions. Moreover by using such a donor as leucomalachite green the overall reaction can also be measured spectrophotometrically by the production of a green colour. By an elegant application of the HARTRIDGE–ROUGHTON flow method, the concentration† of ES and the amount of product formed can be followed over a very short period (under 2 sec) after mixing, within which time the reaction is usually complete with the very small amounts used. Chance has now developed such methods to a high pitch of refinement and sensitivity for this and other purposes.

† Later work has shown that two different complexes with peroxide are involved and the formation of the active complex takes place by two successive reactions, which can however be treated as one. The mechanism will be discussed in detail in Chapter VII.

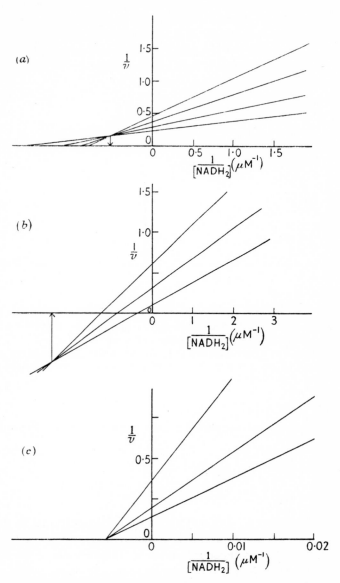

Fig. IV.28. *Frieden's method for determining affinity of enzyme for the first-combining substrate.*

(a) Lactate dehydrogenase.
(b) Liver alcohol dehydrogenase.
(c) Yeast alcohol dehydrogenase.

from *779*

On mixing enzyme and H_2O_2 in the absence of added donor, and following the change of p with time, it was found that the combination was very rapid and practically complete; the value of the bimolecular constant k_{+1} was $1 \cdot 2 \times 10^7$ l. per mole per sec and the equilibrium constant K_s was found to have a maximum value of 2×10^{-8} moles per l., hence k_{-1} must be $0 \cdot 2$ per sec or less.

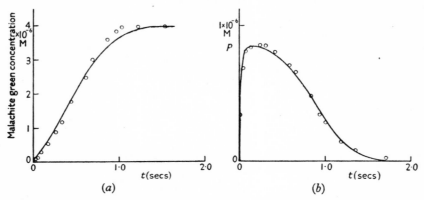

Fig. IV.29. *Kinetic curves of peroxidase* (1.11.1.7) *obtained by Chance's method.* Initial concentrations : 10^{-6} M horseradish peroxidase, 4×10^{-6} M H_2O_2, 15×10^{-6} M leucomalachite green. Acetate buffer pH 4.

    (a) shows amount of product formed; (b) shows the changes in the concentration of peroxidase-peroxide complex. Circles are experimental points; curves are calculated.

from *418*

When enzyme, substrate and donor are present together, the following reactions occur

IV.108 $E + H_2O_2 \rightleftharpoons ES$

IV.109 $ES + AH_2 \rightarrow E + A + 2H_2O$

The rate of reaction IV.109 will therefore be proportional to the concentration a of the donor AH_2. It is convenient to treat the reaction for any fixed donor concentration as a unimolecular reaction with velocity constant k_{+2}; k_{+2} therefore includes the donor concentration so that

IV.110 $k_{+2} = k'_{+2} a$

where k'_{+2} is the true bimolecular velocity constant (cf. equation IV.41).

    k_{+2} was determined in two ways. If the rate of oxidation (v) of the donor and the concentration of ES(p) are simultaneously determined, k_{+2} may be determined from the equation

IV.111 $\qquad v = k_{+2}p$

A typical experiment with peroxidase is shown in Fig. IV.29, in which both curves were determined at the same time. It will be seen from curve (b) that the complex is formed rapidly, remains constant for a short time and finally falls off as the substrate is exhausted. The rate of formation of product, which is given by the slope of curve (a), is seen to vary directly with the concentration of the complex. The velocity rises during the formation of the complex, reaches a maximum at the time corresponding to the peak of curve (b), and slowly falls to zero. Simultaneous values of v from curve (a) and p from curve (b) will give k_{+2} by equation IV.111.

The second method depends on the measurement of the area under curve (b). Since the amount of donor oxidized in a short interval of time dt is, by equation IV.111, equal to $k_{+2}p.dt$, the total amount oxidized is given by $k_{+2}\int_0^\infty pdt$. The integral is the area under the curve. Assuming that the total amount of donor oxidized is equal to s_0, the initial amount of peroxide, which is known,

IV.112 $\qquad s_0 = k_{+2}\int_0^\infty pdt$

from which k_{+2} may be determined. This method does not depend on measurements of the product of oxidation and can be applied to donors giving colourless products, e.g. ascorbate. Fig. IV.30 shows in (a) some typical results obtained with ascorbate and in (b) the proportionality of the resulting values of k_{+2} to the donor concentration, giving a value for k'_{+2} of $1\cdot8\times10^5$ l. per mole per sec.

Having obtained values for the three velocity constants k_{+1}, k_{-1} and k_{+2} it is now possible to interpret K_m for this enzyme. Inserting in equation IV.87 the appropriate values for the experiment shown in Fig. IV.29, we obtain for $K_m \dfrac{0\cdot2+4\cdot2}{1\times10^7}$ or $4\cdot4\times10^{-7}$M. This may be compared with the value of $5\cdot0\times10^{-7}$M calculated for these conditions from the data of MANN (1704) on the assumption that K_m is proportional to the donor concentration, as it would be if k_{-1} were negligible.

K_m can also be obtained from the peak value of p and equation IV.83.

Rearranging the latter equation and writing p_{max} for the peak value of p which corresponds to the steady state

IV.113 $$K_m = \frac{(e - p_{max}) s_m}{p_{max}}$$

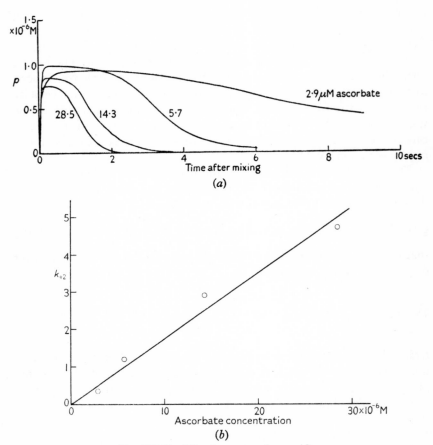

Fig. IV.30. *Kinetic curves of peroxidase.*
Initial concentrations: 10^{-6} M horseradish peroxidase, 4×10^{-6} M H_2O_2, ascorbate concentration as indicated. Acetate buffer pH $4 \cdot 2$.

   (a) shows the experimental curves; (b) shows the values of k_{+2} obtained from them by the second method described in the text.

                                                                    from *418*

s_m, the peroxide concentration when $p = p_{max}$, can be calculated from that part of the area under the p, t curve which lies between the time of mixing and the time of the peak. Such calculations for the experiment of Fig. IV.29 gave a value for K_m of $4 \cdot 1 \times 10^{-7}$. Further confirmation is given by the agreement of the experimental points with the curves showing computer solutions of the equations using the following values: $k_{+1} = 0 \cdot 9 \times 10^7$ l. per mole per sec, $k_{-1} = 0$, $k_{+2} = 4 \cdot 5$ per sec (see Fig. IV.29). The agreement of these values of K_m obtained in different ways gives confidence in the method.

The values show clearly that under these conditions K_m for this enzyme is almost equal to k_{+2}/k_{+1}, so that it represents a dynamic rather than a thermodynamic equilibrium; K_s in fact makes only a small contribution. k_{+2}, however, depends on the donor concentration, and by reducing this concentration it can be reduced to the same value as k_{-1}, or even less. Thus it is possible to vary K_m between the two extreme values of $K_m = K_s$ and $K_m = k_{+2}/k_{+1}$ with the same enzyme. K_s represents the extrapolated value of K_m obtained as k_{+2} approaches zero.

For cases like this in which there is some means of varying k_{+2} independently of k_{+1} and k_{-1}, for instance by varying a second reactant involved in the breakdown reaction, this gives a method of determining K_s and the three velocity constants. SLATER and BONNER (*2428*) suggested that if K_m is plotted against V in such a case a straight line should be

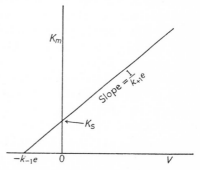

Fig. IV.31. *Extrapolation of K_m to give K_s.*

obtained with intercepts of K_s and $-k_{-1}e$ on the vertical and horizontal axes respectively, as shown in Fig. IV.31. This is readily shown as follows. From equation IV.87, $K_m = K_s + k_{+2}e/k_{+1}e$ and substituting $V = k_{+2}e$ from equation IV.85 we get

IV.114 $$K_m = K_s + \frac{V}{k_{+1}e}$$

For the determination of the absolute values of the velocity constants the enzyme concentration must be known, but even when it is not known the ratios of the constants may be obtained.

It should be possible to apply this method to many enzymes, but the literature at present only provides fragmentary data to which it can be applied. SLATER (*2425*) has applied it to the available measurements of other workers on certain enzymes, including glucose oxidase of moulds (1.1.3.4) and $NADH_2$ cytochrome c reductase (1.6.2.1), and since the graph passes through the origin in these two cases he has concluded that

k_{-1} must be zero. DIXON (624), however, pointed out that this conclusion could not be drawn in such cases, in which the flavin group of the enzyme is reduced by the substrate and reoxidized probably after the product has dissociated. The application of steady-state kinetics to this mechanism shows that the graph must always pass through the origin, whatever the values of any of the individual velocity constants, and therefore no conclusions can be drawn as to their magnitude. This criticism, which has been accepted by SLATER (2426), means that caution must be exercised in drawing conclusions from graphs which pass through the origin, since the explanation might be either that $k_{-1} = 0$ or that a product is liberated at some intermediate stage in the series of reactions.

We have mentioned in the previous section Frieden's method for obtaining K_s for the first substrate in a two-substrate system by extrapolating reciprocal plots for one substrate at various concentrations of the other to the common point of intersection (Fig. IV.28). MAIN (1693) has used an analogous method to obtain K_s for a hydrolytic system, namely cholinesterase (3.1.1.8). Reciprocal plots at various concentrations of butanol, which increases the rate, were found to extrapolate to a single point, which was interpreted as giving K_s.

If for any enzyme k_{-1} is negligible, we should expect that anything which affects V will produce a proportionate change in K_m. Some results of this kind have been obtained for carboxypeptidase A (3.4.2.1) by E. SMITH and his co-workers (1632), who found that over a limited range changes of pH, D_2O concentration and substrate structure produced parallel changes in V and K_m.

It should be noted that although k_{-1} may be small, it can never be zero for an enzyme which catalyses a reversible reaction, for in the reverse direction it is k_{-1} which determines the rate of dissociation of the product from the enzyme and if k_{-1} were in fact zero the reaction would not proceed. In view of the fact that in most enzyme reactions the substrate and product are rather similar molecules, it seems likely that where the dissociation of the substrate is slow the dissociation of the product will also be slow. In other words, where k_{-1} is very small there will be a tendency for the enzyme reaction to be limited by the rate at which the product leaves the enzyme.

A different method of measuring the velocity constants has been developed by GUTFREUND and ROUGHTON (2258); this depends on estimations of the product during the very short initial time interval while the ES complex is building up and the reaction is accelerating, that is to say, before the steady state is reached. This initial acceleration is visible in Fig. IV.29(a); it only lasts for a fraction of a second, and can only be measured by special techniques.

Considering a system of the type represented in IV.81, we have from IV.82

IV.115
$$\frac{dp}{dt} = k_{+1}es - (k_{+1}s + k_{-1} + k_{+2})p$$

and from IV.84, writing z for the concentration of product,

IV.116
$$v = \frac{dz}{dt} = k_{+2}p$$

whence

IV.117
$$\frac{d^2z}{dt^2} = k_{+2}\frac{dp}{dt}$$

From IV.115 and 117

IV.118
$$\frac{d^2z}{dt^2} + \frac{dz}{dt}(k_{+1}s + k_{-1} + k_{+2}) - k_{+1}k_{+2}es = 0$$

The solution of this equation, which applies both to the initial period and to the steady state for so long as s can be considered to be essentially unchanged from its initial value s_0, is

IV.119
$$z = z_0 + \frac{k_{+2}s_0 et}{s_0 + \frac{k_{-1} + k_{+2}}{k_{+1}}} + \frac{k_{+1}k_{+2}s_0 e}{(k_{+1}s_0 + k_{-1} + k_{+2})^2}(\epsilon^{-(k_{+1}s_0 + k_{-1} + k_{+2})t} - 1)$$

where z_0 is the initial concentration of product (included because the product measured by Gutfreund was H^+). Writing the exponential term in the form of a series, in which all terms beyond the third may be neglected for very small values of t, we obtain the simplified equation, valid only for the early part of the acceleration phase

IV.120
$$z - z_0 = \frac{k_{+1}k_{+2}es_0 t^2}{2}$$

Thus by measuring z over this early phase of the reaction it is possible to obtain $k_{+1}k_{+2}e$. $k_{+2}e$ can be obtained by measuring V, in accordance with equation IV.85, and this then gives k_{+1}, while by measuring K_m we can obtain $(k_{-1} + k_{+2})/k_{+1}$. From these values and the enzyme concentration all three of the velocity constants can be calculated.

Equation IV.119 may be used in another way (GUTFREUND, 957). When $z - z_0$ is plotted against t, the equation gives a curve of the form shown in Fig. IV.32. The curvature is due to the exponential terms when t becomes sufficiently large for this term to be neglected (steady-state phase), the curve follows the dotted straight line represented by

IV.121 $$z - z_0 = \frac{k_{+2}\, s_0\, et}{s_0 + K_m} - \frac{k_{+2}\, s_0\, e}{k_{+1}(s_0 + K_m)^2}$$

If the substrate concentration is high enough to saturate the enzyme (s_0 large compared with K_m), this approximates to

IV.122 $$z - z_0 = k_{+2}\, et - \frac{k_{+2}\, e}{k_{+1}\, s_0}$$

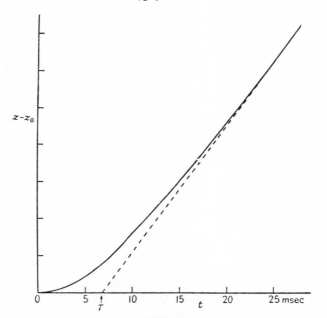

Fig. IV.32. *Pre-steady-state kinetics: method of determining k_{+1}.*

from *957*

The intercept on the base-line (τ), obtained by putting $z - z_0 = 0$, is

IV.123 $$\tau = \frac{1}{k_{+1}\, s_0}$$

Thus a measurement of τ gives k_{+1} directly.

It will be noted that the validity of these equations depends upon the assumption that K_m is represented by the Briggs–Haldane expression IV.87. They apply to systems with a single intermediate complex

ES, in which k_{+1} is the velocity constant of the formation of that complex which breaks down to give the product. They do not apply to systems in which there are two or more intermediate complexes. In such cases, e.g. the system shown in IV.100, the complex ES which is formed by the k_{+1} reaction is different from that which gives the product; the rate of formation of product is no longer necessarily proportional to its concentration, and K_m is represented by a more complex expression. The rate of formation of product may well be limited by one of the intermediate steps, e.g. by k_{+3}, and in this case $1/\tau$ will no longer measure k_{+1} but will be a function of k_{+3} and possibly of other constants as well.

This, however, is easily tested, for these later steps do not involve the free substrate and the resulting expressions do not contain s_0. Thus if τ is found to be proportional to $1/s_0$, equation IV.123 may be taken as valid and k_{+1} determined from it, whereas if τ is independent of s_0, it depends on one of the intermediate constants, though it may not be possible to determine which.

GUTFREUND (956–7) has carried out a number of measurements on the hydrolysis of synthetic aminoacid esters by proteolytic enzymes. For the hydrolysis of benzoyl-L-arginine ethyl ester by trypsin (3.4.4.4), k_{+1} was found to be greater than 4×10^6 and k_{+2} was 15 per sec. Since $K_m = 10^{-5}$ (233), k_{-1} must be greater than 25 per sec; this is only a minimum value and it is possible that k_{-1} is much greater than this. For the hydrolysis of acetyl-L-phenylalanine ethyl ester by chymotrypsin (3.4.4.5), k_{+1} was greater than 10^6, k_{+2} was about 10 per sec and K_m was 10^{-4}; k_{-1} must therefore be greater than 90 per sec (959). For the hydrolysis of benzoyl-L-arginine ethyl ester by ficin (3.4.4.12), k_{+1} was 5×10^2, K_m was $1 \cdot 5 \times 10^{-2}$ and 'k_{+2}' was $1 \cdot 5$ per sec; k_{-1} is therefore about 6 per sec. ('k_{+2}' means here the velocity constant determining the rate of breakdown of ES, but it is placed here in inverted commas because in ficin the breakdown occurs in two steps and the rate is determined by the second, since 'k_{+2}' is the same for amides as for esters (990)).

It will be seen that in all these cases k_{+2} is considerably smaller than k_{-1}, so that K_m practically equals K_s; the agreement may be even closer than appears from these figures since, except for ficin, only a minimum for k_{-1} was obtained. We may conclude that these enzymes, particularly chymotrypsin, form systems for which the original Michaelis assumptions are correct.

It should be noted that the initial acceleration phase which is dealt with in this method is so brief that it would not be detected by ordinary methods of measurement. The phrase 'initial velocity' which we have used hitherto does not refer to this phase, but to the steady-state velocity after the ES complex has been formed.

Kinetic elucidation of reaction sequence

Since, as we have seen, different reaction patterns lead to different kinetic equations, it might be thought that kinetic studies would enable one to determine unambiguously the sequence of steps in the overall reaction. The matter, however, has in practice not proved to be so simple, since several different patterns may lead to kinetics which cannot readily be distinguished. Many authors state that their results 'are consistent with' a particular mechanism, but this is of little value unless it is also shown that they are inconsistent with all other likely mechanisms.

In order to do this one needs a systematic tabulation of the characteristic kinetic features of the different mechanisms. This approach is still

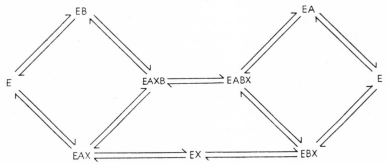

Fig. IV.33. *General reaction scheme for an X-transferase.*
Overall reaction: $AX + B = A + BX$
after *2905*

in its early stages, but WONG and HANES (*2905*) have recently made considerable progress in connection with two-substrate systems. They have tabulated the characteristic features of twenty-three reaction systems which may be derived by making various modifications in the general scheme shown in Fig. IV.33.

They make use particularly of the conception of the 'degree' of a system with respect to each of the substrates and products. The degree with respect to a given reactant means the highest power of the concentration of that reactant which occurs in the rate equation, and is equal to the number of different enzyme-containing species which react with that reactant. Thus the system of Fig. IV.25 is of the second degree in A or B and of the first degree in Z. A degree higher than the first is shown by non-linearity in the plots (*c*), (*d*) or (*e*) of Fig. IV.12. The theory is undergoing rapid development and will no doubt be applied to the kinetic analysis of actual enzyme systems in the near future.

Equilibrium constant of the overall reaction in terms of V and K_m

In a reversible one-substrate system the initial velocity of the reverse reaction can be expressed, like the forward velocity, in terms of a Michaelis equation; the system is then defined by four constants V_f, V_b, K_{mf} and K_{mb}, where the subscripts f and b denote the forward and backward reactions respectively. After a time, such a system will reach an equilibrium point when the velocities of the forward and backward reactions become equal. Unless the affinities for substrate and product are equal, the equilibrium constant K will not be equal to the ratio V/V_b, but can be expressed in terms of the four constants as follows:

Taking the system represented by reactions IV.97 as an example, we may obtain the ratio V_f/K_{mf} from equations IV.98 and IV.99, thus

IV.124 $$\frac{V_f}{K_{mf}} = \frac{k_{+1}k_{+2}k_{+3}e}{k_{-1}k_{-2}+k_{-1}k_{+3}+k_{+2}k_{+3}}$$

In order to write down the corresponding expression for the back reaction, we must interchange k_{-3}, k_{+3}, k_{-2}, k_{+2} and k_{-1} with k_{+1}, k_{-1}, k_{+2}, k_{-2} and k_{+3} respectively. This gives

IV.125 $$\frac{V_b}{K_{mb}} = \frac{k_{-1}k_{-2}k_{-3}e}{k_{+2}k_{+3}+k_{-1}k_{+3}+k_{-1}k_{-2}}$$

Dividing one expression by the other, we get

IV.126 $$\frac{V_f K_{mb}}{V_b K_{mf}} = \frac{k_{+1}k_{+2}k_{+3}}{k_{-1}k_{-2}k_{-3}} = K_1 K_2 K_3 = K$$

where K_1, K_2, K_3 are the equilibrium constants of the three stages in IV.97.

This important relationship was first deduced by HALDANE (*979*, p. 80). It is quite general for one-substrate systems, provided that the substrate does not act as an activator or inhibitor. For two-substrate systems, the situation is more complicated. In certain cases, for example where Michaelis conditions prevail and the two substrates combine independently, an equation analogous with IV.126 holds, namely

IV.127 $$\frac{V_f K_Y K_Z}{V_b K_A K_B} = K$$

where V_f is the velocity with both substrates A and B in excess. For other reaction patterns more complicated forms of the Haldane relationship have been deduced; some of these have been tabulated by ALBERTY (*33*) and by DALZIEL (*534*), involving either the square or the cube of V_f/V_b. If V_f is very different from V_b and K is determined, these relationships may throw light on the type of reaction system involved. For random order of combination the system will be of second degree and since there is no Michaelis constant no Haldane relationship can be formulated.

Integrated Michaelis equations

It was pointed out early in this chapter that it is generally difficult to derive equations which satisfactorily represent the progress curves of enzyme reactions, owing to the numerous factors which may alter the velocity during the course of the reaction; consequently, we have been dealing hitherto with initial velocities. However, in the special case when the decrease in rate during the progress of the reaction is due solely to the decrease in saturation of the enzyme as the substrate concentration falls, the progress curves can be obtained by integrating the Michaelis equation.

If s_0 is the initial substrate concentration and the concentration at time t is s_0-y, the velocity at this time is

IV.128 $$\frac{dy}{dt} = \frac{V(s_0-y)}{K_m+s_0-y}$$

Integrating, we get

IV.129 $$Vt = \int_0^y \frac{s_0-y+K_m}{s_0-y} \cdot dy = y+K_m \log_e \frac{s_0}{s_0-y}$$

An equation of this form was put forward in 1902 by HENRI (*1065*). Provided that no other factors interfere, it may be used to determine K_m and V from measurements during the progress of the reaction, where measurements of initial velocity are difficult. Rearranging, we have

IV.130 $$\frac{2\cdot303}{t} \log\frac{s_0}{s_0-y} = \frac{V}{K_m} - \frac{1}{K_m}\cdot\frac{y}{t}$$

Thus if y is measured at a series of times and $\dfrac{2\cdot303}{t}\log\dfrac{s_0}{s_0-y}$ is plotted against y/t, a straight line will be obtained; this will have a slope of $-1/K_m$ and an intercept on the base-line which will give V. The same line will be obtained also from determinations at one time with varying s_0; a number of measurements for different values of t and s_0 may therefore be plotted on the same graph. Fig. IV.34 shows a series of results on histidine ammonia-lyase (4.3.1.3) plotted by this method (*2762*). A slight modification of the method has also been applied to testosterone 17-β-dehydrogenase (1.1.1.j) (*2582*).

Like the Michaelis equation itself, equation IV.129 reduces to simple forms when s_0 is made very large or very small. When s_0 is very large compared with y and with K_m, $Vt = y$. This represents the usual constant-velocity or zero-order portion at the beginning of a progress curve with high substrate concentration. When s_0 (and therefore y) is very small in comparison with K_m, we get an equation of the standard first-order form

IV.131
$$\frac{2 \cdot 303}{t} \log \frac{s_0}{s_0 - y} = \frac{V}{K_m}$$

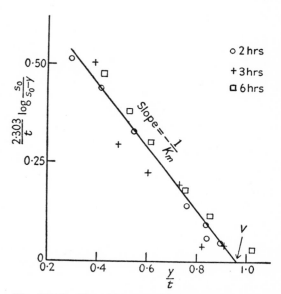

Fig. IV.34. *Use of integrated Michaelis equation for determination of V and K_m.*

Histidine ammonia-lyase (4.3.1.3); measured by NH_3 production at three different times with various initial substrate concentrations.

from *2762*

V/K_m is constant in any given experiment; thus the reaction with very low substrate concentration is first-order, with a velocity constant V/K_m. This does not, of course, give V and K_m separately; for this reason the expression of specificity data in terms of the first-order velocity constants obtained with different substances is not satisfactory, as it does not reveal whether the effect is on affinity or reactivity.

Equation IV.131 is only applicable over a limited range of conditions. A check on whether one is working in the right range is given by plotting

$\log \dfrac{s_0}{s_0-y}$ against t (see *685*). If the equation is obeyed, a straight line is obtained and first-order constants can be used; if an appreciable curvature is obtained, it will be necessary to use equation IV.129.

(c) EFFECT OF pH

In general, enzymes are only active over a limited range of pH and in most cases a definite optimum pH is observed. This optimum may be due to (*a*) a true reversible effect on V itself, (*b*) an effect of pH on the

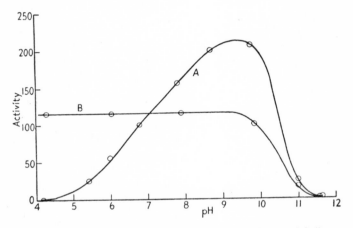

Fig. IV.35. *Effect of pH on monoamine oxidase* (1.4.3.4).

For curve A the activity was tested at the pH values given; for curve B the enzyme was exposed for 5 min to the pH values given and the activity then tested at pH 7·3.

from *1004*

affinity, the fall on either side of the optimum being due to a decreased saturation of the enzyme with substrate, due to a decreased affinity, or (*c*) an effect of pH on the stability of the enzyme, which may become irreversibly destroyed on one or both sides of the optimum. These effects may occur in combination; for instance, the fall on one side may be due to a fall in affinity and on the other to instability of the enzyme.

The effects may easily be distinguished experimentally. The occurrence of irreversible destruction can be tested by exposing the enzyme to a range of pH values and then testing the activity after readjusting the pH to some standard value. Fig. IV.35 shows such pH curves for monoamine oxidase (1.4.3.4) and it will be seen that the fall on the alkaline side is due to destruction of the enzyme. As such a destruction is progressive, the shape of the curve and the apparent optimum pH depend on the time; if the true initial velocities could be measured immediately after the enzyme is brought to the pH of testing, the effect of the destruction would be entirely eliminated. Such an optimum is analogous to the spurious 'optimum temperature' which will be dealt with later.

The effect of pH on the affinity can be eliminated by using a sufficiently high concentration of substrate to saturate the enzyme at all pHs used. Owing to the large changes which may take place in the affinity as the pH is altered, it must not be assumed that a substrate concentration which is sufficient to saturate the enzyme at one pH will do so at other pHs. To define properly the effect of pH on enzyme activity, it is important that enough data should be obtained at each pH to evaluate V and K_m by one of the graphical methods shown in Fig. IV.12. The majority of pH curves in the literature are composite curves depending partly on a change of V and partly on a change of K_m. Curves showing the effect of pH on V are in fact extremely rare; among the few examples are the curves for the forward and backward fumarate hydratase (4.2.1.2) reactions (1751a) and a curve for cholinesterase (3.1.1.8) (1019), given below in Figs. IV. 40–41, and curves for papain (3.4.4.10) at three temperatures (2536a).

The effect of pH on enzymes, like all pH effects, is due to changes in the state of ionization of the components of the system as the pH changes. Either the free enzyme, the enzyme–substrate complex or the substrate may undergo such changes. Since enzymes are proteins containing many ionizable groups, they exist in a whole series of different states of ionization, and the distribution of the total enzyme among the various ionic forms depends on the pH and the ionization constants of the various groups. However, as the catalytic activity is usually confined to a relatively small range of pH, it seems likely that only one of the ionic forms of the enzyme (or rather of the active centre) is catalytically active, as suggested by MICHAELIS and DAVIDSOHN (1814) in 1911. There is some evidence that, as would be expected, the ionization of groups in the protein which are remote from the active centre has little or no effect, while the ionic state of groups in or close to the active centre has a very large effect.

If the enzyme is only active in one state of ionization, it follows that (to a first approximation) the ionization of two particular groups in or near the active centre will largely determine the activity, namely, those groups which ionize (or de-ionize) first as the pH is moved away from the optimum on the acid and alkaline sides respectively. These are sometimes referred to as the acid and basic groups of the enzyme. We are not concerned with other ionization processes which take place at pHs further from the optimum, as they only affect the state of inactive forms of the enzyme. It is true that the enzyme molecule may contain several groups of the same kind, which will ionize together, but it is perhaps not very likely that the active centre will contain more than one of these groups. Thus pH effects on the velocity of enzyme reactions are frequently discussed in terms of two ionizing groups only, using the equations applicable to a dibasic acid or simple ampholyte, although no doubt this is an over-simplification.

The Michaelis pH functions

It will facilitate the discussion of the effect of pH on enzymes, and will simplify the writing of the equations, if we first consider the properties of some functions of pH which play a dominant part in the theory of the effects. Michaelis first drew attention to their importance in 1913 (see *1812*, p. 48). The Michaelis pH functions are defined as follows:

IV.132 $$f = 1 + \frac{K_1}{H} + \frac{K_1 K_2}{H^2}$$

IV.133 $$f^- = 1 + \frac{H}{K_1} + \frac{K_2}{H}$$

IV.134 $$f^= = 1 + \frac{H}{K_2} + \frac{H^2}{K_1 K_2}$$

where H is written for the concentration of H^+ ions.† These functions apply to a substance which undergoes two successive ionizations with ionization constants K_1 and K_2, for instance, a symmetrical dibasic acid AH_2 such as succinic acid, which will exist in three states of ionization thus

IV.135 $$AH_2 \overset{K_1}{\rightleftharpoons} AH^- \overset{K_2}{\rightleftharpoons} A^=$$

It should be clearly understood that K_1 and K_2 refer to the first and second stages of ionization of the molecule and are defined by equations

---

† We shall use the simple term 'hydrogen ion' throughout the book, rather than such terms as 'proton', 'oxonium ion', 'hydronium ion', 'hydroxonium ion', etc. The last three terms refer to the hydrated form of the hydrogen ion, i.e. OH_3^+. It is usual to neglect the hydration of reactants in chemical thermodynamics. Although hydrogen ions exist in aqueous solution in the hydrated form (*988*, p. 41), we write equations involving hydrogen ions in terms of H^+ rather than OH_3^+.

IV.137; they are not the ionization constants of the individual carboxyl groups. The importance of this distinction will become clear later.

It will be convenient to use the subscript t to denote the sum total of the concentrations of all the different forms of a given substance; thus for this system we have

IV.136 $A_t = [AH_2] + [AH^-] + [A^=]$

From this, inserting the definitions of the constants K_1, K_2, namely

IV.137 $K_1 = \dfrac{[AH^-]H}{[AH_2]}, \qquad K_2 = \dfrac{[A^=]H}{[AH^-]} = \dfrac{[A^=]H^2}{[AH_2]K_1}$

we get

IV.138 $A_t = [AH_2]\left(1 + \dfrac{K_1}{H} + \dfrac{K_1 K_2}{H^2}\right) = [AH_2].f$

IV.139 $A_t = [AH^-].f^-$

IV.140 $A_t = [A^=].f^=$

Thus the amount of any ionic form of a substance is obtained by dividing the total amount of the substance by the appropriate pH function.

The three functions are interrelated, and it may be convenient for later discussion if we set out the relationships between the three functions and the three states of the substance as follows:

IV.141 $A_t = [AH_2].f = [AH_2].f - \dfrac{K_1}{H} = [AH_2].f - \dfrac{K_1 K_2}{H^2}$

$$= [AH^-].f\,\dfrac{H}{K_1} = [AH^-].f^- = [AH^-].f - \dfrac{K_2}{H}$$

$$= [A^=].f\,\dfrac{H^2}{K_1 K_2} = [A^=].f - \dfrac{H}{K_2} = [A^=].f^=$$

The reciprocals of the three functions, which are respectively proportional to the amounts of the three forms of the substance, are plotted against the pH in Fig. IV.36(a), assuming $K_1 = 10^{-5}$ and $K_2 = 10^{-10}$. Similar curves may be drawn for any system with two successive ionizations; they are not restricted to dibasic acids, for which the intermediate form carries one negative charge, but might for instance equally well represent an aminoacid for which the intermediate form is a dipolar ion with no net charge. The curve for the intermediate form $(1/f^-)$ may quite well represent that fraction of an enzyme which is in the catalytically active ionic form, even though we may not know what charge it carries; in fact it was the resemblance between such curves and the pH activity curves of many enzymes which led Michaelis and Davidsohn to put forward their theory.

The curve for the intermediate form rises to a maximum at a pH

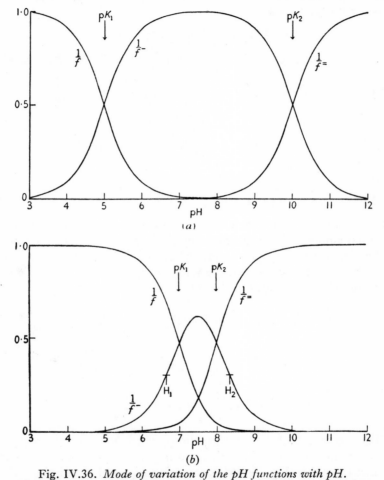

Fig. IV.36. *Mode of variation of the pH functions with pH.*
(a) Reciprocals of pH functions for a system with two ionizing groups with pKs of 5 and 10 respectively.
(b) Reciprocals of pH functions for a symmetrical system with pKs of 7 and 8.

(pH_0, which corresponds to the optimum pH in the case of an enzyme) half-way between the two pK values,† which means that

IV.142 $H_0 = \sqrt{(K_1 K_2)}$

† $pK = -\log_{10} K.$

When the two pKs are well separated, as in this case, practically the whole of the substance is in the intermediate form at pH_0, but this is not so if the two constants are more nearly equal, as shown in Fig. IV.36(*b*). In fact when the two constants are equal the peak of the curve for the intermediate form reaches only one-third of the total. In this case all three terms in each of the functions are equal to 1, and equal amounts of all three forms are present.

When the two pKs are well separated, they may readily be determined from the half-maximal values or mid-points of the two sides of the curve for the intermediate form (which might correspond to the pH-activity curve of an enzyme) as shown in Fig. IV.36(*a*), but when the pKs are more nearly equal this method is not applicable and gives large errors, as will be evident from Fig. IV.36(*b*). ALBERTY and MASSEY (*38*) have given a rule for determining the Ks in such cases; they derived it from equations relating to enzymes, but it is a general rule and may readily be obtained from the definition of f^- as follows. From equations IV.133 and IV.142 the height of the $1/f^-$ peak at pH_0 is

IV.143
$$\frac{1}{f_0^-} = \frac{1}{1 + 2\sqrt{\dfrac{K_2}{K_1}}}$$

The value of H at which $1/f^-$ is half this maximum height will be obtained by putting $1/f^-$ equal to half $1/f_0^-$, or

IV.144
$$\frac{1}{f^-} = \frac{K_1 H}{K_1 H + H^2 + K_1 K_2} = \frac{1}{2 + 4\sqrt{\dfrac{K_2}{K_1}}}$$

This simplifies to

IV.145
$$H^2 - (K_1 + 4H_0)H + H_0^2 = 0$$

This equation has two real roots, which we will call H_1 and H_2, corresponding to the half-maximal points on the two sides of the optimum; their sum will be given by the expression in brackets, so that

IV.146
$$H_1 + H_2 = K_1 + 4H_0$$

This simple rule gives K_1, since the hydrogen ion concentrations at the maximum and the two half-way points are all known. K_2 can then be obtained from equation IV.142. This is a useful method for determining enzyme ionization constants from pH-activity curves, though unfortunately its accuracy is least in those cases in which it is most useful.

Considering Fig. IV.36(*b*) as an illustration of the rule, by taking the mid-points of the two sides of the $1/f^-$ curve we should obtain pKs of

$6\cdot64$ and $8\cdot36$, instead of the true values of $7\cdot0$ and $8\cdot0$. Applying the rule, however, we find that $H_1 = 10^{-6\cdot64} = 10^{-7+0\cdot36} = 2\cdot29\times10^{-7}$; similarly $H_2 = 4\cdot37\times10^{-9}$, so that $H_1+H_2 = 2\cdot33\times10^{-7}$. As $H_0 = 10^{-7\cdot5}$, $4H_0 = 1\cdot26\times10^{-7}$. Thus $H_1+H_2-4H_0 = 1\cdot07\times10^{-7}$, in reasonable agreement with the true value of $1\cdot00\times10^{-7}$.

The three pH functions for a system existing in three different forms each contain three terms and as the pH is gradually increased, each of these three terms becomes dominant in turn. If the pKs are fairly well separated, each term has a range of pH within which the other two terms are negligibly small in comparison. For instance, considering f^- (equation IV.133) in the case of Fig. IV.36(a), at pH 3 the second term is 100, which may be considered large in comparison with 1, and the third term is 10^{-7}; the second term is therefore dominant in this pH range. At pH 7 the second and third terms are 10^{-2} and 10^{-3} respectively and are both small compared with 1, while at pH 12 the second term is 10^{-7} and the third term is 100, which is large compared with the other two. Between these regions there are limited ranges in which two terms simultaneously contribute to the value of the function.

If $-\log f^-$ $\left(\text{which we shall call } pf^-\text{, and which is equal to } \log\dfrac{1}{f^-}\right)$ is plotted against pH, the graph which is obtained consists of straight-line portions, each corresponding to a region where only one term is important, with short curved portions joining them, corresponding to the parts where two terms are contributing. The slope of the straight-line sections is equal to the power of H occurring in the corresponding dominant term. For instance, at pH 3, where the second term is dominant,

$$pf^- = -\log\frac{H}{K_1} = pH - pK_1,$$ so that the curve of pf^- against pH is here a straight line with a one-unit slope; in other words the pf^- increases by 1 for every pH increase of 1 in the region where the dominant term contains the first power of H. At pH 12 $pf^- = -\log\dfrac{K_2}{H} = pK_2 - pH$,

and has a slope of -1, while in the region of pH 7 pf^- is independent of pH, as shown in Fig. IV.37. It is easily shown that if the straight portions are produced they intersect at a pH value equal to the pK, and every pK produces a change of slope of 1 in the graph. Similar considerations of course apply also to the pf and $pf^=$ graphs; here the last terms will produce two-unit slopes, as they contain the second power of H. DIXON (618, 621) has made these facts the basis of a unified theory for the treatment of the effects of pH on the equilibria involved in hydrogenation and phosphorylation reactions and in enzyme–substrate and enzyme–inhibitor combination. This is discussed in greater detail in the section on K_m below.

Returning to the Michaelis pH functions for a dibasic acid, we must point out that it does not seem to have been sufficiently realized (although pointed out by ADAMS (*15*) in 1916) that K_1 and K_2 refer to the first and second *stages* of ionization of the molecule and are not the ionization constants of particular groups. The importance of the distinction was not very obvious with the symmetrical dibasic acids considered by Michaelis, since the same anion is produced whichever carboxyl

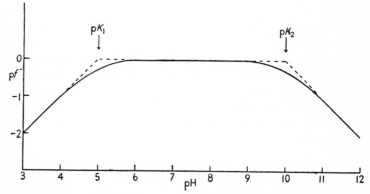

Fig. IV.37. *Plot of* $pf^- = -\log f^- = \log 1/f^-$ *for the system of Fig. IV.36 (a).*

group ionizes, so that there are only three possible ionic states of the substance. With an unsymmetrical molecule, however, such as

$$R \cdot CH \cdot COOH \ (x)$$
$$CH_2 \cdot COOH \ (y)$$

in which we may distinguish the two carboxyl groups by the letters x and y, there will be two different intermediate forms, namely, the singly-charged anions produced by the ionization of x and y respectively. The substance has therefore four states and not three. For titration purposes it is quite immaterial which group is ionized, since the amount of alkali required is the same in each case and the two intermediate forms are equivalent. In titration, therefore, one is interested only in the stages of ionization and hence in K_1 and K_2. In dealing with enzymes, however, it is most probably the state of ionization of the particular groups in the active centre which is important for the activity; it is very probable that only one of the two intermediate forms will be active and consequently we are more interested in the group ionization constants K_x and K_y.

Each group may ionize either from the undissociated molecule or from the anion, in other words in the first or second stage; we therefore need four ionization constants to represent the ionization of an unsymmetrical dibasic acid completely, as follows:

$$
\begin{array}{c}
\text{R.CH.COO}^- \\
K_{1x} \nearrow \quad \overset{|}{\text{CH}_2.\text{COOH}} \quad \searrow K_{2y}
\end{array}
$$

IV.147 $\text{R.CH.COOH}\,(x)$ R.CH.COO^-

               $\overset{|}{\text{CH}_2.\text{COOH}}\,(y)$ $\overset{|}{\text{CH}_2.\text{COO}^-}$

$$
\begin{array}{c}
K_{1y} \searrow \quad \text{R.CH.COOH} \quad \nearrow K_{2x} \\
\overset{|}{\text{CH}_2.\text{COO}^-}
\end{array}
$$

If we are dealing with a molecule in which the two ionizing groups are sufficiently far apart to have no influence on one another, K_{1x} will equal K_{2x} and K_{1y} will equal K_{2y}.

Calling the two intermediate forms produced by the ionization of groups x and y AH_x^- and AH_y^- respectively, we have the following equations defining the four group ionization constants

IV.148

$$
K_{1x} = \frac{[\text{AH}_x^-]\text{H}}{[\text{AH}_2]}, \quad K_{1y} = \frac{[\text{AH}_y^-]\text{H}}{[\text{AH}_2]}, \quad K_{2x} = \frac{[\text{A}^=]\text{H}}{[\text{AH}_y^-]}, \quad K_{2y} = \frac{[\text{A}^=]\text{H}}{[\text{AH}_x^-]}
$$

From these equations we have the relation

IV.149 $K_{1x}\,K_{2y} = K_{1y}\,K_{2x}$

The relationship between the molecular ionization constants K_1, K_2 and the group ionization constants just mentioned may be seen as follows. The total concentration of intermediate form is the sum of the concentrations of AH_x^- and AH_y^-. Inserting $[\text{AH}_x^-]+[\text{AH}_y^-]$ for $[\text{AH}^-]$ in the definitions of K_1 and K_2 (equations IV.137), we obtain (cf. ADAMS, 15)

IV.150 $K_1 = \dfrac{([\text{AH}_x^-]+[\text{AH}_y^-])\text{H}}{[\text{AH}_2]} = K_{1x}+K_{1y}$

IV.151 $K_2 = \dfrac{[\text{A}^=]\text{H}}{[\text{AH}_x^-]+[\text{AH}_y^-]} = \dfrac{1}{\dfrac{1}{K_{2x}}+\dfrac{1}{K_{2y}}}$

It is interesting to consider again the case of a symmetrical dibasic acid in the light of these results. In this case $K_{1x} = K_{1y}$ and $K_{2x} = K_{2y}$. If we further suppose that the two ionizing groups do not influence each other, all four of the group ionization constants will be equal. It then follows from equations IV.150–1 that $K_1 = 4K_2$. Moreover, for the symmetrical acids considered by Michaelis, it follows from equation IV.150 that the first ionization constant of the molecule K_1 is equal to twice the true ionization constant of a carboxyl group (the reason being that the concentration of carboxyl groups is twice the molecular concentration of the acid). In fact if we prevent the ionization of one of the carboxyl groups, e.g. by esterifying it, K_1 immediately drops to half its previous value (being now the true group constant), although the carboxyl group remains just as strong an acid as it was before. Adams has pointed out that these deductions are in agreement with observation; they are sufficient to demonstrate the importance of the distinction between the two types of constants.

Returning to the consideration of the unsymmetrical molecule, we now require four pH functions to give the amounts of the four components. Inserting the definitions of the four group ionization constants (equations IV.148) into the conservation equation

IV.152　　　$A_t = [AH_2] + [AH_x^-] + [AH_y^-] + [A^=]$

and making use of equation IV.149, we obtain the new pH functions

IV.153　　　$f = 1 + \dfrac{K_{1x}}{H} + \dfrac{K_{1y}}{H} + \dfrac{K_{1x}K_{2y}}{H^2}$

IV.154　　　$f_x^- = 1 + \dfrac{K_{1y}}{K_{1x}} + \dfrac{H}{K_{1x}} + \dfrac{K_{2y}}{H}$

IV.155　　　$f_y^- = 1 + \dfrac{K_{1x}}{K_{1y}} + \dfrac{H}{K_{1y}} + \dfrac{K_{1x}K_{2y}}{K_{1y}H}$

IV.156　　　$f^= = 1 + \dfrac{H}{K_{2y}} + \dfrac{K_{1y}H}{K_{1x}K_{2y}} + \dfrac{H^2}{K_{1x}K_{2y}}$

As before, the reciprocals of these functions (which we have not found in the literature) will give the fractions of the total amount which are present in the corresponding states of ionization.

These functions are only important when the two groups do not differ very greatly in their strength of ionization, as may well be the case in the active centres of enzymes. Where the pKs are widely separated, as in Fig. IV.36(a), such complications do not arise. This may be seen by making K_{1x} very much larger than K_{1y} in the above expressions, when it will be found that f, f_x^- and $f^=$ reduce to expressions identical in form with the three Michaelis functions IV.132–4, while f_y^- becomes very large, which means that $[AH_y^-]$ is negligible, so that effectively only one intermediate form exists. This is the case for example with an average aminoacid where (in round figures) we might take pK_{1x} (carboxyl) as 3 and pK_{1y} (amino) as 10, so that the only intermediate form

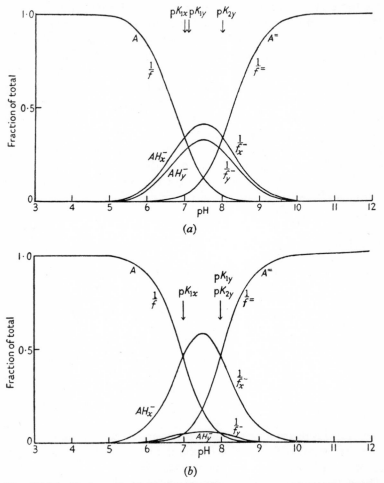

Fig. IV.38. *Reciprocals of pH functions for an unsymmetrical system with pKs as shown.*

is the dipolar ion; the amount of the uncharged form is infinitesimal and the Michaelis expressions apply.

It will be noted that the application of the functions does not depend on the chemical nature of the ionizing groups; they are not restricted to molecules with two carboxyl groups, but apply equally to ampholytes like aminoacids and to the active centres of enzymes where the nature of the ionizing groups may not be known. The $1/f_x^-$ curve might, for instance, very well represent the effect of pH on the amount of the active form of an enzyme, corresponding to the pH-activity curve.

The reciprocals of the four pH functions (which give the fractions of the total substance present in the four forms) are plotted in Fig. IV.38. assuming values for K_{1x} and K_{2y} of 10^{-7} and 10^{-8} respectively. The relative amounts of the two intermediate forms depend on the relative

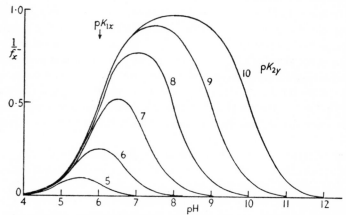

Fig. IV.39. *Effect on amount of one intermediate form of altering pK of one ionizing group while keeping that of the other constant.*

pK_{1x} kept constant at 6; values of pK_{2y} shown on the curves. Plotted from equation IV.154.

modified from *38*

values of K_{1x} and K_{1y}; in (*a*) the two are assumed to be nearly equal, while in (*b*) K_{1y} and K_{2y} are assumed equal. (*a*) might represent a molecule with two similar groups, with some interaction between them (cf. Fig. 3 of *205* for cysteine); (*b*) might represent a molecule with two somewhat different groups, without interaction. The curves for the two intermediate forms lie in the same pH region, have maximum values as before at pH_0, and are of the same general form as the previous curve for $1/f^-$. When all the group ionization constants are made equal to one another and to the pH, each of the four terms in each of the four functions becomes 1 and each form amounts to one-quarter of the total, so that the total intermediate form amounts to one-half of the total, not one-third as previously when K_1 was made equal to K_2.

It is convenient to use the letter x for the more strongly ionizing group; the value of K_{1y} will then lie between the values of K_{1x} and K_{2y}, for it will not be less than the latter since the effect of ionization of one group will be to decrease rather than increase the ionization of the other.

In Fig. IV.39 is plotted a family of curves from the function $1/f_x^-$ showing the effect on the amount of one intermediate form (e.g. the active form of an enzyme, in which case the ordinates might represent velocity) of changing pK_{2y}, while keeping pK_{1x} constant. This is very similar to the effects which certain kinds of inhibitors exert on the pH curves of enzymes (e.g. MYRBÄCK, *1911*, Fig. 1). When the two constants are equal, the maximum height is one-quarter of the total. This figure resembles the set of curves given by ALBERTY and MASSEY (*38*, Fig. 1), but their curves are given in terms of K_1 and K_2 and the maximum when these two constants are made equal is shown as one-third of the total. Since we are dealing here with activity phenomena produced by factors affecting actual groups in enzymes, and not with titration results, we deem it preferable to draw the curves in terms of group ionization constants. A set of curves showing the effect of simultaneously changing both constants of an ampholyte was given much earlier by Michaelis (*1812*).

In the sections which follow, when the functions are written simply as f, etc., it is assumed that the appropriate expressions will be used.

Effect of pH on V

As already mentioned, the effect of pH on V itself can be determined by carrying out a series of velocity measurements at different pHs with a sufficiently high substrate concentration to saturate the enzyme in all cases. Any effects on the affinity are thus eliminated. Under these conditions the whole of the enzyme is in the form of ES complex and since the velocity of the reaction is simply the rate of breakdown of the complex into free enzyme and product, the effect of pH on V will be determined only by the state of ionization of the complex. Changes in the state of ionization of the free enzyme or substrate will not affect V; they will affect K_m, but effects on K_m are eliminated by the use of high substrate concentrations. This consideration greatly simplifies the discussion.

From equation IV.84, $v = k_{+2}p$, where p is the concentration of the ES complex, which becomes equal to the total enzyme concentration when excess substrate is present, so that $V = k_{+2}e$ (equation IV.85). p is the sum of the concentrations of all the different ionic forms of the complex and might be written p_t (= total complex concentration), but since we have already frequently used p in this sense we shall drop the suffix, and similarly with e. The constant k_{+2} is the velocity constant with respect to the total amount of complex and will vary with the pH. This variation is due to the fact, already suggested by the pH-activity curves, that only one ionic form of the complex breaks down (or at any rate that one form breaks down more rapidly than any of the others) and the fraction of the total complex which is in this form varies with the pH. Thus k_{+2} consists of two parts, the velocity constant of breakdown of this particular form (which is independent of the pH and which we will call $\tilde{k}_{+2}$) and the appropriate pH function which determines the concentration of this form at any pH. The fact that the velocity falls off on either side of the pH optimum suggests that the active state is an intermediate form, so that the pH function involved is of the form given in the expression for f^- (equation IV.133). Thus we write

IV.157 $$k_{+2} = \frac{\tilde{k}_{+2}}{f_{es}}$$

where the subscript es refers to the ES complex. Since we do not know the nature of the ionizing groups in the enzyme which affect the activity, or which is the active ionic form of the complex, it will be convenient (cf. 38) to write ES^n for the latter, n being the net negative charge carried by the active form. Then

IV.158 $$v = \tilde{k}_{+2} \frac{p}{f_{es}^-}$$

where $\tilde{k}_{+2}$ is the velocity constant of breakdown of ES^n and p/f_{es}^- is the concentration of ES^n. The expression for V is obtained by putting $p = e$, and may thus be written out as

IV.159 $$V = \frac{\tilde{k}_{+2} e}{1 + \dfrac{H}{K_{es1}} + \dfrac{K_{es2}}{H}}$$

Here K_{es1} is the ionization constant of the complex which affects the acid side of the pH curve and K_{es2} is that which affects the alkaline side. A similar equation was given by WALEY (2760).

The underlying assumption is made that the ionization processes take place rapidly in comparison with the formation and breakdown of the enzyme–substrate complex, so that the various ionic forms of each of the components of the system are in equilibrium with one another. This seems a safe assumption in view of the nature of the processes. LAIDLER (1504) has worked out the complete equations for the case in which it does not hold, but they are too complicated to be useful and only become manageable when the assumption is made.

F

The system may be set out as follows (cf. *38*):

IV.160

$$
\begin{array}{ccc}
& K_{e1} & \quad K_{e2} \\
E^{n-1} \rightleftharpoons & E^n & \rightleftharpoons E^{n+1} \\
& k_{+1} \Big\Vert k_{-1} & \\
ES^{n-1} \rightleftharpoons & ES^n & \rightleftharpoons ES^{n+1} \\
K_{es1} & \Big\downarrow k_{+2} & K_{es2} \\
& E^n + P &
\end{array}
$$

Here the three velocity constants are defined with respect to the particular ionic species involved in the reaction in each case.

In deriving equation IV.159 we assumed that only one form of the ES complex breaks down, but it is possible that two forms of the complex might undergo breakdown at the same or different rates, though as far as we are aware there is no case in which this has been shown to occur. For instance, both ES^n and ES^{n+1} might break down; a fall of the pH-activity curve to zero on the alkaline side must then be due to a further ionization step with a constant which may be written K_{es3}. If ES^{n+1} breaks down more slowly than ES^n, the alkaline side of the curve will be composite, falling in two steps (which, however, may be fused) corresponding to K_{es2} and K_{es3}.

In certain cases K_{es2} will not affect the shape of the curve. If the group corresponding to K_{es2} is in such a position, either in the enzyme part or the substrate part of the complex, that its ionization has no influence on the reaction, both forms will break down at the same rate. Remembering that in the pH range where both ES^n and ES^{n+1} exist together, that is where H is of the same order of magnitude as K_{es2}, f_{es}^{-} approximates to $1+\dfrac{K_{es2}}{H}$ and $f_{es}^{=}$ to $1+\dfrac{H}{K_{es2}}$, we may write

IV.161

$$
v = \tilde{k}_{+2}\frac{p}{f_{es}^{-}} + \tilde{k}_{+2}\frac{p}{f_{es}^{=}} = \tilde{k}_{+2}p\left(\frac{1}{1+\dfrac{K_{es2}}{H}} + \frac{1}{1+\dfrac{H}{K_{es2}}}\right) = \tilde{k}_{+2}p
$$

In this case therefore, as would be expected, K_{es2} has no effect whatever on the velocity and the case reduces to that of breakdown of only one form of the complex, with the pH curve determined entirely by K_{es1} and K_{es3}.

If, however, the group is in such a position in or near the active centre that its ionization affects the rate of breakdown, the velocity constants $\tilde{k}_{+2}$ and $\tilde{k}_{+2}^{-}$ for the breakdown of ES^n and ES^{n+1} respectively will not be equal. The result then depends upon the nature of the breakdown process, that is to say, on whether the breakdown of both forms of the complex liberates the products in the same ionic forms or not. If $E^n + P$ is produced in both cases it will be clear that the two reactions must be written as $ES^n \rightarrow E^n + P$ and $ES^{n+1} + H^+ \rightarrow E^n + P$ respectively. The velocity will then be given by

IV.162
$$v = \tilde{k}_{+2}\frac{p}{f_{es}} + \tilde{k}_{+2}^- \frac{p}{f_{es}^=}H$$

But from equations IV.141 it may be seen that $H/f^= = K_2/f^-$, so that

IV.163
$$v = (\tilde{k}_{+2} + \tilde{k}_{+2}^- K_{es2})\frac{p}{f_{es}}$$

This is the same as equation IV.158, except for the substitution of one constant for another; thus the effect of pH on the velocity is the same as before and it is only the interpretation of the velocity constant that is altered.

It is possible, however, that the products are produced in different ionic states by the breakdown of the two forms of the complex. For instance, ES^n might liberate E^n, while ES^{n+1} liberates E^{n+1}, which then reacts with a hydrogen ion to become E^n. Though the two breakdown processes are now almost identical, it is possible that they might occur at slightly different rates, owing to the influence of the additional charge on the enzyme. This would give

IV.164
$$v = \tilde{k}_{+2}\frac{p}{f_{es}^-} + \tilde{k}_{+2}^- \frac{p}{f_{es}^=}$$

which does not reduce to the simple form, in the same way as equation IV.161, if $\tilde{k}_{+2}$ and $\tilde{k}_{+2}^-$ are appreciably different.

There remains the possibility (though there is no evidence for it, so far as we know) that in certain cases the breakdown of the ES complex might actually be a process which is catalysed by hydrogen ions, like a number of non-enzymatic breakdown processes. In this case the velocity would be given by

IV.165
$$v = \tilde{k}_{+2}H\frac{p}{f_{es}}$$

Now referring once more to equations IV.141, we find that $H/f^- = K_1/f$, so that

IV.166
$$v = \tilde{k}_{+2}K_{es1}\frac{p}{f_{es}}$$

Thus the effect is precisely the same as if ES^{n-1} broke down and E^n did not.

Returning now to equation IV.159, we note that if we plot $\log V$ against pH, we shall obtain the same type of graph as that in Fig. IV.37, for

IV.167 $$\log V = \log \check{k}_{+2}e + \mathrm{p}f^{-}_{es}$$

and the first term on the right does not vary with pH. This is a valuable rule, for it means that from the positions of the bends in the graph we can obtain the pKs of the ionizing groups in the ES complex which

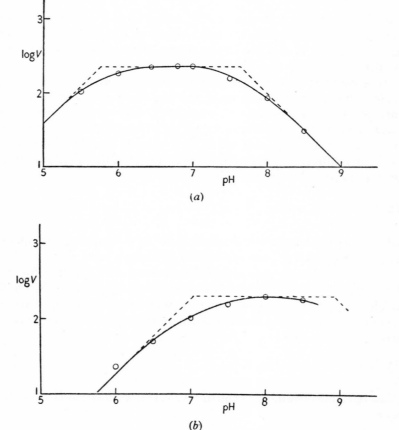

(a)

(b)

Fig. IV.40. *Log V curves for fumarate hydratase (4.2.1.2).*

(a) with fumarate as substrate
(b) with malate as substrate.

plotted from data in *1751a*

affect the activity, in other words groups which either form part of the active centre or are closely associated with it.

In cases where the observations do not extend over a sufficiently wide pH range to enable the linear portions on both sides of the pK value to be plotted, the pK may often be determined by plotting $1/V$ against H or $1/H$ as the case may be. This method is valid only if no other group changes its ionization within the region considered. If this condition is fulfilled one of the two terms H/K_{es1} or K_{es2}/H in equation IV.159 can

be neglected, and $\dfrac{1}{V} = \dfrac{1 + \dfrac{H}{K_{es1}}}{\check{k}_{+2}e}$, or $\dfrac{1}{V} = \dfrac{1 + \dfrac{K_{es2}}{H}}{\check{k}_{+2}e}$. A plot of $1/V$ against

H or $1/H$ respectively will be a straight line of slope $1/K_{es1}\check{k}_{+2}e$ or $K_{es2}/\check{k}_{+2}e$ and intercept on the vertical axis $1/\check{k}_{+2}e$, so that from the slope and intercept K_{es1} or K_{es2} may be obtained. This method has been used by LAIDLER (*1505*) and others.

Unfortunately, as we have already mentioned, very few data are available on the effect of pH on V. Although the literature contains pH curves of numerous enzymes and in some cases it has been shown that more than enough substrate was used to saturate the enzyme at the optimum pH, in very few cases is it certain that this was so at all the pHs tested. One of the few cases for which reliable curves of V have been obtained is that of fumarate hydratase (4.2.1.2) (MASSEY and ALBERTY, *1751a*) and from these data $\log V$ curves have been plotted in Fig. IV.40; (*a*) is for fumarate as substrate and (*b*) for malate. It will be seen that the enzyme–fumarate complex has pKs of about 5·7 and 7·7, while the enzyme–malate complex has pKs of about 7 and (perhaps) 9. There is of course no reason to expect that the two complexes would have the same pK values; in any case a complication is introduced by the fact that fumarate hydratase is an enzyme which has the special property of being sensitive to anions and the curves are greatly affected by salts.

LAIDLER (*1505*) has plotted $\log V$ curves from data in the literature for cholinesterase (3.1.1.8) (HASE, *1019*) and for xanthine oxidase (1.2.3.2) acting on 2-amino-4-hydroxypteridine (LOWRY et al., *1622*); these are shown in Figs. IV.41 and 42. In these two cases only one pK of the ES complex is observable in the range tested and there is no optimum pH for V, which simply rises to a constant maximum value. Further reliable work on the pKs of enzyme–substrate complexes is much needed; comparison of the pKs of the complexes with those of the free enzymes and substrates seems likely to yield interesting information about the effects of combination with the active centre of the enzyme on the substrate molecule.

While measurements of velocity at high substrate concentrations give the pKs of the ES complex, measurements at very low substrate concentrations may give the pKs of the free enzyme and substrate. As already pointed out, at low concentrations $v = (V/K_m)s$. From the quantity V/K_m it is possible to determine the pKs of the free enzyme (cf. *38*) and the free substrate. The reason for this will become clear when the effect of pH on K_m has been considered, but briefly it may be said

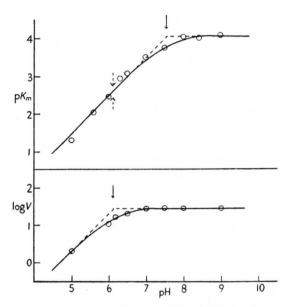

Fig. IV.41. *Effect of pH on K_m and V for cholinesterase (3.1.1.8) acting on acetylcholine.*

data of Hase (*1019*), upper curve from Dixon (*621*),
lower curve from Laidler (*1505*)

that K_m depends upon the ionization constants of all three components, while V is a function of the constants of ES only; in the ratio of the two quantities the ES constants are cancelled out, leaving only the constants of the free enzyme and substrate. Observations on K_m alone, however, are capable by themselves of giving the pKs of all the components, as explained in the next section; the velocity measurements at low and high substrate concentrations are then useful for checking the results. In Fig. IV.42 the three quantities are plotted together; the logarithmic method of plotting, as proposed by DIXON (*621*), makes the observations comparatively easy to interpret.

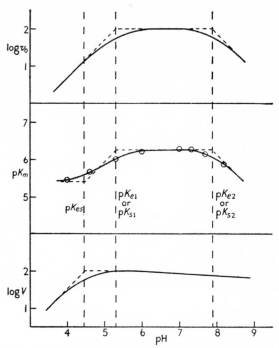

Fig. IV.42. *Effect of pH on K_m, V and v_0 for xanthine oxidase (1.2.3.2) acting on 2-amino-4-hydroxypteridine.*
data of Lowry *et al.* (*1622*), middle curve from Dixon (*621*), upper and lower curves from Laidler (*1505*)

Effect of pH on K_m

WALKER and SCHMIDT (*2762*), in considering the case of histidine ammonia-lyase (4.3.1.3), described the general manner in which ionization of the three components of the system should affect the Michaelis constant and they worked out equations on the assumption that each component has a single ionizing group. DIXON (*621*) later gave a more general theoretical treatment, with a number of rules for interpreting the data. His treatment relates to K_s and it applies equally to K_i for inhibitors; it is thus a theory of the effect of pH on the affinities of enzymes for substrates and inhibitors and it was assumed in deriving it that the ES complex was in equilibrium with the free enzyme and substrate, or in other words that k_{+2} was small compared with k_{-1} and the system fulfilled the Michaelis condition. This treatment is quite valid for K_s and K_i;

the question of the validity of its application to K_m and to steady-state kinetics is considered later.

Considering the system set out in reactions IV.160, we will assume for the moment that, as before, the form E^n of the enzyme combines with the unionized form S of the substrate (which might for example be a dibasic acid) to give the form ES^n of the complex, thus

IV.168 $E^n + S \rightleftharpoons ES^n$

and that equilibrium is set up. We will define an equilibrium constant $\tilde{K}_s$ by the relationship

IV.169 $$\tilde{K}_s = \frac{[E^n][S]}{[ES^n]}$$

This differs from the ordinary substrate constant K_s because the latter is the equilibrium constant defined with respect to the total amounts of E, S and ES and depends on the pH, whereas $\tilde{K}_s$ is defined with respect to particular ionic forms of the components and is independent of the pH. [S] is here the concentration of the unionized form of the substrate.

We have then from equations IV.138–40 and the definition of K_s

IV.170 $$K_s = \frac{E_t \cdot S_t}{ES_t} = \frac{[E^n] f_e^- \cdot [S] f_s}{[ES^n] f_{es}^-} = \tilde{K}_s \frac{f_e^- \cdot f_s}{f_{es}^-}$$

This important equation, which shows how K_s varies with the pH, is also useful in logarithmic form

IV.171 $$pK_s = p\tilde{K}_s + \log f_{es}^- - \log f_e^- - \log f_s$$

$$= p\tilde{K}_s - pf_{es}^- + pf_e^- + pf_s$$

Precisely similar equations express the effect of pH on the affinity of enzymes for inhibitors:

IV.172 $$K_i = \tilde{K}_i \frac{f_e^- \cdot f_i}{f_{ei}^-}$$

IV.173 $$pK_i = p\tilde{K}_i - pf_{ei}^- + pf_e^- + pf_i$$

Since the various ionic forms of each component are in equilibrium with one another, we might have written equations IV.168–9 in terms of any other forms; it is quite immaterial which forms we assume actually to combine and we have only chosen this mode of combination as the simplest in relation to the system as set out in reactions IV.160. It is easy to show that the same result is obtained whatever assumption is made about the mechanism of combination. If, for instance, we assume that it is not the uncharged form but the doubly-charged anion of the substrate which combines, and that the ES complex is the same as before, we must write instead of equations IV.168–9

IV.174 $E^n + S^= + 2H^+ = ES^n$

IV.175 $\bar{K}_{s=} = \dfrac{[E^n][S^=]H^2}{[ES^n]}$

and then we have from equations IV.137–41 and 169

IV.176

$$K_s = \frac{E_t \cdot S_t}{ES_t} = \frac{[E^n] f_e^- \cdot [S^=] f_s^=}{[ES^n] f_{es}^-} = \frac{\bar{K}_{s=}}{H^2} \cdot \frac{f_e^- \cdot f_s^=}{f_{es}^-} = \frac{\bar{K}_{s=}}{K_{s1} K_{s2}} \cdot \frac{f_e^- f_s}{f_{es}^-} = \bar{K}_s \frac{f_e^- f_s}{f_{es}^-}$$

which is the same result as before (cf. equation IV.170).

The selection of the correct functions to use in equation IV.171 is in fact determined not by any assumptions as to the mechanism of combination, but merely by the way in which the equilibrium constant which appears in the equation is defined. Thus the equation as written contains f^- functions for E and ES and an f function for S simply because $\bar{K}_s$ is defined with respect to intermediate forms of E and ES and the uncharged form of S.

It was pointed out by Dixon (621) that if a graph of $-\log K_s$ or pK_s is plotted against pH, the results can easily be interpreted by a few simple rules of which equation IV.171 forms the theoretical basis. This equation shows that, neglecting the first constant term, which merely affects the vertical position of the graph, the curve will represent the algebraic sum of three pf terms, each of which will obey the same rules as the function already plotted in Fig. IV.37. It will, however, be noted that whereas the pf terms for the free enzyme and substrate appear with the same sign as that in the figure, the pf term for the ES complex has the opposite sign and its effect will be inverted. These considerations lead to the following rules.

(a) The graph of pK_s will consist of straight-line sections (if the pK values are sufficiently separated) joined by short curved parts.

(b) The straight portions have integral slopes, i.e. zero or one-unit or two-unit slopes, positive or negative.

(c) Each bend indicates the pK of an ionizing group in one of the components and the straight portions when produced intersect at a pH corresponding to the pK.

(d) Each pK produces a change of 1 unit in the slope.

(e) Each pK of a group situated in the ES complex produces an upward bend, i.e. an increase of (positive) slope with increase of pH, or, in other words, a bend with the concave side upwards; each pK of a group situated in either the free enzyme or the free substrate produces a downward bend.

(f) The curvature at the bends is such that the graph misses the intersection point of the neighbouring straight parts by a vertical distance of $0 \cdot 3$ units ($= \log 2$); if two pKs occur together the distance is equal to $\log 3$.

(g) The slope of any straight-line section is numerically equal to the change of charge occurring in that pH range when the complex dissociates into free enzyme and substrate. For instance, if at a certain pH the enzyme and complex both have n negative charges and the free substrate is present in the uncharged form, the dissociation process will be $ES^n \rightarrow E^n + S$, so that there will be no change of charge and a zero slope; if the complex has $n+1$ negative charges and the substrate has 1, the process will be $ES^{n+1} \rightarrow E^n + S^-$ and the slope will still be zero; if the process is $ES^{n-1} \rightarrow E^n + S$ the change of charge is -1, giving a minus-one-unit slope, and so on. The slope is simply determined by the charges on the particular forms of the components which happen to predominate at the pH in question.

It is not possible in this way to distinguish between ionizations of the free enzyme and those of the free substrate, but since those of the substrate are usually known or can be determined, little difficulty arises in practice.

It should be noted that these rules are independent of assumptions as to which forms of the components combine or react or which pH functions occur in the equations. In fact it is not necessary to be able to write the equations for a given system at all in order to interpret the pK_s curves by means of the rules.

These rules are equally applicable to the effects of pH on pK_i and considerably facilitate the interpretation of the action of inhibitors.

When an ionizing group is not actually involved in the link which is formed between enzyme and substrate, it will still usually ionize in the complex, but the effect of the combination may well produce a change in its pK; this will produce a wave in the graph, as shown in Fig. IV.43, B or C, and the vertical difference in level due to the wave will be equal to the change which occurs in the pK on combination, if the vertical and horizontal scales of the graph are the same, which is desirable. When the combination is actually with the ionizing group itself, its ionization is usually entirely suppressed and an angle in the graph as shown in A is produced.

The effects on K_s of the ionizations of all groups which ionize equally strongly in the free enzyme and the enzyme–substrate complex cancel out (for they can be regarded as producing an infinitely small wave), though they may affect V and appear in the log V curve; this cancellation is valuable, as it means that only those groups which are intimately associated with the active centre, so as to be affected when the substrate combines, are revealed by the graphs. The many ionizing groups in the enzyme protein which are remote from the active centre produce no disturbing effect. It must be remembered on the other hand that some

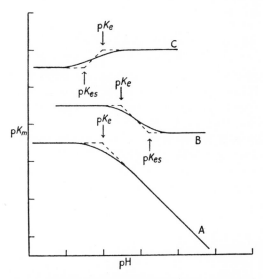

Fig. IV.43. *Diagram illustrating some effects of pH on K_ms.*

groups which do not ionize at all may be responsible for, or involved in, the combination with the substrate and no indication of their presence will be given by the graphs.

The above theory is valid for the effect of pH on K_s. The question naturally arises whether it is equally valid for K_m when Briggs–Haldane conditions apply, that is to say, when K_m is not a true equilibrium constant but is equal to $(k_{-1}+k_{+2})/k_{+1}$, where any or all of the three velocity constants may vary with pH. The kinetic treatment of this problem becomes simplified when we remember that the k_{+1} reaction (formation of the complex from the free enzyme and substrate) will depend on the state of ionization of the enzyme and substrate only and not on that of the complex, whereas the k_{-1} and k_{+2} reactions (breakdown of the complex, either into enzyme and substrate or into enzyme and product) will depend only on the ionization of the complex and will be independent of that of the enzyme and substrate.

We have already seen in the previous section (equation IV.158) that the effect of pH on k_{+2} is allowed for by substituting $\tilde{k}_{+2}/f_{es}^-$ for k_{+2}, the velocity constant and pH function chosen being those for the form of ES which breaks down. Similarly, assuming that the same form of ES is involved in the k_{-1} reaction, as shown in the system of IV.160, we substitute $\tilde{k}_{-1}/f_{es}^-$ for k_{-1}. For the k_{+1} reaction, which involves both free enzyme and substrate, we must write $\tilde{k}_{+1}/(f_e^-.f_s)$. Making these substitutions, we obtain

IV.177 $$K_m = \frac{k_{-1}+k_{+2}}{k_{+1}} = \frac{\tilde{k}_{-1}+\tilde{k}_{+2}}{\tilde{k}_{+1}} \cdot \frac{f_e^- \cdot f_s}{f_{es}^-}$$

Thus the effect of pH on K_m is precisely the same as its effect on K_s (cf. equation IV.170), since $\tilde{k}_{+1}$, $\tilde{k}_{-1}$ and $\tilde{k}_{+2}$ do not depend on the pH because they refer to particular ionic forms. The pH theory is therefore valid for this case also.

An expression of this form was first worked out, using Briggs–Haldane steady-state kinetics, by WALEY (2760). The full expression for the velocity, in the system shown in IV.160, may be written out in full as follows, including Waley's expression for V,

IV.178 $$v = \frac{\dfrac{\tilde{k}_{+2}e}{1+\dfrac{H}{K_{es1}}+\dfrac{K_{es2}}{H}}}{1 + \dfrac{1}{s} \cdot \dfrac{\tilde{k}_{-1}+\tilde{k}_{+2}}{\tilde{k}_{+1}} \cdot \dfrac{\left(1+\dfrac{H}{K_{e1}}+\dfrac{K_{e2}}{H}\right)\left(1+\dfrac{K_{s1}}{H}+\dfrac{K_{s1}K_{s2}}{H^2}\right)}{1+\dfrac{H}{K_{es1}}+\dfrac{K_{es2}}{H}}}$$

It is here assumed that the active form of the complex is ES^n, that this is formed by the combination of E^n with S and that the substrate can undergo ionization as a dibasic acid.

It was mentioned above that in the treatment for K_s, where equilibrium conditions prevail, it was of no consequence which ionic forms were assumed to combine. In the kinetic treatment this is no longer true; if in the system shown in IV.160 there is also combination of E^{n-1} with S to give ES^{n-1}, the velocity of this reaction must be added to that of the $\tilde{k}_{+1}$ reaction and the results will be affected. LAIDLER (1504), extending the theoretical treatment of BOTTS and MORALES (298), has worked out the full kinetic equations for this system and has shown that, provided that the formation of the active form of the complex from E^n is much more rapid than its formation from any of the other forms of the enzyme, the above equations will hold, but that when this is not the case errors of up to $0\cdot3$ pH units may occur in the ionization pK values. Since this is probably within the experimental error in this kind of work, this condition does not seem to be very essential.

It is implicit in the formulation of Laidler and others that the effects of pH on the k_{-1} and the k_{+2} reactions are similar, since they both depend on the state of ES. It is perhaps conceivable that this may not be so in all cases, though it is not easy to formulate conditions in which they

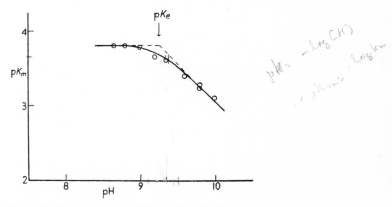

Fig. IV.44. *Effect of pH on K_m of alkaline*
phosphatase (3.1.3.1).
data of Morton (*1878*), from Dixon (*621*)

would be different. If there were an additional effect of pH on k_{+2} only, this constant would have to be multiplied by some function of pH, say f_{+2}, which would not affect the other constants, so that equation IV.177 would have to be replaced by $K_m = \dfrac{\tilde{k}_{-1} + f_{+2}\tilde{k}_{+2}}{\tilde{k}_{+1}} \cdot \dfrac{f_e \cdot f_s}{f_{es}}$. How far this would affect the results would depend on the relative magnitude of $\tilde{k}_{-1}$ and $\tilde{k}_{+2}$ and on the nature of f_{+2}. We are not aware of any evidence which suggests that this ever occurs, but the possibility should not be entirely ruled out. Laidler's conclusion is that, except for the possible slight errors in ionization constants mentioned in the last paragraph, the pH theory applies not only to the equilibrium case but also to the Briggs–Haldane case.

The data in the literature on the effect of pH on K_m, as on V, are very meagre. Dixon plotted six cases, of which four are shown in Figs.

IV.41, 42, 44 and 45. The application of the rules for the interpretation of the curves is well illustrated by Fig. IV.42; the pK_m curve shows a pK of the complex (upward bend) at about $4 \cdot 5$, and two for the free enzyme (or substrate) at $5 \cdot 3$ and $7 \cdot 9$. The pK of the complex also appears in the $\log V$ curve, but not in the $\log v_0$ curve, while the pKs of the enzyme appear in the $\log v_0$ curve, but not in the $\log V$ curve, in full agreement with the theory given above. Fig. IV.41 is an illustration of the fact, already mentioned, that the pK of a group in the enzyme which may affect the velocity and appear in the $\log V$ curve will be cancelled out of the pK_m curve if its ionization is not affected by combination with the substrate.

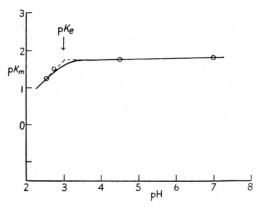

Fig. IV.45. *Effect of pH on K_m of β-fructo-furanosidase* (3.2.1.26).

data of Josephson (*1268*), from Dixon (*621*)

Some interesting results on arylsulphatase (3.1.6.1) obtained by DODGSON *et al.* (*640a*) are shown in Fig. IV.46 for three different substrates. It will be seen that the enzyme has two pKs at about $8 \cdot 1$ and $9 \cdot 4$ and the ES complex has one pK, varying slightly with different substrates, between $7 \cdot 5$ and $7 \cdot 8$. One of the substrates contains an extra phenolic group which was found, from the titration curve of the free substrate, to have a pK of about $6 \cdot 5$. This produces an additional wave in the curve, which shows two extra pKs, one just over $6 \cdot 5$ belonging to the free enzyme or substrate, the other at $6 \cdot 9$ belonging to the ES complex. The pK at $6 \cdot 5$ corresponds with that of the free substrate; it cannot belong to the enzyme since it does not appear in the other curves. The pK at $6 \cdot 9$ is evidently due to the ionization of the same group in the combined substrate, showing that this group is still free in the complex, but that combination of the substrate with the active centre of the enzyme has made it less acidic. It is possible that the study of such effects of combination with the enzyme on various substituent groups in the substrate would give an idea of the electronic changes which occur in the substrate molecule when it becomes activated by the enzyme.

The possibility of determining the pKs of ionizing groups situated in the active centres of enzymes suggests that it might throw valuable light on their chemical nature. This is quite possible, but a cautious approach is recommended. In the first place the fact that a group in the enzyme has a pK of the same value as that of a known chemical group

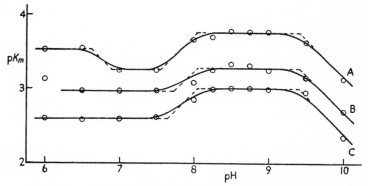

Fig. IV.46. *Effect of pH on K_m of arylsulphatase* (3.1.6.1).

A, on nitrocatechol sulphate
B, on p-nitrophenylsulphate
C, on p-acetylphenylsulphate.

after *640a*

does not prove its identity with that group, for other groups may have the same pK value. In the second place a given group may not have the same pK when it is present in a protein molecule as it has when it is present in a free aminoacid or other small molecule, owing to the influence of other charged groups nearby in the protein. Table IV.1, taken from EDSALL (*469*, p. 445), gives the range of pK values of a number of groups present in proteins, together with the heats of ionization of the groups. In discussing the identification of ionizing groups in proteins, Edsall says, 'These (pK) regions may be shifted owing to interaction of the acid group involved with other neighboring groups within the molecule, but, in general, such shifts are relatively small and even in the most extreme cases known are scarcely ever greater than 2 pH units. . . .

The characteristic heats of ionization of the different groups ... afford a very important clue to their nature. ... If both the pK value of a certain group in a protein and its heat of ionization be known, little doubt generally remains as to the nature of the group.' It has been suggested, however, that this may not apply to groups in the active centres of enzymes, where local electrostatic fields may perhaps be expected to exist. So far there is no evidence that this is so and it is necessary to suspend judgment on the question until more data have been accumulated. The heats of ionization of the groups may be determined by observing the effect of alteration of temperature on the pKs.

TABLE IV.1

pK VALUES AND HEATS OF IONIZATION OF SOME GROUPS
PRESENT IN PROTEINS

Group	pK (25°)	$\Delta H_i (cal/mol)$
Carboxyl (α)	3·0–3·2	($\pm 1,500$)
Carboxyl (aspartyl)	3·0–4·7	($\pm 1,500$)
Carboxyl (glutamyl)	ca. 4·4	($\pm 1,500$)
Phenolic hydroxyl (tyrosine)	9·8–10·4	6,000
Sulphydryl†	8·3–8·6	—
Imidazolium (histidine)	5·6–7·0	6,900–7,500
Ammonium (α)	7·6–8·4	10,000–13,000
Ammonium (α, cystine)	6·5–8·5	—
Ammonium (ϵ, lysine)	9·4–10·6	10,000–12,000
Guanidinium (arginine)	11·6–12·6	12,000–13,000

† From 205.

It should be noted that the bends in the curves of log V and of pK_m against pH give molecular ionization constants (K_1, K_2, etc.) and not group ionization constants (K_x, K_y, etc.). This may be shown as follows. If in equation IV.154, f_x^- is taken as the pH function for the active form of the enzyme, represented by a curve of the type shown in Fig. IV.37, the equation for the middle (pH-independent) portion will be p$f_x^- = -\log(1+K_{1y}/K_{1x})$, that for the left-hand portion will be p$f_x^- = -\log(H/K_{1x})$ and that for the right-hand portion will be p$f_x^- = -\log(K_{2y}/H)$. At the left-hand intersection the first two must be equal, and therefore $H = K_{1x}+K_{1y} = K_1$ (cf. equation IV.150). Similarly at the right-hand intersection the first and third must be equal, and therefore $H = 1/(1/K_{2x}+1/K_{2y}) = K_2$, from equation IV.149.

If the two constants are sufficiently different from one another, the molecular constants thus determined will be equal to the group ionization constants. It is only when the constants are not very different in value that it is necessary to make the distinction, and in any case under these conditions it is difficult to make accurate estimates of pK_1 and pK_2. If such estimates are made, however, care must be taken in interpreting these constants as group ionization constants for the identification of particular groups.

(D) EFFECT OF TEMPERATURE

The effect of temperature on the velocity of enzyme reactions may be due to several different causes. It may be due to an effect on the stability of the enzyme; to an effect on the actual velocity of breakdown of the complex (i.e. on k_{+2}) determined by the heat of activation of the reaction; to an effect on the enzyme–substrate affinity (i.e. on k_{+1} and k_{-1}); to an effect on the pH functions of any or all of the components, due to an alteration of their pKs which is determined by the heats of ionization; to an effect on the affinity of the enzyme for activators or inhibitors, if any; to a transfer of rate-limiting function from one enzyme to another, in a system involving two or more enzymes with different temperature coefficients; or even to such subsidiary causes as a change in concentration of dissolved O_2, due to a change of solubility, in manometric experiments, or a change in the pH of the buffer used.

This might suggest that the effects of temperature are extremely complex. Actually they can readily be analysed experimentally. Effects due to instability of the enzyme itself can be studied by exposing the enzyme to various temperatures for a definite period, before measuring its activity at a temperature at which it is stable. Effects on the affinity can be eliminated by using sufficiently high concentrations of substrate or activator to saturate the enzyme, so that the effect of temperature on V can be determined. The effect of temperature on the Michaelis constant can be measured independently by the usual methods and in some cases its effect on the three velocity constants can be determined. The effect on the pKs of the components may be separately determined by the methods of the last section. In a multi-enzyme system, each enzyme may usually be studied separately, so as to avoid the limiting effects of the other enzymes. Finally, most subsidiary effects can be eliminated by a proper attention to details of technique.

Heat inactivation of enzymes

If a series of progress curves for different temperatures is plotted, the results obtained will in general resemble those shown diagrammatically in Fig. IV.47. It will be seen that, although the true initial velocity increases steadily as the temperature is raised, the amount of substrate transformed at any finite time first rises and then falls, giving an apparent optimum temperature. Further, this optimum temperature is not constant, but falls as the time interval increases; compare, for example, times t_1 and t_2 in the figure.

Two different effects of temperature are operating simultaneously here, namely, the increase in the initial velocity or true catalytic activity of the enzyme, together with a destruction of the enzyme at the higher temperatures, producing a continuous fall in the concentration of active

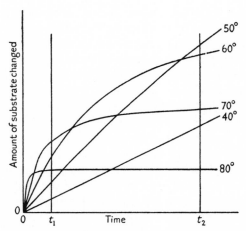

Fig. IV.47. *Typical progress curves of an enzyme reaction at various temperatures, showing dependence of apparent optimum temperature on time.*

enzyme, as shown by the increasing curvature as the temperature rises until the velocity falls to zero. The optimum temperature is determined by the balance between the effect of temperature on the rate of the enzyme reaction and its effect on the rate of destruction of the enzyme; therefore the actual values of the optimum temperature have no special significance.

The rate of inactivation of enzymes in solution increases rapidly with the temperature; in nearly all cases inactivation becomes virtually instantaneous at temperatures well below 100° and in the majority of cases below 70°. The number of enzymes which can withstand a temperature of 100° is extremely small; the classical example is adenylate kinase (2.7.4.3), which will withstand prolonged heating at 100° at pH 1. It is interesting, however, that certain bacteria which normally live at high temperatures (the thermophilic bacteria) contain enzymes which are abnormally heat-stable. For example, a crystalline α-amylase (3.2.1.1) isolated from *Bacillus stearothermophilus* was shown to retain 90 per cent of its activity after 1 hr at 90° (*1708*).

The inactivation of enzymes by heat is nearly always due to the denaturation of the enzyme protein. The temperature coefficient of inactivation is considerably higher than that of any other known process, with the exception of protein denaturation, although showing marked

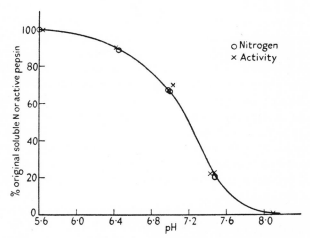

Fig. IV.48. *Equivalence of enzyme inactivation and protein denaturation.*

Pepsin (3.4.4.1) at 20°.

from *1993*

variations and ranging from about 10 to many hundreds. An exact proportionality between inactivation and denaturation has been shown for both pepsin (3.4.4.1) and trypsin (3.4.4.4) by NORTHROP (*1993, 1995*), and one set of observations is shown in Fig. IV.48. Furthermore, in these cases denaturation can be reversed under certain conditions and a recovery of activity parallel with the renaturation of the protein is obtained.

The denaturation of enzymes by heat falls within the field of the protein chemist and will not be considered in great detail here. The measurement of enzyme activity gives the protein chemist a ready method of accurately following denaturation.

The high temperature coefficient implies a high heat of activation for denaturation. By applying the theory of absolute reaction rates (see *2508*) it is possible to calculate the free energy and entropy of activation for denaturation; it is found that the value of the free energy is not exceptional† and the high heat of activation is due to exceptionally high positive entropies of activation. This has been interpreted as indicating the breaking of a large number of weak bonds, such as hydrogen bonds, in the denaturation of proteins and enzymes. This is consistent with the accepted picture of denaturation as an opening up of the molecule by unfolding or separation of adjacent portions of peptide chains. This question is discussed in more detail in Chapter X.

The rate of inactivation of enzymes, like other protein denaturations, is in most cases greatly dependent on the pH of the solution. The effect of pH varies greatly from one enzyme to another. In general there is a zone of maximum stability, not necessarily around the isoelectric point, and the inactivation increases on the acid and alkaline sides. Many enzymes are inactivated even at room temperature at pH 4–5 and 8–10. Since the inactivation parameters vary greatly with pH, caution should be exercised in drawing general conclusions from observations at only one pH. Other factors than pH may also have a considerable effect on the inactivation rate, for example, ionic strength, protein concentration, and the protective action of substrates, inhibitors and other substances. The concentration of water is also of importance and dried enzymes are comparatively heat stable.

In a number of cases heat denaturation is reversible on cooling. One striking example is the nucleotide pyrophosphatase (3.6.1.9) of *Proteus vulgaris*, which is completely inactivated by 10 minutes at 70°, but completely reactivated on cooling to 37°. Unheated preparations of the enzyme contain a thermolabile inhibitor, and the enzyme is inactive until this is removed by heating to 100° in the presence of its substrate pyrophosphate, which acts as a protector against denaturation (*2580*).

In some cases of reversible heat denaturation it is possible to measure the equilibrium between the active and inactive forms, although it is a matter of great difficulty to do this without disturbing the equilibrium. Almost the only enzymes with which this has been done are trypsin (3.4.4.4) (*79*) and the L-aminoacid oxidase of snake venom (1.4.3.2) (*1329*). The equilibrium changes fairly rapidly with temperature; with trypsin in 0·01 N HCl, in which the denaturation is completely reversible, the

† It appears from Table I of *2508* that the free energy of activation for denaturation is remarkably constant. This however, is merely a consequence of the fact that workers have naturally chosen temperatures at which the rate of denaturation is conveniently measurable. Since the rate is determined by the free energy of activation, this implies that constant values of this quantity will be found.

percentage denaturation at equilibrium is 33 at 42°, 50 at 44° and 80 at 50°. Thus the denaturation process is endothermic, with a heat of denaturation of about 68,000 cal per mole and an entropy change (which is independent of temperature) of 213 cal per mole per deg. These figures are considerably higher than the heat and entropy of activation for denaturation, which are 40,200 cal per mole and 44·7 cal per mole per deg. respectively. It is quite unusual for the heat and entropy of a process to be greater than the heat and entropy of activation of the process and this is a remarkable feature of protein denaturation. The relationships are shown diagrammatically in Fig. IV.49, which

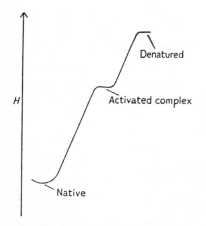

Fig. IV.49. *Diagrammatic representation of ΔHs in the denaturation of trypsin (3.4.4.4).*

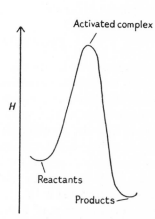

Fig. IV.50. *Diagrammatic representation of ΔHs in a
typical chemical reaction.*

may be compared with the more usual type of relationship shown in Fig. IV.50.

Although the stability of enzymes is usually greatest at low temperatures, so that preparations are frequently carried out in the cold room, there are rare cases where the stability is less at 0° than at room temperature. The bacterial glutamate decarboxylase (4.1.1.15) is stable at 25°, but at 0° the activity falls and reaches a limiting value of about half in 1 hr (*2395*). This fall does not occur if pyridoxal phosphate is first added (the enzyme is a pyridoxal phosphate protein), or in presence of serum albumin or high concentrations of glycine. After inactivation at 0°, the activity is partially restored by adding pyridoxal phosphate, but not by albumin or glycine, or by warming to 25°. The interpretation given is that combination with the prosthetic group stabilizes the protein, and that the dissociation of the prosthetic group from the protein is exothermic and thus favoured by cooling.

An effect of a different kind is the cold-sensitivity of an adenosinetriphosphatase of mitochondria (2124), which undergoes a fairly rapid inactivation at 0°, but which at room temperature is stable or even shows a slow increase of activity. The substrate ATP, which protects the enzyme against inactivation at higher temperatures or on dialysis, does not protect against inactivation at low temperatures. Only partial reactivation is obtained on warming from 0° to room temperature, so that the cold-sensitivity cannot be due simply to a shift in the equilibrium between an active and an inactive form of the enzyme. The kinetics of the effect are complicated (2371) and the explanation is still uncertain.

Effect on the enzyme reaction itself

As discussed earlier in this chapter, the overall enzyme reaction consists of at least three successive stages, namely, formation of the enzyme-substrate complex, conversion of this into the enzyme–product complex and dissociation of the product. The effect of temperature on the reaction will be the resultant of its separate effects on these stages. This means that there are at least 18 thermodynamic parameters for the whole forward reaction, namely, the heat, free energy and entropy of activation, and the heat, free energy and entropy of the process, for each of the three stages (see Table IV.2). There is no case, however, in which more than a small number of these quantities has been determined. In fact it must be admitted that remarkably little is known about any of these quantities and that such values as are given in the literature have meanings which are doubtful because of certain criticisms which are discussed below.

Ideally, what is required is the measurement of the absolute value of each of the separate velocity constants mentioned in section (c) and the effect of temperature on each. The various quantities can then be calculated as follows:

k_{+1}/k_{-1} gives the equilibrium constant for the first stage and the free energy is given by the usual equation

IV.179 $$\Delta F_1^0 = -RT \log_e \frac{k_{+1}}{k_{-1}} = -2 \cdot 303 \times RT \log_{10} \frac{k_{+1}}{k_{-1}}$$

where ΔF_1^0 is the standard free-energy change, which is the free-energy change (in cal per mole) of the reaction $E + S \rightarrow ES$ when E, S and ES are all at unit activity, positive when the formation of ES is endothermic; R is $1 \cdot 986$ cal per deg. per mole.

From the effect of temperature on k_{+1}/k_{-1} the heat change for the first stage may be obtained by means of the equation

IV.180 $$\Delta H_1^0 = 2 \cdot 303 \times RT^2 \frac{d \log \frac{k_{+1}}{k_{-1}}}{dT}$$

and the entropy of the process ΔS_1^0 can be obtained from ΔF_1^0 and ΔH_1^0 by the standard equation

IV.181 $$\Delta S_1^0 = \frac{\Delta H_1^0 - \Delta F_1^0}{T}$$

The most convenient way of using equation IV.180 is to plot $\log_{10}(k_{+1}/k_{-1})$ against $1/T$; the slope of the straight line obtained is then $-\Delta H_1^0/2 \cdot 303\,R$. If $\log K_s$ is plotted instead, the slope will be equal to $+\Delta H_1^0/2 \cdot 303\,R$.

The corresponding quantities for the second and third stages may be obtained in the same way from the ratios k_{+2}/k_{-2} and k_{+3}/k_{-3} respectively. The quantities for the back reaction are simply those for the forward reaction with reversed sign. The algebraic sum of the ΔH^0s for the three stages is equal to the overall heat of conversion of the substrate into the product, which can be independently checked from thermochemical data; similar summations can be carried out for the ΔF^0s and the ΔS^0s.

In the following discussion we shall for convenience omit the small zeros which show that the quantities are standard quantities.

In order to obtain the energies and entropies of activation it is necessary to make use of the theory of absolute reaction rates (EYRING, 711). The central point of this theory is that the rate of any reaction at a given temperature depends only on the concentration of an energy-rich activated complex which is in equilibrium with the unactivated reactants. According to the theory all activated complexes break down at a rate† given by $k_B T/h$, where k_B is the Boltzmann constant (the gas constant per molecule) and h is Planck's constant. In other words the rate of breakdown is independent of the nature of the complex.

Thus the reaction velocity constant k is given by

IV.182 $$k = \frac{k_B T}{h} K^*$$

where K^* is the equilibrium constant for the equilibrium between the activated complex and the unactivated molecules. Starred symbols are used to indicate quantities concerned in the activation process. The

† We omit the transition coefficient κ, which is usually assumed to be unity.

ordinary thermodynamic equations can be applied to this equilibrium, so that

IV.183 $\Delta F^* = \Delta H^* - T\Delta S^* = -RT \log_\epsilon K^*$

Substituting in equation IV.182, we get

IV.184 $k = \dfrac{k_B T}{h} \epsilon^{-\frac{\Delta F^*}{RT}} = \dfrac{k_B T}{h} \epsilon^{-\frac{\Delta H^*}{RT}} \epsilon^{+\frac{\Delta S^*}{R}}$

Assuming that ΔS^* does not vary with temperature, this gives by taking logarithms and differentiating

IV.185 $\dfrac{d\log_\epsilon k}{dT} = \dfrac{1}{T} + \dfrac{\Delta H^*}{RT^2} = \dfrac{\Delta H^* + RT}{RT^2}$

This may be compared with the empirical Arrhenius equation

IV.186 $\dfrac{d\log_\epsilon k}{dT} = \dfrac{E}{RT^2}$

where E was called the energy of activation. It will be noted that

IV.187 $E = \Delta H^* + RT$

Many workers have given values of heats of activation which are in fact E values and require correction by the quantity RT, which will be about 600 calories and is therefore not negligible.

As with equation IV.180, the most convenient method is to plot $\log_{10} k$ against $1/T$. Equation IV.185 can be rewritten

IV.188 $d\log_{10} k = \dfrac{\Delta H^* + RT}{2 \cdot 303\,R} \cdot \dfrac{dT}{T^2} = -\dfrac{\Delta H^* + RT}{2 \cdot 303\,R} \cdot d\left(\dfrac{1}{T}\right)$

so that this method of plotting will give a line with a slope of $-(\Delta H^* + RT)/2 \cdot 303\,R$. It is important to note that this plot gives E and not ΔH^*. The method can be applied directly to velocities expressed in arbitrary units, as any constant factor will merely affect the position and not the slope of the line.

ΔF^*, the free energy of activation, may be obtained from the value of k, using equation IV.184; for this purpose k must be expressed in absolute units. For instance, in the case of k_{+2}, we have from equation IV.85 $k_{+2} = V/e$; thus it will be necessary to know the molar concentration of active centres. This usually implies the use of pure enzymes of known molecular weight. ΔS^*, the entropy of activation, may then be obtained from equation IV.183.

It will be seen that there is a certain analogy between the absolute reaction rate theory and the Michaelis theory of enzyme action, for each involves the formation and breakdown of an active complex which is in equilibrium with the original reactants. However, the Michaelis enzyme–substrate complex and the Eyring activated complex are in quite different states; the Michaelis complex is not activated in the physical sense, but still requires thermal activation in order to react. Furthermore, a transitory activated complex must be formed during the combination of E and S to give the Michaelis complex and it is this which determines the value of k_{+1}. Similarly, the EZ complex also requires thermal activa-

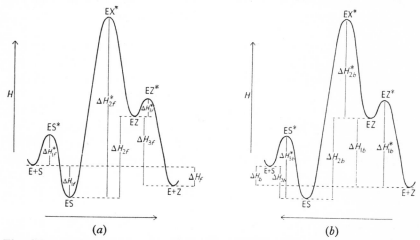

Fig. IV.51. *Diagrammatic representation of ΔHs in a typical reversible enzyme reaction.*

(*a*) forward reaction
(*b*) backward reaction.

tion in order to dissociate. The simple system considered thus involves three activated and two non-activated complexes:

$$E+S \rightleftharpoons ES^* \rightleftharpoons ES \rightleftharpoons EX^* \rightleftharpoons EZ \rightleftharpoons EZ^* \rightleftharpoons E+Z$$

The energy relationships of the different complexes in this system may be made clearer by the diagram given in Fig. IV.51(*a*) and (*b*), based on one given in *831*. This represents the *ΔH*s; similar diagrams may be drawn for the *ΔF*s and the *ΔS*s. The combination of enzyme with substrate or product may be exothermic or endothermic; to illustrate this point ES formation has been shown as exothermic and the combination of E and Z as endothermic. The first diagram (*a*) refers to the forward reaction and the second (*b*) to the reverse reaction of the same enzyme; in each case the stages have been numbered in the order in which they occur. The unactivated complexes lie at the troughs of the diagram and the activated complexes at the peaks; the height of each peak above the neighbouring trough represents the heat of activation,

TABLE IV.2

DETERMINATION OF THERMODYNAMIC QUANTITIES FROM VELOCITY CONSTANTS

Quantity	determined from	using equation	Quantity	determined from	using equation
$\Delta H_f =$ $-\Delta H_b$	effect of T on overall equilibrium	IV.180	$\Delta F_f =$ $-\Delta F_b$	overall equilibrium	IV.179
ΔH_{1f}	effect of T on $k_{+1}/k_{-1} = 1/K_{sf}$	IV.180	ΔH_{1b}	effect of T on $k_{-3}/k_{+3} = 1/K_{sb}$	IV.180
ΔH_{1f}^{*}	effect of T on k_{+1}	IV.185	ΔH_{1b}^{*}	effect of T on k_{-3}	IV.185
ΔF_{1f}	value of $k_{+1}/k_{-1} = 1/K_{sf}$	IV.179	ΔF_{1b}	value of $k_{-3}/k_{+3} = 1/K_{sb}$	IV.179
ΔF_{1f}^{*}	value of k_{+1}	IV.184	ΔF_{1b}^{*}	value of k_{-3}	IV.184
ΔH_{2f}	effect of T on k_{+2}/k_{-2}	IV.180	ΔH_{2b}	effect of T on k_{-2}/k_{+2}	IV.180
ΔH_{2f}^{*}	effect of T on k_{+2}	IV.185	ΔH_{2b}^{*}	effect of T on k_{-2}	IV.185
ΔF_{2f}	value of k_{+2}/k_{-2}	IV.179	ΔF_{2b}	value of k_{-2}/k_{+2}	IV.179
ΔF_{2f}^{*}	value of k_{+2}	IV.184	ΔF_{2b}^{*}	value of k_{-2}	IV.184
ΔH_{3f}	effect of T on $k_{+3}/k_{-3} = K_{sb}$	IV.180	ΔH_{3b}	effect of T on $k_{-1}/k_{+1} = K_{sf}$	IV.180
ΔH_{3f}^{*}	effect of T on k_{+3}	IV.185	ΔH_{3b}^{*}	effect of T on k_{-1}	IV.185
ΔF_{3f}	value of $k_{+3}/k_{-3} = K_{sb}$	IV.179	ΔF_{3b}	value of $k_{-1}/k_{+1} = K_{sf}$	IV.179
ΔF_{3f}^{*}	value of k_{+3}	IV.184	ΔF_{3b}^{*}	value of k_{-1}	IV.184

Quantities relating to the forward and back reactions are distinguished by the subscripts f and b respectively. The velocity constants are numbered in accordance with the following scheme:

$$E+S \underset{k_{-1}}{\overset{k_{+1}}{\rightleftharpoons}} ES \underset{k_{-2}}{\overset{k_{+2}}{\rightleftharpoons}} EZ \underset{k_{-3}}{\overset{k_{+3}}{\rightleftharpoons}} E+Z$$

From each corresponding pair of ΔH and ΔF values, the relevant entropy change ΔS can be calculated by equations IV.181 or IV.183.

It will be noted that

$$\Delta H_{1f} = -\Delta H_{3b}, \quad \Delta H_{2f} = -\Delta H_{2b}, \quad \Delta H_{3f} = -\Delta H_{1b}$$

and similarly for the ΔFs and ΔSs. The following are additional relationships between the ΔHs.

$$\Delta H_{1f} + \Delta H_{2f} + \Delta H_{3f} = \Delta H_f, \qquad \Delta H_{1b} + \Delta H_{2b} + \Delta H_{3b} = \Delta H_b$$
$$\Delta H^*_{1f} - \Delta H_{1f} = \Delta H^*_{3b}, \qquad \Delta H^*_{1b} - \Delta H_{1b} = \Delta H^*_{3f}$$
$$\Delta H^*_{2f} - \Delta H_{2f} = \Delta H^*_{2b}, \qquad \Delta H^*_{2b} - \Delta H_{2b} = \Delta H^*_{2f}$$
$$\Delta H^*_{3f} - \Delta H_{3f} = \Delta H^*_{1b}, \qquad \Delta H^*_{3b} - \Delta H_{3b} = \Delta H^*_{1f}$$
$$\Delta H^*_{1f} + \Delta H^*_{2f} + \Delta H^*_{3f} - \Delta H^*_{1b} - \Delta H^*_{2b} - \Delta H^*_{3b} = \Delta H_f$$
$$(\Delta H_{1f} + \Delta H^*_{2f}) - (\Delta H_{1b} + \Delta H^*_{2b}) = \Delta H_f$$

Similar identities can be written for the ΔFs and ΔSs.

or in other words the energy barrier to be overcome. The unstarred ΔHs remain the same for both directions, except for a change of sign; the heats of activation are different. The unstarred ΔHs add up to ΔH, the heat of the overall reaction.

EX* is the activated complex for conversion of ES to EZ or for the reverse reaction; it is assumed that the same complex is involved in both directions. For each stage the difference between the starred and unstarred ΔHs is equal to the starred ΔH for the reverse direction. The difference between the sums of the starred quantities in the forward and reverse directions is equal to the heat of the overall reaction.

These relationships, together with the method of deriving all the thermodynamic quantities from measurements of the separate velocity constants, are shown in Table IV.2. We believe that there is no enzyme for which such a complete set of data has been obtained, since although in a few cases the separate velocity constants have been determined, the measurements have only been carried out at one temperature. There is a great need for data of this kind and there is no reason why such full data should not be obtained by using the methods described above at different temperatures.

A fair volume of partial data for enzyme reactions has been published (see, for example, 2422, 2508), all of it obtained from measurements of the effect of temperature on K_m and V and in most cases of somewhat doubtful interpretation for the following reasons.

Dealing first with measurements of K_m, we note that the significance of the temperature effects will depend on the meaning of K_m, which has been discussed at length earlier in this chapter. In the extreme cases the situation is fairly simple. If $K_m = K_s = k_{-1}/k_{+1}$, the measurements are those of a true equilibrium constant which can be dealt with by equations IV.179–80, giving the free energy, heat and (from equation IV.181) entropy of combination of enzyme with substrate (i.e. ΔF_{1f}, ΔH_{1f} and ΔS_{1f}). In the opposite extreme, where $K_m = k_{+2}/k_{+1}$, we are dealing with the ratio of the velocity constants of two successive reactions, so that a plot of pK_m against $1/T$ will give the difference between the heats of activation of the processes of formation and breakdown of the complex (i.e. $\Delta H_{2f}^* - \Delta H_{1f}^*$). In order to obtain ΔH_{1f}^*, a knowledge of ΔH_{2f}^* is necessary and this can be obtained from the effect of temperature on V. Another method for determining ΔH_{1f}^* and ΔF_{1f}^* (and hence ΔS_{1f}^*) in this case is by measurements of the velocity constant at low substrate concentration, when the reaction becomes first-order with respect to substrate with a velocity constant of $k_{+2}e/K_m$ (see p. 115) which is here equal to $k_{+1}e$. It will be noted that in the Michaelis case it is the quantities relating to the overall process of combination which are obtained (i.e. unstarred quantities), whereas in the extreme Briggs–Haldane case it is those relating to the activation for combination (i.e. starred quantities).

In the intermediate case, where K_m is a function of three velocity constants, the situation is complex and the 'ΔH' values obtained from the plots of pK_m against $1/T$ will be complex functions of ΔH_{1f}, ΔH_{1f}^* and ΔH_{2f}^* and the three velocity constants. We believe that no method for the interpretation of such data has been given. It is probable that some of the few published values of the heat of formation of ES complexes are of this nature.

Considering now measurements of V, it should be noted that although V is a direct measure of k_{+2} if only one intermediate complex is involved, there are in fact two or more complexes in many cases; V, like K_m, will then be a complex function of several velocity constants, including that for dissociation of the product from the enzyme. When V depends on k_{+2} only, ΔH_{2f}^* will be given by the plot of $\log_{10} V$ against $1/T$ (equation IV.185), then if the concentration of enzyme is known so that the absolute value of k_{+2} can be obtained, ΔF_{2f}^* is given by equation IV.184 and ΔS_{2f}^* can be obtained from equation IV.183. When V is a complex function, the apparent 'ΔH^*' and 'ΔF^*' will likewise be complex functions and difficult to interpret without a knowledge of the separate constants. If in any particular case V/e approximates closely to some single velocity constant representing a later rate-determining step, the quantities obtained will relate to this step. If the different steps have different temperature coefficients, it is possible that different steps will become rate-determining at different temperatures; the plots of $\log V$ against $1/T$ will then be non-linear.

If the values for the energy of activation E, as determined from the Arrhenius plot, are to have the proper significance, care must be taken to see that the true value of V is obtained at each temperature. Since K_m generally depends on the temperature, it is not sufficient to assume that a substrate concentration which saturates the enzyme at one temperature will saturate it at other temperatures. Ideally, V should be obtained by extrapolation of a Lineweaver–Burk or other plot at each temperature. Neglect to do this has resulted in considerable errors in a number of cases, as shown by GIBSON (*831*). He points out that if, as has usually been the case, the velocities are measured with the same substrate concentration at different temperatures

IV.189
$$\Delta H_{2f}^{*\prime} - \Delta H_{2f}^{*} = \frac{K_m}{s+K_m}\Delta H_{1f}^{\prime} = \frac{1}{1+\sigma}\Delta H_1^{\prime}$$

using our notation, where $\Delta H_{2f}^{*\prime}$ is the apparent heat of activation (uncorrected for changes in K_m) obtained at constant substrate concentration assuming the measured velocity to be V, and $\Delta H_{1f}^{\prime}$ is the apparent heat of combination, obtained from the variation of K_m with temperature. If σ is made sufficiently large, this correction becomes negligible; this is also the case when $\Delta H_{1f}^{\prime}$ is small. Gibson, in his Table I, gives a number of examples in the literature in which this error is important, in some cases probably amounting to some thousands of calories.

It has been shown in section (c) that both V and K_m depend on the ionization of groups in the active centre of the enzyme. If these groups have an appreciable heat of ionization, the ionic state of the system will vary with temperature and this will produce an effect on the velocity. For instance, the pH curve may vary with temperature, so that the pH chosen may no longer be the optimum pH, and the effect of pH on the affinity may also change, so that the enzyme may no longer be saturated at the pH chosen. These changes will result, if not allowed for, in further errors in the values of the quantities which appear in Table IV.2.

Provided that all these difficulties can be satisfactorily overcome, it is possible to obtain from measurements on K_m and V at different temperatures in a reversible system all the quantities shown in Fig. IV.51 except those depending on the energy levels of ES* and EZ* (compare the data for fumarate hydratase in Fig. IV.56).

The effect of temperature on enzyme reactions is usually given in terms of the temperature coefficient Q_{10}, which is the factor by which the velocity is increased on raising the temperature by 10°C. From equation IV.186 it is readily shown that approximately

IV.190
$$E = \frac{RT^2 \log_e Q_{10}}{10}$$

The temperature coefficients of enzyme reactions usually lie between 1 and 2. It is a general feature of catalysis that the temperature coefficient of a catalysed reaction is lower than that of the same reaction when un-catalysed. With enzymatic reactions the Q_{10} is even lower than with in-organic catalysts, e.g. hydrogen ions. As most enzymatic reactions do not proceed at a measurable rate in the absence of the enzymes, the tempera-ture coefficients of the uncatalysed reactions are unknown.

Where two or more enzymes catalyse the same reaction, a different activation energy is obtained with each enzyme, but where one enzyme acts on several substrates, the same activation energy is often obtained for all. In fact the activation energy appears to be more characteristic of the enzyme than of the substrate. This is illustrated by the following figures (*2422*):

Reaction	Catalyst	E (cal/mole)
Hydrolysis of sucrose	H+	26,000
,, ,, sucrose	malt 'sucrase'	13,000
,, ,, sucrose	yeast 'sucrase'	11,000
,, ,, raffinose	yeast 'sucrase'	11,000

When the logarithm of the velocity is plotted against $1/T$ a single straight line is not always obtained. In a number of cases the graph has a discontinuity of slope and approximates to two straight lines meeting at an angle. This indicates that there is a change from one value of activation energy to another at the transition temperature. A number of explanations for such discontinuities have been suggested.

(*a*) A phase change in the solvent. Lipase (3.1.1.3), trypsin (3.4.4.4) and pepsin (3.4.4.1) have been studied at very low temperatures and in each case there is a large change in activation energy at about 0°. For lipase the values are 37,000 cal below 0° and 7,600 above 0°. However, it does not appear that a phase change of the water from liquid to solid is the cause of the break, for the same results are obtained if freezing is pre-vented by the addition of high concentrations of glycerol (*2422*).

(*b*) Two parallel reactions, e.g. by different active centres, with differ-ent temperature coefficients. The rate of the reaction with the higher coefficient increases more rapidly with temperature than the other, and therefore this reaction predominates at the higher temperatures. It would therefore be expected that the higher activation energy would be that observed at the higher temperatures and the Arrhenius plot should be concave upwards. This, however, is the reverse of what is usually observed. Moreover, on this theory, unless the two activation energies differ by a very large amount, the discontinuity will not be sharp.

(c) An overall process involving two successive reactions with different temperature coefficients. The reaction with the higher coefficient will tend to become the more rapid of the two at higher temperatures and the overall process will then be limited by the other reaction; the activation energy of the latter will then be that which is observed. This will lead to the more common type of discontinuity, in which the lower activation energy is that observed at the higher temperatures and the Arrhenius plot is concave downwards. Such a system has been discussed theoretically by STEARN (2508).

(d) Enzyme existing in two forms of differing activities. If the enzyme exists in two forms in equilibrium with one another, both forms being active but having different activation energies, and if the effect of temperature on the change from one form to the other is large, a sharp discontinuity will be observed. According to SIZER (2422) urease (3.5.1.5) has an activation energy of 8,700 cal in the reduced form and 11,700 in the oxidized form. No discontinuities are observed with either of these states; with mildly reducing media, however, a discontinuity is observed at 22°, with the activation energy of the reduced form above, and that of the oxidized form below, this temperature. Sizer suggests that as the temperature rises the enzyme changes over rather sharply from one form to the other, but it is not altogether clear why such a change should occur. KISTIAKOWSKY and LUMRY (1391), however, do not obtain such discontinuities and offer an alternative suggestion, which is discussed under (e) below. With fumarate hydratase, discontinuities with higher activation energies at the higher temperatures were obtained in alkaline solutions by MASSEY (1745); so far as we are aware, this is the only known case of an Arrhenius plot with an upward bend. This discontinuity (Fig. IV.52) is distinguished from other discontinuities observed in acid solutions (see (f) below) by the fact that it occurs with either fumarate or malate as substrates, that it is not accompanied by a discontinuity in K_m and that the transition temperature varies with the pH from 22° to 32°. Massey suggests that this is due to a dissociation of enzyme into units of smaller molecular weight as the temperature is increased, these smaller units having a higher activation energy. This dissociation might, like denaturation, have a high temperature coefficient.

Myosin ATPase (3.6.1.3) under certain conditions, for example in the presence of dinitrophenol or actin, shows a downward discontinuity in the Arrhenius plot in the region of 16° with ATP as the substrate, and, with ITP as substrate, even in the absence of these substances (1568–9). This has been interpreted as a change in the protein configuration, which is prevented by combination with substrates containing a 6-amino-group.

(*e*) Reversible inactivation of enzyme. KISTIAKOWSKY and LUMRY (*1391*) state that, if an enzyme is in equilibrium with an inactive form, the heat change of the conversion of one form into the other being ΔH_c, the Arrhenius plot will give straight lines when the enzyme is mainly

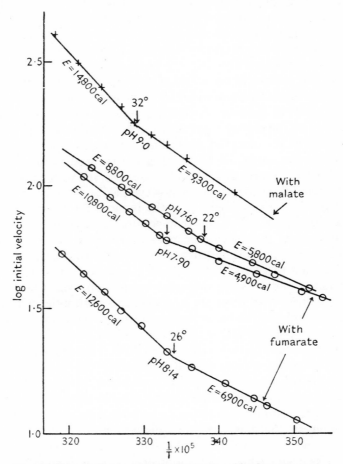

Fig. IV.52. *Arrhenius plots for forward and backward reactions of fumarate hydratase (4.2.1.2) in alkaline solution.*

from Massey (*1745*)

either in the active or in the inactive form. In the former case the slope will give E, and in the latter case $E - \Delta H_c$; thus, whether ΔH_c is negative or positive, the bend will be downwards. They reinvestigated the case of urease and came to the conclusion that the sulphite used as a mild reducer produced such a reversible inactivation of the enzyme.

They suggested that similar effects with other enzymes might be explained in the same way.

(*f*) A discontinuity affecting the forward reaction only. MASSEY (*1745*) showed with fumarate hydratase in acid solutions that a downward bend in the Arrhenius plot occurred with fumarate as substrate at about 18°, this transition temperature being practically independent of pH (Fig. IV.53 (*a*)). In the reverse direction with malate as substrate no such

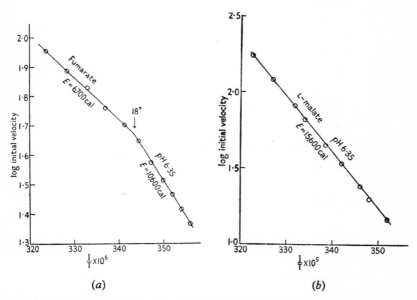

Fig. IV.53. *Arrhenius plots for forward and backward reactions of fumarate hydratase in acid solution.*

(*a*) forward reaction
(*b*) backward reaction.

from *1745*

discontinuity was observed (Fig. IV.53(*b*)). The change in activation energy at the critical temperature is now accompanied by an equal and opposite change in the apparent heat of combination of enzyme with fumarate, obtained from the effect of temperature on K_m, assuming that the latter is an equilibrium constant (Fig. IV.54). The ΔH relationships in the two temperature ranges at pH 6·35 are shown later in Fig. 56. Since the discontinuity occurs only in the hydration reaction, Massey suggests that it might be associated with an effect of temperature on the orientation of the water involved in the reaction. It seems difficult, however, to explain the apparent change in affinity for fumarate on this basis and

G

still more so the later observation (MASSEY, *1746*) that inhibitor affinities also show similar discontinuities (see Fig. IV.55). What seems clear is that in acid solution two different enzyme–fumarate complexes exist on the two sides of the critical temperature, both capable of reacting. In neutral solution no discontinuities of either kind are observed.

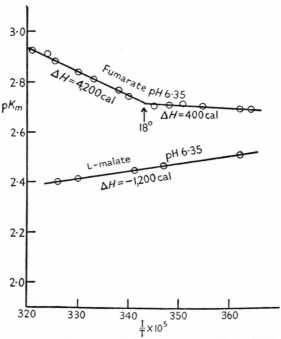

Fig. IV.54. *Effect of temperature on K_m for forward and backward reactions of fumarate hydratase in acid solution.*

from *1745*

In an easily reversible system, it is possible from measurements on K_s and V for the forward and back reactions to determine the heats of formation of ES and EP and the activation energies of the reaction in both directions (i.e. ΔH_{1f}, ΔH_{1b}, ΔH_{2f} and ΔH_{2b}). From the last equation in Table IV.2, the heat of the overall reaction can then be calculated and compared with the known value, and this gives a useful check. It will be noted that the two quantities in brackets in this equation represent the heights of the main peak above the starting level in the two directions, which must equal the overall heat change. Similar calculations can be made for the free energies and entropies.

The only example for which the data are reasonably complete is provided by fumarate hydratase (MASSEY, *1745*). Fig. IV.56 shows the experimental ΔH relationships for this enzyme in acid solution and it will be seen that the quantities check well within experimental error. This applies to both curves, relating to the two temperature ranges, in

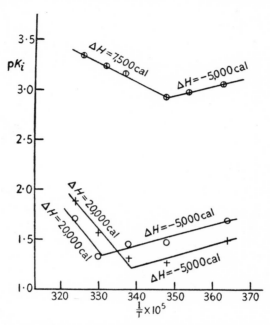

Fig. IV.55. *Effect of temperature on K_i of inhibitors of fumarate hydratase in acid solution.*

The same values of K_i are obtained for forward and backward reactions.

① *trans*aconitate + succinate ○ malonate.

from Massey (*1746*)

which different enzyme–fumarate complexes are involved, as explained above.

The data are also given, along with unpublished data for ΔF and ΔS, in Table IV.3. It will be remembered that while the ΔH values are obtained from the slopes of the V and K_m curves, which are constant over a range of temperature but change abruptly at the critical temperature, the ΔF values are obtained from the actual values of V and K_m, which change continuously with temperature without any abrupt change at the critical point. Thus it is necessary to calculate ΔF at a specified temperature and in the table the values are for 18°.

It has been suggested that the satisfactory summation shown in Fig. IV.56 provides evidence that for fumarate hydratase $K_m = K_s$ and that V is a measure of a single velocity constant, since these assumptions were made in calculating the ΔHs. This is not so. Such a summation is to be expected in any case from the Haldane relationship (equation IV.126)

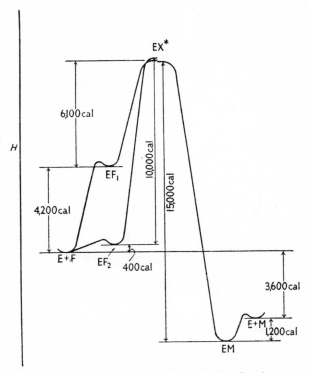

Fig. IV.56. *Scale diagram of ΔHs in the fumarate hydratase reaction in acid solution.*

from *1745*

which is not restricted to systems where K_m and V have such a simple meaning. From equation IV.126, taking logarithms and differentiating with respect to the temperature, we obtain

$$\text{IV.191} \qquad \frac{d\log V_f}{dT} + \frac{d\log\dfrac{1}{K_{mf}}}{dT} - \frac{d\log V_b}{dT} - \frac{d\log\dfrac{1}{K_{mb}}}{dT} = \frac{d\log K}{dT}$$

or, multiplying by $2\cdot303\,RT^2$,

$$\text{IV.192} \qquad (`\Delta H^*_{2f}\text{'} + RT + `\Delta H_{1f}\text{'}) - (`\Delta H^*_{2b}\text{'} + RT + `\Delta H_{1b}\text{'}) = \Delta H$$

Since the RT terms cancel out, this is identical in form with the last equation of Table IV.2. The inverted commas in equation IV.192 are used to signify that these are the apparent quantities obtained from the experimental plots in the usual way. If the original assumptions were valid the inverted commas could be omitted, but the addition follows even if these quantities are complex functions.

TABLE IV.3

THERMODYNAMIC BALANCE SHEET FOR FUMARATE HYDRATASE AT pH 6·35

T	ΔH_{1f}	ΔH_{2f}^*	ΔH_{1b}	ΔH_{2b}^*	$\Delta H_{f,\text{calc.}}$	ΔH
Below 18°	400	10,000	−1,200	15,000	−3,400	−3,600
Above 18°	4,200	6,100	−1,200	15,000	−3,500	−3,600

	ΔF_{1f}	ΔF_{2f}^*	ΔF_{1b}	ΔF_{2b}^*	$\Delta F_{f,\text{calc.}}$	ΔF_f
Immediately below 18°	−3,600	12,900	−2,800	13,600	−1,500	−865
Immediately above 18°	−3,600	12,900	−2,800	13,600	−1,500	−865

	ΔS_{1f}	ΔS_{2f}^*	ΔS_{1b}	ΔS_{2b}^*	$\Delta S_{f,\text{calc.}}$	ΔS_f
Immediately below 18°	13·7	−10	7·1	4·8	−8·2	−9·4
Immediately above 18°	26·8	−23·4	7·1	4·8	−8·5	−9·4

In comparing the ΔH data with Figs. IV.53–4, from which they were obtained, it should be noted that $\Delta H^* = E - RT$ (equation IV.187). The subscript f refers to the hydration of fumarate, the subscript b to the dehydration of malate

Effect on the state of ionization of the enzyme

In the section on pH we discussed the effect of changes in the state of ionization of various groups on the affinities of the enzyme for the reactants and on the velocity of the enzyme reaction. A change of temperature will itself produce a change in the state of ionization of each of these groups and the rate of this change is determined by the heat of ionization of the group concerned. Some part of the effect of temperature on K_m and V will be due to the resulting change in the pH functions of the components, producing changes in the pH curves with temperature.

If pK_m is plotted against pH, as in Figs. IV.41–46, the positions of the bends in the curves give the pKs of the ionizing groups involved in the combination of enzyme with substrate; thus by determining the curves at several different temperatures the change in each pK with temperature can be measured by the displacement of the bends. From this change the heat of ionization of the corresponding group can be obtained from the equation

IV.193 $$\Delta H_i = -2 \cdot 303 \times RT^2 \frac{d\mathrm{p}K}{d\mathrm{T}}$$

There appear to be no cases in which this has been done and as far as we know this is a completely untouched field, although in one case it has been done for an inhibitor (thiocyanate with fumarate hydratase, *1751a*).

By plotting log V against pH, the pKs of ionizing groups which affect the breakdown of the ES complex can often be determined, but owing to overlapping the interpretation of pH-activity curves in terms of pKs is not always easy (see the section on pH). Where such a pK can be determined, however, the heat of ionization can be calculated from its values at several temperatures. This has been done in the case of trypsin by GUTFREUND (*958*), who deduced from the value of the pK and the heat of ionization that a histidine group was responsible.

V

ENZYME CLASSIFICATION

THE LARGE AND rapidly increasing number of known enzymes makes it imperative to have some systematic arrangement and nomenclature, so that any given enzyme can be precisely identified. In the past enzyme nomenclature has been very far from systematic. The uncontrolled naming of enzymes by the discoverers and others has inevitably led to many inconsistencies and incompatibilities. Some names have been definitely misleading; others have conveyed little or nothing about the nature of the reaction catalysed, as for example 'diaphorase', 'catalase', 'zwischenferment', and 'old yellow enzyme'. Two or more names have often been used for the same enzyme by different groups of workers; conversely the same name has quite often been used for two or more different enzymes.

From time to time attempts have been made to bring order into this field, although most of these have been limited to particular groups of enzymes. In recent years two more general schemes of classification, with nomenclatures based on them, have been put forward by HOFFMANN–OSTENHOF (*1118*) and by the authors in the first edition of the present work. Neither of these had any official status, but in 1961 a comprehensive scheme of classification and nomenclature (*2212*) was adopted by the International Union of Biochemistry, and is used throughout the present edition. This was produced by the international Commission on Enzymes which had been set up in 1956 to deal with the unsatisfactory situation referred to above.

The chemical reaction catalysed is the specific property which distinguishes one enzyme from another, and it is logical to use it as the basis for the classification and naming of enzymes. The system involves the arrangement of the enzymes into groups catalysing similar processes, with sub-groups specifying more precisely the actual reaction catalysed. In general, each enzyme will have a name consisting of (*a*) the name of the substrate, and (*b*) a word ending in '-ase' specifying the kind of reaction carried out by all the enzymes of the group to which it belongs, for example 'alanine racemase'. This method provides names which are precise and systematic, but owing to the complexity of many of the substrates and the length of their chemical names, it gives in some cases names which are too long for ordinary use. The Commission dealt with this difficulty by proposing that, in addition to these systematic names, there should be agreed trivial names convenient for everyday use. Where the names already in general use were sufficiently unobjectionable, they were adopted by the Commission as the official trivial names.

This method of classification is facilitated by the fact that the chemical reactions catalysed by enzymes fall into a comparatively small number of types, the large number of enzymes in existence being due to their high specificity towards parts of the substrate molecule other than the group actually undergoing reaction. In the first edition of this book a list of the then known enzymes was given, which was divided into three main sections, namely hydrolysing enzymes, transferring enzymes and other enzymes (the latter including the synthetases, the stereoisomerases and the enzymes adding groups to double bonds). The oxidizing enzymes, which catalyse hydrogen transfer, and were therefore treated as transferring enzymes, formed by far the largest sub-section. It was recognized that the division between the hydrolysing and the transferring enzymes was somewhat arbitrary, since hydrolysis can be regarded as a transfer of one part of the substrate molecule from the other part to a water molecule; in any case many hydrolysing enzymes catalyse other transfer reactions.

In the Enzyme Commission's scheme the oxidizing enzymes are treated, on account of their importance, as a separate group, and it was found possible to arrange all the known enzymes in six main classes, namely oxidoreductases, transferases, hydrolases, lyases, isomerases, and ligases or synthetases.

ENZYME COMMISSION'S NUMBERING SYSTEM

The Commission also adopted a scheme for numbering enzymes, which was closely linked with the classification. Each enzyme number contains four elements, separated by points, and arranged on these principles:

(i) The first figure shows to which of the six main classes the particular enzyme belongs, as follows:

1. Oxidoreductases
2. Transferases
3. Hydrolases
4. Lyases
5. Isomerases
6. Ligases

'Lyases' are enzymes which remove groups from their substrates (otherwise than by hydrolysis), leaving double bonds (these are the same as those referred to in the first edition as adding groups to double bonds); 'ligases' are enzymes which catalyse the joining together of two molecules coupled with the breakdown of a pyrophosphate bond in ATP or a similar triphosphate (otherwise known as 'synthetases').

(ii) The second figure indicates the sub-class. For the oxidoreductases it shows the type of group in the *donors* which undergoes oxidation (1 denoting a –CHOH– group, 2 an aldehyde or keto group, and so on); for the transferases it indicates the nature of the group which is transferred; for the hydrolases it shows the type of bond hydrolysed; for the lyases it denotes the type of link which is broken between the group removed and the remainder; for the isomerases it indicates the type of isomerization involved; for the ligases it shows the type of bond formed.

(iii) The third figure indicates the sub-sub-class. For the oxidoreductases it shows for each type of donor the type of acceptor involved (1 denoting a coenzyme (NAD or NADP), 2 a cytochrome, 3 molecular O_2, and so on); thus the first three figures of the number indicate clearly the nature of the enzyme, for example 1.2.3 denotes an oxidoreductase with an aldehyde as donor and O_2 as acceptor. For the transferases the third figure sub-divides the types of groups transferred (indicating, for example, whether the one-carbon group is a methyl or a carboxyl group, etc.); except that for the phosphotransferases it is used to denote the type of acceptor, as with the oxidoreductases. For the hydrolases this figure shows more precisely the type of bond hydrolysed, and for the lyases the nature of the group removed. For the isomerases it shows more precisely the nature of the transformation, and for the ligases the nature of the substance formed.

(iv) The fourth figure is the serial number of the enzyme in its sub-sub-class.

In a few cases it was necessary to use the word 'other' in the description of sub-classes and sub-sub-classes. They have been given the figure 99, in order to leave space for new sub-divisions.

This method of numbering, in addition to its advantages as a system of classification and as an indication of the nature of the reaction catalysed, avoids the chief disadvantage of consecutive numbering through the whole enzyme list, namely that the discovery of a new enzyme belonging to a class early in the list disturbs the numbers of all those following. On the present system, it is possible to allot to a new enzyme a number at the end of its sub-sub-class without disturbing any other numbers. Similarly, should it become necessary to create new classes, sub-classes, or sub-sub-classes, they can be added without disturbing those already defined.

Table V.1 gives the key to the Enzyme Commission's system of numbering and classification, and at the end of the book will be found a table of all the enzymes known to the authors, based on the literature up to the end of 1961, giving their official numbers and systematic and trivial names. The table is based on the table published by the Commission in their report (*2212*), but includes a number of more recently discovered enzymes. For the purpose of referring to these additional enzymes we have given them temporary and unofficial numbers of the type 1.1.1.a; we have also suggested systematic names, which are shown in italics. In one or two cases recent work has shown the systematic name in the Commission's list to need modification; in these cases we have shown the suggested modification in italics. All the four-figure numbers and systematic names in roman type are officially adopted by the International Union of Biochemistry.

TABLE V.1

KEY TO NUMBERING AND CLASSIFICATION OF ENZYMES

1. OXIDOREDUCTASES

1.1 Acting on the CHOH group of donors

1.1.1 With NAD or NADP as acceptor
1.1.2 With a cytochrome as an acceptor
1.1.3 With O_2 as acceptor
1.1.99 With other acceptors

1.2 Acting on the aldehyde or keto-group of donors

1.2.1 With NAD or NADP as acceptor
1.2.2 With a cytochrome as an acceptor
1.2.3 With O_2 as acceptor
1.2.4 With lipoate as acceptor
1.2.99 With other acceptors

1.3 Acting on the CH—CH group of donors

1.3.1 With NAD or NADP as acceptor
1.3.2 With a cytochrome as an acceptor
1.3.3 With O_2 as acceptor
1.3.99 With other acceptors

1.4 Acting on the CH—NH₂ group of donors

1.4.1 With NAD or NADP as acceptor
1.4.3 With O_2 as acceptor

1.5 Acting on the C—NH group of donors

1.5.1 With NAD or NADP as acceptor
1.5.3 With O_2 as acceptor

1.6 **Acting on NADH$_2$ or NADPH$_2$ as donor**

    1.6.1   With NAD or NADP as acceptor
    1.6.2   With a cytochrome as an acceptor
    1.6.4   With a disulphide compound as acceptor
    1.6.5   With a quinone or related compound as acceptor
    1.6.6   With a nitrogenous group as acceptor
    1.6.99 With other acceptors

1.7 **Acting on other nitrogenous compounds as donors**

    1.7.3   With O$_2$ as acceptor
    1.7.99 With other acceptors

1.8 **Acting on sulphur groups of donors**

    1.8.1   With NAD or NADP as acceptor
    1.8.3   With O$_2$ as acceptor
    1.8.4   With a disulphide compound as acceptor
    1.8.5   With a quinone or related compound as acceptor
    1.8.6   With a nitrogenous group as acceptor

1.9 **Acting on haem groups of donors**

    1.9.3   With O$_2$ as acceptor
    1.9.6   With a nitrogenous group as acceptor

1.10 **Acting on diphenols and related substances as donors**

    1.10.3 With O$_2$ as acceptor

1.11 **Acting on H$_2$O$_2$ as acceptor**

1.98 **Enzymes using H$_2$ as reductant**

1.99 **Other enzymes using O$_2$ as oxidant**

    1.99.1 Hydroxylases
    1.99.2 Oxygenases

2. TRANSFERASES

2.1 **Transferring one-carbon groups**

    2.1.1   Methyltransferases
    2.1.2   Hydroxymethyl-, formyl- and related transferases
    2.1.3   Carboxyl- and carbamoyltransferases

2.2 **Transferring aldehydic or ketonic residues**

2.3 **Acyltransferases**

    2.3.1   Acyltransferases
    2.3.2   Aminoacyltransferases

2.4 **Glycosyltransferases**

    2.4.1   Hexosyltransferases
    2.4.2   Pentosyltransferases

2.5 **Transferring alkyl or related groups**

2.6 **Transferring nitrogenous groups**
    2.6.1 Aminotransferases
    2.6.2 Amidinotransferases
    2.6.3 Oximinotransferases

2.7 **Transferring phosphorus-containing groups**
    2.7.1 Phosphotransferases with an alcohol group as acceptor
    2.7.2 Phosphotransferases with a carboxyl group as acceptor
    2.7.3 Phosphotransferases with a nitrogenous group as acceptor
    2.7.4 Phosphotransferases with a phospho-group as acceptor
    2.7.5 Phosphotransferases, apparently intramolecular
    2.7.6 Pyrophosphotransferases
    2.7.7 Nucleotidyltransferases
    2.7.8 Transferases for other substituted phospho-groups

2.8 **Transferring sulphur-containing groups**
    2.8.1 Sulphurtransferases
    2.8.2 Sulphotransferases
    2.8.3 CoA-transferases

3. HYDROLASES

3.1 **Acting on ester bonds**
    3.1.1 Carboxylic ester hydrolases
    3.1.2 Thiolester hydrolases
    3.1.3 Phosphoric monoester hydrolases
    3.1.4 Phosphoric diester hydrolases
    3.1.5 Triphosphoric monoester hydrolases
    3.1.6 Sulphuric ester hydrolases

3.2 **Acting on glycosyl compounds**
    3.2.1 Glycoside hydrolases
    3.2.2 Hydrolysing N-glycosyl compounds
    3.2.3 Hydrolysing S-glycosyl compounds

3.3 **Acting on ether bonds**
    3.3.1 Thioether hydrolases

3.4 **Acting on peptide bonds (peptide hydrolases)**
    3.4.1 α-aminopeptide aminoacidohydrolases
    3.4.2 α-carboxypeptide aminoacidohydrolases
    3.4.3 Dipeptide hydrolases
    3.4.4 Peptide peptidohydrolases

3.5 **Acting on C—N bonds other than peptide bonds**
    3.5.1 In linear amides
    3.5.2 In cyclic amides
    3.5.3 In linear amidines
    3.5.4 In cyclic amidines
    3.5.99 In other compounds

6. LIGASES

6.1 Forming C—O bonds
6.1.1 Amino-acid-RNA ligases

6.2 Forming C—S bonds
6.2.1 Acid thiol ligases

6.3 Forming C—N bonds
6.3.1 Acid-ammonia ligases (amide synthetases)
6.3.2 Acid-aminoacid ligases (peptide synthetases)
6.3.3 Cyclo-ligases
6.3.4 Other C—N ligases
6.3.5 C—N ligases with glutamine as N-donor

6.4 Forming C—C bonds

RULES FOR SYSTEMATIC AND TRIVIAL NOMENCLATURES

The Enzyme Commission included in their report a set of rules for the construction of systematic and trivial names. These rules have been followed in forming the names given in the table of enzymes, and can be extended to new enzymes. For convenience they are reproduced in detail below.

Systematic nomenclature	*Trivial nomenclature*

(i) *General rules*

Rule 1 The names of substrates, forming parts of enzyme names, should be given as precisely as possible, following the official I.U.P.A.C. rules (see *Handbook for Chemical Society Authors*, Chemical Society, London, 1960), e.g. N-D-ribosyl-purine (not purine riboside), 2-amino-2-deoxy-D-glucose (not glucosamine). The 1, 2, 3, system of locating substituents should be used instead of the α, β, γ system; α, β should be used for indicating configuration, although group names such as β-aspartyl, γ-glutamyl, and also β-alanine, γ-lactone, are permissible. For nucleotide radicals, 'adenylyl-' (not

Generally accepted trivial names of substrates may be used. D- should be omitted for common sugars and L- for individual amino acids. α, β, γ may, if desired, be used instead of numbers to indicate positions where such usage is widely established at present; in general it is not necessary to indicate positions of substituents in the trivial names.

Systematic nomenclature	*Trivial nomenclature*

'adenyl-') will be the form used. For phosphate compounds, the forms glucose phosphate or phosphoglycerate are used, according to whether another acidic group is present or not. The name 'ketoacids' may be used as a class name, but for individual compounds 'oxo-' should be used.

Rule 2

Where the substrate is normally in the form of an anion, its name should end in '-ate' rather than '-ic'; e.g. 'lactate dehydrogenase', not 'lactic acid dehydrogenase' or 'lactic dehydrogenase'. Exception: '2-oxoacid carboxy-lyase' (4.1.1.1).

Rule 3 Commonly used abbreviations for substrates which are to the chemist trivial, e.g. ATP, may be used in systematic names of enzymes, but the use of new abbreviations should be discouraged.

Abbreviations for names of enzymes, e.g. GDH, should be strongly discouraged.

Rule 4

Names of substances such as glucose phosphate, which are normally written with a space, may be hyphenated when they form parts of enzyme names, e.g. 'glucose-6-phosphate dehydrogenase' (1.1.1.49).

Rule 5

The use as enzyme names of *descriptions* such as 'condensing enzyme', 'Zwischenferment', 'acetate-activating enzyme', 'pH 5 enzyme', '"malic" enzyme', should cease as soon as the catalysed reaction is known. The word 'activating' should not be used in the sense of converting the substrate into a

Systematic nomenclature   *Trivial nomenclature*

substance which reacts further; all enzymes act by activating their substrates, and the use of the word in this comparatively new sense may lead to confusion.

Rule 6

Where the systematic name is short enough to be used as a trivial name, there is no need for a separate trivial name.

Rule 7

If it can be avoided, a trivial name should not be based on a substance which is not a true substrate, e.g. enzyme 4.2.1.17 should not be called 'crotonase since it does not act on crotonate.

Rule 8 In general, the name of an enzyme will consist of two parts. The first will consist of the name of the substrate or, in the case of a bimolecular reaction, of the two substrates separated by a colon. The second, ending in '-ase', will indicate the nature of the process. See also Rule 13.

The same will be true of most trivial names, but with less detail. The majority of trivial names will be identical with the names previously in common use. In certain cases the same trivial name may be used for more than one enzyme.

Rule 9

The termination '-ese' (as in 'rhodanese') should not be used.

Rule 10 The systematic name will include one of the following special words which indicate particular types of reaction: 'oxidoreductase', 'racemase', 'isomerase', 'epimerase', 'lyase', 'ligase', 'hydrolase', 'transferase', 'mutase'.

The suffix '-ase' will not be attached directly to the name of the substrate.

Trivial names may be formed with a greater variety of special words, including 'tautomer se', 'kinase', 'phosphorylase', 'reductase', 'oxidase', 'dehydrogenase', 'peroxidase'.

The direct attachment of '-ase' to the name of the substrate will imply a hydrolysing enzyme. Exceptions: thiaminase I (2.5.1.2), ribonuclease (2.7.7.16).

Systematic nomenclature   *Trivial nomenclature*

Rule 11

The name 'dehydrase', which has been used for both dehydrogenating and dehydrating enzymes, will not be used. 'Dehydrogenase' will be used for the former and 'dehydratase' for the latter.

Rule 12 In the case of reversible reactions, the direction chosen for naming should be the same for all the enzymes in a given class, even if this direction has not been demonstrated for all. Thus systematic names may be based on a written reaction, even though only the reverse of this has been actually demonstrated experimentally.

Trivial names will normally be based on a reaction direction which has been demonstrated, e.g. 'dehydrogenase' or 'reductase', 'decarboxylase' or 'carboxylase'.

Rule 13 When the overall reaction includes two different changes, e.g. an oxidative demethylation, the second function should be indicated by adding a suitable participle in parenthesis: 'sarcosine:O_2 oxidoreductase (demethylating)' or 'D-aspartate:O_2 oxidoreductase (deaminating)'; see 1.5.3.1 and 1.4.3.1. Examples of such additions are: '(decarboxylating)', '(cyclizing)', '(acceptor-acylating)', '(isomerizing)'.

Rule 14 When an enzyme catalyses more than one type of reaction or acts on more than one substrate (or pair of substrates), the name will normally refer to only one substrate (or pair of substrates) and one reaction. A general rule has not yet been found for such cases. Each must be considered on its merits, and the choice must be to some extent

Systematic nomenclature   *Trivial nomenclature*

arbitrary. In certain cases it may
by possible to use a term which
covers a whole group of substrates, and this is permissible.

(ii) *Rules for particular classes of enzymes*
      Class 1

Rule 15   All enzymes catalysing oxido-
          reductions will be named
          'oxidoreductases' in the sys-
          tematic nomenclature, and the
          names formed on the pattern
          'donor:acceptor oxido-
          reductase'.

The terms 'dehydrogenase' or
'reductase' will be used much
as hitherto. When hydrogen
transfer from the substance
mentioned as donor in the systematic name is not readily
demonstrated, the latter term
will be used. 'Transhydrogenase' may be retained for a
few well-established cases.
'Oxidase' will be used only for
cases where O_2 acts as an
acceptor, and 'oxygenase' only
for those cases where the O_2
molecule is directly incorporated
into the substrate. 'Peroxidase'
is used for enzymes using H_2O_2
as acceptor. 'Catalase' must be
regarded as exceptional. Apart
from indications given by these
names, the second reactant is
not usually named.

Rule 16   For oxidoreductases using NAD
          or NADP, the coenzyme will
          always be named as the acceptor
          (except for the special case of
          section 1.6). Where the enzyme
          can use either coenzyme, this
          may be indicated by writing
          'NAD(P)'.

Rule 17   Where the true acceptor is
          unknown, and the dehydro-
          genase has only been shown to
          react with artificial acceptors,
          the word 'acceptor' may be
          written in parentheses, e.g.

Systematic nomenclature   *Trivial nomenclature*

'succinate:(acceptor) oxidoreductase'; see 1.3.99.1. (The
substance used experimentally
as acceptor is shown in the
'comments' column of the
enzyme list).

Rule 18 No systematic names are pro-   They may be named on the
posed for the enzymes which   pattern 'substrate n-hydroxyl-
hydroxylate their substrates in   ase' where n represents a figure
the presence of $NAD(P)H_2$ and   giving the position of the
O_2. The reactions are not yet   hydroxylation (see class 1.99.1).
understood and each may
involve more than one enzyme.

Class 2

Rule 19 Enzymes catalysing group-   In the trivial nomenclature, the
transfer reactions will be named   forms 'aminotransferase', etc.,
'transferases', and the names   may be replaced if desired by
formed on the pattern 'Donor: the corresponding forms 'trans-
acceptor group-transferred-   aminase', etc. A number of
transferase', e.g. 'ATP:acetate   special words are used to in-
phosphotransferase' (2.7.2.1). A   dicate reaction types, e.g.
figure may be prefixed to show   'kinase' to indicate a phosphate
the position to which the group   transfer from ATP to the named
is transferred, e.g. 'ATP:D-   substrate (not 'phosphokinase'),
fructose 1-phosphotransferase'   'pyrophosphokinase' for a
(2.7.1.3). The spelling 'trans-   similar transfer of pyrophos-
phorase' will not be used.   phate, 'phosphomutase' for an
apparent intramolecular phos-
phate transfer. The names
'phosphorylase' and 'pyrophosphorylase' are not strictly
consistent with the recommended method of treating
transfer reactions, but some are
so well established that they are
given in the list as alternatives
to the preferred trivial names
for certain enzymes in groups
2.4.1, 2.4.2 and 2.7.7.

Rule 20 In the case of the kinases, ATP
will always be named as the
donor. In the case of the amino-

	Systematic nomenclature	*Trivial nomenclature*
	transferases involving 2-oxoglutarate, the latter will always be named as the acceptor.	
Rule 21	The prefix denoting the group transferred should, as far as possible, be non-committal with respect to the mechanism of the transfer, e.g. 'phospho-'.	
	Class 3	
Rule 22	Hydrolysing enzymes will be named on the pattern 'substrate hydrolase'. Where the enzyme is specific for the removal of a particular group, the group may be named as a prefix, e.g. 'adenosine aminohydrolase' (3.5.4.4). In a number of cases this group can also be transferred by the enzyme to other molecules, and the hydrolysis itself might be regarded as a transfer of the group to water.	The direct addition of '-ase' to the name of the substrate generally denotes a hydrolase. Where this is difficult, e.g. for 3.1.2.1, the word 'hydrolase' may be used. A number of special words for classes of hydrolases may be used, e.g. 'phosphatase', 'deaminase'. Enzymes should not normally be given separate names merely on the basis of optimal conditions for activity. The acid and alkaline phosphatases (3.1.3.1–2) and the ATPases (3.6.1.3–4) should be regarded as special cases and no as examples to be followed.
Rule 23	A systematic nomenclature covering all peptide hydrolases is not possible at present, owing to their overlapping specificities. The separate identity of some of them seems to be somewhat doubtful.	For the present the existing names may be used as trivial names. Trivial names of new enzymes may be formed on the pattern 'source peptide hydrolase', followed if necessary by a letter to distinguish it from other enzymes. Names based on particular proteins as substrates (such as 'collagenase' or 'elastase') or names such as 'coagulase' should be abandoned, as should names of the type 'paratrypsin' and 'homotrypsin'.

Systematic nomenclature   *Trivial nomenclature*

Class 4

Rule 24 Enzymes removing groups from substrates non-hydrolytically, leaving double bonds, (or adding groups to double bonds) will be called 'lyases' in the systematic nomenclature. Prefixes, such as 'hydro-', 'ammonia-', will be used to denote the type of reaction, e.g. 'L-malate hydro-lyase' (4.2.1.2). Decarboxylases will be regarded as carboxy-lyases. A hyphen should always be written before 'lyase', to avoid confusion with hydrolases, carboxylases, etc.

The existing names 'de-carboxylase', 'aldolase', etc., will be retained; and 'de-hydratase' (not 'dehydrase') will be used for the hydro-lyases. 'Synthetase' will not be used for any enzymes in this class; where it has been customary, 'syn-thase' will be used instead, to emphasize the synthetic aspect of the reaction (including those cases in which the adding action of the lyase is accompanied by the cleavage of a thioether bond).

Rule 25 The complete molecule, not either of the parts into which it is separated, will be named as the substrate.

Where the equilibrium warrants it, or where the enzyme has long been named after a particular substrate, the reverse reaction may be taken as the basis of the name, using 'hydratase', 'carboxylase', etc. e.g. 'fumarate hydratase' for 4.2.1.2 (not 'fumarase', which suggests an enzyme hydrolysing fumarate). 'Anhydrase' for 4.2.1.1 should not be taken as equivalent to 'dehydratase'; it is used because the substrate is carbonic anhydride, although the case should be regarded as excep-tional.

Class 5

Rule 26 'Isomerase' will be used as a general name for enzymes of this class.

The majority of the trivial names for this class will resemble the systematic names, somewhat simplified where possible.

Rule 27 The types of isomerization will be indicated by prefixes, e.g. 'maleate *cis-trans*-isomerase'

(5.2.1.1), 'phenylpyruvate keto-enol-isomerase' (5.3.2.1), '3-ketosteroid Δ^4-Δ^5-isomerase' (5.3.3.1). Enzymes catalysing an aldose-ketose interconversion will be known as 'ketol-iso-merases', e.g. 'L-arabinose ketol-isomerase' (5.3.1.4). When the isomerization consists of an intramolecular transfer of a group, the enzyme will be named a 'mutase', e.g. 5.4.1.1, and when it consists of an intra-molecular lyase-type reaction, e.g. 5.5.1.1, it will be named a 'lyase (decyclizing)'.

Rule 28 Isomerases catalysing inversions of asymmetric groups will be termed 'racemases' or 'epi-merases', according to whether the substrate contains one or more than one centre of asym-metry; compare for example 5.1.1.5 with 5.1.1.6. A numerical prefix to the word 'epimerase' will be used to show the position of the inversion.

Class 6

Rule 29 The class of enzymes catalysing the linking together of two molecules, coupled with the breaking of a pyrophosphate link in ATP etc., will be known as ligases (pronounced with a short i in English). These enzymes have hitherto been known as synthetases; recently, however, this term has been used also for synthesizing enzymes not in-volving nucleoside triphosphates. Moreover, this terminology differs from all other systematic enzyme names in that it is based

Since the enzymes of this class are still generally known as 'synthetases', this designation is retained in the trivial names, in order to avoid extensive changes in the existing nomenclature. 'Synthetase' should not be used for enzymes which do not involve nucleoside triphosphates (see Rule 24).

Systematic nomenclature *Trivial nomenclature*

on the product and not on the substrate. For these two reasons a new systematic name was necessary.

Rule 30 The systematic names will be formed on the pattern: 'X:Y ligase (ADP)', where X and Y are the two molecules to be joined together. The substance shown in parenthesis (ADP or AMP in most cases) is the product formed from the triphosphate, so that '(ADP)' may be taken in the sense of '(ADP-liberating)'. In this case it indicates both that ATP is the triphosphate involved, and also that it is the terminal pyrophosphate link that is broken. Thus the reaction is
$$X+Y+ATP = X-Y+ADP+P.$$

The trivial names will be formed on the pattern: 'X–Y synthetase', where X–Y is the substance formed by linking X and Y. Exceptionally, where Y is CO_2, the name 'X carboxylase' may be used. Names of the type 'X-activating enzyme' will not be used (see Rule 5).

Rule 31 In the special case where glutamine acts as an ammonia-donor, the name 'amido-ligase' may be used.

ENZYME REACTIONS

The remainder of this chapter is devoted to a consideration of the chemical reactions brought about by enzymes in the various classes, which are dealt with in the order in which they appear in the list of enzymes.

1. *Oxidoreductases*

These are the enzymes concerned with biological oxidation and reduction, and therefore with respiration and fermentation processes. The class includes not only the dehydrogenases and oxidases (1.1 to 1.10) but also the peroxidases (1.11), which use H_2O_2 as the oxidant, the hydroxylases (1.99.1), which introduce hydroxyl groups by a mechanism which is not fully understood, and the oxygenases (1.99.2), which introduce molecular O_2 in place of a double bond in the substrate.

Dehydrogenases and oxidases

It will be noted that the reaction types catalysed by sub-groups 1.1 and 1.4 are very similar, the essential difference being that instead of –O– we have the chemically similar –NH– group; for it is believed that the first step in the oxidation of the aminoacids is the formation of the imino-acid, which then decomposes to give the ketoacid. Isotopic evidence for this has been obtained with the snake venom oxidase (1.4.3.2) (*782*). If, as is believed, aldehydes are oxidized in the form of their hydrates or of compounds with thiol groups, sub-group 1.2 is also concerned with the oxidation of –CHOH– groups. These three sub-groups together contain no less than 123 enzymes.

A feature of interest among the enzymes of these sub-groups is the occurrence of a number of pairs of enzymes, bringing about the same oxidation but using different hydrogen acceptors, such as pairs where one uses NAD and the other NADP (1.1.1.1–2; 1.1.1.32–3; 1.1.1.38 and 40; 1.1.1.41–42; 1.2.1.3–4; 1.2.1.6–7; 1.2.1.12–13); pairs where one uses a coenzyme and the other a cytochrome (1.1.1.8 and 1.1.2.1; 1.1.1.27 and 1.1.2.3; 1.2.1.2 and 1.2.2.1); pairs where one uses a coenzyme and the other O_2 (1.1.1.47 and 1.1.3.4; 1.1.1.37 and 1.1.3.3). There are also pairs where the two enzymes act on the same substance, but give different oxidation products (1.1.1.9–10; 1.1.1.12–13; 1.1.1.37–8; 1.1.1.43–4; 1.1.2.3 and 1.1.3.2; 1.2.1.3 and 1.2.1.10; 1.2.1.9 and 1.2.1.13; 1.2.2.2 and 1.2.3.3); this is often because one member of the pair also catalyses some associated reaction, such as decarboxylation.

Sub-group 1.1 contains enzymes which convert CHOH to C=O groups in many alcohols, sugar alcohols, hydroxyacids, sugars, and hydroxy-steroids.

Sub-group 1.2 contains not only several unspecific aldehyde-oxidizing enzymes, but also some specific enzymes concerned with energy utiliza-tion, the oxidation being linked with the formation of such 'energy-rich' compounds as thiolesters or mixed anhydrides. Glyceraldehyde-phosphate dehydrogenase (1.2.1.12) had been extensively studied on account of the important part which it plays in carbohydrate metabolism. The mechanism of its action is shown in detail in Table XII.1. The two enzymes requiring thiamine pyrophosphate and using lipoate as ac-ceptor are also important in carbohydrate metabolism; they are discussed in detail in Chapter IX.

Sub-group 1.3 is concerned with the removal of two hydrogen atoms from CH–CH groups to form C=C groups; they are therefore desatu-rating enzymes. Enzymes 1.3.2.1–2 play an important role in fat meta-bolism (see Table XII.4). Succinate dehydrogenase is a very well known enzyme, important in the citric cycle (Table XII.2); it is given the number 1.3.99.1 because the nature of the biological acceptor is unknown.

Sub-group 1.4 consists of enzymes which bring about oxidative deamination, except for 1.4.1.6 which causes cyclization. On the other hand enzymes of sub-group 1.5 oxidize substituted amines without releasing ammonia.

Sub-group 1.6 is exceptional in that the reduced forms of the coenzymes are named as donors. This is because most of these enzymes function as 'coenzyme dehydrogenases', and act in the cell as part of the hydrogen transport chain linking the reduced coenzymes with O_2. They are comparatively unspecific with regard to the other reactant, so that a classification taking the coenzyme as acceptor would be rather unsatisfactory. Enzymes 1.6.6.1–4 are concerned with the reduction of nitrate to ammonia or amino-groups in plants or bacteria.

Sub-groups 1.9–10 contain important enzymes which act as the terminal steps of hydrogen transport chains. In particular 1.9.3.1 is of the greatest importance in the respiration of a great many aerobic organisms, and is discussed in some detail in Chapter IX. Many of the enzymes of these sub-groups are copper-proteins.

Peroxidases

Sub-group 1.11 contains a variety of enzymes using H_2O_2 as oxidant. The classical peroxidases (1.11.1.7) are haemoproteins specific for peroxide, but using a wide range of substances as donors. Catalase (1.11.1.6), which decomposes H_2O_2, is included here in view of the fact that it is generally similar in structure and properties and is able to bring about certain oxidations by H_2O_2. The decomposition of H_2O_2 can be regarded as the oxidation of one molecule by the other. It is widespread in aerobic cells and may have some more important function. The coenzyme peroxidases 1.11.1.1–2 are not haemoproteins, and one at least is a flavoprotein. Other flavoproteins such as xanthine oxidase (1.2.3.2) will also use H_2O_2 among other acceptors, and the coenzyme peroxidases resemble these rather than the classical peroxidases in not being specific for H_2O_2.

Hydroxylases and oxygenases

Sub-group 1.99 contains enzymes which incorporate oxygen atoms from O_2 into their substrates. Many, and perhaps all, of the hydroxylases, unlike the oxygenases, require the presence of the reduced form of one of the coenzymes, which is oxidized by O_2 in the process. Details of the mechanism of this coupled oxidation remain to be worked out. The hydroxylases are important in the metabolism of steroids and other cyclic compounds. The oxygenases, on the other hand, incorporate the whole O_2 molecule in the course of oxidative cleavage of a carbon–carbon double bond.

Hydrogenase (1.98.1.1) is clearly an oxidoreductase and is included in group 1.

2. Transferases

Methyltransferases

Biological methylation is brought about by transfer of methyl groups by the enzymes of sub-group 2.1.1. For many of these enzymes the methyl-donor is S-adenosylmethionine, which is produced by 2.4.2.13. Enzyme 2.1.1.4, which is localized in the pineal body, is responsible for the formation of the hormone melatonin.

Other one-carbon transferases

As discussed in Chapter IX, tetrahydrofolate acts as a carrier for $-CH_3$, $-CH_2OH$, $-CHO$ or $-CH=NH$ groups. The enzymes concerned with transfer of these groups, which are important in the biosynthesis of purines etc., are listed in sub-group 2.1.2. Carboxylations are also important in biosynthesis, and the resulting carboxyl or carbamoyl groups are transferred by enzymes of sub-group 2.1.3.

Transaldolase and transketolase

These two enzymes are brought together as sub-group 2.2.1. Transketolase may be regarded as transferring glycolaldehyde from combination with one aldehyde to combination with another; transaldolase transfers dihydroxyacetone from one aldehyde to another by way of a dihydroxyacetone-enzyme intermediate (*2731*). Thus in one case an aldehyde–aldehyde combination is involved, and in the other an alcohol–aldehyde combination. The first enzyme, but not the second, depends on thiamine pyrophosphate for its action. They are both important in photosynthesis and the pentose phosphate oxidation system (Tables XII.19 and 5).

Acyltransferases

The enzymes of sub-group 2.3.1 all catalyse acyl-group transfers through coenzyme A; coenzyme A thus occupies much the same position with regard to acyl transfer as ATP does with regard to phosphate transfer, though the acyl groups are not all of the same kind. It is interesting to note that here also the links involved are of the energy-rich type; the carboxyl group of the acid is linked with the –SH group of the coenzyme A, forming a thiolester, and the free energy of hydrolysis of this bond is of the same order as that of the pyrophosphate bond in ATP. These enzymes are important in many lines of metabolism, especially that of fats. Phosphate acetyltransferase (2.3.1.8), which occurs only in bacteria, is important as establishing a connection between energy-rich thiolester bonds and energy-rich phosphate bonds. Enzyme 2.3.1.12 forms part of the pyruvate oxidase system (see Table XII.1).

Glycosyltransferases

The enzymes of sub-group 2.4 catalyse the transfer of sugar residues to various acceptors, especially to an –OH group of another sugar or a phosphate molecule, or to a nitrogen atom of a heterocyclic ring. Few of the compounds involved contain high-energy bonds, and most of these systems are freely reversible. The hexosyltransferases are mainly bacterial and plant enzymes, although there are some important exceptions.

This group includes the phosphorylases, which transfer glycosyl groups to or from phosphate; of these, 2.4.1.1, 2.4.1.8 and 2.4.2.1–4 are true phosphorylases, always involving phosphate. Although 2.4.1.7 can act as a phosphorylase, it is not a true phosphorylase, since phosphate need not be involved in the reaction; it is rather a transglycosylase which can use phosphate as one of a number of acceptors.

The best known phosphorylase (2.4.1.1) transfers glucose reversibly from combination with phosphate to the non-reducing end of a polysaccharide chain. It therefore requires the presence of a polysaccharide to start the reaction, and then builds up long unbranched chains. Phosphate is not involved with enzyme 2.4.1.18, which forms the branched structures of glycogen and amylopectin from the unbranched chains by transferring a part of the chain to the 6-position of one of the intermediate glucose residues in the remainder, forming as it were a T-structure. Enzyme 2.4.1.2 brings about a similar transfer, except that only the terminal glucose is transferred, and that it is transferred to another chain, so that by repeated transfer a chain is built up in which *all* the links are 1,6-links.

Enzyme 2.4.1.19 transfers part of the chain, not to another position in the remainder, but to its own non-reducing end, thus removing part of the molecule in the form of a ring:

V.1

$$
\begin{array}{ccc}
& \overset{\displaystyle H-I-J\ldots}{\underset{\displaystyle G}{}} & \\
\overset{\displaystyle F}{\underset{\displaystyle E}{}} & & \overset{\displaystyle A}{\underset{\displaystyle B}{}} \\
& \underset{\displaystyle D\!-\!-\!C}{} &
\end{array}
\quad = \quad
\begin{array}{ccc}
& G-H-I-J\ldots & \\
\overset{\displaystyle F\!-\!A}{} & & \\
\overset{\displaystyle E}{} & & \overset{\displaystyle B}{} \\
& \underset{\displaystyle D\!-\!C}{} &
\end{array}
$$

Here the letters represent successive glucose residues, counting from the non-reducing end. The reducing group of F is transferred from the 4-position of G to the 4-position of A, giving a non-reducing cyclic dextrin, usually containing 6 or 7 glucose residues. This enzyme also catalyses reactions similar to those of 2.4.1.3, namely transfer of one glucose of maltose to the 4-position of a terminal glucose, e.g. 2 maltose = maltotriose+glucose; 2.4.1.3, however, is not known to form cyclic dextrins. Enzyme 2.4.1.3 is a representative of a class of enzymes, including also 2.4.1.4–5 and 2.4.1.9–10, which like phosphorylase build up polysaccharide chains of various types by glycosyl transfer, although not from phosphate but from combination as a disaccharide. Enzyme 2.4.1.4 transfers the glucose from combination with fructose to the terminal 4-position; 2.4.1.5 does the same, but to the terminal 6-position (even of sucrose itself to form leucrose); with 2.4.1.9–10 it is the fructose which is transferred, to either the 1- or the 6-position, accompanied by much hydrolysis.

In the case of maltose phosphorylase (2.4.1.8) it is interesting that an optical inversion to the β-form takes place during the transfer; this has been correlated with the mechanism of the reaction (see Chapter VII). When 2.4.1.7 does not act as a phosphorylase and R′ is a ketose, the 1,2-(non-reducing)-link is formed; when, however, R′ represents L-arabinose it is the 1,3-link which is formed. When R′ is arsenate, a rapid hydrolysis takes place, owing to spontaneous hydrolysis of the glucose arsenate.

It will be noted that 2.4.1.11–17 act on uridinediphosphate derivatives. Enzyme 2.4.1.11 is involved in the formation of glycogen in animal tissues, 2.4.1.13 in the formation of sucrose in plants, where 2.4.1.7 does not occur, and 2.4.1.c in the formation of the lactose of milk.

Enzymes 2.4.2.1–6 are enzymes which can form nucleosides; here the sugar is linked directly to an N-atom and not, as in the other cases, with an O-atom.

Enzymes 2.4.2.7–12 are similar to the phosphorylases, but involve pyrophosphate rather than orthophosphate. These enzymes, which are often referred to as pyrophosphorylases, are essentially transribosylases, and should not be confused with the pyrophosphorylases in section 2.7.7, which are essentially transphosphorylating enzymes. The pyrophosphorylases in sub-group 2.4.2 bring about the formation of mononucleotides, whereas those in sub-group 2.7.7 form dinucleotides.

Enzyme 2.4.2.13 converts methionine into a source of active methyl groups. The essential feature of the reaction is the conversion of

$$\underset{\overset{|}{\text{CH}_3}}{\text{S}.\text{CH}_2.\text{R}} \text{ into } \underset{\overset{|}{\text{CH}_3}}{\text{R}'.\text{CH}_2.\overset{+}{\text{S}}.\text{CH}_2.\text{R}}, \text{ from which the methyl group is}$$

subsequently removed by a transmethylase to give R′.CH_2.S.CH_2.R.

Alkyltransferases

Sub-group 2.5 consists of some recently-discovered enzymes which transfer at carbon atoms in somewhat complicated substrates. 2.5.1.1 is important in the biosynthesis of isoprenoid compounds including carotenoids, steroids, rubber, ubiquinone, etc. 2.5.1.a brings about the formation of thiamine monophosphate from a substituted thiazole and the appropriate pyrimidine pyrophosphate; this is still another kind of 'pyrophosphorylase' reaction. 2.5.1.2, on the other hand, brings about the breakdown of thiamine by a similar transfer to a variety of bases. 2.5.1.b catalyses an internal transfer, producing a lactone.

Enzymes transferring nitrogenous groups

The transaminases are important in aminoacid metabolism. The number of authenticated transaminases (sub-group 2.6.1) has greatly increased recently. Many of these involve glutamate and, when coupled with the glutamate dehydrogenases (1.4.1.2–4), can form a variety of aminoacids from ketoacids and ammonia, the glutamate acting as an ammonia carrier. There are also two transaminases for glutamine, one transferring the α-amino group (2.6.1.15) and the other (2.6.1.16) transferring an amino group from the amide group. In the latter case the acceptor is a sugar. Enzyme 2.6.1.14 resembles 2.6.1.15, but is specific for asparagine. Enzymes 2.6.1.11, 13, b and c transfer the ω-amino group, and differ from the other enzymes of this section in that the product is an aldehyde. Enzyme 2.6.1.10 is involved in the formation of specific peptides containing D-aminoacids in *B. subtilis*. The activities of enzymes 2.6.1.1–2 in serum have been widely used in clinical diagnosis, since heart is rich in the first and liver in the second and when the tissues undergo degeneration they are liberated into the blood.

Glycine transamidinase (2.6.2.1) is a unique enzyme, bringing about transfer of the $-C(=NH).NH_2$ group, and is concerned in the biological synthesis of creatine; 2.6.3.1 transfers a $=NOH$ group.

Enzymes transferring phosphate groups

By far the majority of transphosphorylations go through ATP and the enzymes involved are known as kinases (sub-groups 2.7.1–4). Such reactions are important because of the possibility of transferring energy from one system to another in the form of an energy-rich phosphate bond (see p. 618). In the majority of cases (2.7.1), however, the phosphate is transferred to a hydroxyl group in an alcohol or sugar, giving a low-energy bond. Since the bond in ATP is a high-energy bond, we then have a high-energy bond on one side of the reaction and a low-energy bond on the other, so that in these cases the reaction is irreversible to all ordinary tests.

In the reactions catalysed by the kinases in sub-groups 2.7.2–4, however, there is an energy-rich bond on both sides of the reaction, and these systems are readily reversible.

Of the considerable number of these enzymes which phosphorylate sugars it will be noted that the phosphorylation takes place specifically at one or other of the terminal carbons, unless both positions are blocked, as in the cases of NAD (2.7.1.23) and dephosphocoenzyme A (2.7.1.24). The preference is for the formation of an ester on the terminal primary hydroxyl group (position 5 or 6, and also position 1 in the ketoses). However, a number form glycosidic phosphates.

Sixteen enzymes phosphorylate primary alcohols, namely 2.7.1.26–39. It has been shown by BUBLITZ and KENNEDY (351), using isotopically labelled ATP, that 2.7.1.30 always phosphorylates the same end of the glycerol molecule, although this molecule has a plane of symmetry. BURNETT and KENNEDY (365) have shown that 2.7.1.37 phosphorylates almost exclusively the serine hydroxyl groups of proteins. Several of these enzymes are important for the synthesis of various coenzymes.

Recently a very large number of transfer reactions involving nucleoside polyphosphates have been studied. The literature on the enzymes concerned is somewhat conflicting, but it appears certain that there are two main enzymes or groups of enzymes, typified by 2.7.4.4 and 6. The essential difference between the two enzymes is shown by the following reactions:

V.2   (2.7.4.4) XMP+YTP = XDP+YDP

V.3   (2.7.4.6) XDP+YTP = XTP+YDP

Adenylate kinase (2.7.4.3) catalyses a reaction of the same type as 2.7.4.4, but is restricted to adenosine derivatives.

The enzymes of sub-group 2.7.2 form acyl-phosphates, while those of sub-group 2.7.3 form amido-phosphates. Enzyme 2.7.4.1 catalyses the interchange of pyrophosphate bonds between ATP and inorganic polyphosphate.

Sub-group 2.7.6 contains two enzymes in which the bond which is split in ATP is the second pyrophosphate link, so that a pyrophosphate group is transferred instead of a phosphate group. Enzyme 2.7.6.1 forms a specific glycosyl-pyrophosphate which is important in the synthesis of nucleotides by enzymes 2.4.2.7–14 (1370).

Sub-group 2.7.7 contains a number of important enzymes of comparatively recent discovery, which bring about the transfer of groups from pyrophosphate to other molecules, liberating inorganic pyrophosphate, thus:

V.4 $X-P-P-P+P-Y \rightleftharpoons X-P-P-Y+P-P.$

This reaction consists of a transfer of the substituted phosphate group X–P from pyrophosphate to another substituted phosphate group forming a new pyrophosphate bond in the product X–P–P–Y. These enzymes are thus important in the synthesis of dinucleotides and analogous molecules. Isotope experiments on enzyme 2.7.7.1 have shown that the pyrophosphate liberated arises from the two terminal phosphate groups of the triphosphate, thus confirming the mechanism suggested above *(1437)*. The reaction catalysed by enzyme 2.7.7.4, though similar, does not strictly conform to the above equation V.4; here sulphate acts instead of the acceptor phosphate, forming a mixed acid anhydride.

These enzymes catalyse a special type of transphosphorylation, but the term 'pyrophosphorylase' has also been applied to another group of enzymes forming pyrophosphate, which, however, do not catalyse transphosphorylations but transglycosylations. These enzymes are given in section 2.4.2.

The phosphomutases (sub-group 2.7.5) do not involve ATP or other nucleotide polyphosphates. At one time they were believed to catalyse intramolecular phosphate transfers, moving the phosphate group from one position to another in the same molecule, for instance, in the case of phosphoglucomutase (2.7.5.1) from the 1- to the 6-position in a glucose molecule. It is now known that this is not so; the transfer is from position 1 in one molecule to position 6 in another, and the reaction is as set out in the table. The reaction must be started by the addition of a trace of the diphosphate, but since one molecule of this appears for every molecule disappearing, it remains constant in amount, and acts catalytically as a 'coenzyme' of the reaction. All but one of the phosphomutases appear to act in a similar way; in each case the process is a transfer in which 'coenzyme' is converted into product and substrate into 'coenzyme', a very interesting type of reaction. A phosphoglycerate phosphomutase from cereal germ, however, does not need a cofactor, and has therefore been placed among the isomerases (5.4.2.1).

All the enzymes of sub-groups 2.7.7–8 can be regarded as transferring substituted phosphate groups. The ribonucleases 2.7.7.16 and g might be supposed to act in a similar way to deoxyribonuclease (3.1.4.5.), but actually the breakdown of ribonucleate occurs by a phosphate-transfer reaction, which may be written as shown in V.5, where Py represents a pyrimidine. An examination of this will show that it consists essentially of the transfer of the linking phosphate group from the 5'-position of the terminal nucleotide to the 2'-position of the pyrimidine nucleotide, giving a cyclic phosphate which is then slowly hydrolysed *(1720)*.

V.5

Sulphur- and sulpho-transferases

Enzyme 2.8.1.1 acts by means of a disulphide group in its molecule, which probably acts as a carrier of S from combination with sulphite to cyanide (*907, 2473*). The sulphotransferases of sub-group 2.8.2 bring about the formation of a number of organic sulphates; in all cases 3'-phosphoadenylylsulphate acts as an 'active sulphate' intermediate (*2227–8, 2272*).

Coenzyme A transferases

These enzymes (sub-group 2.8.3), like the transacylases, act on acyl-CoA compounds, but differ from them in transferring coenzyme A and not the acyl group.

3. Hydrolases

Esterases

This group (3.1) includes some enzymes of comparatively low specificity, that is to say, although they are specific for the ester link they hydrolyse a very large number of different esters, though not all at the same rate. Some of these also act slowly on lactones, but the group includes three enzymes which are true lactonases, that is to say, they act only on internal esters.

Thiolesterases

These enzymes are important because the thiolester link plays an essential part in the metabolism of acyl groups generally. 'Glyoxalase II' (3.1.2.6) acts on the lactylglutathione formed by 'glyoxalase I' (4.4.1.5), the two together forming the glyoxalase system which converts methylglyoxal into lactate.

Phosphatases

The phosphomono-(and di)-esterases (3.1.3–4) are often, within their respective fields, enzymes of comparatively low specificity. Some enzymes in the group, however, especially those acting on sugar phosphates, are quite highly specific. The deoxyribonucleases are included here because they act by a phosphodiesterase type of reaction; ribonuclease (2.7.7.16) is placed in another section because it acts by a phosphate-transfer reaction to form cyclic phosphates.

Glycosidases

Sub-group 3.2 includes not only enzymes hydrolysing true glycosides (3.2.1), but also enzymes hydrolysing N-glycosyl compounds (3.2.2) and one hydrolysing S-glycosyl compounds (3.2.3.1). The true glycosidases (sub-group 3.2.1) include not only enzymes acting on simple glycosides, but also enzymes such as the amylases, which hydrolyse glycoside links in polysaccharides. α-amylase might be termed an endo-amylase and β-amylase an exo-amylase, by analogy with the peptidases, since α-amylase can split glycosidic links in the middle of polysaccharide chains, whereas β-amylase works from the non-reducing end of the chains, splitting off maltose residues one at a time. The maltose is split off in the β-form, so that there is an optical inversion at the point of hydrolysis.

Enzymes acting on a considerable variety of glycosidic links are known. Enzymes 3.2.1.1–3 and 12–13 act on α-1,4 glucose links, 3.2.1.9–11 on α-1,6 glucose links, 3.2.1.4 on β-1,4 glucose links, 3.2.1.27 on α-1,3 glucose links, 3.2.1.7 on β-1,2 fructose links, 3.2.1.8 on β-1,4 xylose links, 3.2.1.a on β-1,3 xylose links, 3.2.1.14 and 29 on α-1,4 2-acetyl-amino-2-deoxyglucoside links, 3.2.1.15 on α-1,4 galacturonide links, 3.2.1.16 on β-1,4 mannuronide links, 3.2.1.19 on α-1,4 links between 2-amino-2-deoxyglucose and glucuronate, 3.2.1.28 on α-α-diglucose links, and others on a variety of other groups, the nature of which will be clear from the table. Enzymes 3.2.1.14 and 29 are known to be different enzymes. Enzyme 3.2.1.17 (hitherto known as lysozyme) has been studied by means of its action in lysing bacterial cells, especially of *M. lysodeikticus*.

The breakdown of nucleotides and nucleosides in animal tissues takes place mainly by a phosphorolytic mechanism, but some hydrolytic enzymes specific for nucleoside links are known and comprise sub-group 3.2.2.

Peptidases, etc.

Ideas on proteolytic enzymes (sub-group 3.4) have changed considerably in recent years. It used to be thought that some enzymes, the proteinases, were adapted to attack only large molecules, while others only hydrolysed small molecules. It is now realized that it is not a matter of

H

the size of the substrate molecule at all; it is really a matter of specificity. By no means all peptide links are hydrolysed by all peptidases; whether a given enzyme will act or not depends on the nature of the other chemical groups in the neighbourhood of the peptide link. Some enzymes do not require an adjacent terminal carboxyl or amino group, and may even be prevented from acting by such groups, while others require such a free terminal group. The former (termed by Bergmann endopeptidases) can thus act in the middle of a peptide chain, breaking protein molecules up into smaller fragments, but will generally hydrolyse small peptides only if the terminal groups are artificially blocked by chemical means. The latter (Bergmann's exopeptidases) cannot hydrolyse links in the middle of the chain, but act, some from the carboxyl and others from the amino end of the chain, removing the terminal aminoacids successively one at a time.

The endo- and exo-enzymes co-operate very effectively in protein digestion, in which it may be said that the main function of the former is to produce a large number of free ends at which the latter can act. The same two types of action are also seen in the enzymes which digest polysaccharides, as illustrated by the α- and β-amylases.

Peptidase action, however, is far more than a matter of terminal groups; the nature of the aminoacid side-chains in the neighbourhood of the link has a powerful determining action. In fact, proteinases are rather specific and the percentage of the peptide links in a protein which can be broken by a given proteinase is not very large. The matter is discussed in more detail in Chapter VI. Although quite a number of proteinases have been purified or even crystallized, the specificity of only a few has been studied. Several are known to be capable of transferring peptides to other molecules as well as hydrolysing them.

Sub-groups 3.5.1–2 comprise a number of enzymes hydrolysing –CO–NH– links which are not concerned with protein breakdown, but are involved in other lines of metabolism. It will be seen that some of these open heterocyclic rings.

Sub-groups 3.5.3–4 hydrolyse a C–N bond within the structure =N—CH=N-. According to the groups attached to the nitrogen atoms, the result will be liberation of ammonia or urea, or the opening of a ring. A number of these enzymes are involved in the formation of excretory products of nitrogen metabolism. It should be noted that most biological deaminations occur not by the hydrolytic mechanism discussed here, but by oxidation or by transfer to another molecule.

Although the substrates of the enzymes in sub-group 3.5.99 contain the amidine structure, the bond hydrolysed is external to this structure, which remains intact in the product.

Pyrophosphatases, etc.

The group of enzymes hydrolysing acid anhydrides (3.6), with one exception (3.6.1.7), act on pyrophosphate links. The pyrophosphatases are usually classed with the phosphatases, but, in fact, they are not esterases and form a quite distinct class. This group includes a number of important enzymes acting on nucleotides. Myosin (3.6.1.3) is especially important because of its close connection with muscle contraction. Nucleotide pyrophosphatase (3.6.1.9) attacks pyrophosphate links in which both phosphate groups are substituted and has been much used in elucidating the structure of nucleotide coenzymes.

4. *Lyases*

Decarboxylases

The decarboxylase reaction can be written either as a hydrolytic process producing H_2CO_3, or as a lyase reaction producing CO_2. Owing to the rapid interconversion of these two substances, it is not an easy matter to establish which is the primary product. The case of pyruvate decarboxylase (4.1.1.1) has been much studied, with contradictory results (*495–6, 1465*); the latest investigation (*2050*) shows that CO_2 is first formed. It does not immediately follow, however, that this is true of all decarboxylases, for this enzyme is exceptional among decarboxylases in requiring thiamine pyrophosphate (like 4.1.1.7–8). Many of the decarboxylases act on nitrogenous substrates and depend on pyridoxal phosphate, and for a number of these there is isotopic evidence (*2254*) that CO_2 is the first product. The remaining decarboxylases do not seem to require a coenzyme, and we are not aware of any evidence as to the mechanism of their action, but for convenience all the decarboxylases have been grouped together as carboxy-lyases.

Pyruvate decarboxylase is the important enzyme in yeast which diverts carbohydrate metabolism towards alcoholic fermentation. It has close relations with pyruvate dehydrogenase (1.2.4.1), and these are discussed in Chapter IX under thiamine pyrophosphate.

The aminoacid decarboxylases (4.1.1.11–28) are mostly of bacterial origin, and these have important actions in bacterial infections and in putrefaction. They are specific enzymes and have been of great practical use for the estimation of aminoacids on a micro-scale. A few occur in animal tissues and play a part in the metabolism of certain aminoacids.

The last four enzymes of the decarboxylase sub-group have secondary reactions associated with the decarboxylation. Three of these are phosphorylations; the fourth is a dehydration coupled with the breakdown of ATP, and can be regarded as the converse of a ligase reaction.

Aldehyde-lyases

These enzymes (4.1.2), are mainly known as aldolases, since they bring about reactions that are essentially aldol condensations or the reverse. Like all the enzymes of sub-group 4.1, they are concerned with the formation or dissolution of C–C bonds. The aldolases have an outstanding importance in carbohydrate metabolism. The classical aldolases (4.1.2.7 and *b*) bring about the breakdown of hexoses into three-carbon units for their further metabolism.

Ketoacid-lyases

The enzymes of this sub-group (4.1.3) are mainly concerned with the synthesis of di- or tri-carboxylic acids from two smaller fragments, and some of them are important in connection with the citrate and glyoxylate cycles. The classification of these enzymes presents some difficulty, since the overall reactions can be regarded in various ways, and information about their mechanism is somewhat scanty. The enzymes listed here, however, have much in common and can clearly be regarded as lyases, although several have secondary reactions, usually acetylation of co-enzyme A, associated with the lyase reaction.

Hydro-lyases

This large sub-group (4.2.1) includes such well known and important enzymes as fumarate and aconitate hydratases. Enzymes 4.2.1.13–16 act on hydroxy-aminoacids; removal of water is followed by rearrangement of double bonds in the product and subsequent hydrolysis liberating ammonia. The synthases (4.2.1.20–23) also act on a hydroxy-aminoacid, but here the lyase reaction is associated with the addition of other molecules. In the case of 4.2.1.24 the lyase reaction is associated with the addition of a second molecule of the substrate, followed by cyclization.

Other lyases

Enzyme 4.2.99.1, which is a bacterial enzyme, may be contrasted with hyaluronidases (3.2.1.d–e), which break down hyaluronate hydrolytically.

The ammonia-lyases (4.3.1) provide another method of deamination of aminoacids, giving unsaturated acids. The amidine-lyases (4.3.2), on the other hand, bring about amination by addition of an aminoacid followed by removal of the corresponding unsaturated acid, leaving the amino group attached. Enzymes of sub-group 4.4 bring about the removal of H_2S or substituted forms thereof.

5. *Isomerases*

Racemases and epimerases

Racemizations may often be brought about by pairs of enzymes, respectively specific for the two isomers and producing a common symmetrical product. In the cases included in sub-group 5.1, however, there is evidence that single enzymes are responsible for a direct racemization. These enzymes are concerned either with the racemization of aminoacids or the epimerization of sugars. Enzyme 5.1.3.3 catalyses mutarotation.

Cis–trans *isomerases*

These enzymes are not concerned with optical activity, but bring about a change of geometrical configuration at a double bond. They may act by the formation of a symmetrical intermediate by additions to the double bond; in two cases it is known that the –SH group of glutathione acts in this way.

Intramolecular oxidoreductases

The isomerases interconverting aldoses and ketoses (5.3.1) bring about the oxidation of a CHOH group with the simultaneous reduction of an adjacent C=O group. The tautomerase 5.3.2.1 and the Δ-isomerases 5.3.3 can also be regarded as intramolecular oxidoreductases.

Intramolecular transferases

These enzymes (5.4), known as mutases, bring about the transfer of a group from one part of the substrate molecule to another part of the same molecule. Enzyme 5.4.2.1 should be contrasted with the phosphomutases of sub-group 2.7.5, which transfer phosphate groups from one molecule to another. Enzymes 5.4.99.1–2 depend on the cobamide coenzymes, which are discussed in Chapter IX.

6. *Ligases*

These are enzymes bringing about the synthetic linking together of two molecules, simultaneously with breakdown of ATP. The energy liberated by the ATP breakdown supplies the energy for the synthesis. The importance (and even the existence) of this class of enzymes has only recently been recognized. Previously it was thought that such syntheses were brought about by the combined action of phosphokinases and transferases, so that the process could be represented as (1) $B+ATP = B-P+ADP$, followed by (2) $A+B-P = A-B+P$. It had been shown that starch could be synthesized by such a process. It is now known, however, that most of the synthetase reactions are brought about by single enzymes, acting by mechanisms which are discussed in Chapter VII.

The enzymes in sub-group 6.1.1 are often referred to by the unsatisfactory name of 'aminoacid-activating enzymes', although this conflicts with Rules 5 and 30 of the Enzyme Commission's recommendations (see pp. 175 and 183). These enzymes bring about the first stage in the biosynthesis of proteins, in which each aminoacid residue becomes attached to the ribose of the terminal adenylate residue of its own soluble RNA. This process is discussed in Chapter XI.

The enzymes of sub-group 6.2.1 are concerned with the formation of acyl-CoA derivatives, and since these are energy-rich compounds these reactions are freely reversible.

The reactions of the remaining synthetases will be clear from the table. All of those in section 6.4 depend on biotin as cofactor.

VI

ENZYME SPECIFICITY

THE HIGH SPECIFICITY of enzymes, that is to say the strict limitation of the action of each enzyme to one substance or to a very small number of closely related substances, is one of their most striking characteristics. Enzyme specificity is one of the most important biological phenomena, without which the ordered metabolism of living matter would not exist and life itself would be impossible. As HOPKINS (*1155*) said in 1932, 'The organising potentialities inherent in highly specific catalysis have not, I believe, been adequately appraised in chemical thought. The concentration of a catalyst or, alternatively, the extent of its active surface will determine the velocity of changes due to its influence, but highly specific catalysts determine in addition just what particular materials, rather than any others, shall undergo change. In this respect they are like the living cell itself, for they select from their environment. Finally the specific catalyst, in virtue of its own intimate structure, determines which among possible paths the course of change shall follow. It has directive powers. . . . I do not expect that all will feel able to admit as much as I myself would like to claim, namely, that the control of events by intracellular enzymes, exerted in the specialized colloidal apparatus of the cell by itself secures the status of the cell as a system which can maintain itself in dynamic equilibrium with its environment. I am not denying for a moment that the cell has esoteric qualities which may call for organizing influences of a greatly different kind, exerted maybe at some higher level. It is at any rate sure that the inter-related activity of highly specific catalysts represents a notable device of Nature which has supported during the course of evolution those dynamic manifestations which characterize living things.'

No one who examines the tables given in Chapter XII can doubt the essential part played by enzyme specificity in creating organized and fruitful lines of metabolism from diverse types of chemical reactions. If enzymes were not specific, their action would result in rapid degradation of the cell material, with no energy-rich intermediates and with no biosynthetic possibilities. The subject of 'organization by specificity' is discussed in Chapter XII.

The degree of specificity observed varies with different enzymes. In many cases the enzyme acts, so far as is known, on one substance only, and carries out only one reaction. In other cases it can act on a small number of closely related substances, carrying out the same reaction in all cases. In such a case it is often possible to recognize a common chemical structure which must be present in a substance if the enzyme is to act on it. With the less specific enzymes this necessary structure is a relatively small part of the substrate molecule, e.g. an aldehyde or ester grouping, so that a large number of related substances can be attacked.

There are several circumstances which make it somewhat difficult to present a satisfactory account of enzyme specificity.

(a) A great many enzymes are apparently absolutely specific for a single substrate or (in the case of a bimolecular reaction) for a single pair of substrates. When this has been recorded, there is little more that can be said. It is only with the less specific enzymes, acting on a whole series of related substrates, that a detailed discussion is possible of the effect of modifications in various parts of the substrate molecule, and of the underlying causes of these effects. Thus, inevitably, the greater part of the discussion is taken up with the less specific enzymes, giving a misleading picture.

(b) In many extensive studies of the specificity of particular enzymes, involving much careful chemical work in the preparation of a large number of pure substrates, it is unfortunate that equal care was not taken to work with pure enzymes. Several such studies in fact have been carried out with relatively crude enzymes, and this greatly detracts from their value, since it is impossible to be certain that all the reactions observed were due to the same enzyme. Perhaps this is especially true in the case of enzymes acting on carbohydrates.

(c) Conversely, in several cases in which trouble was taken to obtain a pure enzyme, an equal degree of trouble was not taken to ensure complete purity of the substrates. With certain methods of following enzyme reactions, e.g. by observing the appearance of the $NADH_2$ absorption band in dehydrogenase reactions, the presence of a small amount of an unsuspected impurity which acts as a substrate may give completely misleading results.

(d) In certain studies in which crystalline enzymes were used, a relatively very large amount of enzyme was used. If a slow reaction is observed with an added substance under such conditions, it is difficult to be certain that it is really due to the enzyme in question and not to a very small amount of some other enzyme present in the crystals. Even if the crystals of enzyme were 99·99 per cent pure, the presence of 0·01 per cent of another active enzyme would give ample activity to be observed.

(*e*) The vast majority of specificity studies consist only of determinations of the reaction velocity with a series of substances at a constant concentration. A difference between one substance and another might be due either to a difference of rate of reaction of the ES complexes or to a difference of affinity; in other words, the difference might be one either of V or of K_s. In only very few studies has the effect of substrate structure on V and K_s been separately determined.

THE INVESTIGATION OF ENZYME SPECIFICITY

The satisfactory investigation of the specificity of a given enzyme calls for attention to a number of points, some of which have just been mentioned. The enzyme should be as pure as possible, preferably recrystallized several times, and in any case should be quite free from any other enzyme acting on similar substrates. The substrates also should be as pure as possible, and quite free from any other substances on which the enzyme may act. In the case of optically active substances, the two isomers should if possible be tested separately, as it is likely that the enzyme will act on one only (see p. 204) and it is possible that the presence of the other may inhibit the reaction. For instance, D-asparagine competitively inhibits the deamination of L-asparagine by asparaginase (*938*).

In carrying out a specificity study it is usual to select a reference substrate, which is generally the most readily attacked biological substrate, and to work out the optimum conditions for this. Other possible substrates are then examined under the same conditions of pH, temperature and concentration. However, to obtain quantitative information in cases where several substrates are attacked, the most desirable procedure is to construct a Lineweaver–Burk plot for each substrate and to determine V and K_m by extrapolation (examples are given in Table VI.4). Moreover, in the case of ionizing substrates, this should be done over a range of pH values, since each substrate may have a different pH optimum. This procedure is important because the different substrates may have different affinities, so that the standard concentration may produce different degrees of saturation, and they may have different pH curves, so that the standard pH may give a different fraction of the optimum velocity for each substrate. In any case V and K_m are needed separately in order to assess the influence of structure both on the affinity of the enzyme for the substrate and on the lability of the enzyme-substrate complex.

Even when the enzyme only acts on one substrate, the influence of structure on affinity can still be studied by extending the investigation to competitive inhibitors, in other words substances for which $V = 0$, in which case K_i is measured instead of K_m.

The enzyme should always be used at reasonably low concentration, in order to avoid reactions due to traces of contaminating enzymes, which may be observed even with comparatively pure enzymes if excessive amounts are taken.

The general procedure in investigating specificity is, having first obtained an active substrate, to make small chemical modifications in every part of the molecule separately, and to determine the effect on affinity and reactivity. It may be necessary to do this with more than one substance. The majority of enzyme reactions are reactions involving more than one substrate, for example, transferring enzymes catalyse reactions between donor and acceptor molecules, and even hydrolysing enzymes, when catalysing the reverse reaction, are concerned with two different molecules at the same time. In all such cases two series of compounds must be studied in order to determine the specificity towards each substrate independently.

From the results it is possible to formulate the minimal structures necessary for combination and for reaction, and to determine the quantitative effects of additional groups. From such data a picture may frequently be drawn showing the manner in which the substrate unites with the enzyme, the groups involved and the mechanism of the reaction.

When two or more different reactions are found to be catalysed by the same enzyme preparation it is necessary, unless the enzyme is known to be pure and homogeneous, to determine whether both are in fact due to the same enzyme. A number of criteria of identity of enzymes can be formulated, possibly none absolutely conclusive by itself, but providing very strong evidence when taken together. Lists of such criteria have been put forward by HALDANE (979) and by DIXON (615). Among the best criteria may be mentioned the following.

(a) Failure to separate the two activities by all the available fractionation procedures. This may only mean that the two enzymes are very similar in physical properties; however, by using a large number of different procedures it may be made very convincing.

(b) Maintenance of a constant ratio between the two activities as the enzyme undergoes inactivation. If two different enzymes were involved, this could only be true if precisely the same fraction of each were inactivated under all conditions. The inactivation may be carried out by controlled heating, by adjustments of pH, by treatment with irreversible inhibitors, by irradiation, or by other means. It is inconceivable that all these treatments would inactivate two different enzymes equally.

(c) If only one enzyme is concerned, a competitive inhibitor should give the same value of K_i when tested with either substrate.

(d) When the substrates for the two reactions are added together, the total rate of reaction will be less than the sum of the rates of the reactions measured separately, provided that the substrate concentrations used are sufficient to saturate or nearly saturate the enzyme when added separately (the 'mixed-substrate' method). When additive effects are obtained, it is good evidence that two independent enzymes are concerned, but less-than-additive effects are not conclusive evidence for identity, since each enzyme might be competitively inhibited by the substrate of the other. The quantitative effects observed with one enzyme catalysing two reactions simultaneously are discussed on p. 84.

A number of less valid criteria have been suggested and used from time to time. Similarity of pH curves for the two substrates is not necessarily to be expected, even when both are acted upon by the same enzyme, especially if one or both of the substrates undergoes ionization. A given concentration of a competitive inhibitor will not usually inhibit both reactions to the same extent, since the inhibition will depend on the affinity of the particular substrate for the enzyme. Cofactors may not affect the two reactions similarly, for example, Table IX.7 shows how the specificity pattern of single enzymes may be markedly influenced by the nature of the activating metal ion.

GENERAL OBSERVATIONS ON SPECIFICITY

Different groups of enzymes vary markedly in their degree of specificity. A very large number of the enzymes shown in the table of enzymes are highly specific; we may mention particularly the dehydrogenases, the kinases and the synthetases. In the majority of these the high degree of specificity applies to both reactants in the bimolecular reaction (or all three in the case of the trimolecular synthetase reactions). However, in a few cases, for example, alcohol dehydrogenase (1.1.1.1), the enzyme is highly specific for one substrate (NAD) but fairly unspecific for the other, which can be any one of a number of alcohols. At the other end of the scale come a few hydrolysing enzymes such as esterases, phosphatases and peptidases, which act on a wide range of carboxylic esters, phosphate esters and peptides respectively. But even here there are considerable differences of specificity and some esterases, for example, the phospholipases, are quite highly specific, as also are some phosphatases and peptidases.

In rare cases a dual specificity is shown; xanthine oxidase (1.2.3.2), which is quite highly specific within the purine series, also oxidizes aldehydes (*615*), and the liver aldehyde oxidase (1.2.3.1) also oxidizes derivatives of pyridine and quinoline. These are cases where the enzyme brings about the same type of reaction with two different groups of substrates. On the other hand, there are some cases where an enzyme may act on its substrate in two different ways; this is true, for example, of the decarboxylating malate and isocitrate dehydrogenases (1.1.1.38, 40, 42), which will either reduce or decarboxylate the corresponding keto-acids. It should also be noted that there are a number of cases where a given oxidation reaction may be brought about by a number of different enzymes, using different acceptors (see Chapter V).

Stereospecificity of enzymes

Enzymes are not only chemically specific; they are also sterically specific when they act upon or form substances containing asymmetric centres. The substrate may contain an asymmetric carbon atom, in which case it is usually found that the enzyme acts on only one of the optical isomers. Specificity of this type appears usually to be absolute, in other words the opposite isomer is not acted upon at all, in those cases in which the asymmetric group itself undergoes the actual enzymatic reaction, for instance the oxidation of a CHOH group in a hydroxyacid. Where, however, the asymmetric group forms part of the substrate molecule at some distance from the reacting group, both isomers are often attacked, although there is usually a more or less marked disparity in the actual velocity with the two isomers, for example in the hydrolysis of optically active esters by carboxylesterase (see the review by WEBB (*2806*)).

In the table of enzymes, wherever the substrate is given as D- or L-, it may be taken that the antipode is not attacked at a detectable rate. When a DL-mixture is acted on by the enzyme in such cases, it is found that only half of the substrate is broken down, and this is one way of resolving a racemate. Where the stereochemical specificity is absolute, the un-attacked antipode does not usually inhibit the utilization of the sub-strate. In certain cases, however, the unattacked antipode does inhibit competitively and is therefore bound at the active site of the enzyme. By making use of this effect the affinity of this combination can be measured. Surprisingly, it is found in some cases that the affinity of the inhibitory antipode is even greater than that of the substrate. An example of this is shown in Table VI.1, which gives a comparison of the action of chymo-trypsin (3.4.4.5) on a number of pairs of stereoisomers. It will be seen that for each of the first four pairs the affinity is greater for the form which does not react than for the substrate, assuming that K_m is not very different from K_s, which is probably the case for this enzyme (see p. 111).

Even when neither isomer is attacked by the enzyme, the affinity for the D-form is greater than that for the L-form.

In cases of this kind either configuration will allow the enzyme to combine with the substance, provided that it contains the correct combining groups, but only one configuration produces the mutual orientation of enzyme and substrate groups which causes activation and reaction.

TABLE VI.1

AFFINITIES OF SOME PAIRS OF STEREOISOMERS
FOR CHYMOTRYPSIN (from *2806*)

	K_m (mM)	K_i (mM)
Acetyl-L-tryptophanamide	5·3	
Acetyl-D-tryptophanamide		2·7
Acetyl-L-tyrosinamide	30·5	
Acetyl-D-tyrosinamide		12·0
Nicotinyl-L-tryptophanamide	2·7	
Nicotinyl-D-tryptophanamide		1·4
Nicotinyl-L-tyrosinamide	15·0	
Nicotinyl-D-tyrosinamide		6·2
Acetyl-L-tryptophan		17·5
Acetyl-D-tryptophan		4·8
L-tryptophanamide		6·3
D-tryptophanamide		3·2

Where the substrate is a symmetrical molecule and the product contains an asymmetric carbon atom the enzyme nearly always produces only one optical isomer, or, in other words, it carries out an 'asymmetric synthesis'. For example, the reduction of pyruvate by the lactate dehydrogenase (1.1.1.27) gives only L-lactate, whereas the same reaction carried out by a different dehydrogenase (1.1.1.28) yields only D-lactate; reduction of ammonium 2-oxoglutarate by the L-glutamate dehydrogenases (1.4.1.2–4) gives only L-glutamate; the phosphorylation of glycerol by glycerol kinase (2.7.1.30) gives only L-glycerol 3-phosphate; the condensation of glycine with acetaldehyde by threonine aldolase (4.1.2.5) gives only L-threonine, whereas the same reaction carried out by another aldolase (4.1.2.6) gives only L-allothreonine. In the formation of threonine two asymmetric carbon atoms are produced simultaneously. In compounds which have two or more asymmetric centres, each centre may have its own influence on enzyme specificity (*2887*).

In addition to D-L-isomerism, enzymes are also influenced by other types of geometrical isomerism. In cases where the substrate has a *cis*- or *trans*-configuration it is usual to find that the corresponding *trans*- or *cis*-isomers respectively are not attacked. For example, fumarate hydratase acts only on fumarate and not at all on maleate, and it forms only fumarate from malate. It will be noticed that this enzyme shows both types of stereospecificity, being specific for fumarate in one direction and for L-malate in the other. Numerous examples of both types of stereospecificity can be found in the table of enzymes.

A number of enzymes, however, act equally well on both isomers. Where this occurs in relation to D-L-isomerism, and the reaction destroys the asymmetry of the centre, the enzymes concerned act as racemases, for they can convert the L-form into the symmetrical intermediate, and then by the reverse reaction produce a racemic mixture. This is the case for the enzymes of sub-group 5.1. Moreover, where an enzyme acts equally on the *cis*- and *trans*-forms of a substance to produce a compound with free rotation about the relevant bond, e.g. by the addition of a molecule such as glutathione to the double bond, it will act as a *cis-trans*-isomerase (sub-group 5.2). The epimerization of a sugar can be regarded as a D-L-change on a particular carbon atom of the sugar ring, and may be brought about in a similar way by enzymes which are not specific for one particular configuration on the carbon atom involved. Such reactions are brought about by enzymes of sub-group 5.1.3.

In addition to the types of stereospecificity mentioned, enzymes are able to distinguish between groups in symmetrical molecules which would be considered identical by the chemist. For instance, in a reaction

VI.1 $\qquad Cx_2yz \longrightarrow Cx'xyz$

where the small letters represent the four groups attached to the carbon atom, the enzyme may act on only one of the two chemically indistinguishable x groups. This is shown by the fact that only one optical isomer of the asymmetric molecule $Cx'xyz$ is produced; for example, only L-glycerol 3-phosphate is formed in the phosphorylation of glycerol by enzyme 2.7.1.30 (*350*). This asymmetric phosphorylation of the symmetrical glycerol molecule has been confirmed by the use of isotopes (*351*). Glycerol labelled with C^{14} in the 1-position only, previously obtained by yeast fermentation of carboxyl-labelled acetate or 3,4-labelled glucose (*2587*), was phosphorylated with highly purified glycerol kinase and ATP, and the reaction was found to take place as follows:

VI.2
$$
\begin{array}{ccc}
C^*H_2OH & & C^*H_2OH \\
| & & | \\
HO{-}C{-}H \quad + \text{ ATP } = & HO{-}C{-}H & + \text{ ADP} \\
| & & | \\
CH_2OH & & CH_2.O.H_2PO_3
\end{array}
$$

A similar specificity is shown by the enzymes of the citric cycle concerned in the formation and breakdown of citric acid. If citric acid is formed enzymatically from $C*OOH.CH_2.CO.COOH$, chemical breakdown shows that the C^{14} occurs only in a terminal carboxyl group of the citric acid. Since citric acid is a symmetrical molecule, it is impossible to distinguish chemically between the two $-CH_2.COOH$ groups. However, enzymatic oxidation of this citric acid by a mitochondrial preparation gives 2-oxoglutarate with the label entirely in the α-carboxyl (*1617*); thus only one of the terminal carboxyl groups of the citric acid could have been labelled, and the oxidation system is able to distinguish between them. The reactions involved may be written in an abbreviated form as

$$
\begin{array}{l}
\text{VI.3} \quad
\begin{array}{c}
C*OOH \\
| \\
CH_2 \\
| \\
CO.COOH \\
+ \\
CH_3 \\
| \\
COOH
\end{array}
\rightarrow
\begin{array}{c}
C*OOH \\
| \\
CH_2 \\
| \\
C(OH).COOH \\
| \\
CH_2 \\
| \\
COOH
\end{array}
\rightarrow
\begin{array}{c}
C*OOH \\
| \\
CHOH \\
| \\
CH.COOH \\
| \\
CH_2 \\
| \\
COOH
\end{array}
\rightarrow
\begin{array}{c}
C*OOH \\
| \\
CO \\
| \\
CH_2 \\
| \\
CH_2 \\
| \\
COOH
\end{array}
+ CC_2
\end{array}
$$

The full reactions are written out in Table XII.2.

The first two stages here are catalysed by citrate synthase (4.1.3.7) and aconitate hydratase (4.2.1.3) respectively. In the first reaction the 2-carbon residue might be expected to add indiscriminately to the front or back of the $=C=O$ group. The fact that only the upper carboxyl group of the citric acid is labelled shows that this is not so, but that the enzyme causes it to add to only one face; addition to the other face would have caused the lower carboxyl group to be labelled. This is more easily seen in molecular models. In the second reaction it might be expected that the two $-CH_2.COOH$ groups would be equivalent, but, in fact, the aconitate hydratase only acts on the upper of these two groups.

This type of specificity may readily be explained in terms of the considerations advanced by OGSTON (*2016–7*). If an enzyme has groups in the active centre which combine with any three of the substituent groups in the substrate Cx_2yz, it is clear that the substrate can only be bound by the enzyme in one orientation, in spite of it being a symmetrical molecule. Therefore an x-binding group in the enzyme always binds the same x group in the substrate, and if it is the group which brings about the reaction, only this particular x group will ever react. Fig. VI.1, which shows two possible structures of the enzyme–substrate complex, may help to make this clear.

If the two x groups in a molecule of the structure Cx_2yz differ not chemically but isotopically one has a case of what is known as 'isotopic asymmetry'. We have already seen two cases of this in enzyme reactions (equations VI.2 and VI.3) and it is, in fact, a general method for the investigation of this type of enzyme stereospecificity. The various types of rotational and reflective asymmetry which are important in this connection have been considered in detail by HIRSCHMANN (*1111*).

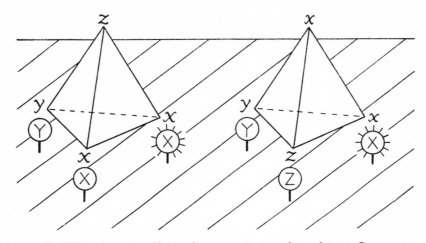

Fig. VI.1. *Stereospecificity of an enzyme towards a substrate* Cx_2yz.

The diagram shows two possible structures of the enzyme-substrate complex. The substrate molecule is shown as a tetrahedron with the groups x, y and z at the corners. In the left-hand diagram the enzyme is assumed to combine with both x groups and the y group, and in the right-hand diagram with only one x group and in addition with the y and z groups. The spheres X, Y and Z represent the specific combining groups of the enzyme; the X group marked with rays is that which makes the attached x group reactive. On either supposition only one particular x group can undergo reaction.

One much studied example of the phenomenon discussed in the few paragraphs is the reduction of NAD by dehydrogenases. As is discussed at some length in Chapter VII, it can be shown by using deuterium as a marker that the hydrogen transferred from the substrate is added by a given enzyme only on to one face of the nicotinamide ring. Some dehydrogenases catalyse the addition of hydrogen to one face, and others to the other face (Table VII.1). These enzymes catalyse two-substrate reactions and they exhibit stereospecificity towards both substrates. The specificity towards the donor is often an absolute optical specificity (i.e. for the L- or D-form, as in the case of lactate), whereas that towards the acceptor is of a kind only revealed when isotopes are used. Even if the donor is symmetrical, it may be possible to show an asymmetric action of the enzyme by means of isotopes, as was first shown with yeast alcohol dehydrogenase by LOEWUS, WESTHEIMER and VENNESLAND (*1608*). By reducing $CH_3.CDO$ with $NADH_2$, only one isomer of $CH_3.CHDOH$ was formed; the other isomer was obtained by reducing $CH_3.CHO$ with NADHD. These forms are, in fact, somewhat optically active, and possess opposite rotations ($\alpha_D = 0 \cdot 18°$).

In an enzymatic reaction between two optically active substrates there are theoretically four possibilities with respect to stereoisomerism, but any given enzyme normally only catalyses the reaction between one pair of forms, the other three possibilities being eliminated by its specificity. For a particular reaction, however, there may be enzymes with different stereospecificities (for example the L- and D-lactate dehydrogenases), although not all the four possibilities will in fact be found (all the lactate dehydrogenases known react with the same face of the ring in NAD).

ILLUSTRATIVE EXAMPLES OF ENZYME SPECIFICITY

The amount of information available on enzyme specificity varies greatly from one enzyme to another. The specificity of some enzymes or groups of enzymes has been studied in great detail, while in other cases only a few scattered observations have been made. In a number of cases, although a considerable amount of work on specificity has been published, the enzyme preparations used have been so crude that, unfortunately, the work is not of great value. In still other cases, although much valuable work has been done, the action appears to be limited to one substance only, and therefore little can be added to the information in the table of enzymes.

In this section we shall give tables for a number of enzymes which have been studied in detail, as far as possible including only work with highly purified enzymes. We shall consider the enzymes in the order in which they appear in the Table of Enzymes.

Dehydrogenases

With the exception of a few enzymes of rather wide specificity, such as the alcohol dehydrogenases (1.1.1.1–2), the aldehyde dehydrogenases (1.2.1.3–6), and the acyl-CoA dehydrogenases (1.3.2.1–2) the enzymes in this category are much more highly specific than most of the enzymes which we have discussed hitherto. In many cases only one pair of substrates is known, i.e. one hydrogen donor and one acceptor. In general, these enzymes only act on the pair of substrates shown; where any enzyme has been found to act on other substrates, the fact is mentioned.

The peroxidases, however (sub-group 1.11), are for the most part unspecific with respect to the hydrogen donor, though, of course, they are highly specific with respect to the peroxide grouping.

Glucose oxidase

One of the best studies of specificity which has been carried out with any enzyme is that of KEILIN and HARTREE (*1343–4*) on pure glucose oxidase of *Penicillium* (1.1.3.4). As seen in Table VI.2 the enzyme is highly specific for β-D-glucose. Any alteration whatever in this molecule enormously reduces the rate of oxidation. Of the eight aldo-D-hexoses, only three others (D-mannose, D-altrose and D-galactose) are oxidized at all, and these at extremely low rates. Even the other anomer of D-glucose

TABLE VI.2

SPECIFICITY OF GLUCOSE OXIDASE

Sugar	*Relative rate of oxidation* (β-D-*glucose* = 100)
β-D-glucose	100
2-deoxy-D-glucose	25
6-deoxy-6-fluoro-D-glucose	3
6-methyl-D-glucose	1·85
4,6-dimethyl-D-glucose	1·22
D-mannose	0·98
D-xylose	0·98
α-D-glucose	0·64
Trehalose	0·28
Maltose	0·19
D-altrose	0·16
D-galactose	0·14
Melibiose	0·11
Cellobiose	0·09

The enzyme does not oxidize D-fructose, L-fucose, D-idose, D-talose, L-arabinose, D-allose, D-gulose, D-ribose, L-sorbose, L-rhamnose, D-tagatose, glucoheptose, sucrose, lactose, melizitose, raffinose, D-glucuronate, D-galacturonate, 2-amino-2-deoxy-D-glucose, 2-amino-2-deoxy-D-galactose, 2-methyl-D-glucose, 3-methyl-D-glucose, 2,3-dimethyl-D-glucose, 2,3,6-trimethyl-D-glucose, 2,4,6-trimethyl-D-glucose, 2,3,4,6-tetramethyl-D-glucose, 2,4-dimethyl-α-D-galactose, 4,6-dimethyl-α-D-galactose, 2,4,6-trimethyl-α-D-galactose, 2-methyl-β-D-galactose, 2,6-dimethyl-β-D-galactose, 3,4-dimethyl-β-D-galactose, 3,4,6-trimethyl-D-fructofuranose, α-D-methylglucoside, 2-methyl-α-D-methylglucoside, 2-methyl-β-D-methylglucoside, 2,3-dimethyl-α-D-methylglucoside, 2,3,6-trimethyl-β-D-methylglucoside, 2,3,4,6-tetra-acetyl-D-glucose, penta-acetyl-D-glucose, 3,4,6-triacetyl-2-deoxy-D-glucose, α-D-glucose 1-phosphate, D-glucose 6-phosphate, D-fructose 6-phosphate, D-fructose 1,6-diphosphate. References: *262, 1343–4, 2470.*

(i.e. α-D-glucose) is oxidized 150 times more slowly. Substitution on C_2 (except of –H for –OH) or on C_3 completely abolishes the activity, but the enzyme is slightly less specific as regards C_4 and C_6, since small changes can be made on these positions without complete loss of activity. Thus substitution of –F for –OH in the 6-position reduces the rate to 3 per cent, methylation here reduces it to about 2 per cent, but phosphorylation reduces it to zero. Removal of the –CH_2OH group to form a pentose reduces the rate 100-fold.

The high specificity of this enzyme makes it one of the most useful reagents for the detection and estimation of glucose in biological material.

Methyltransferases

The methyltransferases, like the dehydrogenases, seem to have a rather high specificity for both reactants. Dimethylthetin:L-homocysteine methyltransferase (2.1.1.3) has been studied in some detail by MAW (1763) and by DURELL et al. (660), using partially purified preparations from rat liver and horse liver respectively. As acceptor, only L-homocysteine will act, except for a very slow reaction with the D-isomer. A number of other thiols, including glutathione, cysteine and mercaptoethanol, were inactive, as were homocystine, aminobutyrate, threonine and dimethylglycine.

The best donor is dimethylthetin, $(CH_3)_2\overset{+}{S}.CH_2.COOH$, but a number of methylsulphonium compounds show some activity. One methyl group can be replaced by ethyl (with some loss in activity), but the diethyl compounds are completely inactive, as the enzyme can only transfer methyl groups. Lengthening of the chain between the sulphur atom and the carboxyl group greatly reduces the activity; some activity is obtained with methionine methylsulphonium. Sulphur cannot be replaced by nitrogen. The small activity observed with betaine has been shown (1394) to be due to a separate specific enzyme (2.1.1.5).

Transketolase and transaldolase

Transketolase (2.2.1.1) has a fairly wide specificity, catalysing reactions of the type

VI.4 $R–CHOH–CO–CH_2OH + R'–CHO$
$$= R–CHO + R'–CHOH–CO–CH_2OH$$

where R and R' represent a variety of groups, a glycolaldehyde group being transferred from one substrate to the other. In the earlier work with the crude enzyme it seemed that D-ribulose 5-phosphate could act as a donor, but this was later shown to be due to the presence of the epimerase 5.1.3.1, the actual substrate of the transketolase reaction being D-xylulose 5-phosphate (*1161, 2489*). The following are known (*587*) to act as donors: sedoheptulose 7-phosphate, D-fructose 6-phosphate, D-xylulose 5-phosphate, L-erythrulose, and hydroxypyruvate. Since the above equation is symmetrical, it is only necessary to consider the specificity with respect to the donor. In the case of hydroxypyruvate, the group R with the adjacent hydrogen atom have been replaced by an oxygen atom, so that the reaction becomes

VI.5 $HOOC-CO-CH_2OH+R'-CHO$
$$= CO_2+R'-CHOH-CO-CH_2OH.$$

Thus in the presence of a suitable acceptor aldehyde the enzyme acts as a decarboxylase for this substrate.

Transaldolase (2.2.1.2) catalyses reactions of the type

VI.6 $R-CHOH-CHOH-CO-CH_2OH+R'-CHO$
$$= R-CHO+R'-CHOH-CHOH-CO-CH_2OH$$

a dihydroxyacetone group being transferred in this case. The following are known (*2731*) to act as donors: octulose 8-phosphate, sedoheptulose 7-phosphate, fructose 6-phosphate, fructose, L-sorbose 6-phosphate, and erythrulose.

Glycosyltransferases

Some of the glycosyltransferases in sub-group 2.4 are specific for glycosyl transfer to or from inorganic phosphate (or arsenate). In these cases the reaction can be looked upon as a phosphorolytic cleavage of a glycoside bond (or the reverse) and the enzymes may be described as phosphorylases. Thus the typical phosphorylase reaction is

VI.7 $A-G + P = A + G-P$

where G represents a glycosyl group, P represents phosphate and A the other glycosyl acceptor. Thus the specificity towards both A and G must be considered.

So far as is known, each phosphorylase is highly specific for one particular glycosyl group in the role of G. Thus α-glucan phosphorylase (2.4.1.1) is completely specific for α-D-glucosyl transfer. In the case of maltose phosphorylase (2.4.1.8) the glycosyl group undergoes an inversion during transfer, so that in one direction the enzyme is specific for α-D-glucose and in the other direction for β-D-glucose residues.

With regard to the nature of A, there is also a fairly high degree of specificity, although this is not absolute. Thus, for the α-glucan phosphorylase of potato, A must be a polysaccharide chain of at least four glucose units, although very slight activity can be detected with three (*134, 775, 2816*). The glucosyl group is transferred only to the 4-position of the non-reducing terminal unit. For good activity all the links in the chain must be 1,4-α-glucoside links; lichenin (containing 1,4-β-glucoside links) and dextran (containing 1,6-α-glucoside links) are not acted upon (*2816*), and glycogen is acted on much more slowly and less completely than by the animal enzyme (*1582*). Branched dextrins derived from amylopectin and containing one or two 1,6-α-glucoside links instead of 1,4-α-glucoside links, may be actually inhibitory (*775*). Dextrins of four or more units containing a phosphate group on the 6-position of the second or third glucose residue can act, but the presence of this phosphate group reduces the activity to one-fifth (*2108*).

The muscle α-glucan phosphorylase differs significantly from the potato enzyme in that it does not act with these small straight-chain dextrins and works best with larger branched molecules. In the phosphorolysis it acts much more rapidly on amylopectin or glycogen than on amylose, and in the reverse direction it can act with the limit dextrin produced from amylopectin or glycogen by the phosphorolysis, though not with the limit dextrin produced by β-amylase, which contains four fewer glucose residues in the main chain (*503, 1089*). In other words, this phosphorylase is unable to act within five glucose units of the branching point in the main chain, although it can degrade the side chain down to the unit attached by the 1,6-link. This difference in specificity towards the main and side chains is somewhat surprising.

The specificity is somewhat influenced by the size of the substrate molecule, the liver enzyme working best with smaller glycogen molecules than the muscle enzyme (*2527*).

Sucrose glucosyltransferase (2.4.1.7) may catalyse reactions involving inorganic phosphate, and was originally regarded as a phosphorylase, but unlike the true phosphorylases it can catalyse transglucosylations from one sugar to another, without involving phosphate at all. Its specificity has been studied in detail by HASSID and DOUDOROFF (*1022*). It transfers only α-D-glucosyl groups and does not act with α-L-glucosyl, α-D-mannosyl, α-D-galactosyl, α-D-xylosyl or melibiosyl radicals. The α-D-glucosyl group can be transferred to phosphate, arsenate, D-fructose, L-sorbose, D-xylulose, L-arabinulose or L-arabinose, but not to L-fructose, D-tagatose, D-fructose-6-phosphate, D-fructose-1,6-diphosphate, D-mannoheptulose, D-glucose, D-mannose, D-galactose, L-rhamnose, L-fucose, D-xylose, D-lyxose, D-arabinose, L-xylulose, D-arabinulose, erythrulose, dihydroxyacetone or turanose. Of the five sugars which act as acceptors, the four ketoses produce non-reducing disaccharides, namely, the β-D-fructofuranoside, the α-L-sorbofuranoside, the

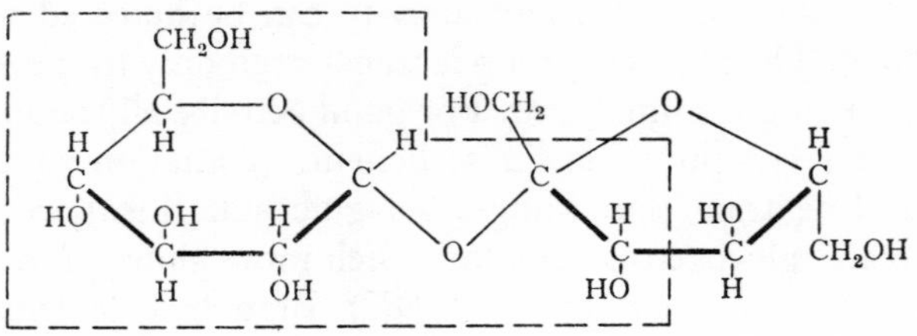

Sucrose

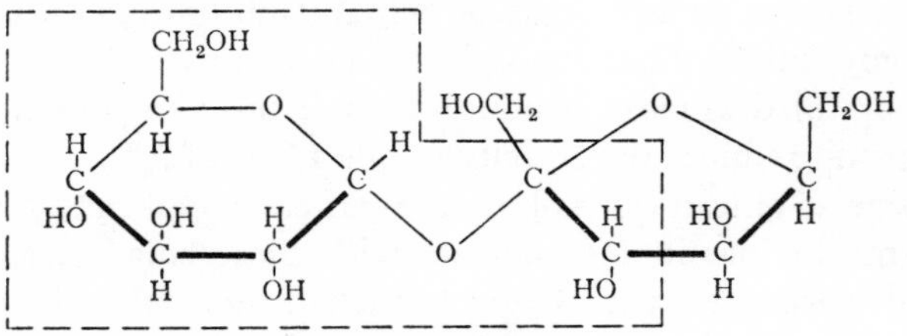

α-D-glucosyl-α-L-sorbofuranoside

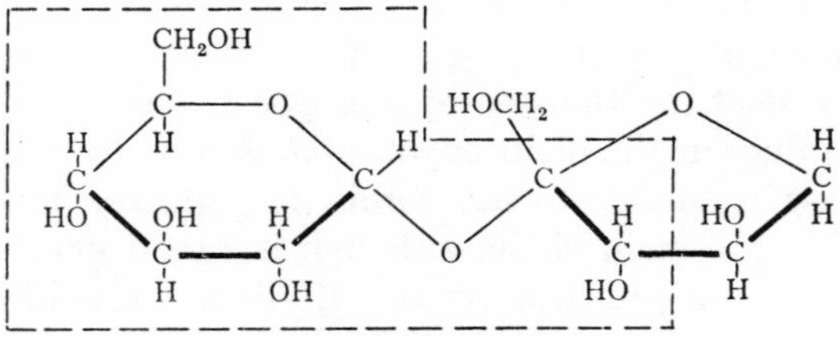

α-D-glucosyl-β-D-xylulofuranoside

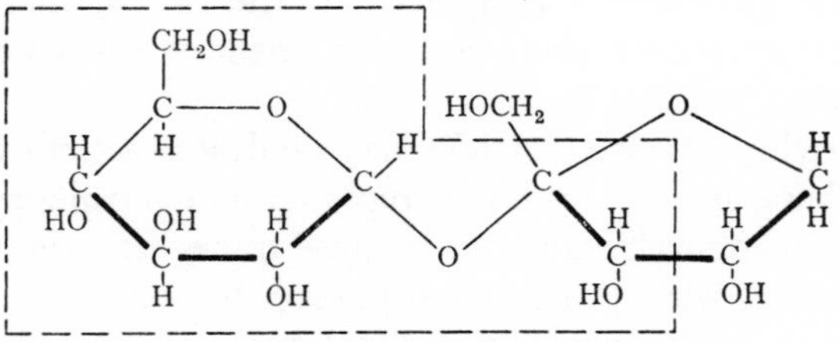

α-D-glucosyl-α-L-arabinulofuranoside

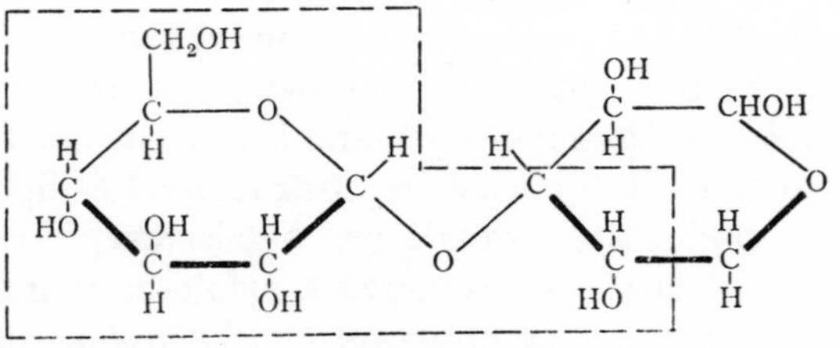

3-(α-D-glucosyl)-L-arabinose

Fig. VI.2. *Products of the sucrose glucosyltransferase reaction.*

β-D-xylulofuranoside and the α-L-arabinulofuranoside respectively, but on the other hand the L-arabinose has the glucosyl residue transferred to its 3-position, giving a reducing disaccharide, 3-(α-D-glucopyranosyl)-L-arabinopyranose. This result becomes less surprising on consideration of Fig. VI.2, which shows that all the five disaccharides have the common structure within the dotted line (*879*).

Phosphotransferases

Kinases

Here, as with the dehydrogenases, we have a series of enzymes for which the specificities with respect to donor and acceptor have to be considered separately, but in this case the donor and acceptor are for phosphate and not for hydrogen. In general, they are even more specific than the dehydrogenases, and this specificity applies to both donor and acceptor. For instance, creatine kinase (2.7.3.2) has been studied by KUBY *et al.* (*1480*), who showed that creatine cannot be replaced by creatinine, L-arginine, D-arginine or L-histidine; ATP cannot be replaced by ADP, adenosine 2'-phosphate, adenosine 3'-phosphate, adenosine 5'-phosphate or ITP; and ADP cannot be replaced in the reverse reaction by ATP. This is typical of the kinases, although in one or two cases other nucleoside triphosphates can replace ATP, for example, with phosphofructokinase (2.7.1.11) and pyruvate kinase (2.7.1.40).

The specificity of three hexokinases have been investigated in some detail, and the results are shown in Table VI.3. This shows for each enzyme the maximum velocity for each substrate (relative to that for D-glucose) and also the affinity for each substance (relative to that for D-glucose), based on the assumption that the reciprocal of K_m is a measure of the affinity. Where the velocity is zero or very small, the affinity is based on measurements of K_i with fructose as substrate. The actual values of K_m for glucose were $1 \cdot 0 \times 10^{-4}$M for the yeast enzyme, $8 \cdot 0 \times 10^{-6}$M for the brain enzyme, and $1 \cdot 6 \times 10^{-4}$M for the *Aspergillus* enzyme.

It will be seen that the crystalline yeast enzyme is capable of phosphorylating a number of different sugars. The α- and β-forms of D-glucose and D-mannose both react at about the same speed, without undergoing preliminary interconversion; D-fructose reacts only in the β-furanose form (*876–8*). As well as the substances shown in the table, the yeast enzyme can phosphorylate 2,5-anhydro-D-mannitol (*366*). These facts show that the enzyme is specific for the 3,4,5,6-region of the molecule but not for the 1,2-part, provided that no large groups are attached thereto (see Fig. VI.3, based on *879*).

TABLE VI.3

SPECIFICITY OF HEXOKINASES

	Yeast		Brain		Aspergillus	
	Relative affinity	Relative maximum velocity	Relative affinity	Relative maximum velocity	Relative affinity	Relative maximum velocity
D-glucose	1·0	1·0	1·0	1·0	1·0	1·0
D-fructose	0·14	1·8	0·0005	1·5		0·28
D-mannose	2·0	0·8	1·6	0·4		0·64
2-amino-2-deoxy-D-glucose	0·07	0·7	0·1	0·6	0·47	0·55
D-galactose	<0·002	0	0·0001	0·02	0·75	0·88
2-amino-2-deoxy-D-galactose					0·37	0·41
2-deoxy-D-glucose	0·33	1·0	0·3	1·0		
L-sorbose	0	0	0	1·0		0·02
1,5-sorbitan	0·03	0·01	0·0003	0·9		
1,5-mannitan			0·0004	0·1		
D-arabinose	<0·001	0	0·000004	0·5		0·04
D-allose	<0·001	<0·1	0·001	0·08		
D-glucosone	5·0	0·2	0·8	0·2		
3-deoxy-D-glucose			0·0005	0·11		
D-altrose			0·003	0·08		
2,5-sorbitan			0·00006	0		
D-xylose	0·01	0	0·004	0		
D-lyxose			0·006	0		
6-deoxy-D-glucose			0·004	0·01		
D-mannoheptulose	0·67	0	0·16	0·01		
D-glucoheptulose			0·04	0		
2-acetylamino-2-deoxy-D-glucose	0·1	0	0·1	0		
2-methylamino-2-deoxy-D-glucose			0·04			
References:	218 1493 2471		2469		548	

The following are inactive: (yeast) α-methylglucoside, 1-methylglucoside, 1-methylfructose, 3-methylglucose, 3-methylfructose, sorbitol, L-rhamnose, sucrose, lactose, maltose, trehalose, raffinose; (brain) α- and β-methylglucosides, 2-methylglucose, 3-methylglucose, sorbitol, α-glucose 1-phosphate, glucono-δ-lactone, D-ribose.

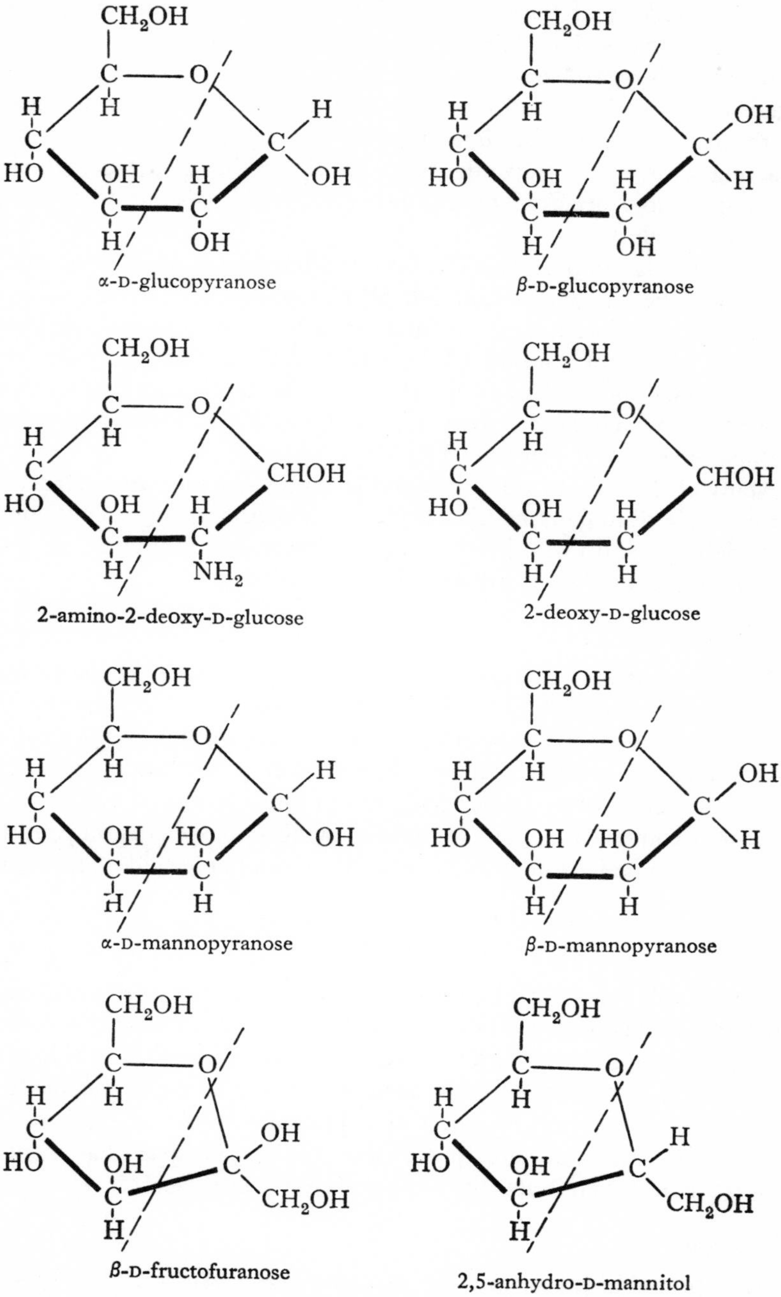

Fig. VI.3. *Substrates of yeast hexokinase.*

The specificity of the other two hexokinases is broadly similar, but there are some striking differences. The brain enzyme is much less exacting with regard to substitution on C_5, as shown by the high rate of attack on 1,5-sorbitan and 1,5-mannitan, which are only slowly attacked by the yeast enzyme. The *Aspergillus* enzyme, on the other hand, is non-exacting with regard to configuration at C_4, so that galactose, which is not appreciably attacked by the other enzymes, is almost as good a substrate as glucose.

Phosphorylation of hexoses in liver and bacteria appears to be due to more specific enzymes. Glucose is phosphorylated by glucokinase (2.7.1.2) which does not act on fructose; fructose instead is phosphorylated by ketohexokinase (2.7.1.3), which differs from the other two enzymes mentioned in phosphorylating at the 1-position instead of the 6-position, which is also true of rhamnulokinase, galactokinase and arabinokinase (2.7.1.5–6 and d).

Many of the kinases are quite specific for a particular sugar structure, for example ribulokinase (2.7.1.16) from *Aerobacter aerogenes* only phosphorylates D- and L-ribulose and, more slowly, adonitol and L-arabitol, out of a large number of substances tested (*2406*).

Phosphomutases

Phosphomutases are very specific enzymes. In an extensive study of phosphoglyceromutase (2.7.5.3) PIZER and BALLOU (*2091*) showed that only 2,3-diphospho-D-glycerate and 2,3-diphospho-D-*erythro*-dihydroxy butyrate acted as donors, while of twenty substances tested only those containing two adjacent hydroxyl groups capable of assuming the D-*erythro*-configuration, one of these carrying a phosphate group, and an adjacent terminal acidic group (carboxyl or sulphonic acid), could act as acceptors.

Esterases

The simple esterases and lipases are concerned with the hydrolysis of uncharged substrates, and here the main factors influencing the specificity are the lengths and shapes of the hydrocarbon chains on either side of the ester link. The classical division into esterases and lipases was based on an assumed preference for short or long chains in the acyl groups, but we have shown elsewhere (p. 92) that pancreatic lipase has a special requirement in that it acts only at an oil–water interface.

Carboxylesterases

It is probable that a number of carboxylesterases (3.1.1.1) exist, of somewhat varying but wide specificities. The specificity of purified horse

TABLE VI.4

SPECIFICITY OF CARBOXYLESTERASE FROM HORSE LIVER

	$-O.CH_3$	$-O.C_2H_5$	$-O.C_3H_7$	$-O.C_4H_9$	$-O.C_5H_{11}$	$-O.C_6H_{13}$	$-O.C_7H_{15}$	$-O.C_8H_{17}$
$H.CO-$	1.0 / 0.2							
$CH_3.CO-$	0.26 / 0.02	0.07 / 0.28	0.12 / 1.55	0.28 / 3.1	0.18 / 1.1	0.45 / 0.87	0.3 / 2.5	0.13 / 1.8
$C_2H_5.CO-$	1.28 / 0.025	0.46 / 0.43		2.0 / 4.7	1.5 / 2.2			
$C_3H_7.CO-$	2.0 / 0.46	1 / 1	2.0 / 0.93	4.5 / 2.9	3.5 / 6.7	2.5 / 11.7	1.1 / 5.3	
$C_4H_9.CO-$	1.85 / 1.1	1.04 / 2.3		3.2 / 3.3				
$C_5H_{11}.CO-$	2.35 / 1.18	0.6 / 2.2		1.7 / 4.2		0.32 / 2.5		
$C_6H_{13}.CO-$	1.75 / 1.3	0.92 / 4.0						
$C_7H_{15}.CO-$	1.25 / 2.85	0.8 / 3.4						
$C_8H_{17}.CO-$	1.05 / 10.0							
$C_9H_{19}.CO-$	0.36 / 22.0							

Explanation of table: The left-hand column shows the acyl group and the top row the alkyl group of the straight-chain esters tested. For each ester the upper figure shows the maximum velocity and the lower figure the affinity, both in relation to those for ethyl n-butyrate taken as unity. The affinity is taken as the reciprocal of K_m.

liver carboxylesterase has recently been studied in detail (WEBB, *2807*). The enzyme attacks both aliphatic and aromatic neutral esters, so that the old name 'ali-esterase' was incorrect. Results for some straight-chain esters are shown in Table VI.4.

The effects of changes in the acyl and alkyl parts of the substrate molecule are largely independent. Taking the acyl group first, the affinity and reactivity increase together up to a chain length of 4 to 6 carbon atoms; further increase in length causes a fall in reactivity, but a sharp rise in affinity. In the case of the alkyl group there is a similar

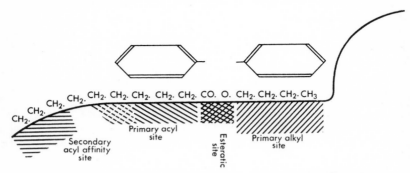

Fig. VI.4. *Possible configuration of active centre of carboxylesterase.*
from *2807*

increase of affinity and reactivity to a maximum with 4 to 6 carbon atoms; but a further increase of chain length produces a fall in both affinity and reactivity. With the smaller esters the alkyl group has a much greater effect on the affinity than the acyl group, while the reverse is true for the reactivity. The effect of branching in the chains has been studied, and in general it produces a considerable increase in affinity but some decrease in reactivity. The best substrates contain non-polar groups at both ends of the molecule.

Fig. VI.4 shows a schematic diagram of a possible configuration of the active centre of carboxylesterase which might account for these facts. Although the esteratic site binds the ester grouping and therefore locates the molecule, its binding power is less than that of the acyl and alkyl sites. As the latter combine with non-polar chains, van der Waals forces must play the main part in enzyme-substrate binding. The width of the shading is intended to give a qualitative indication of the magnitude of the forces at the different sites. The alkyl group is shown constricted, being filled by a n-butyl chain or a phenyl ring. On the acyl side a secondary acyl site is shown which strongly increases the binding, but decreases the reactivity by interfering with the orientation at the esteratic site.

Cholinesterases

It has been known since the work of MENDEL and his colleagues in 1943 (*1794–5*) that these enzymes are of two types, which we have shown in the list as 'acetylcholinesterase' (3.1.1.7) and 'cholinesterase' (3.1.1.8); these were formerly known by the rather unsatisfactory names 'true cholinesterase' and 'pseudo-cholinesterase' respectively. Acetylcholinesterase is the predominant acetylcholine-decomposing enzyme of nervous tissue and the erythrocytes of most species, whereas cholinesterase predominates in the blood plasma of most species (see the review by AUGUSTINSSON (*97*) and the survey by ORD and THOMPSON (*2031*)).

The cholinesterases have not been highly purified, apart from the horse-serum enzyme, which has been purified 6,000 times, but which has not been used in this state of purity for any extensive specificity studies. When tested with a number of esters, crude preparations from different sources show different specificity patterns. It is not clear whether this is to be interpreted as due to variants of the enzymes themselves, or as due to mixtures of more than two enzymes in various proportions. The investigation of the specificity of these enzymes is made more difficult by the fact that many of the esters are almost insoluble in water, so that it is impossible to study the different substrates under comparable conditions, or to obtain V in these cases. Moreover, the standard substrate, acetylcholine, shows a very marked high-substrate inhibition, in the case of acetylcholinesterase only, which is not shown by other substrates. Thus, it is difficult to determine for this enzyme a reference value with which the other rates can be compared. In view of these difficulties it is not surprising that the literature and nomenclature of these enzymes is very confused.

An investigation of the specificity of the acetylcholinesterase of human erythrocytes and the cholinesterase of human plasma was made by ADAMS (*5*) and ADAMS and WHITTAKER (*6*), and although they did not purify the enzymes to any considerable extent, they did show that their preparations were free from carboxylesterase which is present in blood, and also, by means of mixed-substrate and inhibitor experiments, that the reactions were in the main due to a single enzyme in each preparation. Each enzyme was found to hydrolyse both choline and non-choline esters. On varying the nature of the acyl group attached to choline they found that with acetylcholinesterase the rate decreased sharply with increase of chain length, butyrylcholine being hydrolysed at only one or two per cent of the rate with acetylcholine; with the cholinesterase, on the other hand, the reverse effect was found, and butyrylcholine was hydrolysed twice as fast as acetylcholine. The enzyme from houseflies, although regarded as an acetylcholinesterase, is intermediate in properties, the rate with butyrylcholine being 50 per cent of that with acetylcholine (541). MYERS (1908) has found that the cholinesterases of a number of different species show a similar increase of activity with chain length, the order with choline esters being butyryl > propionyl > acetyl; but in some other species the order is propionyl > butyryl > acetyl, butyryl > acetyl > propionyl (100) or even propionyl > acetyl > butyryl.

With normal non-choline aliphatic esters, Adams and Whittaker studied the effects of variations of chain length in the acyl and alkyl parts of the molecule independently. With variation of the length of the alkyl chain, using acetates throughout, the effects are generally similar with both cholinesterases, showing an optimum with butyl acetate. Similar results were obtained with other series. However, when the size of the acyl group is varied, keeping the alkyl chain constant, a striking difference is seen between the two cholinesterases, the acetylcholinesterase showing a sharp optimum with the 2-carbon acyl group (acetate) and falling to zero with butyrate, whereas the cholinesterase shows a fairly sharp optimum for butyrate.

Many facts suggest that both cholinesterases have a special affinity for methyl groups, hence branching of the alkyl chain (except at the carbon atom next to the ester group) increases the susceptibility of esters. The optimum alkyl group in both cases appears to be 3,3-dimethyl-butyl, which is in fact a carbon analogue of choline:

$$CH_3 \; CO.O.CH_2.CH_2.\overset{+}{N}{\overset{\displaystyle CH_3}{\underset{\displaystyle CH_3}{-CH_3}}} \qquad CH_3.CO.O.CH_2.CH_2.C{\overset{\displaystyle CH_3}{\underset{\displaystyle CH_3}{-CH_3}}}$$

Acetylcholine   3,3-dimethyl-butyl acetate

It is interesting that the charged nitrogen atom of choline is not essential for either enzyme, and the shape of the molecule is clearly one of the most important factors. However, the cholinesterase is more specific for the choline structure than the acetylcholinesterase. Thus the carbon analogue is hydrolysed by acetylcholinesterase at 60 per cent of the acetylcholine rate, but by cholinesterase at only 35 per cent of the rate.

The cholinesterases, like carboxylesterase, can hydrolyse aromatic as well as aliphatic esters, often quite rapidly. For example, with a purified acetylcholinesterase from the electric eel the relative rates of attack on acetylcholine:phenyl acetate:p-methoxyphenyl acetate:p-nitrophenyl acetate are as $1:2\cdot4:0\cdot85:0\cdot1$ (225).

ORMEROD (2033) studied the effect of a series of substituents in the ring of benzoylcholine on the rate (V) of its hydrolysis by horse-serum cholinesterase, and found that there was a correlation between V and the electron-attracting power of the substituent group (Fig. VI.5). Non-enzymatic hydrolysis by alkali was similarly affected. This effect is evidently not connected with the shape of the substrate molecule, but with the reactivity of the ester linkage. Similar effects have been found with the glycosidases.

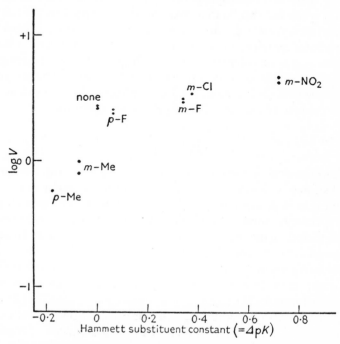

Fig. VI.5. *Effect of substituents in the ring of benzoylcholine on its maximum rate of hydrolysis by cholinesterase.*

Log V is plotted against the 'Hammett constant', which is the change of pK of benzoic acid produced on substitution by the group in question (see *988*, p. 186).

after *2033*

Phosphatases

Both specific and unspecific phosphatases exist. Acid and alkaline phosphatases (3.1.3.1–2) both act on a wide range of monoesters of orthophosphoric acid, although they have no effect on pyrophosphates, metaphosphates or phosphoric diesters such as diphenyl phosphate (*815, 1496, 1875*). The purified alkaline phosphatases from intestinal mucosa and *Esch. coli* are very similar in specificity pattern, except that the animal enzyme, but not the bacterial one, will hydrolyse the amidophosphate link of creatine phosphate.

In a detailed study of the specificity of the acid phosphatase of *Neurospora*, it was found (*1496*) that the presence of a polar group close to the phosphate ester link had an inhibitory effect. When a free amino group and a phosphomonoester group are attached to adjacent carbon atoms, as in the case of O-phosphoserine or O-phosphoethanolamine, no hydrolysis whatever can be detected. However, separation of the polar and phosphomonoester groups by three or more carbon atoms completely restores activity; for example 2-amino-2-deoxyglucose 6-phosphate is an excellent substrate, whereas the 1-phosphate is completely inert. The effect of the amino group can be partly abolished by acetylation, and 2-acetylamino-2-deoxyglucose 1-phosphate is hydrolysed at about a sixth of the rate of 2-amino-2-deoxyglucose 6-phosphate.

Glycosidases

This large and important group of enzymes is concerned in the main with substrates which have no charged groups. Furthermore, all the determining groups are either hydroxyl groups or hydrogen atoms, so that the specificity must be determined by the pattern in which these are arranged, including the configuration of each –CHOH– group. In general, the enzymes are each specific for a particular monosaccharide ring, but the attached aglycone group may have a more or less marked influence, and in some cases (e.g. nucleosidases) the enzyme may be as specific for the aglycone as for the sugar. For example, inosinase (3.2.2.2), which hydrolyses ribosyl-hypoxanthine, will not act on ribosyl-xanthine.

A good deal of work has been done with the less specific glycosidases, such as 3.2.1.20–26, but it is unfortunate that most of this work has been done with impure enzymes, and it is difficult to know whether the results were due to single enzymes or mixtures of enzymes. Most of this work will be found in reviews by HELFERICH (*1056*), PIGMAN (*2087*) and GOTTSCHALK (*879*). In general, the interchange of hydrogen and hydroxyl on any single carbon atom of a glycoside substrate is sufficient to prevent the action of the corresponding enzyme; for example, β-glucosidase does not act on β-D-mannosides, and probably not on β-D-galactosides, nor does it act on α-D-glucosides. In the case of the epimers involving carbon atoms 1, 2 and 4 of the aldohexose ring, separate enzymes exist for each structure. Thus we have α- and β-glucosidases, α- and β-galactosidases and α- and β-mannosidases.

Substitution on the hydroxyl groups of the sugar usually has a profound effect; with β-glucosidase any substitution on carbon atoms 2, 3 or

4 completely prevents hydrolysis. Substitution on carbon atom 6 lowers the rate of hydrolysis, the effect increasing with the volume of the substituent group. Replacement of the $-CH_2OH$ group attached to C_5 by $-H$, i.e. conversion to a β-D-xyloside, produces a 200-fold reduction in rate. Thus, in general, an intact unsubstituted hexose ring is required.

The nature of the aglycone has a considerable influence on the rate of hydrolysis. Most of the available data are expressed in terms of 'enzyme efficiencies', which are essentially v_0 (but see *987*). Thus the variations found might be due to the effect of the aglycone structure on either K_s or V. Here it appears that the electron-attracting power of the group, rather than its size, is the operative factor (*1928*).

Peptidases

It was at one time considered that the specificity of proteolytic enzymes was largely related to the molecular size of the substrate, and that these enzymes could be divided into proteinases and peptidases. The availability of a large number of synthetic peptides, however, has shown that this distinction was unreal, since proteinases are in fact capable of hydrolysing very small peptides of suitable structure. This has brought about a revolution in the subject, mainly due to BERGMANN. It is now clear that the determining factor is not the size of the substrate molecule, but the nature of the aminoacid side-chains and other groups in the neighbourhood of the bond which undergoes hydrolysis. Each enzyme, in fact, has fairly strict requirements and will hydrolyse only those peptide bonds in proteins which satisfy these requirements. Table VI.5 shows the action of eleven crystalline or highly purified peptidases on some 400 synthetic peptides and related compounds. The results have been collected from a large number of papers, and although in many cases the data are given quantitatively in terms of either 'proteolytic coefficient' or maximum velocity, it is not possible to express them all in comparative figures, owing to the fact that different enzyme preparations and conditions were chosen by different authors. We have therefore expressed the results semi-quantitatively in terms of a scale of plus signs. As the range of velocities observed is very great, the scale may be thought of as a logarithmic rather than a linear one.

A good deal of the earlier work with synthetic peptides was done with crude mixtures of peptidases; this is difficult to interpret and has been omitted. The results for the first six enzymes in the table relate to crystalline preparations; the others were obtained with highly purified preparations which were apparently free from other peptidases.

The abbreviations used in the table are explained on p. 239.

I

TABLE VI.5

SPECIFICITY OF SOME PEPTIDASES

#	Substrate	Pepsin (3.4.4.1)	Trypsin (3.4.4.4)	Chymotrypsin (3.4.4.5)	Cathepsin C (3.4.4.9)	Papain (3.4.4.10)	Carboxypeptidase A (3.4.2.1)	Leucine amino-peptidase (3.4.1.1)	Aminotripep-tidase (3.4.1.3)	Glycyl-glycine dipeptidase (3.4.3.1)	Iminodipeptidase (3.4.3.6)	Imidodipeptidase (3.4.3.7)
1	Form-Phe						○					
2	Ac-Gly		○	○			○					
3	Ac-Phe		○	○			○					
4	Ac-Try						○					
5	ClAc-Leu	○					○					
6	ClAc-Phe						+					
7	ClAc-Tyr						+					
8	ClAc-NMeTyr						○					
9	ClAc-Try						+					
10	Bz-Phe						○					
11	Bz-Tyr						○					
12	CB-Phe						○					
13	CB-Tyr						±					
14	CB-Try						○					
15	PhPyr-Gly						±					
16	PhPyr-Leu					○	±	±		○		
17	PhPyr-Phe						+					
18	PhPyr-Glu						±					
19	Gly-NH₂			○		±						
20	Ac-Gly-NH₂			○								
21	Bz-Gly-NH₂			○								
22	Nic-Gly-NH₂			○								
23	Ac-Gly-OMe			+								
24	Bz-Gly-OMe			+								
25	Gly-OEt											
26	Bz-Gly-Oβphenyllact		○	○		±	+	+	±	○		
27	Gly-Gly						+			+		
28	Bz-Gly-Gly		○				+			+		
29	CB-Gly-Gly						+			○		○
	Me │						○			○		
30	Gly-Gly		○				±			○		+

31 Me — CB-Gly-Gly		o	o			o			+ + o o + + +	o o + + +	
32 CB-Gly-dlAla											
33 CB-Gly-Ala									+ +		
34 Gly-βAla		o ++	o						+ +		+ + o
35 Gly-dlVal											
36 CB-Gly-AmiB			++			o		++			
37 Gly-Leu											
38 CB-Gly-Leu											
39 CB-Gly-dLeu											
40 CB-Gly-Ileu											
41 CB-Gly-Met		++	++		o	+	c	+	++		
42 CB-Gly-dMet											
43 Bz-Gly-PhGly											
44 Gly-dlPhe											
45 Bz-Gly-Phe		o ++	++ ++ o+ +o+ ++ o ++o +++	o+ +o+	+++ +++ o++o +++ +++	o			+ +o ++o	++ o	o
46 CB-Gly-Phe											
47 CB-Gly-dPhe											
48 Bzs-Gly-dPhe											
49 CB-Gly-dehydroPhe											
50 Gly-Tyr		o		o		o		o			
51 CB-Gly-Tyr											
52 Gly-Pro											
53 Gly-dPro											
54 Gly-Hypro											
55 CB-Gly-Hypro		o		o	o		o		o	o	o
56 CB-Gly-Hypro Me											
57 Gly-Hypro		o			o		o		o		o
58 Gly-alloHypro											
59 Gly-Try											
60 CB-Gly-Try				++							
61 CB-Gly-dTry											
62 Gly-His											
63 CB-Gly-His											
64 Bz-Gly-Lys CB											
65 Bz-Gly-Lys											
66 Gly-Asp											
67 CB-Gly-Glu											
68 Me — Gly-Gly											
69 Me2 — Gly-Gly											
70 Bz-PhGly-OEt											

	Pepsin (3.4.4.1)	Trypsin (3.4.4.4)	Chymotrypsin (3.4.4.5)	Cathepsin C (3.4.4.9)	Papain (3.4.4.10)	Carboxypeptidase A (3.4.2.1)	Leucine aminopeptidase (3.4.1.1)	Aminotripeptidase (3.4.1.3)	Glycyl-glycine dipeptidase (3.4.3.1)	Iminodipeptidase (3.4.3.6)	Imidodipeptidase (3.4.3.7)
71 Ala-NH₂			o				+		o		o
72 Bz-Ala-NH₂							+				
73 Ala-Gly							+				o
74 Ala-Leu							+				
75 CB-Ala-Phe						+	+				
76 CB-Ala-Tyr						+					
77 βAla-Gly						+	o		o		
78 βAla-βAla						+			o		
79 βAla-Pro						+	+				
80 βAla-His						+	+				
81 DlαAmB-NH₂							o				o
82 αAmiB-NH₂							+				
83 Val-NH₂							+		o		o
84 DlNorval-NH₂							o				
85 Bz-Norval-OEt		o	+				+				
86 Leu-NH₂					+		+	+			
87 DLeu-NH₂					o		o				
88 Bz-DLeu-NH₂			o		+		+				
89 CB-Leu-NH₂		o	o			o	+				
90 Leu-NHnaph	o	o	o		o		+	+			
91 Leu-Gly							+				
92 Bz-Leu-Gly							o				
93 DLeu-Gly							+				
94 Leu-Ala							+				
95 Leu-DAla							o				
96 Leu-βAla							+				
97 Leu-Val							+				
98 Leu-DVal							+				
99 Leu-Leu		o	o				+				
100 Leu-DLeu							+				
101 Leu-Ileu							+				
102 Leu-DIleu							+				
103 Leu-Phe							+				
104 Leu-DPhe							+				
105 Leu-Tyr		o					+				

										+

No.	Substrate									
106	DLeu-Tyr			0						0
107	Ileu-NH₂			+	+					
108	alloIleu-NH₂			+						
109	DLNorleu-NH₂			+	++					
110	Bz-Norleu-OEt			+	+					
111	DLTerleu-NH₂									
112	DLαAmCapr-NH₂									
113	Ser-NH₂				0 0					
114	CB-Ser-NH₂									
115	Bz-DLSer-OEt									
116	Ac-DLThr-OEt				0 0					
117	Bz-DLThr-OEt									
118	CySH-Tyr									
119	CB-CySH-Tyr									
120	Bz / CB-CyS-Tyr									
121	Nic-Met-NH₂			+	0 +					
122	Bz-Met-OEt			+	+					
123	CB-Met-Met			+						
124	Met-Tyr									
125	CB-Met-Tyr									
126	Phe-NH₂						+H			
127	Ac-Phe-NH₂					+	+++			
128	Nic-Phe-NH₂					+	+++			
129	Nic-Phe-NHnaph					+				
130	Ac-Phe-NHOH									
131	Bz-Phe-NHOH							++		
132	Bz-Phe-OMe							++		
133	Phe-OEt							+		
134	Ac-Phe-SEt							++		
135	Ac-Phe-OEt							+		
136	Bz-Phe-OEt							+ +		
137	Phth-DLPhe- OMe							0 +		
138	Ac-Phe-OβNaph							+ + 0		
139	Phth-Phe-OβNaph							+ +		
140	Nic-Phe-OpAnisidide							0		
141	Ac-Phe-Gly				+ +					+ +
142	Ac-Phe-Phe				+ +					+ 0
143	Ac-DPhe-Tyr				+ +					+
144	I₂ / Ac-DPhe-Tyr				+					0
145	Phe-Hypro									

	Pepsin (3.4.4.1)	Trypsin (3.4.4.4)	Chymotrypsin (3.4.4.5)	Cathepsin C (3.4.4.9)	Papain (3.4.4.10)	Carboxypeptidase A (3.4.2.1)	Leucine amino-peptidase (3.4.1.1)	Aminotripep-tidase (3.4.1.3)	Glycyl-glycine dipeptidase (3.4.3.1)	Iminodipeptidase (3.4.3.6)	Imidodipeptidase (3.4.3.7)
146 CB-Phe-Glu	+		±			±					
147 Bz-dehydroPhe-NH₂			o			o					o
148 Ac-dehydroPhe-OEt											
149 Ac-dehydroPhe-Leu											
150 Ac-dehydroPhe-Phe											
151 DehydroPhe-Pro		o	+		o						
152 Ac-hexahydroPhe-NH₂			±								
153 Tyr-NH₂			+				+				
154 Form-Tyr-NH₂							+				
155 Ac-Tyr-NH₂			+				o				
156 ClAc-Tyr-NH₂		o	+								
157 F-Ac-Tyr-NH₂			+								
158 Bz-Tyr-NH₂			+								
159 Nic-Tyr-NH₂			+								
160 iNic-Tyr-NH₂			+								
161 Tyr-NHOH	+	±	+								
162 Ac-Tyr-NHOH	+	+	+								
163 Nic-Tyr-NHNH₂	+		+								
164 Tyr-OEt	+		+								
165 Ac-Tyr-OEt	+		+								
166 Bz-Tyr-OEt			+								
167 oNO₂			+								
168 Bz-Tyr-OEt			o								
169 CB-Tyr-Gly			+								
170 Tyr-CySH / CB-Tyr-CySH			+								
171 CB-Tyr-Phe			+								
172 Ac	/ CB-Tyr-Phe											
173 CB-Tyr-Phe	+					±					
174 Tyr-Tyr	+										
175 Ac-Tyr-Tyr	+										
176 Tyr-Arg	+					±					
177 Bz-dehydroTyr-NH₂	+		±			±					
178 Ac-dehydroTyr-Tyr	+										

No.	Compound
179	Pro-NH₂
180	Pro-Gly
181	Pro-Tyr
182	Pro-Pro
183	CB-Pro-Pro
184	Pro-Hypro
185	Pro-Asp
186	Hypro-NH₂
187	Hypro-Gly
188	Hypro-Ala
189	Hypro-Leu
190	Hypro-Phe
191	Hypro-Tyr
192	Hypro-Asp
193	Hypro-Glu
194	alloHypro-Gly
195	Me–Hypro-Gly
196	Try-NH₂
197	Ac-Try-NH₂
198	Nic-Try-NH₂
199	Ac-Try-OEt
200	CB-Try-Gly
201	CB-D-Try-Gly
202	CB-Try-Ala
203	CB-Try-Tyr
204	CB-Try-Pro
205	CB-Try-Try
206	His-NH₂
207	Bz-His-NH₂
208	CB-His-NH₂
209	Nic-His-NH₂
210	His-Gly
211	CB-His-Gly
212	CB-His-Phe
213	CB-His-Tyr
214	Arg-NH₂
215	Bz-Arg-NH₂
216	Ts-Arg-NH₂
217	CB–Bz-Arg-NH₂–NO₂
218	CB-Arg-NH₂

		Pepsin (3.4.4.1)	Trypsin (3.4.4.4)	Chymotrypsin (3.4.4.5)	Cathepsin C (3.4.4.9)	Papain (3.4.4.10)	Carboxypeptidase A (3.4.2.1)	Leucine aminopeptidase (3.4.1.1)	Aminotripeptidase (3.4.1.3)	Glycyl-glycine dipeptidase (3.4.3.1)	Iminodipeptidase (3.4.3.6)	Iminodipeptidase (3.4.3.7)
219	Bz-Arg-OMe		+	+		+	0					
220	Ts-Arg-OMe		+			+						
221	Bz-Arg-OEt		+	+		+						
222	Ts-Arg-OEt		+	+		+						
223	Arg-Gly		+			0						
224	Arg-Leu		+			0						
	NO$_2$					+						
225	CB-Arg-Leu		+			+						
226	Arg-Phe		0			+						
	NO$_2$					0						
227	CB-Arg-Phe		+			+						
228	Arg-Glu		+			+						
229	Lys-NH$_2$		+			0						
230	Bz-Lys-NH$_2$		+					+				
231	CB—Lys-NH$_2$ CB		0									
232	Bz-Lys-NH$_2$		+									
233	Lys-OEt CB		+			0						
234	Lys-OMe		0									
235	Bz-Lys-Lys		0									
236	NH$_2$ Asp-NH$_2$							+				
237	Glu-NH$_2$		0					+				
238	Bz-Glu-NH$_2$		0			+						
239	CB-Glu-NH$_2$ NH$_2$					+						
240	CB-Glu-NH$_2$					+						

No.	Substrate										
241	CB-Glu-Gly								++		0
242	CB-Glu-Met										+0
243	CB-Glu-Phe										+
244	CB-Glu-DPhe NH₂										
245	CB-Glu-Phe					+	++	0		±+0+	
246	Glu-Tyr										
247	CB-Glu-Tyr							0			+0
248	CB-DGlu-Tyr I₂										0
249	CB-Glu-Tyr							0			
250	CB-Glu-Glu									0	
251	εAmCapr-OEt							0			
252	Lβphenyllact-OMe							++++			
253	Dβphenyllact-OMe										
254	DLαClβphenylprop-OMe							00			
255	Hydrocinnam-OMe							0			
256	αAcβphenylprop-OEt							++		0	
257	αBenzylmalon-OEt NH₂							0			
258	αBenzylmalon-NH₂									±	
259	HO.C₆H₄.CH₂.CH₂.CO-CH₂.COOH	0	0	0	±1+++	+?		+			
260	HO.C₆H₄.CH₂.CH₂.CO-CH₂.COOEt			0				+		0	
261	C₆H₄.CH₂.CH₂.CO-CH₂.COOH										
262	NH₂:(CH₂)₅.CO-CH₂.COOEt										
263	Gly-Gly-NH₂										
264	Gly-Gly-OEt										
265	Gly-Gly-Gly										
266	CB-Gly-Gly-Gly Me	00									
267	Gly-Gly-Gly										
268	Gly-Gly-βAla					+					
269	Gly-Gly-Leu				++						
270	Gly-Gly-DLeu				+++						
271	Gly-Gly-Pro										
272	Gly-Gly-Hypro				++++						
273	Ala-Gly-Gly	0			+++						
274	DAla-Gly-Gly				±						
275	βAla-Gly-Gly				0						
276	βAla-Gly-βAla	0	0	+++	0+		±			0	
277	Leu-Gly-Gly				++	+?					
278	DLeu-Gly-Gly				0+						
279	CB-Leu-Gly-Gly				0	+++					

	Pepsin (3.4.4.1)	Trypsin (3.4.4.4)	Chymotrypsin (3.4.4.5)	Cathepsin C (3.4.4.9)	Papain (3.4.4.10)	Carboxypeptidase A (3.4.2.1)	Leucine amino-peptidase (3.4.1.1)	Aminotripep-tidase (3.4.1.3)	Glycyl-glycine dipeptidase (3.4.3.1)	Iminodipeptidase (3.4.3.6)	Iminodipeptidase (3.4.3.7)
280 Phe-Gly-NH₂		0	+		+						
281 Bz-DLPhe-Gly-NH₂			0		+						
282 Tyr-Gly-NH₂		0	+1								
283 Bz-Tyr-Gly-NH₂			+								
284 Bz-DTyr-Gly-NH₂			+2								
285 CB-Tyr-Gly-NH₂			+				+1	+1			
286 CB-DTyr-Gly-NH₂		±	0				+	+		o	
287 Ac-Tyr-Gly-NH₂ (Ac)			+2					+1		o	
288 CB-Tyr-Gly-OEt			0				+	+			
289 Pro-Gly-Gly			++					0			
290 Hypro-Gly-Gly			0								
291 CB-Try-Gly-NH₂		±1	±2				+++?	±1			
292 His-Gly-Gly				+			++	0			
293 Lys-Gly-NH₂ Me				+			++	0			
294 Ala-Gly-Gly											
295 Leu-Ala-NH₂							+++?				
296 Gly-βAla-Gly							++				
297 Gly-βAla-βAla											
298 βAla-βAla-Gly											
299 βAla-βAla-βAla											
300 Leu-Val-NH₂											
301 Gly-Leu-NH₂							+	+1			
302 CB-Gly-Leu-NH₂							0	+			
303 Gly-Leu-OEt								+1			
304 Gly-Leu-Gly								±1			
305 Gly-DLeu-Gly								+			
306 Bz-Gly-Leu-Gly					++2		+++	+1			
307 Gly-Leu-DLeu							++				
308 Ala-Leu-NH₂							+1,2				
309 DAla-Leu-NH₂							o o				
310 βAla-Leu-NH₂								+1			

No.	Compound										
311	Bz-Leu-Leu-Gly								0		
312	γGlu-CySH-Gly	± 0	+ 0	+ + 0	+						
313	Gly-Phe-NH₂			+ + +	+	0					
314	Gly-DPhe-NH₂										
315	CB-Gly-Phe-NH₂										
316	Gly-Phe-OEt			+							
317	CB-Gly-DLPhe-OEt			H	+	0					
318	Gly-Phe-NH₂ (Me)			+++			0				
319	Gly-Phe-OEt										
320	βAla-Phe-OEt				H						
321	AmiB-Phe-OEt			+ + + + +							
322	Leu-Phe-OEt			0							
323	Ser-Phe-NH₂			H							
324	Phe-Phe-NH₂			0							
325	CB-Phe-Phe-NH₂			0	H					0	
326	Pro-Phe-NH₂										
327	Pro-Phe-OEt										
328	Lys-Phe-NH₂ (Ac)			0							
329	Lys-Phe-NH₂ (Bz)			+ + + +	0 H						
330	Lys-Phe-NH₂			H	+						
331	Lys-Phe-OEt (Ac)			+							
332	Lys-Phe-OEt			+ + +	H						
333	CB-Glu-Phe-NH₂	0			+						
334	γGlu-Phe-NH₂										
335	Gly-NMePhe-NH₂										
336	Gly-Tyr-NH₂										
337	CB-Gly-Tyr-NH₂										
338	Gly-Tyr-OEt										
339	CB-Gly-Tyr-OEt										
340	Gly-Tyr-NH₂ (Me)			H	+						
341	Gly-Tyr-NH₂			+ ++ +	+						
342	Gly-Tyr-OEt										
343	Ala-Tyr-NH₂										
	Ala-Tyr-OEt										

	Pepsin (3.4.4.1)	Trypsin (3.4.4.4)	Chymotrypsin (3.4.5)	Cathepsin C (3.4.9)	Papain (3.4.4.10)	Carboxypeptidase A (3.4.2.1)	Leucine amino-peptidase (3.4.1.1)	Aminotripep-tidase (3.4.1.3)	Glycyl-glycine dipeptidase (3.4.3.1)	Iminodipeptidase (3.4.3.6)	Imidodipeptidase (3.4.3.7)
344 dAla-Tyr-OEt				+++							
345 AmiB-Tyr-OEt				+							
346 Ser-Tyr-NH_2			++								
347 Phe-Tyr-NH_2			++								
348 Tyr-Tyr-NH_2			++	++							
349 CB-Tyr-Tyr-NH_2				++							
350 Pro-Tyr-NH_2				++							
351 Pro-Tyr-OEt				++							
352 Bz-Lys-Tyr-NH_2				0							
353 Lys-Tyr-NH_2				0							
354 Ac-Lys-Tyr-OEt				0							
355 Ac-Lys-Tyr-NH_2				±							
356 Lys-Tyr-OEt				++							
357 CB-Glu-Tyr-NH_2	+2										
358 CB-Glu-Tyr-Gly-NH_2	++2										
359 CB-Glu-Tyr-NH_2	±2		0								
360 γGlu-Tyr-NH_2			++	++							
361 Me-Gly-Tyr-NH_2											
362 Gly-Pro-Gly...						0		0		0	?
363 CB-Gly-Try-NH_2			++		+2						
364 Bz-Gly-His-NH_2											
365 CB-Gly-His-NH_2			0								
366 CB-Bz-Gly-Arg-NH_2		++++									
367 Bz-Gly-Arg-NH_2		0									

No.	Compound								
368	Gly-Lys-NH₂								
369	Bz-Gly-Lys-NH₂							0	
370	Tyr-Lys-Glu								
371	Lys-Lys-NH₂								
372	Lys-Lys-Lys								
373	Bz-Lys-Lys-Lys CB								
374	Bz-Gly-Lys-NH₂								
375	Gly-Glu-Gly								
376	Gly-Glu-Tyr								
377	CB-Gly-Glu-Tyr								
378	Nic-Phe-Urea-OβNaph								
379	Gly-Gly-Gly-NH₂								±1
380	Gly-Gly-Gly								±1
381	CB-Tyr-Gly-Gly-NH₂ Me								
382	CB-Gly-Gly-Gly-Gly								0
383	CB-Gly-Leu-Gly-NH₂								
384	Gly-Leu-Gly-Leu								
385	Gly-Phe-Gly-NH₂								
386	CB-Gly-Phe-Gly-NH₂								
387	Gly-Tyr-Gly-NH₂								
388	CB-Gly-Tyr-Gly-NH₂							+?	
389	Glu-Tyr-Gly-NH₂								0
390	CB-Glu-Tyr-Gly-NH₂								
391	CB-Gly-Glu-Gly-NH₂								
392	Gly-Glu-Gly-OEt								
393	Ala-Ala-Ala-Ala								
394	Gly-Gly-Leu-Gly								
395	Gly-Gly-Phe-NH₂								
396	Gly-Gly-Phe-OEt							+	±1
397	Lys-Lys-Lys-Lys								
398	Gly-Glu-Glu-Gly								
399	Tyr-Lys-Glu-Tyr								
400	Ala-Ala-Ala-Ala-Ala								
401	Tyr-Tyr-Lys-Glu-Tyr								
402	Gly-Gly-Gly-Gly-Gly								
403	(Lys)>₄								

	Pepsin (3.4.4.1)	Trypsin (3.4.4.4)	Chymotrypsin (3.4.4.5)	Cathepsin C (3.4.4.9)	Papain (3.4.4.10)	Carboxypeptidase A (3.4.2.1)	Leucine aminopeptidase (3.4.1.1)	Aminotripeptidase (3.4.1.3)	Glycyl-glycine dipeptidase (3.4.3.1)	Iminodipeptidase (3.4.3.6)	Iminodipeptidase (3.4.3.7)
404 (DLys)>$_4$		o	:	:	:	:	:	:	:	:	:
405 (Orn)>$_4$		o	:	:	:	:	:	:	:	:	:
406 CyS-Tyr	+		:	:	:	:	:				
CyS-Tyr / CB-CyS-Tyr	⊦		:	:	:	:	:				
407 CB-CyS-Tyr / Tyr-CyS	+		:	:	:	:	:				
408 Tyr-CyS / CB-Tyr-CyS	⊦		:	:	:	:	:				
409 CB-Tyr-CyS	+		:	:	:	:	:				
References	142 223 584 1007 2097	220a 1122 1561 1959 2377 2720 2761	221-3 562 643 764 859 1177 1322 1959 2351 2367 2463	794 1223	562 1381 2720	562 1123 1959 2351 2503	562 2438 2448	11 691 795	2438	563-4	12 14 565 2442

Explanation of Table : The substrates are arranged systematically in increasing order of complexity. Each aminoacid residue, or α-amide, α-amide, α-hydroxamide, α-hydrazide or ester group is treated as one unit (acylated or ω-substituted aminoacids being treated as a unit), and the table is arranged in blocks of 1-, 2-, 3- and 4-unit compounds, with finally a few more complex compounds. Within each block the compounds are arranged on the basis of the nature of the penultimate unit, which in many cases largely determines the specificity. In each peptide the N-terminal residue is on the left and the C-terminal residue on the right. The order of arrangement is that of the abbreviations given below. Acyl groups substituting on the terminal α-NH₂ group are written on the left; groups substituting on the side-chains are written above the aminoacids concerned. The rate of hydrolysis is indicated semi-qualitatively by the number of plus signs; since the affinities are usually not large, the rate in most cases approximates to v_0 rather than to V. Unless otherwise indicated, the bond hydrolysed is that indicated by the right-hand hyphen; in other cases the figure against the result indicates the number of the bond hydrolysed, counting from the left. Where the point of splitting has not been determined, a question mark is given instead of a figure. Unless otherwise indicated, all aminoacids are L-isomers.

Abbreviations : (a) aminoacids : Gly, glycine ; PhGly, phenylglycine ; Ala, alanine ; AmB, α-amino-n-butyric acid ; AmiB, α-amino-iso-butyric acid ; Val, valine ; Norval, norvaline ; Leu, leucine ; Ileu, isoleucine ; alloIleu, allo-isoleucine ; Norleu, norleucine ; Terleu, tertiary leucine ; αAmCapr, α-amino-n-caproic acid ; Ser, serine ; Thr, threonine ; CySH, cysteine ; Met, methionine ; Phe, phenylalanine ; Tyr, tyrosine ; Pro, proline ; Hypro, hydroxyproline ; alloHypro, allo-hydroxyproline ; Try, tryptophan ; His, histidine ; Arg, arginine ; Lys, lysine ; Asp, aspartic acid ; Glu, glutamic acid ; εAmCapr, ε-amino-n-caproic acid.

(b) Carboxyl-substituent groups : -NH₂, amide ; -NHnaph, β-naphthylamide ; -NHOH, hydroxamide ; -NH.NH₂, hydrazide ; -OMe, methyl ester ; -OEt, ethyl ester ; -OβNaph, β-naphthyl ester.

(c) Amino-substituent groups: Form-, formyl ; Ac-, acetyl ; ClAc-, chloroacetyl ; F₃Ac-, trifluoroacety l ; Bz-, benzoyl ; Bzs-, benzenesulphonyl ; Ts-, toluene-sulphonyl ; CB-, carbobenzoxy (C₆H₅.CH₂.CH₂.O.CO-); Nic-, nicotinyl ; iNic-, isonicotinyl ; PhPyr-, phenylpyruvyl.

Nothing like a complete study of peptidase specificity has been made, although much work has been done. The number of di- and tri-peptides which could theoretically be synthesized from the usual aminoacids is of the order of 10,000 or twenty-five times the number of compounds given in the table, which in any case includes many acylated peptides and non-peptide substances. Moreover, the great majority of the substances in the table have only been tested with one or two peptidases, so that even with these substances not much more than 10 per cent of the possible combinations have been tested. However, enough has been done with each enzyme to establish the general features of its specificity fairly clearly.

The specificity of these enzymes is unexpectedly sharply defined. Although they all hydrolyse peptide links, none of them hydrolyses all peptides. A given substance which is rapidly hydrolysed by one peptidase may show little or no hydrolysis by any of the others; in fact, a number of substances have been proposed as 'specific substrates', whose hydrolysis is brought about only by one particular enzyme, thus enabling that enzyme to be estimated in crude mixtures. Such substrates have been described for most of the enzymes listed. The specificity requirements of each enzyme in turn will now be considered.

Pepsin

The exact specificity of this enzyme is somewhat uncertain. Although it was the first of these enzymes to be crystallized, less data appear to be available than for most of the other enzymes. On a molecular basis, it acts much more slowly than other proteinases on proteins, and even more slowly on peptides. In fact, it has at times been doubted whether the action on synthetic peptides is due to pepsin or to a contaminating enzyme. Crystalline salmon pepsin does not attack synthetic peptides which are hydrolysed by mammalian pepsin (*1988*). However, there is evidence that the mammalian enzyme does itself attack some synthetic peptides (*1133*).

In contrast to some other peptidases, pepsin has only been found to hydrolyse peptide links, not amides or esters. It is absolutely specific for the optical configuration of the aminoacids on both sides of the bond hydrolysed (compare the pairs 142–3, 174–5, 243–4, 247–8). An aromatic ring in the side-chain of either aminoacid is particularly favourable for hydrolysis by pepsin, as shown by substances 118–20, 124–5, 243, 247, 358, 376–7, 388 and 390, in which the bond which is split involves the amino group of a tyrosine or phenylalanine residue; by substances 169–71 and 408–9, in which the link involves the carboxyl group of an aromatic aminoacid; and by substances 142, 171 and 174, in which both residues involved are aromatic and which are split much more rapidly than any others. Substitution on the aromatic ring prevents the action (compare compounds 171–2, 247 and 249), as does the substitution of dehydrotyrosine for tyrosine (compare compounds 174 and 178).

The action of pepsin on substrates containing an aromatic aminoacid residue on the right of the bond hydrolysed is facilitated if the residue on the left is glutamyl (compare substrates 51 with 247 and 388 with 390). Amidation of the side-chain carboxyl group reduces the effect somewhat, but does not abolish it (compare compounds 243 with 245 and 357 with 359). No glutamyl peptides have been found to be hydrolysed unless they contain also an aromatic residue (compare 241 and 250 with 243). A sulphur-containing residue also facilitates the action on tyrosine-containing peptides (see substances 118–20, 124–5 and 169–70). A free side-chain thiol group is not required, since benzoylatior does not abolish the action (compound 120) and the $-S.CH_3$ group of methionine is also effective (compounds 124–5).

Amidation of the C-terminal carboxyl group tends to prevent the action of pepsin (compare 247 with 357). A free α-amino group near the bond in question also tends to prevent the action (compare 118 with 119, 124 with 125, 246 with 247 and also with 376 and 377). These examples show that either acylating the amino group or increasing its distance from the susceptible bond reduces its influence.

The synthetic peptides shown in the table can only illustrate the action on small molecules, but it is now possible to study the specificity of the action on long-chain peptides and proteins by the identification of the terminal groups produced, e.g. by Sanger's method. In the case of a protein of unknown structure, it is not possible to determine completely the nature of the bonds hydrolysed; for example, if N-terminal groups A and B and C-terminal groups C and D are produced, the bonds split might have been either A–C and B–D or A–D and B–C. On the other hand, with a polypeptide chain of known structure, such as the A- or B-chains of insulin, this difficulty can be overcome. Even in this case, however, it is usually difficult to determine the order in which the various bonds are split.

The action of pepsin on the A- and B-chains of insulin (*2299, 2300*) and on globin and ovalbumin (*598, 2261*) is in general agreement with the results shown in the table; however, some additional bonds are also hydrolysed, as, for example, a leucyl-valine link, as shown by the arrows marked P in Fig. VI.6.

The specificity of crystalline rennin (3.4.4.3) appears to resemble that of pepsin (*741*) (see the action on the B-chain shown by the arrows marked R in Fig. VI.6; the action on the A-chain has not yet been tested).

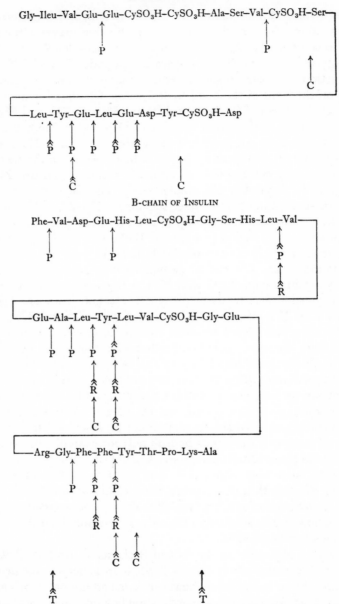

Fig. VI.6. *Action of some peptidases on peptide chains of insulin*

The arrows show the points of splitting by the various peptidases, the feathered arrows indicating the principal points of action. P represents pepsin, R rennin, C chymotrypsin and T trypsin. Trypsin has no action on the A-chain; the action of rennin on this chain has not been investigated.

Trypsin

Trypsin hydrolyses links (not necessarily peptide links) involving the carboxyl groups of the basic aminoacids lysine and arginine. Amides are split more rapidly than peptides, and esters even more rapidly. The rate of hydrolysis of the esters is not affected by the nature of the alcohol group; only two (compounds 219 and 221) of a series of esters of benzoyl-arginine, all behaving similarly (*1959*), are given in the table. Even such a simple substance as lysine ethyl ester (233) is rapidly hydrolysed by trypsin. Substitution on the side-chain $-NH_2$ group entirely prevents the action (compare the pairs 215 and 217, 230 and 232, 366 and 367, 369 and 374), while substitution on the α-NH_2 group facilitates the action (compare 229 with 230, 368 with 369, 372 with 373), although complete removal of this group entirely prevents hydrolysis (see compound 251). The side-chain must not be shorter than in lysine (compare 403 with 405). An acidic side-chain on the neighbouring aminoacid residue tends to retard hydrolysis, as shown by the low activity with substrates 399 and 401 and the complete inactivity with 370. Trypsin has been shown (*2377*) to have a slow hydrolysing action on a β-ketoacid with a lysine-like side-chain (compound 262).

Chymotrypsin

This enzyme, like trypsin and unlike pepsin, hydrolyses amides and esters as well as peptides and, like pepsin and unlike trypsin, it shows a marked preference for links involving aromatic aminoacid residues. Again the best substrates are esters, especially of N-acyl-tyrosine (substances 165–7); phenylalanine esters are more slowly hydrolysed. Some esters of tryptophan and methionine are also hydrolysed (substances 122 and 199) and, very much more slowly, esters of arginine, norleucine and norvaline (substances 85, 110, 219, 222).

Nitration of the tyrosine ring in the *ortho*-position has no effect (compound 167), but removal of the methylene group from the phenylalanine side-chain completely prevents action (compare 70 with 136).

In general, acylation of the α-amino group of the aromatic aminoacid increases the action of chymotrypsin, like that of pepsin (compare 153 with 154–60, 161 with 162, 164 with 165–6, 282 with 283 and with 285 and 287) and this may be true also when the amino group is further removed from the bond hydrolysed (compare 389 with 390). Unlike the effect with pepsin, however, the nature of the acyl group has a large influence with chymotrypsin, being particularly well-marked with aromatic acyl groups such as benzoyl, carbobenzoxy and nicotinyl groups (compare 23 with 24, 127 with 128, 154–5 with 158–60). Groups of this type apparently increase both the affinity of the enzyme for the substrate and the rate of breakdown of the ES complex (see Table VI.6). The benzoyl group may in fact be able to satisfy the requirement of the enzyme for an aromatic ring in the substrate; in 24 it is the only such ring in the molecule (cf. 23). If both hydrogen atoms of the α-amino group are substituted, as, for example, by forming a phthalimide group (compound 137), no activity is found.

TABLE VI.6

KINETIC CONSTANTS FOR SOME SUBSTRATES OF CHYMOTRYPSIN

No. in Table VI.5	Substrate	$K_m \times 10^3$	$V \times 10^3$ (moles/min/mg N/ml)
24	Bz-Gly-OMe	6·5	2·2
122	Bz-Met-OEt	0·83	8·0
127	Ac-Phe-NH$_2$	31	0·8
128	Nic-Phe-NH$_2$	19	2·0
136	Bz-Phe-OEt	5·7	390
152	Ac-hexahydroPhe-NH$_2$	27	0·65
154	Form-Tyr-NH$_2$	12	0·45
155	Ac-Tyr-NH$_2$	32	2·4
156	ClAc-Tyr-NH$_2$	27	4·0
157	F$_3$Ac-Tyr-NH$_2$	26	2·6
158	Bz-Tyr-NH$_2$	2·5	4·0
159	Nic-Tyr-NH$_2$	12	5·0
160	iNic-Tyr-NH$_2$	9·0	6·4
161	Tyr-NHOH	41	3·6
162	Ac-Tyr-NHOH	43	33
165	Ac-Tyr-OEt	74	4500
166	Bz-Tyr-OEt	3·9	820
167	oNO$_2$ | Bz-Tyr-OEt	11·4	3400
197	Ac-Try-NH$_2$	5·0	0·55
198	Nic-Try-NH$_2$	2·5	1·5
199	Ac-Try-OEt	4·8	363
252	Lβphenyllact-OMe	10	14
253	Dβphenyllact-OMe	35	2·4
254	DLαClβphenylprop-OMe	2·3	83
255	Hydrocinnam-OMe	0·2	22
259	HO.C$_6$H$_4$.CH$_2$.CH$_2$.CO-CH$_2$.COOH	140	0·8
260	HO.C$_6$H$_4$.CH$_2$.CH$_2$.CO-CH$_2$.COOEt.	40	2·5
287	Ac-Tyr-Gly-NH$_2$	23	7·5
336	Gly-Tyr-NH$_2$	122	4·1

If instead of being acylated, the α-amino group is removed and replaced by hydrogen, the substrate is still hydrolysed, as shown by substance 255, which can be regarded as phenylalanine methyl ester without the amino group. The amino group may also be replaced by hydroxyl (compounds 252–3), or by chlorine (compound 254), but not by a carboxyl group (compound 257) or by a CH_3. CO– group (compound 256).

Like trypsin, chymotrypsin is capable of hydrolysing β-ketoacids which contain the appropriate side-chain (compounds 259–60).

In the case of chymotrypsin data are available for a number of substrates showing the effect of structure on K_m and V independently, as shown in Table VI.6, from *643, 764, 1322* and *2463*.

In general the optical configuration of the aromatic aminoacid must be L- in order that the substrate may be hydrolysed, although chymotrypsin has a high affinity for the corresponding D-isomers, which are competitive inhibitors (see Table VI.1).

There is one case of optical specificity which is of special interest. In the compound

the ester bond of the D-compound is hydrolysed but the L-compound is not acted on, contrary to the behaviour of the enzyme with open-chain phenylalanyl esters. Since the optically active carbon atom is in a saturated ring, the configuration of the molecule is fixed. The fact that the enzyme acts on the D-form is taken to indicate that the active centre is specific for this configuration. The open-chain L-forms, on account of their flexibility, can assume this shape, whereas steric hindrance prevents the D-forms from doing so (*108*).

Cathepsin C

This enzyme, like pepsin and chymotrypsin, acts particularly on compounds containing an aromatic aminoacid; unlike them, however, it requires a free α-amino group, and this must be carried by another aminoacid attached to the amino group of the aromatic aminoacid, although the bond which is split involves the carboxyl group of the latter. Most of the substrates which have been tried are amides or esters of dipeptides. Acylation of the α-amino group of these compounds abolishes the activity. Thus the enzyme appears to be an aminopeptidase which splits off dipeptides from the N-terminal end (cf. β-amylase). The N-terminal aminoacid is preferably one with a small side-chain, such as glycine, alanine or serine, although proline is also effective (compounds 313, 316, 323, 326–7, 336, 338, 342–3, 350–1). The hydrogen atom of the left-hand peptide bond must be unsubstituted, although this is not the bond which is hydrolysed (compare 313 with 335). Methylation of the glycine amino group considerably slows the action (compare 338 with 341), while increasing the distance of the α-amino group from the susceptible bond by interposing one methylene group makes the compound completely inactive (compare 316 with 320). K_m and V have been separately determined for some of these substrates (794).

The enzyme does not act on proteins unless they contain the appropriate N-terminal dipeptide grouping (2094).

Papain

Although a certain amount of work has been carried out with the crystalline enzyme, it is insufficient to enable us to form as clear a picture of its specificity as of that of some of the other peptidases. It hydrolyses amides and esters, particularly (like trypsin) those of basic aminoacids (substances 215, 220, 230) which should not be substituted on the side-chain amino group (compare 215 with 218). Some glycine and leucine derivatives are also hydrolysed, as also are some glutamic derivatives when aminated in the side-chain (substance 240).

Carboxypeptidase

This enzyme, in contrast to those hitherto considered, requires a free carboxyl group, and does not hydrolyse amides or esters of simple alcohols. The specificity of the enzyme is determined primarily by the aminoacid bearing the free carboxyl group, and only to a small extent by the part of the molecule on the left of this aminoacid; this part may even be an acyl group instead of an aminoacid, as in substances 6, 7, 9, 14, and 16–18. Like pepsin and chymotrypsin, this enzyme acts best on substances containing an aromatic aminoacid; in this case, however, the aromatic residue is on the right of the bond split (compounds 45–6, 51, 60, 75–6, 125, 203). This residue may even be an aromatic hydroxyacid, as in the case of the ester 26. The configuration of the aromatic acid residue must be L- (compare 38 with 39, 41 with 42, 46 with 47, 60 with 61), but with this enzyme the length of the side-chain is not critical, since a C-terminal phenylglycine residue is removed (substance 43).

A number of other aminoacid residues are removed more slowly, and the enzyme has been used for the identification of C-terminal end-groups. As pointed out in Chapter XI, however, a negative result does not necessarily mean the absence of any C-terminal group. The enzyme acts only slowly on dipeptides unless the amino group is acylated (see 173, 176 and compare 50 with 51), although in tripeptides or higher peptides the length of the peptide chain has little effect. Even in the case of proteins and long peptide chains, the enzyme has been found capable of removing fifteen of the twenty naturally-occurring amino-acids from the C-terminal end.

Leucine aminopeptidase

This enzyme requires a free α-amino group and is therefore properly termed an aminopeptidase; blocking of this group prevents its action (compare 91 with 92). The bond hydrolysed in most of the cases in the table is that adjacent to this amino group, but in at least one case it is the second peptide bond from this group (compound 301). The amides of most aminoacids are hydrolysed, although those of leucine, nor-leucine, norvaline and 2-aminocaproic acid are attacked more rapidly than the others. Replacement of the amide ammonia by glycine has little effect, so that the dipeptides are hydrolysed at about the same rate as the amides. Unlike trypsin and chymotrypsin, it does not hydrolyse the corresponding aminoacid esters at all (2448). In agreement with this lack of esterase activity, the enzyme is not inhibited by di-isopropyl phos-phorofluoridate (see p. 346). It is not strictly a leucine-specific peptidase, but acts particularly on compounds with an N-terminal aminoacid with an aliphatic side-chain, the efficiency increasing with the size of the side-chain. It also acts on compounds with an N-terminal phenylalanine, tyrosine, histidine or tryptophan residue. The configuration of the aminoacids on both sides of the bond which is split is important, par-ticularly that on the left (see the pairs 86–7, 91–3, 94–5, 99–100, 101–2, 103–4, 105–6, 308–9). A leucine residue has a particularly favourable effect on either side of the bond which is hydrolysed (compare 74 with 94).

Aminotripeptidase

This enzyme is only known to act rapidly on tripeptides, most of those which have been tried being peptides of glycine, alanine and leucine (substrates 265, 269, 271, 273, 277, 289–90, 304). Since tri-peptides of other aminoacids do not appear to have been tried, little can be said about the specificity of the enzyme towards particular amino-acid side-chains. The small activity ($\pm$) shown in the table towards some dipeptides is possibly due to traces of other enzymes, as the tripeptidase has not been completely purified. The enzyme requires both a free α-amino group (compare 265 with 266, 277 with 279) and a free α-carboxyl group (compare 265 with 379), and thus is a specific tripeptidase. It is, however, termed an aminotripeptidase rather than a carboxytripeptidase because it removes the N-terminal aminoacid (795). The enzyme is stereochemically specific for the L-isomers of the aminoacids in all three positions; this stereospecificity is absolute for the N-terminal residue (compare 273 with 274, 277 with 278), very high for the middle residue (compare 304 with 305), and least for the C-terminal residue (compare 269 with 270). The hydrogen atom of the susceptible peptide link must be present (compare 273 with 294 and 362), but not that of the right-hand peptide link (compare 265 with 267). The free amino group must be in the α-position (compare 273 with 275). The enzyme has no amidase activity and it is doubtful whether it possesses any esterase activity (2438).

Glycyl-glycine dipeptidase

This enzyme has been tested with even fewer substrates than the last. The best substrate is glycyl-glycine, and the enzyme must be rather specific for this, since it does not hydrolyse such closely related dipeptides as glycyl-alanine or alanyl-glycine, or amides such as glycineamide. It is a true dipeptidase, requiring both α-amino and α-carboxyl groups on adjacent aminoacids (compare 27 with 28-9, 27 with 263, 27 with 265). The question of optical specificity does not arise with this enzyme. The peptide link must be unsubstituted (compare 27 with 30); however, one (but not both) of the hydrogen atoms of the amino group may be replaced by a methyl group (compare 27 with 68 and 69).

Iminodipeptidase

This enzyme acts on dipeptides containing proline or hydroxyproline, but is stated not to act on other dipeptides (564). It appears to be a dipeptidase, and does not act on tripeptides containing proline (compounds 289-90, 362). The best substrates have the iminoacid in the N-terminal position (substrates 180-1, 187-91, 194-5), but it may also be in the C-terminal position (substrate 52). Amides of iminoacids are not attacked (compounds 179, 186). The action is prevented by the presence of an aspartic or glutamic residue (compounds 185, 192-3). The hydroxyl group in hydroxyproline is not essential and can be substituted or inverted without loss of activity (compare 187 with 195 and 194).

Imidodipeptidase

This enzyme differs from all the peptidases considered above in hydrolysing an imide bond formed between an α-carboxyl group and a cyclic iminoacid, proline or hydroxyproline; normal peptides of these iminoacids are not attacked (compounds 179–80, 186–7). A typical substrate is glycyl-L-proline (substance 52). The enzyme is a specific dipeptidase, requiring α-carboxyl and α-amino groups on adjacent residues (compare 52 with 54, 182 with 183, 52 with 271 and with 362). It is specific for the L-form of the iminoacid (compare 52 with 53). The introduction of the hydroxyl group in hydroxyproline lowers the susceptibility (compare 52 with 55, 182 with 184) and methylation of this group has a still more marked effect (compound 57). Removal of the hydroxyl group to the other side of the ring partially removes its inhibitory effect (compound 58). This has been interpreted as showing that the enzyme combines with one face of the pyrrolidine ring (*2443*). It is particularly interesting that, provided that the peptide contains an imide bond, the pyrrolidine ring is not necessary, for glycyl-sarcosine is hydrolysed, although glycyl-glycine is not (compare 27 with 30).

General conclusions on peptidase specificity

Although a great deal more information will be required before it is possible to form a detailed picture of the mechanisms underlying peptidase specificity, it is already possible to make a few generalizations from the known facts. The presence or absence of charged groups in particular positions in relation to the bond hydrolysed is often a determining factor; this underlies the distinction between exopeptidases and endopeptidases and between aminopeptidases and carboxypeptidases. Some peptidases have no special requirement for a charged group, some require a positive charge near the susceptible bond, others require a negative charge, others again require both a negative and a positive charge separated by a definite distance. The charge may be required on an α-amino group or in a side-chain. A charge on the substrate, however, is not always essential, for example, chymotrypsin hydrolyses benzoyl-glycine methyl ester, benzoyl-phenylalanine methyl ester and a number of other neutral compounds.

Charged groups are not the only specificity-determining factors, and in some cases uncharged or even non-polar groups have an important effect. Aromatic groups are particularly important and phenylalanine and tyrosine are usually equivalent in this respect, the phenolic hydroxyl group having no effect on the affinity. In other cases the pyrrolidine ring of an iminoacid is required. In at least one case (leucine amino-peptidase) there is even a requirement for a hydrocarbon chain, the effect of which must presumably be due to van der Waals forces between enzyme and substrate.

Provided that the foregoing requirements are met, the nature of the bond to be hydrolysed is not always of determining importance. In many cases it need not be a peptide bond, but may be represented as R.CO–X. If the appropriate structures are present in R, the bond CO–X is activated, and the nature of X is only important in so far as it affects the inherent chemical stability of this bond. In such a case, where the enzyme is not specific for X, it may catalyse not only a hydrolysis but also an interchange of one X for another. Thus those peptidases which hydrolyse esters and amides also catalyse transpep-tidations of the acyl type (325, 793). On the other hand pepsin catalyses transpeptidations of the amino-transfer type to the free carboxyl groups of acceptors (1953).

Lyases

Fumarate hydratase

This is a highly specific enzyme (4.2.1.2), acting only on L-malate in one direction and on fumarate in the other. It shows two types of stereo-specificity, since in the first direction it acts only on one of a pair of

TABLE VI.7

SPECIFICITY OF FUMARATE HYDRATASE

Substrates	Competitive inhibitors	Inactive substances
L-malate	D-malate	L-aspartate
fumarate	citrate	D-aspartate
	D-tartrate	fumarate monomethyl ester
	L-2-hydroxy-3-sulphopropionate	fumaric dimethyl ester
	maleate	crotonate
	mesaconate	acetoacetate
	*trans*aconitate	acetate
	succinate	butyrate
	malonate	acetylenedicarboxylate
	adipate	L-cysteate
	glutarate	
	glycine	

optical enantiomorphs, and in the other on only one of a pair of geo-metrical isomers. The substrates cannot be replaced by any of the other substances shown in Table VI.7, although many of them act as com-petitive inhibitors (1746).

From this table it may be seen that two acidic groups are necessary to enable the substance to combine with the enzyme; thus related monocarboxylic acids, or the mono- or di-esters of the substrates are completely inactive. However, if one carboxyl is replaced by a sulphonic acid group the substance, although not a substrate, still combines with the enzyme. Substitution of an α-hydrogen atom, either by a methyl group or by a $-CH_2.COOH$ group (as in mesaconate (i.e. 2-methyl-fumarate), citrate and *trans*aconitate), or addition of two further α-hydrogen atoms (as in succinate, etc.), has a similar effect, while removal of both α-hydrogen atoms from fumarate (as in acetylenedicarboxylate) renders it completely inactive. It is surprising to note that the stereo-isomers of both substrates (D-malate and maleate), though not acted upon, combine fairly strongly with the active centre of the enzyme and are competitive inhibitors.

Phosphopyruvate hydratase

This enzyme (4.2.1.11) is also highly specific, acting only on 2-phospho-D-glycerate in one direction and phosphoenolpyruvate in the other. However, other substances are also able to combine with the active centre, as shown in Table VI.8 (*2894*).

TABLE VI.8

SPECIFICITY OF PHOSPHOPYRUVATE HYDRATASE

Substrates	*Competitive inhibitors*	*Inactive substances*
2-phospho-D-glycerate	3-phospho-3-hydroxypropionate	D-lactate
phosphoenol-pyruvate	2-phospho-D-lactate	D-glyceraldehyde 3-phosphate
	3-phospho-D-glycerate	dihydroxyacetone phosphate
	2-phospho-D-*erythro*-2,3-dihydroxy-butyrate	glycerol 2-phosphate
	3-phospho-D-*erythro*-2,3-dihydroxy-butyrate	

Homoserine dehydratase

Until fairly recently it was thought that the dehydration of homoserine and the cleavage of cystathionine to cysteine, oxobutyrate and ammonia were due to different enzymes. It is now known that they are due to a single enzyme (4.2.1.15), which has been crystallized, and whose specificity has been examined in some detail (*1758*). It removes R–OH or R–SH groups from a variety of aminoacids containing hydroxyl, thiol or thioether groups (see Table VI.9).

TABLE VI.9

SPECIFICITY OF HOMOSERINE DEHYDRATASE

Aminoacid	Relative velocity of cleavage
L-homoserine	100
L-cystathionine	80
L-djenkolate	30
L- (and *meso-*) lanthionine	17
L-cysteine	5
L-serine	2
O-acetyl-DL-homoserine	2
S-carbamidomethyl-L-cysteine	1
S-carboxyethyl-L-homocysteine	1
DL-homocysteine	0·7

The following show little or no activity: L-threonine, L-allothreonine, DL-2-amino-5-hydroxyvalerate, DL-2-amino-6-hydroxycaproate, 3-hydroxy-DL-aspartate, 3-hydroxy-DL-glutamate, 2-amino-2-deoxy-D-glucose, S-methyl-L-cysteine, S-ethyl-L-cysteine, L-methionine, DL-methionine and L-penicillamine.

It is believed that the product formed by removing water from homoserine, or cysteine from cystathionine, is in both cases vinylglycine. Subsequent rearrangement and hydrolysis produces oxobutyrate and ammonia.

Enoyl-CoA hydratase

This enzyme (L-3-hydroxyacyl-CoA hydro-lyase, 4.2.1.17) presents a number of very interesting points of specificity (*2516*). It only acts on the CoA thiolesters of appropriate acids, and does not even act, as does for example 1.1.1.35, with simpler analogues of CoA or other thiols. It reversibly hydrates a number of unsaturated esters of CoA, at least up to C_9, the rate decreasing with increasing chain length (Table VI.10).

The enzyme is exceptional among hydro-lyases in hydrating both *cis* and *trans* isomers, the relative rates of the two depending on the chain length. In the dehydration reaction, however, only the L-isomers are attacked, the enzyme having no action whatever on D-3-hydroxybutyryl-CoA. Hydration of *trans* unsaturated substrates has been shown to produce L-hydroxy-isomers; the products from hydration of the *cis*-compounds are of uncertain configuration, although the balance of the evidence is in favour of their also being L-derivatives.

It is remarkable that both 2,3- and 3,4-unsaturated compounds can be hydrated by the enzyme, but in both cases it is the 3-hydroxy-compound which is produced.

TABLE VI.10

SPECIFICITY OF ENOYL-CoA HYDRATASE

Substrate	Relative velocity of hydration
(trans) crotonoyl-CoA	100
(cis) isocrotonoyl-CoA	30
trans-2-pentenoyl-CoA	77
cis-2-hexenoyl-CoA	20
trans-2-hexenoyl-CoA	15
trans-3-hexenoyl-CoA	0·86
3-methylcrotonoyl-CoA	14
cis-2-methylcrotonoyl-CoA	+
acryloyl-CoA	+
vinylacetyl-CoA	1·5
methacryloyl-CoA	+
sorboyl-CoA	+
S-crotonoyl-pantetheine	0·01

A + sign indicates that the substance serves as a substrate, but the specific activity has not been determined. The following are inactive: crotonate, 4-pentenoyl-CoA, 3-hydroxy-4-hexenoyl-CoA, maleyl-CoA, itaconyl-CoA, mesaconyl-CoA, trans-cinnamoyl-CoA, fumarate, cis-aconitate.

Aspartate ammonia-lyase

Another example of a very specific lyase is aspartate ammonia-lyase (4.3.1.1). In this case ammonia and not water is added to fumarate, and the enzyme acts only on fumarate and L-aspartate. The purified aspartate ammonia-lyase of *Propionibacterium* has no action on D-aspartate, maleate, fumarate monoethyl ester, fumaric diamide or diethyl ester, pyruvate, crotonate, mesaconate, aconitate, glutaconate, 2,4-hexadieno-ate, glycine, alanine, leucine, phenylalanine, tyrosine, histidine or glutamate (686). Thus any simple change in the substrate molecule, either by substitution or by stereoisomerization, renders it completely inactive.

Aldose mutarotase

This enzyme (5.1.3.1) catalyses a reaction, namely, the interconversion of α- and β-sugars, which also takes place in the absence of the enzyme. Thus it is possible to compare the rates of the enzyme-catalysed reactions with the inherent reactivity of the substrates. This has been done for the enzymes from the mould *Penicillium* and from mammalian kidney (1368–9, 1567) and the results are shown in Table VI.11, in which the rates of the enzyme-catalysed mutarotations (corrected for the spontaneous reactions), together with the rates of the non-enzymatic reactions themselves, are expressed as percentages of the rates with α-D-glucose. It will be seen that the animal and mould enzymes have a similar specificity and act only on those sugars containing the same configuration at C_2 and C_3 as D-glucose, although at very different rates, D-galactose being the best substrate. It is interesting that there is

TABLE VI.11

SPECIFICITY OF ALDOSE MUTAROTASES

Rates of mutarotation, given as percentages of the corresponding rate with α-D-glucose

Substance	Non-enzymatic reaction	Penicillium mutarotase at pH 4·7	Kidney mutarotase at pH 7·1
α-D-glucose	100	100	100
α-D-galactose	110–70	131	165
L-arabinose	436		119
α-D-xylose	320	30	60
β-lactose	72	23	
β-D-fructose	680	10	0
β-maltose	84	6	
α-D-mannose	260–480	0	0
2-amino-2-deoxy-D-glucose	112	0	
D-arabinose	420		0
L-rhamnose	420		0
3-methyl-D-glucose			0
sucrose	0		0
raffinose	0		0
mannitol	0		0
sorbitol	0		0
References:	*1368*	*1567*	*1368–9*
	1567		

no correlation whatever between the enzyme specificity and the reactivity of the substrate, since glucose and galactose, which are the best substrates for the enzymes, are comparatively unreactive, while the very reactive D-mannose, D-arabinose and L-rhamnose are not acted upon at all by mutarotase.

Enzymes with substrates containing hydrocarbon chains

When an enzyme acts on a substrate which contains an alkyl chain with more than one or two carbon atoms, the length of the chain is usually not very critical, so that the enzyme acts on a range of homologous substrates. It is of interest in the case of such enzymes to investigate the effect of chain length. These enzymes are of various types, but it seemed useful to collect some of the more extensive sets of observations into one section, and these are shown in the form of histograms in Fig. VI.7 (pp. 256–7).

The diagram illustrates a number of general features of the effect of chain length. In all cases the rate varies with chain length in a more or less regular manner. In most cases there is a definite optimum chain length, and such an optimum would probably be found in all cases if the data were complete. The optimum chain length varies greatly from one enzyme to another, the actual optimum values ranging from 2 to 17 carbon atoms. In some cases the same type of reaction is carried out by two or more different enzymes having different optimum chain lengths, so that one enzyme deals with the lower members and another with the higher members of a series, as, for example, the dehydrogenases 1.3.2.1–2 and the synthetases 6.2.1.2–3. An interesting feature is that the peak of the curve shows considerable variation in width, the rate falling to 50 per cent of the maximum in some cases with a change of chain length of only two carbon atoms from the optimum, while in other cases this fall is only produced by a change of chain length of six carbon atoms or more. It is rather surprising that a sharp optimum can occur with a chain containing a large number of carbon atoms, as in the acyltransferase 2.3.1.15.

GENERAL CONCLUSIONS

The phenomena of specificity throw some light on the relations between an enzyme and its substrate, and they form an important part of the experimental evidence on which any theory of enzyme mechanism must be based. It is clear that in most cases the presence of a definite pattern of chemical groups, peculiar to each enzyme, is required in a substance to give it the power of combining with the active centre of the enzyme. However, not all substances having the necessary combining structure are capable of reacting when they are combined with the active centre; thus the structural requirements for competitive inhibitors are somewhat less stringent than those for substrates. The size and complexity of the structure required in a substance to make it a substrate is a measure of the specificity of the enzyme; an enzyme requiring in its substrate only a relatively simple structure or small grouping, e.g. an ester link, will be relatively unspecific, whereas one requiring a large and complex grouping, such as that of NAD, is highly specific.

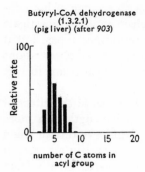

Butyryl-CoA dehydrogenase
(1.3.2.1)
(pig liver) (after *903*)

Relative rate

number of C atoms in
acyl group

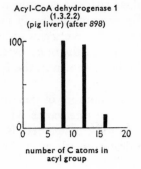

Acyl-CoA dehydrogenase 1
(1.3.2.2)
(pig liver) (after *898*)

number of C atoms in
acyl group

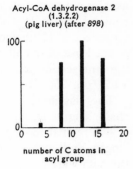

Acyl-CoA dehydrogenase 2
(1.3.2.2)
(pig liver) (after *898*)

number of C atoms in
acyl group

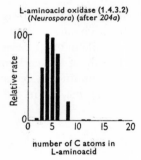

L-aminoacid oxidase (1.4.3.2)
(*Neurospora*) (after *204a*)

Relative rate

number of C atoms in
L-aminoacid

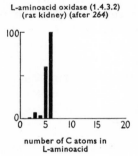

L-aminoacid oxidase (1.4.3.2)
(rat kidney) (after *264*)

number of C atoms in
L-aminoacid

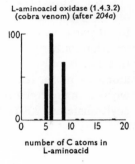

L-aminoacid oxidase (1.4.3.2)
(cobra venom) (after *204a*)

number of C atoms in
L-aminoacid

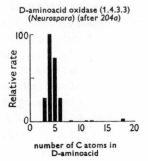

D-aminoacid oxidase (1.4.3.3)
(*Neurospora*) (after *204a*)

Relative rate

number of C atoms in
D-aminoacid

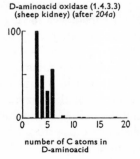

D-aminoacid oxidase (1.4.3.3)
(sheep kidney) (after *204a*)

number of C atoms in
D-aminoacid

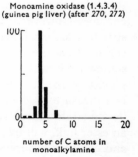

Monoamine oxidase (1.4.3.4)
(guinea pig liver) (after *270, 272*)

number of C atoms in
monoalkylamine

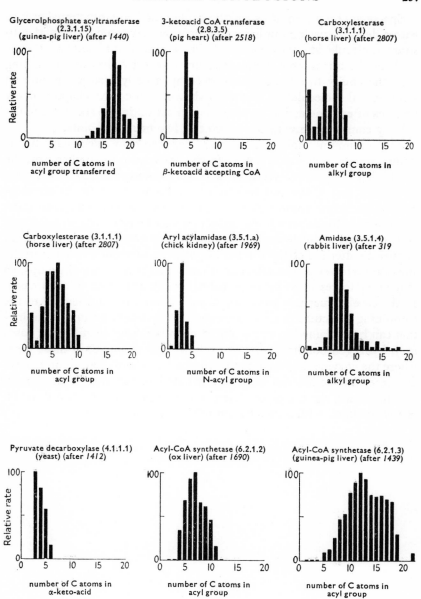

Fig. VI:7. *Effect of chain length of alkyl or acyl groups in substrates on various enzyme reactions.*

In all cases the substrates are of the type $CH_3.(CH_2)_n.X$. In each case the activities are expressed as percentages of the rate obtained with the best substrate.

K

Specificity for a complex structure containing many functional groups with a definite spacing implies a combination between enzyme and substrate molecule at many points. Such a multipoint contact at once explains the remarkable stereospecificity shown by enzymes, including even the ability to distinguish between apparently identical groups in symmetrical molecules (p. 206). As shown in the next chapter, many theories of enzyme action involve a strain set up in the substrate molecule by combination with the enzyme at two or more points.

The minimum combining structure deduced from specificity studies differs greatly in chemical nature from one enzyme to another, and the combining groups involved may be of very different natures. It is clear from this that many different types of forces must be involved in enzyme–substrate combination. In cases where a charged group must be present in the substrate, the attraction may be primarily electrostatic, and if the attraction were purely due to electrostatic forces one could picture a pattern of charges in the enzyme complementary to that in the substrate. However, the substrate often contains no charged groups, so that other forces must be responsible for the attraction in such cases. In the case of enzymes acting on sugars, where the main feature of the combining structure is an arrangement of hydroxyl groups, combination can be explained in terms of hydrogen bonding. In still other cases even hydrogen bonding must be excluded, for example, in those cases where the enzyme is specific for a hydrocarbon chain of a certain length. In these, interaction can only be attributed to van der Waals forces. In a few cases, e.g. the peroxidases, combination is due to co-ordination of the substrate with a metal atom in the enzyme.

VII

ENZYME MECHANISMS

IT MAY TRULY be said that the most fundamental problem of enzymology is the elucidation of the mechanism by which enzymes act. Enzymes are very remarkable catalysts, bringing about in many cases with great speed and in 100 per cent yield chemical reactions which are difficult to carry out in the laboratory, and the mechanism of their action cannot fail to interest the chemist as well as the biologist. It is, however, a very difficult problem, and although some progress has been made, an enormous amount remains to be done. It is only in the last few years that effective methods of obtaining definite evidence have been developed.

That the process of enzyme catalysis depends on a combination of substrate with enzyme had already become clear from kinetic studies, before any pure enzymes were available for chemical investigation. These kinetic studies have been dealt with at some length in Chapter IV and we do not propose to consider them further here. What we are now concerned with is the nature of the enzyme–substrate combination, its effects and the manner in which the catalysis takes place. A number of theories have been put forward from time to time; all these theories have in common the idea that the combination produces some kind of 'activation' of the substrate molecule, due to a polarization, electron displacement, strain or other distortion of the bonds involved in the reaction.

Recently the phrase 'mechanism of an enzyme reaction' has been applied merely to the reaction pattern of the overall process in the sense which we have discussed on p. 112, i.e. the order of combination of the reactants with the enzyme, the number and order of the intermediate complexes, and the order of dissociation of the products. We feel that the use of the term in this limited sense is unfortunate, since genuine understanding of the mechanism involves not only a knowledge of the reaction pattern, but also an insight into the reason for the occurrence of the reactions.

In the first edition of this book we gave an account of some of the theories which have been put forward in the past. All of these were suggested in relation to particular groups of enzymes. As many of them are now only of historical interest, we shall not repeat the account in this edition. They all depended on the idea of some change produced in the substrate molecule by combination with a pattern of chemical groups in the active centre of the enzyme; some kind of strain, distortion or polarization resulting in reactivity was postulated in some cases, or in others the initiation of chain reactions by the formation of free radicals. One valuable theory, based on analogy with non-enzymatic 'bifunctional catalysts', was that of concerted attack by one electrophilic and one nucleophilic group in the enzyme (SWAIN and BROWN, 2578).

No general theory of enzyme activation has so far been developed. It was seen in Chapter V that although enzymes catalyse a multiplicity of reactions, the number of reaction types is very small and in fact over 90 per cent of the known enzymes can be regarded as catalysing transfer reactions. It may well be, therefore, that the activations brought about by all enzymes have much in common and there is no reason why a general theory should not be developed in the light of modern physical organic chemistry.

It must be emphasized, however, that it is dangerous to assume that because a non-enzymatic reaction proceeds by a certain mechanism, a similar reaction which is brought about enzymatically will take place by the same mechanism. The enzymatic and non-enzymatic reactions may well proceed by quite different mechanisms.

In this chapter we shall describe some of the recently developed experimental methods of studying enzyme mechanisms and review the advances which they have brought about in our knowledge of the mode of action of enzymes.

MECHANISM OF HYDROGEN-TRANSFER REACTIONS

As WIELAND pointed out many years ago, the great majority of biological oxidations are really dehydrogenations, consisting of the removal of two hydrogen atoms with a rearrangement of the bonds within the molecule. Typical reactions, of which many examples may be found in group 1 of the enzyme list, are

VII.1
$$\begin{array}{c}\diagdown \\ \diagup\end{array}\!\!C\!\!\begin{array}{c}\diagup H \\ \diagdown O\,H\end{array} \; -2H \; = \; \begin{array}{c}\diagdown \\ \diagup\end{array}\!C\!=\!O$$

VII.2
$$\begin{array}{c}\diagdown \\ \diagup\end{array}\!\!C\!\!\begin{array}{c}\diagup H \\ \diagdown N\,H \\ \;\;H\end{array} \; -2H \; = \; \begin{array}{c}\diagdown \\ \diagup\end{array}\!C\!=\!NH$$

VII.3
$$
\begin{array}{ccc}
\overset{\displaystyle |}{\text{H–C–H}} & & \overset{\displaystyle |}{\text{H–C}} \\
| & -\,2\text{H} \;=\; & \| \\
\text{H–C–H} & & \text{H–C} \\
| & & |
\end{array}
$$

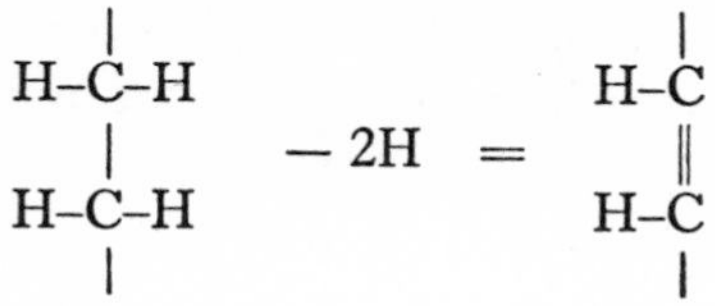

VII.4
$$
\begin{array}{ccc}
\text{–S–H} & & \text{–S} \\
& -\,2\text{H} \;=\; & | \\
\text{–S–H} & & \text{–S}
\end{array}
$$

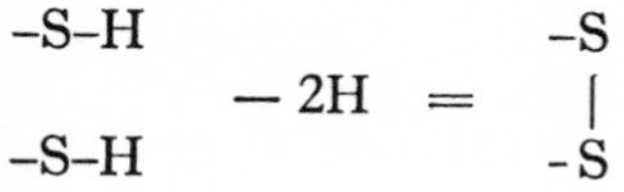

VII.5

$$
\begin{array}{ccc}
\text{O–H} & & \text{O} \\
\bigcirc & -\,2\text{H} \;=\; & \bigcirc \\
\text{O–H} & & \text{O}
\end{array}
$$

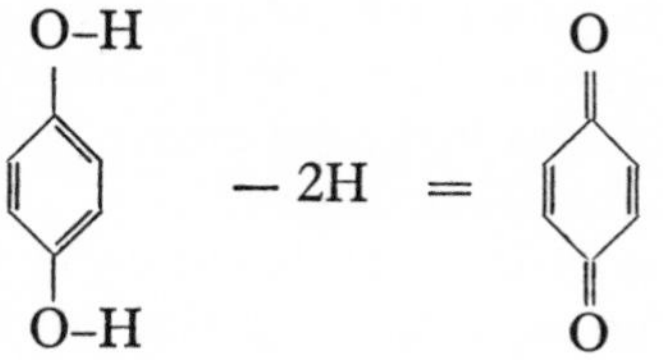

Reaction VII.2 is believed to be that catalysed by the amino acid oxidases, with the formation of the iminoacid as the primary product followed by its decomposition to the ketoacid and ammonia.

Even the oxidation of aldehydes, which at first sight appears to be a reaction of a different type, is almost certainly a dehydrogenation. Aldehydes exist in aqueous solution mainly as hydrates and can react in this form, thus

VII.6 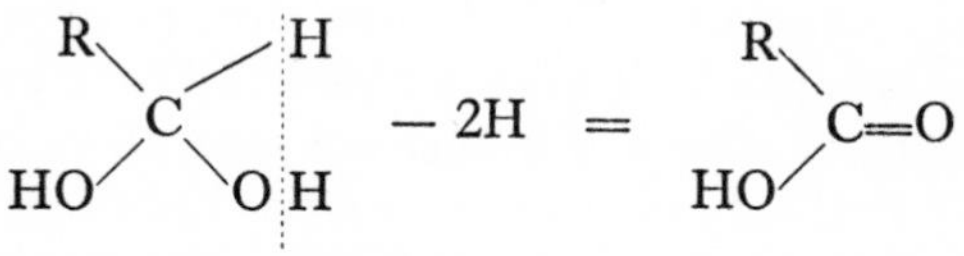
$$
\overset{R}{\underset{HO}{>}}C\overset{H}{\underset{OH}{<}} \quad -\,2\text{H} \;=\; \overset{R}{\underset{HO}{>}}C{=}O \quad (\text{cf. VII.1})
$$

In some enzymatic aldehyde oxidations, particularly by glyceraldehyde-phosphate dehydrogenase, they are believed to be oxidized by the de-hydrogenation of a compound of the aldehyde with an –SH group of the enzyme, thus

VII.7
$$
\begin{array}{ccccccc}
\overset{R}{\underset{|}{C}}\overset{H}{\underset{O}{<}} & & \overset{R}{\underset{|}{C}}\overset{H}{\underset{OH}{<}} & & \overset{R}{\underset{|}{C}}{=}O & & \overset{R}{\underset{|}{C}}{=}O \\
& = & | & & | & & | \\
& & \text{S} & -\,2\text{H} \;=\; & \text{S} & = & \text{OH} \\
\text{S–H} & & | & & | & & | \\
| & & \text{E} & & \text{E} & & \text{S–H} \\
\text{E} & & & & & & | \\
& & & & & & \text{E}
\end{array}
$$

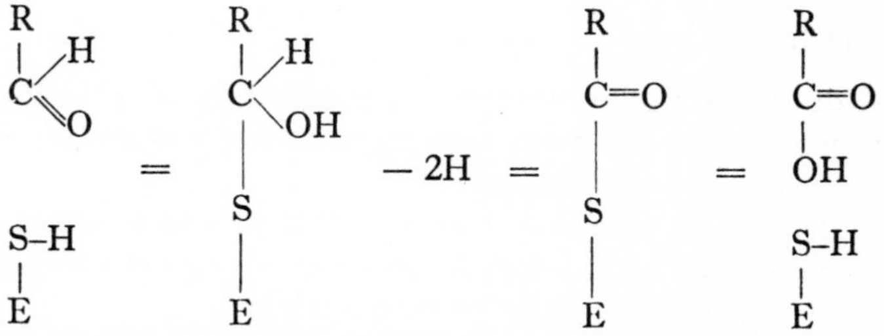

In many oxidation systems the substrates are not directly oxidized by O_2, but the hydrogen transfer takes place through one or more

intermediate substances (coenzymes, flavins, etc.) which act as carriers. For instance, the reactions which are brought about by glucose oxidase (1.1.3.4), namely

$$\text{VII.8} \qquad \overset{-O}{\underset{-C}{>}} C \overset{OH}{\underset{H}{<}} + F = \overset{-O}{\underset{-C}{>}} C{=}O + FH_2$$

$$\text{VII.9} \qquad FH_2 + O_2 = F + H_2O_2$$

(where F denotes the flavin prosthetic group of the enzyme and only the relevant part of the β-glucose molecule is written) are most easily interpreted as a transfer of two hydrogen atoms from glucose to the flavin group and thence to molecular oxygen.

This view gave rise to a terminology based on hydrogen, in which the substance oxidized (glucose in the first reaction and flavin in the second) is called the hydrogen-donor, the oxidizing agent (flavin in the first reaction and O_2 in the second) is known as the hydrogen-acceptor, the flavin is called a hydrogen-carrier and the overall process is referred to as hydrogen transport.

Later, however, another terminology has grown up and is used by many workers. This is based on the electron and the reactions are considered to take place by a transfer of electrons from one molecule to the other. In this terminology hydrogen-carriers are spoken of as electron transmitters, the reactants are called electron-donors or acceptors and the overall process is termed electron transport. The reasons for this change are not altogether clear and it does not seem to be based on any concrete evidence.† Probably the main factor has been that cytochrome is involved in many respiratory systems. The oxidation of cytochrome involves a change of valency of the iron atom, and although the mechanism of the process is still unknown, it is tempting to regard it as analogous to the oxidation of free ferrous ions, which is most simply written as a removal of an electron, thus

$$\text{VII.10} \qquad Fe^{++} - e = Fe^{+++}$$

A desire for a uniform theory of the mechanism of biological oxidation processes then led many workers to extend this assumption also to the dehydrogenation reactions.

It must be admitted, however, that this view seems very artificial when applied to the dehydrogenation of organic compounds. On this view a hydrogen transfer reaction such as

$$\text{VII.11} \qquad AH_2 + B = A + BH_2$$

† We shall not use the 'electron' terminology, which we consider misleading.

takes place in stages as follows:

VII.12 $$AH_2 = A^{--} + 2H^+$$

VII.13 $$A^{--} + B = A + B^{--}$$

VII.14 $$B^{--} + 2H^+ = BH_2$$

The two hydrogen atoms involved first dissociate as hydrogen ions, giving the anion of the donor, which is the form in which it reacts. The anion then transfers two electrons to B and the resulting anion B^{--} then takes up two hydrogen ions to form BH_2. It will be noted that this process involves not only an electron transfer but also a proton transfer in the same direction; it differs from the classical hydrogen transfer in two respects: (a) the electrons and protons pass separately and not together as hydrogen atoms, and (b) the hydrogen atoms in the product BH_2 may not be the same as those originally present in AH_2, but may have been derived from the water.

While it may be possible to explain in this way the oxidation of a few substances like diphenols (reaction VII.5), in which the two hydrogens involved show weakly acidic properties, the majority of the hydrogen atoms concerned in biological oxidations show no acidic properties whatever and there seems no justification for postulating the formation of an anion as the first step.

Moreover, there is considerable doubt as to whether the oxidation and reduction of cytochrome takes place by the simple removal or addition of electrons. The state of the iron atom in such haemoproteins, in which it is united by covalent bonds with six nitrogenous rings, is very different from that in free ferrous or ferric ions, and it is not necessary to suppose that the same mechanism is responsible in both cases. Redox potential measurements show that at pHs more alkaline than about $7\cdot5$ the charge on the cytochrome c molecule does not change on reduction, as it would if the process were a simple addition of an electron to the iron atom (though it does show a change in acid solution). The marked change in the spectrum on reduction shows that the conjugated double-bond system of the haematin structure has been affected. Thus the change is probably not quite as simple as it might appear at first sight. It must be admitted, however, that the nature of the process which occurs in the oxidation and reduction of cytochrome is still largely unknown.

The following mechanism for the oxidation of iron compounds deserves consideration:

VII.15 $$RFe^{++} : OH_2 - H = RFe^{+++} : OH^-$$

where one of the groups with which the iron is co-ordinated is a water molecule; this mechanism might conceivably apply to the ions also. Ferrous and ferric ions in solution are not free, but are combined with water, thus $Fe^{+++}(OH_2)_6$, so that they are in effect surrounded by a shell of hydrogen atoms.

THEORELL (2627) has suggested that the reduction of cytochrome c takes place by a hydrogenation of one of the imidazole groups which are co-ordinated with the iron, followed by a redistribution of charge between this ring and the iron atom. Some such mechanism appears

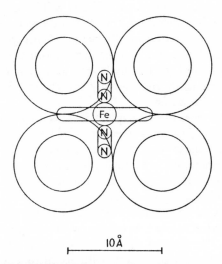

10 Å

Fig. VII.1. *Diagram of structure of cyto-chrome c according to Ehrenberg and Theorell (679).*

necessary in the light of the structure of cytochrome c which has been put forward by EHRENBERG and THEORELL (679) (shown in Fig. VII.1). The figure shows the haem group tightly packed between four helical peptide chains, seen in end view, with the iron in the centre within the porphyrin disc, which is shown edgewise with histidine side-chains of the protein above and below the iron. Theorell points out that the iron is thereby protected from direct attack by oxidizing agents, and he suggests that the point of attack is the uppermost histidine nitrogen atom, which is the most accessible point. This histidine ring acts as a carrier between re-ducing or oxidizing molecules and the iron atom, probably by means of its conjugated double-bond system. The actual mechanism by which this occurs remains undetermined.

Since it is possible to imagine various mechanisms by which the oxidation and reduction may take place, and the actual mechanism is unknown, studies on cytochrome have not afforded much evidence one way or the other on the question whether dehydrogenation reactions should be regarded as occurring by electron or hydrogen transfer. This question remained open until 1953, when VENNESLAND and others began a series of studies by isotopic methods, using deuterium, and obtained clear evidence that a number of oxidation reactions catalysed by de-hydrogenases and similar enzymes take place by the direct transfer of hydrogen atoms.

The work is based mainly on the point made above, that in hydrogen transfer the H-atoms found in the product are the same as those removed from the donor, whereas in electron transfer they will in general not be the same, since they are derived from the hydrogen ions of the water.

Ethanol labelled with deuterium on the first carbon atom $(CH_3.CD_2OH)$ was first prepared (742) and this was used as substrate with alcohol dehydrogenase (1.1.1.1). The reaction which then took place may be written as follows:

VII.16

$$CH_3.C\begin{matrix} \diagup D \\ | \\ D \diagdown OH \end{matrix} + \begin{matrix} H \\ \diagup C \diagdown \\ HC \quad C\text{-}CONH_2 \\ \| \quad | \\ HC \quad CH \\ \diagdown N^+ \diagup \\ | \\ R \end{matrix}$$

$$= CH_3.C{=}O \begin{matrix} | \\ D \end{matrix} + \begin{matrix} D \quad H \\ \diagdown C \diagup \\ HC \quad C\text{-}CONH_2 \\ \| \quad \| \\ HC \quad CH \\ \diagdown {}_H N^+ \diagup \\ | \\ R \end{matrix} = \begin{matrix} D \quad H \\ \diagdown C \diagup \\ HC \quad C\text{-}CONH_2 \\ \| \quad \| \\ HC \quad CH \\ \diagdown N \diagup \\ | \\ R \end{matrix} + H^+$$

where R is written for the residue of the NAD molecule. The reduced coenzyme was isolated and found to contain one atom of deuterium per molecule, as also did the acetaldehyde formed. The reduced coenzyme containing deuterium (which we will write NADHD) could then be reoxidized, either by alcohol dehydrogenase with acetaldehyde or by lactate dehydrogenase with pyruvate. In both cases the whole of the deuterium was thereby removed from the coenzyme and the lactate formed from the pyruvate was found to have one deuterium atom per molecule.

A number of interesting deductions may be made from these observations. (a) The reaction takes place by a direct transfer of hydrogen (or deuterium) atoms from one molecule to the other; since the reaction was carried out in H_2O and not in D_2O, if electron transfer had taken place it would have been followed by the uptake of hydrogen ions and not deuterium ions. The only deuterium atoms initially present were in the substrate, and these atoms were transferred to the coenzyme without passing through any state which could exchange with hydrogen ions or atoms.

(b) The relative orientation of the substrate and coenzyme is always the same during the reaction; the hydrogen (or deuterium) atom attached to the carbon is always transferred to the carbon at position 4 of the coenzyme ring, and the hydroxyl hydrogen to the nitrogen, never the reverse. If some of the molecules had reacted in the reverse position, the D atoms transferred to the nitrogen would have been lost by ionization, and the deuterium content of the reduced coenzyme would have been less than one atom per molecule.

(c) The reaction is stereochemically specific, occurring with one face of the ring only. The bonds uniting the D and H atoms with the carbon in the ring of NAD lie in a plane at right angles to the plane of the ring; thus if the ring lies in the plane of the paper, the H atom will lie below and the D atom above the paper. We may regard the ethanol and NAD as being combined side by side on the enzyme with one face of the nicotinamide ring presented to the substrate, and the ring prevented from turning over by combination of the amide group with the enzyme, so that the H or D atom from the ethanol always goes on in the same position (see below). If the amide group were absent, so that both faces of the ring were equivalent, or if the substrate could react with either face of the ring, the D atoms in the reduced coenzyme molecules would be distributed equally between the two positions and only half the deuterium would be removed in the enzymatic reoxidation. In other words, the deuterium would be 'diluted' by the hydrogen already attached to the carbon atom in position 4. The fact that the whole is removed shows that only one position is involved. It is of interest that when the coenzyme is reduced non-enzymatically by dithionite in D_2O, the reduced coenzyme likewise contains one D atom per molecule, but the deuterium is distributed between the two positions.† If this NADHD labelled in both positions is reoxidized by lactate dehydrogenase with pyruvate, only about one-half of the deuterium is removed, showing that the enzyme only reacts with one position.

(d) The substrates of the alcohol and lactate dehydrogenases both react with the same face of the ring, so that any D atoms added by one enzyme can be removed by the other. However, not all the dehydrogenases react with the same face, in fact the majority react with the opposite face. In a system consisting of two dehydrogenases and NAD, together with the reduced substrate of one (labelled with deuterium) and the oxidized substrate of the other, the deuterium will be transferred from one substrate to the other if both enzymes react with the same face of the nicotinamide ring, but will be retained in the coenzyme if they react with opposite faces. This gives a convenient method of testing to which of the two groups a given dehydrogenase belongs.

The terms 'form A' and 'form B'‡ have been proposed (2301) to denote the forms NADHD which are produced by alcohol dehydrogenase and β-hydroxysteroid dehydrogenase respectively. The two forms of NADPHD have been related to those of NADHD by the action of phosphatase, which merely removes the 2'-phosphate group without changing the configuration of the ring. 'Form A' of NADPHD is defined as that which gives rise to form A of NADHD, thus both A forms have the same configuration (1921). The absolute configurations of the A and B forms have been determined by CORNFORTH et al. (505a). If the molecule is placed as shown in equation VII.16, the A form is that in which the D atom is situated above the plane of the paper and the H atom below.

Table VII.1 shows the forms produced by those enzymes which have been tested up to the present time. It will be noted that a few enzymes appear in both the NAD and the NADP sections; these are enzymes which can react with either coenzyme, and as might be expected, they are found to produce the same form with both. When an enzyme reacts with a series of substrates (e.g. alcohol dehydrogenase) it always produces the same form of NADHD, and the form produced is independent of the source of the enzyme.

† Actually in the case of NAD, unlike simple nicotinamide compounds, the distribution between the two positions is not quite indiscriminate, even in these non-enzymatic reductions. It appears from the observations of PULLMAN et al. (2125) and of FISHER et al. (742) that dithionite reduction in D_2O always gives rather more of 'form A' than of 'form B', although there is some disagreement as to the exact ratio of the amounts of the two forms produced.

‡ Subsequently other workers (656, 1571) have spoken of 'the α and β configurations', 'the α and β faces' and 'the α and β positions'. We prefer to speak of 'form A' and 'form B' as originally proposed, since the α-β terminology may easily lead to confusion with the α and β isomers of the coenzymes (see Chapter IX), or even with the designation of particular carbon atoms.

TABLE VII.1

STEREOSPECIFICITY OF REDUCTION OF NAD AND NADP

(1) *Enzymes producing Form A*

With NAD	*With NADP*
1.1.1.1 Alcohol dehydrogenase (liver)	1.1.1.42 Isocitrate dehydrogenase (heart)
1.1.1.27 L-lactate dehydrogenase (heart)	
1.1.1.28 D-lactate dehydrogenase	
1.1.1.29 Glycerate dehydrogenase (spinach)	
1.1.1.37 Malate dehydrogenase (heart, wheat germ)	
1.2.1.3 Aldehyde dehydrogenase (liver)	
1.3.3.1 Dihydro-orotate dehydrogenase (bacteria)	
1.6.2.2 $NADH_2$ cytochrome b_5 reductase (liver)	

(2) *Enzymes producing Form B*

With NAD	*With NADP*
1.1.1.8 Glycerolphosphate dehydrogenase (muscle)	1.1.1.44 Phosphogluconate dehydrogenase (yeast)
1.1.1.35 3-hydroxyacyl-CoA dehydrogenase (heart)	1.1.1.49 Glucose-6-phosphate dehydrogenase (yeast)
1.1.1.47 Glucose dehydrogenase (liver)	
1.1.1.50 3-α-hydroxysteroid dehydrogenase (bacteria)	
1.1.1.i Oestradiol 17-β-dehydrogenase (placenta)	
1.1.1.51 β-hydroxysteroid dehydrogenase (bacteria)	
1.2.1.12 Glyceraldehydephosphate dehydrogenase (yeast, muscle)	
1.4.1.3 Glutamate dehydrogenase (liver)	1.4.1.3 Glutamate dehydrogenase (liver)
1.6.1.1 NAD(P) transhydrogenase (bacteria)	
1.6.2.1 $NADH_2$ cytochrome c reductase (liver, heart)	
1.6.4.2 Glutathione reductase (yeast, bacteria)	1.6.4.2 Glutathione reductase (yeast, bacteria)

References: 658, 1251, 1576, 1714, 1921, 2514

The specificity given for enzyme 1.6.1.1 is with respect to NAD. It would be interesting to know with which face of $NADPH_2$ it reacts; if the two coenzymes lie side-by-side it would be expected that side A of $NADPH_2$ would react with side B of NAD.

The factor determining which face is involved must presumably be the relative position of the substrate and coenzyme on the active centre. There appears to be no correlation with the structure of the substrate or the nature of the oxidation.

It may be pointed out that if the reacting groups are drawn with the correct bond lengths, it is easy to see how the typical dehydrogenase reaction may take place. We assume that we are looking down on the enzyme surface and that the reactants are combined side by side with their active groups close together. The nicotinamide ring of the coenzyme, seen on edge, is assumed to present one face to the substrate and to be prevented from turning by the amide group. The two hydrogen atoms of the CHOH group of the substrate are then not far from the positions which they will occupy in the reduced coenzyme. Thus not much more than a redistribution of electrons is necessary in order to transfer the attachment of the two hydrogen atoms from the substrate to the coenzyme or vice versa. One may probably picture the activated complex as a resonance-stabilized structure in which the hydrogen atoms can be regarded as shared between the substrate and the coenzyme, and which may break down in either direction, that is to say, either into substrate and coenzyme or into oxidized substrate and reduced coenzyme. The reversibility of the reaction is thus readily accounted for, in fact this mechanism accounts simply and satisfactorily for the observed phenomena of dehydrogenase reactions.

VII.17

The electron redistribution suggested has many similarities with the concerted displacement mechanism of Swain and Brown, mentioned earlier in this chapter. The simultaneous transfer of two hydrogen atoms is thus accounted for.

Here the curved arrows represent migrations of pairs of electrons, always in a clockwise direction round the circuit. In an alternative formulation, for which there is something to be said, half the electrons move clockwise and half anticlockwise, thus

$$
\begin{array}{c}
R_1 \diagdown \qquad H \\
R_2 \!-\! C \qquad \qquad CH\!-\!CH \\
\qquad \qquad \quad \overset{\|}{CH} \\
\qquad \qquad \quad \overset{\|}{CH} \\
O \diagdown \qquad \qquad N_{\!\!+}\!-\!CH \\
\qquad H \qquad \qquad | \\
\qquad \qquad \qquad R
\end{array}
$$

Here the arrows denote migrations of single electrons. In this case there is no electric current round the circuit. It would no doubt be an extremely difficult matter to distinguish between these formulations experimentally.

It is of interest to note that in dehydrogenase reactions generally the distance between the two hydrogen atoms of the substrate which are removed is about the same as in this case.

The work with deuterium leads clearly to the conclusion that biological dehydrogenation reactions catalysed by coenzyme-dependent dehydrogenases take place by hydrogen atom transfer, and not by the transfer of a pair of electrons, as many people have implied by the use of the 'electron transport' terminology.

There have been a few suggestions recently that such reactions may occur by the transfer of a hydride ion (H^-), but no evidence has ever been produced that this is the case for any enzymatic reaction. All these suggestions appear ultimately to have been derived from one by HAMMETT (988) that the Cannizzaro reaction of aldehydes in alkaline solution, which had been shown by experiments with deuterium to involve the transfer of a hydrogen atom from one aldehyde molecule to another without interchange with the solvent, proceeds by the transfer of a hydride ion from an anionic form of the aldehyde. It should be noted, however, that Hammett merely says that the phenomena 'are consistent' with this mechanism and, as INGOLD (1211, p. 708) points out, other mechanisms are possible, especially for the heterogeneous reaction.

It is true that in the reduction of NAD the *components* of a hydride ion (one proton and two electrons) are added, if the overall reaction including the ionization of the reduced form is considered, but this does not mean that they are transferred as a unit and one cannot deduce mechanisms merely from overall reactions.

A number of studies on the reduction of organic substances by LiAlH$_4$ in absolute ether have been quoted in support of the hydride ion mechanism. The example which most closely resembles the coenzyme is the reduction of quinoline methiodide to 1,2-dihydroquinoline, a very unstable substance which could only be isolated in the strict absence of oxygen (*2333*). The authors say 'it must be assumed that the H$^-$ from the metal hydride combines with the ammonium base to an unstable ammonium hydride' which is converted into the reduced product. No evidence is given that hydride ions are actually involved in the reaction; in any case it is difficult to argue from reactions of metal hydrides in anhydrous ether to enzyme-catalysed reactions in aqueous solution.

The coenzymes can be reduced in aqueous solution by NaBH$_4$ (*1756*), giving a product which shows an absorption spectrum similar to that of normal NADH$_2$, but which has less than half its activity with dehydrogenases. In other cases differences have been noted between reduction by metal hydrides and by more normal reducing agents such as dithionite. For instance, thiamine, which is reduced by dithionite with separation of the two rings, is reduced by LiAlH$_4$ to an *ortho*-dihydro compound; this, however, is practically inactive biologically (*1310*).

Reduction by LiAlH$_4$ invariably gives addition of hydrogen *ortho* to the nitrogen in such compounds, as would be expected if the hydrogen atom and the electron are added together in the form of a single particle. In the case of the enzymatic reduction of the coenzyme, however, experiments with deuterium (see Chapter IX) have shown that the addition is in the *para*-position, and that in the dehydrogenase reactions there is no hydrogen transfer to or from either of the *ortho*-positions. The addition of the hydrogen atom to one end of the ring and the electron to the other is less easy to explain if they are added together as one particle.

There is of course no question of *free* hydride ions in reactions occurring in aqueous solutions, because of their great reactivity. However, in such an intimate complex as that shown in VII.17, the distinction between the transfer of two hydrogen atoms and the transfer of a hydride ion and a hydrogen ion breaks down. The mechanism which we there put forward to show the transfer of two hydrogen atoms by a movement of electrons can be regarded also as a transfer of a hydride ion at one end and a hydrogen ion at the other. It is an important feature of this mechanism that the two transfers are simultaneous, both being part of the same electronic rearrangement, and the reaction is not a two-stage process involving successive transfers of H^- and H^+.

We have discussed mainly dehydrogenase reactions because their mechanisms have been studied by means of experiments with deuterium. The method owes its success to the fact that we are here concerned with hydrogen atoms that do not exchange with the solvent. When however, we come to the next step in the oxidation chain, i.e. flavoproteins, the hydrogen atoms of the carrier are exchangeable, so that any deuterium atoms transferred to it will be lost. Failure to demonstrate a direct transfer of deuterium from substrate to flavoprotein has led to claims that flavoproteins act by electron transfer and not by hydrogen transfer, but clearly these claims are invalid and the failure is simply due to loss by exchange.

However, in some cases the exchange is sufficiently slow to allow direct transfer of deuterium through the flavin group to be demonstrated. With glutathione reductase the rate of transfer of deuterium from NADHD to glutathione through the flavin group is 35 times as rapid as the loss by direct exchange between the flavin and the water (2514). Furthermore, with $NADH_2$ cytochrome b_5 reductase (1.5.2.2) on addition of NADHD the deuterium is transferred to the flavin group and can be subsequently transferred to an analogue of NAD, showing that the reduction and oxidation of flavoproteins takes place by the direct transfer of hydrogen atoms (658). In the case of the flavins there is sufficient similarity of the reducible grouping to that of the coenzyme, especially in the spacing of the two hydrogen atoms added, to suggest that a similar mechanism of simultaneous transfer of two hydrogen atoms may apply. In the case of the cytochromes there is no great difficulty in representing on paper their oxidation and reduction either as a transfer of hydrogen atoms or electrons, but the question remains open.

The case of O_2 is of special importance, as it is almost invariably the terminal acceptor in aerobic cells. The direct reduction of O_2 to H_2O_2, predicted by Wieland, was first shown for an enzyme system by THURLOW (2653) in the case of xanthine oxidase, and this is a general phenomenon in the autoxidation of flavoproteins. It can be imagined to take place either by the direct addition of two hydrogen atoms to give H_2O_2, or by addition of two electrons to give O_2^{--}, the anion of hydrogen peroxide, followed by the addition of two hydrogen ions. It is also conceivable that it could take place in two one-equivalent steps, with the intermediate formation of free radicals, such as HO_2-. In the case of xanthine oxidase kinetic considerations led GUTFREUND and STURTEVANT (960) to postulate an intermediate complex of reduced flavoprotein with O_2, which is formed very rapidly compared with the oxidation of the flavin group. More recently WELLNER and MEISTER (*2837*) have given spectroscopic evidence of such an O_2-flavoprotein complex in the case of L-aminoacid oxidase. The formation of a complex of this kind would facilitate the direct transfer of two hydrogen atoms between $FADH_2$ and O_2.

In several cases it has been shown that during the action of flavoprotein enzymes the half-reduced semiquinone form FADH– is involved. This will be further discussed on p. 276.

We shall now discuss a few dehydrogenases whose mechanism has been investigated in some detail.

Alcohol dehydrogenase

With this enzyme, as with several others, the combination of $NADH_2$ with the enzyme protein can be measured by changes in the absorption spectrum or in fluorescence (*2629*). The process catalysed can be represented as

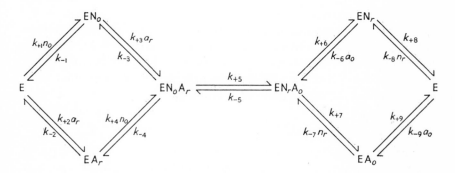

where for brevity N_o and N_r are written for the oxidized and reduced forms of NAD, and A_r and A_o for alcohol and aldehyde respectively.

The yeast alcohol dehydrogenase gives kinetics which indicate the formation of ternary complexes as represented, the overall reaction being limited by the interconversion of these complexes (i.e. by the actual oxidoreduction reaction) so that Michaelis conditions prevail (*534, 2003*). The K_ms for the two forms of NAD and for aldehyde agree reasonably well with the K_s values determined directly by ultracentrifugal methods (*1044*).

The liver enzyme, on the other hand, obeys different kinetics (*2635–6*). Here the interconversion of the ternary complexes is rapid, the dissociation of the coenzyme from these complexes is much slower than that of the substrate or product, and the combination of the enzyme with the coenzyme is independent of its combination with substrate or product. This means that k_{+5} and k_{-5} are large, k_{+7} and k_{+8} are relatively small (and in the reverse reaction k_{-1} and k_{-4}). Consequently the overall forward reaction with excess substrate is limited by the dissociation of the reduced coenzyme (i.e. by k_{+8}), and the kinetic behaviour will give no indication of the presence of ternary complexes, $E.N_o$ being rapidly converted into $E.N_r$ in the presence of alcohol. This has been called the 'Theorell-Chance mechanism', which may be represented for the back reaction by the equations

VII.18 $E + N_r = E.N_r$

VII.19 $E.N_r + A_o = E.N_o + A_r$

VII.20 $E.N_o = E + N_o$

THEORELL and McKINLEY McKEE (*2636*) have given a picture of the configuration of the ternary complexes which shows the coenzyme and substrate in the same relative position as that shown on p. 269, the coenzyme and the oxygen atom of the substrate being bound to the protein through a zinc atom.

A considerable amount of work on the nature of the groups in various dehydrogenases which are concerned with the binding of NAD has been done, largely by measurements of fluorescence. This has been reviewed by SHIFRIN and KAPLAN (*2388*). It is now well established that thiol groups play an important part in the binding.

Glyceraldehydephosphate dehydrogenase

This enzyme presents a number of unusual features. These are partly due to the fact that the normal oxidation of glyceraldehyde phosphate is coupled with a phosphorylation, and partly to the fact that, when suitably treated, the enzyme catalyses a number of other reactions. Moreover there are important differences between the yeast and muscle enzymes. The affinity of the enzymes for NAD is high, particularly that of the muscle enzyme, which as usually crystallized contains two molecules of NAD per molecule of enzyme. This can be removed by adsorption on charcoal.

The NAD is bound to the enzyme protein through thiol groups in the latter, and is released when these groups are combined with –SH reagents. It is not yet clear with what point in the NAD molecule the thiol group combines.

The view of the mechanism of the normal reaction which is most generally accepted is that of RACKER, which is as follows.

VII.21 $E-SH + NAD^+ = E-S-NAD + H^+$

VII.22 $\quad$ E–S–NAD + CHO.R = E–S–CO.R + NADH

VII.23 $\quad$ E–S–CO.R + H_3PO_4 = E–SH + H_2PO_3–O–CO.R

Here the aldehyde group of the substrate is assumed to undergo a double decomposition with the E–S–NAD, with the transfer of the acyl group to the –SH group. This acyl group is subsequently transferred to ortho-phosphate, giving an acyl phosphate. This scheme is undoubtedly a simplification; for example it fails to explain the high specificity of the enzyme for its substrate, which presumably depends on combination of R.CHO with a specific site in the active centre.

With the normal substrate (R = $-CHOH.CH_2.O.PO_3H_2$) the acyl-enzyme intermediate is stable and in the absence of phosphate the oxidation of the substrate does not proceed. With the non-phosphorylated glyceraldehyde as substrate, however, the reaction occurs at a slow rate in the absence of phosphate, owing to a slow hydrolysis of the acyl-enzyme intermediate, although the reaction is somewhat accelerated by the addition of phosphate.

The animal enzyme also catalyses transacylation, for example transfer of acetate from acetyl phosphate to various –SH compounds, or from one –SH compound to another, or the breakdown of acetyl phosphate by arsenolysis. These reactions, like the normal oxidation, are inhibited by –SH reagents but not by cyanide. The enzyme also catalyses direct hydrolysis of acetyl phosphate, but this is not affected by –SH reagents, although it is inhibited by 10^{-5}M cyanide. After all NAD has been removed from the enzyme by charcoal treatment the dehydrogenase will catalyse slow hydrolysis of p-nitrophenyl acetate; this reaction, unlike the acyl phosphatase activity, is inhibited by DFP and –SH reagents, but not by cyanide (*2053*). It is thus possible by appropriate treatment to convert the dehydrogenase into an acetyltransferase, a phosphatase, or an esterase. Table VII.2 summarizes the properties of these reactions.

TABLE VII.2

ENZYMATIC ACTIVITIES OF GLYCERALDEHYDEPHOSPHATE
DEHYDROGENASE

Reaction	Relative rate	pH optimum	Effect of IAA	Effect of cyanide	Combined NAD
Dehydrogenase	100	8+	Inhibits	None	Required
Acetyltransferase	0·006– 0·02	8+	Inhibits	None	Required
Esterase	0·018	8+	Inhibits	None	Inhibits
Acylphosphatase	0·023	7–	None	Inhibits	Required

References: 1011, 2053.

The secondary activities of this enzyme have only come to light because of the availability of large quantities of the crystalline enzyme. The interpretation of these results in terms of specific binding groups must await further investigation.

Lipoamide dehydrogenase

MASSEY (*1749*) has identified this enzyme with the flavoprotein previously known as 'diaphorase', which was only known to catalyse the oxidation of $NADH_2$ by artificial acceptors. It forms a part of the systems oxidizing pyruvate and 2-oxoglutarate. Its mechanism has been investigated by MASSEY and VEEGER (*1755*).

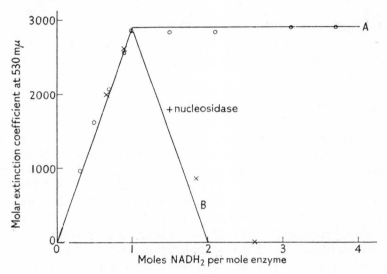

Fig. VII.2. *Titration of lipoamide dehydrogenase with $NADH_2$.*
Circles and crosses show the results in absence and presence of NAD(P) nucleosidase (3.2.2.6) respectively.

after *1755*

They showed that the enzyme is reduced by excess $NADH_2$ to a form in which the flavin is only half reduced. This can be detected by its absorption at 530 mμ; at this wavelength neither the oxidized nor the fully reduced form have any appreciable absorption. $NADH_2$ preparations usually contain small amounts of NAD; on removing all traces of NAD with NAD nucleosidase, Massey and Veeger found that the enzyme was converted into its fully reduced form. On titrating the flavoprotein with ordinary $NADH_2$, curve A of Fig. VII.2 was obtained.

This shows that on adding one molecule of $NADH_2$ per flavin group the whole of the enzyme was converted into the half reduced form, and on adding further amounts no change took place. With the $NADH_2$ preparation which had been freed from NAD, however, one molecule produced the same effect, but a second molecule completely reduced the enzyme. Since one molecule of $NADH_2$ yields two equivalents of hydrogen, whereas the conversion of the flavin to the half reduced form

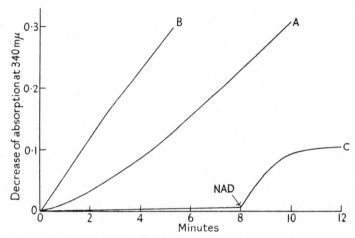

Fig. VII.3. *Necessity of NAD for $NADH_2$-lipoate reaction with lipoamide dehydrogenase.*

Lipoamide dehydrogenase, oxidized lipoate and $NADH_2$, with
   A, no additions
   B, 0·5 μmole NAD
   C, NAD(P) nucleosidase, 1 μmole NAD at arrow.
In A the production of NAD by the reaction increases the rate; in C the destruction of traces of NAD prevents the reaction and after the addition of NAD its destruction soon brings the reaction to a standstill again.

from *1755*

requires only one, it is evident that some other group in the enzyme was reduced at the same time, and they have produced evidence that this is a disulphide group. The three forms of the enzyme might be represented as

$$
\begin{array}{ccccc}
\left|\begin{array}{c}\text{-F} \\ \text{-S—S-}\end{array}\right| & \overset{2H}{\rightleftharpoons} & \left|\begin{array}{c}\text{-FH} \\ \text{-S } \text{ HS-}\end{array}\right| & \overset{2H}{\rightleftharpoons} & \left|\begin{array}{c}\text{-FH}_2 \\ \text{-SH } \text{ HS-}\end{array}\right|
\end{array}
$$

The catalytic activity of the flavoprotein was shown to be due to a reversible interconversion of the first two forms, and not of the first and third forms. Fig. VII.3 shows that when the enzyme is fully reduced by NAD-free $NADH_2$ it is catalytically inactive, and the presence of some NAD to prevent full reduction is necessary.

The scheme given by Massey and Veeger involves the formation of two neighbouring free radicals, and is somewhat more complicated.

MECHANISM OF TRANSFERRING (OR HYDROLYSING) ENZYMES

The hydrolysing enzymes are included with the transferring enzymes partly because, as already mentioned, hydrolysis can be regarded as a transfer of a part of the substrate molecule to a hydroxyl group from water, partly because it is now clear that there is much in common between the mechanisms of the two types, and partly because in fact many of the hydrolysing enzymes can also transfer to other molecules the group which is split off and conversely many transferring enzymes also bring about a certain amount of hydrolysis. The dividing line between the two types is therefore not sharp; it will be seen in section (d) below that it is based only on the stability towards water of the link formed between the enzyme and the group transferred.

In one respect views on enzyme action have undergone an important modification in recent years as a result of experimental investigations. Enzyme reactions used to be regarded as taking place between molecules on the surface of the enzyme, which acted purely as a catalytic influence and did not really enter into the reaction at all. There is now a strong tendency to bring the enzyme into the reaction as one of the reactants. This change of view is reflected in a change in the form of the equations representing the reaction. A reaction involving the transfer of a group B from combination with A to combination with D used to be written as

$$\text{VII.24} \qquad \overset{E}{A–B + D = A + B–D}$$

Nowadays it is much more likely to be written in two steps as

$$\text{VII.25} \qquad A–B + E = A + B–E$$

$$\text{VII.26} \qquad D + B–E = B–D + E$$

involving the formation of a definite compound of the enzyme with the group which is transferred. If, for example, the reaction is a phosphate transfer, the first step is the formation of the phosphorylated enzyme; if an acetyl-transfer, of an acetylated enzyme, and so on. It is now clear that very many, though apparently not all, transfer reactions do occur in this way.

(a) *Identification of the bond affected*

In reactions of this kind, which involve the division of the substrate molecule into two parts, it is frequently not immediately obvious where the division occurs. The two parts are usually united by a linking atom, most frequently an 'oxygen atom, and the division might occur on either side of this atom. For example, in the hydrolysis of sucrose the bond broken might be that between the bridging O atom and the glucose part, in which case the oxygen would remain as part of the free fructose molecule, or it might be the bond between the oxygen and the fructose part. In a phosphoric ester either the C–O or the P–O bond might be broken. Which bond is broken makes a good deal of difference to the mechanism of the enzyme action, especially in connection with the question of optical inversions (see section (c) below).

The question has been studied especially by M. Cohn (*471*) by isotopic methods, using O^{18}. The most direct way of testing would be to synthesize substrates in which O^{18} was the bridging atom, and to determine which part of the molecule contained it after the reaction. However, the synthesis may present difficulties and there are two much easier methods.

The first method is as follows. If the hydrolysis of the unlabelled substrate is carried out in H_2O^{18}, it is clear that O^{18} will be found in one part of the molecule or the other, according to the position at which the break occurs. Thus, considering a molecule represented as A–O–B,

$$A \text{----} \vdots \text{--} O \text{----} B \qquad A \text{----} O \vdots \text{----} B$$
$$O*H \ \vdots \ H \qquad\qquad H \ \vdots \ HO*$$

in the first case the O^{18} will be found in AOH and in the second case in BOH. This method is due to Polanyi and Szabo (*2099*), who used it to study the alkaline hydrolysis of an ester.

In the second method ordinary water is used, and free AOH and $BO^{18}H$ are added to the enzyme. Then in the reverse (synthetic) reaction, which will always be catalysed by the enzyme to some extent, we have the two possibilities, one of which will give $A–O^{18}–B$ while the other will give unlabelled A–O–B, thus

$$A\text{-}\boxed{\text{-O—H} \quad \text{H-}\text{-O*—B}} \qquad\qquad A\text{—O-}\boxed{\text{-H} \quad \text{H—O*-}}\text{-B}$$
$$\downarrow \qquad\qquad\qquad\qquad\qquad \downarrow$$
$$A\text{—O*—B} \qquad\qquad\qquad A\text{—O—B}$$
$$\downarrow \qquad\qquad\qquad\qquad\qquad \downarrow$$
$$A\text{—O—H} \quad H\text{—O*—B} \qquad\qquad A\text{—O—H} \quad H\text{—O—B}$$

On hydrolysis by the enzyme, as shown in the second step, the first case will give $BO^{18}H$, as at the beginning, while the second will give un-labelled BOH, since the reaction occurs in ordinary water. Thus, if time is allowed for the reaction to go backwards and forwards a sufficient number of times, in the second case the $BO^{18}H$ will lose practically all its O^{18}, but in the first case it will lose none. In the particular cases to which this method was applied, BOH was $H_3PO_4^{18}$, with all its O atoms labelled. It could only be expected to lose one O^{18} each time it reacted,

TABLE VII.3

Catalyst	Breakage point	Substrate
Acid	C$\overset{\downarrow}{-}$O–P	Glucose 1-phosphate
Acid	C$\overset{\downarrow}{-}$O–P	Trimethyl phosphate
Alkali	C–O$\overset{\downarrow}{-}$P	Trimethyl phosphate
Glyceraldehydephosphate dehydro-genase (1.2.1.12)	C$\overset{\downarrow}{-}$O–P	Acetyl phosphate
α-glucan phosphorylase (2.4.1.1) ..	C$\overset{\downarrow}{-}$O–P	Glycogen+phosphate
Sucrose glucosyltransferase (2.4.1.7) ..	C$\overset{\downarrow}{-}$O–P	Glucose 1-phosphate+ phosphate
Ribonuclease (2.7.7.16)	C–O$\overset{\downarrow}{-}$P	Polynucleotide
Alkaline phosphatase (3.1.3.1).. ..	C–O$\overset{\downarrow}{-}$P	Glucose 1-phosphate
Alkaline phosphatase (3.1.3.1).. ..	C–O$\overset{\downarrow}{-}$P	Phenyl phosphate
Acid phosphatase (3.1.3.2)	C–O$\overset{\downarrow}{-}$P	Glucose 1-phosphate
Phosphodiesterase (3.1.4.1)	C–O$\overset{\downarrow}{-}$P	Polynucleotide

but since all its groups react indiscriminately a sufficient number of reversals of the reaction should remove all the O^{18} atoms.

This method is also applicable to transfer reactions, for example, to phosphorylases, using $H_3PO_4^{18}$ as the acceptor D in reaction VII.26. If the B group (in this case a glycosyl group) is transferred in the form B–O–, the O^{18} will be displaced from D, but if in the form B–, D will retain its label. Some results obtained by this method are shown in Table VII.3, where the arrow indicates the point of breakage.

These results may be compared with non-enzymatic hydrolysis of carboxylic esters, where either bond may be broken, according to the conditions of the hydrolysis and the nature of the ester, although acyl-oxygen fission is most common (see, for example, chapter 14 of *1211*). It will be seen that all the phosphatases attack the P–O link, whereas the phosphorylases attack the C–O link.

The enzyme results strongly suggest that the break comes on that side of the bridging atom which is nearest to the part of the molecule for which the enzyme is most specific (*1451*), that is to say, it occurs as closely as possible to the group which is being transferred. The phosphatases are specific for the phosphate part of the molecule, and both can transfer phosphate groups to other molecules, so that the break comes next to the phosphorus atom; the phosphorylases, on the other hand, are glycosyl-transferring enzymes, specific for the glucose part of the molecule, and the break comes next to the glucose carbon atom.

In confirmation of this, KOSHLAND and STEIN (*1451*) have examined the action of yeast invertase (a fructofuranosidase) on sucrose. This enzyme is specific for the fructose part of the molecule and can catalyse the transfer of fructosyl groups to other molecules. As expected, the bond which is broken is that nearest to the fructose part of the molecule.

The number of enzymes which have been examined by these methods is not large enough to establish the rule as one of universal validity, but it appears to be an important principle and it is to be hoped that additional evidence will soon be forthcoming.

M. COHN (*472–3*) has also studied glyceraldehydephosphate dehydrogenase (1.2.1.12) and phosphoglycerate kinase (2.7.2.3) (see Table XII.1.h–j). On carrying out the overall dehydrogenase reaction, namely

VII.27   Glyceraldehyde phosphate+phosphate+NAD
$$\rightleftharpoons \text{diphosphoglycerate}+\text{NADH}_2$$

using $H_3PO_4{}^{18}$, she found no change in the O^{18} content of the phosphate group, and this was also true when the reaction was carried out in the reverse direction. This shows that it is the C–O and not the P–O bond which is involved, as might be expected from the fact that the enzyme is specific towards the aldehyde. With the kinase, on the other hand, it is the P–O bond which is affected, in agreement with the fact that this is a phosphate-transferring enzyme. When the kinase reaction XII.1.j is carried out with the diphosphoglycerate formed in the above reaction (and therefore containing O^{18} atoms in its 1-phosphate group) the molecule of phosphoglycerate which is formed is left with a $-CO.O^{18}H$ group, because the linking O atom which originally belonged to the phosphate is left attached to the C atom when the P–O bond is broken. Thus one effect of this two-enzyme system is to transfer one of the O atoms of the phosphate to the carboxyl. The whole system, however, is reversible, so that an O atom from the carboxyl can be taken back into the phosphate; but since the two O atoms in a –COOH group are chemically equivalent, either atom can be taken back. This results ultimately in a dilution of the O^{18} by the amount of O^{16} initially attached to this C atom in the substrate, and only by this amount, as found by Cohn.

Similar studies have shown (473) that the P–O bond is involved in the action of yeast hexokinase (2.7.1.1) and adenylate kinase (2.7.4.3).

(b) *Isotope exchange methods*

These methods make it possible to decide between the two mechanisms of enzyme-catalysed transfer reactions given above, namely, reaction VII.24, in which there is a direct transfer of the group from one molecule to the other, and reactions VII.25–6, in which an intermediate compound of the group with the enzyme is formed.

If VII.24 represents the true mechanism, no reaction will occur unless both substrates A–B and D are added. Reaction VII.25, on the other hand, only requires the presence of one substrate, and if A–B is added to the enzyme in the complete absence of D a small amount of free A (not exceeding the equivalent of the amount of enzyme present) will be reversibly formed. Now if we add, in addition to A–B, some isotopically labelled A (A*), we should expect to find reaction VII.25 followed by the reverse reaction

VII.28   B–E $+$ A* $=$ A*–B $+$ E

and although the amount of enzyme present may be stoichiometrically very small this process will proceed until isotopic equilibrium is reached. In other words, in the absence of the acceptor D the enzyme will catalyse an isotopic exchange reaction involving that part of the substrate molecule which is *not* transferred to the enzyme. A similar experiment may be performed with the product; if B–D and D* are added to the enzyme in the absence of A, an isotopic exchange of D will be catalysed. On the other hand, if B* were added no exchange would be observed in either case.

The method is a powerful one for the investigation of reactions which occur by intermediate group-transfer to the enzyme, and it is being increasingly used. The following are a few cases in which it has given clear evidence as to the reaction mechanism.

Sucrose glucosyltransferase (2.4.1.7) catalyses the reaction

VII.29 α-G-1-Ph $+$ F $=$ α-G-1-F $+$ Ph

where Ph represents phosphate, G glucose and F fructose, so that α-G-1-F represents sucrose; the reaction is thus a reversible transfer of the glucose group from phosphate to fructose. If only glucose phosphate is added, with or without free phosphate, no *chemical* reaction would be expected to occur, since in the absence of fructose there would be no acceptor for the phosphate. However, it was found (*650*) that when $H_3P^{32}O_4$ and glucose phosphate are added the enzyme rapidly catalyses the isotope exchange reaction

VII.30 $\qquad \alpha\text{-G-1-Ph} + \text{Ph*} = \alpha\text{-G-1-Ph*} + \text{Ph}$

This indicates that the enzyme forms a compound with the glucose group, liberating the phosphate, the exchange then taking place as follows

VII.31 $\qquad \text{G-1-Ph} + \text{E} = \text{G-1-E} + \text{Ph}$

VII.32 $\qquad \text{G-1-E} + \text{Ph*} = \text{G-1-Ph*} + \text{E}$

This was confirmed by the use of fructose labelled with $C^{14}(F^*)$ (*2901*). In the absence of phosphate, the enzyme catalyses the exchange

VII.33 $\qquad \alpha\text{-G-1-F} + \text{F*} = \alpha\text{-G-1-F*} + \text{F}$

which again is to be expected if the enzyme forms a compound with the glucose part of the molecule, which is the part for which it is specific and which it transfers to other molecules. The enzyme is thus not a true phosphorylase, since phosphate is not necessarily involved in the reaction. In fact, it can transfer glucose groups to a variety of other molecules, and this fact provides further support for the mechanism proposed. Still further evidence for an intermediate transfer of the glucose group to the enzyme is given in section (c) below.

When we turn to maltose phosphorylase (2.4.1.8) the position is quite different. The reaction catalysed can be represented as

VII.34 $\qquad \alpha\text{-G-G} + \text{Ph} = \beta\text{-G-1-Ph} + \text{G}$

The fact that an optical inversion occurs is an indication of a direct transfer rather than a transfer by way of the enzyme (see section (c)), and in agreement with this the enzyme does *not* catalyse the isotope exchange

VII.35 $\qquad \beta\text{-G-1-Ph} + \text{Ph*} = \beta\text{-G-1-Ph*} + \text{Ph}$

(*746*), nor (in the absence of phosphate) does it catalyse the reaction

VII.36 $\qquad \alpha\text{-G-G} + \text{G*} = \alpha\text{-G-G*} + \text{G}$

In the presence of phosphate, VII.36 is catalysed, but this is bound to happen simply by the reversal of VII.34.

The evidence suggests therefore that in this case no enzyme–glucose compound is formed, and that the transglycosylation takes place by a direct transfer of the glucose group from one substrate to the other in accordance with equation VII.24. α-glucan phosphorylase (2.4.1.1) also fails to catalyse the isotope exchange reaction VII.30 (476).

These results are confirmed by the behaviour of the enzymes in the presence of arsenate. With sucrose glucosyltransferase the addition of arsenate causes a rapid hydrolysis of sucrose to free glucose and fructose, and of glucose 1-phosphate to free glucose and phosphate. This is because arsenate can take the place of phosphate, forming the very unstable glucose arsenate which spontaneously breaks down with high velocity. Thus reactions VII.37 and VII.38 are followed respectively by reactions VII.39–40:

VII.37 $G\text{-}1\text{-}F + E = G\text{-}1\text{-}E + F$

VII.38 $G\text{-}1\text{-}Ph + E = G\text{-}1\text{-}E + Ph$

VII.39 $G\text{-}1\text{-}E + As = G\text{-}1\text{-}As + E$

VII.40 $G\text{-}1\text{-}As + H_2O = G + As$

where As represents H_3AsO_4.

On the other hand maltose phosphorylase, which does not form the glucose–enzyme intermediate, is unable to catalyse the hydrolysis of β-glucose 1-phosphate in the presence of arsenate, and this agrees with its inability to catalyse reaction VII.35. As would be expected, however, it does catalyse the hydrolysis of maltose in the presence of arsenate, as this can take place by a direct transfer of glucose to arsenate, thus

VII.41 $\alpha\text{-}G\text{-}G + As = \beta\text{-}G\text{-}1\text{-}As + G$

followed by reaction VII.40. Thus the results clearly show the difference in reaction mechanism between the two enzymes which was found by the isotope exchange method.

Several other enzymes have been tested similarly. 3-ketoacid CoA-transferase (2.8.3.5) catalyses the exchange

VII.42   succinyl–CoA+succinate* = succinyl*–CoA+succinate

(see *1639a*), showing that again the enzyme forms an intermediate compound with the group which it transfers, in this case coenzyme A. Arylamine acetyltransferase (2.3.1.5) catalyses the exchange

VII.43   acetyl–arylamine+arylamine*
                    = acetyl–arylamine*+arylamine

but not the exchange

VII.44   acetyl–arylamine+acetate*
                                  = acetyl*–arylamine+acetate

(see *240*), indicating that again it is the group transferred (the acetyl group) which combines with the enzyme, and not the arylamine.

With the kinases, on the other hand, the available evidence suggests that the phosphate group which is transferred does not form an intermediate enzyme–phosphate compound. Acetate kinase (2.7.2.1) has been shown (*2246*) not to catalyse the incorporation of labelled ADP into ATP (unless acetate is also added), or of labelled acetate into acetyl phosphate (unless ADP is also added), or of labelled phosphate into ATP (even when acetate is added). If an enzyme–phosphate compound were formed, the first two exchanges might have been expected. Similarly, pyruvate kinase (2.7.1.40) will not catalyse the incorporation of labelled pyruvate into phosphopyruvate unless ADP is also added (*305*). On the basis of other evidence mechanisms have been suggested, in the case of phosphoglycerate and pyruvate kinases, which are consistent with these observations (see section (d) below).

Among the hydrolysing enzymes, NAD(P) nucleosidase (3.2.2.6) has been shown (*2959*) to catalyse the exchange

VII.45   N–R + N* = N*–R + N

where N is written for nicotinamide and R stands for the rest of the coenzyme molecule. This suggests that the mechanism of the hydrolysis is

VII.46   N–R + E = E–R + N

VII.47   E–R + H_2O = E + R

Since alkaline phosphatase (3.1.3.1) can transfer phosphate groups in addition to removing them by hydrolysis, it would be expected that the process takes place through an intermediate enzyme–phosphate compound, and if so, since it is the P–O bond which is broken, it should catalyse the incorporation of O^{18} from H_2O^{18} into phosphate. This has been shown to occur (*2510*), though at a rather slow rate. It has also been shown (*474*) to occur with inorganic pyrophosphatase (3.6.1.1).

ATPase (3.6.1.3) has been shown to break the bond between the P atom of the terminal group and the linking O atom (*473*). Both in the form of myosin and actomyosin, it catalyses the incorporation of O^{18} from H_2O^{18} into inorganic phosphate, but in the case of myosin this requires the presence of ATP or other nucleoside triphosphates. The effects are complicated, depending on the nature of the activating metal ion and of the nucleoside triphosphate (*591, 1570*). They may be due to structural changes in the protein, which are known to take place in the presence of ATP, or to an exchange with an intermediate formed during ATP hydrolysis. A definite conclusion is not possible at present.

The case of chymotrypsin (3.4.4.5) is also one in which the incorporation of O^{18} provides evidence of a definite compound with the enzyme. When carbobenzoxyphenylalanine is added to the enzyme in H_2O^{18}, a rapid incorporation of O^{18} into the aminoacid occurs, owing to a reversible combination of the carboxyl group with the enzyme and elimination of water (*2486*). This does not occur with phenylalanine itself, in agreement with the specificity of the enzyme when acting on peptides, etc., nor does it occur with serum albumin.

(c) *The optical inversion method*

A direct group-transfer reaction may be regarded as a case of the well-known 'displacement reaction', in which, as the group *to* which the transfer takes place approaches the atom *at* which it takes place, the group *from* which it takes place simultaneously recedes from the opposite side. For example, the methyl-transfer reaction from X to Y

$$\text{methyl-X} + \text{Y} = \text{methyl-Y} + \text{X}$$

may be regarded as taking place somewhat as follows:

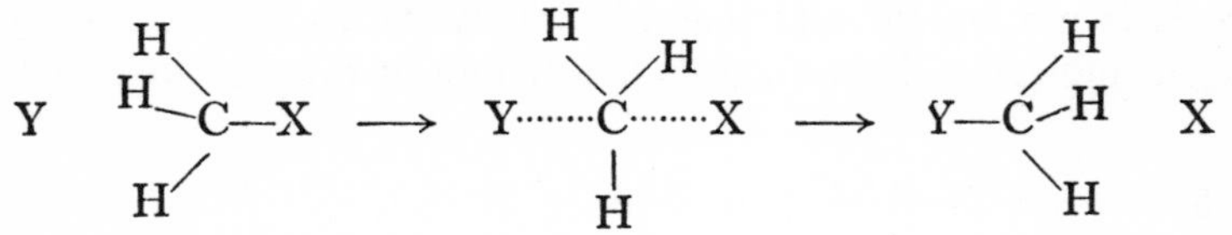

Here the displacement takes place at the C atom of the methyl group, and Y approaches from the side opposite to X. As Y gets nearer to the C atom, X recedes, and at the same time the three C–H bonds also recede, until in the intermediate state of the system they lie in a plane at right angles to the X–Y axis, as shown in the central configuration. Finally, they move still further, so that they lie on the side opposite to Y; the result is that the configuration of the C atom has become reversed, as shown in the right-hand diagram.

Now if the displacement had occurred on an optically active atom, or, in other words, if these three bonds had been attached to three different groups, a little reflection will show that an optical inversion would have accompanied the transfer, for the group transferred would have been converted into its mirror image. This is in fact a known characteristic of the displacement reaction.

KOSHLAND (*1448*) has pointed out that the occurrence or non-occurrence of an optical inversion in an enzyme reaction may afford evidence of the mechanism of the reaction. If the reaction involves only one transfer (or an odd number of successive transfers) of the group, the result will be an optical inversion; if it involves two successive transfers (or an even number), the effects will cancel and no inversion will be observed. Thus if the reaction occurs by a direct transfer of the group from one substrate to the other, in accordance with reaction VII.24, an inversion of the group B will be produced. If it takes place through the formation of an intermediate compound of group B with the enzyme, as shown in reactions VII.25–6, the transfer of B from A to the enzyme will cause an inversion, but the transfer of B from the enzyme to D will cause a second inversion, cancelling the effect of the first and restoring B to its original configuration.

It is important to remember, however, that the inversion can only affect the particular atom at which the transfer occurs; hence the importance of determining the actual bond involved in the reaction, as described in section (a) above. For instance, no inversion is observed as a result of the action of phosphatase. This might at first sight be regarded as indicating a two-step mechanism. But it has been shown that in the C–O–P grouping it is the P–O bond which is broken, therefore the displacement is not on the C atom at all; it is impossible for inversion of the C to take place, because its bond remains attached to the O atom, so that all its bonds must retain their relative position. In this case therefore the absence of an inversion provides no evidence of mechanism, since it is to be expected from either mechanism.

For the same reason also in the case of a disaccharide substrate

it is impossible ever to get an inversion of *both* hexoses. If it is bond A which is broken, no inversion can occur in the right-hand hexose, though there may be one at the C_1 atom of the left-hand hexose; if bond B is affected, the left-hand hexose must retain its configuration, though the other may suffer an inversion at its C_4 atom.

Now if we compare sucrose glucosyltransferase and maltose phosphorylase, we find that this method gives results in good agreement with the isotope exchange method. We have seen that the bond affected is that between the glucosidic carbon atom and the oxygen atom, so that no inversion should be found in the other half of the molecule, and this is in agreement with observation. We have seen also that the isotope method indicates that the two enzymes differ in their mechanism. In the case of sucrose glucosyltransferase, the α-glucose is first transferred to the enzyme, presumably with an inversion to the β-form; this is then transferred from the enzyme to phosphate or some other molecule, which should cause a second inversion to give α-glucose 1-phosphate, as is actually found. In the case of maltose phosphorylase the isotope evidence indicates a direct transfer of the α-glucose to the phosphate, and the resulting inversion should give β-glucose 1-phosphate, which is what is actually found.

Another illustration of the same principle is amidophosphoribosyltransferase (2.4.2.14), for which the lack of incorporation of labelled pyrophosphate into phosphoribosyl-pyrophosphate shows that the reaction does not proceed through the formation of a phosphoribosyl-enzyme intermediate. Thus the process must take place by a single displacement reaction, and inversion would be expected; this is actually found, the α-phosphoribosyl-pyrophosphate being converted into β-phosphoribosylamine (*1015*).

In the case of α-glucan phosphorylase there is an unexplained discrepancy between the two methods. As we have seen, it resembles maltose phosphorylase in being unable to catalyse the isotope exchange, which would suggest a direct transfer. This should result in an inversion, as in the case of the maltose enzyme, but no such inversion occurs. α-glucose 1-phosphate is formed from the polysaccharide chains, which contain only α-links. It is to be hoped that further work will reveal the cause of this discrepancy. The system is probably more complex than it appears; the enzyme active centre contains pyridoxal phosphate (*160*), and the enzyme action depends on the presence of a phosphate-containing group, the phosphate of which can be removed and restored enzymatically. If the mode of action of this group were known, the reason for the lack of inversion would probably become clear.

(d) *Inferences from competition and other effects*

Apart from the more general methods, inferences as to the reaction mechanism may be made in a number of cases from special features in the behaviour of the systems. For instance, in the case of the phosphatases (3.1.3.1–2), which can bring about both hydrolysis and transfer, MORTON (*1879*) found that there is a definite competition between water and the phosphate acceptor for the phosphate removed from the substrate. This is most easily explained by an initial (rate-determining) transfer of phosphate from the substrate to the enzyme, followed by a partition of the enzyme-bound phosphate between water and the acceptor in accordance with their concentrations and the velocity constants of the two reactions. This is in agreement with the evidence from isotope experiments already mentioned.

These phosphatases are specific for the phosphate group and comparatively unspecific for the remainder of the molecule. Other phosphatases, however, are specific for the substrate as a whole (e.g. 3.1.3.5 and 3.1.3.11), and with these enzymes no phosphate transfer has been detected (*1879*).

Another type of competition effect has been used by BÜCHER (*354*) to deduce a reaction mechanism for phosphoglycerate kinase (2.7.2.3), which catalyses the reversible transfer of phosphate from the carboxyl group in diphosphoglycerate to ADP. This reaction may be represented symbolically as

VII.48 $PGP + ARPP = PG + ARPPP$

where PG is written for 3-phosphoglycerate and A, R and P for the adenine, ribose and phosphate groups of ADP and ATP, so that ARPPP stands for ATP. Bücher found that ATP does not compete with ADP in this system, suggesting that they combine at different sites on the enzyme, but that both ATP and ADP compete with diphosphoglycerate. To explain this, he proposed the following picture of the process

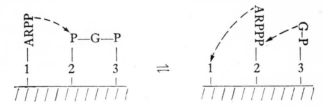

Here 1, 2 and 3 represent three sites on the enzyme; 1 can combine with the adenine end of the ADP molecule, 2 can combine either with ATP through its terminal phosphate group or with the 1-phosphate of diphosphoglycerate, and 3 can combine with the 3-phosphate of phosphoglycerate or diphosphoglycerate. Thus the latter combines with sites 2 and 3 simultaneously. The phosphate group which is transferred is the one which is combined with site 2, and the reaction can be pictured as taking place by the terminal phosphate of ADP coming on to this phosphate group and displacing the glycerate from it, so that we are left with ATP on site 2 and phosphoglycerate on site 3, as shown above. The process may be regarded as a direct displacement of the type represented by reaction VII.24.

L

This mechanism appears quite probable, although the evidence from competition cannot be regarded as conclusive. It explains the competition between ATP and diphosphoglycerate, but it does not entirely account for the absence of competition between ATP and ADP for it is not clear why ATP should not combine with site 1 as ADP does, and since ADP competes with diphosphoglycerate as well as ATP it seems that both ADP and ATP must combine with site 2 and should compete with one another. Perhaps the explanation is a matter of relative affinities of the different reactants for the three sites.

The mechanism of pyruvate kinase (2.7.1.40) has been investigated by BOYER et al. (*1020, 2213*), who find that ADP does not compete with phosphoenolpyruvate (PEP), that ATP competes with ADP and with PEP, that pyruvate competes weakly with PEP, while AMP does not inhibit. This indicates that there is one site combining with either ADP or ATP and one combining with either pyruvate or PEP. Competition between ATP and PEP is caused by the overlap of the phosphoryl group which is directly transferable in the reaction. The competition of ATP with ADP and PEP has been confirmed by direct measurement of the binding. The K_ms for ADP and PEP were shown to be approximately equal to the K_ss thus obtained.

The kinetics of adenylate kinase (2.7.4.3) have been studied by CALLAGHAN and WEBER (*381*), who find that ATP and AMP compete with ADP in one direction, and ADP with ATP and AMP in the opposite direction, but ATP does not compete with AMP. They interpret this to mean that there is a single site combining with any of the three reactants to form a complex which then reacts with an appropriate second molecule. For all three reactants, K_m values obtained as substrates are identical with K values obtained as inhibitors.

(e) *Identification of intermediate complexes*

Light on mechanism can sometimes be obtained by the actual isolation and identification of an intermediate complex.

In the case of phosphoglucomutase (2.7.5.1), the occurrence of a phosphate–enzyme compound has been demonstrated directly (*1651, 2123*). When a rather large amount of the crystalline enzyme is added to glucose 1-phosphate, there is an instantaneous formation of glucose 1,6-diphosphate and the amount formed depends on the amount of enzyme added. Evidently the enzyme as isolated is partly or wholly in the phosphorylated state and the phosphate can be transferred to the glucose phosphate.

VII.49   E–P + glucose 1-phosphate = E + glucose 1,6-diphosphate

The resulting free enzyme can then be rephosphorylated by glucose diphosphate, with the formation of an equivalent amount of glucose 6-phosphate (cf. reaction XII.1.b). Similar results have been obtained with crystalline muscle phosphoglyceromutase (2.7.5.3) (*2090*).

VENKATARAMAN and RACKER (*2731*) were able to isolate a dihydroxy-acetone-transaldolase complex by chromatography on a column of carboxymethyl-cellulose. This shows that the reaction takes place by a transfer of a dihydroxyacetone group from the substrate to the enzyme, from which it was shown to be removed by a suitable acceptor. The dihydroxyacetone-enzyme complex is a Schiff's base involving the ϵ-group of a lysine residue in the enzyme (*892*).

In some cases the group is transferred, not to the enzyme protein, but to a prosthetic group bound to the enzyme protein. In the case of trans-ketolase, a glycolaldehyde-thiamine-pyrophosphate compound has been identified (see p. 414). Another example is the isolation of a biotin-CO_2 compound from the carboxylases of sub-group 6.4 (see p. 415). Pyridoxal phosphate functions as the prosthetic group of many enzymes acting on aminoacids by forming Schiff's bases with them (p. 411).

A number of hydrolases also catalyse the transfer of the group removed to other acceptors than water, and this has been widely interpreted as due to the transfer of the group to the enzyme in the first place. Such intermediates cannot normally be isolated, since they are rapidly hydro-lysed by water. In the case of chymotrypsin, however, it is possible by using an unusual substrate to produce a stable analogue of the normal intermediate. Chymotrypsin at neutral pH hydrolyses p-nitrophenyl acetate, but at acid pH hydrolysis is very slow and a monoacetylchymo-trypsin can be isolated (*149*).

MECHANISM OF LYASES

Apart from the decarboxylases, many of which depend on pyridoxal phosphate or thiamine pyrophosphate and are discussed in the chapter on cofactors (see also p. 195), the lyase which has been most studied is fumarate hydratase (4.2.1.2). We shall therefore discuss this in some detail.

Fumarate hydratase

The question of the mechanism of this enzyme is closely bound up with the stereochemistry of the reaction. It shows optical specificity in one direction (using only L-malate) and geometrical specificity in the other (using only fumarate). Thus it is specific with respect to the placing of the hydroxyl group onto fumarate, and ALBERTY and his colleagues (*39,*

715) showed that it is also specific with respect to the placing of the hydrogen on the other carbon atom. This is shown by the fact that if fumarate is allowed to equilibrate with D_2O in the presence of the enzyme, and the malic and fumaric acids isolated and allowed to exchange with H_2O, the malic acid is found to contain one atom of deuterium and the fumaric acid to contain none. Thus any deuterium added in the forward reaction is removed in the reverse reaction.

On the evidence of proton magnetic resonance measurements on the isolated malic acid, it was at first thought that the –H and –OH had been added to the double bond of fumarate in the *cis*- configuration. However, ANET (*71*) and GAWRON and. FONDY (*818*) synthesized *trans*-monodeuteromalic acid, and by comparison with the form produced by the enzyme they showed conclusively that the addition by the enzyme was *trans*. Similar results have been obtained for other hydro-lyases. ENGLARD (*696*) independently came to the same conclusion by some rather complicated deductions from deuterium-transfer by a mixture of citrate synthase, aconitate hydratase and isocitrate dehydrogenase.

Alberty also considered the question of whether the water molecule is added as such by a concerted mechanism, or in two steps as OH^- and H^+ ions. From the fact that the hydration of fumarate was found to proceed at the same rate in D_2O as in H_2O, he concluded that a simultaneous addition of OH^- and H^+ ions was excluded, but in his experiments it seems quite possible that the limiting step was the initial formation of the enzyme-substrate complex, since he was working under 'first order conditions' with low substrate concentration. If this were so a difference would not be expected. In fact it has later been shown (*2491*) that under 'zero order conditions' an isotope effect on the velocity occurs, although it is not large. We consider that the question remains quite open, although analogy with the enzyme discussed in the next paragraph would suggest the addition of a water molecule as such.

Aspartate ammonia-lyase

The behaviour of this enzyme is closely similar to that of fumarate hydratase; they both add groups across the double bond of fumarate, and they have the same L- and *cis*-requirements in their substrates. Moreover, they both add the hydrogen atom in the same position, i.e. *trans* to the NH_2 or OH group respectively (*1457a*). If fumarate is converted into aspartate in D_2O with one enzyme, the deuteromalate formed by the action of nitrous acid on the resulting deuteroaspartate is identical with that produced directly from fumarate in D_2O by the other.

The addition of ammonia by this enzyme can hardly be written as a sequential addition of two ions, and must be due to the *trans* addition of a whole NH_3 molecule by a concerted mechanism across the double bond.

Epimerases

Epimerases catalyse D-L-transformations in substrates having more than one asymmetric centre. Diaminopimelate epimerase (5.1.1.7) acts on a substrate in which the two asymmetric groups are well separated. The stereochemical requirements have been studied by ANTIA, HOARE and WORK (*80*). The enzyme will convert the LL-form into the LD- or *meso*-form, but will not interconvert the LD- and DD-forms. This means that the enzyme has two combining sites; one combines with the end having the L-configuration, but has no action on it, the other combines with the other end in either configuration and causes their interconversion.

Aldose mutarotase (5.1.3.3) is a special case in which the asymmetric centre acted on is the reducing group of a sugar. The mechanism of it action has been studied by BENTLEY and BHATE (*207*). They showed that during the reaction there is no exchange of the hydrogen atom on C_1 with deuterium in D_2O, or any loss of $O^{18}H$ from glucose-1-O^{18}. Replacement of the hydrogen atom on C_1 by D has no effect on the rate. These observations appear to rule out any mechanism based on dehydration or on dehydrogenation involving C-bound hydrogen, or a single displacement mechanism involving OH^-. The most probable mechanism is a hydrogen transfer resulting in the intermediate formation of the open-chain aldehyde.

Methylmalonyl-CoA racemase

This enzyme (5.1.99.a) differs from other known racemases in that the carbon atom in the asymmetric centre has three other carbon atoms attached. MAZUMDER *et al.* (*1773*) have shown that the conversion is not due to the direct transfer of the coenzyme A from one carboxyl group to the other. OVERATH *et al.* (*2038*) showed that the hydrogen atom on the asymmetric centre exchanges with tritium when the reaction is carried out in T_2O. They interpret this as supporting the following mechanism:

$$\begin{array}{ccc} \text{H} \quad \text{O} & & \text{O}^- \\ | \quad || & & | \\ \text{HOOC.C---C.CoA} & \rightleftharpoons & \text{HOOC.C=C.CoA} + \text{H}^+ \\ | & & | \\ \text{CH}_3 & & \text{CH}_3 \end{array}$$

The enol form produced has a planar configuration and the enzyme can add a H^+ ion to either side of the plane to produce the D- or L-configuration.

Cis-trans isomerases

These enzymes appear to catalyse a shift in the disposition of groups in planar molecules. Some at any rate depend on reduced glutathione as cofactor. The addition of glutathione across the double bond would produce a saturated compound and allow free rotation:

$$
\begin{array}{ccc}
\text{H} \quad \text{H} & & \text{H} \quad \text{H} \\
\text{–C=C–} & & \text{–C—C–} \\
+ & \rightleftharpoons & \text{H} \quad \text{S} \\
\text{H—S} & & \text{G} \\
\text{G} & &
\end{array}
$$

If the elimination of glutathione now takes place with removal of the hydrogen other than that which was added, isomerization will result. It is known that glutathione catalyses the interconversion of fumarate and maleate non-enzymatically in this way. However, this should result in the incorporation of deuterium if the reaction is carried out in D_2O, and in the reaction catalysed by maleylpyruvate isomerase (5.2.1.a) this is found not to occur (*1500*), nor was it found in the corresponding non-enzymatic reaction catalysed by glutathione. The correct interpretation of these findings is still obscure.

Ketol-isomerases

Triosephosphate isomerase (5.3.1.1) catalyses the reduction of the aldehydic or ketonic group by the adjacent CHOH group. Isotopic experiments (RIEDER and ROSE, *2220*) indicate that the reaction does not take place by direct intramolecular hydrogen transfer, since one tritium atom is incorporated when the reaction takes place in T_2O. They suggest a mechanism in which an enzyme-bound enolate anion is an intermediate. By experiments with this enzyme and with aldolase (4.1.2.b), they showed that one of the hydrogen atoms in the $-CH_2OH$ group is removed by the isomerase and the other by aldolase.

Similar results were obtained with glucosephosphate isomerase (5.3.1.9) by TOPPER (*2671*) who also postulated a bound enolate ion intermediate. He showed that the hydrogen atom in the $-CH_2OH$ group of fructose 6-phosphate which is removed by this enzyme is not the one which is removed by mannosephosphate isomerase (5.3.1.8).

In a more recent study, ROSE and O'CONNELL (*2247*), while confirming Topper's results, showed also that fructose 6-phosphate labelled with tritium on C_1 is converted by glucosephosphate isomerase into glucose 6-phosphate labelled on C_2. Thus, although incorporation occurs, there is also a transfer of tritium from C_1 to C_2 of the same molecule. At low temperatures the transfer is much more rapid than the incorporation. They therefore suggested a modification of the mechanism just given, in which the reaction takes place by transfer of the carbon-bound hydrogen, which is removed when the enolate ion is formed, to a group on the enzyme which only exchanges with the medium comparatively slowly. The same hydrogen can then be transferred back from the enzyme to the adjacent carbon of the same substrate molecule.

Δ-isomerases

Steroid Δ-isomerase (5.3.3.1) catalyses the transposition of a double bond from the 4,5 to the 5,6 position, which implies the migration of a hydrogen atom from the 6 to the 4 position. The mechanism was studied by TALALAY and WANG (*2609*), and compared with the non-enzymatic catalysis of the same reaction by H^+ and OH^- ions. In D_2O the non-enzymatic process is associated with incorporation of deuterium, but the enzymatic process, which proceeds at the same rate as in H_2O, gives no incorporation. This suggests that the enzyme catalyses a direct intramolecular transfer of a hydrogen atom from C_6 to C_4.

Methylmalonyl-CoA mutase

It was earlier thought that this enzyme catalysed the conversion of methylmalonyl-CoA to succinyl-CoA by an intermolecular carboxyl transfer, with propionyl-CoA as a 'cofactor', thus

VII.50
$$
\begin{array}{cc}
\text{COOH} & \text{CH}_3 \\
| & | \\
\text{H—C—CH}_3 + & \text{CH}_2 \\
| & | \\
\text{CO.CoA} & \text{CO.CoA}
\end{array}
$$

$$
\begin{array}{ccc}
\text{H} & & \text{HOOC—CH}_2 \\
| & & | \\
= \quad \text{H—C—CH}_3 + & & \text{CH}_2 \\
| & & | \\
\text{CO.CoA} & & \text{CO.CoA}
\end{array}
$$

This was supported by the fact that labelled propionyl-CoA appeared as labelled succinyl-CoA.

However, EGGERER, STADTMAN, OVERATH and LYNEN (*678*) showed that this was not the correct explanation, the incorporation of propionyl-CoA in these experiments being due to propionyl-CoA carboxylase (6.4.1.3) present as an impurity, and that the isomerization took place by an intramolecular transfer.

The nature of the transfer was established by using C_2-labelled methyl-malonyl-CoA as substrate; the product was shown to be C_3-labelled succinyl-CoA, so that the process must be regarded as a transfer of the –CO.CoA group and not of the –COOH group:

VII.51

$$
\begin{array}{ccccc}
\text{COOH} & & \text{COOH} & & \text{COOH} \\
| & \text{COOH} & | & \text{CO.CoA} & | \\
H_2C\!*\!\!-\!\!CH_2 & \xleftarrow{\hspace{1cm}} & HC\!*\!\!-\!\!CH_3 & \xrightarrow{\hspace{1cm}} & H_2C\!*\!\!-\!\!CH_2 \\
| & \text{transfer} & | & \text{transfer} & | \\
\text{CO.CoA} & & \text{CO.CoA} & & \text{CO.CoA}
\end{array}
$$

The isomerase depends on a cobalt-containing cobamide coenzyme (a derivative of vitamin B_{12}, see p. 402). In some non-enzymatic isomerizations catalysed by trivalent cobalt, the mechanism has been shown to involve the formation of free radicals and the migration of a carbon-linked group within the molecule to the free bond. Arguing by analogy, Eggerer *et al.* suggest that the enzymatic reaction is due to the formation of the free radicals

$$
\begin{array}{ccc}
\text{COOH} & & \text{COOH} \\
| & & | \\
HC\!\!-\!\!CH_2\text{-} & \rightleftharpoons & HC\!\!-\!\!CH_2 \\
| & & | \\
\text{CO.CoA} & & \text{CO.CoA}
\end{array}
$$

MECHANISM OF LIGASES

The isotope exchange method may be extended to more complex mechanisms, such as those involved in synthetase reactions, in which the formation of a bond between two molecules is connected with the breaking of a bond in a third molecule. This may be written as

VII.52 $A\!-\!B + X + Y = A + B + X\!-\!Y$

The mechanism of such enzyme reactions is a matter of great interest, because of the important part which they probably play in biosynthesis. However, this question is still a matter of active debate at the time of writing and it is not possible to give a definite answer which would be generally accepted. It is possible indeed that coupled reactions of this type may not all be brought about by the same mechanism.

Several types of mechanism have been postulated. A reaction of this type would result from the combined action of a kinase and a phosphorylase. For example, taking A–B in equation VII.52 to represent ATP, the kinase might phosphorylate X with the production of X–P and ADP; an X-transferase (a 'phosphorylase') would then transfer the X to Y with the liberation of phosphate. In this case a synthetase reaction would be brought about by a two-enzyme system. The other mechanisms do not involve successive reactions brought about by different enzymes. One consists of a triple-transfer occurring at the same active centre as explained in the next paragraph; another assumes the intermediate formation of an acyl-adenylate mixed anhydride in the manner explained on p. 302.

Triple-transfer mechanism

The three-step transfer mechanism may be represented as follows:

VII.53 $A–B + E = A + B–E$

VII.54 $B–E + X = B + X–E$

VII.55 $X–E + Y = X–Y + E$

The first step is, as before, a transfer of the group B from the first substrate A–B to the enzyme; the second step is the transfer of the enzyme from B to X, or, in other words, the displacement of combined B by X; the third step is the transfer of X from the enzyme to Y. The whole process results in the synthesis of the molecule X–Y from X and Y at the expense of the breakdown of A–B into A and B. In the synthetase reactions given in the table A–B represents ATP or, very rarely, other nucleoside triphosphates.

This mechanism is inferred from the following observations. The enzyme will catalyse the isotope exchange reaction

VII.56 $A–B + A^* = A^*–B + A$

in the absence of X, Y and X–Y, but will not catalyse the reaction

VII.57 $A–B + B^* = A–B^* + B.$

It will also catalyse the reaction

VII.58 $X–Y + Y^* = X–Y^* + Y$

in the absence of A, B and A–B, but will not catalyse the reaction

VII.59 $X–Y + X^* = X^*–Y + X$

Reaction VII.56 is to be expected from the repeated reversal of VII 53, and VII.58 from the repeated reversal of VII.55. The failure to catalyse VII.57 and VII.59 is in agreement with the rule that the enzyme-bound group is not exchanged, since it is not liberated in the free state. If, however, X is added in addition to A–B and B*, reaction VII.57 *is* catalysed, since it can now be brought about by the repeated reversal

TABLE VII.4

TRIPLE-TRANSFER SYNTHETASE MECHANISMS, WITH THE CORRESPONDING ISOTOPE EXCHANGES

Case (a) : E–P *as intermediate*

VII.4.a	ADP–P + E = ADP + E–P
VII.4.b	E–P + X = E–X + P
VII.4.c	E–X + Y = E + X–Y

VII.4.d   ADP–P + ADP* = ADP*–P + ADP
catalysed by E, inhibited by X

VII.4.e   ADP–P + P* = ADP–P* + P
catalysed by E+X, inhibited by Y

VII.4.f   X–Y + Y* = X–Y* + Y
catalysed by E, inhibited by P

VII.4.g   X–Y + X* = X*–Y + X
catalysed by E+P, inhibited by ADP

Case (b): E–ADP *as intermediate*

VII.4.h	ADP–P + E = P + E–ADP
VII.4.i	E–ADP + X = E–X + ADP
VII.4.j	E–X + Y = E + X–Y

VII.4.k   ADP–P + P* = ADP–P* + P
catalysed by E, inhibited by X

VII.4.l   ADP–P + ADP* = ADP*–P + ADP
catalysed by E+X, inhibited by Y

VII.4.m   X–Y + Y* = X–Y* + Y
catalysed by E, inhibited by ADP

VII.4.n   X–Y + X* = X*–Y + X
catalysed by E+ADP, inhibited by P

Case (c) : E–AMP *as intermediate*

VII.4.o	AMP–PP + E = PP + E–AMP
VII.4.p	E–AMP + X = E–X + AMP
VII.4.q	E–X + Y = E + X–Y

VII.4.r   AMP–PP + PP* = AMP–PP* + PP
catalysed by E, inhibited by X

VII.4.s   AMP–PP + AMP* = AMP*–PP + AMP
catalysed by E+X, inhibited by Y

VII.4.t   X–Y + Y* = X–Y* + Y
catalysed by E, inhibited by AMP

VII.4.u   X–Y + X* = X*–Y + X
catalysed by E+AMP, inhibited by PP

of the pair of reactions VII.53–4. Similarly, the addition of B to a mixture of X–Y, X* and enzyme enables reaction VII.59 to proceed, since it can now take place through the pair of reactions VII.54–5.

Certain inhibition effects can also be used for confirmation of the inferred mechanism. The addition of X, while it catalyses reaction VII.57, will tend to inhibit reaction VII.56 by diminishing the concentration of B–E. Similarly, the addition of A, B and Y will tend to inhibit reactions VII.59, 58 and 57 respectively, by reducing the concentration of B–E, X–E and X–E respectively.

This method gives a means of identifying enzyme-bound groups and of determining the sequence of transfers with considerable certainty. It has given interesting information about the reaction mechanisms of the various synthetases, for which A–B represents ATP. It appears that the details may be quite different in different cases. In particular, either of the two pyrophosphate bonds in ATP may be used in different cases to supply the energy for synthesis, so that the ATP may react either as AMP–PP or as ADP–P. Moreover, either part of the molecule might, in theory at any rate, become attached to the enzyme, acting as B. Thus there are four possible cases, but the formation of E–PP has not been suggested as an intermediate in any actual case; the other three are shown in Table VII.4, with the corresponding effects. It should be mentioned that only a few of these effects have been demonstrated for any given synthetase.

γ-glutamyl-cysteine synthetase (6.3.2.2) is an example of case (a). It has been found (*2812*) that the enzyme alone catalyses the exchanges

VII.4.d $\qquad$ ADP–P + ADP* = ADP*–P + ADP $\qquad$ and

VII.60 $\qquad$ Glutamyl-cysteine + cysteine*
$$= \text{glutamyl-cysteine*} + \text{cysteine}$$

If glutamate is also added (but not otherwise) the enzyme catalyses the exchange

VII.4.e $\qquad$ ATP + P* = ATP* + P

The addition of glutamate slows down reaction VII.4.d and the addition of cysteine slows down reaction VII.4.e. All this suggests that the mechanism of this enzyme is an example of case (a) and may be written

VII.4.a $\qquad$ ATP + E = ADP + E–P

VII.61 $\qquad$ E–P + glutamate = E–glutamate + P

VII.62 $\quad$ E–glutamate + cysteine = E + glutamyl-cysteine

The exchange VII.4.d shows that the enzyme combines with the phosphate group from ATP, and the exchange VII.60 that it combines with glutamate ($= X$). The fact that the exchange VII.4.e requires the presence of glutamate shows that glutamate liberates phosphate from the compound, in agreement with VII.61, and incidentally that the E–P compound is a firm one, not spontaneously hydrolysed. The fact that glutamate slows reaction VII.4.d, the incorporation of ADP* into ATP, is due to the diminution in the concentration of E–P and consequent slowing of the reverse reaction of VII.4.a, while the presence of cysteine ($= Y$) diminishes the concentration of E–glutamate, slows the reverse reaction of VII.61 and, consequently, also VII.4.e.

This strongly suggests a triple-transfer mechanism. First the terminal phosphate group of ATP is transferred from its combination with ADP to combination with the enzyme, then the enzyme is transferred from phosphate to glutamate, and finally the glutamate is transferred from the enzyme to cysteine. The enzyme-phosphate link evidently retains enough of the free energy of the original pyrophosphate link to bring about the synthesis of the glutamyl-cysteine. Another synthetase which appears to act by the case (a) mechanism is glutathione synthetase (6.3.2.3) (*2462*).

It seems probable that other synthetases will be found to work by a triple-transfer mechanism. Results have been published for a number of enzymes which appeared to indicate one or other of the mechanisms set out in Table VII.4, but some of these have since been shown to be in error. The isotopic exchange method is particularly apt to be affected by the presence of impurities in either the enzyme or the substrates, since the conclusions as to mechanism frequently depend on whether the exchange reactions occur in the absence of one or other of the reactants. In a number of cases exchanges demonstrated with impure enzyme preparations were found to disappear on further purification of the enzyme, and in other cases phosphate-ATP exchanges were found to be dependent on the presence of traces of ADP in the ATP, or ADP–ATP exchanges to be dependent on the presence of phosphate as impurity.

Ternary complex mechanisms

In a number of cases there is valid evidence that the mechanism is somewhat more complicated than those discussed in the last section. In these it is necessary to postulate an enzyme-bound complex involving two of the reactants. With the succinyl–CoA synthetase of plants (6.2.1.5) (*1316*) the exchange reaction

VII.63   Succinyl–CoA + succinate* = succinyl*–CoA + succinate is catalysed by the enzyme only in the presence of phosphate, which would suggest a 'case (a)' mechanism, with succinate as X. However, the exchange VII.4.e, which should be catalysed by enzyme and succinate, is found to require also coenzyme A. In order to account for this point of difference from the normal cases, KAUFMAN (*1316*) suggests the following mechanism

VII.4.a $ADP–P + E = ADP + E–P$

VII.64 $E–P + CoA = E(CoA–P)$

VII.65 $E(CoA–P) + succinate = E + succinyl–CoA + P$

The alternative possibilities, intermediate formation of succinyl-phosphate or CoA-phosphate, were eliminated.

A similar but slightly more complicated case is that of formyltetrahydrofolate synthetase (6.3.4.3). The following reaction scheme has been suggested (*1229*):

VII.66 $ADP–P + E = E–P + ADP$

VII.67 $E–P + THFA = E(THFA–P)$

VII.68 $E(THFA–P) + formate = E(formyl–THFA–P)$

VII.69 $E(formyl–THFA–P) = E + formyl–THFA + P$

Another variant occurs where the enzyme contains a prosthetic group which binds one of the reactants, for example biotin in the carboxylases of sub-group 6.4 (see also p. 414). Two of these enzymes have been studied in detail by LYNEN et al. (*1639*) and by OCHOA and his colleagues (*1325*). This recent work has shown, contrary to earlier theories, that the phosphate–ATP and ADP–ATP exchanges are both dependent on the presence of all the reactants except the final carboxyl-acceptor. For propionyl-CoA carboxylase (6.4.1.3) the following mechanism was put forward (*1325*):

VII.70 $ADP–P + E + CO_2 = (ADP–P–E–CO_2)$

VII.71 $(ADP–P–E–CO_2) = \left(\begin{bmatrix} ADP \\ P \end{bmatrix} E \sim CO_2 \right)$

VII.72 $\left(\begin{bmatrix} ADP \\ P \end{bmatrix} E \sim CO_2 \right) + propionyl–CoA$
$$= E + ADP + P + methylmalonyl–CoA$$

Here E represents the biotin-containing enzyme, and $E \sim CO_2$ represents carboxybiotin in the enzyme. Step VII.71 consists of the breakdown of

ATP with simultaneous energizing of the enzyme–CO_2 compound, and therefore contains the essence of the synthetase reaction.

For the case of phosphoribosyl-glycinamide synthetase HARTMAN and BUCHANAN (*1016*) have put forward a picture in which the actual synthetase step takes place within a quaternary complex containing all the reactants and the enzyme. The reaction is envisaged as a concerted attack, represented by them as follows:

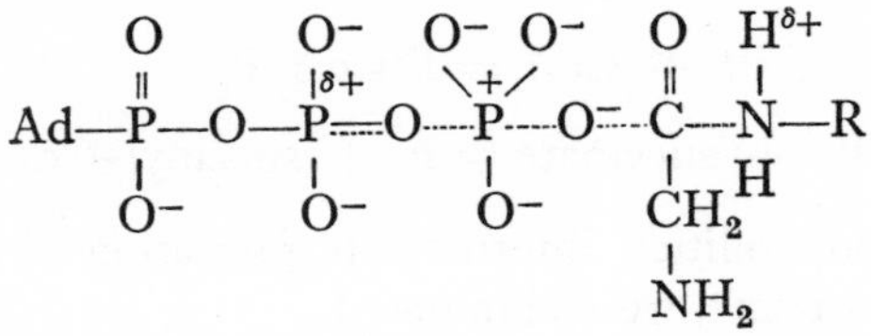

$$
\text{Ad—}\overset{\overset{\textstyle O}{\|}}{\underset{\underset{\textstyle O^-}{|}}{P}}\text{—O—}\overset{\overset{\textstyle O^-}{|\delta+}}{\underset{\underset{\textstyle O^-}{|}}{P}}\text{=O----}\overset{\overset{\textstyle O^-}{\diagdown+\diagup}}{\underset{\underset{\textstyle O^-}{|}}{P}}\text{---O=}\overset{\overset{\textstyle O}{\|}}{\underset{\underset{\textstyle \underset{\textstyle NH_2}{|}}{CH_2}}{C}}\text{---}\overset{\overset{\textstyle H^{\delta+}}{|}}{\underset{\underset{\textstyle H}{|}}{N}}\text{—R}
$$

where Ad is written for adenosine and R for the phosphoribosyl group. The electrophilic attack on the carboxyl by the ATP phosphate reinforces the nucleophilic attack by the amino group of the phosphoribosylamine, resulting in a linear displacement of electrons with formation of a CO–NH bond and simultaneous cleavage of the ADP–P bond. Hartman and Buchanan suggest that this mechanism may be fairly general, and indeed LYNEN *et al.* (*1639*) have considered its application to methylcrotonoyl-CoA carboxylase (6.4.1.4), where the biotin of the enzyme might be regarded as replacing the $R.NH_2$ in the diagram above.

Yet another mechanism is believed to operate with a number of important synthetases. This mechanism, first put forward by BERG (*212–3*) for acetyl–CoA synthetase (6.2.1.1), involves the intermediate formation of an acyl–AMP compound:

VII.73   AMP–PP + acetate = acetyl–AMP + PP

VII.74   acetyl–AMP + CoA = acetyl–CoA + AMP

This is consistent with the fact that both acetate and coenzyme A were required to bring about an AMP–ATP exchange, and that both AMP and pyrophosphate were needed for an acetate–acetyl–CoA exchange. These facts could not be explained by any of the mechanisms in Table VII.4.

Acetyl–AMP was prepared chemically, and the enzyme was shown to catalyse the reaction

VII.75   Acetyl–AMP + PP $\longrightarrow$ ATP + acetate

at about the same rate as the PP–ATP exchange in the presence of acetate. The enzyme also catalyses the formation of acetyl–CoA from acetyl-AMP.

BOYER *et al.* (*306*) have observed that when the reaction

VII.76 $ATP + acetate + CoA \longrightarrow AMP + PP + acetyl\text{–}CoA$

is carried out with acetate containing O^{18} in the carboxyl group, O^{18} is present in the phosphate group of the AMP which is formed, and similar results have since been obtained with several other synthetases. This has been regarded as evidence for Berg's mechanism. To us, however, it seems to be quite compatible with a triple-transfer mechanism. Since the E–CoA bond must be energy-rich, in order to account for the synthesis, it seems reasonable to suppose that the combination of the –SH group of the CoA must be with a carboxyl group in the enzyme. The two oxygen atoms of a carboxyl group are chemically equivalent because of ionization, so that both oxygen atoms in the group must be regarded as labelled initially.

We can picture the process as occurring as follows. Starting with ATP, enzyme and CoA, reactions VII.4.o and VII.4.p in Table VII.4 will first form unlabelled E–CoA, which we shall write in conformity with the above assumption as E–CO–S–CoA. Then will follow

VII.77
$$\begin{array}{ccc} \text{E–CO–S–CoA} & & \text{E–CO} \quad \text{S–CoA} \\ & = & \quad | \qquad | \\ \text{HO*–CO*–CH}_3 & & \text{HO*} \quad \text{CO*–CH}_3 \end{array}$$

VII.78
$$\text{E–CO–O*H} \quad = \quad \text{E–CO*–O*H}$$

VII.79
$$\begin{array}{ccc} \text{E–CO*} & & \text{E–CO*} \\ | & & | \\ \text{AMP} \quad \text{O*} & = & \text{AMP–O*} \\ | \quad | & & \\ \text{PP–O} \quad \text{H} & & \text{PP–O–H} \end{array}$$

VII.80
$$\begin{array}{ccc} \text{E–CO*} \quad \text{HS–CoA} & & \text{E–CO*–S–CoA} \\ | & = & \\ \text{AMP–O*} & & \text{AMP–O*–H} \end{array}$$

Thus if this mechanism is correct, there is bound to be an incorporation of O^{18} into AMP. It will be noted that reactions VII.79–80 involve the formation of a bond on one side of the bridging oxygen atom and the breaking of a bond on the other, but an explanation in terms of Berg's mechanism equally involves this; indeed the appearance of the O^{18} in the AMP is evidence in itself that this has occurred at some point.

The Berg mechanism has been applied quite widely, especially to the so-called 'aminoacid-activating enzymes' (aminoacid–sRNA ligases, sub-group 6.1.1). Fifteen aminoacyl–AMP compounds have been prepared synthetically (*1845*). In aqueous solution these acid anhydrides rapidly degrade to the 2′- or 3′-aminoacyl–AMP esters. The anhydrides are extremely reactive; they *all* form ATP from pyrophosphate with tryptophanyl–sRNA synthetase or methionyl–sRNA synthetase, although in the forward direction both these enzymes are absolutely specific for one particular L-aminoacid. It is remarkable that ATP is formed more rapidly by the former enzyme with D-tryptophanyl–AMP than with the L-compound, although in fact the affinity for L-tryptophanyl–AMP is rather higher than for any other aminoacyl–AMP (*1469*). Aminoacyl–AMP anhydrides can transfer the aminoacid residue non-enzymatically to a variety of acceptors, including ammonia, hydroxylamine, aminoacids, proteins and RNA. The ester forms are less reactive; although they still react with hydroxylamine, they do not form ATP from pyrophosphate with the appropriate enzyme.

The aminoacyl donor for the enzymatic synthesis of aminoacyl–sRNA cannot be the free aminoacyl–AMP compound described above. The intermediate is probably enzyme-bound aminoacyl–AMP anhydride, and WONG and MOLDAVE (*2907*) have shown incorporation of both the AMP and the aminoacid moieties into a complex with the tryptophanyl–sRNA synthetase, starting either from L-tryptophan and ATP or from the synthetic L-tryptophanyl–AMP. The transfer of the aminoacyl residue from the enzyme-bound intermediate is highly specific, in each case being only to a particular sRNA, producing the aminoacyl–sRNA in which the aminoacid is ester-bound to the 2′ or 3′ hydroxyl of the ribose of the terminal adenylate residue.

MECHANISM OF METALLOENZYMES

Enzyme activity is often dependent on the presence of a metal atom. In the true metalloenzymes this atom is firmly bound as a constituent of the enzyme itself, either with some groups in the protein or in combination with some prosthetic group such as a porphyrin. In other cases it is necessary to add some metal ion to 'activate' the enzyme. The distinction may be a matter of firmness of combination; in cases where the metal has to be added it is usually easily removed again, either by dialysis or by precipitation of the protein. A finite concentration of the free activating ion must then be maintained in order to hold the enzyme in the form of the active 'metalloenzyme'. Sometimes the metal activator may combine with the substrate rather than with the enzyme, the true substrate of the enzyme then being a metallosubstrate rather than the substance actually added. The activation of enzymes by metal and other ions is discussed in detail in Chapter IX. We are dealing here with four groups of metalloenzymes for which there is some evidence as to mechanism.

Metal-activated peptidases

A number of peptidases contain or require metal atoms, without which they are inactive. For example, carboxypeptidase A (3.4.2.1) contains zinc (*2710*), glycylglycine dipeptidase (3.4.3.1) specifically requires cobalt for its activity, and leucine aminopeptidase (3.4.1.1) requires manganese or magnesium. EMIL SMITH has suggested (adopting an earlier suggestion of HELLERMAN's for arginase (*1057–8*) that these metals act by forming chelate compounds with two or three groups in the substrate and with a similar number of groups in the enzyme (see, for example, *2443, 2447*). By considering specificity he was able to suggest definite structures for a number of these enzyme-substrate complexes, as, for example, in the case of leucine aminopeptidase acting on a dipeptide

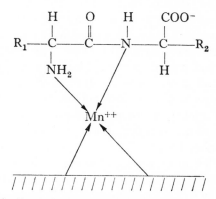

or in the case of glycylglycine dipeptidase

or in the case of carboxypeptidase A

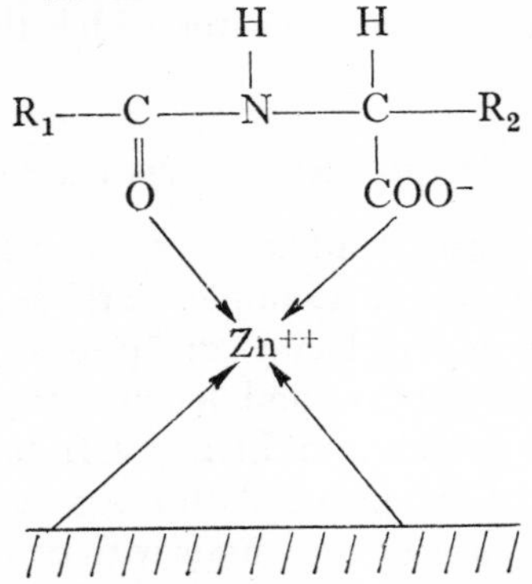

$$R_1-\underset{\underset{O}{\|}}{C}-\underset{\underset{H}{|}}{N}-\underset{\underset{COO^-}{|}}{\underset{\overset{H}{|}}{C}}-R_2$$

$$Zn^{++}$$

These diagrams show only the connections with the metal, but in order to explain the specificity of the enzymes it is necessary to postulate other bonds directly between the R groups and the enzyme protein.

It will be noted that in the first of these enzymes the combination takes place with the terminal amino group and in the last enzyme with the terminal carboxyl group, these being the respective groups with which the enzymes are known from specificity data to react, while the dipeptidase requires both terminal groups. The first two enzymes act only on peptides and not on aminoacid esters; therefore the NH group of the peptide bond is shown as involved in the combination. On the other hand, carboxypeptidase does act on certain esters with a free terminal carboxyl group and therefore the NH group is not essential; chelation is here shown with the carbonyl oxygen.

Smith's mechanism for glycylglycine dipeptidase was based partly on an apparent parallelism between the ability of the enzyme to hydrolyse the substrate and the ability of cobaltous ion to form a co-ordination compound with the substrate, as judged by the change in the absorption spectrum. However, it has been shown (836) that the spectrum observed was not that of a cobaltous complex, but that of a cobaltic complex which is not hydrolysed by the enzyme. WILLIAMS (2869) has reviewed a number of criticisms of Smith's formulations and in some cases has suggested alternatives. One criticism is that the cobalt complex with co-ordinated nitrogen atoms, shown in the above diagram, is readily oxidized; Williams states that an oxygen-nitrogen complex is to be preferred, for example he suggests for glycylglycine dipeptidase the complex

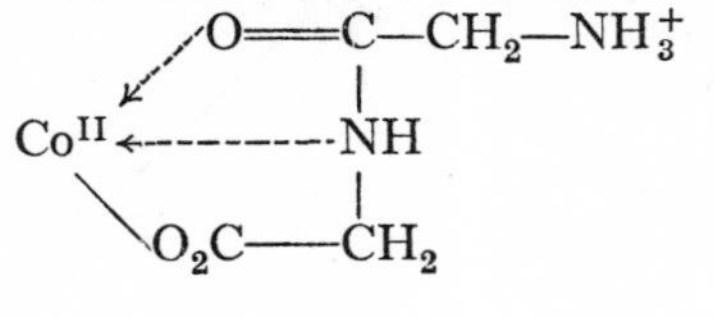

$$\begin{array}{c} O=\!\!=\!\!C-CH_2-NH_3^+ \\ | \\ Co^{II}\cdots\cdots NH \\ | \\ O_2C-\!\!-CH_2 \end{array}$$

It is not clear what is the feature in Smith's formulated complex which brings about the breakdown of the susceptible bond in the substrate. KLOTZ (*1400*) has suggested that the formation of such a complex might tend to stabilize the substrate rather than to facilitate its breakdown, and thinks that the true function of the metal may be to combine with the substrate in its activated rather than its normal form and to facilitate the activation by attracting a hydroxyl ion, thus catalysing the reaction.

Zinc-containing dehydrogenases

VALLEE has shown that a number of non-flavoprotein dehydrogenases contain zinc (see *2708*), in particular alcohol dehydrogenase (1.1.1.1) and glutamate dehydrogenase (1.4.1.3). The zinc forms an integral part of the structure and there is one zinc atom in each active centre. Because of this the number of zinc atoms is equal to the number of NAD molecules bound per molecule of enzyme.

Yeast alcohol dehydrogenase (molecular weight 151,000) contains 4 Zn atoms per molecule and binds 4 molecules of NAD, while the liver enzyme (molecular weight 84,000) has 2 Zn atoms and binds 2 NAD molecules. With both the alcohol and glutamate enzymes, removal of the zinc by treatment with zinc-complexing agents causes not only an inactivation but also a dissociation of the enzyme protein into sub-units; for example the yeast alcohol enzyme (containing 4 Zn atoms) dissociates into 4 inactive sub-units of molecular weight 36,000 when the zinc is removed (*1281*).

Various pictures have been proposed to explain the action of the zinc. It is known that zinc can bind to NAD, to thiol groups in proteins and to a number of substances which act as enzyme substrates. Its function in these dehydrogenases is undoubtedly that of binding, either of the reactants to the active centre or of the protein sub-units to one another.

Metalloflavoproteins

In 1950 ALBERT (*30*, see also *31*) showed that riboflavin, containing a grouping resembling the well-known metal chelating agent 8-hydroxyquinoline, has the property of binding divalent ions of heavy metals. In comparison with ordinary chelating agents, it has a very high avidity for Fe^{++}; no evidence was obtained of combination with Fe^{+++}. A series of chelated metal-riboflavin compounds has been isolated by FOYE and LANGE (*767*); these contain two metal atoms per molecule of flavin, but it is not clear how these atoms are combined.

Albert first suggested 'that the activity of some riboflavin-containing enzymes may be associated with metal ions', and this has more recently been confirmed in a number of cases. Some, but by no means all, flavo-protein enzymes contain heavy metal atoms, which may be iron, molyb-denum, copper or manganese in different cases. Usually it appears that one heavy metal atom is present for each flavin group, but occasionally iron is found in addition to the other metals in amounts many times the equivalent of the flavin, and this obviously cannot be present as a flavin complex.

All the metalloflavoprotein enzymes are dehydrogenases; a number can act with a variety of acceptors, though for some of these the presence of phosphate is also required. It has been shown that while the metal is necessary for the reduction of some of the acceptors, it is not necessary for others. It is often possible to remove the metal, for instance, by dialysis against cyanide, dilute alkali, thiocyanate or 8-hydroxyquinoline. This gives a metal-free enzyme which has lost its power of reacting with such acceptors as cytochrome c, ferricyanide or nitrate, but which still retains its original power of reducing such acceptors as O_2, dyes, quinones or coenzymes. The metal is therefore not concerned in the activation of the hydrogen donor. It is possible to restore all the original activities by incubating the metal-free enzyme with a compound of the metal in question; other metals are usually inactive.

For example, the xanthine oxidase of milk (1.2.3.2) and the aldehyde oxidase of liver (1.2.3.1), which are molybdoflavoproteins, normally reduce all the acceptors mentioned above. GREEN and his co-workers claim that after removal of the molybdenum by alkaline dialysis these enzymes lose the ability to reduce cytochrome c, nitrate or ferricyanide, although they still react normally with other acceptors (*1665, 1686*). The lost activities can be restored by incubation with a suitable molybdenum compound, or to some extent with uranium compounds for xanthine oxidase and tungstates for aldehyde oxidase. The chemistry of molyb-denum compounds is complicated, and it is not clear what is the true activator; simple compounds like MoO_3 or MoO_4^{--} are inactive alone, and the presence of phosphate or silicate is necessary in addition. This indicates that the activation is really due to a phosphomolybdate or silicomolybdate (*853*). *Neurospora* nitrate reductase needs phosphate; this can be replaced completely by selenate, tellurate or arsenate and to a lesser extent by sulphate or silicate (*1966*).

The molybdenum- and iron-containing flavoprotein xanthine oxidase (1.2.3.2) has been studied by BRAY et al. (*320*), using electron spin resonance and magnetic susceptibility methods. By the first method signals were obtained due to flavin semiquinone, Mo^V and Fe^{II}. As in the case of lipoamide dehydrogenase (p. 276), the substrate reduced the flavin in two one-equivalent steps, first to the semiquinone and then to

$FADH_2$. The molybdenum also was probably reduced in two one-equivalent steps, from Mo^{VI} to Mo^V and then to Mo^{IV}, since the Mo^V signal disappeared on complete reduction. There was some evidence that the iron also underwent reduction from Fe^{III} to Fe^{II} (317). However, Bray et al. found that the strongest signals were given by inactive enzyme, and they advocate extreme caution in the interpretation of such results.

The evidence for participation of iron in the action of metalloflavoproteins is by no means decisive. The iron in $NADH_2$-cytochrome c reductase (1.6.2.1), which is not required for the reaction with dyes but only for the reaction with cytochrome, can be removed by dialysis against 8-hydroxyquinoline, and the enzyme can then be partially reactivated with Fe^{+++}, though not at all with Fe^{++}, which strongly inhibits (1682). However, SINGER and MASSEY (2414) have given some evidence that the iron is completely in the ferric form and does not undergo oxido-reduction. In the case of succinate dehydrogenase MASSEY (1747) showed that the iron is normally in the ferric form and that there is no valid evidence that it undergoes valency changes during the action of the enzyme. Moreover half of the iron can be removed without loss of activity. Acyl–CoA dehydrogenase (1.3.2.2) can be prepared almost free from iron without any loss of activity.

MAHLER (1683–4) has suggested that the metal is necessary for the reaction with those acceptors which require only one equivalent of hydrogen for their reduction, and is not necessary for those requiring two equivalents. It is easy to see why this might be so. In a system involving only two-equivalent reactants the reduction might readily occur by the simultaneous transfer of two hydrogen atoms by the mechanism shown in VII.17 for the reduction of coenzyme. It is interesting to note that in the reduction of flavins by reduced coenzyme the spacing between the two hydrogens does not change appreciably during the transfer from one molecule to the other, so that a resonance-stabilized intermediate of the type discussed earlier would presumably be possible. The same considerations apply to the further transfer to the two-equivalent acceptors which act with flavoproteins. MAHLER and GLENN (1683) represent the transition state in the reduction of a quinone by a flavoprotein enzyme diagrammatically as in Fig. VII.4.

On the other hand, the reduction of a one-equivalent acceptor by a two-equivalent donor presents a difficulty, since unless a trimolecular reaction occurs the donor can only be oxidized by two successive reactions, the first involving its oxidation to a free radical, and the second the oxidation of the free radical by a second molecule of acceptor. Thus unless the donor is capable of forming a free radical, the only method of reacting is through the formation of a termolecular complex. Flavins differ from most redox dyes in the ease with which they form half-reduced free radicals ('semiquinones') (*196–7, 1483, 1813*) and they might therefore be expected to link two-equivalent with one-equivalent systems. For instance, one may perhaps imagine the flavin group of a cytochrome reductase as taking up hydrogen atoms two at a time from the dehydrogenation systems and passing them on one at a time to cytochrome.

However, the semiquinone-forming properties of flavoproteins are apparently not sufficient to bring about such linking, although free flavins can do so (*2412*). With some flavoproteins a combined metal is obligatory for the reduction of one-equivalent acceptors, as already mentioned. This might facilitate the reaction in three ways. (*a*) It might make the formation of the semiquinone easier; in other words the metal-chelated flavin group might form a semiquinone even more readily than the free flavin. (*b*) The metal might act as a carrier between the flavin and the one-equivalent acceptor. (*c*) The metal might stabilize a termolecular complex of the flavin with two acceptor molecules, within which the whole oxidoreduction would take place, so that the formation of a flavin semiquinone would be unnecessary (*1683*).

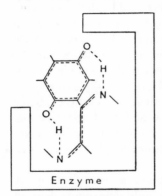

Fig. VII.4. *Diagrammatic representation of transition state in the reduction of a quinone by a flavoprotein enzyme.*

from *1683*

All of these suggestions have been advanced at various times as possible explanations of the requirement for metal, but so far there appears to be insufficient evidence to decide between them.

The division of acceptors into two groups, one containing the one-equivalent acceptors and requiring metal, the other containing the two-equivalent acceptors and not requiring metal, is not in fact clear cut. The reduction of nitrate to nitrite requires not one but two equivalents, and yet the reduction invariably needs molybdenum. In answer to this objection it has been argued (*a*) that the reduction may proceed in two one-equivalent steps, though there is no evidence of this, (*b*) that nitrate, which is a sluggish oxidizing agent, may require activation in order to function as an acceptor, and that this may be brought about by complexing with the metal. Many of the acceptors here described as two-equivalent, on the other hand, can undoubtedly form semiquinones as intermediates and can therefore undergo reduction by two one-equivalent steps, yet they do not require metal. In fact many of these substances can react freely with one-equivalent systems in the absence of enzymes; for example, hydroquinone is readily oxidized to quinone by cytochrome c.

The metal in metalloflavoproteins is not always concerned with the reduction of one-equivalent acceptors. Highly purified liver xanthine oxidase can scarcely react with cytochrome c or ferricyanide, although it contains its full complement of one atom of molybdenum and four of iron per flavin group, and addition of extra iron, molybdenum and flavin has no effect (*1373*). Similar results have been obtained with crystalline milk xanthine oxidase (*106*).

A number of molybdoflavoproteins and other enzymes contain variable amounts of iron, the amounts ranging from 40 atoms per flavin group in *Micrococcus* succinate dehydrogenase to one-sixth or less in acyl-CoA dehydrogenase. Iron is, of course, readily bound by proteins, especially on –SH groups, and it is not clear whether the iron in these enzymes has any functional significance.

It will be seen that the present position is far from satisfactory, and more work will be necessary before we can give a clear picture of the function of the metal in metalloflavoproteins.

Haemoprotein enzymes

Some of the enzymes which act specifically on hydrogen peroxide or its derivatives, namely, the catalases and peroxidases, contain ferri-protoporphyrin (haematin) prosthetic groups. The action of these enzymes is different from that of the dehydrogenases or the enzymes of the cytochrome system in that the prosthetic group is involved directly in the activation of the substrate. The enzymes thus bring about the oxidation of various substances by H_2O_2: peroxidases oxidize a wide range of substances, including phenolic substances, cytochrome c, nitrite, leucomalachite green, etc., but not H_2O_2 itself or alcohols; catalases oxidize particularly H_2O_2 itself (which thus acts in a double capacity) and also ethyl alcohol, but not most of the substances oxidized by peroxidases. Catalases can be regarded as peroxidases with a different specificity, and the general features of the mechanism of action are probably the same for both. The ensuing discussion relates mainly to horseradish peroxidase (1.11.1.7).

In Chapter IV we have mentioned that peroxidase forms complexes with H_2O_2 which can be detected spectroscopically, and the kinetics of the formation and breakdown of these complexes can account for the quantitative features of the enzymatic catalysis. Four distinct types of complex have been distinguished. Complex I is that which is first formed on adding H_2O_2; it is a green compound of transitory existence, which normally rapidly changes to the red Complex II. In the early kinetic work of CHANCE (418) discussed in Chapter IV (p. 102), the complex which was measured was actually Complex II, but in later work (421) the measurements were extended to the formation and breakdown of both complexes and their interconversion. Complexes III and IV are red compounds formed with excess of H_2O_2; these complexes are catalytically inactive and the reaction is inhibited when they are formed. For the consideration of the enzymatic mechanism, we can confine our attention to Complexes I and II.

The conversion of Complex I to Complex II proceeds more rapidly in the presence of a hydrogen donor (polyphenol, nitrite, etc.) and may therefore be assumed to contribute to the formation of the product of the reaction. The overall process can then be represented by the following equations, which are inferred from the observed kinetics (421):

VII.81 $$E + H_2O_2 \underset{k_{-1}}{\overset{k_{+1}}{\rightleftharpoons}} ES_I$$

VII.82 $$ES_I + AH_2 \xrightarrow{k_{+2}} ES_{II} + -AH$$

VII.83 $$ES_{II} + AH_2 \xrightarrow{k_{+3}} E + -AH$$

VII.84 $$2-AH \longrightarrow A + AH_2$$

The reactions have been written for the case of a two-equivalent donor AH_2; since the transitions from ES_I to ES_{II} and from ES_{II} to E are both one-equivalent processes it is necessary to postulate the formation of the free radical $-AH$, and there is evidence that such radicals are formed (2938). These equations make no implications about the chemical nature of ES_I and ES_{II}, except that ES_I possesses two oxidizing equivalents above the enzyme and ES_{II} possess only one. This has been established by titration with ferrocyanide (821).

For the donors examined, k_{+2} was considerably greater than k_{+3}, so that V is determined by reaction VII.83. This explains the transitory nature of ES_I and the failure to detect it in the earlier work. The enzyme–substrate complex whose existence would be predicted from the kinetics of the enzyme-catalysed reaction is in fact ES_{II}.

As to the chemical nature of the two complexes there are two schools of thought. CHANCE formulates Complex I as $Fe_p^{+++}(H_2O_2)$, i.e. an addition compound of the enzyme with H_2O_2; the subscript p denotes that the iron forms part of the haemoprotein enzyme. Complex II is considered to be $Fe_p^{+++}(OH\cdot)$, where the group $(OH\cdot)$ is merely written as a symbol for half-reduced H_2O_2, for electronic resonance absorption measurements show that in fact Complex II does not contain a free radical. Thus the nature of Complex II is uncertain in Chance's formulation.

GEORGE (*821–2*) on the other hand believes that the H_2O_2 oxidizes the iron in the enzyme to a valency state higher than that normally found, and suggests that Complex I contains quinquevalent and Complex II quadrivalent iron: 'Several possibilities may be considered for the structure of such a compound: (i) simple quadrivalent iron Fe^{++++} ... (ii) ... the ferryl ion $(FeO)^{++}$ ... (iii) a biradical structure in which the tervalent iron forms 'one end' of the radical, the other end being a normal radical grouping at a methine carbon atom ... or some other atom ... within the conjugated network ... (iv) a higher oxidation state of the haematin group in which the electron has been removed from a π-orbital common to the ring as a whole.' For various reasons George prefers (ii) and in this case the mechanism can be written as

VII.85
$$Fe_p^{+++} + H_2O_2 \longrightarrow (Fe_pO)^{+++} + H_2O$$

VII.86
$$(Fe_pO)^{+++} + AH_2 \longrightarrow (Fe_pO)^{++} + -AH + H^+$$

VII.87
$$(Fe_pO)^{++} + AH_2 + H^+ \longrightarrow Fe_p^{+++} + -AH + H_2O$$

VII.88
$$2 -AH \longrightarrow A + AH_2$$

In contrast to the previous mechanism this process involves an oxidation and reduction of the enzyme. This is supported by George's observation that under certain conditions one molecule of H_2O_2 gives rise to considerably more than one molecule of Complex II, which he explains by an oxidation of free enzyme by Complex I as follows

VII.89
$$Fe_p^{+++} + (Fe_pO)^{+++} + H_2O \longrightarrow 2(Fe_pO)^{++} + 2H^+$$

BRILL and WILLIAMS (*329*) have investigated the nature of Complex I formed with ethylhydroperoxide by both catalase and peroxidase. They concluded that Complex I is a mixture of two complexes, which they call A and B. Form A is a simple ferric porphyrin complex, whereas in compound B there has been an oxidation of one of the methine bridges in the porphyrin ring. Their work supports George's formulation of the structure of Complex II.

The other haemoprotein enzymes are concerned with the reduction and oxidation of cytochrome *c*. The yeast lactate dehydrogenase (1.1.2.3) (cytochrome b_2) contains one haem group for every flavin mononucleotide group (*82*). The crystalline enzyme brings about the oxidation of lactate by cytochrome *c*; on addition of lactate, both the flavin and the haem groups are rapidly reduced. The flavin dissociates spontaneously from the enzyme in the presence of O_2, and the haem group is then no longer reduced by lactate, suggesting that its reduction takes place through the flavin.

The cytochrome oxidases (1.9.3.1) contain a special haem (haem a), the probable structure of which is shown in Fig. IX.10. The enzyme from heart muscle contains one atom of firmly bound copper per haem group, and it has been shown that this undergoes oxidation and reduction at the same time as the haem group (GRIFFITHS and WHARTON, *933*). Cyanide has been shown to prevent the oxidation of the haem group by O_2 by combining with the copper. Thus the function of the copper may be to bring about the aerobic oxidation of the haem a group.

VIII

ENZYME INHIBITORS

THE POISONING OF any single enzyme involved in a main metabolic chain will render the whole chain inoperative and will have a profound or even fatal effect upon the organism. Such an inactivation of an essential enzyme has been called by PETERS (*817*) a 'biochemical lesion'. The most obvious example of the fatal effects which may be caused by the specific poisoning of a single enzyme is the toxicity of cyanide, which is primarily due to the inhibition of cytochrome oxidase, resulting in a cessation of the aerobic oxidation processes and death in a very few minutes.

The increasing realization of these facts has changed the study of enzyme inhibitors from an interesting sideline of enzyme kinetics into a study which is now becoming recognized by many pharmacologists and toxicologists as of fundamental importance to their subjects. It thus has immediate practical applications, and has become even of military importance—the 'nerve gases', for instance, are essentially specific enzyme inhibitors. An increasing use of related compounds as insecticides is now the basis of a large and expanding industry. The *in vitro* study of the action of toxic substances as inhibitors is proving valuable also in the development of antidotes to specific poisons.

However, these developments are fairly recent, and so far the action of only a few poisons has been interpreted in terms of the inhibition of particular enzymes. It is clear from the work which has been done that fruitful developments may be expected in the future. But even in those cases where the action of a drug or toxic substance has been definitely traced to an effect on a known enzyme, it is not always easy to see how the resulting physiological changes are produced; for instance, it is not known why substances which poison thiol enzymes give rise to trains of electrical impulses in the corneal nerve fibres, resulting in lachrymation. Such a gap in knowledge between the primary biochemical mechanism and the final effect is general, applying also, for example, to the lesions produced by deficiencies of vitamins whose biochemical action is known.

On the purely academic plane, specific enzyme inhibitors are frequently useful as tools; for instance, many of the intermediates in glycolysis and yeast fermentation were discovered largely by the use of inhibitors blocking the various successive steps and allowing the corresponding intermediates to accumulate in sufficient quantities for isolation and identification. Similarly, the use of malonate, a competitive inhibitor of succinate dehydrogenase, provided evidence for the existence of the citric cycle.

TYPES OF INHIBITORS

A mere irreversible destruction of an enzyme, as, for example, denaturation by heat, strong acid, or other means, is not usually regarded as an inhibition. Inhibitors in the usual sense, working by a definite chemical action, may be reversible or irreversible. The word 'reversible', however, has been used in the literature in two different senses. The sense in which we shall use it implies that the activity returns on merely removing free inhibitor by dialysis or other means, showing that there is an equilibrium between free inhibitor and enzyme. By contrast, with the irreversible inhibitors no such equilibrium is set up and the activity does not return on dialysis. The word 'reversible', however, has been applied also in another sense to cases in which it is possible to remove the inhibiting group from the enzyme by a chemical reaction, although it does not dissociate spontaneously. Irreversibility in this sense denotes that all attempts to remove the group by chemical means have been unsuccessful, although the possibility is not thereby excluded that the inhibition may become 'reversible' as the result of further work. We shall use the term 'reactivation' rather than 'reversal' for such chemical removal of the inhibiting group.

Reversible inhibition is characterized by an equilibrium between enzyme and inhibitor, defined by an equilibrium constant which is a measure of the affinity. The effectiveness of the inhibitor is normally expressed by this constant K_i, which is the reciprocal of the enzyme–inhibitor affinity. This type of system is characterized by a definite degree of inhibition, depending on the inhibitor concentration, which is usually reached fairly rapidly and thereafter is independent of time, provided that the inhibitor is stable.

Irreversible inhibition on the other hand is characterized by a progressive increase with time, ultimately reaching complete inhibition even with very dilute inhibitor, provided that the inhibitor is in excess of the amount of enzyme present. The effectiveness of the inhibitor is here expressed not by an equilibrium constant but by a velocity constant, which determines the fraction of the enzyme inhibited in a given period of time by a certain concentration of inhibitor (ALDRIDGE, 41).

Examples of irreversible inhibitions are the action of cyanide on xanthine oxidase (1.2.3.2) and of the 'nerve gases' on cholinesterases

(3.1.1.7–8); reversible inhibitions are numerous, e.g. the action of cyanide on cytochrome oxidase (1.9.3.1) and of malonate on succinate dehydrogenase (1.3.99.1). We shall deal here mainly with reversible inhibitions.

As with other factors influencing the velocity of enzyme reactions, reversible inhibitors may act either on the apparent K_m or on V; those which act by increasing the effective K_m are termed 'competitive inhibitors', since the inhibitor and substrate tend to drive one another off the enzyme so that the inhibitor competes with the substrate for the enzyme; those which have no effect on K_m, but act simply by reducing V, are termed 'non-competitive'. The effect of a competitive inhibitor is abolished in high substrate concentration, which means that V is not affected; that of a non-competitive inhibitor remains.

A 'competitive' type of effect may sometimes be observed with irreversible inhibitors also, in that the substrate will protect the enzyme from the inhibitor by reducing the velocity constant of the inhibition. However, a reversibly-combining substrate can never prevent the ultimate complete inhibition by an irreversible inhibitor, since there must always be a small amount of *free* enzyme in reversible equilibrium with the substrate, and this will be available for irreversible attack by the inhibitor. Moreover, once the inhibition has taken place, it cannot be reduced by the substrate. This 'competitive' effect occurs when the inhibitor combines with a substrate-binding group in the active centre, and is therefore due to much the same cause as the reversible competitive type of inhibition.

Substances, especially those related in structure to the substrate, which combine with the enzyme at the same site as the substrate produce the competitive type of inhibition (type I); substances which combine at another site, sufficiently far removed from the substrate-binding site to have no influence on the binding of the substrate, produce the non-competitive type (type II).

In the non-competitive type the enzyme may combine with both inhibitor and substrate at the same time; in the competitive type this may or may not be the case. If the inhibitor and the substrate combine with the same site (type I a), the enzyme may be in combination with either substrate or inhibitor, but not both. It is also possible, however, that the inhibitor, while not combining with the substrate-binding site, may combine with another site sufficiently close to reduce the affinity of the enzyme for the substrate (type I b). It will thus produce competitive effects, although the enzyme can still be combined with both substrate and inhibitor at the same time. The EIS complex, when formed, breaks down at the same rate as the ES complex in this type of system.

In type I a combination with inhibitor completely abolishes the power of combining with substrate; in type I b the effect is only partial, consisting in a reduction in the affinity for substrate. A similar division into complete and partial effects can be made for the type II inhibitors, which affect V; in type II a the EIS complex does not break down at all, while in type II b it breaks down, but with a reduced velocity. There are thus four typical cases. Another possibility, to which the rather unfortunate name of 'uncompetitive inhibition' has been applied, has been suggested (667), namely, where the inhibitor can combine only with the ES complex. This, however, seems to be exceedingly rare. There is also, of course, the possibility that an inhibitor may act in more than one way, giving mixed types; the fact that it increases K_m does not exclude an action on V as well, and vice versa.

We will now consider the kinetics of the various typical cases in turn.

Competitive inhibitors

Type I a. Dealing first with *the fully competitive type*, in which the inhibitor combines with the substrate-binding site, we may represent the system by the following reactions (1815):

VIII.1 $E + S \rightleftharpoons ES$

VIII.2 $E + I \rightleftharpoons EI$

VIII.3 $ES \xrightarrow{k} E + P$

It is assumed that EI undergoes no further reaction and that a complex EIS cannot be formed. The reaction VIII.2 is an equilibrium, with dissociation constant K_i (the 'inhibitor constant'); reaction VIII.1 will be an equilibrium in the Michaelis case, with dissociation constant K_s, but it will not reach equilibrium in the Briggs–Haldane case. Dealing first with the Michaelis case, we have the following equations, in which p is the concentration of ES and q that of EI:

VIII.4 $(e - p - q)s = K_s p$

VIII.5 $(e - p - q)i = K_i q$

VIII.6 $v = kp.$

Solving these equations for v, we get

VIII.7 $$v = \frac{ke}{1 + \dfrac{K_s}{s}\left(1 + \dfrac{i}{K_i}\right)}$$

or, using relative concentrations and velocities (see p. 65) and writing ι for i/K_i,

VIII.8 $$\phi = \frac{\sigma}{1+\sigma+\iota}$$

(cf. equation IV.15).

Dealing with the same system, but without assuming that reaction VIII.1 reaches equilibrium (the general Briggs–Haldane case), we write, inserting velocity constants into reactions VIII.1–3

VIII.9 $$E+S \underset{k_{-1}}{\overset{k_{+1}}{\rightleftharpoons}} ES$$

VIII.10 $$E+I \underset{k_{-2}}{\overset{k_{+2}}{\rightleftharpoons}} EI$$

VIII.11 $$ES \overset{k_{+3}}{\rightarrow} E+P$$

Applying steady-state kinetics we obtain the equations

VIII.12 $$k_{+1}s(e-p-q) = (k_{-1}+k_{+3})p$$

VIII.13 $$k_{+2}i(e-p-q) = k_{-2}q$$

VIII.14 $$v = k_{+3}p$$

Solving for v, we obtain

VIII.15 $$v = \frac{k_{+3}e}{1+\dfrac{k_{-1}+k_{+3}}{k_{+1}s}\left(1+\dfrac{k_{+2}i}{k_{-2}}\right)}$$

and writing K_m for $(k_{-1}+k_{+3})/k_{+1}$ and K_i for k_{-2}/k_{+2}, we have

VIII.16 $$v = \frac{V}{1+\dfrac{K_m}{s}\left(1+\dfrac{i}{K_i}\right)}$$

It will be noted that this is the same equation as VIII.7, with the substitution of K_s by the usual steady-state expression for K_m (equation IV.87), but still retaining the true equilibrium constant K_i. The latter point follows from the fact that by definition of a competitive inhibitor EI does not break down and reaction VIII.10 will always be a true equilibrium.

The effect of the competitive inhibitor is thus to produce an apparent increase of K_m by the factor $1+i/K_i$; this means that the apparent K_m

increases without limit as i is increased. At any finite inhibitor concentration, the limiting velocity with excess of substrate is always equal to V, which is the maximum velocity for the uninhibited reaction.

Type I b. In *the partially competitive type* of system the inhibitor affects the affinity of the enzyme for the substrate, although the inhibitor and substrate combine with different groups. For this system we may write the following equations, which differ from those just given in assuming that a complex EIS may exist:

VIII.17 $E+S \rightleftharpoons ES$

VIII.18 $E+I \rightleftharpoons EI$

VIII.19 $EI+S \rightleftharpoons EIS$

VIII.20 $ES+I \rightleftharpoons EIS$

VIII.21 $ES \overset{k}{\rightarrow} E+P$

VIII.22 $EIS \overset{k}{\rightarrow} EI+P$

Here it is assumed that the inhibition is purely an effect on affinity, so that the complexes ES and EIS break down at the same rate; hence the same velocity constant k applies to the breakdown of both and the overall velocity will be the sum of these two reactions. If this were not so the inhibitor would be acting in two ways, affecting V as well as K_m.

Writing K_s, K_i, K_s' and K_i' for the equilibrium constants of reactions VIII.17–20 respectively, and p, q and p' for the concentrations of ES, EI and EIS respectively, we obtain the equations

VIII.23 $(e-p-p'-q)s = K_s p$

VIII.24 $(e-p-p'-q)i = K_i q$

VIII.25 $qs = K_s' p'$

VIII.26 $pi = K_i' p'$

VIII.27 $v = k(p+p')$

Solving for v, we get

VIII.28 $$v = \cfrac{ke}{1 + \cfrac{K_s}{s} \cdot \cfrac{\left(1 + \dfrac{i}{K_i}\right)}{\left(1 + \dfrac{i}{K_i} \cdot \dfrac{K_s}{K_s'}\right)}}$$

This may be written more simply in terms of relative quantities, using r for K'_s/K_s as in equation IV.49, as follows

VIII.29 $$\phi = \frac{\sigma}{\sigma + (1+\iota)\dfrac{r}{r+\iota}}$$

When i is zero, these equations reduce to those of the simple uninhibited Michaelis type IV.11 and IV.15. When i is very large, equation VIII.28 reduces to

VIII.30 $$v = \frac{ke}{1 + \dfrac{K'_s}{s}}$$

In other words the effect is to produce a new enzyme EI with a different affinity for the substrate $1/K'_s$. This system is completely indistinguishable from the fully competitive type (type I a) merely by varying the substrate concentration at fixed inhibitor concentrations, as in the Lineweaver and Burk graphical method (see p. 69). It may, however, be distinguished by varying the inhibitor concentration at fixed substrate concentration, for the inhibition does not increase indefinitely with increase of inhibitor concentration (as in the fully competitive case), but increases to a definite limit when all the enzyme is combined with inhibitor, and can then increase no further. This is true of the apparent Michaelis constant also.

It should be noted that it is not possible in this case to determine K_i by simple graphical methods; this is partly because the effective affinity of the enzyme for inhibitor varies with the substrate concentration over the range from $1/K_i$ to $1/K'_i$. Combination of the enzyme with substrate must affect the affinity for inhibitor to the same extent as combination with inhibitor affects the affinity for substrate, since it may be shown from the definitions of the equilibrium constants that

VIII.31 $$\frac{K_i}{K'_i} = \frac{K_s}{K'_s}$$

Moreover, a plot of $1/v$ against i will not give a straight line, as it does in the fully competitive or non-competitive cases (p. 328).

It should be noted that r in equation VIII.29 is not necessarily greater than 1, that is to say, the treatment is not restricted to cases of inhibition; it may cover activation also. This is a general equation dealing with interaction of the affinities of the enzyme for the substrate and other substances. If r is less than 1, the substance is an activator increasing the affinity for the substrate, although it will not affect V. If r is 1, the

M

substance has no effect. If r is greater than 1, we have the case of partially competitive inhibition just discussed. If r is infinite, so that EI has no affinity for the substrate, we have the case of fully competitive inhibition.

Non-competitive inhibitors

Type II. In *the non-competitive type* of inhibition the inhibitor does not affect the combination of the substrate with the enzyme, but affects only V. There are two possibilities; either the complex EIS may not break down at all (type II a) and the velocity is entirely that of the breakdown of ES, the effect of the inhibitor being equivalent to a reduction in the amount of active enzyme; or EIS may break down at a different velocity from ES (type II b) and the velocity is the sum of the two reactions.

Type II a. The equations for this type are

VIII.32 $\quad$ E+S $\rightleftharpoons$ ES

VIII.33 $\quad\quad$ E+I $\rightleftharpoons$ EI

VIII.34 $\quad$ EI+S $\rightleftharpoons$ EIS

VIII.35 $\quad$ ES+I $\rightleftharpoons$ EIS

VIII.36 $\quad\quad$ ES $\overset{k}{\rightarrow}$ E+P

As now combination with each substance does not affect the affinity for the other, we may write K_s for the equilibrium constants of reactions VIII.32 and VIII.34 and K_i for those of reactions VIII.33 and VIII.35 so that

VIII.37 $\qquad (e-p-p'-q)s = K_s p$

VIII.38 $\qquad (e-p-p'-q)i = K_i q$

VIII.39 $\qquad\qquad qs = K_s p'$

VIII.40 $\qquad\qquad pi = K_i p'$

VIII.41 $\qquad\qquad v = kp$

These give

VIII.42 $\qquad v = \dfrac{\dfrac{ke}{1+\dfrac{i}{K_i}}}{1+\dfrac{K_s}{s}}$

or using relative quantities

VIII.43
$$\phi = \frac{\sigma}{(1+\sigma)(1+\iota)}$$

The effect is thus to divide V by the factor $1+i/K_i$, leaving K_s unaffected. If i becomes infinite, v becomes zero under all conditions.

Type IIb. For this type equation VIII.41 becomes

VIII.44
$$v = kp + k'p'$$

and equation VIII.42 becomes

VIII.45
$$v = \frac{\dfrac{ke + k'\dfrac{i}{K_i}e}{1 + \dfrac{i}{K_i}}}{1 + \dfrac{K_s}{s}}$$

or in relative quantities

VIII.46
$$\phi = \frac{\sigma + R\iota\sigma}{(1+\sigma)(1+\iota)}$$

where $R = k'/k$. With excess of substrate the velocity is equal to ke in the absence of inhibitor and $k'e$ with excess of inhibitor; it therefore falls to a definite limit and not to zero. If k' is zero, equation VIII.45 reduces to VIII.42; if k' is greater than k, I is an activator of the enzyme.

Equation VIII.45 can be written

VIII.47
$$v = \frac{ke}{\left(1 + \dfrac{K_s}{s}\right)\dfrac{\left(1 + \dfrac{i}{K_i}\right)}{\left(1 + \dfrac{i}{K_i} \cdot \dfrac{k'}{k}\right)}}$$

On comparison of this equation with VIII.28 it will be seen that the same function of I is involved as in type Ib, but with the ratio of the substrate affinities of E and EI replaced by the ratio of the activities of E and EI, and now affecting V instead of K_s. As before, the determination of K_i by the usual methods will present difficulties; in particular, methods depending on the plotting of functions of the velocity with variable i (p. 329) fail. K_i may, however, be obtained as explained on p. 328, if K'_s or k' (as the case may be) are independently determined by measurements of the apparent affinity or the maximum velocity in presence of excess of the inhibitor.

'Mixed-type' inhibitors

As already mentioned, an inhibitor may act on both V and K_m, giving a mixture of competitive and non-competitive effects. Thus we may have a type combining I b and II a or I b and II b; it is not, however, possible to combine I a with II a or II b, for with a fully competitive inhibitor no EIS complex can be formed and hence effects on its breakdown are meaningless.

It should be noted that inhibitors may affect both V and K_m, and hence be classified as mixed types, even when their mechanism of action is in fact quite simple. Thus for an enzyme obeying Briggs–Haldane kinetics, in which k_{+2} makes an important contribution to K_m, any inhibitor affecting k_{+2} must affect K_m as well as V, so that no purely non-competitive inhibitors can exist in this case. In the limiting case, where k_{+2} is very large compared with k_{-1} so that K_m approximates to k_{+2}/k_{+1}, an inhibitor simply affecting the breakdown of ES will produce proportional changes in V and K_m. Consequently the reciprocal plots in the presence of different constant amounts of inhibitor will all be straight lines parallel to that obtained in the absence of inhibitor. The case would then appear to be one of so-called 'uncompetitive inhibition' (although not, as originally suggested, because the inhibitor can only combine with the ES complex). It is not uncommon to obtain approximately parallel reciprocal plots with inhibitors, and the most likely cause of this is a direct effect on k_{+2}. Of course if k_{+2} is very greatly reduced, so that it becomes small in comparison with k_{-1}, the effect on K_m will disappear. Thus as the inhibitor concentration is greatly increased the reciprocal plots will begin to diverge, and in the limit will become typically non-competitive.

Various 'mixed-type' inhibitions can arise in other ways, for example when an inhibitor combines not with the initial enzyme-substrate complex but with a later intermediate in the reaction pattern. KRUPKA and LAIDLER (1470) have considered the case of an inhibitor of acetylcholinesterase which slows the decomposition of the acetylated enzyme, and have shown that mixed-type effects are obtained.

A general equation for mixed competitive and non-competitive inhibition was derived by the application of steady-state kinetics by BOTTS and MORALES (298). The equation is complicated and requires simplification before it can be applied to actual cases.

A less general case, in which a fully non-competitive action is associated with a partially competitive action, has been treated theoretically by FRIEDENWALD and MAENGWYN-DAVIES (783); they presented it as a general case, although in fact their assumptions imply that the inhibitor not only affects enzyme–substrate combination, but also completely prevents the breakdown of the complex. The assumptions are the same as those made for type I b, as shown in equations VIII.17–21, with the exception that, whereas there it was assumed that both ES and EIS broke down with the same rate constant k, here it is assumed that k for reaction VIII.22 is zero, i.e. the complex EIS does not break down. Equations VIII.23–6 thus remain the same, but VIII.27 is replaced by

VIII.48 $\qquad v = kp$

We obtain by solution of these equations

VIII.49 $\qquad v = \dfrac{ke}{1+\dfrac{K_s}{s}+\dfrac{i}{K_i}\left(\dfrac{K_s}{s}+\dfrac{K_s}{K_s'}\right)}$

or in terms of relative quantities

VIII.50 $\qquad \phi = \dfrac{\sigma}{1+\sigma+\iota+\dfrac{\iota\sigma}{r}}$

Equation VIII.49 can be rewritten as

VIII.51 $\qquad v = \dfrac{\dfrac{ke}{\left(1+\dfrac{i}{K_i}\cdot\dfrac{K_s}{K_s'}\right)}}{1+\dfrac{K_s}{s}\cdot\dfrac{\left(1+\dfrac{i}{K_i}\right)}{\left(1+\dfrac{i}{K_i}\cdot\dfrac{K_s}{K_s'}\right)}}$

It will be seen that equation VIII.51 resembles equation VIII.28, but with an additional term affecting V, due to the non-competitive part of the effect of the inhibitor. The Lineweaver–Burk plot showing the effect of such an inhibitor is distinguished from the plots for the purely competitive or non-competitive types by the fact that both intercepts change on addition of the inhibitor.

Graphical presentation of inhibition effects

The effect of inhibitors of various types on the five ways of plotting the Michaelis equation is shown in Fig. VIII.1; the arrow shows the direction in which the graph is displaced in presence of the inhibitor

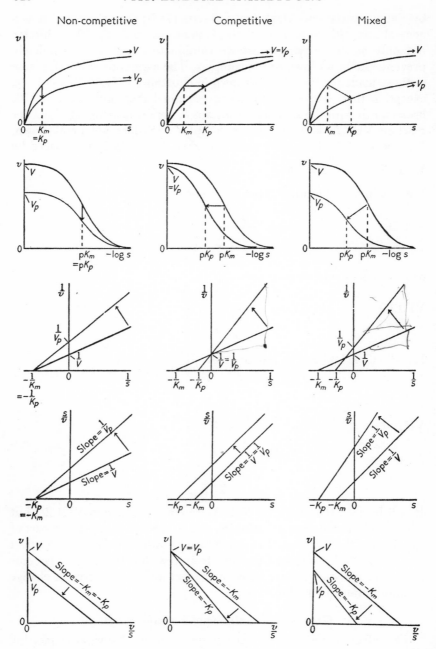

Fig. VIII.1. *Effect of inhibitors of various types on the five ways of plotting the effect of substrate concentration on enzyme reaction velocity.*

in each case. The *a* types are represented by the same figures as the *b* types, because the direction of displacement is the same in both, but in the *b* types the displacement reaches a finite limit as the inhibitor concentration is increased, whereas this is not the case with the *a* types.

The five rows of Fig. VIII.1 correspond with the five methods of plotting the Michaelis equation shown in Fig. IV.12. The Lineweaver–Burk method of plotting, shown in the third line, has been particularly widely used for distinguishing types of inhibition. With fully competitive inhibitors, the lines intersect on the vertical axis, whereas with fully non-competitive inhibitors they intersect on the base line; with mixed types the point of intersection is between the two axes.

Determination of inhibitor constants

(i) The Lineweaver–Burk plot can be used to determine K_i from the values of the appropriate intercepts in presence and absence of inhibitor. Expressions for the intercepts on both axes for the various types of inhibition can be obtained from the equations already given; for convenience they are summarized in Table VIII.1.

TABLE VIII.1

INTERCEPTS OF RECIPROCAL PLOTS IN PRESENCE OF INHIBITOR

Type	Intercept on vertical axis	Intercept on base line
Ia Purely competitive	$\dfrac{1}{V}$	$\dfrac{1}{K_m(1+i/K_i)}$
Ib Partially competitive	$\dfrac{1}{V}$	$\dfrac{1+iK_m/K_iK_m'}{K_m(1+i/K_i)}$
IIa Purely non-competitive	$\dfrac{1+i/K_i}{V}$	$\dfrac{1}{K_m}$
IIb Partially non-competitive	$\dfrac{1+i/K_i}{V+V_i'/K_i}$	$\dfrac{1}{K_m}$
Ib+IIa Mixed	$\dfrac{1+iK_m/K_iK_m}{V}$	$\dfrac{1+iK_m/K_iK_m'}{K_m(1+i/K_i)}$

In the competitive case the points of intersection with the base line of the reciprocal plots without and with inhibitor give $1/K_m$ and $1/K_p$ respectively, where K_p is written for $K_m(1+i/K_i)$, the effective Michaelis constant in presence of inhibitor at concentration i. Thus K_i can be obtained from the expression

VIII.52
$$K_i = \frac{i}{\dfrac{K_p}{K_m} - 1}$$

With a non-competitive inhibitor the points of intersection with the vertical axis give $1/V$ and $1/V_p$ respectively, where V_p is written for $V/(1+i/K_i)$. Then

VIII.53
$$K_i = \frac{i}{\dfrac{V}{V_p} - 1}$$

For the partial cases the expressions for K_i are

VIII.54
$$K_i = \frac{i}{\dfrac{K_p}{K_m} - 1}\left(1 - \frac{K_p}{K'_m}\right) \qquad \text{(case I b)}$$

VIII.55
$$K_i = \frac{i}{\dfrac{V}{V_p} - 1}\left(1 - \frac{V'}{V_p}\right) \qquad \text{(case II b)}$$

where V' is the velocity in presence of excess inhibitor and substrate, and K'_m is the Michaelis constant in presence of excess of inhibitor. These two quantities must be obtained independently by extrapolating V_p and K_p to infinite inhibitor concentration.

(ii) DIXON (622) has given a simple graphical method which gives K_i directly without calculation. If the velocity is determined with a series of inhibitor concentrations, keeping the substrate concentration constant, a straight line is obtained on plotting $1/v$ against i, as shown in Fig. VIII.2. This can be seen from the reciprocal forms of equations VIII.16 and VIII.42. The former gives for the competitive case

VIII.56
$$\frac{1}{v} = \frac{K_m}{Vs} + \frac{1}{V} + \frac{K_m}{Vs}\cdot\frac{i}{K_i}$$

If a second series of points is determined with another substrate concentration s_2, a second straight line will be obtained which cuts the first, as shown in Fig. VIII.2 (a). The point of intersection gives $-K_i$ directly.

The proof is as follows. At the point of intersection $1/v$ and i will be the same for both lines, as also will V since the inhibition is competitive. Therefore

$$\frac{K_m}{s_1} + 1 + \frac{K_m}{s_1}\cdot\frac{i}{K_i} = \frac{K_m}{s_2} + 1 + \frac{K_m}{s_2}\cdot\frac{i}{K}$$

or

VIII.57
$$\frac{1}{s_1}\left(1+\frac{i}{K_i}\right) = \frac{1}{s_2}\left(1+\frac{i}{K_i}\right)$$

Equation VIII.57 can only be true if either $s_1 = s_2$ (which is not the case) or $i = -K_i$.

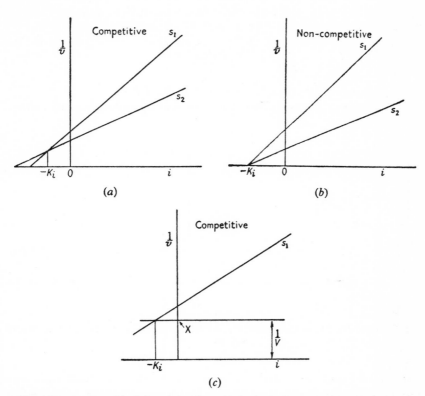

Fig. VIII.2. *Graphical determination of inhibitor constant (method of Dixon).*

It may be that K_m has already been determined in the absence of inhibitor. It is then only necessary to carry out inhibition experiments at one substrate concentration, for the point which gives K_i lies at a height of $1/V$, as may be seen by putting $i = -K_i$ in equation VIII.56, and this is already given by the point X in Fig. IV.12(c). Thus it is only necessary to draw a horizontal line through point X on the $1/v$ axis, as shown in Fig. VIII.2(c), and it will cut the graph obtained in presence of inhibitor at $-K_i$. This method, however, is restricted to competitive cases.

If desired, K_m as well as K_i can be obtained from Fig. VIII.2(a), for each line cuts the base-line at a value of i equal to $-K_i\left(\dfrac{s}{K_m}+1\right)$.

The method is also applicable to non-competitive inhibitors. This case is shown in Fig. VIII.2(b). The intersection of the lines still gives $-K_i$, but it now lies on the base-line. This can be seen by putting $1/v = 0$ in the reciprocal form of the non-competitive equation VIII.42, namely

VIII.58 $$\frac{1}{v} = \frac{1}{V}\left(1+\frac{K_m}{s}\right)\left(1+\frac{i}{K_i}\right)$$

which represents the straight lines of Fig. VIII.2(b).

(iii) The previous methods require series of measurements with either

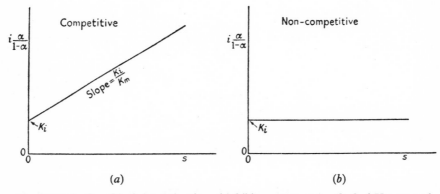

Fig. VIII.3. *Graphical determination of inhibitor constant (method of Hunter and Downs).*

constant substrate and varying inhibitor or constant inhibitor and varying substrate concentrations. It may be, however, that it is desired to obtain K_i from a number of existing measurements in which both substrate and inhibitor concentrations vary, perhaps in a more or less haphazard manner. This may be done by the method of HUNTER and DOWNS (*1191*) which enables all the data to be recalculated so that they are brought on to a single line.

If for each observation a velocity ratio α is defined by

VIII.59 $$\alpha = \frac{v_i}{v}$$

where v_i is the velocity in the presence of inhibitor and v the velocity in its absence with the same substrate concentration, it is easy to show for the competitive case from equations IV.11 and VIII.7 that

$$\text{VIII.60} \qquad i\frac{\alpha}{1-\alpha} = K_i + \frac{K_i}{K_m}s$$

If then $i\dfrac{\alpha}{1-\alpha}$ is plotted against s, as shown in Fig. VIII.3 (a), a straight line will be obtained which cuts the vertical axis at K_i and has a slope of K_i/K_m.

Actually, instead of $i\dfrac{\alpha}{1-\alpha}$, it is quicker to calculate $i\dfrac{v_i}{v-v_i}$, which is the same thing.

For the non-competitive case, it follows from equations IV.11 and VIII.42 that

$$\text{VIII.61} \qquad i\frac{\alpha}{1-\alpha} = K_i$$

and is independent of substrate concentration, as shown in Fig. VIII.3 (b).

Other types of inhibitors

All the cases of inhibition which we have so far discussed involve a direct combination of the inhibitor with the enzyme, but inhibition will also be produced by a substance which combines with the substrate, coenzyme or metal activator, so rendering them unavailable for the enzyme. In such cases inhibition will only be produced if the concentration of the inhibiting substance is of the same order as that of the substrate or cofactor affected, and the addition of more substrate or cofactor will abolish the inhibition.

Two further types of inhibition arise by competition, but when the inhibitor competes not with the substrate but with a coenzyme or metal activator. Several examples of both types are shown in Fig. IX.29 and Table IX.6. Although these are competitive as far as the cofactor is concerned, and can be reversed by increasing the concentration of the latter, they are non-competitive in the usual sense, since the inhibition will be independent of the substrate concentration.

Inhibitors with very high affinities

With the majority of inhibitors the amounts needed to produce a significant inhibition are very large compared with the amount of enzyme taken; consequently the amount of inhibitor bound by the enzyme will always be a negligible fraction of the total, and the concentration of free inhibitor can be taken as equal to the total concentration. This has been implicitly assumed in developing the equations for inhibition, and is analogous to the assumption for substrate concentration normally made in enzyme kinetics.

Certain inhibitors, notably the highly potent anticholinesterases (Fig. VIII.14), have K_i values of the order of 10^{-9} M, so that the molarities of inhibitor and enzyme taken may be of the same order. In this case the binding of inhibitor by the enzyme may greatly reduce the concentration of free inhibitor, so that the equations, which are expressed in terms of free inhibitor, require modification. Equations expressed in terms of total inhibitor concentrations have been developed by EASSON and STEDMAN (665), STRAUS and GOLDSTEIN (2548) and GOLDSTEIN (862).

Considering the case of a purely non-competitive inhibitor as represented by equations VIII.32–6 (type II a), we must now write instead of equations VIII.38 and VIII.40

VIII.62 $\qquad (e-p-p'-q)(i_t-p'-q) = K_i q$

VIII.63 $\qquad\qquad p(i_t-p'-q) = K_i p'$

where e and i_t are the total molar concentrations of enzyme and inhibitor, and p, p' and q are the concentrations of ES, EIS and EI respectively. Since the system is non-competitive, the affinities of E and ES for the inhibitor will be the same, so that K_i as before will represent the dissociation constant either of EI into E and I or of EIS into ES and I.

Let α be the fraction of the total enzyme which is not combined with inhibitor; then

VIII.64 $\qquad \alpha = \dfrac{e-p'-q}{e}$

Since combination with inhibitor does not affect the equilibrium with the substrate, α will also be the fractional activity v_i/v, where v_i is the velocity in the presence of inhibitor and v that in its absence with the same substrate concentration. α is thus identical with that already defined in equation VIII.59. Eliminating p, p' and q from equations VIII.62–4, we obtain

VIII.65 $\qquad i_t \dfrac{\alpha}{1-\alpha} = K_i + \alpha e$

If the amount of enzyme e is very small in comparison with K_i, the last term may be neglected, i_t becomes i, and the equation becomes identical with that of Hunter and Downs (equation VIII.61).

The last term produces a distortion in the plots of velocity in terms of inhibitor concentration. This is shown, for example, in Fig. VIII.4, where activity is plotted against $\log i_t/K_i$. With low enzyme concentration, the usual symmetrical curve is obtained, with the mid-point at $i_t = K_i$. As the enzyme concentration is increased, two effects become apparent, namely, a change in the form of the curve with a downward displacement of the point of inflection, and a displacement of the whole curve towards the right. In the case shown in the right-hand curve practically all the inhibitor is combined with the enzyme. At the inhibitor concentrations corresponding to 50 per cent of full activity

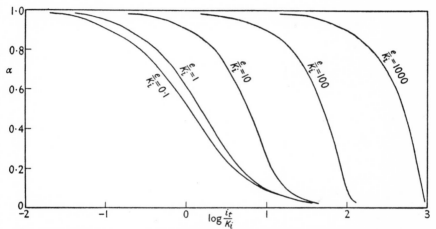

Fig. VIII.4. *Effect of binding of inhibitor with high affinity on inhibition curve.* Theoretical curves plotted from equation VIII.65.

from *2548*

(known as I_{50}) $\alpha = 0 \cdot 5$ and, as pointed out by MYERS (*1907*), equation VIII.65 gives

VIII.66 $I_{50} = K_i + 0 \cdot 5e$

The half-inhibition points of the curves in Fig. VIII.4 are therefore displaced to the right of the pK value by an amount which depends on the enzyme concentration.

These distortions can be used to determine e, or more strictly the absolute concentration of inhibitor-binding sites, or of enzyme active centres if, as is usually the case, each centre combines with one molecule of inhibitor. This method has been used to estimate the number of active centres of cholinesterases in a given volume of solution, and hence their catalytic centre activity (*665, 1907, 2548*). This may be done by varying the inhibitor concentration with a constant enzyme concentration, and plotting $i_t/(1-\alpha)$ against $1/\alpha$, as shown in Fig. VIII.5. The intercepts on the vertical and horizontal axes are e and $-e/K_i$ respectively.

MYERS (*1907*) has found it possible to use this principle with the cholinesterase inhibitor Nu-683 (see Fig. VIII.15), in spite of the fact that this is properly speaking a competitive inhibitor, because the displacement of inhibitor from the enzyme by the substrate is very slow. Thus, provided the activity is measured within a few minutes of adding the substrate to the inhibited enzyme, the system behaves as a non-

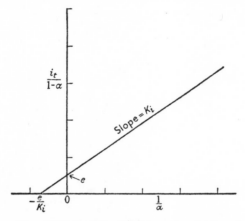

Fig. VIII.5. *Determination of molarity of enzyme with inhibitor of high affinity.*
Theoretical curve plotted from equation VIII.65.

from *2548*

competitive one. The method Myers used was to determine I_{50} values for several amounts of enzyme, and to plot these against the amount of enzyme expressed in terms of activities in the absence of inhibitor. If these activities are expressed in μmoles of substrate per minute, they will be equal to Ae, where A is the catalytic centre activity (see Chapter II). Then from equation VIII.66, we have

VIII.67 $$I_{50} = K_i + \frac{0 \cdot 5}{A} \cdot Ae$$

The plot will therefore give a straight line with a slope of $0 \cdot 5/A$, and from the intercepts on the two axes, which will be K_i and $-\dfrac{A}{0 \cdot 5}K_i$, the catalytic centre activity and hence the absolute enzyme molarities can readily be obtained. Fig. VIII.6 shows the data of Myers for the inhibition of human serum cholinesterase acting on benzoylcholine, plotted in this way. For the experiment shown, the intercepts are $0\cdot88\times10^{-9}$ M and $-3\cdot45\times10^{-5}$ moles per minute per litre, giving $A=1\cdot96\times10^{4}$ for benzoylcholine.

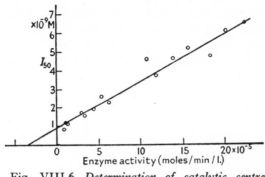

Fig. VIII.6. *Determination of catalytic centre activity of cholinesterase.*

Application of equation VIII.66 to inhibition of human serum cholinesterase by Nu-683. Each I_{50} has been determined from a curve of the type shown in Fig. VIII.4.

after *1907*

EFFECT OF pH ON INHIBITION

The inhibition of enzymes may be very greatly affected by pH, in the irreversible no less than the reversible case. In the former, the rate of reaction of inhibitor with enzyme may be affected by pH because the different ionic forms of the enzyme may react at different rates with the inhibitor, or because the inhibitor itself ionizes. The effects can be dealt with quantitatively in the same way as that which we have developed for the effect of pH on k_{+2} (equation IV.157 ff.). An example will be given in the section on organophosphorus inhibitors (p. 350).

The effect of pH on reversible inhibitions may be the result of several different mechanisms, depending on the mechanism by which the inhibitor itself acts. If the inhibitor acts by reducing V, it may do so either by reducing $\check{k}_{+2}$ or by affecting K_{es1} or K_{es2} (equation IV.159). A pure effect on $\check{k}_{+2}$ will result if the rate of breakdown of the active ionic species of EIS is less than that of the active ionic species of ES; the effective value of $\check{k}_{+2}$ will then lie between those of $\check{k}_{+2}$ for ES and $\check{k}_{+2}$ for EIS. These are both pH-independent quantities, but their relative contributions to the effective $\check{k}_{+2}$ will vary with pH if K_i changes with pH; in this case therefore the value of the effective $\check{k}_{+2}$ may vary between these limits as the pH changes.

The inhibitor may affect K_{es1} or K_{es2} either by direct combination with the acidic or basic group in the active centre, producing an apparent change in these constants, or by combining with a neighbouring group to produce a true change. Again, the effective values of these constants will lie between the values for ES and those for EIS, and the pH-activity curve will be affected as discussed in the section on unspecific anionic effects (p. 443; cf. Fig. IX.35). Then the inhibition produced will vary markedly with pH; such a shift of the pH-activity

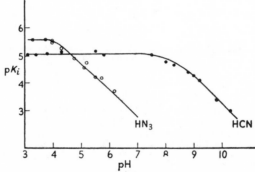

Fig. VIII.7. *Effect of pH on inhibition of catalase by HN₃ and HCN.*

after *422*

curve may even result in the substance acting as an inhibitor at one pH and as an activator at another.

In the competitive case EIS is not formed, but the effective Michaelis constant K_p may vary with pH if either K_m or K_i varies, because if the affinity of the enzyme for either substrate or inhibitor changes with pH the degree of inhibition will also change. The interpretation of pH effects on K_m in terms of the pKs of the groups which are affected by combination of the enzyme with the substrate has already been discussed in Chapter IV, section (c), and it has been pointed out that this treatment also applies to the interpretation of the effect of pH on K_i in terms of the pKs of the groups affected by combination with the inhibitor (equations IV.172–3). Thus by plotting pK_i against pH a graph is obtained in which the pKs of these groups show up as bends, and the rules set out on pp. 137–8 for the pK_s graph apply also to this graph. As an illustration, Fig. VIII.7 shows the pK_i curves, drawn from data of CHANCE (422), for the inhibition of catalase by hydrazoic acid and hydrocyanic acid. The bend in each curve corresponds roughly with the pK of the inhibitor, and the slopes show that combination with the free acid occurs without any alteration of charge, while combination with the inhibitor anion also produces a neutral compound with disappearance of the negative charge. MASSEY (Figs. 2 and 3 of 1746) has published a number of pK_i curves for inhibition of fumarate hydratase by a variety of dibasic acids; these well illustrate the great importance of pH in enzyme inhibition and the kind of effects which may be obtained, but as pointed out in the following chapter, the case of fumarate hydratase is complicated by anion effects. Few other inhibitors seem to have been studied in this way; this is regrettable since such studies may throw a good deal of light on the nature of the active centre and the mechanism of action of competitive inhibitors. It should be noted in this connection that the study of K_i has an advantage over the study of K_m, in that the former is always a true equilibrium constant expressing the affinity and is free from the kinetic element which may be present in K_m.

SOME IMPORTANT INHIBITORS

A vast number of enzyme inhibitors are mentioned in the literature, particularly competitive inhibitors related to the enzyme substrates. In many cases little has been reported beyond the mere fact of the inhibition. It would be an impossible task to bring together all this material in a reasonably small space and we have not attempted to do so. We shall limit ourselves to mentioning the more important classes of inhibitors.

Poisons of heavy metals

A number of substances, such as cyanide and H_2S, inactivate heavy metal catalysts by forming very stable complexes with the metal. Since the cytochrome oxidase system involves catalysis by iron and copper, these substances are powerful inhibitors of the respiration of many tissues and are often referred to as the respiratory poisons. They inhibit many, though not all, of the enzymes which contain iron or copper atoms as an essential part of their catalytic mechanism. Other inhibitors which have been included in this group are azide and carbon monoxide. The inhibition of respiration by this group of inhibitors provides the main evidence for the importance of the cytochrome system in biological oxidation; this evidence is critically reviewed in the following chapter.

Cyanide has been considered to be the standard inhibitor for detecting metal catalysis. It has now become clear, however, that in fact cyanide

TABLE VIII.2

ENZYME INHIBITIONS BY THE RESPIRATORY POISONS

	Cyanide Conc. (M)	Cyanide Inh. (%)	Azide Conc. (M)	Azide Inh. (%)	Sulphide Conc. (M)	Sulphide Inh. (%)	CO CO/O_2 ratio	CO Inh. (%)
Cytochrome oxidase (1.9.3.1)	10^{-8}	50	10^{-3} (pH 7·5)	80		++	6	50 (Reversed by light)
Cytochrome peroxidase (1.11.1.5)	10^{-4}	50	10^{-2} (pH 5·5); 10^{-2} (pH 7·5)	95; 0				None
Catalase (1.11.1.6)	5×10^{-6}	50	2×10^{-5}	50				None
Peroxidase (1.11.1.7)	10^{-5}–10^{-6}	++	10^{-3}	++	10^{-5}–10^{-6}	++		None
Homogentisate oxygenase (1.99.2.5)		++		++				None
Ascorbate oxidase (1.10.3.3)		++						None
Catechol oxidase (1.10.3.1)	2×10^{-3}	++	2×10^{-3} (pH 8)	++	5×10^{-4}	++	4	40
Urate oxidase (1.7.3.3)	3×10^{-5}	83	2×10^{-3} (pH 6·8)	28	4×10^{-3}	0		None
Carbonic anhydrase (4.2.1.1) (blood)	10^{-4}–10^{-5}	50	10^{-4}–10^{-5} (pH 6·8)	50	10^{-4}–10^{-5}	50		(?)
Carbonic anhydrase (4.2.1.1) (plants)	10^{-3}	50–75	10^{-3}	70–90		80		
Carnosinase (3.4.3.3)	10^{-2}	80			10^{-3}			
Isocitrate dehydrogenase (1.1.1.42)	10^{-2}	50	10^{-2}	50				
Aconitate hydratase (4.2.1.3)		+++				++		
Hydroxylamine reductase (1.7.99.1)	5×10^{-6}	50		++				
NADH$_2$ nitrate reductase (1.6.6.3)		++		++				
Tryptophan oxygenase (1.99.2.c)		+		+		+		+

Enzyme						
Monoamine oxidase (1.4.3.4)	10^{-3}	100				
Diamine oxidase (1.4.3.6)		+				
Arginine decarboxylase (4.1.1.19)	10^{-3}	98	10^{-3}	21		
Glutamate decarboxylase (4.1.1.15)	10^{-4}	93	10^{-2}	27		
Histidine decarboxylase (4.1.1.22)	10^{-2}	97	10^{-1}	38	10^{-1}	42
Lysine decarboxylase (4.1.1.18)	10^{-4}	81	10^{-4}	61	10^{-2}	32
Ornithine decarboxylase (4.1.1.17)	10^{-4}	40	10^{-4}	36		
Tyrosine decarboxylase (4.1.1.25)	10^{-3}	64	10^{-1}	15	10^{-2}	0 (None)
L-serine dehydratase (4.2.1.13)		+++				
Trytophan synthase (4.2.1.20)	10^{-3}	95				
Histidine ammonia-lyase (4.3.1.3)		+				
Alkaline phosphatase (3.1.3.1)	3×10^{-3}	50				++
Aldolase (4.1.2.b) (yeast)		+ (pH 8·5)				
Acetoacetate decarboxylase (4.1.1.4)	10^{-4}	82	10^{-2}	53		
Formate dehydrogenase (1.2.1.2)	10^{-4}	80	5×10^{-7}	65		
Alcohol dehydrogenase (1.1.1.1) (liver)	10^{-4}	67 (pH 10)				
L-iditol dehydrogenase (1.1.1.14)	10^{-2}	53				
Mannitol-1-phosphate dehydrogenase (1.1.1.17)	$1 \cdot 5 \times 10^{-2}$	50				
Phospholipase B (3.1.1.5)	10^{-3}	87				
Progressive inactivations						
Thiosulphate sulphurtransferase (2.8.1.1)		+++				
Xanthine oxidase (1.2.3.2)		+	10^{-3}	0		
Aldehyde oxidase (1.2.3.1)		+++		++		
Succinate dehydrogenase (1.3.99.1) (particulate)		+				
Hydrogenase (1.98.1.1)		++		++ (Reversible, but not by light)		

is a very unspecific inhibitor and that it inhibits a large number of enzymes which do not involve a metal catalysis. It has been much used in determining the fraction of cell-respiration which depends on cytochrome oxidase, but in view of the possibility of actions other than the poisoning of the oxidase it must be regarded as giving only a maximum value for this fraction. Table VIII.2 shows a list of cyanide-sensitive enzymes, together with some quantitative data both for cyanide and for other members of the group. It will be seen that the list contains a number of haemoproteins, copper-containing enzymes and enzymes containing zinc or other metals, but in addition it contains many enzymes depending on pyridoxal phosphate or on disulphide groups.

Thus cyanide may inhibit enzymes by several different mechanisms. It may combine with an essential metal in the enzyme; it may remove a metal from the enzyme as an inactive complex; it may combine with a carbonyl group in the enzyme itself, in a cofactor or prosthetic group (e.g. pyridoxal), or even in the substrate; it can act as a reducing agent to break essential disulphide links in the enzyme, or it may act in still other ways as in the slow progressive cyanide inhibitions. In their specificity of inhibition, azide and sulphide generally resemble cyanide, although the table shows some differences. Carbon monoxide, on the other hand, has a much narrower range of action, inhibiting only enzymes containing iron or copper and not all of these. It inhibits particularly those enzymes in this group which react directly with oxygen, with which it competes, combining with the reduced forms of the enzymes, in contrast to cyanide, which combines most stably with the oxidized forms and does not compete with oxygen. Owing to the competition with oxygen, the inhibition by carbon monoxide is determined by the ratio of the pressures of carbon monoxide and oxygen to which the system is exposed. The carbon monoxide compounds of the haemoprotein enzymes, unlike those of the cuproprotein enzymes, are dissociated by light, and this effect has been much used in the identification of cytochrome oxidases (see the following chapter). Cyanide also combines to a relatively small extent with the reduced forms of haemoproteins, and these compounds resemble the carbon monoxide compounds in being dissociated by light (see *1346*).

Most of the inactivations of metalloenzymes by heavy metal poisons are rapid and reversible. Occasionally, however, relatively slow, progressive and irreversible inhibitions are observed with cyanide, and these are shown at the end of Table VIII.2. The first examples of this effect was found with xanthine oxidase (*626*), studied with purified soluble preparations. In contrast, succinate dehydrogenase in the soluble form is not inhibited by cyanide, but in particulate preparations shows similar effects to xanthine oxidase (943). In this case the effects vary with the acceptor used. They are not yet completely explained, but it has been suggested that they may be due to combination of the cyanide with iron atoms in the enzyme.

1,10-phenanthroline is becoming increasingly used as a metal-complexing agent. By its use MASSEY (1747) was able to show that at least half the iron in succinate dehydrogenase could be removed without loss of activity. It has also been used for Zn-containing enzymes (see p. 307). VALLEE et al. (2713) have made a detailed study of its action on the alcohol dehydrogenases of yeast and liver. The latter enzyme shows only an instantaneous reversible inhibition, whereas with the former there is also a slow irreversible inactivation.

Reagents for thiol groups

In 1925 SCHWARTZ and OSCHMANN (2348) showed that muscle glycolysis is inhibited by iodoacetate; this was confirmed some years later by LUNDSGAARD, who showed that alcoholic fermentation in yeast is also inhibited. It was not until some years later that iodoacetate was shown to be a specific inhibitor of certain enzymes, notably yeast alcohol dehydrogenase (614, 2747) and glyceraldehydephosphate dehydrogenase (614). Between 1931 and 1935 it was shown that iodoacetate reacts with the thiol groups of thioglycollate (1060), α-thiolactate (238), cysteine and glutathione (606, 2131, 2172) and proteins (1833) to give alkylated derivatives with the liberation of HI.

Not all thiol reagents act by alkylation. These reagents may be divided into three groups: (a) alkylating reagents, (b) mercaptide-forming reagents, and (c) oxidizing agents converting thiol into disulphide groups (for reviews, see 173, 2129).

Thiol-alkylating reagents

Halogenated acetic acids were the first-described reagents of this class. Free iodoacetate, however, although it inhibits a few thiol enzymes strongly, fails to react with many others. It is therefore not a general thiol enzyme poison, in contrast to its esters and iodoacetamide. The most effective members of this class of reagents are the halogenated compounds ethyl iodoacetate, iodoacetamide, chloroacetophenone and bromobenzyl cyanide; less effective, though still active, compounds contain an ethylenic group instead of the halogen, for example, ethyl acrylate or acrolein. All these compounds have lachrymatory properties (617). The various reactions involved may be written as shown in Fig. VIII.8.

The compounds of the first group contain a 'positive halogen' atom. FORD-MOORE (760) showed a correlation between lachrymatory power and the positiveness of the halogen resulting from electron displacement under the influence of neighbouring groups, such as a carbonyl group, e.g.

$$\overset{\displaystyle \curvearrowright O^{(-)}}{\underset{(+)}{R-C-CH_2-Cl}}$$

The same groups which bring about this electron displacement also cause a polarization of the ethylenic double bond in the second type of compound. In both types of compound the lachrymatory properties were shown to be associated with reactivity towards –SH groups (*127, 617, 1666*). The reaction between the polarized ethylenic group and the thiol group may be pictured thus

$$\begin{array}{ccccc}
R-S^{(-)} & & CH_2^{(+)} & & R-S-CH_2 \\
| & & \| & & | \\
H_{(+)} & + & CH & \longrightarrow & CH_2 \\
& & | \quad {}^{(-)} & & | \\
& & C=O & & C=O \\
& & | \curvearrowright & & | \\
& & R' & & R'
\end{array}$$

Carboxyl groups, unlike the carbonyl groups of esters, ketones, aldehydes and amides, do not make the halogen atom or ethylenic group reactive; thus acrylate and iodoacetate have no lachrymatory properties, whereas their esters are lachrymators. Correspondingly, acrylate and iodoacetate react feebly with most –SH groups in comparison with the esters.

MORGAN and FRIEDMANN (*1857–8*) have shown that even maleic acid itself can form addition compounds with –SH groups, when high concentrations are used and the mixture is incubated for a number of hours. Since the molecule is symmetrical in the free acid and its disodium salt, this would not be expected on the above view, since the double bond would not be polarized; however, in the monosodium salt the charge on only one carboxyl group would presumably produce some polarization. The fact that fumarate does not act supports this idea, for the first and second ionization constants of fumaric acid are not very different, whereas those of maleic acid differ by a factor of more than 5,000. Consequently, the concentration of the singly charged anion may be large in the case of maleate, but is always small in the case of fumarate.

All the compounds shown in Fig. VIII.8 behave as general irreversible poisons of –SH enzymes; iodoacetamide and chloroacetophenone have been particularly used in the identification of essential thiol groups in enzymes. Mustard gas ($S(C_2H_4Cl)_2$) has sometimes been classed with these as a thiol reagent, but this is misleading. In fact it reacts much less readily with thiol groups, and much more readily with other groups in proteins, than do these compounds (*300*).

Iodoacetate is not completely specific for thiol groups. At certain pHs it reacts with a histidine residue in native ribonuclease, and it can also react with a methionine group (*2507*).

$$R-SH + ICH_2.CO.O.C_2H_5 \longrightarrow R-S-CH_2.CO.O.C_2H_5 + HI$$

$$R-SH + ICH_2.CO.NH_2 \longrightarrow R-S-CH_2.CO.NH_2 + HI$$

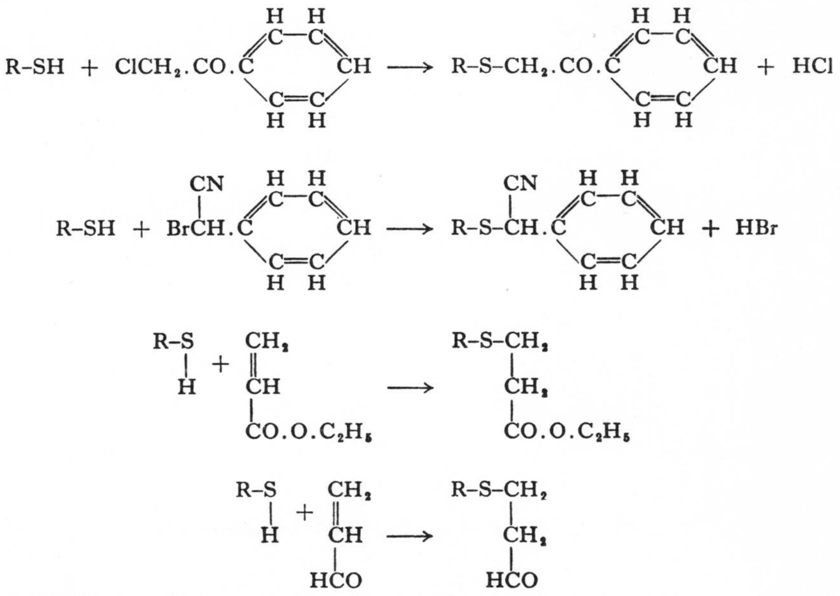

$$R-SH + ClCH_2.CO.\overset{\displaystyle H\ H}{\underset{\displaystyle H\ H}{C\underset{}{\diagdown}}} CH \longrightarrow R-S-CH_2.CO.\overset{\displaystyle H\ H}{\underset{\displaystyle H\ H}{C}} CH + HCl$$

$$R-SH + Br\overset{\displaystyle CN}{\underset{}{CH.C}}\overset{\displaystyle H\ H}{\underset{\displaystyle H\ H}{}} CH \longrightarrow R-S-\overset{\displaystyle CN}{CH.C}\overset{\displaystyle H\ H}{\underset{\displaystyle H\ H}{}} CH + HBr$$

$$\overset{\displaystyle R-S}{\underset{\displaystyle H}{|}} + \overset{\displaystyle CH_2}{\underset{\displaystyle CO.O.C_2H_5}{\overset{\displaystyle \|}{CH}}} \longrightarrow \overset{\displaystyle R-S-CH_2}{\underset{\displaystyle CO.O.C_2H_5}{CH_2}}$$

$$\overset{\displaystyle R-S}{\underset{\displaystyle H}{|}} + \overset{\displaystyle CH_2}{\underset{\displaystyle HCO}{\overset{\displaystyle \|}{CH}}} \longrightarrow \overset{\displaystyle R-S-CH_2}{\underset{\displaystyle HCO}{CH_2}}$$

Fig. VIII.8. *Reactions of thiol-alkylating reagents.*

Mercaptide-forming reagents

Organic compounds of mercury or arsenic reversibly form mercaptides with thiol groups. The most widely used of the mercury compounds is *p*-chloromercuribenzoate. However, in fairly high concentrations the mercury compounds inhibit enzymes by reactions not involving –SH groups (*2466a*). Trivalent arsenicals also readily react with –SH groups, although they have not been used for their estimation. The reactions involved are shown in Fig. VIII.9.

In contrast to the alkylating reagents, inhibitions by mercaptide-forming reagents are readily reversed, particularly by adding an excess of a thiol compound such as cysteine. An equilibrium is then set up, with the reagent partitioned between the thiol groups of the enzyme and those of the added thiol compound in proportion to the concentrations and affinities. With dithiol compounds resembling reduced lipoic acid the arsenical reagents form stable ring structures, as shown in the last line of Fig. VIII.9, and this combination is not reversed by excess of a monothiol compound. Thus the inhibition of the pyruvate oxidase

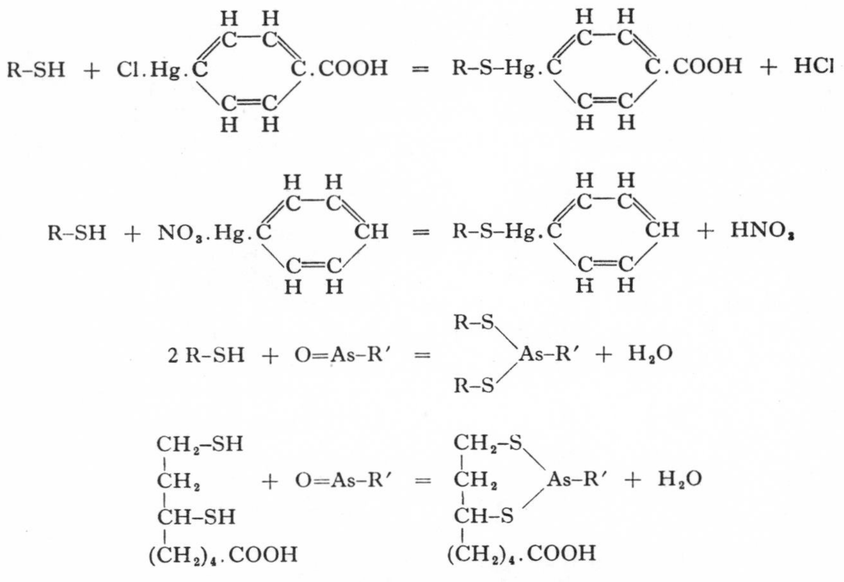

$$R-SH + Cl.Hg.\underset{\underset{C=C}{\overset{\overset{H\ H}{C-C}}{}}}{C}.C.COOH = R-S-Hg.\underset{\underset{C=C}{\overset{\overset{H\ H}{C-C}}{}}}{C}.C.COOH + HCl$$

$$R-SH + NO_3.Hg.\underset{\underset{C=C}{\overset{\overset{H\ H}{C-C}}{}}}{C}\ CH = R-S-Hg.\underset{\underset{C=C}{\overset{\overset{H\ H}{C-C}}{}}}{C}\ CH + HNO_3$$

$$2\,R-SH + O{=}As{-}R' = \overset{R-S}{\underset{R-S}{\diagdown\ \diagup}}As{-}R' + H_2O$$

$$\begin{matrix} CH_2-SH \\ | \\ CH_2 \\ | \\ CH-SH \\ | \\ (CH_2)_4.COOH \end{matrix} + O{=}As{-}R' = \begin{matrix} CH_2-S \\ | \quad\ \diagdown \\ CH_2 \quad\ \diagup As{-}R' + H_2O \\ | \\ CH-S \\ | \\ (CH_2)_4.COOH \end{matrix}$$

Fig. VIII.9. *Reactions of mercaptide-forming reagents.*

system by arsenicals, which is due to an attack on the lipoate cofactor, cannot be reversed by cysteine (see *2645*). It can, however, be reversed by other *di*thiol compounds, and this led to the development by PETERS and his group (*2537*) of 'British Anti-Lewisite' (BAL), which has the structure

$$\begin{matrix} CH_2SH \\ | \\ CHSH \\ | \\ CH_2OH \end{matrix}$$

It is remarkable that, at a time when lipoate was unknown, a substance so similar to it should have been produced purely from the application of chemical principles to enzyme inhibition studies. The arsenical compound Lewisite was one of the more dangerous war gases, and the development of an effective antidote in this way demonstrates the important practical consequences which may result from studies of enzyme inhibitors.

The fact that the mercaptide-forming reagents react with the same groups in enzymes as do the alkylating reagents was elegantly demonstrated by R. VAN HEYNINGEN (see *617*), who showed that the –SH groups of hexokinase could be protected by an arsenical (Lewisite) against attack by an alkylating reagent (ethyl iodoacetate), with recovery of full activity on subsequent removal of the arsenical.

Thiol-oxidizing reagents

Thiol groups are relatively easily oxidized by a wide variety of oxidizing agents, but the majority of these substances are not regarded as

$$2\,R\text{–SH} + G\text{–S–S–G} = R\text{–S–S–R} + 2\,G\text{–SH}$$

$$2\,R\text{–SH} + I_2 = R\text{–S–S–R} + 2\,HI$$

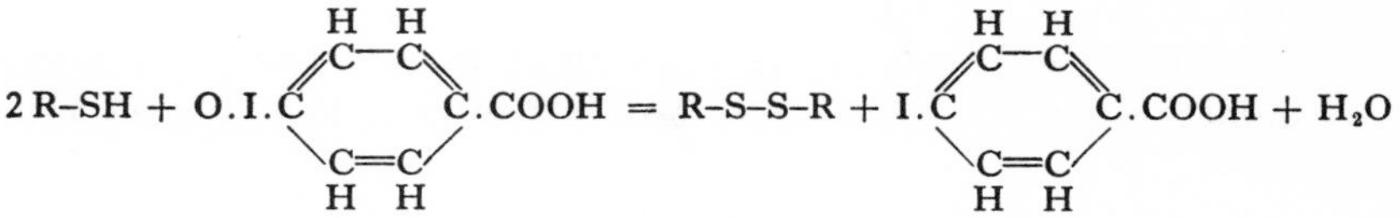

Fig. VIII.10. *Reactions of thiol-oxidizing reagents.*

specific reagents for thiol enzymes. Enzymes contain other oxidizable groups, and even the thiol groups themselves may be oxidized by some reagents to products other than disulphide groups. The most specific reagents for oxidizing the thiol groups of enzymes to disulphide links are probably disulphides themselves, e.g. oxidized glutathione, which inhibits –SH enzymes and was early used by HOPKINS (*1158*) as a test. Iodosobenzoate appears to be the most preferred reagent of this type at the moment, but it must be used under strictly controlled conditions, or it may attack other groups, such as methionine. The reactions involved in inhibition by some thiol-oxidizing reagents are shown in Fig. VIII.10.

Heavy metals

Salts of heavy metals, such as silver, copper, mercury and lead, inactivate most enzymes in high concentrations, and are in fact general protein precipitants. A few enzymes are extremely sensitive to low concentrations of such metals. A well-known case is the inhibition of β-fructofuranosidase by Ag, and malt amylase is inactivated even by saturated AgCl solution (*2024*)! The mechanism of such inhibitions is unknown; some workers have suggested that the metal ions combine with thiol groups, others that carboxyl groups are involved. However, in the case of β-fructofuranosidase, MYRBÄCK (*1914*) has shown that the inhibition is due to a combination of Ag^+ with a histidine residue. It does not appear that any general rules for such inhibitions can be formulated.

In most cases heavy metal inhibitions are reversible by the addition of metal-complexing agents, e.g. cyanide or EDTA (ethylenediamine-tetra-acetate). This is a point of some practical importance in estimating the activity of enzymes. An increase in total activity during purification of an enzyme may often be due to removal of an inhibitory metal by some added substance, e.g. cysteine, ATP, many buffers such as pyro-phosphate, or glycyl-glycine. Denatured protein is a much better metal-complexing agent than most native proteins, so that denaturation of protein during the manipulations may cause an increase of activity. Reagents, especially ammonium sulphate, and even ordinary distilled water, are apt to contain a sufficient amount of heavy metal ions to produce an appreciable inhibition of sensitive enzymes. In such cases, in order to avoid the trouble of using highly purified reagents and glass-distilled water, it may be convenient to carry out all activity determinations in the presence of an efficient complexing agent such as EDTA.

Irreversible organophosphorus inhibitors

Substances of the general formula

$$\begin{array}{ccc} R-O & O & \\ & \diagdown P \diagup & \\ R'-O & X & \end{array} \quad \text{or} \quad \begin{array}{ccc} R-O & O & \\ & \diagdown P \diagup & \\ R' & X & \end{array}$$

where R and R' are alkyl groups and X is $-F$, $-CN$, or $-O.C_6H_4.NO_2$, are highly specific inhibitors of enzymes which possess esterase activity, particularly cholinesterase and acetylcholinesterase, as first shown independently in 1941 by ADRIAN *et al.* (see *20*) and MACKWORTH (see *1667*). They also inhibit chymotrypsin, trypsin, thrombin, plasmin, acetylesterase, carboxylesterase and some lipases (*146*, *1820*, *1887*, *2804–5*). All of these enzymes have esterase actions, but the inhibition is not confined to this action, as the proteolytic activity of chymotrypsin is similarly inhibited. This group of substances is collectively known as 'the nerve gases', since the high sensitivity of the cholinesterases to them makes them highly toxic to the central nervous system. Many of them have found practical application in clinical medicine and as insecticides (*2309*).

These are enzyme inhibitors of a unique and extremely interesting type. The reason that their action is confined to enzymes which can hydrolyse esters is that the inhibitory group is formed from them by the enzyme itself, by a process analogous to the first stage of the hydrolysis of the substrate. As we have pointed out in the two preceding chapters, the reactions catalysed by enzymes of this group take place in two stages, namely, (a) transfer of the acyl group to the enzyme, with the formation of an acylated enzyme and liberation of the free alcohol, and (b) hydrolysis of the acylated enzyme (reactions VIII.68 and VIII.70). Similarly, with the organophosphorus inhibitors the substituted phosphoryl group is transferred to the enzyme (reaction VIII.69), with the formation of a phosphorylated enzyme and liberation of the substance HX. The phosphorylated enzyme, however, is a comparatively stable compound, hydrolysing only at a negligible rate in the case of the more effective inhibitors. It is true that in the case of the less effective members of the series the substituted enzyme hydrolyses at a measurable rate (reaction VIII.71); thus in these cases the enzyme slowly hydrolyses the P–X bond of the organophosphorus compound and the full activity ultimately returns, but with the more effective members of the series the enzyme remains for all practical purposes permanently inhibited.

$$\text{VIII.68} \quad R.\overset{\overset{\displaystyle O}{\|}}{C}.O.R' + EH = R.\overset{\overset{\displaystyle O}{\|}}{C}.E + HO.R'$$

$$\text{VIII.69} \quad \begin{matrix} R\text{-}O \\ R' \end{matrix}\!\!>\!\!P\!\!<\!\!\begin{matrix} O \\ X \end{matrix} + EH = \begin{matrix} R\text{-}O \\ R' \end{matrix}\!\!>\!\!P\!\!<\!\!\begin{matrix} O \\ E \end{matrix} + HX$$

$$\text{VIII.70} \quad R.\overset{\overset{\displaystyle O}{\|}}{C}.E + H_2O = R.\overset{\overset{\displaystyle O}{\|}}{C}.OH + EH$$

$$\text{VIII.71} \quad \begin{matrix} R\text{-}O \\ R' \end{matrix}\!\!>\!\!P\!\!<\!\!\begin{matrix} O \\ E \end{matrix} + H_2O = \begin{matrix} R\text{-}O \\ R' \end{matrix}\!\!>\!\!P\!\!<\!\!\begin{matrix} O \\ OH \end{matrix} + EH$$

Since the group X is removed in the first step, its nature cannot affect the rate of recovery by reaction VIII.71. This has been shown by ALDRIDGE and DAVISON (46) for a series of inhibitors of the formula $(C_2H_5O)_2 : PO.X$ (see Fig. VIII.11).

On the other hand, the rate of combination with the enzyme is strongly influenced by the nature of X. This appears to affect the rates of reaction with the enzyme and with water in a similar way; in other words the inhibitors which react most rapidly with the enzyme also undergo the most rapid non-enzymatic hydrolysis (45) (see Fig. VIII.12). The nature of the R groups, which are still present in the phosphorylated enzyme and affect both the rate of combination with the enzyme and the rate of recovery, has a reverse effect. In a series in which X is the same throughout and the R groups are varied, the compounds which undergo the most rapid spontaneous hydrolysis may be the weakest inhibitors.

With the organophosphorus inhibitors it is necessary to distinguish between inhibitory power, as measured by the velocity constant of the enzyme–inhibitor combination, and the inhibiting capacity, as measured

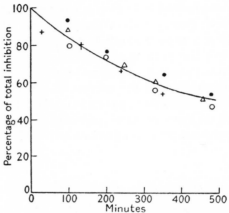

Fig. VIII.11. *Recovery of cholinesterase activity after poisoning with organophosphorus inhibitors containing two ethoxy groups.*

Incubation, 30 min, followed by removal of free inhibitor by hydrolysis with DFPase (3.8.2.1). Symbols as in Fig. VIII.12.

from *46*

by the number of molecules of enzyme ultimately inhibited by one molecule of inhibitor. If the phosphorylated enzyme is hydrolysed at an appreciable rate, the maximum inhibition attained may be low even when the rate of combination is high, because the inhibition achieved is the resultant of two different processes having opposite effects. Furthermore, the inhibition will then depend on the time, reaching a maximum and then falling off ultimately to zero. On the other hand, if the rate of breakdown of the phosphorylated enzyme is negligible, each molecule of inhibitor will ultimately inhibit one molecule of enzyme or at any rate one active centre, even if the rate of combination is low. Fig. VIII.13 shows the difference between the effect of dimethyl *p*-nitrophenyl-phosphate, where the rate of breakdown of the enzyme compound is high, and that of diethyl *p*-nitrophenylphosphate, where it is low (*44*).

The inhibiting capacity is also greatly dependent on the degree of specificity for the active centre and on the purity of the enzyme. If the inhibitor combines with other groups, either in the enzyme or in contaminating proteins, its inhibiting capacity will fall far below unity. The very high toxicity of the more effective members of this group of inhibitors is due to their great specificity as well as to the high stability of the substituted enzyme.

While the dimethyl compounds are comparatively weak inhibitors, for the reasons mentioned, the diethyl compounds are much more effective, and such compounds as di-isopropyl phosphorofluoridate† (DFP) are extremely potent inhibitors, showing definite inhibition of cholinesterase in a concentration of 10^{-10} M. DFP hydrolyses only slowly, forms an extremely stable compound with the enzyme (which can be crystallized in the case of chymotrypsin (*146*)), and is highly specific in its action. It has been shown that complete inhibition of chymotrypsin and trypsin is produced by only one molecule per molecule of enzyme (see Chapter X). It has also been used as a radioactive label for the active centre in investigations on its structure (see p. 474).

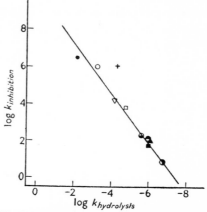

Fig. VIII.12. *The relation between stability to hydrolysis and inhibitory power of some organophosphorus inhibitors.*

The logarithm of the bimolecular velocity constant for the reaction between acetylcholinesterase and inhibitor is plotted against the logarithm of the velocity constant of hydrolysis of the inhibitor at 37° and pH 7·6.

$\triangle$ $(C_2H_5O)_2PO.F$
● $(C_2H_5O)_2PO.O.PO(OC_2H_5)_2$
◑ $(C_2H_5O)_2PO.O.C_6H_5$
+ $(C_2H_5O)_2PO.O.C_6H_4.NO_2$ (*p*)
□ $(C_2H_5O)_2PO.O.C_6H_4.NO_2$ (*m*)
$\triangledown$ $(C_2H_5O)_2PO.O.C_6H_4.NO_2$ (*o*)
○ $(C_2H_5O)_2PO.S.C_6H_4.NO_2$ (*p*)
▲ $(C_2H_5O)_2PO.O.C_6H_4.Cl$ (*p*)
◓ $(C_2H_5O)_2PO.O.C_6H_4.Cl$ (*o*)
◒ $(C_2H_5O)_2PS.O.C_6H_4.NO_2$ (*p*)
■ $(C_2H_5O)_2PS.O.8$-quinolyl

from *45*

The rate of reaction of enzymes with these inhibitors depends on the state of ionization of certain groups in the active centre and therefore

† The naming of these compounds has given rise to some difficulty and several systems have been recommended at different times. Equivalent names in the various systems have been tabulated in *1523*.

on the pH. WILSON and BERGMANN (2883) showed that the inhibition of cholinesterase by tetraethyl pyrophosphate has an optimum rate at pH 8, which is similar to that for the hydrolysis of the substrate, acetylcholine. HARTLEY (1011a) showed that the rate of the reaction of diethyl p-nitrophenylphosphate with chymotrypsin falls off in acid solution and, between pH 6 and 8, obeys the equation

VIII.72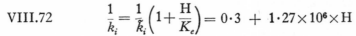

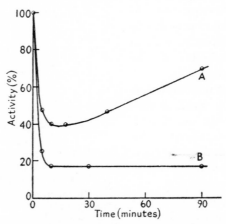

Fig. VIII.13. *Inhibition of acetylcholinesterase in rabbit blood by dialkyl nitrophenylphosphates.*

A: $(CH_3O)_2PO.O.C_6H_4.NO_2$ (p) $4·7 \times 10^{-7}$ M
B: $(C_2H_5O)_2PO.O.C_6H_4.NO_2$ (p) $4·1 \times 10^{-7}$ M
                                                      from 44

where k_i is the bimolecular velocity constant for the reaction between enzyme and inhibitor ($M^{-1}min^{-1}$) and $\check{k}_i$ is the corresponding constant for the reacting form of the enzyme. This gives $pK_e = 6·62$, in reasonable agreement with the pK_e determined from the reaction with substrate (see Table X.3). Thus the organophosphorus inhibitor appears to react with the same ionizable group in the active centre as the substrate. The value of the pK_e has been used as further support for the suggestion that a histidine residue is involved.

Some of the more active and commonly-used of this group of inhibitors are shown in Fig. VIII.14; others may be found in a review by SARTORI (2306). The most effective members of the group are the most potent enzyme inhibitors known. The inhibition is apparently permanent and the activity does not return spontaneously; reactivation is, however, possible by treatment with certain oximes or hydroxamic acids (*449, 558, 895, 2881*) with removal of the phosphoryl group. On incubation, DFP-or sarin-in hibited acetylcholinesterase is converted into another form which is no longer capable of such reactivation. This conversion is due to the loss of one isopropyl group from the di-isopropyl-phosphoryl-enzyme, the monoisopropylphosphoryl-enzyme being more stable towards nucleophilic attack (*211*).

Although these inhibitors are so powerful, the presence of the substrate protects the enzyme against their action, as also do competitive

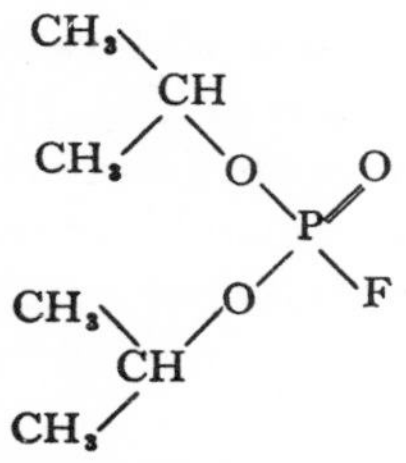

Di-isopropyl phosphorofluoridate
(DFP)

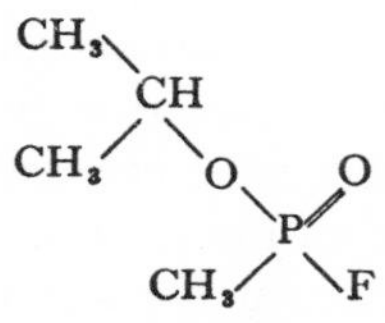

Sarin

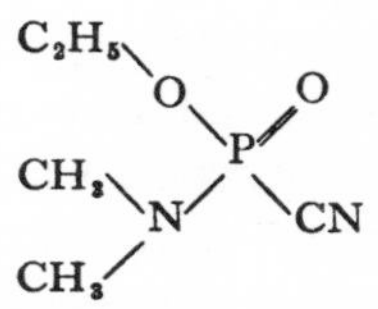

Tabun

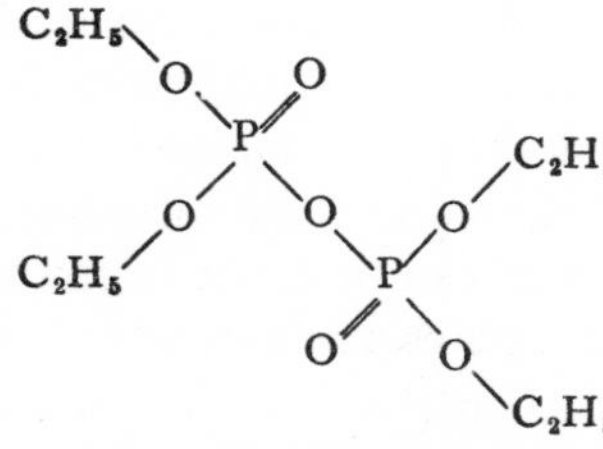

Tetraethyl pyrophosphate
(TEPP)

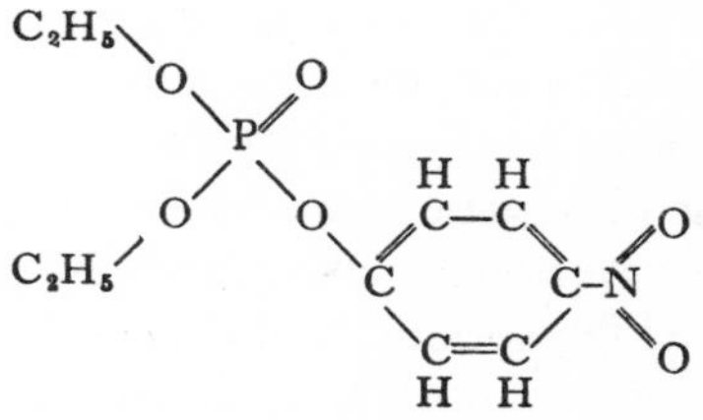

Diethyl *p*-nitrophenylphosphate
(E600, paraoxon)

Fig. VIII.14. *Structures of some organophosphorus inhibitors.*

inhibitors (*1417*). This would be expected if the inhibitors only react with the *free* active centre.

Inhibitors of respiration and phosphorylation

We have already mentioned, in the section on poisons of heavy metals, a number of inhibitors of cytochrome oxidase, such as cyanide, which act at the terminal step of the respiratory chain. There are, however, a number of other inhibitors which act at intermediate steps in the chain. Some of these have been widely used in attempts to elucidate the sequence of carriers, for example urethane, antimycin, $BAL+O_2$, which act between cytochromes b and c_1 or between ubiquinone and cytochrome c_1, and amytal and chloropromazine, which inhibit the reduction of ubiquinone by $NADH_2$. These substances differ from ordinary enzyme inhibitors in that they only act on particulate preparations obtained from mitochondria, and have never been shown to act on isolated enzymes catalysing the corresponding reactions. Thus their action may depend at least in part on physical effects; such systems are well known to be sensitive to many surface-active substances, as well as to such enzymes as lecithinase.

Other substances inhibit the link between oxidation and phosphorylation, releasing the respiration from the retarding effect of the coupled phosphorylation. These are known as 'uncoupling agents'. Examples are dinitrophenol, gramicidin and dicoumarol. A discussion of these inhibitors and uncoupling agents has been given by RACKER (2155). Their mode of action is in most cases not clear, and they may act in a number of different ways. In one case an uncoupling agent, dicoumarol, has been shown to be a specific and extremely powerful enzyme inhibitor, inhibiting menadione reductase (1.6.5.2) strongly at a concentration of 10^{-8} M.

Competitive inhibitors

The literature contains a great many references to substances, closely related to enzyme substrates, which act as competitive inhibitors. Most of these are limited in their action to one enzyme, so far as is known. The observations are too numerous, too scattered and too disconnected to be worth tabulating, and few generalizations can be made from them. The high specificity of enzymes for their substrates also extends to competitive inhibitors, as already discussed in Chapter VI. A systematic study of competitive inhibitors is a fruitful way of adding to our knowledge of enzyme–substrate combination and of the nature of the groups involved in both enzyme and substrate.

The classical example is malonate, which acts as a powerful competitive inhibitor of succinate dehydrogenase (QUASTEL and WOOLDRIDGE, 2134). It owes its inhibitory power to the fact that it possesses two carboxyl groups with approximately the same spacing as in succinate, but without the oxidizable $-CH_2-CH_2-$ group between them. It has been extensively used to provide evidence for the importance of succinate dehydrogenase in metabolism, and for the existence of the citric acid cycle. The kinetics of the inhibition have been studied by THORN (2647). Pyrophosphate, which also possesses two acid groups with approximately the same spacing, also inhibits this dehydrogenase, but not other dehydrogenases (1542).

The enzymes of the citric cycle are concerned with di- or tricarboxylic acids, and several of them have been shown to be inhibited by a range

of such acids. Fumarate hydratase, for example, has been shown by
MASSEY (*1746*) to be inhibited by the salts of every one of about a dozen
di- or tri-carboxylic acids tested, including malonate, but not by those of
mono-carboxylic acids. In nearly all cases it was shown that these inhibitors compete with the substrate.

PETERS (*2077–8*) has shown that fluorocitrate

$$\text{CHF.COO}^-$$
$$\text{HO.C.COO}^-$$
$$\text{CH}_2.\text{COO}^-$$

specifically inhibits aconitate hydratase. This might appear to be another
case of the type just mentioned, but there are several differences which
make it a unique case. The inhibition appears to be limited to aconitate
hydratase, is only slowly set up (requiring at least 15 minutes' incubation
to become fully established), and with synthetic (in contrast to enzymatically formed) fluorocitrate, is not truly competitive.

Fluorocitrate was discovered as a result of work with the highly toxic
substance fluoroacetate $FCH_2.COO^-$, which has been shown to owe
its toxicity to what PETERS (*2076*) has described as a 'lethal synthesis'
in the body, namely, the conversion to fluorocitrate by the citrate synthesizing enzymes. It is this product which is the real toxic agent, which
blocks the citric cycle at the aconitate hydratase stage and causes an
accumulation of citrate. The naturally formed product has been isolated
and compared with synthetic fluorocitrate. With purified aconitate
hydratase, the synthetic substance is 10–15 times more effective than the
naturally formed fluorocitrate, and the inhibition by the former becomes
non-competitive on incubation. On the other hand, with a particulate
enzyme preparation the natural material has twice the activity of the
synthetic. These differences have not been explained, but are no doubt
connected with the presence of different stereoisomers of fluorocitrate.

The stereochemistry of fluorocitrate, which possesses two asymmetric centres, presents a number of interesting features in relation to
enzyme inhibition; these have been discussed by KACSER (*1280*).

Glyceraldehydephosphate dehydrogenase (1.2.1.12) is strongly inhibited by D-threose 2,4-diphosphate (*755, 2158*). The oxidation of
D-glyceraldehyde 3-phosphate by NAD is strongly but non-competitively
inhibited by 10^{-6} M tetrose diphosphate, while the oxidation of $NADH_2$
by 1,3-diphosphoglyceric acid is only slightly affected. The inhibition
appears to be due to the oxidation of the tetrose diphosphate by NAD to
a stable diphosphotetronoyl-enzyme. This is analogous to the formation
of the 3-phosphoglyceroyl-enzyme in the normal reaction, but whereas

N

the phosphoglyceroyl group is removed by transfer to a molecule of inorganic phosphate on a neighbouring site, in the inhibited enzyme this site is occupied by the 2-phosphate of the diphosphotetronoyl group so that removal in this way is impossible, and it cannot be removed competitively by glyceraldehyde phosphate. Little inhibition of the reverse reaction would be expected because NAD is needed to oxidize the tetrose to the inhibiting tetronoyl group, and the only NAD available is that formed by oxidation of the added $NADH_2$ by the reverse reaction.

In the same way as dicarboxylic acids are competitive inhibitors of enzymes whose substrates are also dicarboxylic acids, many substituted diamines are competitive inhibitors of diamine oxidases. Thus BLASCHKO et al. (271) have studied a series of compounds of the formula

$$H_2N.C.NH.(CH_2)_n.NH.C.NH_2$$

$$\overset{\|}{\underset{\overset{|}{H}}{N}} \qquad\qquad \overset{\|}{\underset{\overset{|}{H}}{N}}$$

and other compounds related to the substrate $H_2N.(CH_2)_n.NH_2$. These were found to be powerful inhibitors of diamine oxidase, the inhibitory effect depending on the value of n in much the same way as do the substrate affinities, being high with small values and falling off as n increases until it becomes zero for $n = 18$. The monoguanidine compounds inhibit only slightly. With monoamine oxidase, on the other hand (269), the inhibition by diguanidines only becomes appreciable when n is so large that each end of the molecule may be regarded as effectively a monoguanidine compound. With this enzyme acting on the substrate $CH_3.(CH_2)_n.NH_2$, monoguanidines, monoamidines, and even compounds of the type $CH_3.(CH_2)_n.NH.CH_3$, are all powerful inhibitors (2968).

A great many substances containing basic nitrogen atoms, especially when these are in hererocyclic rings, act as drugs; such substances, when of natural plant origin, are known as alkaloids, and they form a very large and important group. They probably produce their effects by acting as enzyme inhibitors, but in only a few cases has the action been traced to the inhibition of particular enzymes. One such case which has been fully elucidated is that of eserine (physostigmine), obtained from the Calabar bean and well known as a potent parasympathomimetic drug. This owes its pharmacological activity and its toxicity to the fact that it is an extremely powerful inhibitor of cholinesterase and acetylcholinesterase, and thus prevents the removal of the acetylcholine formed during the nerve impulse. A number of other alkaloids inhibit cholinesterases to varying extents, among them nicotine, muscarine, morphine and its derivatives, cocaine and related compounds (but not atropine), the quinine alkaloids, and strychnine. Of the natural inhibitors of cholinesterase, eserine is the most potent, with $K_i = 5 \times 10^{-8}$.

The cholinesterases are in fact inhibited by more substances, natural and synthetic, than any other group of enzymes. The more powerful inhibitors have a quaternary or basic nitrogen atom, they often contain some ester-like grouping such as a urethane group, and are highly methylated. All of these features might be expected to produce competition with the substrate acetylcholine, which has a highly methylated nitrogen atom in the choline residue, which is linked by the susceptible ester group to the methyl-containing acetyl residue. Fig. VIII.15 shows the structures of the substrate and of some of the most active inhibitors. More complete lists have been given by AUGUSTINSSON (97) and (with much quantitative information) by TODRICK (2664).

Inhibitors of the type of eserine and prostigmine, containing a carbamoyl or substituted carbamoyl grouping, at first sight appear to behave as typical competitive inhibitors, the effect being reduced by the presence of the substrate. There is a pronounced time effect, however; if the inhibitor is added before the substrate, a much greater immediate inhibition is obtained than if they are added simultaneously, and on addition of the substrate the velocity rises only slowly. Recently WILSON et al. (2886) have shown that these inhibitors have an action similar to that of the organophosphorus compounds, transferring their carbamoyl group to the active centre of the enzyme, giving a carbamoyl-enzyme which is only relatively slowly hydrolysed. Carbamoylcholine, which is a rather poor substrate, produces the same carbamoyl-enzyme as does eserine. Recovery from the inhibition is due to the slow decarbamoylation by water, and is greatly accelerated by hydroxylamine.

$$CH_3.CO.O.CH_2.CH_2.\overset{+}{N}(CH_3)_3$$

Acetylcholine

$$CH_3.CH_2.CHOH.CH.\overset{+}{N}(CH_3)_3$$
$$\vert$$
$$CHO$$

Muscarine

Eserine (physostigmine)

Prostigmine

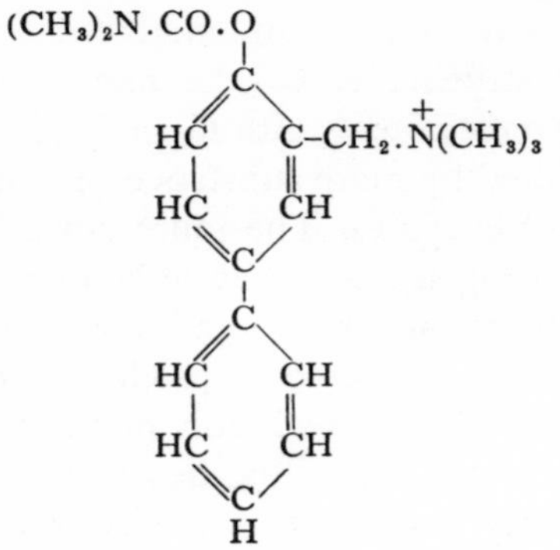

Nu-683

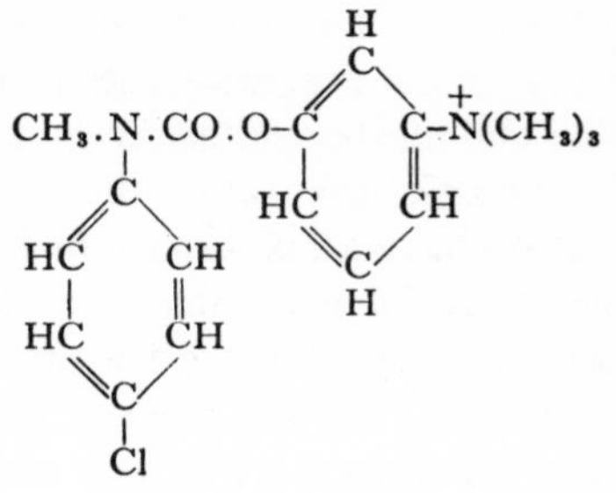

Nu-1250

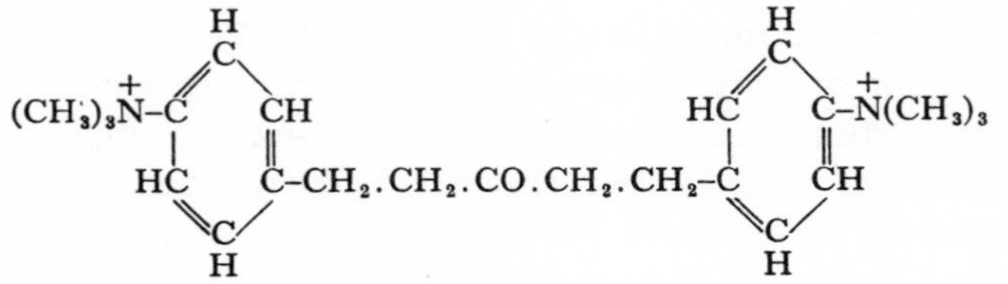

62C47

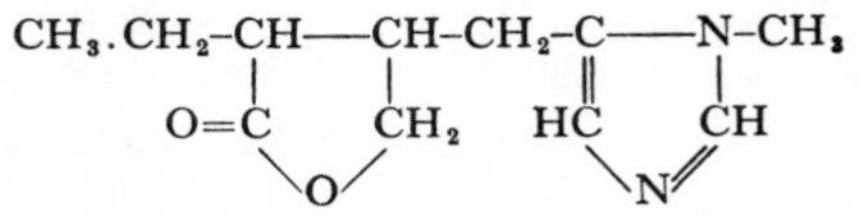

Pilocarpine

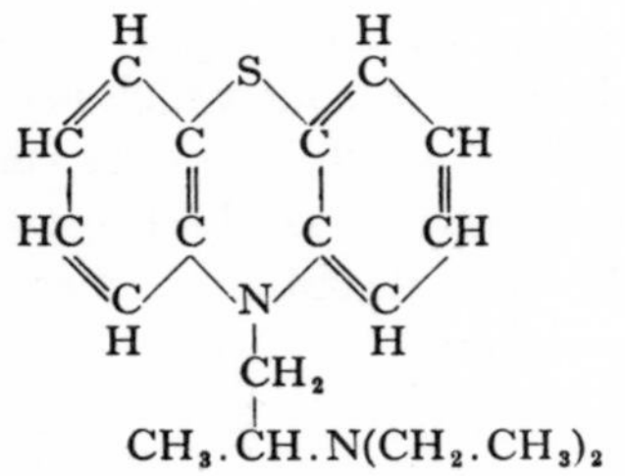

Lysivane

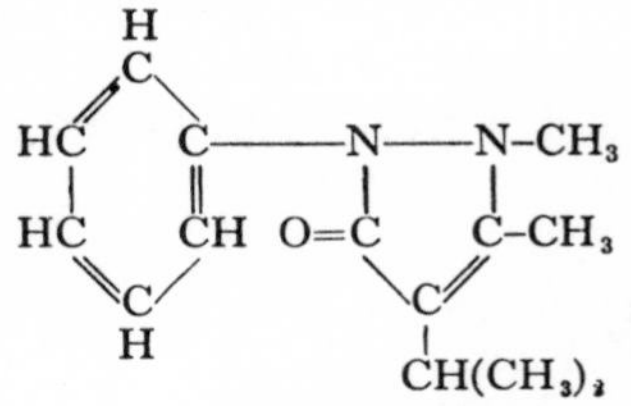

isopropylantipyrine

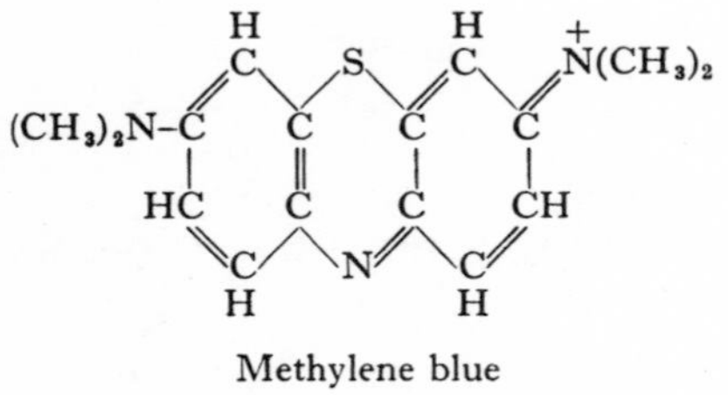

Methylene blue

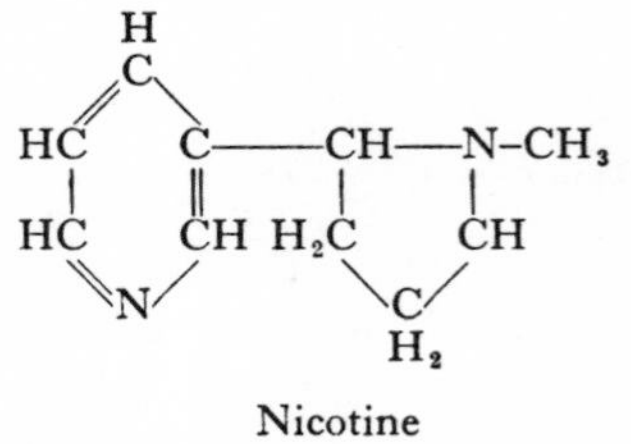

Nicotine

Fig. VIII.15. *Structures of some specific inhibitors of cholinesterases.*

The various cholinesterases are not always equally inhibited by these compounds. In particular the acetylcholinesterases differ considerably from the cholinesterases in their sensitivity towards the different competitive inhibitors; so much so that Nu-683 (*1030*) and lysivane (*180*) have been proposed as specific inhibitors for cholinesterase and Nu-1250 (*1031*) and 62C47 (*180*) for acetylcholinesterase. Thus the ratio of the concentration necessary to half-inhibit cholinesterase to that necessary for acetylcholinesterase is 500 for Nu-1250 and 50,000 for 62C47 (*180*),

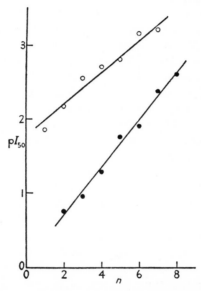

Fig. VIII.16. *Dependence of inhibitory power for cholinesterases on chain length for compounds of the type* $CH_3 . (CH_2)_n . N(CH_3)_3$.

● cholinesterase at 37°
○ acetylcholinesterase at 23°

from *226*

so that at suitable concentrations acetylcholinesterase may be practically completely inhibited while cholinesterase is unaffected.

A careful study of a homologous series of inhibitors on the two cholinesterases has been made by BERGMANN and SEGAL (*226*). Fig. VIII.16 shows the concentrations for half-inhibition (on a logarithmic scale) for compounds of the type $CH_3 . (CH_2)_n . \overset{+}{N}(CH_3)_3$, plotted against n. The inhibition increases with chain length in all cases. Since, with a constant substrate concentration, the pI_{50} is proportional to the pK_i, the free energy of combination increases linearly with n, except in one case, showing that the free energy of combination of a $-CH_2-$ group with the enzyme remains constant throughout each series. It is difficult to compare the curves for cholinesterase with those for acetylcholinesterase, since the two enzymes were studied at different temperatures. By extrapolating to $n = 0$, the contribution of the hydrocarbon chain to the binding force is assumed to be eliminated, leaving the free energy of combination with the tetramethylammonium ion.

All the competitive inhibitors mentioned so far in this section are substances with acidic or basic groups, but non-ionizable molecules such as sugars often act as competitive inhibitors for enzymes acting on similar molecules. For example, brain hexokinase is competitively inhibited by D-xylose, D-lyxose and 6-deoxy-D-glucose (*2469*); phenyl-β-thiogalactoside inhibits β-galactosidase, and D-glucose (a product of the reaction) competitively inhibits α-glucosidase. These substances are all identical with the respective substrates except for one small change, such as the substitution of $-H$ for $-OH$ in the 6-position, of $-H$ for $-CH_2OH$ in the 5-position, or of $-S-$ for $-O-$ in the glycoside link.

As would be expected, competitive inhibitors containing an asymmetric carbon atom usually show the same marked stereochemical specificity as do the substrates (see p. 204). For instance, arginase is inhibited by L-leucine but not by D-leucine (*1191*). However, if the asymmetric arrangement affects only the part of the molecule which does not combine with the enzyme, this may not be observed. In some cases the optical antipode of the specific substrate, although not acted upon, is unexpectedly found to be a competitive inhibitor. Presumably, here there is enough binding force in some of the individual groups to hold the substance on to the enzyme, even though other groups cannot combine because of the configuration. Thus carbobenzoxyglycyl-D-phenylalanine inhibits the action of carboxypeptidase on carbobenzoxyglycyl-L-phenylalanine (*2503*).

Antienzymes

Since enzymes are proteins, they may give rise to antibodies when injected into the blood-stream of an animal. A number of antisera containing such antibodies for particular enzymes have been obtained, and a few antienzymes have been purified. In some cases the enzyme itself provides a highly specific means of precipitating the antibody and can be removed from the precipitated antibody by denaturation.

Antibodies are produced in response to particular groups and arrangements of groups in the protein molecule, and there is no particular reason to suppose that these will be groups associated with the active centre of the enzyme. Thus, unlike the inhibitors which we have been discussing, antienzymes will in general not be specific for the active centre, but for the enzyme protein as a whole. If the antigenic groups of the enzyme are not situated in the active centre, the latter may still be exposed in the enzyme–antienzyme complex, and the enzyme may therefore be precipitated without appreciable loss of activity. On the other hand, if the antigenicity of the enzyme lies partly in the active centre, the antibody will be a powerful inhibitor, competing with the substrate.

Both types of effect have been found; catechol oxidase remains fully active when precipitated with its antibody, whereas lecithinase is almost completely inactive. Intermediate cases are urease, catalase, papain and ribonuclease, which are still partially active when precipitated by their specific antibodies. In the case of alkaline phosphatase, definite evidence has been obtained that the antigenic centre is distinct from the active centre of the enzyme (*2328*).

The whole subject of antienzymes has been reviewed by MARRACK (*1729*).

Antienzymes provide a powerful tool for investigating differences between enzymes from different sources and for the study of the nature of isoenzymes. Both these topics are discussed in some detail in Chapter XIII.

IX

ENZYME COFACTORS

AS WE HAVE already mentioned in Chapter I, an additional substance besides the enzyme and substrate is required in many cases in order that the reaction may proceed. Such 'cofactors' are found unchanged at the end of the reaction and may therefore be regarded as an essential part of the catalytic mechanism. The majority of enzyme cofactors may be broadly divided into two classes: (*a*) specific coenzymes, usually organic molecules of somewhat complicated structure, which play a part in the reaction itself, often as carriers of some chemical grouping, and (*b*) activators, frequently of a very simple nature, e.g. inorganic ions, which in various ways bring the enzyme itself into a catalytically active state.

SPECIFIC COENZYMES

A number of these, especially those which act as carriers, may justifiably be regarded either as coenzymes or as substrates, according to the enzyme system which is being considered. As explained in Chapter XII, they frequently act by linking two enzymes together to form a system, particularly in group transfer reactions; one enzyme transfers the group in question from a substrate to the coenzyme, the other transfers it from the coenzyme to a second substrate. Thus the coenzyme is equally truly a coenzyme for the enzyme system as a whole and a substrate for each of the enzymes considered separately. In practice, however, this may only become clear when the system has been resolved into its component enzymes. The aldehyde mutase system will illustrate the point (see p. 542). It was formerly believed that this was a single enzyme, acting with a coenzyme (NAD) to catalyse the dismutation of two molecules of aldehyde into one of acid and one of alcohol. It is now known to consist of two dehydrogenases, for each of which NAD acts as one of the substrates. It is nevertheless quite proper to regard it as a coenzyme for the mutase *system*.

In the Table of Enzymes, cofactors which must be added in order to get the reaction to proceed are written in square brackets; where, however, the separate reactions are written, the coenzymes are regarded as substrates and written as reactants.

We shall first consider the various coenzymes which act as carriers of particular groups, and afterwards prosthetic groups which act as bound cofactors.

Hydrogen carriers

NAD and NADP†

These two coenzymes are closely related dinucleotides containing adenine and nicotinamide; for a detailed review see KAPLAN (*1302*). Their existence has been known for many years, but their chemical structure and mechanism of action have only been fully elucidated comparatively recently.

The existence of a thermostable coenzyme involved in fermentation (cozymase, now identified with NAD) was shown in 1904 by HARDEN and YOUNG (*1002–3*), but it was not then isolated. It was obtained in a highly purified form by VON EULER et al. (*710*) and by WARBURG and CHRISTIAN (*2785*) independently in 1936. NADP was discovered by WARBURG and CHRISTIAN (*2783*) in 1931 as the coenzyme of glucose-6-phosphate dehydrogenase (1.1.1.49). The demonstration that the active group in both coenzymes is nicotinamide, and that it acts by undergoing reduction and oxidation, is due to WARBURG and CHRISTIAN (*2785, 2790*). NADP differs from NAD only in possessing an additional phosphate group, which may easily be removed, for example, by phosphatase; it was not until 1950 that the position of this phosphate group was determined by KORNBERG and PRICER (*1435*).

Structure. The structure of the oxidized forms of NAD and NADP is shown in Fig. IX.1. This is the cationic form of the molecule, in which the positive charge on the nitrogen atom may be regarded as balanced by some anion, e.g. Cl^-, in the solution. At pH 7·5 the acidic groups of the two phosphate residues in NAD are in the ionized state, giving a net single negative charge on the molecule, which may be regarded as a dipolar ion with an additional negative charge; in NADP these two groups, and also the two acidic groups of the extra phosphate residue, are ionized, giving a net charge of -3.

† These coenzymes have been known by various names and for convenience these are given here.

Nicotinamide-adenine dinucleotide (NAD)	Nicotinamide-adenine dinucleotide phosphate (NADP)
Coenzyme I (CoI)	Coenzyme II (CoII)
Cozymase	Phosphocozymase
Diphosphopyridine nucleotide (DPN)	Triphosphopyridine nucleotide (TPN)

The first name in each case has now been officially adopted both by the International Union of Biochemistry and by the International Union of Pure and Applied Chemistry. The reasons for their adoption have been fully set out in Chapter 4 of the Report of the Commission on Enzymes of the International Union of Biochemistry (*2212*).

The D-ribose residues are linked to the adenine and nicotinamide nitrogen atoms respectively by β-glycosidic links. It was first shown by TODD and his co-workers (*569*) that adenosine and other natural nucleosides contain β-riboside links, and they suggested that this might be a general rule. Both coenzymes give normal adenylic acid on hydrolysis by nucleotide pyrophosphatase (3.6.1.9) and therefore must contain β-linked adenine. Information about the nicotinamide-riboside link has

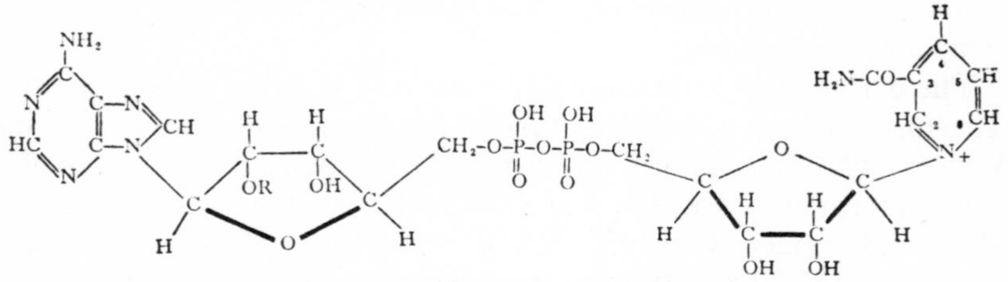

Fig. IX.1. *Structure of NAD and NADP (oxidized forms).*
In NAD, R = —H; in NADP, R = —PO(OH)$_2$.

come from a study of an isomer of NAD which forms about 10–15 per cent of commercial preparations even of high purity (*1304*). This isomer is inactive with many enzymes which act on normal NAD, including the common dehydrogenases and NAD(P) nucleosidase (3.2.2.6). It may be isolated after destruction of the normal isomer by the last-named enzyme. It has the same composition as normal NAD and

TABLE IX.1

	Optical rotation $[\alpha]$	
	Normal NAD	*Inactive isomer*
Original dinucleotide . . .	−34·8	+14·3
Nicotinamide mononucleotide . .	−38·3	+58·2
Ribose 5-phosphate therefrom . .	−2·7	−4·7

(Normal AMP −40·0)

gives normal adenylic acid on hydrolysis, together with a nicotinamide mononucleotide whose optical rotation is opposite in sign to that of normal nicotinamide mononucleotide; both nicotinamide mononucleotides, however, give the same ribose-5-phosphate on further hydrolysis. Thus the isomer differs from normal NAD apparently only in the configuration of the nicotinamide-riboside link. A study of the rotations of the two isomers and their hydrolysis products (Table IX.1) suggests that in the normal form this link has the β-configuration, and that the inactive isomer has an α-link.

The complete synthesis of NAD has now been accomplished by HUGHES, KENNER and TODD (*1187*). Methods for the synthesis of nucleotide co-enzymes have been reviewed by BADDILEY and HUGHES (*130*).

Mode of reduction. The coenzymes can be readily and reversibly re-duced, either by chemical reducing agents such as dithionite or by those dehydrogenases for which they are specific; the reduced form is the same in either case. In the reduction two equivalents of hydrogen per molecule are required. Warburg and Christian showed that it is the nicotinamide ring which is involved in the reduction. When the co-enzymes are reduced, the ultraviolet absorption spectrum undergoes a change; the oxidized form shows only a band at 260 mμ, due to the purine and pyridine rings, but the reduced form shows in addition a band at 340 mμ (see Fig. IX.2). This band is due to the quinonoid bond structure of the reduced nicotinamide ring and is shown also by a number of simple de-rivatives of nicotinamide (e.g. nicotinamide methiodide) in the reduced state. Nucleotides which do not contain nicotinamide do not give this band.

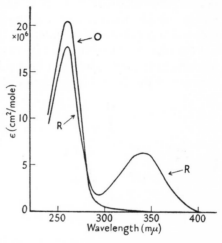

Fig. IX.2. *Spectra of oxidized* (O) *and reduced* (R) *forms of NAD and NADP.*

Further evidence that it is the nicotinamide ring which is re-duced in the dehydrogenase reac-tions was obtained by Warburg and Christian as follows. When the coenzymes are reduced by H_2 in the presence of a platinum catalyst, not two but six equivalents are taken up, and the pyridine ring is reduced to a piperidine ring, giving an enzymatically inactive product which does not show the 340 mμ band. Now if the co-enzyme is first reduced by a dehydrogenase (taking up two equivalents of hydrogen), and then further reduced with H_2+Pt, not six but four equivalents are taken up in the latter reaction. This shows that the two hydrogen equivalents added by the enzyme had gone into the same positions as two of the six hydrogen atoms which were added in the reduction of the oxidized form by H_2+Pt. Had they been added to any other point in the molecule, six further equivalents would have been taken up in the second stage of the reduction. The natural inference is that the enzymatic reaction brings about the hydro-genation of one of the double bonds in the ring; this would give a bond structure resembling that of *o*-quinone and would account for the appearance of the 340 mμ band. Experiments on the chemical behaviour of model compounds suggested that it was the bond adjacent to the nitrogen atom which was reduced, but the actual point of hydrogenation remained undetermined, some workers favouring carbon atom 2 and others carbon atom 6.

It is only fairly recently that the mode of reduction of the coenzymes has been cleared up by the use of deuterium. We have already referred in Chapter VII to the work of VENNESLAND *et al.*, showing that in the reduction of NAD by deuterium-containing substrates catalysed by dehydrogenases a deuterium atom is transferred to one specific position of the nicotinamide ring. It has been possible to locate this deuterium by chemical means and thus to establish the structure of the reduced form of the coenzyme.

PULLMAN, SAN PIETRO and COLOWICK (*2125*) made use of the fact that nicotinamide methiodide can be oxidized by alkaline ferricyanide to a mixture of the 2- and 6-pyridones, thus

IX.1

2-pyridone   6-pyridone

The two pyridones can be separated. If the nicotinamide had contained a deuterium atom attached to the 2-carbon atom, the 6-pyridone would contain a deuterium atom, while the 2-pyridone would contain none, since it would have been removed in the oxidation. Conversely, if the deuterium atom had been attached to the 6-carbon atom, only the

2-pyridone would contain deuterium. In order to apply this test to NAD, it is necessary to isolate the nicotinamide from the coenzyme after introducing the deuterium into the latter by reduction. This may be done by the use of NAD(P) nucleosidase (3.2.2.6) from spleen, which hydrolyses the nicotinamide-riboside bond. However, this enzyme does not act on the reduced form of NAD; consequently, this must first be reoxidized. If both the original reduction and the reoxidation are carried out enzymatically, the deuterium will all be removed again; it is therefore necessary either to reduce chemically and oxidize enzymatically, or to reduce enzymatically and oxidize chemically.

Both these procedures were used by PULLMAN *et al.* In the first method the coenzyme was reduced with dithionite in D_2O, giving a mixture of the two stereoisomers

IX.2

in one of which the deuterium is in front of the plane of the ring and in the other behind it. We have written the two forms in this incomplete way in order to avoid any assumption about the place of the reduction. The two faces of the ring are not equivalent, because of the existence of the amide side-chain in the 3-position (see p. 266). When this mixture was reoxidized with alcohol dehydrogenase and aldehyde, the hydrogen (or deuterium) was removed from one face only, giving a mixture of two forms of the oxidized coenzyme, namely

IX.3

with the hydrogen and deuterium atoms now in the plane of the ring. From this mixture the nicotinamide was isolated after enzymatic hydrolysis and converted into the pyridones as described above. It was found that the 2- and the 6-pyridones contained equal amounts of deuterium, and it was further observed that no deuterium was removed by the alkaline ferricyanide treatment. This showed, contrary to previous views, that the deuterium (and consequently hydrogen) had not been added either in the 2- or the 6-position, but it was in harmony with the only other possibility, namely, that it had been added to the 4-position, so that the reduction had taken place across the whole ring and not across a single double bond.

This experiment was open to the criticism that the deuterium atom which had been located was in a position with which the enzyme does *not* react, since this was the atom which had not been removed by the enzyme. To meet this criticism the experiment was repeated in the reverse way by the second method, with enzymatic reduction followed by chemical oxidation with neutral ferricyanide, which unlike alkaline ferricyanide merely oxidizes $NADH_2$ back to the normal oxidized form. The enzymatic reduction of the coenzyme gives one isomer only; the chemical reoxidation, being sterically unspecific, removes a deuterium atom from half the molecules and a hydrogen atom from the others. It therefore gives the same mixture as before (i.e. IX.3), but in this case the deuterium atom is attached to the carbon atom to which the enzyme transferred it. Exactly the same results as before were obtained.

Final proof that a 1,4-reduction of the nicotinamide ring of the coenzyme, and not a 1,2- or a 1,6-reduction, takes place in dehydrogenase reactions was given by LOEWUS, VENNESLAND and HARRIS (*1607*). By chemical synthesis they prepared three nicotinamides, each containing a deuterium atom, attached to carbon atoms 2, 4 and 6 respectively. These three labelled nicotinamides were separately introduced into NAD by an enzymatic exchange using NAD(P) nucleosidase, giving preparations of oxidized coenzyme labelled in the three different positions. These were then reduced by dithionite in H_2O, each giving a mixture of the two isotopic stereoisomers (IX.2). When these three preparations of $NADH_2$ were oxidized separately with pyruvate and lactate dehydrogenase, and the lactate formed was isolated and analysed for deuterium, it was found that no deuterium at all was transferred from either the 2- or the 6-position, whereas an amount approximating to the theoretical was transferred from the 4-position. This shows convincingly that the 2- and the 6-positions are not concerned in the dehydrogenase reactions and that these reactions are exclusively 1,4-reductions. The reduction may be represented as in IX.4.

This structure has also been proved by infra-red and nuclear magnetic resonance comparison with 2-, 4- and 6-deuterated nicotinamides (*343, 1200*).

$NADPH_2$ must have the same ring structure as $NADH_2$, since it can be converted into $NADH_2$ merely by removal of the phospho-group by alkaline phosphatase (*1921*).

This 1,4-reduction of the ring is not associated only with enzyme reactions, since the above results show that the reduction by dithionite takes place exclusively in this way. This type of reduction is not a general property of pyridine compounds, but depends on the presence of the CO group in the side-chain.

Properties and distribution. NAD is reduced by many different substrates in the presence of the appropriate dehydrogenases; NADP seems to be reduced by fewer enzymes. The enzymes which reduce NAD do not usually reduce NADP and vice versa, though there are exceptions. The coenzymes are also reduced by certain chemical reducers, of which the best known is dithionite.

The reduced forms are not oxidized at significant rates by O_2, or by dyes such as methylene blue, or by cytochrome c. They are of course oxidized by many dehydrogenases acting in reverse in the catalysis of anaerobic fermentations, by dyes in the presence of several flavoproteins, by cytochrome c or b_5 in the presence of the respective cytochrome reductases (1.6.2.1–3), by cystine, glutathione or lipoamide in the

IX.4

presence of their respective reductases (1.6.4.1–3), by H_2O_2 in the presence of the specific peroxidases (1.11.1.1–2) and by quinones in the presence of the enzymes 1.6.5.1–3. They are also oxidized non-enzymatically by a variety of substances including especially phenazines, porphyrindines and porphyrexides (*2327*).

The stabilities of the oxidized and reduced forms vary with pH in opposite directions; the reduced form is extremely unstable in acid but relatively stable in alkaline solutions, while the oxidized form is fairly stable in acid but rather less stable in alkali (*1623*). In neutral solution the reduced form is less stable than the oxidized form, and on freezing and thawing a derivative of unknown structure is produced, which acts as a strong inhibitor in enzymatic reactions involving $NADH_2$ (537, 717). This fact has invalidated many kinetic studies in the past, and great caution is necessary in the use of the reduced coenzymes. On treatment of $NADH_2$ with huge quantities of glyceraldehydephosphate dehydrogenase in the presence of pyrophosphate, a derivative of unknown structure which has been called 'DPNH-X' is formed (443, 1779). This substance, which is inactive, appears to have only one double bond in the reduced nicotinamide ring. It can be reconverted into $NADH_2$ by treatment with ATP and a yeast enzyme.

During hydrogen transport from succinate in heart muscle particles a labile phosphorylated derivative of NAD is formed. This derivative, which is not NADP, has been purified. It decomposes spontaneously into the free coenzyme and inorganic phosphate, but with heart muscle particles and Mg^{++} it phosphorylates ADP to ATP, liberating $NADH_2$. It may well be important in oxidative phosphorylation (931a).

The two coenzymes are widely distributed in living matter. GLOCK and McLEAN (856) have carried out a survey of animal tissues, using specific enzyme methods, which, unlike the dithionite method, give the true amounts of the unfragmented coenzyme molecules; their results for the rat are rounded off and summarized in Table IX.2. In most cells other than plant leaves NAD is present in much larger amounts than NADP, but the ratio of the amounts of reduced and oxidized forms is much higher for NADP than for NAD. In plant leaves NAD and NADP are present in almost equal amounts, the concentration of each being about 10 μg per g wet tissue (69).

Analogues. A number of modifications of NAD and NADP have been prepared and studied with respect to enzymatic properties, especially by KAPLAN and his co-workers.

Considering first changes in the molecule apart from the nicotinamide residue, we note that nicotinamide methiodide and nicotinamide mononucleotide are completely inactive with dehydrogenases, as is NAD with the adenine replaced by nicotinamide. Replacement of the amino group of the adenine by a hydroxyl group (thus giving nicotinamide-hypoxanthine dinucleotide) reduces the activity to an extent which varies with different dehydrogenases. Its activity varies with different enzymes from about half that of NAD down to zero (2122); it is also active with NAD(P) transhydrogenase. Modification of the sugar residue also affects the biological activity; NAD containing deoxyribose in the adenylate residue shows only low activity with dehydrogenases (1397). Thus the adenylic half of the molecule is no less important than the NMN half for coenzyme activity.

In the case of NADP, the position of the third phosphate group is important. In acid solution, this phosphate group migrates spontaneously from the 2'- to the 3'-position, giving an analogue which is inactive with those dehydrogenases which are specific for NADP but is active to the same extent as NADP itself with most, though not all, of those which are able to use both coenzymes (*2398*).

Turning to modifications of the nicotinamide group, we note again that when the group is attached by an α-link the dinucleotide is inactive,

TABLE IX.2

AMOUNTS OF NAD AND NADP IN VARIOUS TISSUES OF THE RAT

(μg per g moist weight)

Tissue	Total NAD	Percentage in reduced form	Total NADP	Percentage in reduced form
Liver	570	36	210	97
Heart	480	38	36	95
Adrenal ..	470	33	130	87
Kidney	440	48	57	95
Diaphragm ..	430	32	13	100
Mammary gland	310	27	50	100
Brain	220	40	8	100
Spleen	200	30	12	100
Pancreas ..	190	40	12	100
Lung	160	33	27	67
Thymus ..	150	23	12	100
Testis	150	47	6	100
Seminal vesicles	140	8	12	100
Ventral prostate	100	18	11	100
Placenta	100	11	3	100
Blood	90	40	8	40

as is also NAD with the ring fully reduced. By means of NAD(P) nucleosidase (3.2.2.6) it is possible to substitute other bases for nicotinamide, giving a series of inactive analogues. By using this enzyme also a number of analogues containing nicotinamide modified in the side-chain have been made (*66, 68*). Results obtained with these analogues and five different dehydrogenases are shown in Table IX.3.

It will be seen that a CO group attached to the ring, or some other unsaturated structure, is necessary for any coenzyme activity or even reduction by dithionite. Replacement of $-CO—NH_2$ by $-CS—NH_2$ produces a dramatic increase of activity with one enzyme, but considerable falls in activity with the others. Substitution or modification of the

–NH$_2$ group usually decreases but does not abolish the activity, although replacement of the –NH$_2$ by –CH(CH$_3$)$_2$ produces an enormous increase with one enzyme, and complete abolition of activity with another. The specificity shown by the different enzymes differs greatly, and analogues have been used to differentiate enzymes from different species and even isoenzymes in the same species.

TABLE IX.3

RATES OF REDUCTION OF SOME NAD ANALOGUES

(Rate with NAD = 100)

Side-chain in 3-position	Horse liver alcohol dehydro-genase	Yeast alcohol dehydro-genase	Rabbit muscle lactate dehydro-genase	Ox heart lactate dehydro-genase	Rabbit muscle glycer-aldehyde-phosphate dehydro-genase	Dithionite
–CO—NH$_2$	100	100	100	100	100	+
–H	0	0	0	0	0	
–CH$_3$	0	0	0	0	0	—
–NH$_2$	0	0	0	0	0	—
–NH—CO—CH$_3$	0	0	0	0	0	—
–CS—NH$_2$	348	16	3	41	16	+
–CO—NH—OH	44	3	20	10	19	+
–CO—NH—NH$_2$	68	8	33	9	38	+
–CO—H	30	2	20	30	0	+
–CO—CH$_3$	90	10	60	15	55	+
–CHOH—CH$_3$	0	0	0	0	0	—
–CO—CH$\big\langle{}^{CH_3}_{CH_3}$	792	52	125	37	0	+
–CO—C$_6$H$_5$	31	0	0	0	0	+
–CH=NOH	50	6	7	1	1	+
–CH=CH—CO—NH$_2$	0	0	0	0	0	+

NAD forms a series of addition compounds with substances such as aldehydes, ketones, thiols, sulphite and cyanide in which a group becomes attached to the 4-position, and which, like NADH$_2$, show an absorption band in the region of 340 mμ. These compounds can be oxidized with ferricyanide to 4-substituted analogues of NAD; both the oxidized and the reduced compounds are enzymatically inactive (*371, 2717*).

Lipoate

History. This important and widely distributed hydrogen carrier originally came to light in 1941 as a growth factor for the protozoon *Tetrahymena* (DEWEY, *603-4, 1371-2*), called at that time 'Factor II'. This was concentrated by STOKSTAD *et al.* (*2539*) and called 'Protogen' and later 'Protogen A'. Meanwhile, GUIRARD *et al.* (*944*) had shown the existence of a factor which could replace the requirement for acetate in the growth of certain bacteria, which they called the 'Acetate-replacing factor', and O'KANE and GUNSALUS (*2019*) had discovered a 'Pyruvate oxidation factor' for *Streptococcus faecalis*. These factors were eventually shown to be identical with protogen (see *2460*).

The substance was crystallized in 1951 by REED, DeBUSK, GUNSALUS and HORNBERGER (*2196*), who proposed the name 'α-lipoic acid' on account of its solubility in organic solvents, the α- being used not in a chemical sense but to distinguish it from a modified form produced by the method of preparation. On chemical grounds (see below) it was also called 'Thioctic acid'. The name 'lipoic acid' is now most commonly used, often only for the oxidized form. We shall use the term for both oxidized and reduced forms, by analogy with the practice for glutathione.

Structure. The structure of the oxidized and reduced forms (*2195*) is shown in Fig. IX.3.

$$CH_2-CH_2-CH-(CH_2)_4-COOH \qquad CH_2-CH_2-CH-(CH_2)_4-COOH$$

$$S-\!\!\!-\!\!\!-\!\!\!-\!\!\!-S \qquad\qquad SH \qquad SH$$

Oxidized lipoic acid   Reduced lipoic acid

Fig. IX.3. *Structure of the two forms of lipoic acid.*

The essential change is the reduction of a disulphide group to two thiol groups. It will be seen that one of the carbon atoms is asymmetric, so that two optical isomers exist. The natural isomer of the oxidized form is dextrorotatory, but gives rise on reduction to the lævorotatory reduced form. Only the natural isomers are active in the pyruvate oxidase system.

A considerable part of the lipoate in cells appears to exist bound to protein, attached by a peptide bond to a lysine group, and can be removed by an enzyme from yeast or bacteria (*2195*).

Properties. In the oxidized form the substance is yellowish, with an absorption spectrum as shown in Fig. IX.4. The absorption band at about 335 mμ is due to the five-membered ring (*382*) which this form contains. Powerful reducing agents, such as zinc in hydrochloric acid (but not borohydride), open the ring by the reduction of the disulphide bond. It is reduced by pyruvate and by 2-oxoglutarate in the presence of their respective dehydrogenases (1.2.4.1–2) and thiamine pyrophosphate; in these cases the reduction is accompanied by the transfer of an acyl group from the substrate through thiamine to the lipoate, giving acetyl-hydrolipoate and succinyl-hydrolipoate respectively (reactions XII.1.s and XII.2.g). The acetyl group has been shown by GUNSALUS et al. (948) to be attached to the thiol in the 6-position.

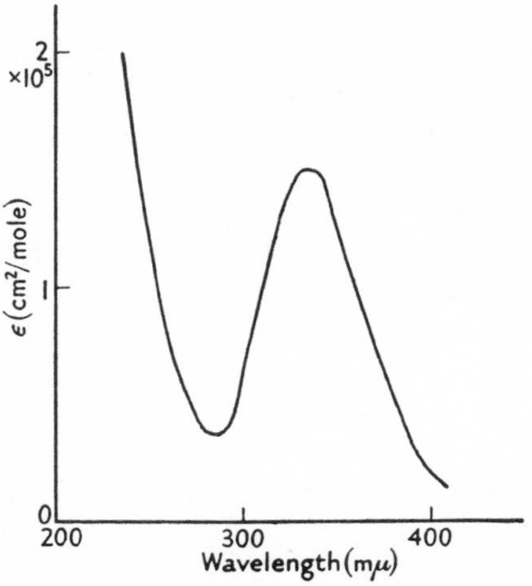

The reduced lipoate, after removal of any attached acyl group, is oxidized by NAD in the presence of lipoamide dehydrogenase (1.6.4.3). It may also be oxidized by mild chemical oxidizing agents, such as iodine.

Fig. IX.4. *Spectrum of oxidized lipoic acid.*

after *382*

Glutathione

This widely-distributed sulphur-containing peptide was discovered in 1921 by HOPKINS (1153). The reduced form of glutathione was first isolated in a non-crystalline state and believed to be a dipeptide of cysteine and glutamic acid. Later Hopkins devised a very elegant method for its isolation in crystalline form from tissue extracts (1154); it was also crystallized almost simultaneously by KENDALL et al. (1358). In both these papers it was shown that it was a tripeptide of cysteine, glutamic acid and glycine; the order in which the aminoacids were combined was not determined by Hopkins, and the suggestion of Kendall as to the order was later shown to be incorrect. The structure was finally established as γ-L-glutamyl-L-cysteinyl-glycine by synthesis (HARINGTON and MEAD, 1006).

The functional group in the molecule is the thiol group and it is customary to represent reduced glutathione by the convenient abbreviation GSH.

Properties. Reduced glutathione is oxidized to the disulphide by mild oxidizing agents, e.g. iodine or ferricyanide. This oxidation is analogous to the oxidation of cysteine to cystine and can be represented by the equation

IX.5 $2GSH - 2H = GSSG$

It is also oxidized by molecular oxygen under suitable conditions in the presence of traces of catalytic metals, and by cytochrome *c*. It is oxidized enzymatically by dehydroascorbate in the presence of glutathione dehydrogenase (1.8.5.1). Powerful reducing agents are needed to reduce the oxidized form back to the thiol form; but enzymatically it can be reduced by NAD or NADP (particularly the latter) in the presence of glutathione reductase (1.6.4.2). Since glutathione undergoes enzymatic oxidation and reduction, it can act as a biological hydrogen carrier, and it was in fact the first such carrier to be discovered.

Thiol-disulphide systems come fairly readily into oxidation-reduction equilibrium with one another in the absence of enzymes; glutathione and cysteine (CSH) are thus in equilibrium in accordance with the following reaction

IX.6 $\qquad$ 2GSH + CSSC $\rightleftharpoons$ GSSG + 2CSH

One such reaction is catalysed by an enzyme, glutathione-homocystine transhydrogenase (1.8.4.1).

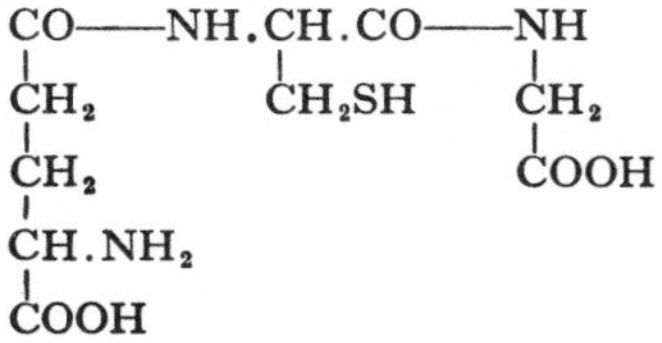

$$
\begin{array}{lll}
CO\text{---}NH.CH.CO\text{---}NH \\
| \qquad\quad | \qquad\quad | \\
CH_2 \qquad CH_2SH \quad CH_2 \\
| \qquad\qquad\qquad\qquad | \\
CH_2 \qquad\qquad\qquad COOH \\
| \\
CH.NH_2 \\
| \\
COOH
\end{array}
$$

Fig. IX.5. *Structure of reduced glutathione.*

Although glutathione has been known for so many years and has given rise to a very extensive literature, its functions are still somewhat obscure. It can undoubtedly act as a biological hydrogen carrier, as originally shown by Hopkins. It can provide a path for the oxidation of the coenzymes through ascorbate and either ascorbate oxidase in plants or cytochrome oxidase in animals. There is no evidence as yet as to the physiological importance of these pathways. As discussed in more detail later on in this chapter, glutathione also acts as a specific coenzyme for the glyoxalase system (see Table XII.8), for maleylacetoacetate and maleylpyruvate isomerases (5.2.1.2, a) and for formaldehyde dehydrogenase (1.2.1.1). The action of glutathione in the glyoxalase system has been much studied, but the metabolic significance of this system is still completely unknown. Many enzymes are –SH enzymes, only active in the thiol state, and it has been suggested that a very important function of glutathione is to keep these enzymes in the reduced form.

Ascorbate

L-ascorbic acid (vitamin C), previously partially purified by several workers, was crystallized by SZENT-GYÖRGYI (*2590*) in 1928; its structure was established by HAWORTH et al. and confirmed by synthesis (*101*).

It will be noted that although the substance exists in an oxidized and a reduced form, the name 'ascorbic acid' is given to the reduced form only and the oxidized form is known as 'dehydroascorbic acid'.

Properties. Ascorbate is an effective reducing agent, rapidly reducing many dyes and even reducing neutral silver nitrate to metallic silver. It is of course also oxidized by the usual oxidizing agents (e.g. iodine) and by oxygen in the presence of traces of catalytic metals. In plants a specific copper-containing ascorbate oxidase (1.10.3.3) brings this reaction about; this enzyme is not present in animal tissues, where ascorbate may be oxidized through the cytochrome system.

Both forms of ascorbic acid are lactones. The reduced form is acidic because of ionization of the ene-diol structure, while the oxidized form

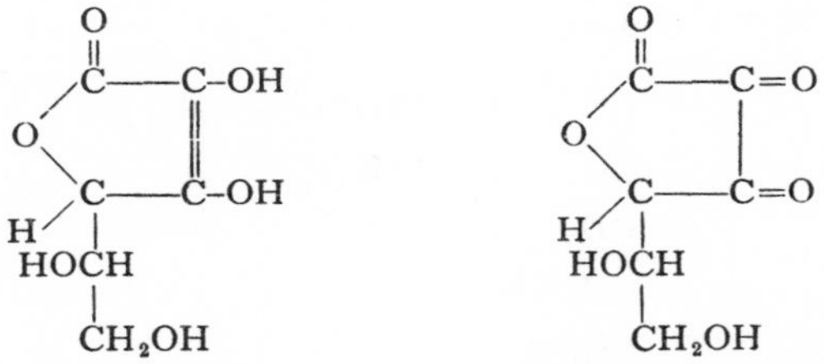

L-ascorbic acid   L-dehydroascorbic acid

Fig. IX.6. *Structure of ascorbic acid and its oxidation product.*

is neutral. The lactone ring is stable in ascorbic acid, but readily hydrolyses in dehydroascorbic acid to give an open-chain acid

$$CH_2OH.CHOH.CHOH.CO.CO.COOH$$

The lactone form of dehydroascorbic acid can readily be reduced to ascorbic acid by H_2S, or by glutathione in the presence of glutathione dehydrogenase (1.8.5.1). The open-chain form is not reduced back to ascorbic acid by H_2S; this form undergoes further irreversible changes in solution, so that the oxidation of ascorbic acid becomes effectively irreversible if the product is not reduced within a short time. An oxidized form of ascorbic acid, which appears not to be dehydroascorbic acid, but to be fairly rapidly converted into it, can bring about the oxidation of $NADH_2$ and $NADPH_2$ (especially the former) in the presence of oxidized ascorbate reductase (1.6.5.4). This oxidized form is produced, at least transitorily, in the action of ascorbate oxidase (*1365, 1927*). It may be concluded from these observations that ascorbate can act as a biological hydrogen carrier, although its significance in this respect is not yet entirely clear. Some of these reactions are shown in Fig. IX.7, where the arrows show the direction of hydrogen transfer.

The wide distribution of ascorbate in animal tissues and other organisms, despite the fact that it is an essential vitamin only in the case of the primates and the guinea-pig, shows that it probably plays an important role in animal metabolism.

Being a good reducing agent, ascorbate, like glutathione, may play a part in maintaining the activity of –SH enzymes. *In vitro* it has been shown to have such an action in a number of cases.

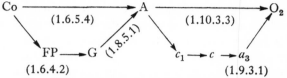

Fig. IX.7. *Hydrogen transport through ascorbate.*

The symbols have the following meanings: Co, $NADH_2$ or $NADPH_2$; A, ascorbate; FP, a flavoprotein enzyme; G, glutathione; c_1, c and a_3, cytochromes c_1, c and a_3 respectively. The numbers are those of the enzymes concerned.

Quinones

Quinones are widespread in living cells. Recent work has shown that some of them play an important part as intermediate hydrogen carriers in the respiratory system, especially methylated quinones with polyisoprenoid side-chains. These include two families of compounds, the ubiquinones and the vitamins K, whose structures are shown in Fig. IX.8.

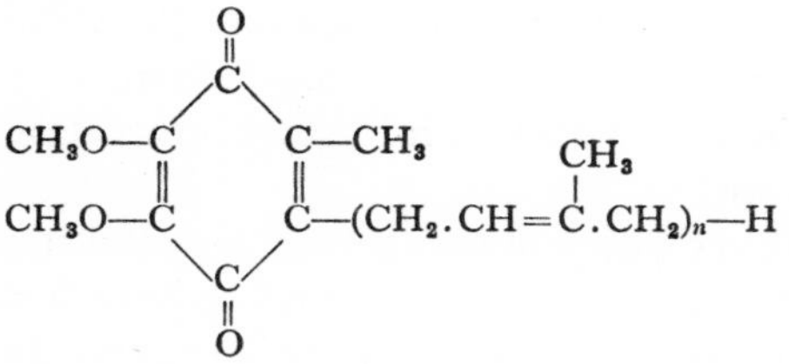

Ubiquinone (UQ$_n$)

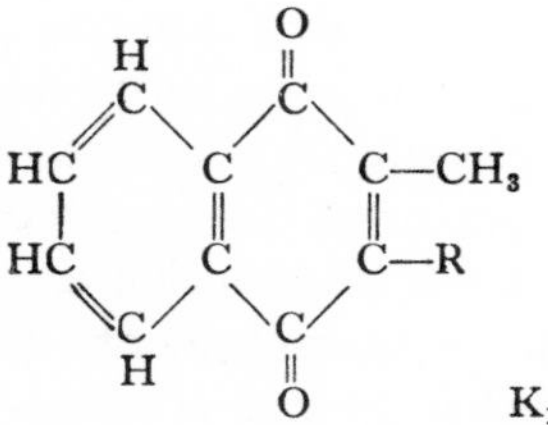

Vitamins K

K_1, R $= -CH_2.CH=C.CH_2-(CH_2.CH_2.CH.CH_2)_3-H$

K_2, R $= -(CH_2.CH=C.CH_2)_n-H$

Menadione, R $= -H$

Fig. IX.8. *Structure of ubiquinones and vitamins K.*

The ubiquinones and the vitamins K_2 are each a group of closely related compounds, differing only in the value of n. For the ubiquinone occurring in animal and higher plant tissues $n = 10$, but in lower organisms homologues with n values of 6 to 9 have been identified. For K_2, n may be 6, 7 or 9.

History of ubiquinone. Ubiquinone was first discovered by R. A. MORTON and his group in 1953 and by CRANE, HATEFI, LESTER and WIDMER in 1957. The structure was essentially given by Morton and his coworkers in 1958; the full structure was published in 1958 simultaneously by Morton in collaboration with the research laboratories of Hoffmann-La Roche and Co., and by GREEN, CRANE and LESTER in collaboration with FOLKERS and his group at the Merck, Sharp and Dohme research laboratories. For an account of the history and chemistry see *1872, 2903*. The greater part of the work on the enzymatic functions of ubiquinone has been carried out at the Institute for Enzyme Studies at Wisconsin.

Ubiquinone has been variously known as '272 mμ substance', 'SA', 'Q_{275}', 'ubiquinone', 'mitoquinone', 'coenzyme Q', 'ubiferon Q'; we use 'ubiquinone' in accordance with the recommendation of the Enzyme Commission of the International Union of Biochemistry, but 'coenzyme Q' is still widely used.

Properties of ubiquinone. Like other quinones, ubiquinone undergoes reduction to a hydroquinone form, and its main physiological function depends on this. It occurs in the mitochondria to the extent of 2–3 mg per g of protein, and forms an essential constituent of the mitochondrial respiratory chain. Like some other components of this system, it is insoluble in water, so that the reactions with which it is concerned take place *in vivo* in a non-aqueous phase.

Extraction of mitochondria with acetone containing 4 per cent of water removes the ubiquinone, and the particles are then found to have lost their power of oxidizing succinate by O_2 through cytochrome c; activity can be fully restored by adding ubiquinone, but not other quinones, including vitamin K (*1553*). It is concluded that ubiquinone forms an essential link between succinate and cytochrome c, and this has been confirmed by spectroscopic observations. The spectra of the oxidized and reduced forms are shown in Fig. IX.9, and it will be seen that it is possible to follow the oxidation and reduction by measurements at 275 mμ. CHANCE and REDFEARN (*425*) have shown that the rate of reduction of endogenous ubiquinone in mitochondrial preparations is of the same order as the rate of succinate oxidation.

After extraction with 10 per cent of water in acetone, the succinate oxidase activity of the particles is not restored by the addition of ubiquinone alone, but is restored by ubiquinone together with the mixture of lipids extracted by the acetone. This lipid can be replaced by certain pure phospholipids, for example phosphatidyl inositol, but not as efficiently as by the mixture (*1553*).

At present it is difficult to say how many substrates depend for their oxidation on ubiquinone. After extraction with acetone the oxidation of $NADH_2$ by mitochondrial particles disappears, and is not restored by the addition of ubiquinone, apparently because the necessary enzyme

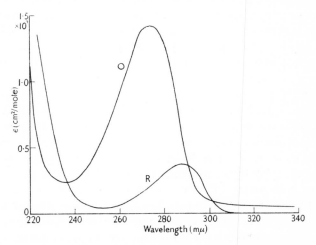

Fig. IX.9. *Spectra of oxidized* (O) *and Reduced* (R) *forms of ubiquinone.*

Curves obtained with UQ_{10} in ethanol.

from *2903*

has been destroyed by acetone. However, a particulate enzyme (1.6.5.3) can be prepared from mitochondria which brings about the reduction of ubiquinone by reduced coenzymes (*1026*). This preparation, like other mitochondrial preparations, contains much non-haem iron, which may play some part in the reaction.

The reduced form of ubiquinone (ubiquinol) is oxidized by another sub-mitochondrial preparation through the cytochrome system (*1025*). The oxidation depends on cytochrome c and cytochrome oxidase, is inhibited by antimycin A (unlike the reduction of ubiquinone, which, contrary to earlier statements, is not inhibited) (*2126*) and is coupled with phosphorylation. Antimycin contrasts with amytal, which inhibits the reduction of ubiquinone by $NADH_2$, though not by succinate.

Vitamin K. There is some doubt as to whether any vitamin K occurs in mitochondria, and although it has been suggested that it acts as a carrier in the respiratory chain, there is little convincing evidence for this (see *2903*). However, vitamin K, and especially menadione, can undergo reduction and oxidation in mitochondrial suspensions, and a very active menadione reductase (1.6.5.2) exists, which brings about the reduction of menadione (but not vitamins K_1 or K_2 or ubiquinone) by $NADH_2$ or $NADPH_2$ (*1722*). This enzyme is inhibited by minute concentrations of dicoumarol, which have no effect on either O_2 uptake or phosphorylation in mitochondria. If therefore this enzyme is involved in the respiratory chain, there must be an alternative pathway which comes into operation when the inhibitor is added.

There is more evidence that vitamin K is involved in the hydrogen transport processes of photosynthetic phosphorylation in chloroplasts.

Cytochromes

The name 'cytochrome' was given by KEILIN in 1925(*1331*) to a group of intracellular haemoproteins which in the reduced form show a marked absorption spectrum in the visible region. The name as at present used appears to include all intracellular haemoproteins with the exception of haemoglobin, myoglobin, peroxidase and catalase. The group includes substances with many different functions. The functions of a number of the cytochromes are unknown, but they all appear to act by undergoing oxidation and reduction. Some of those whose functions are known are enzymes, while the remainder are simply oxidation-reduction carriers.

The four-banded visible absorption spectrum of the typical system of cytochromes (components *a*, *b* and *c*) was originally observed in a great variety of animal tissues by MACMUNN(*1669*) in 1886, but the importance of these observations was not realized until KEILIN confirmed and extended them, extracted the *c* component, and showed the fundamental role of the cytochrome system in cell respiration. Keilin analysed the nature and mode of action of the system (cytochrome+cytochrome oxidase) in a classical series of papers (*1331–3, 1338, 1340–2*) from 1925 onwards.

In addition to the three originally observed cytochromes, a number of others have been discovered by Keilin and other workers and over twenty are now known. Table IX.4 gives a list of the best known cytochromes with some of their properties.

The nomenclature of individual cytochromes has become difficult owing to the isolation from different sources of cytochromes with similar properties. The cytochromes fall into four groups, differing in the nature of the haem prosthetic group. The Enzyme Commission has

TABLE IX.4

CYTOCHROMES

Cytochrome	Occurrence	Absorption bands				MW	Haem groups per mole	E_0' at pH 7 (volts)	Function	References
		reduced			oxidized					
		α	β	γ	γ					
a	Widely distributed	603	none	450	407			+0·29	Component of cytochrome oxidase	933, 1341, 1547, 2020, 2452, 2949
a_1	Bacteria, yeast	590	none	445					?	1335, 2451
a_3	Similar to a	603	none	445					Component of cytochrome oxidase	933, 1341, 1 47, 2020, 2452, 2949
b	Widely distributed	563	532	429	418	28,000	1	+0·08	Carrier in succinate oxidation ?	858, 1143, 1341
b_1	Bacteria	560		430					?	1335, 2451, 2732
b_2	Yeast	557	528	424	413	170,000	2		Lactate dehydrogenase (1.1.2.3)	82, 119, 1880–1
b_3	Plants	559	529	425				+0·04	?	513, 1099, 1736
b_5	Animal tissues	556	526	423	413	14,000	1	+0·02	Carrier in respiration	424, 427, 2186, 2553, 2556, 2728
b_6	Plant chloroplasts	563						−0·06	Carrier in photosynthesis ?	1096–8
b_7	Arum spadix	560	529					−0·03	Carrier in cyanide-insensitive respiration	202, 204

TABLE IX.4—*continued*

Cyto-chrome	Occurrence	Absorption bands reduced α	Absorption bands reduced β	Absorption bands reduced γ	Absorption bands oxidized γ	MW	Haem groups per mole	E'_0 at pH 7 (volts)	Function	References
B (559, *Streptomyces*)		559	530	428	408				?	249
c	Widely distributed	550	521	415	407	13,000	1	+0·254	Carrier in respiration	679, 708, 1062, 1333, 1338, 1716, 2058, 2238, 2630
c_1	Widely distributed	554	524	418	410	37,000	1	+0·220	Carrier in respiration	284, 707, 1346a, 2732, 2924
c_2	Photosynthetic bacteria	552	522	418	410	15,600		+0·33	Carrier in photosynthesis ?	1168, 1860
c_3	*Desulphovibrio*	552	522	418	409	11,300	2	−0·205	Carrier in sulphate reduction	1168, 2110–1
c_4	*Azotobacter*, etc.	551	522	414	409			+0·30	Carrier in bacterial respiration	450, 1298, 1954, 2658–9
c_5	*Azotobacter*	555	524	418	414			+0·32	Carrier in bacterial respiration	1954, 2658–9

C (551, *Pseudomonas*)	551	521	416	409	7,600	1	$+0\cdot286$	Carrier in respiration	*1166*
C (552, *Chromatium*)	552	523	416	410	97,000	3	$+0\cdot01$	Carrier in bacterial photosynthesis	*176*
C (552, *Euglena*)	552	523	417	412			$+0\cdot36$	Carrier in photosynthesis ?	*543, 1973*
C (553, *Chlorobium*)	553	522	417	408	*c.* 50,000	1	$+0\cdot16$	?	*830*
C (554, *Chlorobium*)	554	523	417	412	*c.* 12,000	1	$+0\cdot14$	?	*830*
C (554, halotolerant bacteria) (formerly b_4)	554	521	415					?	*675*
C (555, plant chloroplasts) (formerly *f*)	555	525	423	413	110,000	2	$+0\cdot365$	Carrier in photosynthesis ?	*426, 542–3, 1098–9, 1633*
C (556, *Helix pomatia* hepatopancreas) (formerly *h*)	556	527	422	408	18,500	1		?	*1350*
CD (625, 554, 549, *Pseudomonas aeruginosa*) (formerly GB or a_2)	625 554 549	521	418	408	90,000	2		Cytochrome (c_4+c_5) oxidase (1.9.3.a)	*172, 423, 1167, 1335, 1547, 2451, 2656, 2934*
Cytochromoids									
C (*Rhodospirillum rubrum*) (formerly RHP)	568 550	none	424	390	28,000	2	$-0\cdot008$	Terminal oxidase	*175, 1168*
C (*Chromatium*) (formerly RHP)	565 547	none	426	400	36,000	2	$-0\cdot005$	Carrier in photosynthesis ?	*176*

recommended that this should be the basis for naming cytochromes, the groups being designated by the letters A, B, C and D, as follows:

A. cytochromes with a haem group containing formyl-porphyrin,
B. cytochromes with a protohaem group,
C. cytochromes with a substituted mesohaem group covalently linked with the protein,
D. cytochromes with a haem group containing dihydroporphyrin.

Various criteria for assigning cytochromes to the different groups are given in Chapter 5 of the Commission's report (2212).

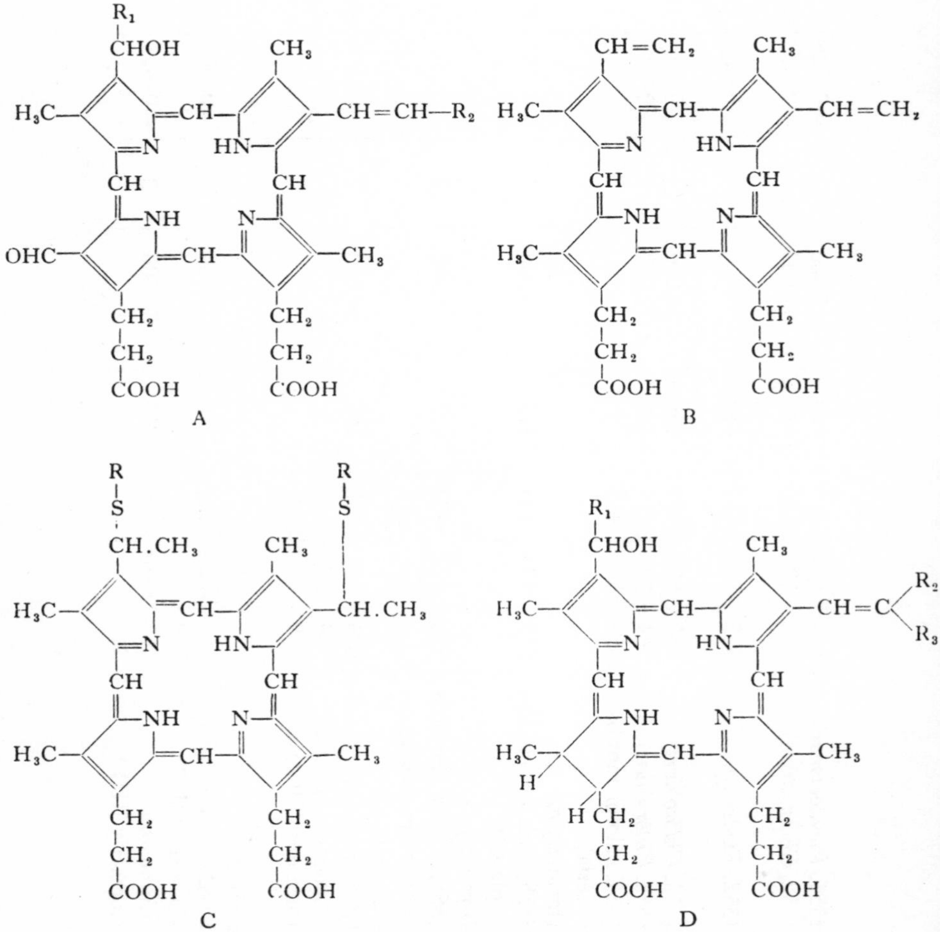

Fig. IX.10 *Porphyrins of cytochromes A, B, C and D.*

Individual cytochromes whose identity is well established are distinguished by a small italic letter denoting the group, with a numerical subscript: these designations are allotted by international agreement, and a list is given in Appendix C of the report. The more recently discovered cytochromes which have not yet been allotted a final name are defined in the meantime by a capital letter denoting the group, with the wavelength of the α-band of the absorption spectrum and the source. This system

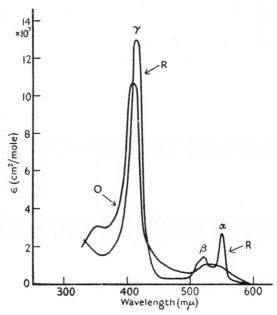

Fig. IX.11. *Spectra of oxidized* (O) *and reduced* (R)
forms of cytochrome c.

after *1715*

will probably need modification as the number of known cytochromes increases.

Fig. IX.10 shows the probable structures of the porphyrins of the four prosthetic groups of cytochromes A, B, C and D.

Haems b and c are based on protoporphyrin; haem a differs in containing a formyl, an ethylenic, and two alkyl groups (one of which may be long-chain) (*459, 1547*); haem d contains instead of a formyl-porphyrin a chlorin (a dihydroporphyrin) (*172*). In the c type of cytochromes the prosthetic group can be regarded as protohaem bonded to the protein in an unusual way by the addition of two thiol groups of the protein across the double bonds of the vinyl groups of the protoporphyrin (THEORELL,

2630). This gives a firm thioether link, and when the haem is separated from the protein a fragment of the protein remains attached, so that the product is the substituted mesoporphyrin shown in Fig. IX.10.C.

The nature of the prosthetic group has a considerable influence on the positions of the α-absorption bands of the spectra of the reduced complete cytochromes: the range of the positions of the α-bands of the *a*, *b* and *c* cytochromes are from 590 mμ upwards, from 554 to 563 and from 550 to 557 respectively. The absorption spectra can only be taken as a rough guide to the classification of the cytochromes, particularly in distinguishing between the *b* and *c* types, since there is a slight overlap.

Properties. The spectra of cytochrome *c* (Fig. IX.11) may be taken as typical of those of the oxidized and reduced forms of cytochromes. On oxidation, which is a one-equivalent reaction involving a change of

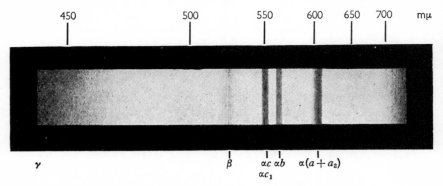

Fig. IX.12. *Typical cytochrome spectrum of aerobic cells.*

state of the iron atom from ferrous to ferric, the sharp α- and β-bands disappear, but the γ-band remains, although it is shifted towards the ultra-violet. However, the reduced *a* cytochromes (and ferrohaemochromes derived from them) show little or no β-band. This was not realized at first, because cytochrome *a* had not been extracted and what was observed was the spectrum resulting from the superimposition of the *a*, *b* and *c* spectra in tissue preparations.

This mixed spectrum (Fig. IX.12) is the typical spectrum given by the cytochrome system of a great variety of aerobic cells, as shown by KEILIN (*1331*; *1334*, Fig. 5); in fact, the normally found group of cytochromes in such cells consists of cytochromes *a*, *b* and *c*, and most of the other cytochromes are special forms of rather limited distribution. However, the normal aerobic system also contains cytochromes a_3, c_1 and frequently b_5, although their absorption bands are obscured by the others and cannot be observed under the usual conditions.

As a general rule the *b* cytochromes are oxidized directly by molecular oxygen, whereas in general the others have not this property of autoxidizability. However, this is not a reliable guide to type, as a_3, c_3, C (552, *Chromatium*) and CD are autoxidizable, and cytochrome *c* becomes autoxidizable at pH values below 4 and above 12; on the other hand, the autoxidation of several of the *b* cytochromes is very slow.

The chief difficulty in studying the cytochrome system, and the cause of much of the obscurity affecting the subject, is the fact that many of the cytochromes cannot be readily obtained in true solution; thus the majority cannot be separated except by rather drastic treatments. Cytochrome *c* is exceptional in being freely soluble and was the first to be extracted and purified (KEILIN, *1333, 1338*; THEORELL and ÅKESSON, *2630*; PALÉUS and NEILANDS, *2046*; MARGOLIASH, *1716*). Cytochrome *c* of the penguin was first crystallized by BODO (*279*); those of many animal tissues, yeast and wheat grain have since been crystallized, especially by HAGIHARA, OKUNUKI and their co-workers (*280, 971, 973–6*). Other cytochromes which have been purified are *a, b, b_2, b_3, b_5, c_1, c_2, c_3, c_4, c_5*, C (551, *Pseudomonas*), C (552, *Chromatium*), C (553, *Chlorobium*), C (554, *Chlorobium*), C (555, plant chloroplasts), C (556, *Helix pomatia* hepatopancreas) and CD (625, 554, 549, *Pseudomonas aeruginosa*).

Purified cytochrome *c* from heart has been studied in considerable detail. The spectrum of the reduced form is unchanged over the whole pH range, showing that the bonds between the iron atom and the four nitrogen atoms of the porphyrin remain covalent. The oxidized form, on the other hand, shows five different spectrum types according to the pH, the transition points indicating pK values of $0\cdot4$, $2\cdot5$, $9\cdot3$ and $12\cdot8$ (*2631*), the acid and alkaline forms being partly ionic. E_0' measurements indicate an additional pK of the oxidized form of $6\cdot8$ (*2058*) or $7\cdot7$ (*2238*); this is associated with the oxidation.

The complete aminoacid sequence of horse heart cytochrome *c* has been determined by MARGOLIASH, EMIL SMITH, KREIL and TUPPY (*1718*). The N-terminal group is acetyl-glycine. There is a marked tendency for the different types of aminoacid to be grouped together, thus there are a number of regions in the chain which consist predominantly of basic residues, and others of large hydrophobic residues. The acidic residues also show some tendency to be associated together. The haem group is attached at a point about one-seventh of the distance along the chain from the N-terminal end; the arrangement is

$$-\text{Lys–Cy–Ala–Glu(NH}_2\text{)–Cy–His–}.$$
$$\overset{|}{\text{S}}\text{———haem———}\overset{|}{\text{S}}$$

o

This sequence represents the two R groups of Fig. IX.10.C; it varies slightly in different species, as discussed on p. 655.

The aminoacid sequence of cytochrome C (551, *Pseudomonas*) has been determined by AMBLER (*58*). The haem is attached at about the same relative distance from the N-terminal end in a similar manner, the $-Ala-Glu(NH_2)-$ group between the two cysteine residues being replaced by $-Val-Ala-$.

Some of the most important cytochromes concerned in cell respiration are located in intracellular particles; in animal tissues cytochromes $a_{(3)}$, b, c_1 and most or all of the c are located in mitochondria. Cytochrome b_5 was believed to be located only in microsomes, but recently it has been found, along with its reductase, in liver mitochondria (*2186*). These cytochromes are not removed by extraction with water (except for some of the c); they can, however, be 'solubilized' by treatment with surface-active substances such as cholate. Cholate and deoxycholate have been extensively used for fractionations of the particulate systems, often coupled with salt fractionations. In this way it has been possible to separate all the cytochromes from one another, though it is debatable whether these are all in true solution, as they precipitate when the solubilizing agent is removed. It has not been possible to separate a_3 from a, and some workers regard these as a single substance.

The purified components of the system fail to react with one another when mixed, unless phospholipids are also added. The particulate respiratory system contains considerable amounts of phospholipid, and some at any rate of the hydrogen transport reactions probably occur in a lipid environment. Cytochrome c, which is normally water-soluble, has been shown to form a complex with lipid which is lipid-soluble and water-insoluble: this has been referred to as 'lipid cytochrome c' (*2859*). The action of phospholipids on cytochrome oxidase has not been entirely cleared up, but Wharton and Griffiths (*2848*) state that its activation is due to protection of the solubilized oxidase from aggregation.

Reduced cytochrome c in neutral solution is not oxidized by molecular oxygen, but it is oxidized by H_2O_2, by ferricyanide and by copper salts. The reaction with H_2O_2 is greatly catalysed by cytochrome peroxidase (1.11.1.5) in some micro-organisms. Reduced cytochrome c is very rapidly oxidized by oxygen in the presence of cytochrome oxidase, and this reaction forms the terminal step of the system. Oxidized cytochrome c is reduced by such chemical reducing agents as dithionite, cysteine, polyphenols and ascorbate. It is also reduced by cytochromes b_5 and c_1, and by a number of enzymes, including the cytochrome c reductases (1.6.2.1,3), yeast lactate dehydrogenase (cytochrome b_2) (1.1.2.3) and indirectly by the succinate and other dehydrogenases. Since its enzymatic oxidation and reduction are both rapid in tissues, it is a very effective carrier in the oxidation of the relevant substrates by molecular oxygen.

It will be seen that its mode of action closely resembles that of the coenzymes, and that, in fact, it acts as a true cofactor in these systems. Cytochrome c, like all the other cytochromes, is a protein (though one of low molecular weight), and the nature of its protein, as well as that of the enzyme proteins concerned, has an influence on the specificity of the reactions. Nevertheless we do not consider it as an enzyme, as it has no such catalytic properties by itself and requires the presence of enzymes for its action.

Several of the systems which reduce cytochrome c are composite and contain other intermediate carriers in addition to the dehydrogenase itself. This field has been reviewed by SLATER (2427). The reduction by succinate probably proceeds through ubiquinone, cytochrome b and cytochrome c_1, in that order. The reduction of cytochrome c by the reduced coenzymes is mediated *in vitro* by the cytochrome reductases, which are flavoproteins, without any additional carriers. The mechanism of this reaction is discussed in Chapter VII (p. 309). However, the oxidation of $NADH_2$ in tissue preparations, like the oxidation of succinate, is sensitive to inhibition by urethane, dimercaptopropanol (BAL) in presence of oxygen, or antimycin A, which do not inhibit the reductases. These three inhibitors all act at the same point, namely between ubiquinone or cytochrome b and cytochrome c_1.

Some of the more important interrelationships of the various cytochrome components of the intracellular oxidation system are shown in Fig. IX.13, in which the arrows indicate the paths of hydrogen transport from substrate to O_2. All the components of this diagram are present in mitochondria, although cytochrome b_5 and its reductase are mainly present in microsomes and much of the NAD, together with its related dehydrogenases, is found in solution in the cytoplasm.

Some of the evidence for the functional order of cytochromes shown in the figure may be briefly summarized as follows. The component which reacts directly with O_2 is clearly $a_{(3)}$, since (a) it is the only one which combines strongly with carbon monoxide, which competes with O_2, (b) it combines strongly with cyanide, and the oxidation of all the other components is then inhibited, and (c) it can be separated from all the other cytochromes, and then acts as a cytochrome oxidase with added cytochrome c. Cytochrome b must be on the substrate side of all the others, since the addition of antimycin A inhibits the oxidation of succinate by O_2, causing b to become reduced and all the others to become oxidized, showing that b is on the substrate side, and the others on the O_2

side, of the point of attack. c_1 is only oxidized by $a_{(3)}+O_2$ when c is added, showing that it is on the substrate side of c, and this is confirmed by the fact that it is reduced by succinate in the absence of c. The exact function of b is still somewhat uncertain.

The order shown is supported by fragmentation studies. By treatment with surface-active substances, such as cholate, it has been

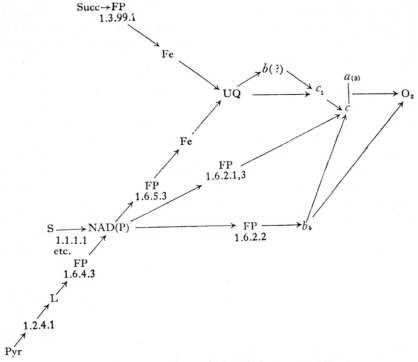

Fig. IX.13. *Some interrelationships of cytochromes.*

The symbols have the following meanings: Succ, succinate; FP, a flavoprotein enzyme; Fe, iron in flavoprotein; UQ, ubiquinone; S, various dehydrogenase substrates; Pyr, pyruvate; L, lipoate (bound); $a_{(3)}$, b, b_5, c, c_1, cytochromes. The numbers are those of the enzymes concerned.

possible to divide the mitochondrial system into four sections, namely (a) $NADH_2 \rightarrow UQ$, (b) $Succ \rightarrow UQ$, (c) $UQH_2 \rightarrow c$, and (d) $c \rightarrow O_2$ (*1026*). These sections can be recombined to re-form the complete system.

Cytochrome oxidase

Reduced cytochrome c does not react with oxygen in neutral solution, but almost all tissues contain cytochrome oxidase, which brings about its rapid oxidation by oxygen. The mode of action of this enzyme, which is still somewhat obscure, has been briefly discussed at the end of Chapter VII. It has been shown by Keilin that it does not oxidize substances such as cysteine, ascorbate or p-phenylenediamine unless cytochrome c is added.

It seems, however, that it does not act simply as a carrier between reduced c and O_2, for the reduced form of $a_{(3)}$ is not oxidized by O_2 unless c is added, when the oxidation is very rapid (2366). This suggests that the active oxidase is a complex of cytochromes c and a.

The oxidase is very sensitive to the inhibitors cyanide, H_2S and carbon monoxide, which are well known inhibitors of metal-catalysed reactions. Its identification with cytochrome a_3 in animal tissues (KEILIN and HARTREE, 1341) and in baker's yeast (CASTOR and CHANCE, 414), and with cytochrome CD or a cytochromoid C, known as cytochrome o, in different bacteria (TISSIÈRES, 2656; CASTOR and CHANCE, 414), is based upon the use of these inhibitors, particularly carbon monoxide. As is well known, this combines with haemoproteins such as haemoglobin; it does not, however, combine with most of the cytochromes.

WARBURG (2782) showed that carbon monoxide reversibly inhibits the oxygen uptake of baker's yeast and certain bacteria. Carbon monoxide compounds of haemoproteins are known to be dissociated into free carbon monoxide and haemoprotein by light, and Warburg found that the inhibition of the respiration was less in light than in the dark, suggesting the dependence of respiration on a catalytic haemoprotein. The effect of monochromatic light was found to be strongly dependent on the wavelength, and on plotting the effectiveness of the light in reversing the carbon monoxide inhibition against the wavelength, a curve similar to Fig. IX.14 was obtained, which in form closely resembled the absorption spectrum of a cytochrome (1475, 2791). Since the amount of carbon monoxide dissociated will depend on the amount of light absorbed, it is reasonable to suppose that this 'photochemical spectrum' represents the actual absorption spectrum of the inactive carbon monoxide compound of the active material, although it could be argued that the spectrum might not be that of the compound actually dissociated by light, but that of an associated substance acting as a photochemical sensitizer.

KEILIN and HARTREE (1341) found that on saturating a reduced preparation of the heart muscle cytochrome system with carbon monoxide, the a spectrum undergoes a change; the α-band at 603 mμ develops a shoulder at about 590 mμ, and the γ-band is largely replaced by a new band at about 430 mμ.

These changes have been interpreted in two ways. Keilin and Hartree suggested that the *a* spectrum represented the superimposed spectra of two components *a* and a_3, of which only a_3 combined with carbon monoxide. The bands at 590 mμ and 430 mμ obtained in the presence of CO thus represent the spectrum of the a_3CO compound. This involves the assumption that the α-band of *a* is stronger than that of a_3, while the γ-band of a_3 is stronger than that of *a*. Keilin and Hartree suggested that the compound which they named 'cytochrome a_3' was, in fact, identical with cytochrome oxidase, because of the fact that, like the oxidase, it combined with CO, and that the absorption bands of the CO compound

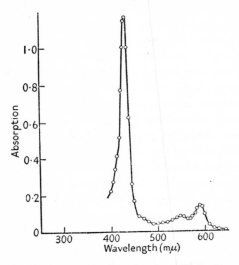

Fig. IX.14. *Photochemical spectrum of respiration of baker's yeast in the presence of carbon monoxide.*

The calculated absorption is expressed in relation to the absorption at 436 mμ.
from *414*

corresponded with those in the photochemical spectrum of CO-inhibited respiration, as shown in Fig. IX.14.

　　The alternative view, which is held by a number of workers, is that there is only one compound, cytochrome *a*, which combines with CO to give the spectrum described by Keilin and Hartree with asymmetric bands. This compound is regarded as the functional oxidase. This view is in agreement with the fact that, although all the other cytochromes of heart muscle have been separated from one another, it has proved impossible to effect any separation of *a* and a_3, and highly purified preparations of cytochrome oxidase show similar spectral changes with CO, although there is only evidence for one type of haem *a*, with one Cu atom per haem group.

YONETANI (*2948*) has obtained some kinetic evidence which he believes proves the separate existence of a and a_3. Using a highly purified but non-crystalline preparation of cytochrome oxidase from heart muscle, and a spectrophotometer recording simultaneously at 445 and 605 mμ, he calculated the state of reduction in each case during the oxidation of ascorbate by O_2 with the addition of cytochrome c. Since the figures for the steady-state percentage reduction were different for the two wavelengths, he concluded that the absorptions at the two wavelengths could not be entirely due to a single compound. The results could be accounted for by assuming that the 605 band is mainly due to a and the 445 band to a_3, as suggested by Keilin and Hartree. Other explanations, however, can be suggested, for example the presence of a catalytically inactive derivative of cytochrome oxidase, which undergoes slow reduction although not contributing to the steady state. It should be noted that even Yonetani's crystalline preparation is only one-fifth as active as the preparation of GRIFFITHS and WHARTON (*933*).

Supporting evidence has been obtained by GIBSON and GREENWOOD (*833*), using Yonetani's preparation, by rapid reaction techniques at different O_2 concentrations. The rates of oxidation by low concentrations of O_2 of the reduced oxidase preparation are higher when measured at 605 mμ than when measured at 445 mμ. At higher O_2 concentration the oxidation is biphasic; a rapid stage dependent on O_2 concentration is followed by a slow step which is independent of O_2 concentration. These effects are explained if at low O_2 concentrations the limiting step is the oxidation of a_3, while at higher O_2 concentrations the reaction is at first limited by the oxidation of a_3 and later by the reduction of a_3 by a.

The nature of the difference between a and a_3 has not been cleared up by the work described in the last two paragraphs. The haem groups are apparently the same, and there is no evidence that more than one protein is present. This suggests that the difference lies in the mode of attachment of the haem to the protein. LEMBERG, NEWTON and O'HAGAN (*1548*) have produced evidence from studies with detergents that the linkage in a_3 involves a lipid molecule which is bound to the haem in such a way that it prevents coordination of nitrogenous groups in the protein with the haem iron, so that the iron is left open to oxidative attack by O_2. Cytochrome a, like cytochrome c, is presumably non-autoxidizable because the iron is protected by coordination with groups in the protein. If Lemberg's suggestions are correct, the distinction between a and a_3 may be much less rigid than many workers have hitherto believed.

Because of the uncertainty about the precise relations between a and a_3, we have denoted the functional cytochrome of the cytochrome oxidase as $a_{(3)}$ in Fig. IX.13 and elsewhere in the chapter.

The view that cytochrome oxidase is responsible for the respiration of aerobic cells in general is not free from difficulties, though widely accepted. Photochemical spectra have only been obtained with a very limited number of different kinds of cells, in particular those which contain a large amount of cytochrome such as baker's yeast, heart muscle and certain bacteria. Many other cells and tissues, however, are known to contain very little cytochrome c; further, the respiration of most animal tissues is insensitive to carbon monoxide, and that of many cells is even insensitive to cyanide. Other respiratory systems must presumably operate in such cells, such as that shown in Table XII.6. It is of interest in this connection that those animal tissues with a lower content of cytochrome oxidase have been shown to have a relatively high content of peroxidase (*1949*).

In certain bacteria the photochemical α-bands are in different positions, indicating that cytochromes a_1 or CD, rather than a_3, are probably acting as cytochrome oxidases. In two cases a photochemical spectrum with α- and β-bands of equal intensity was obtained and ascribed to a different haemoprotein oxidase capable of combining with carbon monoxide, 'cytochrome o' (CASTOR and CHANCE, *414–5*).

Specificity effects also show that the cytochrome oxidases of some bacteria are different from that of animal tissues; for example, the *Pseudomonas* and *Azotobacter* oxidases will only slowly oxidize cytochrome c, but will oxidize cytochrome c_4, which occurs in these organisms, and, conversely, the mammalian oxidase will not oxidize cytochrome c_4 (*1526, 2659*).

Other hydrogen carriers

Any substance which is reduced by one enzyme and oxidized by another may be said to act as a hydrogen carrier, and it is possible for normal metabolites to act in this way. An example is shown in Table XII.6, where the glyoxylate-glycollate pair can be seen to function as a hydrogen carrier in exactly the same way as NAD.

Another important hydrogen carrier is the flavin group, but as this is found as part of the prosthetic group of the flavoprotein enzymes, rather than as a free carrier, it is dealt with later in the chapter (p. 405).

Amino-group carriers

Just as there are many dehydrogenases reacting with common carriers, and thus bringing about distribution of hydrogen, so there are many transaminases reacting with a common ketoacid (2-oxoglutarate), which can therefore act as a carrier of amino groups (cf. p. 545). This is an illustration of a metabolite acting as a coenzyme.

2-oxoglutarate

The aminated form of 2-oxoglutarate is L-glutamate; the structure of the two forms is given in Fig. IX.15.

It will be seen from the Table of Enzymes that the great majority of the known transaminases react with this carrier pair, by which they can therefore be linked together. A small number of transaminases catalyse reactions which are independent of glutamate (see *2268*).

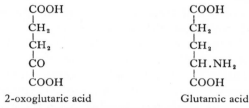

2-oxoglutaric acid   Glutamic acid

Fig. IX.15. *An amino-group carrier system.*

There is no evidence that any other aminoacid can act as a general carrier in transaminations.

The vast majority of the enzymes involved depend on pyridoxal phosphate for their action. This acts as the prosthetic group of the transaminases, as well as of some other enzymes acting on aminoacids, and is dealt with on p. 410.

Phosphate carriers

Probably the two most important types of transport reaction are hydrogen transport and phosphate transport; the hydrogen-transfer reactions are concerned with the production of energy in living matter and the phosphate-transfer reactions with its transfer from one process to another. The biological carriers of phosphate are nucleoside diphosphates, which act as cofactors in transphosphorylation processes, and the enzymes which catalyse the transfer reactions to and from these diphosphates are the kinases (sub-groups 2.7.1–4).

Nucleoside 5'-diphosphates

The main biological phosphate carrier is adenosine diphosphate (ADP), which can take on a third phosphate group to form adenosine triphosphate (ATP). It is not clear how far other nucleoside diphosphates can act as phosphate carriers; it will be seen from the Table that practically all the kinases react with ADP, but in fact very few of them have been tested for specificity towards other diphosphates. Eight kinases have in fact been shown to react with one or more of the other nucleoside diphosphates whose structure is shown in Fig. IX.16. On the other hand, of kinases which have been tested with ITP, only six were capable of reacting with it, so that there is at any rate some degree of specificity towards the nucleoside triphosphate. A great deal remains to be investigated, but the field is a difficult one because of the rarity of the triphosphates, the mutual contamination which is frequently found, and the presence in some of the kinase preparations of nucleoside-diphosphate kinase.

It should be noted that these carriers have the phosphate groups attached to the 5-position of the ribose residue, and not to the 2- or 3-position as in the usual nucleotides obtained from nucleic acid.

In all cases the triphosphates have three phosphate groups in series and therefore contain two pyrophosphate bonds. Only the terminal phosphate group is normally involved in phosphate transfer reactions.

Although ADP is generally recognized as being the main phosphate carrier, the fact that some of the kinases can also react with other nucleoside diphosphates (and also the fact that one kinase does not react with ADP) suggests that these also can act as biological phosphate carriers. However, it is not yet possible to assess their importance in this respect, because of lack of knowledge of the specificity of the enzymes and of the amounts of these substances in living cells. These other phosphate carriers may well form interlinked systems *in vivo* through the action of nucleosidediphosphate kinase (2.7.4.6), thus:

IX.7 $X–P + GDP = X + GTP$

IX.8 $GTP + ADP = GDP + ATP$

IX.9 $ATP + Y = ADP + Y–P$

Here both GDP and ADP act as phosphate carriers; reaction IX.8 is catalysed by nucleosidediphosphate kinase, and reactions IX.7 and IX.9 by other kinases.

It is important to note that such phosphate carriers can not only link two kinases together, they can also link together kinases and synthetases:

IX.10 $X–P + ADP \rightleftharpoons X + ATP$

IX.11 $Y + Z + ATP = Y–Z + ADP + P$

or the reverse process. The linking of a phosphokinase with a synthetase may involve two nucleoside diphosphates and nucleosidediphosphate kinase, see, for example, reactions XII.2.m–n.

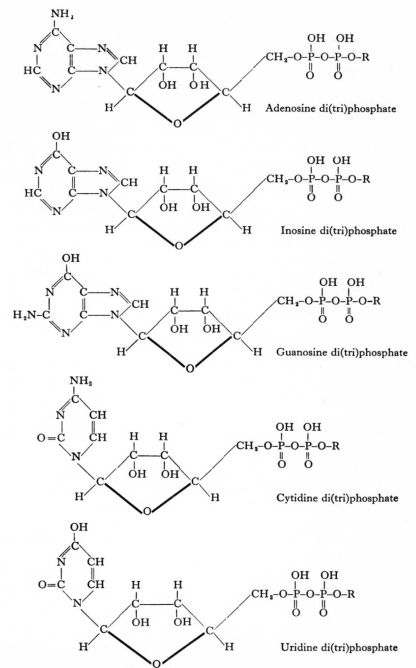

Fig. IX.16. *Structures of nucleoside di- and tri-phosphates.*
In XDP, R = –H; in XTP, R = –H$_2$PO$_3$.

ATP has many other biological functions; it provides the energy for muscular contraction, for bioluminescence, for absorption and secretion, for generation of high voltages for defence, and probably for other processes. It also acts as an adenosine donor in connection with trans-methylation (reactions XII.10.a–b), and as an adenylate donor in the formation of dinucleotides by nucleotidyltransferases (reactions XII.16.d, XII.17.e). GTP, CTP and UTP also act as nucleotide donors in other nucleotidyltransferase reactions, these then link up with reactions described in the next section.

Mixed phosphate and glycosyl transfers

Some nucleoside 5'-diphosphates, particularly UDP, CDP and GDP, have specialized functions as carriers in an unusual type of gly-cosyl transfer, which involves phosphate transfer to complete the cata-lytic cycle. In the simple type of phosphate transfer, involving the transfer of a phosphate group from B to C by means of a phosphate carrier A, we may write the process as

IX.12 $\qquad A + BP = AP + B$

IX.13 $\qquad AP + C = A + CP$

If we assume that a similar simple transfer of a glycosyl group G from C to D could be brought about independently by means of the same carrier A, acting now as a glycosyl carrier, we can write

IX.14 $\qquad A + CG = AG + C$

IX.15 $\qquad AG + D = A + DG$

In actual fact, glycosyl group transfer by a carrier does not occur bio-logically in the simple way shown in reactions IX.14–15; in the known systems the glycosyl and phosphate transfers are interlocked by the combination of the two simple transfer reactions IX.13 and IX.14 into a single double-exchange reaction IX.17, so that the whole process is as follows

IX.16 $\qquad A + BP = AP + B$

IX.17 $\qquad AP + CG = AG + CP$

IX.18 $\qquad AG + D = A + DG$

For example, UDP acts as a carrier of both phosphate and glucose in the system for the biosynthesis of sucrose, thus

IX.19 $\qquad UDP + ATP = UTP + ADP$

IX.20   UTP + glucose 1-phosphate = UDPglucose + pyrophosphate

IX.21   UDPglucose + fructose = UDP + sucrose

Here the carrier A is UDP, B is ADP, C as well as P is phosphate so that in this system CP is pyrophosphate, D is fructose, G is glucose; and the process is catalysed by nucleosidediphosphate kinase (2.7.4.6), UDPG pyrophosphorylase (2.7.7.9) and sucrose-UDP glucosyltransferase (2.4.1.13) (see Table XII.19). UDP plays a similar part in the synthesis of a number of other glycosides, for example, sucrose phosphate, trehalose phosphate, starch, glycogen, cellulose and chitin.

Similar systems involving the combined transfer of phosphate and other groups exist, as, for example, the synthesis of phosphatides, in which CDP acts as a carrier using the enzymes of sub-group 2.7.8.

Another system, in which UDP acts as a cofactor by a different mechanism, is the system interconverting galactose and glucose (Table XII.9). Here the inverting enzyme only acts on hexoses when they are combined with UDP; thus the UDP acts as a 'handle' which is transferred to the sugar before the inversion takes place and is removed by transfer to another molecule when it is completed.

Acyl-group carriers

Recent developments in the study of intermediary metabolism of fats and carbohydrates have focused attention on the importance of acyl-group transfer, particularly by carriers containing thiol groups, with which they form thiolesters. These energy-rich compounds share with energy-rich phosphate compounds the important function of biological energy transfer.

Coenzyme A

This important coenzyme was originally discovered as a coenzyme for acetylations in liver and micro-organisms by LIPMANN in 1947; its structure was established largely as the result of work by his school, and it has been synthesized partly by chemical and partly by enzymatic means (*128*). An enzymatic pathway for the biosynthesis of coenzyme A has been completely elucidated, and is shown in Table XII.17. The structure is shown in Fig. IX.17 and will be seen to be 3'-phospho-ADP-pantoyl-β-alanyl-cysteamine. It thus has some similarity to an adenine dinucleotide in which the second nucleoside is replaced by pantetheine (i.e. pantothenyl-cysteamine). Like NADP, it has a third phosphate group on the ribose residue of the adenylic acid, but in this case it is in the 3-position instead of the 2-position. As in NAD and

NADP, as well as in flavin-adenine-dinucleotide (to be discussed later), the functional group, in this case the –SH group, is in the part furthest removed from the adenine.

For a review of coenzyme A, see *1230*.

The 'two-carbon fragment' or 'active acetyl' known to be involved in carbohydrate metabolism was identified as acetyl-CoA by the work of LIPMANN, OCHOA and their co-workers. This substance was isolated and characterized as the thiolester, namely, S-acetyl-CoA, by LYNEN and REICHERT (*1640*). It was later found that not only acetyl-CoA but acyl-CoA compounds generally were very important in metabolism. This is shown by the fact that over 60 enzymes act on acyl-CoA compounds.

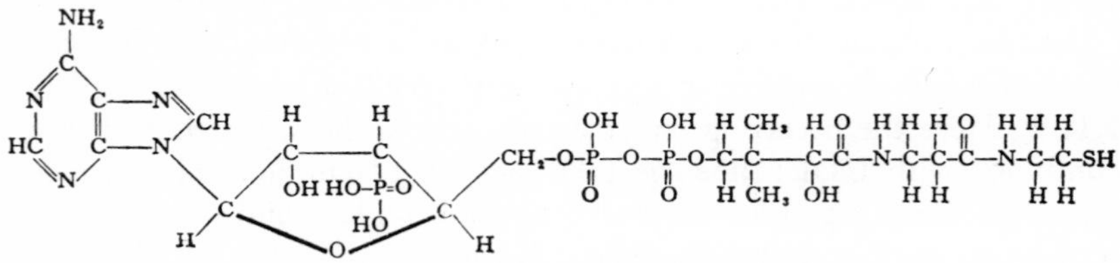

Fig. IX.17. *Structure of coenzyme A.*

Properties. Coenzyme A is a colourless substance having an absorption band in the ultraviolet at 257 mμ due to the adenine residue.

Acyl groups can be added to the thiol group of coenzyme A either by transfer of the acyl group from another molecule or by a synthetase reaction. All the enzymes of sub-group 6.2.1 bring about the formation of coenzyme A thiolesters from free acids, making use of the energy of ATP, or in one case GTP. All the acyltransferases of sub-group 2.3.1 transfer acyl groups to or from coenzyme A. The transfer may be from combination with another S atom (enzymes 2.3.1.10–12), from N (enzymes 2.3.1.1–5, 13–14), from O (enzymes 2.3.1.6–7, 15, c), from C (enzymes 2.3.1.9, 16), or from phosphate (enzymes 2.3.1.8, b). In 13 cases out of 19, it is an acetyl group which is transferred.

Acetyl-CoA is also involved in reactions of a different type, which have been classified under lyases (enzymes 4.1.3.2, 4–5, 7, a). The acetyl group is added to a double bond in the acceptor molecule, either with or without hydrolysis of the thiolester bond. The three synthase reactions form the important metabolites citrate, malate and hydroxymethyl-glutaryl-CoA.

Many of the enzymes involved in these reactions can use simple analogues of coenzyme A, for example N-acetylcysteamine. Others, however, are specific for coenzyme A itself. Where applicable, these model carriers, which are relatively easily synthesized, have proved useful tools in elucidating metabolic interrelationships of these enzymes.

Coenzyme A is essential for the initiation of the citrate cycle, for the oxidative breakdown of fatty acids, and for various biosynthetic processes (see the tables in Chapter XII).

Carriers of one-carbon groups

In the synthesis and breakdown of certain aminoacids and purines, single carbon atoms are transferred in the form of hydroxymethyl, formyl and formimino groups, as well as methyl groups. These groups appear to be carried by tetrahydrofolate or its derivatives; methyl groups are carried also by adenosylhomocysteine and vitamin B_{12}. Biotin, a prosthetic group which acts as a carrier of CO_2, is considered later.

Tetrahydrofolate

It has been known for some time that a folic acid derivative is important in one-carbon transfer reactions, but the exact nature of this factor was long in doubt and is still not entirely clear, although the nature of the reacting group is now known. It is clear from the work of BLAKLEY (259) that the active carrier is not folic acid itself, but that the pteridine nucleus must be reduced to the tetrahydro-form (see Fig. IX.18). This reduction occurs enzymatically in crude enzyme

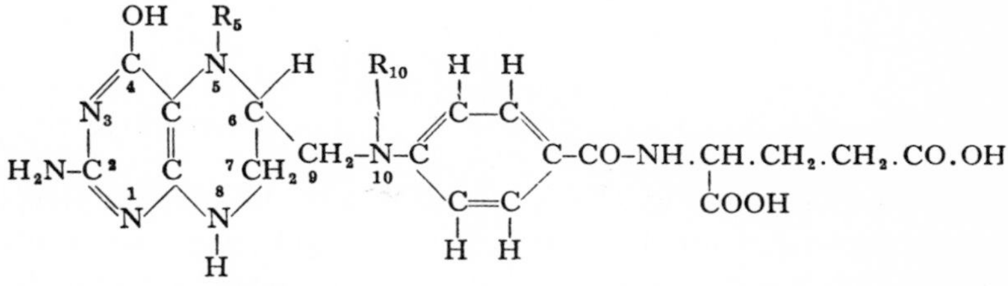

Name	R_5	R_{10}
Tetrahydrofolic acid (THFA)	—H	—H
5-formyltetrahydrofolic acid	—CO.H	—H
10-formyltetrahydrofolic acid	—H	—CO.H
5,10-methenyltetrahydrofolic acid (anhydroleucovorin)	$>\overset{+}{N}=CH—N<$ (5, 10)	
5,10-methylenetetrahydrofolic acid	$>N—CH_2—N<$ (5, 10)	
5-hydroxymethyltetrahydrofolic acid	—CH$_2$OH	—H
5-formiminotetrahydrofolic acid	—CH=NH	—H

Fig. IX.18. *Structures of tetrahydrofolate derivatives.*

preparations, so that added folate itself is active, but with purified preparations of the enzyme system from animal tissues which converts glycine to serine, only di- or tetrahydrofolate are active. With the same enzyme system from bacteria, however, not even tetrahydrofolate itself is active, but only a polyglutamate thereof. This derivatve has been called 'coenzyme C' (*2920*).

HUENNEKENS and OSBORN (*1185*) have reviewed tetrahydrofolate and its metabolic reactions.

Properties. Tetrahydrofolate is a colourless compound, but it and its derivatives have characteristic absorption spectra in the ultraviolet, some

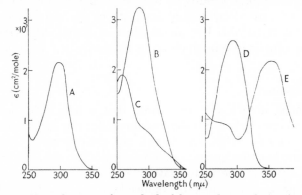

FIG. IX.19 *Spectra af tetrahydrofolate and some derivatives.*

A, THFA
B, 5–formyl–THFA
C, 10–formyl–THFA
D, 5,10–methylene–THFA
E, 5,10–methenyl–THFA

after *1185*

of which are shown in Fig. IX.19. It is highly autoxidizable and is rapidly converted into dihydrofolate by O_2. It is also oxidized enzymatically by NADP. Folate is reduced to di- and tetrahydrofolate by $NADPH_2$ and the liver enzyme 1.5.1.3; the bacterial enzyme 1.5.1.4 is specific for the reduction of dihydrofolate to tetrahydrofolate (*263, 2957*).

THFA acts as a carrier of methyl, hydroxymethyl, formyl or formimino groups. For hydroxymethyl and formyl groups combination with the carrier can take place in three ways, giving the 5-, the 10- and the 5,10-compounds respectively (Fig. IX.18). Each enzyme appears to be specific for one particular form, but there has been a good deal of confusion, owing to the ready enzymatic and non-enzymatic interconversion of the various forms. In particular the wide distribution of the cyclohydrolase 3.5.4.9 in the preparations has made it difficult to determine

which of the forms is involved with any given enzyme. Further purification has largley removed these difficulties (HARTMANN and BUCHANAN,
1017).

Fig. IX.20 summarizes some of the more important reactions in
which THFA is involved; the numbers are those of the enzymes involved,
as given in the Table of Enzymes. Free one-carbon compounds can be

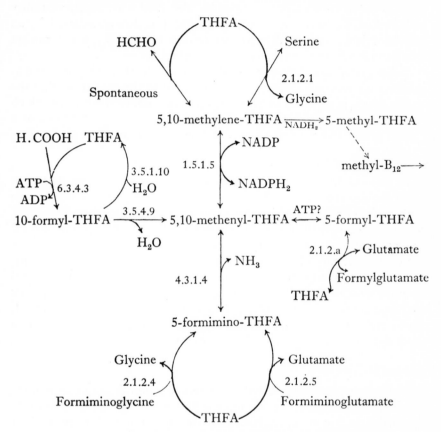

Fig. IX.20. *Some metabolic reactions of THFA and its derivatives.*

utilized metabolically; formaldehyde reacts with THFA non-enzymatically, whereas formate requires ATP and a synthetase for combination with THFA. Enzymatic transfer of hydroxymethyl to THFA
has only been shown to give the methylene bridge compound, although
the intermediate formation of 5-hydroxymethyl-THFA has not been
altogether excluded (*261*); enzymatic formimino-transfer gives only
5-formimino-THFA, while formyl transfer enzymes may form either

the 5-formyl, the 10-formyl or the methenyl bridge compounds. The formyltransferase shown in the Figure (2.1.2.a) gives 5-formyl-THFA; two others, important in purine synthesis (2.1.2.2–3), which are not shown in the Figure, involve the bridge compound and 10-formyl-THFA respectively.

The methylene bridge compound can be reduced by $NADH_2$ and a dehydrogenase to a methyl compound, identified with high probability as 5-methyl-THFA (*2291*). The methyl group is then transferred, by an enzyme system not yet fully characterized, to vitamin B_{12}, which can act as a further methyl-carrier (*942*), as described below.

Tetrahydrofolate differs from other carriers in that the group transported may undergo a change while attached to the carrier, so that the group which is given up to the acceptor is not identical with that which was taken up in the first place. For example, it may be accepted as a formyl group and handed on as a hydroxymethyl group.

Adenosylhomocysteine

In transmethylation from methionine to other substances, CANTONI (*394*) showed that ATP is needed and that two enzymes are involved in each case. The first enzyme, methionine adenosyltransferase (2.4.2.13), forms S-adenosylmethionine by transferring the adenosyl group of ATP to methionine, with the release of one pyrophosphate and one phosphate molecule (reaction XII.10.a). In the second step, a CH_3^+ group is transferred from this sulphonium compound (leaving adenosylhomocysteine) to other substances such as nicotinamide or guanidinoacetate by specific methyltransferases (2.1.1), of which eight have been characterized so far. Since these transfers are reversible, adenosylhomocysteine acts as a methyl-carrier, linking pairs of methyltransferases.

Cobamide coenzymes

These are coenzymes related to vitamin B_{12}, and therefore containing a cobalt atom within a corrin ring, a complex ring structure reminiscent of porphyrin but differing from it in several important respects. The chemistry and terminology of vitamin B_{12} and its derivatives are clearly set out in the monograph by LESTER SMITH (*2440*). In vitamin B_{12} as isolated (cyanocobalamin) the cobalt is coordinated also with a dimethyl-benzimidazole nucleotide and with a cyanide group.

The structure of the main naturally occurring coenzyme (variously called 'DBC coenzyme' or 'coenzyme B_{12}') is shown in Fig. IX.21. Instead of the cyanide group of vitamin B_{12} (which in any case is an artifact), the coenzyme contains 5'-deoxyadenosine, containing the normal β-link unlike the dimethylbenzimidazole nucleotide, which contains an α-link. The deoxynucleoside is directly attached at the 5-position of the ribose by a carbon–cobalt link. It appears that the greater part of the vitamin B_{12} present in cells is in the form of coenzyme B_{12} or closely related coenzymes.

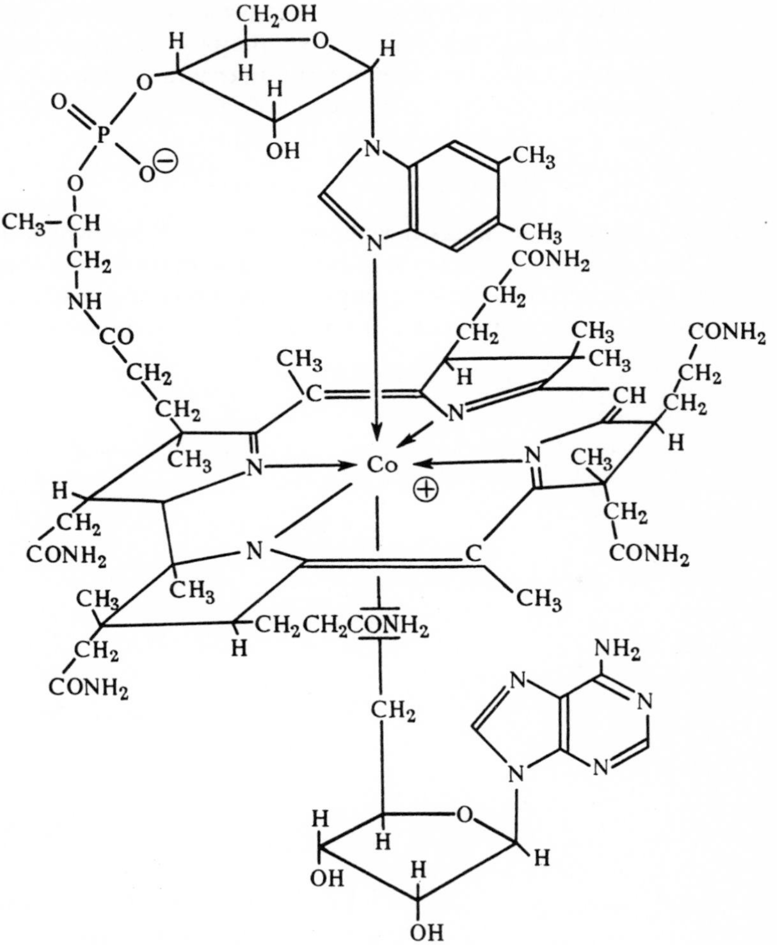

Fig. IX.21. *Structure of coenzyme B_{12}.*

after *163, 1549*

Coenzyme B_{12} acts as a coenzyme of isomerizations involving intramolecular transfer at C–C bonds. It acts as an essential cofactor for enzymes 5.4.99.1–2 and for an as yet uncharacterized enzyme in *Aerobacter* which converts 1,2-propanediol into propionaldehyde (see BARKER,

163). The mechanism of the second of these enzymes has been discussed on pp. 295–6.

Vitamin B_{12} can act as a carrier of methyl groups, as shown by GUEST *et al.* (*942*). By enzymatic transfer of the methyl group from 5-methyl-THFA, a methyl-cobalamin is formed, in which the methyl group is directly attached to the cobalt in place of the deoxyadenosine group shown in the lower part of Fig. IX.21. This methyl group can readily be transferred to homocysteine to form methionine by an enzyme which has been purified, without the necessity for any other cofactor.

Prosthetic groups as carriers

Hitherto we have been discussing non-enzymatic carriers which link together two enzymes. In some case prosthetic groups of enzymes themselves act as carriers, transferring groups from one non-enzymatic substance to another. These prosthetic groups are often firmly-bound parts

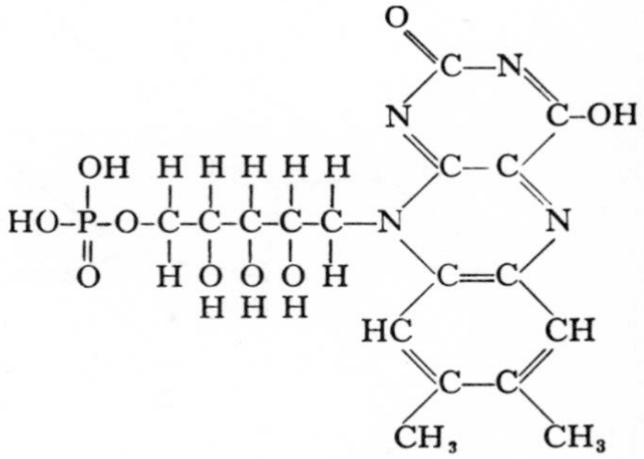

Flavinmononucleotide

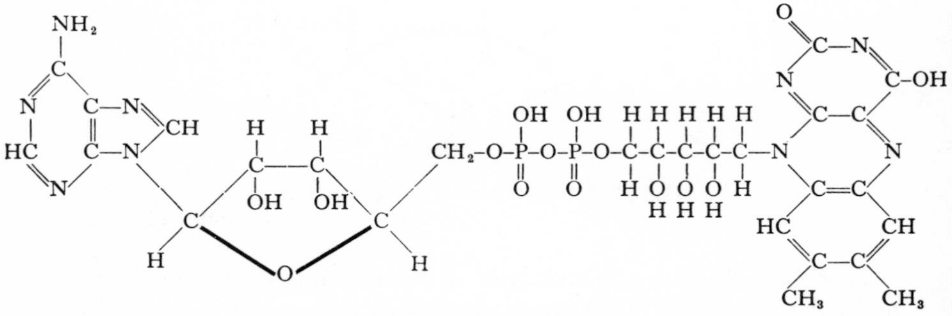

Flavin-adenine-dinucleotide

Fig. IX.22. *Structures of flavin prosthetic groups.*

of the enzyme, and it might therefore be thought that they would be more appropriately dealt with in the following chapter. However, since they act as carriers, we think it more convenient to consider them in juxtaposition to the other carriers, particularly as in some cases they are not firmly bound and can therefore be considered as cofactors.

Flavin groups

The first flavoprotein enzyme to be discovered (1.6.99.1) was that of WARBURG and CHRISTIAN (*2784*), which they extracted from yeast in 1932

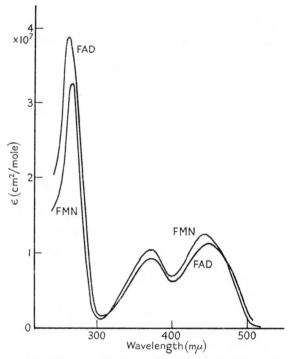

Fig. IX.23. *Spectra of oxidized forms of flavinmono-nucleotide (FMN) and flavin-adenine-dinucleotide (FAD).*

and resolved into a yellow flavin group (which would now be called ribo-flavin phosphate or flavinmononucleotide) and a colloid which was later shown by Theorell to be a protein. The constitution of riboflavin was established by synthesis in 1935 by KUHN *et al.* (*1482*) and by KARRER *et al.* (*1311*).

The original flavoprotein of Warburg and Christian was later re-garded by them (*2786*) as an artifact, but about 40 flavoprotein enzymes are now known, and these are listed in Table IX.5. A few of these have riboflavin 5′-phosphate (flavinmononucleotide, FMN) as prosthetic group, but the majority contain flavin-adenine-dinucleotide (FAD). The structures of these groups are shown in Fig. IX.22. That of FAD has been confirmed by complete synthesis (453); this was the first synthesis of a dinucleotide.

The structures shown are those of the oxidized forms, which are yellow fluorescent substances, showing the absorption spectra given in Fig. IX.23. They are very readily reduced to the leuco-forms by chemical reducers, and on reduction lose their yellow colour and fluorescence, owing to the disappearance of the absorption band at 450 mμ. The reduction involves the addition of two hydrogen atoms across the quinonoid structure in the isoalloxazine nucleus as shown in

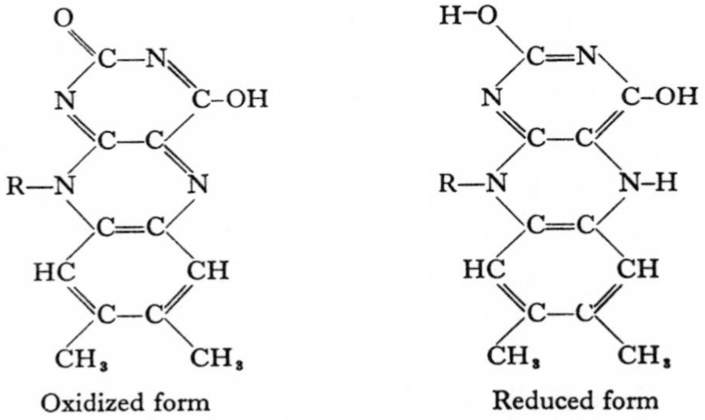

Oxidized form   Reduced form

Fig. IX.24. *The two states of flavin groups.*

Fig. IX.24. The reduced forms of the flavin nucleotides are readily oxidized by oxygen.

Some investigations have been made on the mode of binding of the prosthetic group to the protein in flavoproteins. THEORELL (2002, 2637) suggested that in addition to ionic bonds involving the phosphate the flavin ring might be bound to tyrosine in the protein. P. STRITTMATTER (2554) has shown that in the case of enzyme 1.6.2.2 protein –SH groups are not involved, but the binding takes place through a single tyrosine group.

The biological activity of flavin groups in flavoproteins is due to their oxidation and reduction, that is to say, they act as hydrogen carriers. In the protein-bound state, however, the flavin groups are not often fluorescent, nor are the reduced forms always autoxidizable. The prosthetic group of a flavoprotein enzyme is readily reduced by its specific substrate, activated by combination with the active centre in the enzyme protein.

In certain cases spectroscopic evidence has been obtained for the formation of the half-reduced flavin semiquinone during this process (BEINERT, *198*). The importance of semiquinone formation in the case of lipoamide dehydrogenase is discussed on p. 276.

In Table IX.5 the flavoprotein enzymes are arranged in groups according to the type of reaction they catalyse. The first fourteen are those which react directly with O_2, reducing the oxygen molecule to H_2O_2. The fact that they react with O_2 does not imply that they do not react with other acceptors; most of them react with dyes such as indophenols and

TABLE IX.5

FLAVOPROTEINS

Number	Name	Source	Flavin	Metal atoms per flavin	Flavin groups per mol.	Maximum catalytic centre activity
			Oxidases			
1.1.3.1	Glycollate oxidase	Plants	FMN	—	2 or 4	530
1.1.3.2	Lactate oxidase	Bacteria	FMN		2	470
1.1.3.4	Glucose oxidase	Moulds	FAD	—	2	17,000
1.2.3.1	Aldehyde oxidase	Liver	FAD	$\frac{1}{2}$ Mo $\frac{1}{2}$ H ?		500
1.2.3.2	Xanthine oxidase	Milk	FAD	$\frac{1}{2}$ Mo 4 Fe	2	240
1.2.3.3	Pyruvate oxidase	Bacteria	FAD			
1.2.3.4	Oxalate oxidase	Mosses	FMN or RF			
1.3.3.1	Dihydro-orotate dehydrogenase	Bacteria	FAD+ FMN	1 Fe	2	1,200
1.4.3.1	D-aspartate oxidase	Kidney	FAD			
1.4.3.2	L-aminoacid oxidase	Animal tissues	FMN	—	2	
1.4.3.2	L-aminoacid oxidase	Snake venom	FAD	—	1	3,000
1.4.3.3	D-aminoacid oxidase	Kidney	FAD	—	1	2,000
1.4.3.5	Pyridoxamine-phosphate oxidase	Liver	FMN			
1.5.3.2	N-methylamino-acid oxidase	Kidney	FAD			

TABLE IX.5—*continued*

Number	Name	Source	Flavin	Metal atoms per flavin	Flavin groups per mol.	Maximum catalytic centre activity
			Dehydrogenases			
1.1.2.3	Lactate dehydrogenase	Yeast	FMN	1 H	2	6,000
1.1.2.4	D-lactate dehydrogenase	Yeast	FAD	3 Zn	1	90,000
1.1.99.a	D-2-hydroxyacid dehydrogenase	Yeast	FAD	M		
1.2.2.2	Pyruvate dehydrogenase	Bacteria	FAD		4	10,000
1.3.2.1	Butyryl-CoA dehydrogenase	Animal tissues	FAD	—	4 ?	
1.3.2.2	Acyl-CoA dehydrogenase	Animal tissues	FAD	1 Fe		
1.3.99.1	Succinate dehydrogenase	Heart muscle	FAD	4 Fe	1	
			NAD(P)H$_2$ dehydrogenases			
1.6.2.1	NADH$_2$ cytochrome c reductase	Heart muscle	FMN	4 Fe	1	7,000
1.6.2.2	NADH$_2$ cytochrome b_5 reductase	Liver	FAD	2 Mg	1	
1.6.2.3	NADPH$_2$ cytochrome c reductase	Yeast	FMN	—		1,300
1.6.2.3	NADPH$_2$ cytochrome c reductase	Liver	FAD			1,140
1.6.4.2	Glutathione reductase	Animal tissues, plants	FAD			
1.6.4.3	Lipoamide dehydrogenase	Heart muscle, bacteria	FAD	—	2	80,000
1.6.5.1	Quinone reductase	Bacteria	FMN	—		88,000
1.6.5.2	Menadione reductase	Liver	FAD	—	1	700,000

TABLE IX.5—*continued*

Number	Name	Source	Flavin	Metal atoms per flavin	Flavin groups per mol.	Maximum catalytic centre activity
1.6.5.3	Ubiquinone reductase	Heart muscle	FAD	Fe		
1.6.6.1	NADH$_2$ nitrate reductase	Plants, bacteria	FAD	M		
1.6.6.2	Nitrate reductase	Plants	FAD ?			
1.6.6.3	NADPH$_2$ nitrate reductase	Plants, moulds	FAD ?	Mo		
1.6.6.4	Nitrite reductase	Moulds	FAD	M		
1.6.99.1	NADPH$_2$ diaphorase	Yeast	FMN	—	2	50
1.6.99.1	NADPH$_2$ diaphorase	Plants	FAD	—		4,000
1.11.1.1	NAD peroxidase	Bacteria	FAD	—		5,000

Other flavoprotein enzymes

1.7.99.1	Hydroxylamine reductase	Bacteria	FAD	Mn		
1.7.99.2	Nitric oxide reductase	Bacteria	FAD or FMN	M		
1.7.99.a	Nitrite reductase	Bacteria	FAD	Cu		

In this table RF denotes riboflavin, FMN and FAD denote flavin mono- and di-nucleotides respectively, H denotes a haem group, and M denotes a divalent metal not conclusively identified.

methylene blue, and some, for example xanthine oxidase, are very unspecific with regard to the acceptor. Dihydro-orotate dehydrogenase is exceptional in reacting also with NAD, so that it can act as a dihydro-orotate oxidase, an NAD-linked dihydro-orotate dehydrogenase or an NADH$_2$ oxidase. It is also exceptional in containing one FAD and one FMN group per molecule, each associated with one Fe atom.

The next group in the table cannot use O$_2$ or NAD(P) as acceptor, but react *in vivo* with acceptors whose nature is not in all cases clear. The coenzyme dehydrogenases vary considerably in their specificity for acceptors. The first four enzymes in this group are exceptional flavoproteins in being able to react specifically with a cytochrome, a property which is also shown by two dehydrogenases (1.1.2.2–3). At the other extreme the so-called NAD peroxidase can react, like xanthine oxidase, with a wide variety of acceptors, including H$_2$O$_2$, ferricyanide and quinones. Some of these enzymes act as important links in the respiratory chain, being concerned with the oxidation rather than the reduction of the coenzymes.

It will be seen that a number, but by no means all, of these flavoproteins contain one or more metal atoms, which are probably associated with the flavin group; their mode of action has already been discussed in Chapter VII.

The figures for catalytic centre activity should be taken as no more than a rough guide, given in order to indicate the wide variations which exist.

Pyridoxal phosphate

This forms the prosthetic group of a number of enzymes which catalyse a wide variety of reactions involving aminoacids. In some of its reactions which are transaminations it acts as an amino-carrier; in

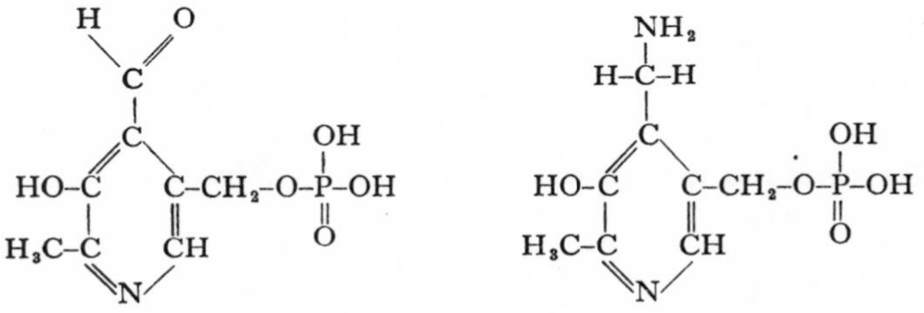

Pyridoxal phosphate   Pyridoxamine phosphate

Fig. IX.25. *Structures of pyridoxal phosphate and pyridoxamine phosphate.*

the other cases it forms a reactive compound with the aminoacid, and thus may act as a 'handle'.

GALE and EPPS (*809*) in 1943 resolved lysine decarboxylase (4.1.1.18) into protein and prosthetic group and partially purified the latter, which they called 'codecarboxylase'. In the following year they purified this cofactor 15,000 times from yeast (*811*). In 1943 also BRAUNSTEIN and KRITZMAN (*315*) showed that the transamination between aspartate and pyruvate was dependent on an acid-labile dialysable cofactor ('coamino-pherase'), which they concentrated. In 1944 GUNSALUS and BELLAMY (*949*) showed that bacteria which had grown on pyridoxin-deficient media and had failed to form tyrosine decarboxylase (4.1.1.25) had their activity restored by the addition of pyridoxal. In the same year they showed with UMBREIT (*950*) that if such cells were dried they were not activated by pyridoxal alone, but required ATP in addition; they also prepared pyridoxal phosphate and showed that it activated the dried cells. In 1945 BADDILEY and GALE (*129*) showed that such synthetic pyridoxal phosphate activated the specific apo-decarboxylases for lysine, arginine, tyrosine and ornithine. In 1946 UMBREIT, O'KANE and GUNSALUS (2698) showed that pyridoxamine phosphate also possessed cofactor activity for aminoacid transaminases but not for aminoacid decarboxylases. This finding with transaminases has been denied by some other workers, but their negative results were shown by MEISTER et al. (1788) to be due to the slower rate of activation of these enzymes by pyridoxamine phosphate than by pyridoxal phosphate.

The structure of pyridoxal phosphate was finally established in 1952 by BADDILEY and MATHIAS (131) by total synthesis as that shown in Fig. IX.25.

The mechanism of action of pyridoxal phosphate has been discussed by SNELL (see, for example, 1802–3) and by BRAUNSTEIN (312). It is believed to act in all cases by forming an azomethine (Schiff's base) by combination of its aldehyde group with the amino group of the substrate. This can undergo tautomerism in the following way

IX.22

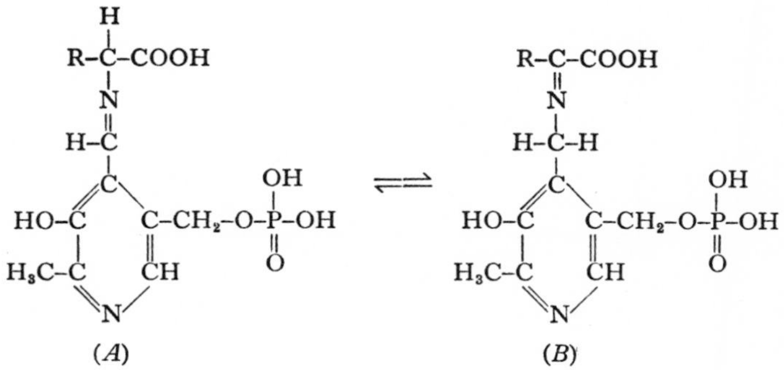

(A)   (B)

The fate of this substance depends on the nature of the enzyme protein to which the pyridoxal phosphate is attached and on the group R. The action of the racemases is immediately explained, since the asymmetry of the α-carbon is lost in form (B). In the transaminases, by hydrolysis at the double bond in form (B) pyridoxamine phosphate and the ketoacid are formed, and by the reversal of these reactions the amino group can be transferred back to another ketoacid (1253). In the aminoacid decarboxylases, the carboxyl group becomes labile and is readily given off, leaving combined amine which is then readily liberated by hydrolysis. In yet other cases, water or some other molecule is eliminated from the substrate, leaving an unsaturated residue which is then hydrolysed off from the pyridoxal phosphate, for example, with serine, homoserine and threonine dehydratases (4.2.1.13–16) and alliin lyase (4.4.1.4).

Pyridoxal phosphate and pyridoxamine phosphate show absorption bands in the near ultra-violet, at 395 mμ and 330 mμ respectively. The spectrum of pyridoxal phosphate is shown in Fig. IX.26; other spectra will be found in *312* and *1253*.

It has been shown spectrophotometrically (*260*) that free pyridoxal phosphate can combine unspecifically with aminoacids in the absence of enzymes (see Fig. IX.26). Furthermore the transfer of –NH$_2$ from pyridoxamine has been studied (*157*), and it has been shown that the

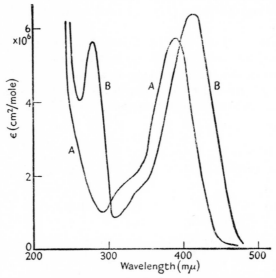

Fig. IX.26. *Spectra of pyridoxal phosphate and its glycine compound.*

A, pyridoxal phosphate alone; B, pyridoxal phosphate + 0·1 M glycine. In bicarbonate buffer pH 7·2.

from *260*

formation of the Schiff's base is rapid, the rate-limiting step in the transamination being the tautomerization shown in Equation IX.22. Moreover, the K_m values of pyridoxal phosphate enzymes for their aminoacid substrates are in most cases equal to the dissociation constants of their pyridoxal phosphate complexes, and in at least one case the dissociation constant and K_m vary similarly with pH (*1626*). However, the specificity for particular aminoacids, and the type of reaction undergone, are determined by the protein part of the enzyme; the transaminases do not decarboxylate and the decarboxylases do not transaminate, and neither group has any racemase activity. Furthermore, nearly all of these enzymes are highly specific for their particular amino-acid substrates.

In addition to the enzymes just mentioned, pyridoxal phosphate is also involved in the action of certain other enzymes. A reaction presenting some unusual features is the conversion of phosphohomoserine into threonine and phosphate catalysed by threonine synthase (4.2.99.2). FLAVIN and SLAUGHTER (751) have produced isotopic evidence for a mechanism involving the removal of phosphate from the Schiff's base, leaving a double bond to which water is then added.

Pyridoxal phosphate also forms the prosthetic group of one enzyme of an entirely different type, namely α-glucan phosphorylase from muscle (2.4.1.1). Here it has been shown that it is attached firmly to the enzyme through its aldehyde group, but without forming a Schiff's base (1207, 1362). The phosphate group is essential for its activity, but is not exchanged during the reaction. The mode of action is still not understood.

Thiamine pyrophosphate

This was first recognized as a cofactor by LOHMANN and SCHUSTER (1611) in 1937; they prepared the crystalline substance from yeast, determined its chemical nature, and showed it to be the prosthetic group of

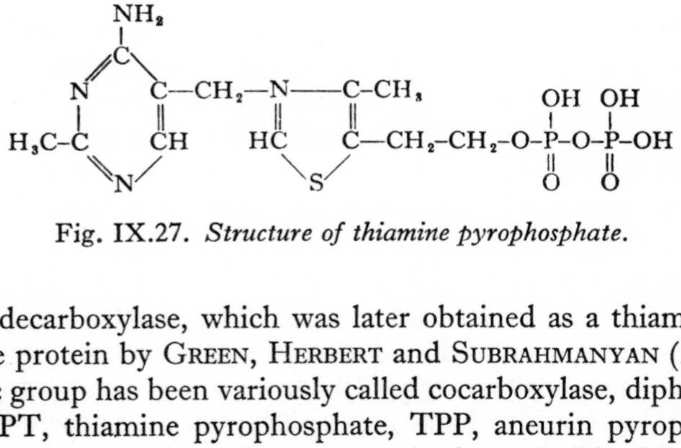

Fig. IX.27. *Structure of thiamine pyrophosphate.*

pyruvate decarboxylase, which was later obtained as a thiamine pyrophosphate protein by GREEN, HERBERT and SUBRAHMANYAN (902). The prosthetic group has been variously called cocarboxylase, diphosphothiamine, DPT, thiamine pyrophosphate, TPP, aneurin pyrophosphate, vitamin B_1 pyrophosphate. Its structure is shown in Fig. IX.27.

In addition to the decarboxylase system, thiamine pyrophosphate is involved in the pyruvate oxidase system, the 2-oxoglutarate oxidase system and in the formation of acetoin. It has long been recognized that in all the reactions involving pyruvate, decarboxylation produces an 'active acetaldehyde' residue which becomes attached to the cofactor, and a variety of formulations, with the group attached to different points in the thiamine molecule, has been put forward. The structure of the

intermediates has now been unambiguously cleared up by the work of
BRESLOW, KRAMPITZ, HOLZER and their co-workers (*1147*, *1457*).

The point of attachment is the reactive C atom between the S and the
N of the thiazole ring. The enzymes first cause the attachment of the
pyruvate thus

$$
\text{IX.23} \quad
\begin{array}{c} CH_3.CO \\ | \\ COOH \end{array}
\; + \;
\begin{array}{c} \overset{+}{-N-} \\ \| \\ H-C \\ \diagdown \quad \diagup \\ S \end{array}
\; = \;
\begin{array}{c} HO \quad \overset{+}{-N-} \\ | \qquad \| \\ CH_3.C-C \\ | \qquad \diagdown \;\; \diagup \\ COOH \quad S \end{array}
$$

where only the relevant part of the thiazole ring is shown. This compound
undergoes rapid decarboxylation thus

$$
\text{IX.24} \quad
\begin{array}{c} HO \quad \overset{+}{-N-} \\ | \qquad \| \\ CH_3.C-C \\ | \qquad \diagdown \;\; \diagup \\ COOH \quad S \end{array}
\; = \;
\begin{array}{c} HO \quad \overset{+}{-N-} \\ | \qquad \| \\ CH_3.C-C \\ | \qquad \diagdown \;\; \diagup \\ H \qquad S \end{array}
\; + \; CO_2
$$

giving α-hydroxyethyl-thiamine pyrophosphate, which is the 'active
acetaldehyde' compound referred to above.

The fate of this compound depends on which enzyme is involved. The
decarboxylase brings about its direct breakdown to free acetaldehyde.
The pyruvate dehydrogenase in the oxidase system brings about its
oxidation by lipoate to an acetyl derivative (as can also be done by other
acceptors, such as ferricyanide or indophenol) and a transfer of the acetyl
group to the reduced lipoate. It is not clear whether the acetyl transfer
occurs simultaneously with the hydrogen transfer or immediately after
it (compare reaction XII.1.5).

Other enzymes acting on 2-ketoacids, for example the 2-oxoglutarate
dehydrogenase, presumably act in a similar way, the thiamine pyrophosphate serving as a carrier of more complex groups. Transketolase
(2.2.1.1), which transfers a glycolaldehyde group from sedoheptulose
7-phosphate to glyceraldehyde 3-phosphate, has been shown to form an
intermediate which is believed to be α,β-dihydroxyethyl-thiamine pyrophosphate (*1149*).

Biotin

Biotin has long been known as an essential vitamin, but its function
has only comparatively recently been shown to be that of a cofactor in
enzymatic reactions involving incorporation or transfer of CO_2 (enzymes
2.1.3.1 and group 6.4) (LYNEN *et al.*, *1638*). The 'egg white injury' caused

by feeding large amounts of egg-white is a biotin deficiency caused by the presence of the protein avidin, which has a very high affinity for biotin, and acts as a specific inhibitor for biotin-dependent reactions. In biotin deficiency, as LARDY showed in about 1950, various CO_2-incorporation reactions in liver are impaired. The mode of action of biotin was studied by LYNEN et al. in 1959 (1638–9), who showed the formation of an N-

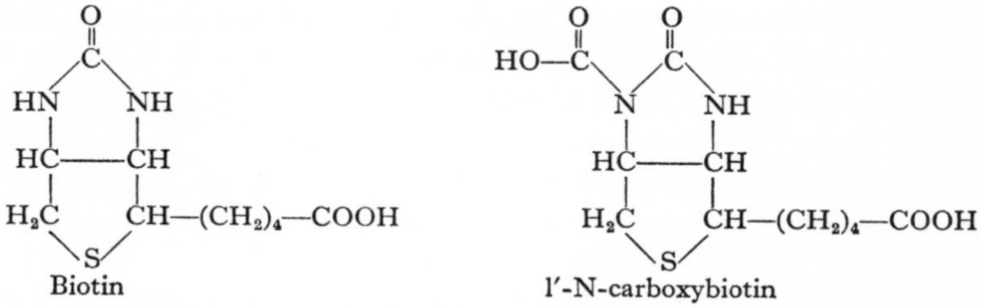

Fig. IX.28 (a). *Structure of biotin and its carboxylated derivative.*

carboxylated derivative of added biotin by methylcrotonoyl-CoA carboxylase (6.4.1.4).

More recently, however, WAKIL and WAITE (2757) have shown with acetyl-CoA carboxylase (6.4.1.2) that the biotin bound as the prosthetic group of the enzyme behaves in a different manner. On treating the enzyme with ATP, Mn and C^{14}-labelled CO_2, but without the acceptor

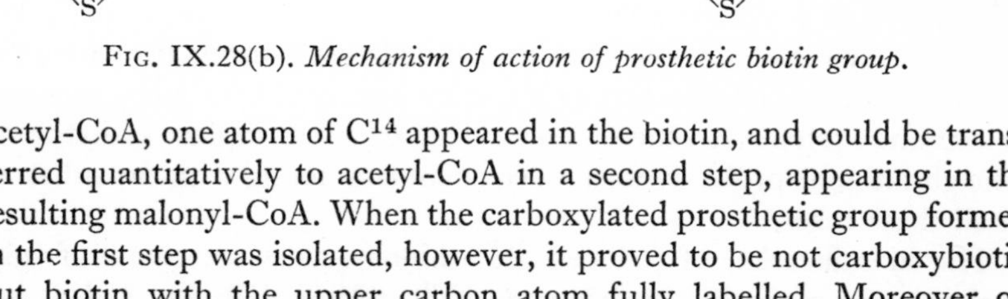

FIG. IX.28(b). *Mechanism of action of prosthetic biotin group.*

acetyl-CoA, one atom of C^{14} appeared in the biotin, and could be transferred quantitatively to acetyl-CoA in a second step, appearing in the resulting malonyl-CoA. When the carboxylated prosthetic group formed in the first step was isolated, however, it proved to be not carboxybiotin but biotin with the upper carbon atom fully labelled. Moreover on isolation of the prosthetic group after the second step, it was found to be not biotin but a substance tentatively identified as 'diaminobiotin'. From these results it may be inferred that the changes undergone by the prosthetic group are as shown in Fig. IX.28(b).

Biotin forms a firmly bound prosthetic group in the enzymes of group 6.4; with these enzymes free CO_2 becomes attached by a synthetase reaction involving the breakdown of ATP; the mechanism has been discussed on p. 301.

Other coenzymes

Phosphomutase coenzymes

The unusual mechanism of the phosphomutase reaction has already been referred to on p. 191. It differs from all other cases in that the coenzyme is converted into product and an equivalent amount of substrate converted into coenzyme by the same transfer of a single phosphate residue. In nearly all cases (2.7.5.1–3), if the phosphate is regarded as being transferred from position a to position b, the coenzyme is the a,b-diphosphate (see reactions XII.1.b and XII.1.k). In one case (2.7.5.4), however, an a,b-diphosphate is converted into a b,c-diphosphate, the coenzyme being the b-monophosphate, thus

IX.25

$$
\begin{array}{lllll}
CH_2.O.H_2PO_3 & & CH_2.O.H_2PO_3 & & CH_2.O.H_2PO_3 \\
|\ \ CHOH & +\ CH_2.O.H_2PO_3 & |\ \ CHOH & +\ CH_2.O.H_2PO_3 \\
|\ \ CO.O.H_2PO_3 & |\ \ CHOH & \longrightarrow\ |\ \ COOH & |\ \ CH.O.H_2PO_3 \\
 & |\ \ COOH & & |\ \ COOH
\end{array}
$$

These phosphomutase reactions are special cases of the general transfer reaction

IX.26 $AP + B = A + BP$

In the first type AP is identical with BP; in the second, A is identical with B. Enzyme 5.4.2.1 works by a different mechanism.

Glutathione as a specific coenzyme

Glutathione has already been mentioned as a hydrogen carrier, but reduced glutathione also acts as a specific coenzyme for a few enzymes or enzyme systems. In these cases cysteine cannot replace glutathione. The glutathione probably forms a covalent compound with the substrate in all these cases.

The identification of reduced glutathione as the coenzyme of 'glyoxalase' was made by LOHMANN (1610) in 1932. KÜHNAU (1484) had shown the spontaneous formation of a compound of glutathione and methylglyoxal. This was confirmed by JOWETT and QUASTEL (1271) who suggested that this compound was the true substrate of the enzyme. YAMAZOYE (2939) showed the formation of another compound in the presence of the enzyme; this compound slowly broke down to lactic acid and glutathione above pH 7, and the breakdown was accelerated by crude glyoxalase preparations. HOPKINS and MORGAN (*1157*) showed that when methylglyoxal was the substrate the system consisted of two protein components in addition to glutathione; they partially purified these and called them 'enzyme' and 'factor'. The factor played no part when phenylglyoxal was the substrate.

The mechanism of the conversion of methylglyoxal to lactic acid was cleared up by the work of RACKER (*2150*) and CROOK and LAW (*521*) independently, and is set out in Table XII.8. The 'enzyme' and 'factor' of Hopkins and Morgan are now known as lactoyl-glutathione lyase (4.4.1.5) and hydroxyacylglutathione hydrolase (3.1.2.6) respectively. The former enzyme converts the above-mentioned compound of Jowett and Quastel into that of Yamazoye; the second enzyme hydrolyses a number of glutathione thiolesters of α-hydroxy-acids. However, it does not hydrolyse the compound formed from phenylglyoxal, and the conversion of the latter into mandelic acid therefore depends upon the spontaneous hydrolysis of the compound. Thus 'methylglyoxalase' is a two-enzyme system, but 'phenylglyoxalase' is a single enzyme.

Another case in which the true substrate of an enzyme is a compound formed between the –SH group of glutathione and an aldehyde is that of formaldehyde dehydrogenase of liver (1.2.1.1). STRITTMATTER and BALL (*2555*) found no other thiol which would act. They suggested that the reaction catalysed by the enzyme is

$$\text{IX.27} \qquad \text{G.S.CH}_2\text{OH} + \text{NAD} = \text{G.S.CO.H} + \text{NADH}_2$$

The resulting formyl-glutathione is then hydrolysed, probably by an enzyme in the preparation, since the preparations also rapidly hydrolysed S-acetyl-glutathione.

Reduced glutathione is also the specific coenzyme of some of the *cis–trans* isomerases (group 5.2); the mechanism of this action has already been discussed on p. 294.

Relationship between coenzymes and vitamins

It will have been noticed that many of the coenzymes to which we have referred are derivatives of vitamins. Taking them in the order in which they are given, NAD and NADP contain nicotinamide (a member of the vitamin B group), lipoate is a growth factor for some micro-organisms, ascorbate (vitamin C) is a vitamin for the primates and the guinea pig, coenzyme A contains pantothenic acid (another member of the vitamin B group), tetrahydrofolate is derived from folic acid (also a vitamin of the

P

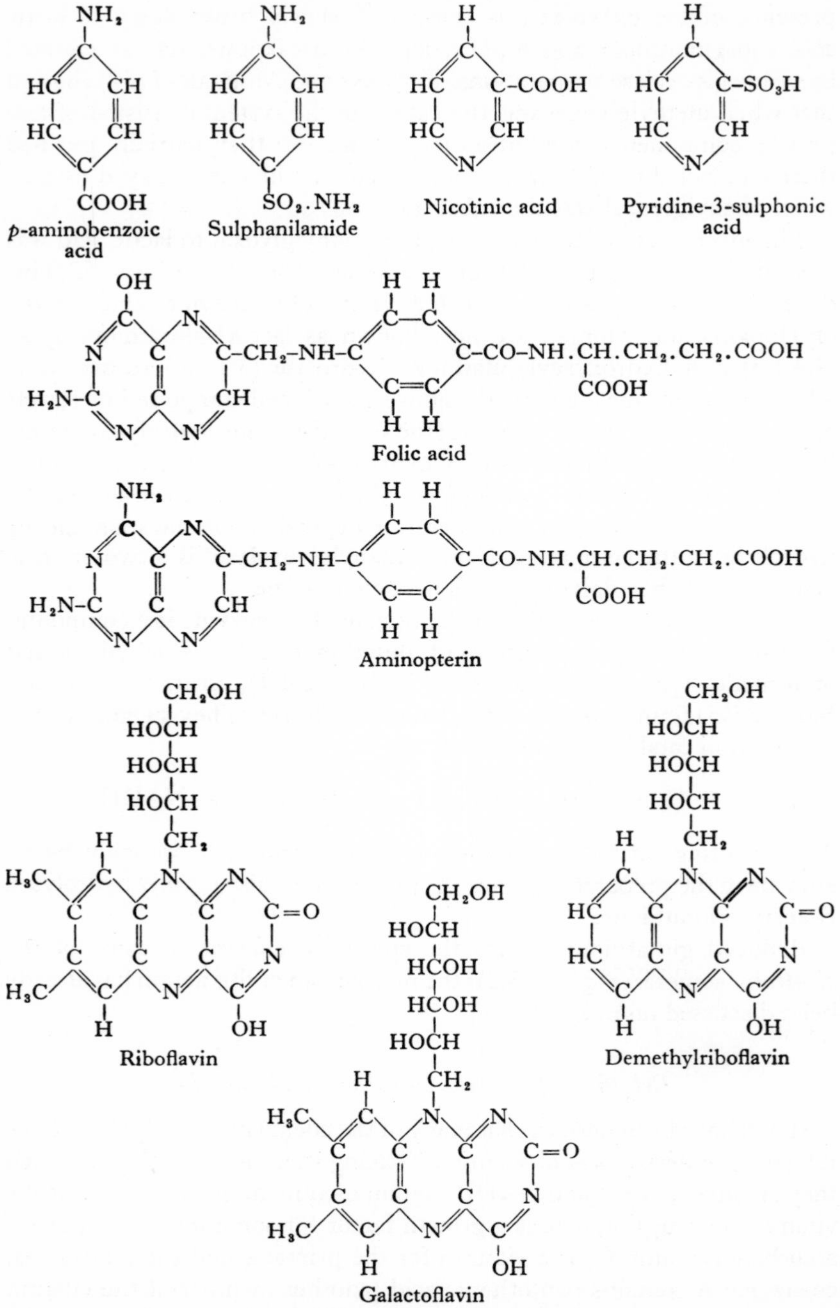

NH₂ ... NH_2

p-aminobenzoic acid

Sulphanilamide

Nicotinic acid

Pyridine-3-sulphonic acid

C-CH₂-NH-C ... C-CO-NH.CH.CH₂.CH₂.COOH

H_2N-C ... COOH

Folic acid

NH_2

C-CH₂-NH-C ... C-CO-NH.CH.CH₂.CH₂.COOH

H_2N-C ... COOH

Aminopterin

CH₂OH
HOCH
HOCH
HOCH
CH₂

H_3C ... C=O ... OH

Riboflavin

CH₂OH
HOCH
HCOH
HCOH
HOCH
CH₂

Galactoflavin

CH₂OH
HOCH
HOCH
HOCH
CH₂

HC ... C=O ... OH

Demethylriboflavin

Fig. IX.29. *Structures of some vitamins and anti-vitamins.*

B group, which itself contains the simpler vitamin p-aminobenzoic acid), the cobamide coenzymes are closely related to vitamin B_{12}, the flavin prosthetic groups contain riboflavin (vitamin B_2), pyridoxal phosphate is a derivative of pyridoxin (vitamin B_6), thiamin pyrophosphate contains thiamine (vitamin B_1), and biotin is itself a member of the vitamin B group.

It may well be that the main function of the vitamins is to serve as the operative part of specialized coenzymes and prosthetic groups; in other words, organisms are often unable to synthetize important parts of many of their essential enzyme systems, which have to be supplied. There are almost certainly other cases which are not mentioned in the above list. We have already mentioned on p. 378 the suggestion of Martius that vitamin K acts as a hydrogen carrier in the phosphorylating system for $NADH_2$ oxidation. Vitamin A has been shown to function (in the form of its aldehyde, retinene) as a cofactor in the visual cycle by WALD and his collaborators (see *1178*).

Substances closely related to vitamins, but incapable of working in the same way, would be expected to combine with the enzymes in the place of the active group and thereby act as a special type of competitive inhibitor. Such substances have been called 'antivitamins'. When administered, often in very small quantities, they produce the symptoms of a deficiency of the corresponding vitamin, and may be highly toxic. For example, aminopterin (folate with an amino group in place of the hydroxyl group) antagonizes the action of tetrahydrofolate and also competitively inhibits its formation from folate. In a concentration of one part per million in the diet it kills rats and mice within one week. The important group of drugs related to sulphanilamide also owe their activity to an anti-folate activity, due to their resemblance to p-aminobenzoic acid. The bacteriostatic action of sulphonamides can be overcome by either p-aminobenzoate or by folate. Other anti-vitamins are pyridine-3-sulphonic acid, which competes with nicotinic acid, and 6,7-didemethylriboflavin and galactoflavin, both of which compete with riboflavin. The chemical basis for some of these competitions will be clear from Fig. IX.29.

Significance of 'nucleotide' structure in coenzymes

A striking feature of the structure of coenzymes is that the majority are either actual nucleotides or have some structural analogy with nucleotides. Many have a nitrogenous base at one end of the molecule and a phosphate group at the other, with or without a carbohydrate between, or have two such structures joined in the form of a dinucleotide. This is true of the phosphate carriers shown in Fig. IX.16, which are actual nucleotide phosphates, also of NAD and NADP, which are true dinucleotides but contain nicotinamide instead of a purine or pyrimidine, and also of the flavin nucleotides, in which one ribose is replaced by ribitol and the base is dimethylisoalloxazine. Further, one-half of the coenzyme A molecule is a nucleotide, although the functional group is not, and thiamine pyrophosphate may be regarded as a pyrimidine nucleotide phosphate in which the sugar is replaced by a thiazolinium ring, while in pyridoxal phosphate the phosphate is directly attached to the base. Four of these coenzymes, namely, NAD, NADP, coenzyme A, and FAD, contain, in addition to the reactive moiety, an adenylic acid residue.

In Chapter XI we shall discuss the evidence for the formation of enzymes on nucleic acid templates. If this is the mode of formation it may well be that the enzyme protein may retain some impress of the nucleic structure, so that certain parts of it are particularly adapted to combine with nucleotide-like molecules. Although no definite evidence can be adduced, it is possible that this may be the reason that so many coenzymes have this type of structure.

It may not be without significance that three of the hydrogen carriers contain as part of their structure a grouping which when free is associated with phosphate transport, in view of the fact that the oxidations in which these carriers take part are coupled with phosphorylation *in vivo*. Moreover, NAD can itself accept a phosphate residue from ATP, becoming NADP. No doubt the significance of these interrelationships will become clearer as a result of future research.

ENZYME ACTIVATORS

In this part of the chapter we deal with such cofactors as act by bringing the enzyme into a catalytically active state, without themselves taking part in the reactions catalysed by the enzyme.

Simple electrolytes

While the activity of some enzymes is not noticeably affected by the presence or absence of salts, others are greatly influenced by the nature and concentration of the ions present. Certain ions are absolutely necessary for the activity of some enzymes, while others (e.g. Ag^+, Hg^{++}, Pb^{++}) are highly toxic to nearly all enzymes. An exceptional case is diphosphoglycerate phosphatase (3.1.3.13), which is strongly activated by low concentrations of Hg^{++} or Ag^+(*2174*). Some ions are poisons for some enzymes and activators for others; some may even inhibit an enzyme at one concentration and be an activator of the same enzyme at another. The effects, like reactions between ions and proteins in general, may be extremely complex, particularly so since, in addition to the purely colloid effects, there may be specific requirements by the active centre of an enzyme for a particular type of ion. The effects of ions on enzymes may be produced in many different ways and in most cases the separate factors have not been properly disentangled. The literature is somewhat scattered and few serious attempts have been made to reduce the subject to order.

Some of the effects, particularly those of anions, are fairly unspecific; the enzyme is usually active to some extent without electrolytes, and almost any anion will have an effect. In other cases, particularly with cations, the enzyme is inactive by itself and the requirement for a cation is usually fairly specific; in some cases only one particular cation is effective, in other cases two or three different cations can act. Examples of the two extreme cases are fumarate hydratase, the activity of which is greatly affected by a wide range of anions, and inorganic pyrophosphatase, which specifically requires Mg^{++} ions for its activity, and these cannot be replaced by any other ions.

The fact that as far as our present knowledge goes the cation effects are much more specific than the anion effects may be partly due to the way in which investigation has been carried out. The effect of cations has usually only been studied in cases where the enzyme becomes inactive in their absence, whereas a variety of anions are usually automatically tested in determining pH curves, for a number of different buffers have to be used in order to cover a wide pH range, and these are usually sodium or potassium salts of weak organic or inorganic acids. Nevertheless, there is probably a more fundamental difference between the nature of the actions of cations and anions, although the underlying physicochemical factors are still not understood.

We shall first consider the more specific effects of inorganic cations.

Specific metal ion activators

Fifteen different metal cations have been found to activate one or more enzymes, namely, Na^+, K^+, Rb^+, Cs^+, Mg^{++}, Ca^{++}, Zn^{++}, Cd^{++}, Cr^{+++}, Cu^{++}, Mn^{++}, Fe^{++}, Co^{++}, Ni^{++}, Al^{+++}, as well as NH_4^+. Molybdenum compounds also activate certain enzymes, but the ionic form of the activator is obscure.

All of the metals in the list have atomic numbers between 11 and 55 and the majority lie between 19 and 30. No metal with an atomic number greater than 55 is known to activate by itself.

Probably one of the important factors which determine which metal ions activate enzymes is the size of the ion. The metal ion activators listed above all have radii which lie within a fairly narrow zone, in the middle range of observed atomic radii.

The ions in the list, however, are by no means interchangeable; with some enzymes only one, in more cases two or three, of these ions are capable of activating. For instance, Mg^{++} is the natural activator of the great majority (though not all) of the enzymes which act on phosphorylated substrates, notably the kinases, the synthetases and the enzymes which hydrolyse phosphoric acid anhydrides, but not the phosphorylases; in nearly all these cases Mg^{++} can be replaced by Mn^{++}, but not usually by any other metal. The similarity between Mg^{++} and Mn^{++} would hardly be expected on chemical grounds. On the other hand, although Na^+ is chemically so similar to K^+, it cannot replace it as an activator of pyruvate kinase (2.7.1.40), though it can replace it

TABLE IX.6

ION ANTAGONISMS

Enzyme	Activating ions	Inhibiting ions
Phosphate acetyltransferase (2.3.1.8)	K^+ or NH_4^+	Na^+ or Li^+
Aldehyde dehydrogenase (1.2.1.5) (yeast)	K^+, NH_4^+ or Rb^+	Na^+, Li^+ or Cs
Glycerol dehydrogenase (1.1.1.6) (bacteria) ..	NH_4^+, K^+ or Rb^+	Zn^{++}
Methionine adenosyltransferase (2.4.2.13) (yeast) ..	$(Mg^{++}$ or $Mn^{++})$ plus $(K^+, NH_4^+$ or $Rb^+)$	Ca^{++} or Zn^{++} —
Acetyl-CoA synthetase (6.2.1.1)	$(Mg^{++}$ or $Mn^{++})$ plus $(K^+, NH_4^+$ or $Rb^+)$	— Na^+ or Li^+
Pantothenate synthetase (6.3.2.1)	$(Mg^{++}$ or $Mn^{++})$ plus $(K^+$ or $NH_4^+)$	Ca^{++} or Zn^{++} Na^+
Pyruvate kinase (2.7.1.40)..	(Mg^{++}) plus $(K^+, Rb^+$ or $Cs^+)$	Ca^{++} Na^+ or Li^+
ATPase (3.6.1.4)	Mg^{++} or Mn^{++}	Ca^{++}
5-nucleotidase (3.1.3.5) ..	Mg^{++}	Ca^{++}
Argininosuccinate synthetase (6.3.4.5)	Mg^{++}	Ca^{++} or Mn^{++}
Glutamine synthetase (6.3.1.2)	Mg^{++} or Mn^{++}	Ca^{++}

TABLE IX.6—*continued*

Enzyme	Activating ions	Inhibiting ions
Riboflavin kinase (2.7.1.26) (animal tissues)	Mg^{++}, Zn^{++}, Co^{++} or Mn^{++}	Ca^{++}
Riboflavin kinase (2.7.1.26) (plants)	Mg^{++}, Zn^{++} or Mn^{++}	Hg^{++}, Fe^{++} or Cu^{++}
Inorganic pyrophosphatase (3.6.1.1)	Mg^{++}	Ca^{++} or Zn^{++}
Phosphopyruvate hydratase (4.2.1.11)	Mg^{++}, Zn^{++}, Mn^{++} or Cd^{++}	Ca^{++} or Sr^{++}
Myosin ATPase (3.6.1.3) ..	Ca^{++} *or* K^+ or NH_4^+	Mg^{++}
Glycyl-leucine dipeptidase (3.4.3.2)	Zn^{++} or Mn^{++}	Ca^{++}
Imidodipeptidase (3.4.3.7)	Mn^{++}	Zn^{++}
Alkaline phosphatase (3.1.3.1)	Mg^{++}, Mn^{++}, Ca^{++} or Zn^{++}	Zn^{++} or Be^{++}
Creatine kinase (2.7.3.2) ..	Mg^{++}, Mn^{++} or Ca^{++}	Zn^{++}
Malate dehydrogenase (decarboxylating) (1.1.1.40)	Mn^{++}, Co^{++}, Zn^{++}, Ni^{++} or Cu^{++}	Hg^{++}
Malate dehydrogenase (decarboxylating) (1.1.1.38)	$(Mn^{++}$, Co^{++} or $Mg^{++})$ *plus* $(K^+$, Rb^+ or $Cs^+)$	
Ketohexokinase (2.7.1.3) ..	$(Mg^{++}$ or $Mn^{++})$ *plus* $(K^+$ or $Na^+)$	
DFPase (3.8.2.1)	Ca^{++}, Mg^{++}, Mn^{++} or Co^{++}	
Pyruvate decarboxylase (4.1.1.1)	Mg^{++}, Mn^{++}, Co^{++}, Cd^{++}, Zn^{++}, Ca^{++}, Fe^{++}, Al^{+++} or Fe^{+++}	
Oxaloacetate decarboxylase (4.1.1.3)	Mn^{++}, Cd^{++}, Co^{++}, Mg^{++}, Ni^{++}, Zn^{++}, Fe^{++} or Ca^{++}	
Aldehyde dehydrogenase (1.2.1.4) (yeast)	Ca^{++}, Mg^{++}, Mn^{++} or Ba^{++}	
Trimetaphosphatase (3.6.1.2)	Co^{++}, Mn^{++}, Fe^{++} or Mg^{++}	
Pantetheine kinase (2.7.1.34)	Mn^{++}, Mg^{++} or Ca^{++}	

in the case of ketohexokinase (2.7.1.3). For another group of enzymes, including some of the peptidases and other enzymes which act on nitrogenous groupings, Mn^{++}, Co^{++}, Ni^{++} and sometimes Zn^{++} are interchangeable. Zn also forms a firmly bound part of several enzymes (see *2707*). Much information about activation of enzymes by metals has been collected in reviews by LEHNINGER (*1533*) and by MALMSTRÖM and ROSENBERG (*1699*).

Cases of ion antagonism are fairly common (see Table IX.6). Na^+ often acts as a competitive inhibitor of K^+ activation, as do other alkali metals. This is illustrated by the first two enzymes in the table. The

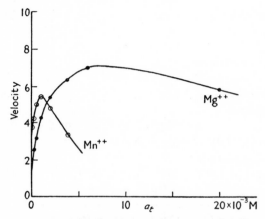

Fig. IX.30. *Activation of NAD kinase* (2.7.1.23) *by* Mg^{++} *and* Mn^{++}.

a_t denotes the total concentration of activating metal ion (either Mg^{++} or Mn^{++}).

from *1427*

alkaline earth metals often compete with one another, in particular a number of Mg^{++}-activated anzymes are inhibited by Ca^{++} (ATPase (3.6.1.4) and related enzymes) and the Ca^{++}-activated myosin ATPase is inhibited by Mg^{++}. Divalent ions of other series often compete with one another, for instance Mn^{++} and Zn^{++} in the case of imidodipeptidase (3.4.3.7).

In several cases two ions, usually of different valency, are required simultaneously for activation, though the reason for this is not clear. For instance, the entry in the table for pantothenate synthetase means that either Mg^{++} or Mn^{++} ions, and in addition either K^+ or NH_4^+ ions, are required. Frequently in such cases a double ionic antagonism is found; in this particular case Ca^{++} or Zn^{++} compete with the activating divalent ion and Na^+ with the univalent ion. However, ions which usually act as mutual antagonists, like Ca^{++} and Mg^{++}, do not invariably do so, but may even act as alternative activators of the same enzyme. We have included in the table below the line a few cases to illustrate this point. It will be noted that pyruvate decarboxylase and oxaloacetate decarboxylase show cation effects which are almost as unspecific as the anion effects which will be dealt with later. However, these reactions are decarboxylation reactions, which are catalysed by these metal ions in the absence of the enzyme, and the latter is merely accelerating a general metal catalysis.

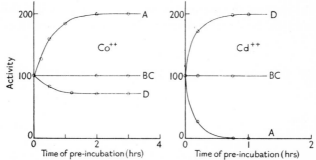

Fig. IX.31. *Effect of pre-incubation with Co^{++} and Cd^{++} on the peptidase and esterase activities of carboxypeptidase B.*

Pre-incubation with 0.01 M Co^{++} at $40°$ or 0.01 M Cd^{++} at $25°$. Activities expressed in percentage of activities without metal ions.

A and D. Pre-incubated with metal ions.
B and C. Pre-incubated without metal ions.
A and B. Peptidase activity (substrate hippuryl-arginine).
C and D. Esterase activity (substrate O-hippuryl-argininic acid).

from *757*

On plotting the velocity of the enzyme reaction against the concentration of the activating ion, a curve resembling the Michaelis curve for substrate concentration is usually obtained. As the concentration is increased, however, the velocity frequently falls off again. This is especially marked in the case of Mn^{++} activation; Mg^{++} also shows the effect, but to a less extent. In enzymes which are activated by both Mg^{++} and Mn^{++}, activation and inhibition are both shown at much lower concentrations of Mn^{++} than of Mg^{++}; a pair of typical activation curves is shown in Fig. IX.30. In such cases, with a concentration of Mg^{++} sufficient to produce maximal activation, the addition of Mn^{++} produces inhibition. In this way many of the divalent ions given in Table IX.6 as alternative activators can be shown to compete with one another.

Activation with Mg^{++} is usually a rapid process, but with some other ions activation may take an appreciable time to reach equilibrium; this is particularly true in those cases where Mn^{++}, Co^{++} and Ni^{++} are activators, when the process may take many hours, e.g. *479, 2251.*

With a given enzyme, a particular ion may have different effects with different substrates. Conversely, the activating ion may in this way have a profound effect on the specificity of the enzyme. Two examples will show this very clearly. Fig. IX.31 shows the effect of pre-incubation with Co^{++} and Cd^{++} on the peptidase and esterase activities of carboxypeptidase B (3.4.2.2). It will be seen that Co^{++} doubles the peptidase activity, but reduces the esterase activity; conversely Cd^{++} doubles the esterase activity, while completely eliminating the peptidase activity

TABLE IX.7

EFFECT OF IONS ON MYOSIN ATPase SPECIFICITY (*1376*)

	Relative rates of hydrolysis in		
Substrate	0·005 M $CaCl_2$	0·4 M K^+ +*versene*	0·2 M NH^+ +*versene*
ATP ..	1·00	2·90	17·2
GTP ..	1·82	0	0
ITP ..	4·51	0	0·92
CTP ..	0·45	1·09	1·97
UTP ..	1·59	0·37	2·58
ATetraP	1·09	0	0

(*757*). Similar results have been obtained with carboxypeptidase A (3.4.2.1) (*479*).

The other case is that of the hydrolysis of nucleoside triphosphates by myosin, shown in Table IX.7. The divalent-metal-complexing agent versene was added to remove any such metals already present in the preparations. The results speak for themselves.

The effect of particular activating ions on an enzyme may vary not only with the substrate and with the pH, but also with the purity and age of the enzyme. Partially purified arginase (3.5.3.1) is activated by Co^{++}, Mn^{++} and Ni^{++} (in descending order of effectiveness), but the highly purified enzyme is activated only by Mn^{++} (*122*). Phosphorylase kinase (2.7.1.38) is activated by Mn^{++} and Ca^{++}, but not by Mg^{++}, in crude extract, but the purified enzyme is activated by Mn^{++} and Mg^{++}, but not by Ca^{++} (*1459*). The ATPase which is combined with the protein actin in the myofibrils (actomyosin) is activated by either Ca^{++} or Mg^{++}, whereas free myosin is activated only by Ca^{++} (*2073*). The explanation of these differences is unknown.

Possible mechanisms of metal ion activation. Ions may produce activating effects on enzymes by a variety of mechanisms. Some of these mechanisms are not sharply differentiated from others, and in a particular case it may be difficult to decide experimentally which mechanism is operative. There are few cases in which the precise mechanism has been definitely established. Some of the possible modes of action will now be enumerated.

The metal may form an essential part of the active centre of the enzyme. This is probably the most widely assumed mechanism and in certain cases is unquestionably true. For instance, the diphenol oxidases (1.10.3.1–2) contain Cu, and after this has been removed they are specifically reactivated by Cu^{++} ions, which are incorporated into the active centre of the enzyme (*1474*). In this position the copper acts as an oxidation-reduction carrier; the metal may or may not act in this way in other cases, such as the haemoprotein enzymes.

The metal may act as a binding link between enzyme and substrate, combining with both and so holding the substrate at the active centre of the enzyme. There are three possible cases according to the order of combination, which will be related to the affinities of the metal for the enzyme and substrate:

IX.28 $\quad$ $E + M + S = EMS$

IX.29 $\quad$ $E + M = EM; \quad EM + S = EMS$

IX.30 $\quad$ $M + S = MS; \quad E + MS = EMS$

In the first case (IX.28) it is assumed that the active complex is formed directly from the free components. This, however, is a trimolecular reaction, which is unlikely, and it is more probable that the metal would combine with either the enzyme or the substrate first, giving one of the other two cases.

In the second case (IX.29) the metal may be regarded as forming a part of the active enzyme EM, where its function is to act as a point of combination of the substrate.

In the third case (IX.30) the metal may be regarded as combining with the added substrate to give the true substrate MS of the enzyme. The last two cases have been regarded as fundamentally different, but if the metal in the complex is combined with both enzyme and substrate, the difference is merely a matter of order of combination, and the final complex will be the same in each case. In fact with any particular enzyme both pathways are likely to be followed simultaneously, their relative contribution depending on the velocity constants and on the concentrations of the components.

In the complex EMS the metal may merely act as a 'handle' holding the substrate in the required position, or it may be itself involved in the activation of the substrate. The latter type of action is an essential part of the theories developed by Hellerman and E. Smith for the metal activation of such enzymes as arginase and certain peptidases. The formation of a chelate compound between the metal atom on the enzyme and the substrate plays an important part in the activation of the latter. We have already discussed this theory in some detail in Chapter VII (see p. 305).

There is independent evidence that metal ions are capable of binding organic molecules to proteins. Klotz and Ming (*1401*) studied the influence of metal ions on the binding of azo-dyes by a number of proteins, including serum albumin and pepsin, and showed a marked increase in binding in the presence of ions such as Zn^{++}, which was strongly pH-dependent. They considered that the effects could be adequately explained by co-ordination, without the necessity of assuming chelation, and regarded the system as a model of metal-activation of enzymes.

Another way in which metal ions can produce an activation, although it is an apparent rather than a real effect on the enzyme, is by changing the equilibrium constant of the enzyme reaction. Such a shift of equilibrium often occurs in the cases already mentioned and will be discussed in more detail later in this chapter. In cases where the reaction in question cannot be observed because the equilibrium constant is unfavourable for its occurrence, a change of the constant in a favourable direction may enable the reaction to take place and so produce an apparent activation. This may take place in two different ways. Where the true substrate is a metal complex, addition of the metal will increase the concentration of this complex and will therefore displace the equilibrium in the desired direction. On the other hand, the metal may form a complex with the product of the reaction and so remove it from the equilibrium, thus giving an apparent activation even though no metal is involved in the enzyme–substrate interaction and the enzyme acts on the form which is *not* complexed with the metal. An example of the latter type of action is the glucose-1-phosphate phosphodismutase (2.7.1.41) of rabbit muscle, in which the dismutation is accelerated by Mg^{++} although the reverse reaction is inhibited. This has been explained (*2399*) by the formation of a magnesium complex of glucose 1,6-diphosphate, so that this product is removed from the equilibrium. A rather similar case is the general accelerating effect of Ca^{++} on hydrolysis by lipases, which is probably due to formation of complexes or even gross precipitates with the products.

There are probably other ways in which metal ions may produce a direct activation of enzymes. For example, it is possible that the reaction may be affected by a change of surface charge on the enzyme protein; it is well known that cations, particularly polyvalent cations such as Al^{+++}, may produce very marked changes in the electrokinetic potential of proteins.

There are also a number of indirect ways in which metal ions may accelerate enzyme reactions. They may remove an inhibitor present in the enzyme preparation by forming a complex or precipitate with it. They may displace ineffective metal ions from combination with the active centre of the enzyme or with the functional groups of the substrate. Furthermore, a metal which does not itself activate the enzyme may produce an activation by displacing the true activating metal, already present in the enzyme preparation, from combination with groups other than the active centre, thus setting the activator free to combine with the effective site. This may explain why partially purified arginase is activated by several ions, while the highly purified enzyme is activated only by Mn^{++}, as mentioned earlier.

If an enzyme can exist in two forms with different activities in equilibrium with one another, and the addition of metal ion affects the equilibrium in favour of the more active form, it will act as an activator. That metal ions can affect equilibria between two forms of an enzyme has been shown in the case of phosphopyruvate hydratase (*1696, 2846*), although in this case it happens to be the less active form which is stabilized. On the other hand Mg^{++} stabilizes the more active form of phosphoprotein phosphatase (3.1.3.16) (*2041*), and Zn^{++} stabilizes the active tetrameric form of yeast alcohol dehydrogenase (*1281*).

Kinetics of activation by metal ions

Combination of metal ion with components of the system may affect either the velocity of the enzyme reaction or the equilibrium reached, or both. We first consider the effect on velocity.

(a) *Velocity effects.* As we have already mentioned, a plot of reaction velocity against concentration of added metal ion commonly gives a rectangular hyperbola, resembling the normal substrate concentration curve, and such data may be treated by any of the usual graphical methods (Fig. IV.12). The 'K_m' for the metal so obtained has been taken by many authors to be simply the dissociation constant of the enzyme–metal complex. This assumption is rarely true, as can be shown by simple calculation; the 'constant' has a number of different meanings, varying with the mechanism of action and the conditions.

Case I. If the metal acts by combining with the enzyme independently of the substrate (compare equation IX.29) the following reactions must be considered

IX.31 $E + M \rightleftharpoons EM$

IX.32 $E + S \rightleftharpoons ES$

IX.33 $EM + S \rightleftharpoons EMS$

IX.34 $ES + M \rightleftharpoons EMS$

IX.35 $EMS \rightarrow EM + \text{products}$

Equation IX.34 is redundant, since the first three are sufficient to define the equilibria between the components. For simplicity we assume equilibrium between enzyme, activator and substrate as in Michaelis kinetics; the same result, with the usual substitution of K_m for K_s, is given by a steady-state analysis. The corresponding mass-action equations are

IX.36 $K_A q = (e-p-q-r)a$

IX.37 $K_s r = (e-p-q-r)s$

IX.38 $K_s p = qs$

IX.39 $v = kp$

where e denotes total concentration of enzyme; a and s are the concentrations of free activating ion and substrate, which will be equal to the total concentrations so long as the concentration of enzyme is small; p, q and r are the concentrations of EMS, EM and ES; and K_A and K_s are the dissociation constants of the enzyme complexes with respect to the activating metal and the substrate respectively. If the combination with substrate and with metal are truly independent, K_A will be the same for reactions IX.31 and 34 and K_s will apply to both reactions IX.32 and 33. It is necessary to postulate the formation of the complex ES, otherwise there is an implied influence of metal on the combination of enzyme with substrate. The equations assume that there is no combination of metal with substrate and that only the complex EMS is active in the formation of products.

Solving these equations for v by the usual methods we get

IX.40 $v = \dfrac{ke}{\left(1+\dfrac{K_s}{s}\right)\left(1+\dfrac{K_A}{a}\right)}$

At a constant substrate concentration this may be written

IX.41 $v = \dfrac{V_a}{1+\dfrac{K_A}{a}}$

where V_a is the maximum velocity with excess M at the particular substrate concentration, which is given by

IX.42
$$V_a = \frac{ke}{1+\dfrac{K_s}{s}}$$

In this case a reciprocal plot with respect to a will give the same value of K_A at all concentrations of substrate and this will be the true dissociation constant of EM. Since equation IX.40 is symmetrical in s and a, the graphically determined K_m will conversely be independent of the concentration of the activating ion.

Case II. If the combination of enzyme with substrate and with metal are not independent, so that E and EM have different affinities for the substrate, the dissociation constants for reactions IX.32 and 33 are not equal and may be written as K_s and K_s' respectively. The equation for the velocity is then

IX.43
$$v = \frac{ke}{\left(1+\dfrac{K_s'}{s}\right)\left(1+\dfrac{K_A}{a}\cdot\dfrac{\left(1+\dfrac{s}{K_s}\right)}{\left(1+\dfrac{s}{K_s'}\right)}\right)}$$

This is a general equation, covering all degrees of interaction, but the two extreme cases are of interest. One of these, that in which $K_s = K_s'$, has already been dealt with as Case I. The other is that in which only the enzyme–metal complex is able to combine with substrate, so that ES is not formed and K_s is infinite. Equation IX.43 then reduces to

IX.44
$$v = \frac{ke}{\left(1+\dfrac{K_s'}{s}\right)\left(1+\dfrac{K_A}{a\left(1+\dfrac{s}{K_s'}\right)}\right)}$$

A similar equation for this limiting case has been derived by ALBERTY (*33*).

Equation IX.44 is of the form

IX.45
$$v = \frac{V_a}{1+\dfrac{K_{Ap}}{a}} \qquad \text{(compare equation IX.41)}$$

where V_a as before is given by equation IX.42 (but with K'_s instead of K_s) and K_{Ap}, the apparent dissociation constant of EM, is given by

IX.46 $$K_{Ap} = \frac{K_A}{1+\dfrac{s}{K'_s}}$$

Thus the graphically-determined constant for the metal will only be equal to its true dissociation constant K_A at low substrate concentration (relative to K'_s). At more normal substrate concentrations the apparent affinity of enzyme for metal will be increased because the concentration of EM is reduced by conversion to EMS, so that reaction IX.31 proceeds further to the right.

As the substrate concentration influences the apparent affinity of the enzyme for the metal ion, so the metal ion concentration affects the apparent affinity for the substrate. Rearranging equation IX.43 gives the apparent substrate constant as

IX.47 $$K_{sp} = K'_s \cdot \frac{\left(1+\dfrac{K_A}{a}\right)}{\left(1+\dfrac{K'_s}{K}\cdot\dfrac{K_A}{a}\right)}$$

In the limiting case discussed above, where K_s is infinite, this reduces to

IX.48 $$K_{sp} = K'_s\left(1+\frac{K_A}{a}\right)$$

Thus the usual methods will only yield the true substrate constant for the metal-activated enzyme (K'_s) at high concentrations of activator, when the enzyme is virtually completely converted into the active form EM.

Case III. The third case is that represented in equation IX.30, in which the metal combines with the substrate rather than with the enzyme. This is the most difficult case to deal with mathematically and a complete treatment has never been published. The difficulty arises from the fact that, whereas combination of the metal with the enzyme in the two previous cases left the concentration of free metal ions essentially equal to the amount added (since the amount of enzyme present was very small), combination with substrate may remove an appreciable part of the metal ion. Conversely, the metal ion may remove an appreciable part of the substrate. Thus neither the concentration of the free metal ion nor that of the free substrate will equal the amounts added. It is thus necessary to convert the simple equilibrium equations, which are expressed in terms of the *free* forms, into equations containing only *total* concentrations. This usually leads to equations which are somewhat complicated. As RABIN and CROOK (*2138*) point out, the first essential is to calculate the concentration of the free metal ions. This has generally not been done, and authors have been content to express their results in terms of total metal concentrations. This is equally true of the substrate concentrations in cases where the substrate combines with the metal ion.

Deriving first the equations in terms of free components, we have, assuming that S does not combine with the enzyme and that the products do not combine with metal (although this is unimportant if only initial velocities are being considered)

IX.49 $$M + S \rightleftharpoons MS$$

IX.50 $$E + MS \rightleftharpoons EMS$$

IX.51 $$EMS \rightarrow E + M + products$$

The corresponding mass-action equations are

IX.52 $$K_0 q = as$$

IX.53 $$K_{AS} p = (e-p)q$$

IX.54 $$v = kp$$

where e denotes total concentration of enzyme; a and s are the concentrations of *free* activating ion and substrate; p and q are now the concentrations of EMS and MS; and K_0 and K_{AS} are the dissociation constants corresponding to reactions IX.49 and IX.50 respectively. From these equations we get

IX.55 $$v = \frac{ke}{1 + \dfrac{K_0 K_{AS}}{as}}$$

This leads to the somewhat surprising result that the maximum velocity reached by increasing either a or s is the same

IX.56 $$V_a = V_s = ke$$

provided that s or a respectively are maintained constant. Thus the enzyme can apparently be saturated with substrate even at low substrate concentration by increasing the metal concentration. This, however, is illusory; it is due to the fact that these equations relate to *free* metal ion and substrate and, in order to hold the concentration of free substrate s constant as the metal concentration is increased, it would be necessary greatly to increase the total substrate concentration. This is equivalent to saturating the enzyme with its true substrate by increasing the concentration of metal-substrate complex.

Equation IX.55 is symmetrical in a and s, and the two constants K_0 and K_{AS} might seem to be analogous constants, defining the effect of activator and substrate concentration respectively on the enzyme velocity. It will be seen from the derivation of the equation, however, that they have quite different meanings. K_{AS} relates to the normal affinity of enzyme for substrate MS, but K_0 is not an enzyme affinity constant at all, as it relates to the combination of activator with substrate. In this equation $K_0 K_{AS}$ forms effectively one constant, which could be obtained by plotting velocity against the concentration of either free substrate or free activating ion. The apparent Michaelis constants thus obtained are

IX.57 $$K_{sp} = \frac{K_0 K_{AS}}{a}$$

IX.58 $$K_{Ap} = \frac{K_0 K_{AS}}{s}$$

There is no way of determining either K_0 or K_{AS} separately. It should be noted that the apparent affinity constant for substrate at a fixed metal concentration is identical with the apparent affinity constant for metal at the same fixed substrate concentration.

The velocity can be expressed in terms of the total added concentrations of substrate and activator (s_t and a_t respectively) by substituting

IX.59 $$s = s_t - q$$

IX.60 $$a = a_t - q$$

into equations IX.52–3. This leads (remembering that q cannot be greater than a_t or s_t, whichever is the smaller) to the equation

IX.61 $$v = \frac{ke}{1 + \dfrac{2K_{AS}}{(K_0 + a_t + s_t) - \sqrt{\{(K_0 + a_t + s_t)^2 - 4a_t s_t\}}}}$$

From this equation v can be readily calculated for particular values of the constants and the total concentrations, although the equation cannot be arranged into the usual form to give simple algebraical expressions for the effective Michaelis constants for substrate and activator.

It is clear that, as with the simpler expression IX.55, the interchange of a_t and s_t leaves this expression unchanged. Therefore the conclusions already given about the identity of the values of the observed Michaelis constants for activator and substrate will still apply when total concentrations are used. A case in which this result has been found experimen-

tally is that of creatine kinase. Both ASKONAS (*93*) and KUBY *et al.*
(*1480*) found that the apparent affinity of the enzyme for a given
metal ion in presence of a certain concentration of ADP was the same

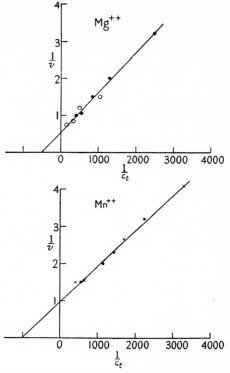

Fig. IX.32. *Equivalence of apparent affinities of creatine kinase (2.7.3.2) for
activating metal and substrate.*

Reciprocal plots for the reaction of ADP
with creatine phosphate. c_t denotes the total
molar concentration of

● ADP (with $0·005$ M Mg^{++})
○ Mg^{++} (with $0·003$ M ADP)
■ ADP (with $0·005$ M Mn^{++})
× Mn^{++} (with $0·003$ M ADP)

from *93*

as that for ADP in the presence of the same concentration of that
metal. Fig. IX.32 shows the results of Askonas, in reciprocal form, for
the dependence of velocity on total Mg^{++} and Mn^{++} concentration in
the presence of $0·003$ M ADP and on total ADP concentration in the

presence of $0\cdot005\,\mathrm{M}$ added $\mathrm{Mg^{++}}$ or $\mathrm{Mn^{++}}$. It will be seen that the K_m for ADP in the presence of $\mathrm{Mg^{++}}$ differs from that in the presence of $\mathrm{Mn^{++}}$, but each K_m agrees closely with the K_m for the respective metal. These observed Michaelis constants are presumably complicated functions of K_0 and K_{AS} which could be deduced from equation IX.61, but if both a and s are high compared with K_0 the equation simplifies to

IX.62
$$v = \frac{ke}{1+\dfrac{K_{AS}}{s}}$$

Thus the Michaelis constant for the true substrate can be obtained by varying the amount of added substrate at sufficiently high concentrations of activator.

Case IV. In the previous case it was assumed that the enzyme only combined with substrate in the presence of the metal; in other words, the dissociation constant of the complex ES was infinite. We shall now consider the more general case in which the enzyme combines with both S and MS, but with different affinities, that is to say, there is some influence of metal on substrate combination, but this is not complete. In addition to equations IX.49–51 we must now introduce the equilibrium

IX.63
$$\mathrm{E + S \rightleftharpoons ES}$$

with dissociation constant K_s. We then have

IX.64
$$K_0 q = as$$

IX.65
$$K_{AS}p = (e-p-r)q$$

IX.66
$$K_s r = (e-p-r)s$$

IX.67
$$v = kp$$

where r is the concentration of ES. This gives

IX.68
$$v = \frac{ke}{1+\dfrac{K_0 K_{AS}}{as}\left(1+\dfrac{s}{K_s}\right)}$$

This equation is no longer symmetrical with respect to the activator and substrate concentrations. The apparent Michaelis constants are

IX.69
$$K_{sp} = \frac{K_{AS}}{\left(\dfrac{a}{K_0}+\dfrac{K_{AS}}{K_s}\right)}$$

IX.70
$$K_{Ap} = K_0 \left(\frac{K_{AS}}{s}+\frac{K_{AS}}{K_s}\right)$$

Two limiting cases are of interest. Where the enzyme does not combine at all with free substrate, K_s is infinite and the equation IX.68 reduces to IX.55, i.e. to Case III. If, on the other hand, the enzyme combines with equal affinity with S and MS, or, in other words, when there is no influence of metal on enzyme–substrate combination, $K_{AS} = K_s$ and the equation reduces to

IX.71
$$v = \frac{ke}{1 + \dfrac{K_0}{a}\left(1 + \dfrac{K_{AS}}{s}\right)}$$

These expressions are in terms of concentrations of *free* components; when recalculated in terms of total concentrations, equation IX.68 becomes

IX.72

$$v = \frac{ke}{\left(1 - \dfrac{K_{AS}}{K_s}\right) + \left(1 + \dfrac{s_t}{K_s}\right)\dfrac{2K_{AS}}{(K_0 + a_t + s_t) - \sqrt{\{(K_0 + a_t + s_t)^2 - 4a_t s_t\}}}}$$

When K_s is infinite, this equation reduces to IX.61. If, on the other hand, we put $K_{AS} = K_s$, we get the equation corresponding to IX.71, expressed in total concentrations, namely

IX.73
$$v = \frac{ke}{\dfrac{2(K_{AS} + s_t)}{(K_0 + a_t + s_t) - \sqrt{\{(K_0 + a_t + s_t)^2 - 4a_t s_t\}}}}$$

Case V. If the metal activator combines with added substrate to give a complex which is the true substrate, as in Case III, it is quite possible that the combination of E with MS will take place through the metal atom. In that case the active centre of the enzyme may well combine with free metal as well as with the substrate-bound metal, though not necessarily with the same affinity. We must then consider, in addition to the reactions IX.49–51, the equilibrium

IX.74
$$\text{E} + \text{M} = \text{EM}$$

with dissociation constant K_A. This leads to the equations

IX.75
$$v = \frac{ke}{1 + \dfrac{K_0 K_{AS}}{as}\left(1 + \dfrac{a}{K_A}\right)}$$

and

IX.76

$$v = \cfrac{ke}{\left(1-\cfrac{K_{AS}}{K_A}\right) + \left(1+\cfrac{a_t}{K_A}\right)\cfrac{2K_{AS}}{(K_0+a_t+s_t) - \sqrt{\{(K_0+a_t+s_t)^2 - 4a_ts_t\}}}}$$

These equations, like those of Case IV, are no longer symmetrical in a and s, and the observed Michaelis constants for substrate and activator are different complicated functions of the equilibrium constants and the total concentrations.

It is implicit in the assumptions of Case V that there is competition between M and MS for the enzyme. Excess of metal added after all the substrate has been converted into MS will therefore act as a competitive inhibitor. It is in fact frequently observed that as the concentration of metal activator is increased, the velocity rises to a maximum and falls again at higher concentrations. This is reflected in the competition term $\left(1+\dfrac{a_t}{K_A}\right)$ in equation IX.76, which tends to reduce the velocity with increase of a_t, just as the competitive effect of S with MS in Case IV is reflected in the competition term $\left(1+\dfrac{s_t}{K_s}\right)$ in equation IX.72.

Case VI. The most general case, from which the equations for all the other cases may be deduced, is that in which both free substrate and free metal combine with the enzyme as well as with each other, so that the equilibria, with their corresponding constants may be written as follows:

IX.77 $E + M = EM$ K_A

IX.78 $EM + S = EMS$ K'_s

IX.79 $E + S = ES$ K_s

IX.80 $ES + M = EMS$ K'_A

IX.81 $M + S = MS$ K_0

IX.82 $E + MS = EMS$ K_{AS}

These form three pairs of reactions by which EMS is formed from E, M and S, with the combinations occurring in different sequences.

It is of course unlikely that all of these reactions would be of importance in any one case. EMS is written here for the active complex, but it may represent four different structures, namely, E–M–S, E–S–M, M–E–S or $E\diagup_{\diagdown M}^{S}$. In the first case, where the metal acts as a link, the complex might be formed by reactions IX.78 or IX.82, but hardly by IX.80. Similarly, the complex E–S–M could hardly be formed by reaction IX.78. In the first case there is no combination of E with S, in the second of E with M and in the third of M with S. It is only with the fourth structure that all the reactions would be chemically probable. However, these considerations do not affect the following treatment. They merely make it likely that some of the constants will approach infinity.

From the definitions of the equilibrium constants we get

IX.83 $$K_A K'_s = K_s K'_A = K_0 K_{AS}$$

Any four of the above equilibria are sufficient to obtain the velocity equation in terms of the *free* components

IX.84 $$v = \frac{ke}{1 + \dfrac{K_0 K_{AS}}{as}\left(1 + \dfrac{a}{K_A} + \dfrac{s}{K_s}\right)}$$

which can be converted into a variety of other forms by substitutions from IX.83. Equation IX.40 of Case I can be obtained by putting $K_0 K_{AS} = K_A K'_s$ and $K'_s = K_s$; equation IX.43 of Case II by putting $K_0 K_{AS} = K_A K'_s$; equation IX.55 of Case III by putting $K_A = K_s = \infty$; equation IX.68 of Case IV by putting $K_A = \infty$; and equation IX.75 of Case V by putting $K_s = \infty$.

The corresponding equation in terms of *total* concentrations is unfortunately too complicated for practical use, and experimental data in terms of total concentrations can only be treated by the equations developed for the special cases I–V.

Criteria for determination of mechanism. The general conclusion which follows from these kinetic considerations is that the common assumption, that the observed Michaelis constant for activating metal ion is the reciprocal of its affinity for the enzyme, is usually incorrect. Correspondingly, the observed Michaelis constant for substrate may include functions of the affinities of the activating ion for substrate and enzyme. This is quite apart from the fact that the Michaelis constants may be partly kinetic in nature, as pointed out in Chapter IV, p. 93.

In order to investigate the action of the activating metal ion in any particular case it is desirable to have more information than can be obtained from measurements of velocity with varying amounts of added substrate and metal ion. For instance, physical methods have recently become available for measuring the concentration of free Mg^{++} and other ions in presence of undissociated metal complexes. Also, in some cases the affinity constants of the metal–substrate combination may be determined independently of enzymatic experiments.

The determination of the mechanism is made much easier if there is a time effect in the activation of the enzyme. In many cases the effect of the metal takes some hours to develop. In such cases the full activity requires the incubation of metal with enzyme, because the metal–protein interaction (for which the presence of the substrate is not necessary) takes place only slowly. Previous incubation of metal with substrate in the absence of the enzyme has no effect. Enzymes which behave in this way, for instance arginase, are therefore activated by the mechanism set out in equation IX.29, in which the active form of the enzyme is EM (Case I or II). Such time effects seem to be common for the activation by Mn^{++} or Co^{++} of peptidases and certain related enzymes acting on nitrogenous groupings; they are usually not observed with Mg^{++}-activated enzymes.

If it is found that the Michaelis constants of substrate and activator are the same when each is varied with the same fixed concentration of the other, it is highly probable that the metal and substrate combine to give the true substrate of the enzyme and that only this complex combines with the enzyme to any great extent (Case III). This conclusion is based on the fact that if free metal or free substrate combine with the enzyme as well as MS, the K_ms are no longer the same (Cases IV and V). If, however, both free metal and free substrate as well as MS combine with the enzyme (Case VI) and the affinities for metal and substrate are the same, a symmetrical expression will again be obtained. This last possibility seems rather unlikely.

A conclusion on kinetic grounds that the activation involves metal-substrate combination is strongly reinforced where it is possible to show independently that such combination takes place, and to measure K_0. For example, the combination of Mg^{++} with ATP was shown by titration with and without the metal by HERS (1084) and ASKONAS (93). A number of attempts have been made to measure the constants of dissociation of Mg–ATP complexes into Mg^{++} and ATP, but there is a variation of up to fifty-fold between the different results. From the most recent studies (2035), $K_0 = [Mg^{++}][ATP^{----}]/[Mg-ATP^{--}] = 10^{-5}M$, in reasonable agreement with the value of $1 \cdot 1 \times 10^{-5}M$ calculated from kinetic data on creatine kinase (1983). This supports the conclusion that this complex is the substrate of creatine kinase. In the reverse reaction, where the combination of Mg^{++} with ADP is relatively slight, MORRISON et al. (1869) conclude that the E–Mg–ADP complex may be formed by random-order combination.

The existence of metal–substrate complexes, though not necessarily enzymatically active, is revealed by a change of the equilibrium constant of the enzyme-catalysed reaction with a change in the nature or concentration of the activating metal, and we will now consider such changes.

(b) *Equilibrium effects.* Let us suppose that we have a reversible enzyme reaction $S_f \rightleftharpoons S_b$ with equilibrium constant given by

IX.85 $$K = \frac{s_b}{s_f}$$

and let us suppose that both S_f and S_b form complexes with the metal M with dissociation constants K_{0f} and K_{0b} respectively. Then

IX.86 $$K_{0f} = \frac{s_f a}{q_f}$$

IX.87 $$K_{0b} = \frac{s_b a}{q_b}$$

where a is the concentration of *free* metal ions, s_f and s_b are the concentrations of free S_f and S_b, and q_f and q_b are the concentrations of MS_f and MS_b respectively.

The total concentrations of the substrates are given by

IX.88 $$s_{ft} = s_f + q_f$$

IX.89 $$s_{bt} = s_b + q_b$$

K_t, the apparent equilibrium constant expressed in terms of *total* added concentrations of the substrates, is by definition

IX.90 $$K_t = \frac{s_{bt}}{s_{ft}}$$

Substituting equations IX.85–89 in this, we get

IX.91 $$K_t = K \frac{\left(1 + \dfrac{a}{K_{0b}}\right)}{\left(1 + \dfrac{a}{K_{0f}}\right)}$$

This equation shows how the equilibrium constant changes with the concentration of free metal ion; it shows that, if K_{0f} differs from K_{0b}, the observed equilibrium constant will be different from the true constant obtained in the absence of metal. By extrapolating K_t to $a = 0$, K can be obtained.

Experimental results are normally plotted against the *total* added concentration of metal a_t. From the equation

IX.92 $a_t = a + q_f + q_b$

and the previous equations, we obtain the following cubic equation from which a may be determined

IX.93 $a^3 + a^2(K_{0f} + K_{0b} + s_{ft} + s_{bt} - a_t) +$
$+ a(K_{0f}K_{0b} + K_{0f}s_{bt} + K_{0b}s_{ft} - K_{0f}a_t - K_{0b}a_t) -$
$- K_{0f}K_{0b}a_t = 0$

The appropriate root of this equation can then be substituted for a in equation IX.91. This can be done numerically, but is extremely laborious.

The equations become much simpler in the case where only s_f combines with metal, so that K_{0b} can be taken as infinite. Then equation IX.91 becomes

IX.94 $K_t = \dfrac{K}{\left(1 + \dfrac{a}{K_{0f}}\right)}$

and IX.93 reduces to the quadratic equation

IX.95 $a^2 + a(K_{0f} + s_{ft} - a_t) - K_{0f}a_t = 0$

whence

IX.96 $K_t = K . \dfrac{2K_{0f}}{K_{0f} + a_t - s_{ft} + \sqrt{\{(K_{0f} + s_{ft} - a_t)^2 + 4K_{0f}a_t\}}}$

This equation might be expected to fit the cases of many of the kinases. For instance, in the creatine kinase system affinity measurements show that ATP has a much greater affinity for Mg^{++} than any other component of the system, although that of ADP cannot be entirely neglected in accurate calculations. Combination with other components, e.g. creatine phosphate, is usually entirely negligible. With the kinases in mind, we have plotted from equation IX.96 the curves shown in Fig. IX.33, taking K_{0f} as 10^{-5}M, the most recent value. It will be seen that the effect of moderate concentrations of Mg^{++} on K_t is very great, and this is a very important effect in such systems. The effect of a given metal concentration depends on the substrate concentration and is less the higher the latter becomes. At low substrate concentration the logarithmic plot gives a normal S-shaped curve whose mid-point gives

pK_{0f}. At higher substrate concentrations this curve becomes distorted, because the substrate more effectively counteracts the effect of metal at low metal concentrations, and the mid-point is considerably displaced.

These curves, which can only be regarded as a first approximation, may be compared with the experimental curves for the creatine kinase system obtained by NODA *et al.* (*1982*) and by ASKONAS (*93*). Results obtained by Askonas are shown in Fig. IX.34; these are in general agreement with our theoretical curves, except that at higher metal concentration $1/K_t$ becomes constant, and does not rise to infinity

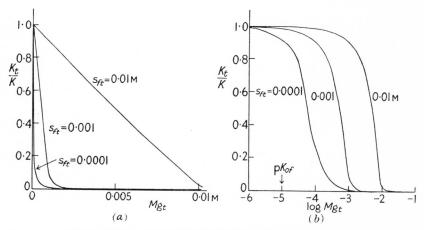

Fig. IX.33. *Theoretical curves showing effect of concentration of added* Mg^{++} *ions* (Mg_t) *on equilibrium constant with different amounts of added substrate.* Plotted from equation IX.96, taking K_{0f} as 10^{-5} M.

as predicted by the simple theory. This is to be expected, because at high metal concentrations the ADP also will combine with Mg^{++}; when the metal concentration is sufficiently high to saturate both ATP and ADP, any further increases will have no effect on the overall equilibrium constant.

Unspecific anionic effects

As first shown by COLE (*478*) in 1904, the activity of some enzymes is greatly influenced by the presence of anions; for example, animal α-amylases are so greatly affected that chloride ion has been regarded as the natural activator of these enzymes. Other monovalent (but not divalent) ions also have some effect on the activity. These effects are paralleled by changes in physical properties of the pure enzyme, e.g.

solubility and electrophoretic mobility (*1905*). Another classical case of an anion-sensitive enzyme is fumarate hydratase as first shown by MANN and WOOLF (*1706*); this, however, is activated only by divalent and trivalent anions. With most enzymes the effects of anions are negligible at ordinary concentrations.

Examination of the effects at various pHs shows that they can be

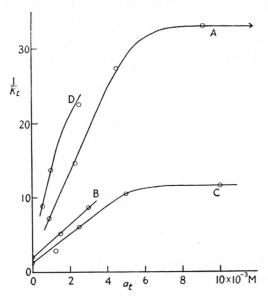

Fig. IX.34. *Dependence of equilibrium constant of creatine kinase on total concentration of activating metal (a_t).*

A, with Mg^{++} at pH 8·45 in glycine buffer.
B, with Mg^{++} at pH 8·8 in glycine buffer.
C, with Mg^{++} at pH 8·8 in ethanolamine buffer.
D, with Mn^{++} at pH 8·45 in glycine buffer.

$$K_t = \frac{[ATP]_t.[creatine]_t}{[ADP]_t.[creatine\ phosphate]_t}$$

from *93*

treated as a displacement of one or both sides of the velocity-pH curve, or, in other words, a real or apparent change in the values of the ionization constants K_{es1} and K_{es2} (see Chapter IV, section c), which determine the two sides of the pH curve.

Fig. IX.35 shows the results obtained by MYRBÄCK(*1912*) with salivary amylase, and Fig. IX.36 shows those of MASSEY (*1744*) with crystalline fumarate hydratase. As would be expected on general grounds, combination with negative ions always produces a displacement to the right; this may affect either side of the pH curve, or both sides. Thus the effect of chloride and bromide ions on amylase, and of phosphate, arsenate, citrate and other ions on fumarate hydratase is on $K_{es\,2}$ only, so that only the right-hand side is affected. This produces an activation, particularly at alkaline pHs, and a shift of the optimum pH towards the alkaline side. On the other hand, the effect of chloride on fumarate hydratase is on the

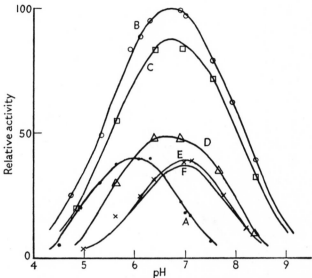

Fig. IX.35. *Activation of salivary α-amylase (3.2.1.1) by anions as a function of pH.*

A, in absence of added anions (apart from phosphate).
B, in 0·005 M or 0·04 M chloride.
C, in 0·04 M bromide.
D, in 0·04 M iodide.
E, in 0·1 M nitrate.
F, in 0·1 M chlorate.
All in 0·03 M phosphate.

from *1912*

left-hand side of the curve only, producing an inhibition, particularly at acid pHs, and a shift of the lowered optimum, still towards the alkaline side. Iodide, nitrate and chlorate shift both sides of the amylase curve, so that the whole curve is displaced; this produces an inhibition on the acid side and an activation on the alkaline side, so that there is little change of the maximum velocity.

Massey explains the fumarate hydratase results by a combination of anion with a basic group adjacent to either of the two ionizable groups in the active centre which determine the pH curve. No matter whether the group in the active centre which is affected is acidic or basic, the suppression of an adjacent positive charge will increase its pK and shift its titration curve in an alkaline direction.

Not all anionic activations are due to displacements of pH curves. WEBB and MORROW (*2809*), with an arylsulphatase B from ox liver,

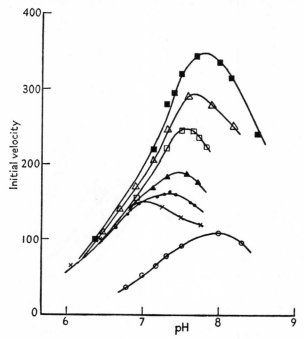

Fig. IX.36. *Activation of fumarate hydratase* (4.2.1.2) *by anions as a function of pH.*

× No added anion.
○ 0·1 M chloride.
● 0·03 M selenate or 0·025 M sulphate.
▲ 0·01 M arsenite.
□ 0·01 M citrate.
△ 0·06 M phosphate.
■ 0·05 M arsenate.

from *1744*

showed that the hydrolysis of *p*-nitrophenyl sulphate (but not of some other substrates) is strongly activated by chloride and some other univalent ions. The pH curves in presence and absence of chloride are of identical form and position, differing only in height. Chloride has no effect on the affinity of the enzyme for this substrate, so that it seems probable that we are dealing here with a direct effect of chloride on $\tilde{k}_{+2}$.

ALBERTY (32) has given a general mathematical treatment of the effect of such buffer salts on the maximum velocity and the effective Michaelis constant in relation to the effect of pH. This has been developed on the assumption that all combinations with the enzyme are rapid compared with the rate of formation of product. The equilibria considered by Alberty may be written, using our symbols, as

IX.97

$$
\begin{array}{ccccc}
& & E^n+P & & \\
& & \uparrow \tilde{k}_{+2} & & \\
ES^{n-1} & \underset{K_{es1}}{\rightleftharpoons} & ES^n & \underset{K_{es2}}{\rightleftharpoons} & ES^{n+1} \\
\updownarrow & & \updownarrow \tilde{K}_s & & \updownarrow \\
E^{n-1} & \underset{K_{e1}}{\rightleftharpoons} & E^n & \underset{K_{e2}}{\rightleftharpoons} & E^{n+1} \\
\updownarrow & & \updownarrow \tilde{K}_A & & \updownarrow \\
EA^{n-1+x} & \underset{K_{ea1}}{\rightleftharpoons} & EA^{n+x} & \underset{K_{ea2}}{\rightleftharpoons} & EA^{n+1+x} \\
\updownarrow & & \updownarrow \tilde{K}'_s & & \updownarrow \\
EAS^{n-1+x} & \underset{K_{eas1}}{\rightleftharpoons} & EAS^{n+x} & \underset{K_{eas2}}{\rightleftharpoons} & EAS^{n+1+x} \\
& & \downarrow \tilde{k}'_{+2} & & \\
& & EA^{n+x}+P & &
\end{array}
$$

where $\tilde{K}_s$ is, as in Chapter IV, the pH-independent equilibrium constant defined by equation IV.169, $\tilde{K}'_s$ is the corresponding constant for the substration of the complex, n is as before the number of negative charges on the active form of the enzyme, and x is the number of negative charges on the anion. x has been introduced to show the actual charge on the complexes, but does not enter into the mathematical treatment. It is not necessary to consider the equilibria for which constants have not been written, since these are already provided for by the existing constants.

Alberty has obtained expressions for V and K_m in the presence of a concentration a of anion. The expression for V is as follows

IX.98

$$
V = \frac{\tilde{k}_{+2}e+\tilde{k}'_{+2}e \cdot \dfrac{a\tilde{K}_s}{\tilde{K}_A\tilde{K}'_s}}{\left(1+\dfrac{H}{K_{es1}}+\dfrac{K_{es2}}{H}\right)+\dfrac{a\tilde{K}_s}{\tilde{K}_A\tilde{K}'_s}\left(1+\dfrac{H}{K_{eas1}}+\dfrac{K_{eas2}}{H}\right)}
$$

In the absence of anion, $a = 0$, and this equation reduces to

IX.99
$$V = \frac{\check{k}_{+2}e}{1 + \dfrac{H}{K_{es1}} + \dfrac{K_{es2}}{H}}$$

This is identical with equation IV.159, already obtained for the effect of pH on an enzyme reaction.

At very high anion concentration, on the other hand, equation IX.98 reduces to

IX.100
$$V = \frac{\check{k}'_{+2}e}{1 + \dfrac{H}{K_{eas1}} + \dfrac{K_{eas2}}{H}}$$

Thus when the enzyme is saturated with anion, the new pH curve determined by the constants of the EAS complex is obtained.

Equation IX.98 can be conveniently expressed in terms of the pH function f^- (equation IV.133), relative concentrations (compare equation IV.13) and the 'relative activation constant' $\tilde{r} = \dfrac{\check{K}_s}{\check{K}'_s}$ (compare equation IV.49) as follows

IX.101
$$V = \frac{\check{k}_{+2}e + \check{k}'_{+2}e\alpha\tilde{r}}{f^-_{es} + \alpha\tilde{r}f^-_{eas}}$$

Alberty's expression for K_s is equivalent to

IX.102
$$K_s = \check{K}_s . \frac{\left(1 + \dfrac{H}{K_{e1}} + \dfrac{K_{e2}}{H}\right) + \dfrac{a}{\check{K}_A}\left(1 + \dfrac{H}{K_{ea1}} + \dfrac{K_{ea2}}{H}\right)}{\left(1 + \dfrac{H}{K_{es1}} + \dfrac{K_{es2}}{H}\right) + \dfrac{a\check{K}_s}{\check{K}_A\check{K}'_s}\left(1 + \dfrac{H}{K_{eas1}} + \dfrac{K_{eas2}}{H}\right)}$$

Expressed in terms of f^- and α, this becomes

IX.103
$$K_s = \check{K}_s . \frac{f^-_e + \alpha f^-_{ea}}{f^-_{es} + \alpha\tilde{r}f^-_{eas}}$$

In the absence of anion, when α becomes 0,

IX.104
$$K_s = \check{K}_s . \frac{f^-_e}{f^-_{es}}$$

This is the same as equation IV.170, f_s being taken as unity, since the substrate has been assumed not to ionize. At high anion concentration, on the other hand, K_s reaches the limiting value given by

IX.105
$$K_s = \check{K}_s . \frac{f^-_{ea}}{\tilde{r}f^-_{eas}}$$

Alberty has considered some additional complications introduced when the anion competes with the substrate as well as activating the enzyme as described above, or when an additional competitive inhibitor is present. The equations obtained were found to be in general agreement with observations on the effect of phosphate on fumarate hydratase obtained earlier by Alberty.

THEORELL *et al.* (*2638a*) determined the effect of anions on the six velocity constants corresponding to the separate steps in the reaction catalysed by liver alcohol dehydrogenase. They found that, for example, $0 \cdot 15 \, \text{M}$ Cl⁻ decreases the rates of combination of the enzyme with oxidized and reduced NAD to about half, while doubling the rate of dissociation of the reduced coenzyme from the enzyme and halving that of the oxidized coenzyme.

Lipophilic ions

Some enzymes acting on water-insoluble, neutral molecules show activation by negatively charged lipophilic molecules. One of the most-studied cases is the lysophospholipase of *Penicillium* (3.1.1.5). This acts readily on lysophosphoglycerides, but does not act on lecithin except in the presence of phosphatidylinositol or anionic detergents, e.g. sodium dodecylsulphate or sodium dicetyl-phosphate (BANGHAM and DAWSON, *155*). This is not due to the increase of surface on emulsification, since the same effect is shown when the enzyme acts on monolayers of the substrate (*156*). The activation is prevented by multivalent cations and by cationic detergents. It was shown that the substrate micelles must have a negative electrokinetic potential exceeding a certain critical value in order to be attacked.

POLYNUCLEOTIDE TEMPLATES

Certain enzymes synthesizing proteins or nucleic acids require cofactors of another type, namely templates which determine the sequence of units in the chains built up. In systems synthesizing nucleic acids, which are discussed in detail in the section on protein biosynthesis in Chapter XI, polynucleotide chains are built up by the enzyme from a mixture of nucleoside triphosphates with liberation of pyrophosphate, and the order in which the different nucleotides are joined together is determined by the order of the nucleotides in the template, so that the chain built up is complementary to the chain in the template. In systems of this type the template cofactor determines the specificity with respect to the non-reacting part of the substrate molecules, i.e. the specificity for particular

Q

purines or pyrimidines, while the enzyme determines the nature of the main chain formed.

It will not have escaped the reader's notice that it is not always possible to make a sharp distinction, for purposes of definition, between a prosthetic group forming a part of the enzyme, a coenzyme distinct from the enzyme but forming a part of the catalytic mechanism, and a substrate acting purely as a reactant in the enzyme-catalysed reaction. It is possible in fact to draw up a series of cases showing a gradual transition from prosthetic group in the strict sense, through coenzymes, to true substrates. In peroxidase (1.11.1.7), the haem group is an undoubted prosthetic group; so it is also in the yeast lactate dehydrogenase (1.1.2.3), where it acts as a carrier by undergoing reduction and oxidation. There seem to be no grounds for making a distinction between such groups and firmly-bound flavin groups in such flavoprotein enzymes as lipoamide dehydrogenase (1.6.4.3), where the flavin group acts in a similar way. The same group (FAD) also occurs in the D-aminoacid oxidase (1.4.3.3), with a similar function, though it differs from the previous case in being less firmly bound to the protein, and has sometimes been called a coenzyme. The difference, however, is only a question of the magnitude of the dissociation constant and is not a fundamental one; among the flavoprotein enzymes there are many which have intermediate values between the very low constant of lipoamide dehydrogenase and the fairly high one of D-aminoacid oxidase. The latter enzyme is very similar to the glutamate dehydrogenase (1.4.1.2), in which the aminoacid is oxidized not by FAD but by NAD. The resemblance is particularly close because the two oxidants are very similar in chemical structure, the nicotinamide group replacing the isoalloxazine group as the actual oxidant. If we consider dehydrogenases as separate enzymes, it is clear that, as we have already seen, each enzyme is merely catalysing a bimolecular reaction between the aminoacid or other substrate and NAD, and in this reaction the latter is a substrate no less than the former. The existence of other enzymes which can reoxidize $NADH_2$, so forming systems in which NAD acts as a catalytic coenzyme, is irrelevant when we are considering the separate dehydrogenases, and there is as little justification for denying the right of NAD to be considered as an enzyme substrate as there is in other cases where substrates act as carriers. In Table XII.6, for instance, glyoxylate and NAD are fulfilling precisely similar functions, and there are no grounds on which a distinction between them could be based. A similar case is that of glutamate in transamination; this is an undoubted substrate.

Thus we have a series in which it seems difficult to draw a dividing line at any point.

It has been suggested that firmness of combination with the enzyme protein should be used as a criterion for deciding whether a given substance is or is not a prosthetic group. This, however, seems impracticable. Many substrates have very high affinities for their enzymes, in fact very much higher than some substances which have been regarded as prosthetic groups. In the flavoprotein series it would be difficult to know just where to draw the line; for instance, it would be illogical to fix an arbitrary limit and say that FAD is a prosthetic group in a flavoprotein if its dissociation constant is $0 \cdot 8 \times 10^{-3}$ but a coenzyme if it is $1 \cdot 2 \times 10^{-3}$!

There is, however, one definite difference between typical prosthetic groups and carriers such as NAD. A true prosthetic group undergoes its whole catalytic cycle while attached to the same enzyme protein molecule; a carrier like NAD must migrate from one enzyme protein to another in order to fulfil its catalytic function. NAD, when combined with glutamate dehydrogenase, can be reduced by glutamate, but as long as it remains attached to the enzyme molecule there is nothing further that it can do. It must leave this enzyme and migrate to another by which it can be oxidized in order to act catalytically. On the other hand, a prosthetic group such as the flavin in glucose oxidase (1.1.3.4) is reduced and oxidized while it remains attached to the same molecule of enzyme protein.

If this difference is adopted as a distinction between prosthetic groups and substrates, as far as present knowledge goes haems, flavins, biotin and pyridoxal phosphate would be considered as prosthetic groups, while NAD, NADP and coenzyme A would be considered as carrier substrates.

X

ENZYME STRUCTURE

AN ENZYME MAY in general be pictured as a protein containing a special structure, the active centre, with sometimes an additional prosthetic group attached. The subject of enzyme structure therefore includes (i) the structure of the protein, which may be subdivided into (*a*) size (molecular weight), (*b*) number of peptide chains and the sequence of aminoacids therein, and (*c*) folding and arrangement of the peptide chains in the whole molecule (tertiary structure); (ii) the nature of the active centre, which involves (*a*) number of active centres per molecule, and (*b*) chemical nature of the substrate-binding and activating groups in the active centre; and (iii) structure of the prosthetic group, if any, and its mode of attachment to the protein. The structure of the known prosthetic groups, however, has already been dealt with in the preceding chapter.

MOLECULAR WEIGHT

The molecular weights of pure enzymes may be determined by the usual physical methods which have been developed for the determination of protein molecular weights in general. We shall not describe these methods in detail; for a general review, see section 1 of Vol. IV of *481*. Table X.1 gives a fairly complete list of the known molecular weights of enzymes. In many cases only one value exists in the literature and we have given this. In a number of cases a wealth of discordant values is available, and instead of giving the separate values we have attempted to produce a representative figure, giving due weight to the reliability of the different methods, preference usually being given to values calculated from sedimentation and diffusion constants. The different methods often give very different results, different workers often obtain different results with the same method, and even with the same authors and the same method, different results may be obtained with different instruments. For instance, the Svedberg type of ultracentrifuge gives values of sedimentation constants about 10 per cent higher than those found with a Spinco ultracentrifuge, owing to difficulty in controlling the temperature of the cell in the former (*1675*), and this difference has not been allowed for in many cases. The figures in the table necessarily vary considerably in their accuracy.

TABLE X.1

MOLECULAR WEIGHTS OF ENZYMES

Hydrogenase (1.98.1.1) (*Desulphovibrio*)	9,000
Aspergillus oryzae ribonuclease (3.1.4.8)	11,000
Cellulase (3.2.1.4)(*Polyporus*)	11,400
Ribonuclease (2.7.7.16)	12,700
Acylphosphatase (3.6.1.7) (ox brain)	13,000
γ-chymotrypsin (3.4.4.5)	15,000–25,000
α-amylase (3.2.1.1) (*B. stearothermophilus*)	15,500
Muramidase (3.2.1.17) (egg white)	17,000
Papain (3.4.4.10)	20,700
Adenylate kinase (2.7.4.3)	21,000
α-chymotrypsin (3.4.4.5)	23,000
Chymotrypsin B (3.4.4.6)	22,500
β-chymotrypsin (3.4.4.5)	23,000
Trypsin (3.4.4.4)	23,800
Phosphoglycerate phosphomutase (5.4.2.1) (wheat and rice germ)..	*about* 30,000
Polymetaphosphatase (3.6.1.10)	33,000
Carbonic anhydrase (4.2.1.1) (human erythrocytes) ..	34,000
Peroxidase (1.11.1.7) (turnip)	34,000–41,000
Carboxypeptidase A (3.4.2.1)	34,300
Carboxypeptidase B (3.4.2.2) (pig)	34,300
Pepsin (3.4.4.1)	35,000
Thiosulphate sulphurtransferase (2.8.1.1)	37,000
Peroxidase (1.11.1.7) (horseradish)	40,000
Rennin (3.4.4.3)	40,000
$NADH_2$ cytochrome b_5 reductase (1.6.2.2) (calf liver)	40,000
Steroid Δ-isomerase (5.3.3.1) (*Pseudomonas*)	40,800
α-chymotrypsin (3.4.4.5) (dimer)	42,900
Chymopapain (3.4.4.11)	45,000
α-amylase (3.2.1.1) (pancreas)	45,000
Glucosephosphate isomerase (5.3.1.9) (ox mammary gland)	48,000
α-amylase (3.2.1.1) (*B. subtilis*)	48,700
Menadione reductase (1.6.5.2) (ox liver)	52,000
Malate dehydrogenase (1.1.1.37) (ox heart supernatant)..	52,000
Peroxidase (1.11.1.7) (Japanese radish)	55,000
Citrate synthase (4.1.3.7) (pig heart)	56,000
Cathepsin D (3.4.4.b) (ox spleen)	56,000
Phosphoglyceromutase (2.7.5.3) (rabbit muscle).. ..	57,000
α-amylase (3.2.1.1) (malt)	59,000
Glutathione reductase (1.6.4.2) (peas)	60,000
Malate dehydrogenase (1.1.1.37) (ox heart mitochondria)	62,000

TABLE X.1—*continued*

Deoxyribonuclease (3.1.4.5)	63,000
Inorganic pyrophosphatase (3.6.1.1)	63,000
Phosphopyruvate hydratase (4.2.1.11) (yeast)	64,000
Isocitrate dehydrogenase (1.1.1.42) (heart)	64,000
meso-inositol oxygenase (1.99.2.6) (rat kidney)	68,000
Phosphoglucomutase (2.7.5.1)	74,000–78,000
NADPH$_2$ cytochrome c reductase (1.6.2.3) (yeast)	75,000
NADH$_2$ cytochrome c reductase (1.6.2.1) (animal)	75,000–80,000
Phosphopyruvate hydratase (4.2.1.11) (rabbit muscle)	80,000
Catechol 1,2-oxygenase (1.99.2.2) (*Pseudomonas*)	*about* 80,000
Leucine aminopeptidase (3.4.1.1)	75,000–80,000
Creatine kinase (2.7.3.2)	81,000
Peroxidase (1.11.1.7) (milk)	82,000
Alcohol dehydrogenase (1.1.1.1) (liver)	84,000
Hexokinase (2.7.1.1) (yeast)	96,600
Urate oxidase (1.7.3.3)	100,000
Catechol oxidase (1.10.3.1)	100,000
Luciferase (fireflies)	100,000
Lipoamide dehydrogenase (1.6.4.3) (pig heart)	100,000
Alkaline phosphatase (3.1.3.1) (calf intestine)	*about* 100,000
Lipoxygenase (1.99.2.1) (soy bean)	102,000
Plasmin (3.4.4.14) (glycerol-activated, human blood)	108,000
Clostridiopeptidase A (3.4.4.19) (*Clostridium*)	109,000
Aspartate aminotransferase (2.6.1.1) (pig heart)	110,000
Lipoamide dehydrogenase (1.6.4.3) (*Esch. coli*)	112,000
Phosphoglyceromutase (2.7.5.3) (yeast)	112,000
p-diphenol oxidase (1.10.3.2) (*Rhus vernicifera*)	120,000
Glyceraldehydephosphate dehydrogenase (1.2.1.12) (yeast)	122,000
L-aminoacid oxidase (1.4.3.2) (animal, snake venom)	130,000
Lactate dehydrogenase (1.1.1.27) (heart)	135,000
Glyceraldehydephosphate dehydrogenase (1.2.1.12) (muscle)	137,000
Glycollate oxidase (1.1.3.1) (spinach)	140,000
Transketolase (2.2.1.1) (yeast)	140,000
Arginase (3.5.3.1)	*about* 140,000
Glucosephosphate isomerase (5.3.1.9) (yeast)	145,000
Ascorbate oxidase (1.10.3.3)	146,000–150,000
Aldolase (4.1.2.b) (muscle)	147,000–180,000
Butyryl-CoA dehydrogenase (1.3.2.1)	150,000–200,000
Glucose oxidase (1.1.3.4) (*Penicillium*)	150,000–152,000
β-amylase (3.2.1.2) (sweet potato)	152,000
Alcohol dehydrogenase (1.1.1.1) (yeast)	151,000
Aldolase (4.1.2.7) (liver)	159,000

TABLE X.1—*continued*

Lactate dehydrogenase (1.1.2.3) (yeast)	170,000
D-aminoacid oxidase (1.4.3.3) (pig kidney)	182,000
Homoserine dehydratase (4.2.1.15) (rat liver) ..	*about* 200,000
Succinate dehydrogenase (1.3.99.1) (heart) ..	*about* 200,000
Fumarate hydratase (4.2.1.2) (heart)	204,000
Enoyl-CoA hydratase (4.2.1.17) (liver)	210,000
Aspartate carbamoyltransferase (2.1.3.2) (*Esch. coli*) ..	220,000
Catalase (1.11.1.6) (horse liver)	225,000
ATPase (3.6.1.3) (myosin, dog heart)	230,000
Catalase (1.11.1.6) (bacteria)	232,000
α-glucan phosphorylase (2.4.1.1) (liver)	237,000
Pyruvate kinase (2.7.1.40)	237,000
Catalase (1.11.1.6) (ox liver)	248,000
α-glucan phosphorylase *b* (muscle)	250,000
Glycerol kinase (2.7.1.30) (yeast)	251,000
Pyruvate dehydrogenase (1.2.4.1) (*Esch. coli*)	265,000
Xanthine oxidase (1.2.3.2) (milk)	290,000
AMP deaminase (3.5.4.6) (rabbit muscle)	320,000
Urease (3.5.1.5) (soy bean)..	480,000
α-glucan phosphorylase *a* (2.4.1.1) (muscle)	495,000
ATPase (3.6.1.3) (myosin, rabbit muscle)	540,000
Phosphoketolase (4.1.2.9) (*Lactobacillus*)	550,000
Propionyl-CoA carboxylase (6.4.1.3) (pig heart)	700,000
Glutamate dehydrogenase (1.4.1.3) (liver)	1,000,000
Pyruvate decarboxylase (4.1.1.1) (wheat germ)	> 1,000,000

The values show a fairly wide range, varying from about 10,000 to a million; the smallest active enzyme molecules found in living matter have molecular weights of not less than 9,000. There is a tendency for the smaller molecules to be comparatively heat-stable, for example, ribonuclease with a molecular weight of 12,700 can be boiled in acid solution without loss of activity.

The great majority of the enzymes in the table form solutions which are monodisperse when examined in the ultracentrifuge. Occasionally, however, an enzyme of higher molecular weight undergoes a spontaneous reversible dissociation into two or four equal parts; this has also been observed with some non-enzymatic proteins. The equilibrium between the two forms may show up in the ultracentrifuge either as two peaks, or as an asymmetry of a single peak, together with a dependence of the sedimentation constant on the concentration of the protein (GILBERT, *834*).

In an appreciable number of cases the naturally occurring forms of enzymes appear to consist of a small number of similar sub-units, often two, three or four. In some cases these enzymes dissociate spontaneously on dilution; in others they are held together by small molecules such as prosthetic groups, coenzymes or substrates, and when these are removed the molecule falls apart; and in yet others the sub-units can only be separated by more drastic treatment, for example in concentrated urea solutions. The monomeric forms are sometimes active enzymatically and sometimes inactive.

The following examples will illustrate these effects. α-chymotrypsin exists in moderate concentration principally as a dimer but dissociates reversibly on dilution, giving an active monomer of molecular weight 23,000. At higher concentrations the trimer is formed (*2170*). Glycollate oxidase from spinach exists in solution in two forms of molecular weight 140,000 and 270,000, the larger one containing four flavin groups per molecule. These are rapidly interconvertible at low ionic strength, although at high ionic strength the forms can be separated. The smaller form as isolated contains no flavin, and is inactive, but can be reactivated by added FMN; while the larger form contains flavin and shows considerable activity without added FMN. The specific activity of the smaller form with added FMN is one-third of that of the larger form. D-amino-acid oxidase, a flavoprotein which has a comparatively low affinity for FAD, exists in a series of polymeric forms of a unit of molecular weight 45,700, each of which can combine with one flavin group. The enzyme dissociates to the monomer on dilution; at moderate protein concentrations FAD favours formation of the tetramer (*437*).

The case of yeast alcohol dehydrogenase, and its dissociation into four sub-units on removal of the four Zn atoms, has already been discussed on p. 307. Muscle α-glucan phosphorylases *a* and *b* form a pair of interconvertible proteins. Phosphorylase *a*, which is active, has a molecular weight of 495,000, contains four molecules of pyridoxal phosphate, and can bind four molecules of AMP per molecule. Phosphorylase *b*, which is inactive, has a molecular weight of 242,000, and can bind two molecules of AMP; in the presence of excess Mg^{++} it forms a crystallizable dimer (*1362*). Conversion of one form into the other is brought about enzymatically in this case, and a definite chemical reaction is involved, namely the addition of two phosphate groups per molecule of phosphorylase *b* by a specific kinase, or the removal of four phosphate groups per molecule of phosphorylase *a* by a phosphatase (*1459–60, 2726a*). *p*-Chloromercuribenzoate can also bring about a dissociation of phosphorylase *a* (*1674*). Glutamate dehydrogenase of liver dissociates into inactive subunits on dilution, and the dissociation is increased by high concentrations of $NADH_2$ by combination with a non-catalytic binding site. $NADPH_2$, which is also a substrate for the enzyme, cannot combine with this site and does not cause dissociation. Low concentrations of the oxidized and reduced forms of either of the coenzymes favour association to the active form (*780*). Propionyl-CoA carboxylase from pig heart has a molecular weight of 700,000 and contains four bound molecules of biotin. In strong urea it dissociates into four inactive sub-units (*1326*).

In a few cases preparations of an enzyme from two different sources are similarly related to each other, though not mutually interconvertible. For instance, alcohol dehydrogenase of yeast, with a molecular weight of 151,000 and four atoms of zinc per molecule, may be compared with alcohol dehydrogenase of liver, with a molecular weight of 73,000 and two atoms of zinc per molecule. This may be compared with the well-known non-enzymatic pair of haemoglobin (molecular weight 68,000, with four haem groups) and myoglobin (molecular weight 17,000, with one haem group). Another case is phosphoglyceromutase; the enzyme from yeast has a molecular weight twice that of the enzyme from rabbit muscle, although the specific activity of the two enzymes (per mg of protein) is about the same (*669*).

PROTEIN STRUCTURE

Number of peptide chains

Only scanty information is available as to the number of peptide chains with free end-groups present in enzyme molecules. The terminal α-amino groups can be determined by the fluorodinitrobenzene method of SANGER. Occasionally the terminal carboxyl group can be detected and estimated by removal with carboxypeptidase; this method, however, is not so reliable as that of Sanger, owing to the restricted specificity of carboxypeptidase, so that in certain cases the C-terminal end-groups may not be attacked.

Most of the enzymes which have been investigated seem to have a single peptide chain. This is true of pepsin, trypsin, papain, carboxy-peptidase A, muramidase, pancreatic α-amylase and ribonuclease. On the other hand, two enzymes have been shown to have two chains, namely, α-chymotrypsin and rabbit muscle aldolase. In the case of myosin, no end-groups can be detected. In the cases mentioned above, where the enzyme reversibly dissociates into two or four portions, the larger molecule must clearly have at least two or four peptide chains.

Aminoacid composition

Until recently, the methods of analysis of proteins needed relatively large amounts of material, consequently most of the proteins analysed

TABLE X.2
AMINOACID ANALYSIS OF SOME ENZYMES
(expressed as g of aminoacid per 100 g of protein)

	Alcohol dehydrogenase (1.1.1.1) (yeast)	Lactate dehydrogenase (1.1.2.3) (yeast)	Glyceraldehydephosphate dehydrogenase (1.2.1.12) (rabbit muscle)	Glyceraldehydephosphate dehydrogenase (1.2.1.12) (yeast)	Catalase (1.11.1.6) (ox liver)	Peroxidase (1.11.1.7) (Japanese radish)	α-glucan phosphorylase (2.4.1.1) (rabbit muscle)	Creatine kinase (2.7.3.2) (rabbit muscle)	Ribonuclease (2.7.7.16) (ox pancreas)	Deoxyribonuclease (3.1.4.5) (ox pancreas)	α-amylase (3.2.1.1) (human saliva)	α-amylase (3.2.1.1) (Aspergillus oryzae)	α-amylase (3.2.1.1) (B. subtilis)	α-amylase (3.2.1.1) (B. stearothermophilus)	Muramidase (3.2.1.17) (egg white)	Muramidase (3.2.1.17) (rabbit spleen)	β-galactosidase (3.2.1.23) (Esch. coli)	Carboxypeptidase A (3.4.2.1) (ox)	Pepsin (3.4.1.1)	Renin (3.4.3)	Papain (3.4.10)	Myosin (3.6.1.3) (rabbit muscle)
Ala	6.6	4.6	6.7	7.3	4.3	10.4	4.9	3.2	7.7	4.9	4.4	5.9	5.3	4.8	5.8	8.3	5.4	5.2	6.4	3.1	5.6	6.5
Gly	5.9	4.1	6.1	4.9	3.3	0.8	3.8	5.4	1.6	3.1	6.8	5.7	6.0	4.2	5.7	6.0	5.4	5.1	7.1	5.2	8.4	1.9
Val	6.6	6.5	12.0	10.3	8.6	8.6	7.3	6.0	7.5	7.7	6.9	6.0	6.1	8.5	4.8	4.8	4.6	5.6	11.5	11.5	8.4	2.6
Leu	7.1	9.5	9.1		8.6	8.6	10.5	10.4	2.0	8.6	5.8	7.6	6.1	7.2	6.9	9.4	}15.9	7.6	}10.8	}15.5	6.1	}15.6
Ileu	7.0	4.8	3.7	3.8	3.8	3.6	6.5	3.3	2.7	4.3	5.8	6.3	4.5	6.0	5.2	6.7		7.6			6.0	
Pro	4.8	4.9	5.5	3.8	4.5	3.7	4.7	5.7	3.9	3.5	3.6	4.2	3.4	16.3	1.4	4.2	3.1	3.7	5.0	5.3	5.1	1.9
Phe	5.7	3.1	4.6	4.9	7.6	5.5	5.9	3.9	3.5	8.3	7.2	4.0	6.0	6.4	3.1	4.1	3.1	3.6	6.4	7.8	3.2	4.3
Tyr	6.0	3.3	2.0	5.2	6.6	1.1	5.0	3.7	7.6	1.6	5.5	3.8	9.0	3.0	3.6	2.7	10.3	7.2	2.4	7.6	14.7	3.4
Try	1.7	0.9	2.0	2.2	3.1	0.9	2.0	2.7	0	10.3	7.2	0	0	0	10.6	6.6	0	0.1	12.2	1.6	14.7	0.4
Ser	5.8	3.7	7.3	4.7	3.3	9.8	6.5	5.7	11.4	8.3	7.8	8.4	5.6	4.2	6.7	6.6	6.6	6.4	9.6	7.8	5.9	4.3
Thr	6.6	3.5	1.1	6.0	2.8	5.9	5.0	3.7	8.9	1.6	4.5	6.3	5.6	4.2	5.5	5.9	5.5	7.8	2.4	7.6	4.6	5.1
Cys	4.4	<0.3	2.7		1.1	1.0	0.4	1.3	0	1.6	2.4	2.1	0	3.4	2.1	4.1	3.0	0.1	1.7	1.0	0	1.4
Met	5.1	4.8	5.2	2.8	2.8	3.4	2.7	3.1	4.0	2.8	2.4	3.0	6.1	4.3	2.1	1.8	8.0	5.1	1.0	1.5	7.7	3.4
Arg	4.9	4.8	5.0	6.0	7.9	3.4	11.6	7.2	4.9	7.0	8.7	1.8	3.9	5.2	12.7	7.4	3.3	3.5	0.9	3.3	0	4.3
His	2.5	1.3	5.0	3.5	7.7	1.8	3.3	11.8	10.5	5.3	6.3	4.8	7.4	5.2	1.0	5.8	7.8	7.8	0.9	5.7	5.7	7.4
Lys	8.6	8.7	9.4	10.7	11.4	12.3	7.2	12.5	15.0	13.9	19.3	15.9	14.5	9.3	18.2	19.1	14.8	11.7	0.9	3.3	5.7	11.9
Asp	8.6	10.4	12.4	9.9	9.7	7.1	13.4	13.0	12.4	10.0	9.6	8.1	12.9	20.4	4.3	11.5	12.1	16.0	16.0	13.3	11.3	22.1
Glu	6.6	11.5	4.8	4.3	9.7	7.1	9.3	13.0	12.4	10.0	9.6	8.1	12.9	20.4	4.3	11.5	12.1	10.7	11.9	13.3	12.4	22.1
Amide	1.7	1.7	0.9		2.2			1.3	2.1	2.2	1.3	1.7	1.7	0.4	(1.7)	2.8	1.8	0.9	1.3	1.6	1.6	1.2
Refs.:	1513	84	2727	2729	2339	1862	2730	777	1110	819	1906	2509	1277	389	1578	1262	2774	2449	2674a	2347	2450	136

'Cys' includes cysteine, if any, as well as cystine.

were non-enzymatic. With the need for analysis of the pure enzymes which became available in relatively small quantities, micromethods have been developed. However, only a small fraction of the enzymes which have been crystallized have been analysed in any detail. Table X.2 contains results for twenty-two enzymes for which complete analyses have been carried out.

With the exception of prosthetic groups, all the enzymes listed are found on analysis to consist entirely of the aminoacids commonly found in non-enzymatic proteins. The analytical figures for the separate aminoacids account within experimental error for the whole of the enzyme molecule, and leave no room for any unusual component responsible for the special activity of the enzyme. There is nothing distinctive in the analyses which would differentiate enzymes from other proteins; these enzymes are in fact a miscellaneous group of typical proteins. Like any other random group of proteins, they differ sufficiently markedly from one another to show that enzymatic activity in general is not due to some peculiarity in aminoacid composition, and also that they cannot be derived from a common protein precursor.

Aminoacid sequence

The methods developed by SANGER (*2283, 2297*), which made it possible to determine the complete structure of insulin, can also be applied to the determination of the aminoacid sequence in enzyme molecules. Since the labour involved in establishing the sequence in a protein molecule of the size of an average enzyme would be very great,

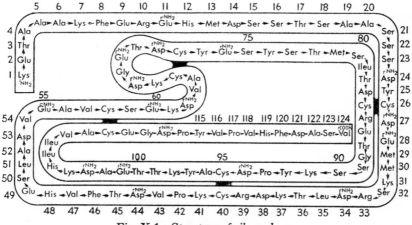

Fig. X.1. *Structure of ribonuclease.*

from *2458*

the enzyme which has been most systematically investigated is ribonuclease, which has the comparatively low molecular weight of 12,700, and it has been possible to determine the complete aminoacid sequence of the enzyme molecule (*1109, 2458, 2479*). Fig. X.1 shows the chemical structure of ribonuclease arrived at by the work of ANFINSEN and his colleagues and of HIRS, MOORE and STEIN. The relation of the structure of the active centre of the enzyme to this sequence will be discussed on p. 470.

The greater part of the aminoacid sequence of chymotrypsin has been determined (see HARTLEY, *1012*), although there are still a number of uncertainties. Work is proceeding on several other enzymes, mainly hydrolytic, including papain (*1591*) and muramidase.

Structure and configuration of the enzyme protein

Even when the complete composition and sequence of the peptide chain or chains (Eyring's 'primary structure') have been determined, one is still far from having a complete picture of the protein molecule. Physical measurements show that most enzymes are globular proteins, the molecules of which are not very far from spherical, with axial ratios not exceeding 5. The peptide chain therefore cannot be linear. In fact, it is now well established that in native proteins generally the peptide chains are coiled, folded or crumpled (Eyring's 'secondary structure'), although there is considerable doubt as to how this occurs. It is widely believed that the peptide chain exists as a helix stabilized by hydrogen bonding between successive turns of the chain. Several such helical models have been proposed, of which the most stable is the α-helix of PAULING and COREY (*2059*). This has been found in polypeptides and may occur in short lengths of the peptide chains of globular proteins, but it is clear that much of the molecule of globular proteins must have other configurations. This is well seen in the one protein whose tertiary structure has been obtained by X-ray methods, namely myoglobin. The elegant model constructed by KENDREW et al. (*1359*) shows that there are four main helical sections and two short sections; but much of the molecule consists of intermediate non-helical sections. On the other hand, in ribonuclease, which is the only enzyme which has been studied in any detail, the X-ray evidence does not appear to be compatible with a structure based on α-helices. The subject of chain configurations within protein molecules is reviewed by LOW (*1619*).

Since the molecule of a globular protein is much thicker than any possible helical or otherwise contracted peptide chain, either a number of chains must be packed side by side or, in molecules consisting of only one chain, this must be folded back on itself (Eyring's 'tertiary structure'). As was mentioned in Chapter VII, the tertiary structure may play some role in the activation of the enzyme substrate, and the enzyme activity is usually lost on denaturation, when the tertiary structure disappears.

THE CHEMISTRY OF THE ACTIVE CENTRE

Number of active centres per molecule

Determination of number of prosthetic groups per molecule

Where an enzyme contains a prosthetic group which takes part in the reaction, the number of active centres can hardly be more than the number of such groups. It is conceivable that other groups of the same chemical nature as the prosthetic group are combined with the protein without taking part in the reaction, so that a mere determination of the total number of these groups gives a *maximum* for the number of active centres.

The number of prosthetic groups may be determined by two main methods, spectroscopic and chemical. In the case of flavoproteins and haemoproteins, measurement of the intensity of the characteristic absorption bands will give the molar concentration of such groups, if the absorption coefficient of the group in the combined state is the same as that of the free substance. In the case of flavoproteins this assumption is probably justified, since the absorption at 450 mμ is roughly the same for different flavin compounds. The case of haemoproteins is more difficult, since the position and intensity of the bands of combined haem are quite different from those of free haem. Two spectroscopic methods are in common use for the determination of haem prosthetic groups. The absorption may be compared with that of a standard haemoprotein of known haem content, for example, other cytochromes may be compared with cytochrome c; or the haem groups may be detached from the protein and converted into a common reference compound, which is usually the pyridine ferrohaemochrome, and compared with a standard solution of the compound. An additional complication with haemoproteins is that the porphyrin may differ and it is necessary to compare it with the appropriate ferrohaemochrome.

Various special methods are available for the determination of particular prosthetic groups when detached from the enzyme protein. For instance, flavin-adenine-dinucleotide may be estimated by adding a known volume of the solution to a flavin-free preparation of the D-aminoacid oxidase, and comparing the rate of oxidation of alanine with that produced by a known amount of FAD. Thiamine pyrophosphate can be similarly estimated with pyruvate decarboxylase and pyridoxal phosphate with an aminoacid decarboxylase. Any of these groups can also be estimated by measuring their activity as growth factors with suitable micro-organisms.

Where the prosthetic group is or contains a metal, chemical methods of estimation or quantitative emission spectrography may be used (see 2707). With metals, more than with other prosthetic groups, the degree of purification of the enzyme is of importance, since proteins readily take up metal ions from solution. Even a purified enzyme may well contain significant amounts of a number of metals which have nothing to do with the activity. We may quote as an example of this the fact that flavoproteins have often been reported to contain amounts of iron which, as already mentioned, may vary from forty atoms to one-sixth of an atom per flavin group.

These methods give the amount of prosthetic group in relation to the total protein present; if the enzyme is pure, one can obtain from this the molecular weight per group, which will be a minimum molecular weight for the enzyme protein. If the actual molecular weight has been determined by physical methods, the number of prosthetic groups per molecule of enzyme is obtained by division.

Determination of number of substrate-binding sites per molecule

If there is a change of some physical property when the substrate combines with the enzyme, it may be possible to determine directly the maximum number of substrate molecules bound by one molecule of enzyme. The best known example of this is the combination of NAD with alcohol dehydrogenase, which is accompanied by a change of ultraviolet spectrum (2633). Using this change, THEORELL and BONNICHSEN showed that the liver enzyme binds two molecules of coenzyme per molecule. The binding of substrate may also be measured by two physical methods which depend on measurements of the amount of free substrate in equilibrium with the enzyme, namely, the dialysis equilibrium method and the analysis of the supernatant layer after ultracentrifugation.

The dialysis equilibrium method was developed by KLOTZ et al. (1402). As usually carried out, an enzyme solution of known volume and molar concentration is placed in a dialysing sac, and dialysed to equilibrium against a solution of a substrate (or competitive inhibitor related thereto), also of known volume and molarity. The substrate must be one which does not react under the conditions chosen. When equilibrium is reached, the concentration of substrate in the external fluid is determined and provided the Donnan effect can be neglected, is assumed to be that of the free substrate in the enzyme solution also. From the total amount of substrate added, making due allowance for any volume changes which may have occurred, the concentration of substrate bound by the enzyme may be calculated, and thus the amount bound by each molecule. This procedure is carried out with several different concentrations of substrate, and extrapolation of the data gives the total number of binding sites per molecule.

It may readily be shown that

X.1 $$r \cdot \frac{K_s}{s} = n - r$$

where r is the average number of substrate molecules bound by one molecule of enzyme, s is as usual the *free* substrate concentration and n is the total number of binding sites in the enzyme molecule. Thus n is the limiting value of r as s is increased to saturation of the enzyme. On plotting r against r/s, a straight line should be obtained, cutting the vertical axis at n.

Fig. X.2 shows the results of LOEWUS and BRIGGS (*1609*) for the binding of α-naphthyl propionate (a competitive inhibi-

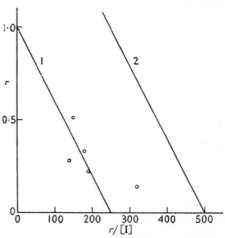

Fig. X.2. *Binding of α-naphthyl propionate by α-chymotrypsin.*

[I] is the concentration of free α-naphthyl propionate. The lines 1 and 2 are the theoretical lines for $n = 1$ and $n = 2$ respectively, since $K_i = 4 \cdot 0 \times 10^{-3}$ M.

from *1609*

tor) by α-chymotrypsin. Using labelled acetyldibromotyrosine, a product of one of the reactions of the enzyme, DOHERTY and VASLOW (*644*) also showed that chymotrypsin has only one binding site per molecule.

The ultracentrifugation method, developed by HAYES and VELICK (*1044*), depends on the same principle, but is carried out by taking samples of the solution at different levels in the tube after ultracentrifugation and estimating substrate and protein. Fig. X.3 shows the results with yeast alcohol dehydrogenase and $NADH_2$. The results are probably to be taken as showing four binding sites per molecule, although for some unexplained reason the extrapolated value falls somewhat short of this. It will be remembered that this enzyme contains four zinc atoms per molecule, and may be contrasted with the liver enzyme, which combines with two molecules of coenzyme and contains two zinc atoms in a molecule of half the size. REYNARD *et al.* (*2213*) have used the same method to determine the binding constants of pyruvate kinase for its substrate.

A related method, which has been used for measuring the number of dye molecules or chloride ions bound by proteins, but which so far as we know has not been used for enzymes, is the electrophoresis method of R. F. SMITH and BRIGGS (*2455*) and ALBERTY and MARVIN (*36–7*), in which it is only necessary to measure the mobilities of the boundaries.

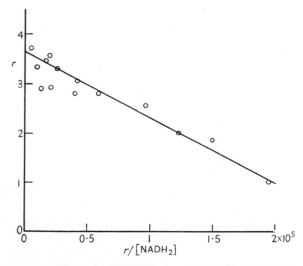

Fig. X.3. *Binding of* NADH$_2$ *by yeast alcohol dehydrogenase.*
r is the number of molecules of NADH$_2$ bound per molecule of enzyme.

from *1044*

Determinations with specific reagents

When an enzyme is completely inhibited by combination with a small number of molecules of an inhibitor, it is usually assumed that this number is the maximum number of active centres in the molecule; this assumption, however, is not always valid. For example, β-fructofurano-sidase (3.2.1.26) is completely poisoned by minute amounts of Ag$^+$ ions, amounting to 7–8 ions added per molecule of enzyme (*1911*); and urease (3.5.1.5) is completely inhibited when four Ag$^+$ ions are bound per molecule (*59*). This might be taken as indicating that these enzymes contain only a small number of active centres per molecule. However, combination of this number of dissociating groups with silver might produce a considerable change in the configuration of the peptide chains, and this might be the cause of the loss of activity. The number of atoms of silver would then give no indication of the number of substrate-binding sites.

Less open to this objection are the results with specific reagents acting as irreversible inhibitors which produce complete loss of activity when only one or two molecules combine per molecule of enzyme. The most specific of such reagents yet found is DFP, which has no action on most enzymes, but inhibits a certain group of enzymes which are capable of hydrolysing carboxylic esters (see p. 346).

BOURSNELL and WEBB (301) found complete inhibition of liver carboxylesterase (3.1.1.1) with labelled DFP when 1 g atom of radioactive phosphorus was bound by 80,000 g of protein; although the molecular weight of this enzyme is not known, the number of active centres could hardly exceed four, and is more likely to be one. JANSEN et al, also using radioactive DFP, showed that complete inhibition of α-chymotrypsin was produced when the enzyme had taken up one atom of radioactive phosphorus (1245) and two isopropyl groups (1246) per molecule. This can only mean that chymotrypsin contains one active centre per molecule. Similar results were obtained with trypsin by JANSEN and BALLS (1241).

An analogous approach was that of KILBY and YOUATT (1378), who measured the liberation of p-nitrophenol during the progressive inactivation of trypsin by diethyl p-nitrophenylphosphate, which transfers a diethylphosphate group to the enzyme. They found complete inhibition when one nitrophenol group was liberated per molecule of 17,000–18,000; the DFP results gave an equivalent weight of 20,700 and the physical methods gave a molecular weight of about 23,000.

A difficulty when using enzymes which have not been obtained in the completely pure state, e.g. acetylcholinesterase (3.1.1.7), is that a part of the DFP may be combining with groups other than the active centre of the enzyme. This has been overcome by COHEN and WARRINGA (461) in the following elegant way. The active centre is first masked by adding a strong competitive inhibitor, and the enzyme preparation is then treated with excess of unlabelled DFP. This saturates all the DFP-binding groups apart from the active centre. The excess DFP and the inhibitor are then completely removed by dialysis; this is shown by the return of the original activity. The preparation is then treated with *radioactive* DFP, which combines only with the active centre, and the labelled phosphorus bound is measured after further prolonged dialysis. No value of the equivalent weight was given, but it was calculated that each ox erythrocyte contained only 520 active centres. Since for this enzyme a number of inhibitors with very high affinities are available, the method of p. 333 can also be used. Another kinetic method (2885), which has been used for acetylcholinesterase, depends on the use of an inhibitor of high affinity which also acts as a poor substrate for the enzyme.

Another group of specific reagents is formed by those which react with thiol groups. Although thiol groups occur in a variety of enzymes they are not always in the active centre, for example, ten thiol groups of aldolase can be destroyed without loss of activity (*2585*). Where the thiol groups do occur in the active centre, these reagents can be used in the same way as DFP to determine the number of such essential groups. VELICK (*2726*) found that the glyceraldehydephosphate dehydrogenase (1.2.1.12) of muscle was completely inhibited by combination with three equivalents of *p*-chloromercuribenzoate. The enzyme as normally obtained contains two molecules of bound NAD per molecule, and these are released as the thiol reagent reacts (*2726*), but it should be noted that after removal of the bound coenzyme by treatment with adsorbents the enzyme combines with *three* equivalents of NAD (*766*). In the case of iodosobenzoate five or more groups react per molecule, but only two of these are connected with the active centres, as shown by the fact that the substrate specifically protects these two from attack (*2361*). It may be concluded that the enzyme contains three active centres per molecule.

Another method is by inactivating the enzyme by photo-oxidation in the presence of methylene blue, which destroys histidine and tryptophan in the protein (WEIL and BUCHERT, *2818*). It was found that with muramidase 70 per cent inactivation occurred when 1 histidine and $1 \cdot 2$ tryptophan residues per molecule had been destroyed (*2819*), and with chymotrypsin complete inactivation corresponded with the destruction of 1 histidine and 3 tryptophan residues (*2820*). These figures give a maximum value for the number of active centres. With phosphoglucomutase a 90 per cent inactivation was produced when 1 histidine residue had been destroyed; the rate of inactivation was compared kinetically with that of the loss of a number of aminoacids. The inactivation shows a fast and a slow component; the former was attributed to the destruction of a reactive histidine and the latter to the destruction of one reactive methionine residue (*1450, 2188–9*).

Chemical nature of the active centre

General considerations

It must be admitted that knowledge of the structure of the active centres of enzymes, as distinct from that of prosthetic groups, is scanty, and in no single case can a complete picture of an active centre be given. The active centre is that special part of the enzyme protein structure which combines with the substrate and is responsible for the enzymatic properties of the molecule. It determines both the specificity and the catalytic activity, and as stated elsewhere it must be a structure of some complexity, adapted to a fairly close fitting of the substrate molecule, or at any rate of those parts of it which are concerned in the reaction. As pointed out in the chapter on specificity (Chapter VI), the fit between the active centre and the combined substrate molecule appears to be close over a patch of possibly up to 15–20 Å in diameter and to fall off rapidly with distance, although there are naturally variations between different enzymes. The general nature of the fit and the facts of specificity show that there must be a number of different groups in the active centre combining with different parts of the substrate, and the evidence relating to the nature of these groups will be considered in the next section.

The active centre need not be considered to lie within one peptide chain only; it may be a pattern of groups extending transversely across two or more adjacent peptide chains or sections of one folded chain, much as in Fig. X.4 (*623*). If so, activity will depend not only on the existence of the combining groups but also on the intactness and configuration of the native protein molecule, which determines the relative positions of these groups; hence the importance of the tertiary structure of the protein for the enzymatic activity. It is well known that when the adjoining peptide chains are separated in denaturation the activity is lost in practically all cases. The fact that some

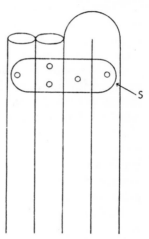

Fig. X.4. *Possible nature of the active centre of an enzyme.*

from *623*

power of combining with substrate has sometimes been found after denaturation, although the activity has been completely lost, would suggest that the individual combining groups are still present although the pattern of the active centre has been disrupted. This pattern may be reformed in certain cases where the denaturation can be reversed, and the activity then returns. Such a picture is consistent with the fact that combination with the substrate often protects the enzyme from denaturation, since it would tend to hold the chains together.

The situation is not unlike that of the haem group in cytochrome *c*, as given in Fig. VII.1, which is there shown as being in combination with four parallel peptide helices.

The peptide chains can in some cases be caused to separate by breaking the disulphide bridges by chemical means. In many proteins these links, formed between cysteine residues in different chains, are the strongest inter-chain bonds, being the only covalent links. Otherwise the attachment is mainly by hydrogen bonding, so that when the disulphide bridges are broken, either by reduction or by oxidation, considerable changes in configuration take place. Thus in ribonuclease, activity is completely lost on oxidation by performic acid (73), although it is retained after the hydrogen bonds have been loosened in 8 M urea (72).

Methods of identifying specific groups in the active centre

Three main types of methods have been used for the identification of the chemical groups in the active centre: (a) deduction of pK values of substrate-binding groups from pH effects, (b) degradation studies, (c) inactivation by specific chemical reagents.

The methods of obtaining pK values of groups in the active centre have already been described in Chapter IV (c). It might be thought that the pKs of the groups would give a clue to their chemical nature, and a number of authors have drawn rather definite conclusions of this kind. We have already pointed out (p. 143) that such results must be treated with due caution, because considerable changes may be produced in the pK of a given group by the influence of neighbouring groups. The influence of temperature on the pKs, however, may provide confirmatory evidence and make the identification more reliable.

Table X.3 shows some of the pK values which have been obtained from kinetic measurements. Column 3 shows pKs of groups in the free enzyme which combine with the substrate, or are sufficiently close to the binding groups to have their pKs appreciably altered when combination

TABLE X.3

IONIZATION CONSTANTS OF GROUPS ASSOCIATED WITH ACTIVE CENTRES OF ENZYMES

Enzyme	Substrate or inhibitor	pK_e	pK_{es}	References: Data	Calc.
Xanthine oxidase (1.2.3.2)	2-amino-4-hydroxy-pteridine	5·3, 7·9	4·4	1622	621
NADH$_2$ cytochrome c reductase (1.6.2.1)	NADH$_2$+cytochrome c	7·7, 8·5	7·6, 8·5	778	778
Peroxidase (1.11.1.7)	H$_2$O$_2$+guaiacol ..		7·8	1172	1172
Carboxylesterase (3.1.1.1)	Ethyl butyrate		5·5	2808	2808
..	Ethyl chloroacetate .. Isopropyl fluoroacetate		6·1, 9·4 } 6·8, 9·2 } 228		228
Acetylcholinesterase (3.1.1.7)	Acetylcholine	6·3, 10·4*	10·4*	2883	2880
..	Ethyl chloroacetate ..		6·7, 9·6	228	228
..	n-propyl fluoroacetate ..		6·2, 9·0	228	228

TABLE X.3—*continued*

Cholinesterase (3.1.1.8)	Acetylcholine	6·2*, 7·7	6·2*	1019	1019
					1505
	n-propyl chloroacetate..		6·2, 9·0	228	228
Alkaline phosphatase (3.1.3.1)	Phenyl phosphate ..	9·2		1878	621
Acid phosphatase (3.1.3.2)	Phenyl phosphate ..		3·3	2341	1505
Arylsulphatase (3.1.6.1)	p-nitrophenyl sulphate	8·1, 9·4	7·75	640a	632
	p-acetylphenyl sulphate	8·1, 9·4	7·65	640a	632
	p-nitrocatechyl sulphate	(6·9),8·1,9·4	7·55	640a	632
Arylsulphatase B ..	p-nitrophenyl sulphate	5·7	5·2	2923	2923
Arylsulphatase C ..	p-nitrophenyl sulphate	7·8		2271	2271
β-amylase (3.2.1.2)	Amylopectin	3·7, 7·0		2641	2641
Dextrin-1,6-gluco-sidase (3.2.1.b) ..	Limit dextrin	7·6		1522	1522
Oligo-1,6-glucosi-dase (3.2.1.10) ..	Limit dextrin	7·0		1519	1519
α-glucosidase (3.2.1.20) ..	Maltose..	7·0		1519	1519
β-fructofuranosidase (3.2.1.26) ..	Sucrose..	3·0, 6·6*	6·6*	1268	621
					1505
	Sucrose..	6·8*	2·6, 6·8*	1916	1916
	Raffinose	6·8*	2·6, 6·8*	1916	1916
Pepsin (3.4.4.1) ..	Ovalbumin		2·2	358	1505
Trypsin (3.4.4.4) ..	Benzoylarginine ethyl ester		6·25	958	958
	Casein		6·25	2494	989
Acetyltrypsin ..	Casein		7·1	2494	989
Chymotrypsin (3.4.4.5)	Acetylphenylalanine ethyl ester ..	c. 8·5, 6·85*	6·85*	{ 989, 525	989†, 525, 632
	Methyl hydrocinnamate		7·2, 8·0	171	1505
Ficin (3.4.4.12) ..	Benzoylarginine ethyl ester	4·35*	4·35*	234	234
Urease (3.5.1.5) ..	Urea		6·1, 9·2	2772	1505
	Urea	9·0*	5·6, 9·0*	2721	632
					1913
Arginase (3.5.3.1) ..	Arginine	6·8	8·3, 12·1	913	621
				2242	2242
Fumarate hydratase (4.2.1.2)	Fumarate	6·2, 6·8	5·3–5·8 / 7·3–7·7	34	34
	Malate	6·2, 6·8	6·6–7·3 / 8·4		
Histidine ammonia-lyase (4.3.1.3) ..	Histidine		7·2, 10·9	2762	1505

† HAMMOND and GUTFREUND (989) use the symbol K_i for our K_e or K_{es} since they treat the relevant hydrogen ion as an inhibitor of the enzyme.

occurs. These may be obtained from measurements on the effect of pH on K_m or on v_0 (compare Fig. IV.42). The pKs in column 4 are those of groups in the complex which similarly undergo a change of ionization on combination; these groups, however, are not necessarily in the enzyme part of the complex, for they may be in the combined substrate. The value shown in brackets is one which clearly belongs to the latter category. The pK values of the complexes may be obtained from measurements on the effect of pH on K_m or V. In addition to groups whose pKs change on combination, there are also groups whose state of ionization affects the reactivity of the enzyme-substrate complex, but which are not concerned in the combination. These pKs may be determined from measurements of V, but cannot be obtained from the K_m measurements (compare Fig. IV.41); they are indicated by an asterisk.

It will be seen that there is a fairly wide range of pK values, varying from about 3 to 11. An interesting point is that in the majority of cases a group with a pK of between 6 and 7 is present in the active centre. As histidine is the only aminoacid with a pK value in this region, many workers have attributed special importance to histidine in enzyme catalysis. However, it is not absolutely certain that no other group could have such a pK in a protein; the two amino groups in cystinyldiglycine have (exceptionally) pKs of $6 \cdot 36$ and $6 \cdot 95$ (921).

Although degradation of enzyme proteins with proteolytic enzymes commonly leads to loss of activity, it will be shown in the next chapter that some proteolytic enzymes can undergo small changes such as the fission of one or two peptide links while remaining active. In four cases it has been found possible to remove a considerable part of the protein by digestion while retaining the activity. PERLMAN(2070) found that after autodigestion of pepsin at pHs removed from the optimum, dialysable fragments showing some enzyme activity could be obtained. The activity was low: per unit weight of nitrogen it was 1–5 per cent of that of the original enzyme if tested with haemoglobin as substrate, but 64 per cent of the original with acetyl-phenylalanyl-diiodotyrosine as substrate. If there had been a removal of some of the inactive part of the protein molecule, leaving the catalytic activity of the active centre unchanged, the specific activity of the remaining part of the molecule should have been increased and not decreased. However, the figures quoted are the average activity of all the dialysable peptides, some of which may have been completely inactive.

Ribonuclease (2.7.7.16) can be completely inactivated by pepsin, with the splitting of only one peptide bond and the removal of the tetrapeptide Asp–Ala–Ser–Val from the C-terminal end. No change can be detected in the remainder of the molecule by physical or chemical methods (73). With carboxypeptidase A, however, the three aminoacids at the C-terminal end (valine, serine and alanine) may be removed without loss of activity, so that these are not essential for enzyme action (2241). It is reasonable to conclude that the aspartic acid residue in the fourth position from the C-terminal end is a part of the active centre. Guanidination of the lysine side-chains with O-methylisourea shows that one of the ten lysine residues is less reactive than the others, and that only this residue is associated with catalytic activity (*1393*). It has now been identified with the lysine in position 41 of Fig. X.1 (*2512*).

RICHARDS and VITHAYATHIL (*2214*) have carried out work of great interest on ribonuclease, using subtilopeptidase A. This splits a single peptide bond in ribonuclease, namely that between residues 20 and 21, without any loss of activity. The resulting mixture of peptide and residual protein can be separated by precipitation of the protein with trichloroacetic acid. They have no enzymatic activity separately, but on simple mixing the activity is restored to nearly the original value. The two parts were shown to have a very strong and specific affinity for one another in neutral solution. These studies show that some groups not far from the ends of the whole peptide chain, as well as one near the middle are essential for activity; it is probable that all these groups are themselves brought near together by the folding of the chain to form the active centre, although they may act by influencing the folding of the chain.

A striking example of the degradation technique is the work of HILL and E. SMITH (*1102*) on the inactive mercury derivative of papain (3.4.4.10). This can be degraded stepwise by leucine aminopeptidase until 109 of the original 185 aminoacid residues have been removed. On removal of the mercury from the residue, the original activity was restored, showing that nearly two-thirds of the molecule is unnecessary for the catalytic activity. Again it appears that the active centre is located near the C-terminal end of the molecule, since the aminopeptidase works from the N-terminal end.

The fourth case is that of phosphopyruvate hydratase (4.2.1.11), which can be degraded by the removal of 150 residues from one end or the other by the use of leucine aminopeptidase or carboxypeptidase A, without loss of activity (NYLANDER and MALMSTRÖM, *2004*). Since the enzyme is a single peptide chain of molecular weight 64,000, this represents a much smaller extent of degradation than was achieved with papain (molecular weight 20,700).

These results may be compared with the effect of digestion of cytochrome c with pepsin (*1717*), which yields a series of more or less denatured products with catalytic properties varying from those of native cytochrome c to those of a simple ferrohaemochrome.

A number of groups have been alleged to be present in active centres of enzymes on the basis of inactivation by chemical reagents. If such studies are to have validity, it is essential that the reagent employed should be really specific for the particular group in question; in other words, it should not attack any of the other groups present in proteins. Moreover, it should be realized that an aminoacid residue in a particular situation in a protein molecule may behave in a very different way from similar residues in other positions or in simpler molecules, owing to the influence of neighbouring groups. In addition, the reagent used must inactivate by an attack on the active centre and not by a denaturation of the protein.

A group of reagents, already discussed in Chapter VIII, act by a more or less specific attack on thiol groups in enzymes, either by oxidation to disulphide, by mercaptide formation or by alkylation. The first two actions are reversible and the third irreversible. As a result of work on inhibitions by these reagents, it has been claimed that thiol groups occur in the active centres of many different enzymes. However, the different reagents frequently give different results (e.g. *985*), authors are by no means agreed as to their specificity for thiol groups, and there are considerable differences of opinion in the interpretation of the observations. Moreover, some of the earlier results have been obtained with complex systems and not with purified enzymes, and some of these systems have since been shown to involve thiol carriers, such as lipoate or coenzyme A, which are also attacked by these reagents. Thus some of the inhibitions which have been obtained are probably not due to attack on enzymic thiol groups, but on the –SH groups of these cofactors. It would be very desirable to establish the specificity for –SH of a standard reagent, and to carry out a fresh survey with purified enzymes by its use. In the meantime, lists of '–SH enzymes' in the literature (e.g. *173*) should be treated with some reserve.

An example of the danger is given by ribonuclease, which contains no –SH groups and yet is inhibited by some so-called –SH reagents, such as iodoacetate and bromoacetate (*170*); this is due to an attack on a histidine residue.

However, certain cases seem to be well established as –SH enzymes, for example, glyceraldehydephosphate dehydrogenase (1.2.1.12), succinate dehydrogenase (1.3.99.1), yeast alcohol dehydrogenase (1.1.1.1), papain (3.4.4.10), and many, if not all, of the kinases.

If combination of the reagents with many –SH groups per enzyme molecule were required to produce inactivation, the effect might be due not to a specific attack on the active centre but to a change in the configuration of the protein as a whole. In several cases, however, there is direct evidence from protection effects that the thiol groups concerned are in the substrate-binding site itself. HOPKINS et al (*1158*) showed that succinate, or the powerful competitive inhibitor malonate, protects succinate dehydrogenase against inactivation by thiol reagents. RAPKINE et al (*2173*) similarly protected glyceraldehydephosphate dehydrogenase by the addition of NAD against inactivation by oxidation of –SH groups; but SEGAL and BOYER (*2361*) were unable to obtain protection against irreversible –SH reagents with NAD, although they did obtain some protection with glyceraldehyde phosphate. In β-amylase iodoacetamide alkylates an –SH, but no other group; cyclohexa-amylose, which is a competitive inhibitor, protects against the reagent (*2641*). The alkylation reduces V by a factor of 50 and the affinity for substrate by a factor of 8.

Another possible way in which alkylating or mercaptide-forming thiol reagents can inactivate enzymes, in which the –SH group is *not* part of the active centre or necessary for the catalytic activity, is by steric hindrance. If the –SH group, although not involved in the catalytic action, is situated close to the substrate-binding point, a bulky reagent attached to this group may interfere with the access of the substrate to the active site. SINGER (*2409*) suggested this mechanism for the inhibition of wheat germ lipase by p-chloromercuribenzoate, because the inhibition increased with the size of the substrate molecule, as if the smaller substrate molecules could pass the obstruction while the larger molecules were blocked. By contrast, he found that the inhibition produced by this reagent with D-aminoacid oxidase was independent of the nature of the substrate.

Another group of highly specific reagents which has already been mentioned is that of the organophosphorus compounds, such as DFP, which react only with certain enzymes having an esteratic action (see Chapter VIII and *2805*). These reagents do not react with proteins generally, or with any of the constituent aminoacids, at an appreciable rate. DFP has been shown by isotopic studies not to combine with a number of native and denatured proteins, including even chymotrypsinogen and denatured chymotrypsin (*301*), although chymotrypsin itself is rapidly attacked, complete inhibition being produced by combination with one molecule (see *146*). Since DFP does not react with any of the individual groups known to be present in proteins, it must be concluded that it reacts with a site formed by two or more groups in juxtaposition, probably in different peptide chains, so that when these groups are separated by denaturation reactivity towards DFP disappears. These reagents, having an ester grouping, probably first combine with the active centre in the same way as the ester substrate, but the phosphoryl group becomes irreversibly attached to the enzyme, whereas the acyl group of the normal substrate is reversibly combined. These considerations would lead us to expect that DFP would throw a particularly good light on the structure of the active centre.

Since the attachment of the substituted phosphoryl group is irreversible, and it is not removed on denaturation or hydrolysis of the protein, a fruitful line of work is the separation and identification of peptides containing it from DFP-inhibited enzymes in an attempt to determine the nature of the groups in the active centre with which it combines. The work is greatly facilitated by the use of DFP labelled with radioactive phosphorus.

SCHAFFER, MAY and SUMMERSON (*2322*) showed that in the case of chymotrypsin the phosphoryl group became attached to the hydroxyl

TABLE X.4

AMINOACID SEQUENCES IN THE ACTIVE CENTRES OF DFP–SENSITIVE ENZYMES

Enzyme	Aminoacid sequence	References
Carboxylesterase (3.1.1.1) (horse liver)	$\overset{\text{P}}{\underset{\mid}{\text{Gly–Glu–Ser}}}$–Ala–Gly–Gly–(Ser, Glu)	1248
Cholinesterase (3.1.1.8) (horse serum)	$\overset{\text{P}}{\underset{\mid}{\text{Phe–Gly–Glu–Ser}}}$–Ala–Gly–(Ala, Ser, Ala)	1247
Trypsin (3.4.4.4) (ox pancreas)		612
$\overset{\text{NH}_2}{\underset{\mid}{\text{Asp–Ser–Cys}}}$–Glu–Gly–Gly–Asp–$\overset{\text{P}}{\underset{\mid}{\text{Ser}}}$–Gly–Pro–Val–Cys–Ser–Gly–Lys		
Chymotrypsin (3.4.4.5) (ox pancreas)	$\overset{\text{P}}{\underset{\mid}{\text{Gly–Asp–Ser}}}$–Gly–Glu–Ala	2323, 2687
Chymotrypsin (3.4.4.5) (ox pancreas)	$\overset{\text{P}}{\underset{\mid}{\text{Gly–Asp–Ser}}}$–Gly–Gly–Pro–Leu	2025
Pancreatopeptidase E (3.4.4.7) (ox pancreas)	$\overset{\text{P}}{\underset{\mid}{\text{Asp–Ser}}}$–Gly	1931
Thrombin (3.4.4.13) (ox blood)	$\overset{\text{P}}{\underset{\mid}{\text{Asp–Ser}}}$–Gly	845
Subtilopeptidase A (3.4.4.16) (*B. subtilis*)	$\overset{\text{P}}{\underset{\mid}{\text{Thr–Ser}}}$–Met–Ala	2298

P denotes the phosphoryl group derived from the organophosphorus reagent used to label the active centre.

group of one of the serine residues. Since there are well over twenty serine residues in the molecule, this single serine group must be in a unique situation. More recently similar results have been obtained with a number of other hydrolysing enzymes, and the identification of the di-isopropylphosphoryl-labelled peptides liberated on partial hydrolysis has led to the sequences shown in Table X.4. They all contain the reactive serine, and with the exception of the last enzyme, which is clearly of a different type, this is attached on the left to a dicarboxylic acid (glutamic acid in the esterases and aspartic acid in the peptidases) and on the right to a neutral aminoacid (alanine in the esterases and glycine in the peptidases). There is an unexplained discrepancy in the results for chymotrypsin between two groups of workers, although this does not affect the groups immediately adjacent to the serine. The second sequence, obtained by OOSTERBAAN *et al*, has been confirmed by them using C^{14}-labelled p-nitrophenyl acetate instead of DFP (*2026*).

Some of these enzymes, for example chymotrypsin, have been shown by other methods to have a reactive histidine in the active centre (see p. 466), but these sequences contain no histidine in the neighbourhood of the reactive serine. The two histidine residues in α-chymotrypsin are in a different peptide chain from that containing the reactive serine (*1012*), so that this must be another example of the involvement of more than one peptide chain in the active centre. The juxtaposition of the two chains must be assumed to confer reactivity on the serine, since this is lost when they are separated by denaturation.

Peptide sequences in some other enzymes containing a reactive serine in their active centres have been obtained by labelling in other ways. MILSTEIN and SANGER (*1830*) labelled phosphoglucomutase by treatment with P^{32}-labelled substrate (either glucose 1-phosphate or glucose 6-phosphate), and found, contrary to previous reports, that the sequence around the reactive serine was

$$
\begin{array}{c}
P \\
|
\end{array}
$$
$$
\text{Thr–Ala–Ser–His–Asp(or Glu).}
$$

In this enzyme both a serine and a histidine have been shown to be essential components of the active centre, and it is interesting that here we have two such residues adjacent in one chain. A serine is also involved in the active centre of alkaline phosphatase, which incorporates labelled inorganic phosphate (*698*).

When α-glucan phosphorylase b is converted into the a form by P^{32}-labelled ATP, the product contains four labelled phosphoserine groups per molecule, i.e. one for each active centre. This is in addition to the four pyridoxal phosphate groups which it contains. The labelled serine residues are each in the sequence (*734*)

$$
\begin{array}{cc}
NH_2 & P \\
| & |
\end{array}
$$
$$
\text{Lys–Glu–Ileu–Ser–Val–Arg}
$$

It will be seen from the preceding discussion that serine and histidine residues are being given increasing prominence in the mechanism of enzyme catalysis. In this connection a number of simple model systems have been studied. The hydroxyl group of N-acetylserineamide, a model of a serine residue in a peptide chain, can be acylated by high energy acetyl derivatives about 1,000 times faster than the hydroxyl of water or ethanol. The hydrolysis of the bond thus formed is strongly catalysed by imidazole (*67*). The rates of these reactions, although high, are very much less than those involved in enzymatic catalysis. Interesting discussions of possible mechanisms of catalysis by serine and imidazole groups will be found in *67* and *169*.

XI

ENZYME FORMATION

THIS HEADING COVERS two distinct topics, namely, (*a*) the extracellular formation of active enzymes from inactive precursors, which may be brought about *in vitro*, and (*b*) the complete biosynthesis of enzymes in the living cell, which is indissolubly linked with growth and is required to replace wastage, but which may also be brought about by a change in environment. The biosynthesis is by far the more important and fundamental process; the formation from protein precursors appears to be limited to proteinases and may perhaps be regarded as the terminal step in their synthesis. We shall deal first with (*b*), as being the more important problem.

THE BIOSYNTHESIS OF ENZYMES

The synthesis of enzymes is a continuous process in every living organism. An increase in the number of molecules of each essential enzyme must clearly take place whenever the quantity of living matter increases during growth. But even when growth is not taking place a continuous synthesis is needed to replace enzyme molecules which have undergone destruction. It is generally believed, largely as the result of work by SCHOENHEIMER and his school (*2340*) on the incorporation of labelled aminoacids, that in animals the intracellular protein is in a state of dynamic equilibrium, in which the proteins are continually being broken down and replaced by resynthesis. Studies with isotopes on the induction of β-galactosidase (3.2.1.23) in *Esch. coli* suggest on the other hand that the proteins of this organism are remarkably stable (*1129*), and because of this it has been suggested that Schoenheimer's results with whole animals might not be due to turnover of protein within individual cells, but to an actual replacement of older by younger cells in the tissues, and also, in those tissues which give the most rapid apparent turnover, by the replacement of protein lost by secretion. However, more recent isotopic experiments (*2586*) have shown that the half-life of liver proteins is 2–4 days.

Moreover, in the case of certain animal enzymes there is direct isotopic evidence of a fairly rapid turnover (*1054, 2407*). Labelled aminoacids were injected into adult rabbits, and three different enzymes were isolated from the muscle after periods of time from two hours upwards. Radioactivity estimations on the aminoacids obtained from the recrystallized enzymes showed that there had been considerable incorporation of the injected aminoacids, and it was calculated that in two cases the breakdown and resynthesis was at the rate of 1 per cent of the total of each enzyme per day, and in the third case about half this. The half-life of aldolase in muscle, a tissue in which the cells are long-lived, has been shown to be about 20 days (2326).

The biosynthesis of enzymes is therefore an extremely important process, without which life would soon come to a halt. The complete synthesis of an active enzyme involves the building up of both the protein part and the prosthetic group, if any. The organism, however, cannot always synthesize all the different prosthetic groups which it' requires from simple metabolites, and these groups must then be supplied. For instance, the animal body cannot synthesize flavin, hence riboflavin is an essential vitamin which must be supplied in the diet, and with insufficient flavin a serious deficiency of flavoprotein enzymes, such as the xanthine and D-aminoacid oxidases, develops (111, 2253). Of course, where enzymes contain particular metals, these metals must also be supplied and consequently are usually growth factors. The existence of such deficiency effects, and their removal by the specific metal, have been used as evidence of the occurrence of this metal in the enzymes affected. For example, molybdenum deficiency reduces the amount of xanthine oxidase in rats, and addition of molybdenum to the diet increases the oxidase level (595, 2218). Such work has not been confined to animals; for instance, the existence of molybdenum in mould nitrate reductase was shown by similar nutritional studies (1962, 1965).

The synthesis of enzymes normally takes place within living organisms, but it can occur in much simpler systems. It can take place in perfused organs or even in tissue slices in vitro, in disrupted bacterial cells, and even (in certain cases) in cell-free extracts from animal tissues. Isolated perfused livers can rapidly form tryptophan oxygenase and threonine dehydratase (2118, 2313). Pigeon pancreas slices, when incubated aerobically (but not anaerobically), form amylase, lipase and ribonuclease, especially if an aminoacid mixture is added (1130, 2343); a fourfold increase of the first two enzymes was observed in $2\frac{1}{2}$ hr. This synthesis was inhibited by dinitrophenol, which interferes with aerobic phosphorylation processes, showing the importance of an energy-yielding process. Well-washed disrupted cells of Staphylococcus aureus, when supplied with an amino-acid mixture and ATP as a source of energy, synthesize catalase, β-galactosidase (if galactose is also present) and the glycolytic system of enzymes (GALE and FOLKES, 812). A fraction from an aqueous extract of acetone-treated pigeon or pig pancreas, with an aminoacid mixture and ATP, showed a steady formation of amylase for 30 to 60 min (STRAUB et al., 2547).

The synthesis of enzymes in the living cell is under two different kinds of control. In the first place their production, like that of proteins in general, is under genic control; a given enzyme can only be formed if the corresponding gene is present in the cell, and if the gene is absent or damaged by a mutation the enzyme will also be lacking. Thus the system of genes (genotype) of the cell fixes its enzyme-forming potentialities; the genes act by producing enzymes, and they contain the plan of the cell's metabolism. The cell cannot produce an unlimited variety of different enzymes, which would lead to chaos, but only those which fall within the range of the genotype. The 'one-gene-one-enzyme' theory (BEADLE, 181), which postulates a separate gene for the formation of every enzyme, is now widely held. It was mainly based on the study of the metabolism of mutant strains, especially of Neurospora, which usually indicates that the mutation of a single gene results in the absence of one single enzyme. This subject is more fully discussed in Chapter XIII.

In the second place the production of many enzymes is strongly influenced by the presence of metabolites, usually but not always either substrates or products. The mere presence of a gene does not guarantee that the corresponding active enzyme will be produced in significant amounts; the presence of an 'inducer' (most frequently the substrate of the enzyme or a related small-molecular substance) may also be required, and may in many cases increase the amount of the corresponding enzyme formed by many hundreds or even thousands of times, without much effect on unrelated enzymes. This phenomenon of enzyme induction is especially marked and easy to demonstrate in micro-organisms. Within the animal body, on the other hand, the composition of the medium surrounding the cells is held comparatively constant, and therefore the enzyme content of any organ in a particular species normally does not show very large variations. A number of cases of induction in animal tissues have, however, been observed; two of these are the tenfold increase in the alcohol dehydrogenase content of rat kidney as a result of adding alcohol to the diet for a month (1544), and the increase in liver arginase in rats kept on a high protein diet and therefore needing to convert large amounts of arginine into urea (1702).

The converse of the induction effect is enzyme 'repression', which is a specific inhibition of the formation of a particular enzyme caused by an accumulation of a product of the reaction which it catalyses. Since the effect of increasing the amount of a given enzyme in the cell will be to decrease the concentration of its substrate and increase that of its product, it is clear that the effects of induction and repression will reinforce in increasing the formation of deficient enzymes and decreasing the formation of those that are present in excess.

We shall now discuss the mechanism of these controlling factors in some detail, beginning with the mechanism of protein biosynthesis under genic control.

Biosynthesis of proteins

Knowledge of this subject is advancing with phenomenal speed at the present time, in fact it is one of those subjects of which it may be said that anything printed is *ipso facto* out of date. Here we can do no more than give an outline of the position as it appears at the moment of writing. The mechanism is an unusually interesting one for the enzymologist, not only because it is the one which gives rise to enzymes, but also because it is based on some exceptionally interesting phenomena of enzyme specificity.

Among general reviews of the subject, covering the developments up to about 1961, we may mention RAACKE (*2137*), McQUILLEN (*1672*) and GALE (*808*); the latter has addenda giving some of the more recent work.

The main seat of protein synthesis is in the ribosomes. These are numerous electron-dense ribonucleoprotein particles of diameter about 150 Å scattered throughout the cell, apparently to some extent even within the nuclei and possibly the mitochondria. Although some protein synthesis occurs in the nuclei and mitochondria, the greater part takes place in the cytoplasm outside these structures. The synthesis of several enzymes, including ATPase, phosphoglucomutase, aldolase and pyruvate kinase, by isolated ribosomes has been directly demonstrated by WEBSTER and LINGREL (see *1010*).

The nature of the protein formed by ribosomes is under genic control. It is now abundantly clear that a gene contains within itself a detailed representation of the actual aminoacid sequence of the particular enzyme or protein whose formation it controls. This information is replicated without limit as the chromosomes divide, and may thus be transmitted unchanged through millions of generations of cells. It is also transmitted within the cell from gene to ribosome, so that the ribosome is caused to form protein molecules with this particular aminoacid sequence.

The whole mechanism is based upon (*a*) the action of polynucleotide templates in determining the sequence in chains built up by enzymes, already briefly referred to on p. 449, (*b*) the strong tendency for association between nucleic acid chains with complementary sequences of bases, and (*c*) the high twofold specificity of the ligases of sub-group 6.1.1, towards aminoacids on the one hand and towards nucleotide sequences on the other.

The gene is composed of deoxyribonucleic acid (DNA), that is to say it consists of a long chain of nucleotides, all identical except for the purine or pyrimidine base. The information specifying the aminoacid sequence of the protein or enzyme to be formed must therefore be stored in the gene in the form of a nucleotide sequence. The mechanism must include provision not only for transmitting the information from gene to ribosome, but also for translating it from a nucleotide sequence to an aminoacid sequence.

The transmission is brought about by an enzyme which uses the gene DNA molecule as a template in building up a molecule of ribonucleic acid (RNA), of which the nucleotide sequence is an exact complement of that of the DNA. This 'messenger RNA' passes to the ribosome, with which it combines, acting as a template for the synthesis of the protein, and causing the ribosome to form that particular protein and no other.

The translation from nucleotide sequence to aminoacid sequence is brought about by the aminoacid:sRNA ligases of sub-group 6.1.1, of which there is probably one for each aminoacid. These enzymes attach to each aminoacid a 'destination label' in the form of a short length of RNA chain with a specific nucleotide sequence, different for each aminoacid. The tagged aminoacids are caused to combine successively with the ribosome by a soluble GTP-dependent enzyme, the order in which they are assembled into a chain being determined by correspondence between the nucleotide sequences in the RNA template on the ribosome and those in the labels specific to the different aminoacids.

Finally, the release of the protein chain thus formed from the ribosome is brought about by another soluble enzyme which is dependent on ATP.

Much of the information about the mechanism of which the above is an outline has been derived from work on bacteria and from experiments with DNA obtained from bacteriophages, but the main features have also been observed with ribosomes from plant and animal tissues. We shall now discuss the different parts of the mechanism in greater detail.

Replication of the gene DNA

DNA usually occurs in the form of two complementary chains of deoxyribonucleotides coiled together (WATSON and CRICK, 2797). The deoxyribose-phosphate chain is on the outside, and the bases lie inside the helix, each purine base being paired with a pyrimidine base of the other chain. The pairing of bases takes place by hydrogen bonding between them, and their configuration is such that adenine will pair only with thymine and guanine only with cytosine. This is what is meant by saying that the two chains are complementary. It will be clear that the composition and sequence of one chain determine those of the other. The

R

deoxyribose-phosphate chains run in opposite directions in the two chains, so that if in one chain each phosphate group is linked to the 3-position of the pentose residue above it and to the 5-position of that below it, in the other chain each phosphate will be linked to the 5-position of the residue above and to the 3-position of that below (see *1270*). The chains are normally very long, each perhaps containing 10,000 nucleotides or more. Figure XI.1 shows an outline of a short section in perspective, and Fig. XI.2 shows a plane representation of the pairing of bases.

RNA, although under certain conditions it can pair with complementary chains, has less tendency to assume a close helical configuration, owing to the bulk of the extra oxygen atom on the 2-position. It appears that usually the chain has a number of small helical regions, involving about half of its nucleotides (*649*).

Soluble RNA (sRNA), however, which has an abnormal base composition (see p. 488), appears to exist mainly as a double helix. Spencer *et al.* (*2482*) have carried out X-ray studies of crystalline yeast sRNA (apparently a mixture of all twenty sRNAs) and conclude that each molecule is doubled back on itself at the centre, the two halves forming the two strands of the double helix, and they suggest that the sequence of one half is complementary to that of the other.

The replication of DNA is brought about by enzyme 2.7.7.7; this has been purified some 4,000-fold from bacteria by KORNBERG and his colleagues (*1429, 1532*), and has also been prepared from other sources, e.g. thymus (BOLLUM, *283*).

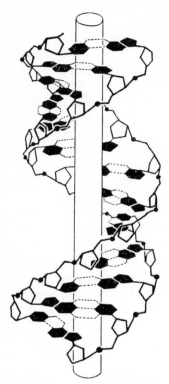

Fig. XI.1.   *Double-stranded helical structure of DNA.*
The dots represent the phosphate groups, the pentagons the deoxyribose rings, the purine and pyrimidine rings are shown in solid black, and the hydrogen bonds are shown as dotted lines.

after *551*

The action of the enzyme, which presents a number of features of unusual interest, is to transfer a nucleotidyl group from a deoxyribonucleoside triphosphate to the end of a DNA chain, releasing free pyrophosphate and lengthening the chain by one unit. It is specific for nucleoside triphosphates, and will not act with diphosphates; it is also specific for deoxyribose compounds, and will not act with ribonucleoside triphosphates.

Although the active centre of the enzyme is thus completely specific for the deoxyribose-triphosphate group, it shows no specificity towards the purine or pyrimidine base. Therefore by a repetition of the above reaction many thousands of times it can build up a complete DNA chain from a mixture of deoxyribonucleoside triphosphates. The incorporation of the different nucleotides, however, is not in a haphazard order; the necessary specificity for one particular base at any given point in the chain is provided by a preformed molecule of DNA acting as a template.

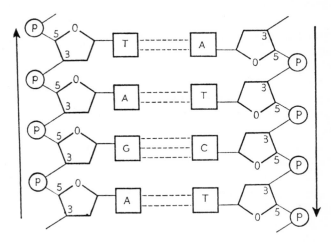

Fig. XI.2. *Pairing of bases in DNA.*

from *1270*

The enzyme is completely inactive without the addition of a DNA template. However, DNA in the double-stranded form is inactive, and the two chains must first be separated, e.g. by heating, before they will serve as templates (*283*). The template chain then combines with the enzyme, and the enzyme builds up on it a new complementary DNA chain, copying exactly the chain with which it was originally combined (*1270*). Thus a double-stranded DNA molecule is produced which is identical in all respects with the original molecule, and since this happens with both chains of the original molecule, there are now two such molecules in the place of one.

In each of the new molecules one chain is newly formed and the other is original, having remained intact. That this is the mechanism also *in vivo* has been shown by MESELSON and STAHL (*1801*) in elegant isotope experiments. DNA containing only N^{15} instead of the normal N^{14} differs sufficiently from ordinary DNA in molecular weight to be distinguished from it in the ultracentrifuge. Bacteria were grown in a N^{15} medium until their DNA was fully labelled ('heavy DNA') and showed a single band well separated from that of ordinary ('light') DNA. They were then transferred to a medium containing only N^{14}. After one generation their DNA showed only one band, in an intermediate position, and neither heavy nor light DNA was seen. Each DNA molecule therefore consisted of one original 'heavy' strand and one new 'light' strand. The second generation cells showed two bands, corresponding to intermediate and 'light' DNA in equal amounts, the 'light' and 'heavy' strands of the intermediate DNA having acted as templates to give 'light' and intermediate DNA molecules respectively. The 'light' and 'heavy' strands of the intermediate DNA could be separated intact.

Considering now the mode of action of the template, we can hardly suppose that the whole molecule is combined with the enzyme and displayed on its surface at the same time, remaining stationary while the new chain is built onto it; nor is it likely that one molecule of the enzyme contains 10,000 active centres specific for the deoxyribose-triphosphate structure, as would seem to be necessary if the template remains fixed during the whole operation. It is much more likely that the template moves step-by-step past the active centre of the enzyme, bringing each of its nucleotides in turn into juxtaposition with it as the new chain grows. The template chain would be fed through the active centre much as a punched tape is fed through a computer. Or perhaps, in view of the size of the template molecule, it would be better to regard the active centre as travelling along the chain. Of course the idea of an enzyme active centre travelling along a substrate chain is not unfamiliar; in the degradation of a long polysaccharide chain by β-amylase or by α-glucan phosphorylase something of the kind must occur. In all cases the position of the active centre in relation to the chain is determined by the position of the end of a chain, in the last two cases by the end of the polysaccharide chain undergoing degradation, and in the case of DNA by the end of the new chain being formed.

We may perhaps regard the particular nucleotide of the DNA template which is at the active centre of the enzyme at a given moment as being itself a temporary part of the whole active centre, completing its structure and conferring upon it the specificity towards purine and pyrimidine bases which was lacking in the permanent part of the centre. The particular base in the operative nucleotide of the template, by virtue of the positioning of its hydrogen bonding groups, will confer upon the centre a specific affinity for a nucleotide containing the complementary base, which will consequently be added to the new chain at that point. For instance, if the template nucleotide contains guanine the complete centre will specifically incorporate a nucleotide of cytosine and no other, the cytosine being hydrogen-bonded to the guanine and the phosphate becoming attached to the deoxyribose at the end of the new chain. The lengthening of the chain will then cause the next template nucleotide to move into position and the specificity of the centre will change. In this way exact replication will be brought about; moreover the new chain will be formed already hydrogen-bonded to the template DNA, and the double-stranded structure will no doubt assume the helical configuration of DNA on leaving the active centre as the chain grows.

As one might expect, the reaction only proceeds if all four of the nucleoside triphosphates are present. Table XI.1 (from *239*) shows the incorporation of deCMP (deoxycytidylic acid); similar results were obtained for the other three nucleotides. With any one alone, only a

TABLE XI.1

INCORPORATION OF deCMP INTO DNA BY
DNA NUCLEOTIDYL-TRANSFERASE (2.7.7.7)

Reactants added	deCMP incorporated ($\mu\mu$moles)
deCTP	2·5
deCTP+deGTP	5·1
deCTP+deGTP+deTTP	15·7
deCTP+deGTP+deTTP+deATP	3,300

minute amount is incorporated and the reaction then stops. Presumably a single residue can be incorporated by those enzyme molecules whose templates are set for the reception of this particular nucleotide, but if the next required nucleotide is not present the process cannot continue. The requirement for the presence of all the reactants may be expected in any case in which the sequence of successive additions is controlled by a template.

The formation of messenger RNA

This is brought about by enzyme 2.7.7.6, an enzyme which has many points of similarity to that just discussed. It builds up polynucleotide chains from nucleoside triphosphates, and it depends on a DNA template which determines the base sequence of the chain formed. It differs from the previous enzyme, however, in using ribonucleoside triphosphates and not deoxyribonucleoside triphosphates, hence it builds up RNA chains which are complementary to those of the DNA templates (see *417, 2009, 2827, 2829*). All four triphosphates are required for the incorporation of each, as well as DNA, and the base composition of the RNA formed is always complementary to that of the template; this has been tested with a variety of DNAs of widely differing composition. The base pairing here is not quite reciprocal, as it was in the previous case, because one of the chains is DNA and the other is RNA. Thus although thymine in the template produces adenine in the RNA, adenine in the template produces not thymine but uracil in the RNA, thymine (methyl uracil) being foreign to RNA.

Messenger RNA (*1225*) forms only a small part of the total RNA of the cell, but it undergoes rapid turnover; it is rapidly formed (several hundred times as fast as any other RNA) and rapidly destroyed during protein synthesis in the ribosomes. A continual stream of messenger RNA, therefore, flows from the nucleus to the ribosomes during protein synthesis. The very rapid formation of fresh messenger RNA can also be seen after the injection into a cell of a DNA foreign to it, e.g. on infection of a bacterial cell with DNA from a bacteriophage.

In the formation of messenger RNA, both strands of the DNA act as templates, so that two complementary RNAs are produced (*820*). Presumably only one of these is active in protein biosynthesis, as the other will contain nucleotide sequences which are complementary to those which fit the sRNA labels attached to the aminoacids. The fate of this RNA chain, and its function, if any, are not known.

Linking of aminoacids with sRNA labels

This is carried out by the ligases (synthetases) of sub-group 6.1.1. These enzymes† catalyse reactions of the **type**

XI.1   aminoacid + sRNA + ATP = aminoacyl − sRNA + AMP +
                                    + pyrophosphate

a typical synthetase reaction, in which the linking together of two molecules is coupled with the breakdown of a molecule of ATP. Their reaction mechanism has already been discussed in Chapter VII.

A number of these enzymes have been separated and highly purified, and it now appears probable that there is one for each aminoacid. It also appears that each enzyme is specific for a different sRNA; that is to say there are many sRNAs containing different nucleotide sequences, each of

---

† These enzymes have often been referred to under the name 'aminoacid-activating enzymes'. This is an unsatisfactory name. All enzymes act by activating their substrates, and the name does not distinguish these enzymes from other aminoacid-activating enzymes such as those of sub-groups 1.4.1, 2.6.1, 4.1.1, 5.1.1, etc. Moreover it gives no idea of the nature of the reaction. The international Commission on Enzymes recommends that it should not be used (see Rule (5) on p. 175, above).

which, because of the high twofold specificity of these enzymes, becomes attached to one particular aminoacid only.

Thus each aminoacid becomes associated with a particular sequence, perhaps of three nucleotides (see the section on coding below), and we may suppose that this sequence is complementary to the nucleotide sequence which specifies the particular aminoacid in the messenger RNA which acts as the template for protein synthesis on the ribosome. For example, it is known that phenylalanine is represented in the template by a sequence of (probably three) UMP nucleotides. If the ligase for phenylalanine is specific for an sRNA containing a corresponding sequence of AMP nucleotides, the pairing of complementary bases will ensure that phenylalanine and no other aminoacid will be incorporated into the polypeptide chain at the points specified by the UMP sequence in the template. In this way the nucleotide sequence of the template (and of the original gene) is translated into an aminoacid sequence, and the different aminoacids are assembled in the correct order for forming the chain of the protein or enzyme specified by the gene.

It will be noted that it is the ligases which translate the nucleotide sequence into an aminoacid sequence; the nucleotide code used in the genes is built into these enzymes in the form of their specificities. There appears to be no obvious chemical relationship between the chemical structure of an aminoacid and that of its specific sRNA, and the only reason why it becomes attached to this particular sRNA is that the enzyme is specific for this aminoacid and this sRNA.

The sRNA serves as a 'destination label' for the aminoacid, or an 'adaptor' (CRICK) enabling it to fit a particular point on the template. Once the aminoacid has been attached to its sRNA and has left the ligase, its destination is determined solely by the sRNA, and is not affected by chemical changes in itself. CHAPEVILLE et al. (429) coupled cysteine enzymatically with its sRNA to give Cys–sRNA$_{Cys}$; then by means of a nickel catalyst they converted the cysteine into alanine, giving Ala–sRNA$_{Cys}$. The alanine then behaved as cysteine in the ribosomal system and was incorporated into the protein in place of cysteine.

So far, few sRNAs have been purified, but enough has been done to make it probable that there is at least one for each aminoacid. They are small molecules in comparison with other forms of RNA, each containing 100–200 nucleotides in its chain. They all appear to terminate with the same sequence, namely with two CMP units followed by one AMP, the latter being terminal (ZAMECNIK et al., 1048). Only one molecule of aminoacid becomes attached to any given sRNA molecule, and this is combined by an ester linkage to the 2'- or 3'-position of the ribose of the terminal AMP nucleotide. This gives a method for the isolation of specific sRNAs from the mixture found in cells, for combination with the aminoacid protects this ribose residue against attack by periodate, to which it is susceptible when uncombined. By treating the sRNA mixture with excess of one aminoacid in presence of its ligase, and then exposing to periodate, the particular sRNA is preserved, while all the others are inactivated and can be converted into derivatives which are easily removed (ZAMECNIK *et al.*, in *1010*).

Since the three nucleotides next to the aminoacid are the same in all cases, the specificity must be determined by more remote parts of the chain. Most likely the residues immediately following give the coding with respect to the template, but it is not known how much of the chain determines the specificity towards the ligases. It is noteworthy that the sRNAs differ from other RNAs in containing unusual bases, for example methylated purines and pyrimidines, and up to 25 per cent of the uracil may be attached to the ribose, not by one of its nitrogen atoms, but through the carbon atom at position 5, giving pseudo-uridine.

There appears to be very little species specificity among the ligases and the sRNAs, and the general interchangeability of preparations of the different components from various species suggests that the same nucleotide code is very widely, if not universally, employed. However, there are some cases showing species specificity between sRNAs and ligases. In the case of leucine, the ligases and sRNAs of yeast and rat liver are mutually interchangeable, but neither ligase works with the sRNA of *Esch. coli*; conversely the ligase from *Esch. coli* works with its own sRNA, but not with those from yeast or liver (*2209*). The extent of the species effect varies with the aminoacid: with lysine, the sRNA from *Esch. coli* works with the ligases from both yeast and *Esch. coli*, while with arginine the sRNA from *Esch. coli* is not used at all by the yeast ligase (*209*). This does not imply any difference in coding, the effects may be due to species differences in the sRNA chain beyond the coding region.

Formation of proteins on ribosomes

Ribosomes consist of roughly equal amounts of protein and high-molecular RNA. Both are comparatively stable; they show little variation in composition and undergo no such rapid turnover as does messenger RNA. They may probably be regarded as structural, forming a base for the template and for the assembly of the protein chain. They carry several times their own weight of water and may have a spongy structure; the RNA is well exposed, not covered by protein as in virus nucleo-proteins. The composition of the RNA differs considerably from those of sRNA and messenger RNA. For a discussion of ribosomal structure see *1672*.

With ribosomes prepared from *Esch. coli*, the electron microscope shows that each consists of two parts, one about twice as large as the other (*1201*). By varying the conditions, these can be caused to separate and recombine. The separate parts bring about little aminoacid incorporation, and nearly all the incorporation is due to the double structure. The significance of this is unknown, but Tissières *et al.* (*2660*) suggest that the protein is formed at the junction of the two parts and is released when they separate.

At any one time it appears that only a minority of the ribosomes are engaged in protein synthesis (*2660*). This is apparently due to an insufficiency of messenger RNA to combine with all the particles; those that are combined incorporate aminoacids at least 40 times as fast as the others, and probably much more. On adding messenger RNA in the presence of Mg^{++}, it combines spontaneously with free ribosomes, and because it has a molecular weight of the order of a million the particle weight is sufficiently increased to sediment at a different rate in the ultracentrifuge. It can be shown in this way that the activity is due to the 'heavy' ribosomes, i.e. those carrying a molecule of messenger RNA (*2225*).

The complex of ribosome and template does not by itself incorporate aminoacyl-sRNA compounds. This is an enzymatic reaction, brought about by a soluble enzyme which has been partially purified (*1929, 2604*). There is much that is still obscure about the nature of the aminoacid incorporation, but since the enzyme reaction involves GTP, one molecule of which is broken down for each aminoacid residue incorporated (*2810*), it is probably of a synthetase type. The aminoacid is thereby attached to the end of the growing polypeptide chain and a molecule of sRNA is released. The sRNA is released in the intact and active form and can be recharged with more aminoacid; thus it acts cyclically as a coenzyme or carrier of aminoacid in the process (*1929*).

The transfer enzyme is unspecific towards the aminoacid, the sRNA and the template, and the same enzyme thus acts for all the aminoacids; it does, however, show a marked species specificity towards the ribosome itself. The enzyme prepared from *Esch. coli* is inactive with liver ribosomes, and the enzyme from liver with ribosomes from *Esch. coli* (*1929*). Presumably this indicates that the enzyme combines with the nucleoprotein of the ribosome.

The rate of the reaction, as calculated from *in vitro* experiments, corresponds to the addition of about two aminoacid residues per second to each chain (*611*), and in the bacterial cell after injection of phage DNA, molecules of new enzymes begin to appear after 2 or 3 minutes.

The manner of assembly of the polypeptide chains is still not entirely settled. The isotopic and other evidence is against a random growth of peptide sections here and there on the template, finally coalescing into a single chain, and in favour of a serial addition of aminoacids, starting from one end of the chain. There has been some difference of opinion as to which end of the polypeptide chain is the starting point, but DINTZIS (611) concludes that the weight of the evidence is in favour of the starting point being the aminoacid which will become the N-terminal end of the protein. This is supported by the observation of BISHOP et al. (252) that in haemoglobin biosynthesis there is at first very little incorporation of labelled valine into what will be the N-terminal position of the protein, suggesting that in the partially formed chains this end has already been laid down. The same deduction can also be made from the results of WAHBA et al. (2748) (see next section).

This means that the process takes place by a transfer of the carboxyl end of the preformed part of the chain from its sRNA to the amino group of the aminoacid residue being added (R), thus:

$$
\begin{array}{c}
\text{sRNA}' \\
\diagdown \\
\text{XI.2} \qquad + \qquad \text{CO}—\ldots—\text{NH}_2 \\[1em]
\text{sRNA}—\text{CO}—\text{R}—\text{NH}_2 \\
\downarrow \\
\text{sRNA}' \\[1em]
+ \qquad \text{CO}—\ldots—\text{NH}_2 \\
\diagup \\
\text{sRNA}—\text{CO}—\text{R}—\text{NH}
\end{array}
$$

where the dotted line represents the preformed part of the chain.

The chain retains only one sRNA molecule, attached to its C-terminal end; it has therefore lost its specific affinity for the template and is presumably held in some way to the ribonucleoprotein of the ribosome. The completed chains do not, however, leave the ribosome spontaneously; the release is brought about by a further soluble enzyme, which requires ATP for its activity (WEBSTER and LINGREL, in 1010). The mode of action of this enzyme, which is unstable but has been purified to some extent, is unknown. It is of interest that puromycin, which inhibits protein synthesis, appears to act by releasing all peptide fragments, however incomplete, from the ribosome (1929).

The messenger RNA is very rapidly broken down during protein synthesis, so rapidly that on the average each molecule only forms one molecule of protein (TISSIÈRES and WATSON, 2662), and this is no doubt the reason why in protein synthesis stoichiometric amounts of messenger RNA, but only catalytic amounts of sRNA, are necessary *(1971)*. The breakdown requires ATP and a soluble enzyme as well as the ribosomes, and it is possible that it is associated with the release of the completed protein from the ribosomes.

In most experiments with ribosomes *in vitro*, aminoacids are readily incorporated into protein, but the main difficulty is to secure the formation of free soluble protein; this is attributed by WEBSTER to a deficiency of the releasing enzyme.

Nature of the polynucleotide code

One of the most interesting questions at the present time is the nature of the biological coding system whereby the different aminoacids are represented by sequences of nucleotides in the genes and templates. Rapid progress is now being made in its elucidation.

Since there are about twenty aminoacids to be distinguished, and only four different nucleotides in DNA, it is clear that each aminoacid must be represented by a combination of two or more nucleotides. A pair of nucleotides could give 16 different combinations, which is insufficient; a triplet could give 64, which is more than enough.

CRICK *et al.* *(519)* have produced strong evidence from a study of mutants that the code is a triplet one, that is to say that each aminoacid is represented by a sequence of three nucleotides, the next three nucleotides representing the next aminoacid in the polypeptide chain. Gene mutations are discussed in Chapter XIII, but we may mention here that they are due to errors in replication of DNA, e.g. the substitution of one base by another, or the insertion or omission of a nucleotide, and the replication of the mutant DNA containing the error. Such errors are naturally very rare (perhaps once in a million replications), but can be caused to occur much more frequently by mutagenic substances, such as analogues of the natural bases or substances which tend to slip in between two nucleotides.

The substitution of one base by another will cause the substitution of a single aminoacid residue in the synthesized enzyme by another, and this will not have much effect on activity, unless the substitution should happen to occur in the active centre of the enzyme. The addition or deletion of a nucleotide, however, will alter all the aminoacids beyond this point, and indeed if a meaningless triplet is reached synthesis may be arrested altogether. For example the template sequence ...UUCAU-GUCUUGAGUC will be read (from the right, see below) as ..UUC .AUG.UCU.UGA.GUC, but if an extra GMP is incorporated to give ...UUCAUGGUCUUGAGUC it will be read as ..U.UCA.UGG. UCU.UGA.GUC. CRICK *et al.* showed that the effect of an addition could be effectively neutraliazed by deletion occurring nearby (provided no meaningless combination intervened), so that the normal reading was restored after a short distance and the only effect on the synthesized enzyme was presumably the alteration of a short length of its polypeptide chain. They also showed, however, that the effect of a deletion could be neutralized by two further nearby deletions; this would be expected for a triplet code, since the omission of three nucleotides will restore the normal reading thereafter, but it would not occur with a doublet or other code.

Information about the actual combinations corresponding to different aminoacids in the code can be obtained in three ways: (a) by using artificial polynucleotides of known composition in place of messenger RNA as ribosome templates, (b) by studying the effect of chemically modifying some of the nucleotide bases, and (c) by deductions from naturally-occurring aminoacid substitutions in proteins.

Enzyme 2.7.7.8 differs from the nucleotidyltransferases mentioned above in two respects; it builds up RNA chains from nucleoside di-phosphates, and it does not require a DNA template. Lacking the base specificity conferred by the template in the case of enzyme 2.7.7.6, it incorporates nucleotides, apparently in random order, in the proportions in which they are supplied; moreover it acts even when only one nucleo-side diphosphate is added. Thus from UDP it forms a polynucleotide chain consisting entirely of UMP units ('poly U'). It is, in fact, found that artificial polynucleotides containing different combinations of bases specifically cause the incorporation of different aminoacids by ribosomes. Poly U produces a protein consisting entirely of phenylalanine residues (*1971*), from which we may conclude that the sequence UUU represents phenylalanine. Using polynucleotides containing two or more different nucleotides, and comparing the incorporation of different aminoacids with the calculated probabilities of occurrence of the different triplets, codes for most of the aminoacids have been deduced by OCHOA *et al.* (*2483*) and by MATTHAEI *et al.* (*1759*), as shown in Table XI.2, and it will be seen that there is a substantial measure of agreement. It should be emphasized that only the composition, not the sequence, of the triplets is shown.

These are the codes in the messenger RNA; the codes in the gene DNA and presumably in the sRNAs will be the complementary triplets.

The results of other methods of attack confirm many of these codes. Deamination with nitrous acid converts cytosine to uracil and adenine to hypoxanthine (which behaves as guanine in the coding). Tobacco mosaic virus RNA treated with nitrous acid produces a number of mutants due to aminoacid replacements in the protein, and of 18 cases studied, all but five would have been predicted from the above chemical changes in the nucleotides (*1759*, *2483*). Moreover E. L. SMITH (*2441*) has examined 15 naturally occurring aminoacid replacements in mutant haemoglobins

TABLE XI.2

NUCLEOTIDE TRIPLETS CODING FOR AMINOACIDS

Composition of nucleotide triplet	Aminoacid	
	(Ochoa)	(Matthaei)
UUU	Phe	Phe
UUC	Ser	Ser
	Leu	Leu
UCC	Pro	Pro
	Thr	
UUA	Tyr	Tyr
	Ileu	Ileu
	Leu	
UAA	Lys	Lys
	AspN	
UAC	His	
	Thr	
	AspN	
UUG	Val	Val
	Leu	Leu
	Cys	Cys
UGG	Try	Try
	Gly	Gly
		Cys
UGA	Met	Met
	Glu	Glu
	Asp	
UCG	Arg	Arg
	Ala	Ala
	GluN	Ser

and other proteins, and has shown that nearly all can be explained on the code of Table XI.2 by the replacement of a single purine or pyrimidine base by another.

Tentative sequences of nucleotides within the triplets have been put forward by JUKES (*1275*), who considered a large number of mutations in the light of results of WAHBA *et al.* (*2748*). The latter authors made use of enzyme 2.7.7.8 to prepare poly-U derivatives with single AMP or GMP residues attached to the left-hand end, i.e. to the 5′-hydroxyl group of the poly-U, thus AUUUUUU....U or GUUUUUU....U. This was done by using the trinucleotides AUU or GUU as primers. When the enzyme is supplied with UDP, it attaches a series of UMP residues to the 3′-hydroxyl group of the primer, building up the above polynucleotides. When the first of these was used as a ribosome template, a proportion of the poly-phenylalanine molecules formed were found to have tyrosine residues in the C-terminal position, and with the guanine-containing polynucleotide as template cysteine residues were present instead of tyrosine. AAUUUUU....U and GGUUUUU....U gave the same results as the templates containing single A or G residues.

From this the following deductions may be made. (*a*) The *sequences* AUU and GUU correspond to tyrosine and cysteine respectively. (*b*) The left-hand end of the polynucleotide formula, i.e. the end with the free 5′-hydroxyl group, corresponds to the C-terminal end of the protein synthesized. (*c*) Since the synthesis begins with the N-terminal end of the protein (see above), the polynucleotide code is ' read' from the right-hand end, i.e. from the end with the free 3′-hydroxyl group. (*d*) Since, in view of the method by which they were prepared, the polynucleotides used must have consisted of mixtures of molecules with various chain lengths, incomplete triplets are disregarded; thus with a chain of $3x$ nucleotides, the left-hand end will be read as AUU.UUU.., giving a C-terminal tyrosine residue, as will also A.AUU.UUU.. with a chain length of $3x+1$, while with $3x+2$ residues AU.UUU.. will incorporate no tyrosine. AAU and GGU evidently do not represent any aminoacid.

Starting with the known code sequences for tyrosine and cysteine, Jukes (*1275*) has been able, from a consideration of a large number of naturally occurring single-aminoacid replacements in proteins, to deduce 25 tentative triplet-sequences corresponding to the known aminoacids, and these are given in Table XI.3. They should be regarded as provisional only, and it is probable that some modifications will be needed.

It will be noticed that every one of these sequences has a U in either the first or the second position. With this restriction, 28 triplet sequences are possible, of which 25 are given in the table. The results of WAHBA *et al.* suggested (deduction (*d*) above) that the sequences AAU and GGU were inoperative, and they do not come within the restriction.

Although the code may need modification in detail, its general features appear to be supported by good evidence. Moreover, evidence for the same coding has now been obtained from such diverse material as to make it probable that it is universal, occurring in all living cells. For example, MAXWELL (*1766*) has shown that seven of the codings in mammalian liver are identical with those in *Esch. coli*.

However, the combinations given may not be the only significant ones. The fact that all these combinations contain UMP may simply be a reflection of the fact that the artificial polynucleotides used all contained a high content of UMP. If these were the only triplets used *in vivo*, messenger RNA should contain a far higher proportion of UMP than any

TABLE XI.3

NUCLEOTIDE CODE-SEQUENCES FOR AMINOACIDS (*1275*)

Nucleotide sequence	Aminoacid	Nucleotide sequence	Aminoacid
UUU	Phe	UUG	Val
		UGU	Leu
UCU	Ser	GUU	Cys
CUU	Ser		
UUC	Leu	UGG	Try
		GUG	Gly
UCC	Pro		
CUC	Pro	UGA	Met
		AUG	Glu
AUU	Tyr	GUA	Asp
UUA	Ileu		
UAU	Leu	GUC	Arg
		CUG	Ala
AUA	Lys	UCG	GluN
UAA	AspN		
AUC	His		
UCA	Thr		
CUA	AspN		

known RNA. This fact has been used as an argument for a doublet, rather than a triplet, code (*2233*). It could, however, be explained if other triplets, not containing UMP, are used as well, so that a given aminoacid is represented by more than one combination. A code in which one aminoacid is represented by more than one combination is described as 'degenerate', whereas one in which a given combination represents more than one aminoacid is called 'ambiguous'; the evidence is that the actual code is degenerate but not ambiguous.

In fact, several cases can be seen in Table XI.3 where a given aminoacid appears in more than one place. The explanation of this degeneracy appears to be the existence of two or more different sRNAs for one aminoacid. WEISBLUM et al. (2826) have, in fact, separated from Esch. coli two sRNAs for leucine which differ in their coding behaviour with artificial polynucleotides. Whether this implies the existence of two ligases for leucine is not clear. It may be that degeneracy merely arises as the consequence of a lack of absolute specificity on the part of the ligases, or it may have some more fundamental function.

The extent of degeneracy appears to be considerable. The results of CRICK et al. (519) indicate that the majority of the chance combinations arising as the result of a deletion or addition must have significance, since it may be some distance before the first meaningless combination is met. This would not be the case if only the 25 given in the table (out of 64 possible) were significant.

The code is built into the biosynthetic mechanism in two places: (a) it is embodied in the DNA of the genes, which use it to represent the structure of the corresponding proteins, and (b) it is built into the specificity of the ligases. One of the most interesting and fundamental questions in biology is how it comes about that the genes and the ligases use the same code. The answer that no life is possible unless they do is unsatisfying; the chances against it coming about without some controlling mechanism to relate the two are enormous, but it is extremely difficult to picture such a mechanism.

The ribosomal synthetic mechanism determines the aminoacid sequence, i.e. the primary structure, of the protein formed. The production of an active enzyme, however, involves also the secondary and tertiary structure, since the active centre may involve several parts of the chain or of different chains. It is therefore necessary that the chain should be correctly folded and hydrogen-bonded. This, however, may be implicit in the aminoacid sequence. ANFINSEN (74) believes that the enzymes contain amino acid sequences so uniquely constructed that the formation of active centers and three-dimensional conformations follow automatically and reproducibly without additional genetic information.

Other biosynthetic mechanisms

GALE (see 808) has separated from bacterial RNA an 'incorporation factor' which can act instead of RNA in bringing about the incorporation of aminoacids by disrupted staphylococcal cells. There is some evidence that there are several such factors differing in specificity; it is not known whether they are true components of the nucleic acid or merely adsorbed on it. The isolated factor also promotes the synthesis of RNA in the preparation, and it is possible that its action is indirect, due to the formation of nucleic acid components. Chemically, it is related to glycerol; it yields glycerol as a breakdown product, and active material can be formed, after a lag period of 1–2 hours, by incubating the cell preparation with glycerol.

Not all polypeptide chains are synthesized by ribosomes. In certain bacteria a cell-wall polypeptide of definite aminoacid sequence is built up by the successive action of a series of specific synthetases, the sequence being determined, not by a template mechanism, but purely by enzyme specificity (ITO and STROMINGER, *1220–1*). The peptide chain is built up step-by-step from a UDP-acetylmuramate group at the N-terminal end, and a different synthetase is required for each step. Each synthetase reaction involves the breakdown of one molecule of ATP to ADP and phosphate, and all are highly specific both for the peptide already formed

TABLE XI.4

PEPTIDE SYNTHESIS BY A MIXTURE OF SYNTHETASES

Addition	*Incorporation of*			
	LAla	*DGlu*	*LLys*	*DAla–DAla*
None	—	—	—	—
UDP–AM	++	—	—	—
UDP–AM–LAla	—	+++	—	—
UDP–AM–LAla–DGlu	—	—	+++	—
UDP–AM–LAla–DGlu–LLys	—	—	—	+++
UDP–AM–LAla–DGlu–LLys–DAla–DAla	—	—	—	—

AM stands for acetyl-muramate.

and for the aminoacid added. Table XI.4 illustrates the process. A mixture of the enzymes was used and tested separately with each of the aminoacids shown; these were isotopically labelled, and the table shows their incorporation into material which could be adsorbed by charcoal. (The UDP peptides were adsorbed, but not the free aminoacids.) The series of intermediates, formed in the building up of the chain, was added as shown in the first column, each substance being the product of the reaction shown in the line above. The incorporation is shown by + signs, rather than by the figures given in the original papers, because this is a composite table from several experiments with preparations whose activities might not have been strictly comparable.

It will be seen that at each stage the aminoacid added is determined by the sequence already formed; the synthetases for the other aminoacids are unable to act, as each is specific for one sequence. Each enzyme is moreover strictly specific for the optical isomer shown, and both D- and

L-isomers are involved. It is also interesting that in the last step a pre-formed dipeptide is added as such. D-alanine itself is not added at this stage, but there is a separate synthetase (6.3.2.4) which forms the dipeptide from D-alanine.

It seems possible that processes of this kind may play a part in protein synthesis in addition to the ribosomal mechanism. This system resembles the ribosomal system in that the sequence of aminoacids produced is determined by the built-in specificity of a series of ligases (synthetases), but it differs from it in that the sequence is fixed and cannot be varied in accordance with a template supplied. It is therefore not under direct genic control, but is adapted more for the synthesis of a product which is invariably needed. Whether it plays any part in the biosynthesis of enzymes is unknown.

Induction and repression

It has already been mentioned that the formation of enzymes is under two kinds of control, namely by genes and by metabolites. For the formation of a given enzyme in a cell, the presence of the corresponding structural gene is an absolute necessity; however, in many cases at least, the mere presence of the gene in the cell does not suffice to ensure the production of the enzyme, and some small-molecular substance related to the reaction catalysed by the enzyme must be either present (induction) or absent (repression) for the enzyme to be formed in significant quantities. This specific influence of metabolites on the production of enzymes gives a most important biological control mechanism whereby the cell's equipment of enzymes is adjusted to the needs of its metabolism. The whole subject, with special reference to work on bacteria, is discussed in the valuable reviews of HALVORSON (*986*) and JACOB and MONOD (*1224-5*).

Repression and induction by metabolites must be clearly distinguished from inhibition or activation by metabolites, which may also be important. Repression and induction affect the actual *amount* of enzyme formed; inhibition and activation affect not the amount but the *activity* of the enzyme. The effects may be distinguished in a number of ways, e.g. by measuring the enzyme activity after removal of the inducing or repressing substance, or by actual isolation of the enzyme. It has been firmly established by isotopic and immunological methods that the appearance of an enzyme under the influence of an inducer corresponds to the synthesis from aminoacids of a protein not previously present in detectable amounts and different from the other proteins in the cell; that is to say 'the inducer brings about the complete *de novo* synthesis of enzyme molecules which are new by their specific structure as well as by origin of their elements' (*1225*).

A list of about two dozen inducible enzymes of micro-organisms is given by MONOD and COHN (Table 1 of *1850*).

Kinetics

On adding an inducer to a growing culture of bacteria the production of the corresponding enzyme begins in two or three minutes and continues

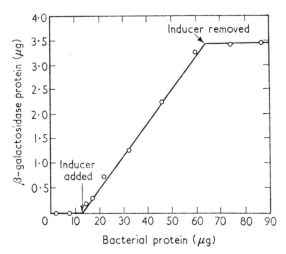

Fig. XI.3. *Time-course of enzyme induction.*
Induction of β-galactosidase in *Esch. coli* ML 30. At first arrow 5×10^{-4} M methyl-β-D-thiogalactoside added as inducer. At second arrow 10^{-2} M phenyl-β-D-thiogalactoside (a strong competitive inhibitor of the inducer) added, effectively removing the inducer from the system.
from *1225*, after M. Cohn

as long as the inducer is present; when the inducer is removed it ceases completely within two or three minutes (except in the case of penicillinase, where the inducing penicillin is retained irreversibly by the cells (POLLOCK, *2101*)). The time-curve of enzyme formation is affected by the fact that the bacteria are growing during the process, so that the number of cells and the total weight of protein are increasing. The process is most clearly shown by plotting the amount of enzyme, not against time, but against the total amount of protein (Fig. XI.3); it is then seen that while the inducer is present the amount of enzyme synthesized forms a constant fraction of all the protein synthesized. This means, in effect, that if the average cell weight remains the same, the amount of enzyme produced per minute per cell is constant.

Similar effects are obtained with repressors. When the repressor is removed from the growth medium, the rate of enzyme formation in relation to protein synthesis at once increases perhaps 1,000-fold and then remains constant, and when the repressor is added again it at once drops to the repressed level. In some cases, where the repressor is the product of the enzyme reaction, its removal produces a burst of rapid enzyme formation, which then ceases because the synthesized enzyme itself forms repressor (872). This can be avoided if steps are taken to prevent accumulation of the repressor, e.g. by continuously renewing the medium in a chemostat, when the enzyme synthesis proceeds linearly.

Specificity

Both induction and repression are extremely specific effects, and the kind of specificity observed is strongly reminiscent of the enzyme-substrate relationship. The action shows not only very high chemical specificity, but also strict stereospecificity as well. This implies that the inducer or repressor molecule must act by combining with a specific 'receptor', different for each enzyme or group of enzymes affected, and specifically fitted to the structure of the particular molecule, much as the active centre of an enzyme is fitted to its substrate. In fact, many of the phenomena of enzyme–substrate combination can be duplicated by receptor–inducer combination. For example, a reciprocal plot of the relationship between inducer concentration and velocity of induced enzyme synthesis gives a straight line resembling the Lineweaver–Burk plot, showing reversible combination between inducer and receptor, and from this a 'Michaelis constant' can be obtained, giving the affinity of the combination (see Fig. XI.4) (1029). The phenomenon of competitive inhibition between different inducers can also be observed.

Since the inducer of any particular enzyme is either the substrate of that enzyme, or is closely related in structure to the substrate, with which the active centre of the enzyme combines, the receptor must be very similar to the active centre in each case. The obvious assumption would be that the active centre of the enzyme is itself the receptor, but it appears that this cannot be the case, for several reasons. (a) There are definite differences in specificity between them; where an enzyme acts on a series of related substrates, although they usually all act as inducers there is no correlation between the two actions, so that a good substrate may be a poor inducer and *vice versa*. (b) Where the affinities for the receptor have been measured, as for instance in the case of valine decarboxylase (1029), it is found that the substrates have a considerably (e.g. tenfold) higher affinity for the receptor than they have for the active centre. Indeed, it is not uncommon for substances which do not combine detectably with the active centre to act as inducers, which implies combination with the receptor. (*c*) Induction by the substrate still occurs when the active centre of the enzyme is no longer functional as the result of a mutation in the

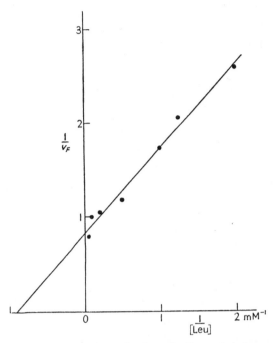

Fig. XI.4. *Reciprocal plot of effect of inducer concentration.*

Induction of valine decarboxylase by leucine in *Proteus vulgaris.* v_F = rate of enzyme formation in arbitrary units, taking rate with 10mM leucine as 1.0.

from *1029*

corresponding structural gene and is unable to combine with the substrate. The formation of β-galactosidase (3.2.1.23) in *Esch. coli* requires induction by a galactoside. The structural gene for this enzyme (known as z) can undergo a mutation (z^-) affecting the active centre, so that instead of active enzyme an inactive protein is produced. This protein appears to be identical with the enzyme in all other respects, for example by immunological tests. It can be isolated, and is found by physical methods to have lost all affinity for galactosides. Nevertheless the synthesis of this protein depends on specific induction by galactosides, showing that the receptor is still present even though the active centre is not (2071). In diploid cells containing both a normal and a mutated gene, the inducer evokes the formation of the enzyme and the inactive protein at the same time.

TABLE XI.5

SPECIFICITY OF INDUCTION OF β-GALACTOSIDASE IN ESCH. COLI

Part I, with Esch. coli, *strain ML, and maltose as carbon source (from 1849)*

No.	Substance (G = D-galactoside)	Enzyme induced (mU/mg after 4 hr in 10^{-3}M)	Relative affinity for purified enzyme (NPG taken as 1,000)	Hydrolysis by purified enzyme
1	Galactose	420	30	
	β-D-galactosides			
2	methyl-β-G..	2,800	10	+
3	n-butyl-β-G	2,800	400	+
4	phenyl-β-G..	560	600	+
5	o-nitrophenyl-β-G (NPG) ..	1,060	1,000	+
6	β-naphthyl-β-G	42	200	+
7	4-glucose-β-G (lactose)	2,500	100	+
8	mannose-β-G	2,500	10	+
9	4(p-aminophenyl-β-glucosido)-β-G	2,200	100	+
	α-D-galactosides			
10	methyl-α-G..	140	0	0
11	6-glucose-α-G (melibiose).. ..	2,400	0	0
12	6-sucrose-α-G (raffinose)	0	0	0
	methyl-substituted galactosides			
13	2-methyl-β-methyl-G	20	0	0
14	2,6-dimethyl-β-methyl-G.. ..	0	0	0
15	3,4-dimethyl-β-methyl-G.. ..	0	0	0
	6-carbon of D-galactose removed			
16	L-arabinose	0	>0	
17	methyl-β-L-arabinoside	0		0
18	o-nitrophenyl-α-L-arabinoside ..	0	50	+
	β-D-thiogalactosides			
19	phenyl-β-thiogalactoside	0	700	0

The following substances do not act as substrates or inducers of the enzyme: deoxygalactose (2- or 6-), D-galacturonates, methyl- or phenyl-β-D-glucosides, D-xylose, D-tagatose, D-mannose, D-glucose, maltose, cellobiose.

TABLE XI.5—*continued*

Part II, with Esch. coli, *strain K12, and glycerol as carbon source* (from *1225*)

No.	Substance (10⁻³M unless otherwise stated) (TG = D-thiogalactoside)	β-galactosidase			Galactoside acetyltransferase	
		Enzyme induced (IPTG taken as 100)	*V* (PG taken as 100)	*Relative affinity for purified enzyme* (PG taken as 100)	*Enzyme induced* (IPTG) taken as 100)	V/K_m
1	Galactose	<0·1	—	4	<1	<1
4	phenyl-β-G (PG)	15	100	100	11	—
7	4-glucose-β-G (lactose)	17	30	14	12	35
11	6-glucose-α-G (melibiose)	35	0	<0·1	37	<1
19	phenyl-β-TG	<0·1	0	100	<1	100
20	methyl-β-TG (10^{-4}M)	78	0	7	74	30
21	isopropyl-β-TG (IPTG) (10^{-4}M)	100	0	140	100	80
22	phenylethyl-β-TG	5	0	10,000	3	—
23	phenyl-β-glucoside	<0·1	0	0	<1	50

V is the maximum velocity of the reaction catalysed by the enzymes. In the case of the acetyltransferase V and K_m could not be measured separately because of the low value of the affinity.

A very large proportion of the work on enzyme induction has been carried out on the β-galactosidase of *Esch. coli*. MONOD and his co-workers have made extensive investigations of the specificity of induction of this enzyme, and their results with two different strains of *Esch. coli* are shown in Table XI.5. Although there are certain quantitative differences between the two organisms, the main features are similar. The figures for the amount of β-galactosidase induced are given in different units in the two parts of the table, and with the data available it is not possible to convert them all into the same units, but as a rough guide it may be stated that the figures in column 3 of Part II should be multiplied by about 75 to make them comparable with those in the same column of Part I.

From these results it may be seen that (*a*) all the galactoside substrates (Nos. 2–9) act as inducers, with varying efficiency; (*b*) in one case (No. 18) a substance can act as a substrate and yet not be an inducer (assuming that this arabinoside is indeed a substrate of β-galactosidase itself); (*c*) substances which are not substrates can act as powerful inducers (Nos. 11, 20–1); (*d*) substances may act as powerful inducers although they have little or no affinity for the active centre of the enzyme (Nos. 2, 8, 11, 20); (*e*) substances may possess powerful affinities for the active centre of the enzyme and yet not act as inducers (Nos. 19, 22); (*f*) all substances shown to act as inducers possess the D-galactose ring; (g) not all substances possessing this ring act as inducers or substrates.

The natural substrate of an enzyme is not necessarily the best inducer. In this case isopropyl-β-D-thiogalactoside (No. 21) is the most powerful inducer; expressed in the units of Part I it gives 7,500, even at 10^{-4}M, and it would probably give well over 10,000 at 10^{-3}M. The rate of induction is usually proportional to the concentration of inducer, but it would not be safe to assume that this is so with such a powerful inducer.

For the induction mechanism, the occurrence of the reaction catalysed by the enzyme is immaterial, in other words it is irrelevant whether the substance complexed with the enzyme breaks down or not (compare for example Nos. 7 and 11). Not only is it unnecessary for the inducer to act as a substrate for the enzyme which it induces, it is not even necessary for the enzyme to be produced in an active form in which it can act on its substrate. If the prosthetic group of the enzyme is a substance which the cell cannot synthesize and it is omitted from the medium, the inactive but specific apo-enzyme may be produced in response to the inducer. For example, in a pyridoxine-deficient medium, certain *Streptococci* produce in the presence of tyrosine (but not in its absence) the protein part of tyrosine decarboxylase (4.1.1.25), which is inactive by itself but can be activated by the addition of pyridoxal phosphate (*201*). This shows that the activity of the enzyme itself is not necessary for the induction, as has been assumed by some theories. Moreover we have seen that induction may still occur when the enzyme formed is incapable of catalysis, being produced without its active centre as the result of the gene mutation.

Not only is reaction at the active centre irrelevant, but so also is combination with the centre; at least there is no correlation between inducing power and affinity of combination. This is shown very clearly in Part II of the table. All this confirms the distinction between the active centre of the enzyme and the receptor for the inducer, and shows that studies on the active centre are not likely to give valid information about the mechanism of the induction. These differences, however, must not cause us to lose sight of the most fundamental feature of induction, namely the remarkable fact that the formation of each of the many inducible enzymes is specifically brought about only by its own substrate or substances closely related thereto. The inducing action of a given substance is limited to those enzymes which catalyse reactions connected in some way with the substance. Thus there *is* a specific connection between the reaction normally catalysed by an enzyme and the induction of its formation, even though the induction does not depend on the occurrence of the reaction. Any satisfactory theory of the process must explain this connection.

It is sometimes found that the addition of a metabolite induces not a single enzyme, but a group of related enzymes by which the substance can be metabolized through a series of intermediates.

Repression differs from induction in two respects. (*a*) The repressor acts to prevent, not to cause, the formation of the enzyme. (*b*) The inducer is (or is related to) the substrate of the enzyme; the repressor is (or is related to) a product of the enzyme reaction. Thus the two processes are complementary control mechanisms. If there is a deficiency of an enzyme involved in a line of metabolism, the concentration of its substrate will be increased, and this will induce the formation of more of the enzyme; if there is an excess of an enzyme, the concentration of its product will be high, and this will tend to repress the formation of the enzyme. In both cases the result is an adjustment of the amounts of the various enzymes in the cell to the needs of its metabolism.

TABLE XI.6

REPRESSION OF ENZYME FORMATION

Repressing substance	Enzymes whose formation is repressed	Organism	References
L-arginine	Acetylornithine deacetylase (3.5.1.d)	Esch. coli W	872–3, 2740
	Ornithine carbamoyl-transferase (2.1.3.3)		
	Argininosuccinate lyase (4.3.2.1)		
L-histidine	Imidazoleglycerol-phosphate dehydratase (4.2.1.19)	Salmonella typhimurium	62
	Histidinolphosphate aminotransferase (2.6.1.9)		
	Histidinolphosphatase (3.1.3.15)		
	Histidinol dehydrogenase (1.1.1.23)		
L-lysine	Aspartate kinase (2.7.2.4)	Esch. coli	2498
L-methionine	A homocysteine methyltransferase	Esch. coli	475, 2864
L-proline	Pyrroline-5-carboxylate reductase (1.5.1.2)	Neurospora crassa	2954
L-tryptophan	Tryptophan synthase (4.2.1.20)	Aerobacter aerogenes	1848

Table XI.6—*continued*

L-tyrosine	Phenylalanine 4-hydroxylase (1.99.1.2)	Rat	*96*
L-asparagine	Asparagine synthetase (6.3.1.1)	*Lactobacillus arabinosus*	*2185*
L-glutamine	Glutamine synthetase (6.3.1.2)	HeLa cells	*589*
Creatine	Glycine amidinotransferase (2.6.2.1)	Birds, rats	*2771*
GMP	IMP cyclohydrolase (3.5.4.10) IMP dehydrogenase (1.2.1.14)	*Salmonella typhimurium*, *Aerobacter aerogenes*	*1558*
UMP	Aspartate carbamoyltransferase (2.1.3.2) Ureidosuccinase (3.5.1.7) Dihydro-orotate dehydrogenase (1.3.3.1)	*Esch. coli* B	*2946*
Phosphate	Alkaline phosphatase (3.1.3.1)	*Esch. coli* W, ML or K12	*814*

The question arises whether the formation of a given enzyme is ever subject to both mechanisms. In other words, can an enzyme which is induced by one substance also be repressed by another, or are there non-overlapping classes of inducible and repressible enzymes? The very incomplete evidence that is available at present seems to suggest that in the majority of cases those enzymes whose formation is controlled by induction are not subject to repression, and vice versa. One or two cases are known, however, where an enzyme that is repressible in one organism is inducible in another.

It is often stated that it is the end-products of lines of metabolism that bring about repression of the enzymes involved in their formation. This statement is not entirely satisfactory. In the complex network of reactions which constitutes metabolism, it is difficult to select particular intermediates as end-products, especially if they undergo further metabolism. The situation would probably be more accurately expressed by saying that when an aminoacid (or more rarely a nucleotide) arises in the course of metabolism, it acts as a repressor of the formation of the enzymes that produce it; for nearly all the known cases are repressions by aminoacids of enzymes involved in their biosynthesis in micro-organisms, as shown in Table XI.6.

The effect is specific to the particular aminoacid which is produced by the enzymes affected, as illustrated in Fig. XI.5.

As in the case of enzyme induction, a large part of the work on repression has been done with various strains of *Esch. coli*, an organism in which the phenomenon is particularly well marked. It is usually necessary to work with mutants in which there is a genetic block (absence of one of the enzymes) in the metabolic pathway leading to the repressing substance, otherwise enough of the substance is produced by the metabolism of the

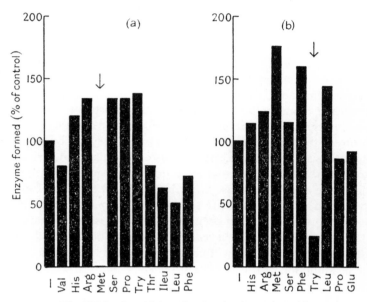

Fig. XI.5. *Specificity of repression by aminoacids*

Effect of growth of bacteria in presence of the aminoacids shown on formation of enzymes. Enzyme formation in control taken as 100. (a) Formation of 'methionine synthase' in *Esch. coli* ML, (b) formation of tryptophan synthase in *Aerobacter aerogenes* L₃. The concentration of aminoacids was M/150 in (a), and varied between M/200 and M/500 in (b).

drawn from data in *475* and *1848*

cell to maintain repression and so to prevent the demonstration of accelerated enzyme formation on release of repression when the substance is removed.

With a suitable mutant it is therefore necessary to supply a certain amount of the repressing substance for growth requirements. If only a limited amount is added, it is usually found that the organism grows without forming the enzyme in question until all the repressing substance is used up; there is then a sudden drop in the growth rate and at the same time formation of the enzyme begins and continues, sometimes at such a high rate that it may account for 5 per cent of the total protein synthesized. If further repressing substance is then added, it stops the formation of the enzyme, which remains at the level reached at the time of addition.

In the absence of a genetic block the addition of any of the intermediates of the particular metabolic pathway may produce repression, simply because they are converted by the series of enzymes into the repressing substance. If there is a genetic block the results will depend on its position: those intermediates which are situated after the block will still be converted into the repressor, but those which occur before the block cannot be so converted, and do not repress.

It is not infrequently found, both in induction and in repression, that a single substance affects the formation of more than one enzyme. The addition of a metabolite may induce not a single enzyme, but a group of metabolically related enzymes by which the substance may be transformed through a series of intermediates. Similarly a repressing substance may prevent the formation of a series of several enzymes bringing about its biosynthesis. For example, the addition of a β-galactoside brings about in *Esch. coli* the induced formation not only of β-galactosidase but also of galactoside acetyltransferase (2.3.1.b) (*2956*), an enzyme of unknown function, and of the so-called 'galactoside permease', an enzyme of unknown nature concerned in some way with the passage of galactosides into the cell, which was believed for a time to be identical with the acetyltransferase (*1224*). As will be seen from Part II of Table XI.5, the degree of induction of the acetyltransferase is identical with that of the galactosidase with a wide variety of inducers. The structural genes of all these enzymes are located in the *lac* segment of the chromosome. Another group of enzymes also connected with galactose is situated in the *gal* segment; these are responsible for the conversion to glucose, and include galactokinase (2.7.1.6), hexose-1-phosphate uridylyltransferase (2.7.7.12) and UDPglucose epimerase (5.1.3.2). These three enzymes are induced to the same extent (but independently of the former group) by 6-deoxygalactose (D-fucose), but are not induced by one of the strongest inducers of β-galactosidase, methyl β-thiogalactoside, which indeed inhibits their induction by D-fucose (*373*).

The same effect has been observed with repressors. For example, in *Salmonella* L-histidine represses the formation of the four enzymes which act consecutively to bring about its biosynthesis (see Table XI.6) and the degree of repression is the same for all; this phenomenon is known as 'coordinate repression' (*62*). Similarly, L-arginine has been shown with *Esch. coli* to repress the formation of three of the enzymes involved in its production, and uracil or derivatives thereof to repress three of those involved in the formation of UMP, as shown in Fig. XI.6. Uracil itself is

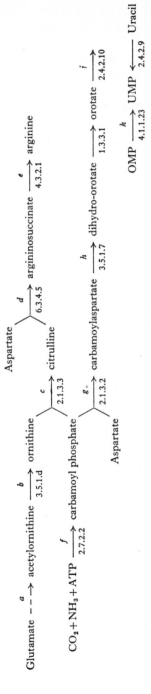

Fig. XI.6. *Enzyme repressions in Esch. coli*
Arginine represses enzymes *b, c* and *e,* but not *f*; uracil (and derivatives) represses *g, h* and *i,* but not *f.*

not, like arginine, an end product of these enzyme reactions, but it can be converted into the end product UMP, which is probably the actual repressor.

It is important to note that enzymes can still be repressed even when one of the enzymes coming between them and the end product is missing as the result of a genetic block. For example, enzyme g in the diagram is repressed by UMP in mutants which lack any of the enzymes $h, i, j,$ or k, although it is metabolically isolated from the repressing substance by the block.

One possible explanation for the induction of a series of enzymes was suggested by STANIER (2504), namely a 'sequential induction' mechanism, with the intermediates formed in the sequence of reactions acting as separate inducers of the respective enzymes which act upon them. The substance added would induce an enzyme which would convert it into the first intermediate; the latter in turn would induce another enzyme converting it into the second intermediate, and so on until a series of enzymes catalysing successive reactions in the metabolic chain has been induced, some acting on substrates bearing little resemblance to the primary inducer. For example, the addition of tryptophan to a *Pseudomonas* culture induces a series of perhaps a dozen enzymes, catalysing the transformation of tryptophan through kynurenine, anthranilate, catechol and muconate to 3-oxoadipate (2505); these enzymes are all absent in the organism grown without inducer.

While this mechanism may play some part, it appears that it is not the main one. It is not only in induction that groups of related enzymes are affected, but in repression also, where this explanation could not hold. A 'sequential repression' might be thought of, in which the repression of one enzyme would cause the accumulation of the product of the preceding enzyme, which would in turn be repressed. This, however, would require that all the intermediates should repress the enzymes forming them, which is not the case; furthermore, the effect would not be able to pass a genetic block, as in fact it does. Moreover, the induction or repression of the different enzymes in the group is not sequential in time; on the contrary, they are affected simultaneously. A different explanation must be sought.

Operons

There is a marked tendency in bacteria (though apparently it is less marked in higher organisms) for the structural genes of groups of metabolically related enzymes to be situated close together in the chromosomes, as we have already seen in the *lac* and *gal* segments of the *Esch. coli* chromosome. It is possible to go further than this, however, by the detailed mapping of the chromosome by the usual genetical methods, which reveals that the genes are arranged in the group consecutively in an order related to the action of their enzymes. HARTMAN *et al.* (*1014*) have shown that in *Salmonella* the structural genes of the series of enzymes leading to histidine are arranged in contact in the exact order of the sequence of chemical reactions catalysed by their respective enzymes, so that it is possible to write the series of consecutive chemical reactions involved in the biosynthesis of histidine below the chromosome map and each gene will appear above the reaction catalysed by its enzyme. The chromosome thus contains a remarkable amount of information, not only (in the internal structure of the genes) about the structures of the enzymes, but also (in the sequence of the genes in the chromosome) about the metabolic pathways catalysed by these enzymes. This is the more remarkable because of the indirect nature of the connection between the structure of the gene and the chemical reaction catalysed by the enzyme; the gene itself does not catalyse these reactions, and it is only when its coded information has been translated into the aminoacid sequences of the enzymes that the nature of the reactions catalysed becomes apparent.

There are, however, considerable differences between different organisms in the grouping of the genes. For example, the genes connected with histidine biosynthesis, which arecollected into one group in *Salmonella*, are widely scattered in *Neurospora* and yeast (*62*). The genes of the arginine-forming enzymes are scattered in *Esch. coli*, at least in several strains.

A group of consecutive genes, functioning as a unit in the chromosome is known as an 'operon' (JACOB and MONOD, *1225*), for example the genes connected with histidine in *Salmonella*, or the group in *Esch. coli* containing the structural genes known as z and y for β-galactosidase and galactoside acetyltransferase respectively. The latter operon is the one on which most work has been done. The enzymes whose genes are situated in one operon are all induced or repressed to the same extent ('coordinate induction or repression'), whereas if the genes of the enzymes are not situated in a single operon they are usually affected to different extents ('non-coordinate induction or repression'), even if the effect is produced by the same substance.

This suggests that the amount of messenger RNA formed in a given time interval is always the same for each of the enzymes in an operon, and this in turn suggests that when the DNA of the operon is copied as messenger RNA the whole operon behaves as a unit, the process starting at one end of the operon and proceeding straight through to the other.

Strong evidence for this mechanism has been obtained from the study of mutations (see JACOB and MONOD, *1224*). The point on the operon at which the formation of the messenger RNA begins is known as 'the operator' (*o*), and in the case of the *lac* operon it has been identified by mapping as the end of the *z* gene away from the *y* gene, in other words one end of the operon. Certain mutations of the operator (known as o^0) make it inactive, so that the formation of RNA cannot begin at this point. The effect of this is to make the whole operon inactive, so that there is no formation of either enzyme, even in the presence of inducers. Thus no RNA can be formed on the *y* gene, although this is normal; the building up of the messenger RNA must begin on the operator. The inactive operon does not interfere, however, with the action of a normal operon carried by another chromosome in the same cell, and the normal operator on this chromosome cannot activate the first operon.

Thus the operator provides a control point for the regulation of the synthesis of all the enzymes in the group, and there is evidence that induction and repression is brought about by an action at this point.

Further evidence that the building up of the RNA is a unidirectional process, starting from the operator and proceeding along the whole operon, is afforded by the effect of mutations within the *y* and *z* genes themselves. Most of these merely produce independent effects on the structure of the acetyltransferase or the galactosidase respectively. One or two mutations in the *z* gene, however, appear to arrest the formation of the RNA, perhaps by producing meaningless combinations, and these prevent the formation of acetyltransferase by the *y* gene also. On the other hand, no mutations in the *y* gene ever affect the action of the *z* gene. This shows that the *z* gene, which contains the operator, is copied before the *y* gene (see *1224*).

The question then arises whether the whole operon is represented by a single molecule of messenger RNA, and if so, whether the whole set of enzymes is synthesized in one operation on a ribosome. The enzymes at any rate are quite distinct proteins and can easily be separated, e.g. by ammonium sulphate fractionation; therefore breaks must occur at some stage, either in the peptide chain or in the RNA chain. It is probably easier to suppose that they occur during the formation of the RNA, perhaps in response to special code combinations, so that it is broken up into lengths corresponding to the separate enzymes; otherwise it would be necessary to assume the formation of a very large messenger RNA molecule, in order to accommodate the structural sequences of all the enzymes represented in the operon.

Operons have so far only been demonstrated in bacteria, though there is no reason to suppose that they do not exist in other organisms. They do not, however, form an essential feature of the mechanism for induction or repression, for groups of enzymes may be induced or repressed by a single substance even when their structural genes are well scattered. In the latter case presumably each of the genes has its own operator, with some structural feature common to all.

Regulator genes

The chromosomes contain not only structural genes, specifying the structures of the corresponding enzymes, but also regulator genes, which specifically control the rate of synthesis of the various enzymes or groups of enzymes. The structural genes are concerned merely with the aminoacid sequences of the enzymes they produce, but not with the rate of formation; in the absence of control, they produce messenger RNA (and hence enzyme) at a constant rate, two or four z genes in one cell producing galactosidase at two or four times the rate of one (*2000*). The regulator genes have no influence on the structure of the enzymes they control, but merely determine the rate at which they are produced by the structural genes. Enzymes produced under their influence have unchanged specific activities; it is only the amount of enzyme which is changed. Regulator genes are not necessarily situated in the chromosome near the structural genes they control. In fact, they may control genes in other chromosomes, which indicates that their action is due to the production of some intracellular substance.

These genes can undergo mutations, and it is the study of the effects of such mutations that has given the main clue to the mechanism of induction and repression.

The regulator gene for the galactosidase operon in *Esch. coli* (known as i) can mutate to a form i^- which gives rise to 'constitutive mutant' cells. Cells containing the normal i^+ form produce galactosidase only when an inducer is present, but cells containing only the i^- form produce the enzyme in the absence of inducer just as well as when inducer is present. If two chromosomes are present, one containing i^+z^- (z^- being a mutant form of z incapable of producing active enzyme) and the other containing i^-z^+, the enzyme is once more formed only in the presence of inducer. In other words i^+ is dominant and i^- recessive.

Thus in the absence of inducer the presence of an i^+ gene prevents the formation of the enzyme and its absence allows its formation, which indicates that i^+ produces a substance which inhibits the formation and i^- does not. In fact the deletion of the region of the chromosome which contains i has the same effect as the i^- mutation.

There is direct evidence from isotope experiments (*1224*) that this 'cytoplasmic repressor' acts by preventing the formation of messenger RNA by the genes it controls. The natural assumption is that it combines with the operator and so prevents the start of the RNA formation. This is

s

supported by the fact that the operator itself can undergo a 'constitutive' mutation (o^c) which apparently makes it unable to combine with the cytoplasmic repressor, for the o^c and the i^- mutations have much the same effect, a repressor which is unable to act behaving as if it were absent.

The effect of the inducer must be to prevent the cytoplasmic repressor from acting, and many workers adopt the hypothesis that the inducer combines specifically with the cytoplasmic repressor to form a compound which can no longer combine with the operator. This means that induction must be seen as a 'derepression', and it becomes possible to regard enzyme induction and repression as variants of the same basic mechanism. In both cases the production of enzyme is blocked by combination of the cytoplasmic repressor with the operator. The essential difference between them is that in an inducible system the free cytoplasmic repressor can combine with the operator while its compound with the inducer cannot, whereas in a repressible system the free cytoplasmic repressor is unable to combine with the operator and it is only a specific compound of it with the aminoacid or other repressing substance that can combine (SZILARD, *2591*). Thus the effect of an inducer is to unmask, and of a repressing substance to mask, the operator.†

We may mention one further mutant form of the regulator gene, known as i^s. When this is present none of the enzymes of the operon can be formed, even in the presence of inducer, although the y and z genes are normal. A normal i^+ gene in a second chromosome has no effect; in other words i^s is dominant over i^+. The interpretation is that i^s forms a modified form of the cytoplasmic repressor which has lost the power of combining with inducer although it can still combine with the operator. Thus the operator is masked in all circumstances. The effects of the mutants mentioned are summarized in Table XI.7.

With regard to the chemical nature of the cytoplasmic repressor, there are several points which might suggest that it is a small-molecular RNA, somewhat resembling the aminoacid-specific sRNA molecules involved in protein synthesis. (*a*) It is formed on the DNA of the regulator gene and its structure is specifically determined by the structure of the DNA. (*b*) Its structure has a specific relationship and affinity to that of the DNA of the operator which it controls. (*c*) Its formation does not involve any protein synthesis, for it is unaffected by chloramphenicol, which prevents

---

† The existing terminology is far from satisfactory. The term 'repressor' is used almost indiscriminately for (*a*) the primary repressing substance, e.g. an aminoacid, (*b*) the cytoplasmic repressor (an RNA ?) produced by the regulator gene, and (*c*) the compound of the cytoplasmic repressor and the repressing substance, which inhibits the operator. One suggestion has been to call (*a*) the 'corepressor', (*b*) the 'aporepressor', and (*c*) the 'repressor', but this has not yet come into general use.

protein formation. (*d*) The repressing substance with which it becomes combined (e.g. an aminoacid or nucleotide) is in practically all cases of a type which is known to be combined with RNA molecules by enzymes, for example by sRNA:aminoacid ligases. (*e*) There is a highly specific connection between its structure and the particular aminoacid with which

TABLE XI.7

MUTATIONS AFFECTING β-GALACTOSIDASE FORMATION

IN *ESCH. COLI*

Muta-tion	Site of mutation	Effect	Result
None	—	Operator blocked by repressor; repressor removed by combination with inducer	Enzyme formed only in presence of inducer
z^-	Part of structural gene forming active centre	Structure of active centre altered	No active enzyme. Inactive protein formed only in presence of inducer
o^0	Operator part of structural gene	Operator inactive, even when **not** combined with repressor; no messenger RNA formed	No enzyme formed, even in presence of inducer
o^c	Operator part of structural gene	Operator active, unable to combine with repressor	Enzyme formed, even in absence of inducer
i^-	Regulator gene	No repressor formed	Enzyme formed, even in absence of inducer
i^s	Regulator gene	Modified repressor formed, unable to combine with inducer	No enzyme formed, even in presence of inducer

it becomes combined, closely resembling the twofold specificity of these ligases.

If this hypothesis is correct, the repressor-RNA presumably contains a nucleotide sequence which is complementary to the operator, i.e. that end of the first structural gene in the operon which determines the N-terminus of the corresponding enzyme. When the same repressor controls a number of enzymes whose genes are scattered, it may be assumed that all these genes have similar terminal sequences, specific for that particular repressor, and if so it is possible that all the enzymes affected would contain the same N-terminal aminoacid, as suggested by JACOB and MONOD (*1224*). This would not necessarily apply to enzymes represented in one operon, where the repressor combines with only one of the genes.

Repression of all the enzymes of one operon is necessarily coordinate, since the copying process produces equimolecular amounts of the messenger RNAs for all the enzymes. Where the genes are scattered, however, the repressor is affecting a number of independently acting genes and there is no reason to suppose that they will all be affected equally; non-coordinate repression would be expected, and is actually observed.

The theory of induction and repression given above leads to the identification of the 'receptor', discussed on p. 500, as the particular repressor RNA with which the inducing or repressing substance becomes combined. This does not, however, explain the high specificity of the combination, or the most striking phenomenon in enzyme induction, namely the close chemical and steric relationship between the inducer and the substrate of the enzyme. For example, it does not account for the fact that galactosidase is only induced by substances containing the D-galactose ring. The enzyme-substrate type of specificity, which the specificity of induction so much resembles, is a distinctive protein property, due to the configuration of a pattern of groups in the active centre. It would be extremely surprising to find centres with similar specificity in polynucleotides, and still more so to find a close connection between the substances which they bind and those which are bound by the polypeptide centres of the particular enzymes whose formation they control.

To avoid this difficulty, we are tempted to suggest (without evidence) that the specificity towards inducing or repressing molecules is not due to a lock-and-key fit between them and the repressor RNAs at all, but that it is a case of enzyme specificity. If, for example, the combination of a repressor RNA with the corresponding aminoacid is brought about by the action of an enzyme, the specificity of the combination might be determined by this enzyme, in the same way as it is in the similar reaction brought about by the aminoacid:sRNA ligases. On this view the specific relationship of a given repressor RNA with the operator of the structural gene it controls is due to complementary polynucleotide sequences, but its relationship with a particular aminoacid is due to the specificity of the combining enzyme. Thus the specific receptor for the repressing amino-acid would be the aminoacid-specific centre of this enzyme, and not the repressor RNA. In this way the similarity of the properties of the receptor to those of the active centres of enzymes would be explained, and the difficulty of having to attribute an enzyme-substrate type of specificity to nucleic acids would be avoided.

It would have to be assumed that a different coupling enzyme acts with each repressing aminoacid, and others with inducers, but these need not necessarily be new enzymes. In fact the combination of aminoacid with repressor RNA resembles the reaction catalysed by the ligases of sub-group 6.1.1 so closely that we wonder whether it might not be brought about by the same enzymes, and indeed whether the repressor RNA for a given aminoacid may not be identical with its normal sRNA. To explain the specific repression effects produced by aminoacids, it would then only be necessary to assume that the operators controlling the formation of the enzymes synthesizing any given aminoacid should contain a nucleotide sequence complementary to one in the sRNA for that aminoacid (not necessarily the coding sequence). On any theory some such specific sequence in the operators must be assumed. The biosynthesis of the various aminoacids would then be automatically controlled by the concentrations of the different aminoacyl-sRNA compounds available for protein synthesis; if, for example, there is a deficiency of tryptophan, there will be a fall in the concentration of tryptophanyl-sRNA, and this will release from repression the genes of the tryptophan-forming enzymes.

If this hypothesis should turn out to be correct, it would mean that the sRNAs have a dual function, and it implies also that sRNAs are formed by regulator genes.

There is evidence that in the case of alkaline phosphatase the mechanism of repression may be of the type suggested above, involving a coupling enzyme. The repression by inorganic phosphate depends on the co-operation of two regulating genes, and it is believed (*814*) that the first forms a precursor of the actual repressor, and the second forms an enzyme which converts the precursor and phosphate into the repressor, in other words it forms a coupling enzyme.

There is much that is still unexplained about induction and repression. No theory has yet accounted for the fact that some repressor RNAs will only combine with the corresponding operators when they are combined with the repressing substances, while others will only combine with their operators when they are *not* combined with the inducers. It is possible that in some cases the mechanism is more complex than has been supposed. For example, EISENSTADT et al. (*684*) have shown the induced formation of β-galactosidase by a system from *Esch. coli* containing ribosomes, soluble enzymes and DNA containing the *z* gene. For this to take place, not only must inducer be present but the DNA itself must be prepared from cells which have been grown in presence of the inducer.

The main theories have been developed from observations on only a very few systems, and it is possible that other systems involve different mechanisms. A number of other theories are discussed by various authors in the symposium containing JACOB and MONOD's article (1224).

Finally, we should mention the more general repressing effect of glucose and certain other carbon sources, discovered by EPPS and GALE (704). A number of theories which have been put forward to explain this effect have been discussed by MAGASANIK (1676); HAUGE (discussion on 1676) has suggested that it is due to an unspecific blocking of the release of finished enzymes from the ribosomes.

Multi-path systems

Some very interesting effects have been observed in cases where a repressible enzyme plays a part in more than one biosynthetic pathway, leading to different products. In *Esch. coli* aspartate kinase (2.7.2.4) is on the pathways leading from aspartate to lysine and threonine respectively. If the formation of the enzyme were repressed independently by both end products, it would be expected that an excess of lysine would give rise to a deficiency of threonine, and vice versa. The system has been studied by STADTMAN *et al.* (2498), who find that two distinct aspartate kinases are present, and can be separated from one another by ammonium sulphate fractionation. Both enzymes catalyse the same reaction and they have identical kinetics. The formation of the first enzyme, however is repressed by L-lysine, while that of the second is not; lysine also inhibits the first enzyme non-competitively, but does not inhibit the second. L-threonine has no action on the first enzyme, but inhibits the second competitively, though it does not repress its formation. Thus the first aspartate kinase is under the control of lysine and the second is under the control of threonine. The effect of this is to set a definite limit to the repressing action of lysine, for no matter how strong this action may be, the second enzyme remains and prevents a threonine deficiency. It is even possible that the two pathways are spatially separated, so that each kinase is concerned only with its own pathway. It is interesting that in yeast, where lysine is not synthesized through aspartate, the first of these enzymes is absent; there appears to be only one aspartate kinase, and this is both repressed and inhibited by L-threonine, but not by lysine.

The case that we have just considered is one where the same enzyme reaction is common to two biosynthetic pathways, and is carried out by two similar enzymes. The converse of this is found where analogous reactions in different pathways are carried out by the same enzyme or

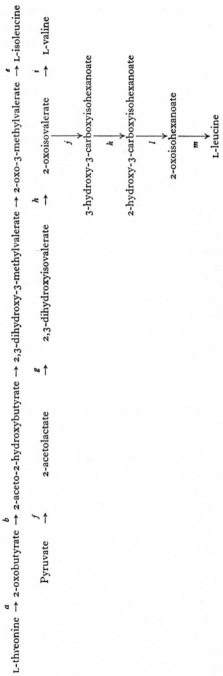

Fig. XI.7.   *A system showing multivalent repression in bacteria.*

enzymes. A case of this kind has been studied with *Esch. coli* and *Salmonella typhimurium* by FREUNDLICH *et al.* (776). The last four steps in the formation of isoleucine from 2-oxobutyrate (derived from threonine) and of valine from pyruvate are analogous reactions, the reactants in the first pathway having one methyl group more than those in the second. The same four enzymes catalyse these four steps in both pathways, that is to say reactions *b* and *f* in Fig. XI.7 are catalysed by one enzyme, *c* and *g* by another, and so on to reactions *e* and *i*. A pathway to L-leucine branches off from 2-oxoisovalerate; the enzymes catalysing reactions *j* to *m* are concerned only with this pathway. Not all the enzymes have been identified with certainty. The authors studied the repression of three of the enzymes, namely those catalysing reactions *a*, *d* (and *h*) and *l* respectively.

It was found that isoleucine and valine separately produced no repression, while leucine by itself repressed the enzyme catalysing reaction *l* only. The formation of the other two enzymes was strongly repressed, but only by a mixture of all three products, namely leucine, valine and isoleucine. Thus the enzyme which is involved only in the production of one of the aminoacids is repressed by that aminoacid by itself, but the enzyme which is involved in the production of each of the three aminoacids is repressed only by a mixture of all three, and not by any one alone. This phenomenon has been called 'multivalent repression'. Its effect is to prevent the causation of a deficiency of any one of the products by an excess of either of the others.

Feedback inhibition

It will not have escaped the reader's notice that repression of enzyme formation does not provide complete control, since it is a 'one way' mechanism. Complete repression merely prevents further formation of enzyme, which then remains constant in amount. Should there have been over-production of an enzyme, or should there be a diminished requirement for the product which it makes, e.g. when growth becomes slower, repression cannot cause a diminution of the amount of enzyme present, and cannot correct the over-production.

Control by induction and repression is therefore supplemented by another method of control, brought about by what has been called 'feedback inhibition'. A number of cases are now known where aminoacid (or in some cases nucleotide) end-products act as specific inhibitors for the first of the enzymes in the chains producing them, even though they may differ considerably in structure from the substrates of these enzymes. This provides the control which would otherwise be lacking, for although the end-product cannot by repression diminish the amount of the initial enzyme of the sequence, it can by inhibition greatly reduce its activity.

This effect should be clearly distinguished from repression, which unfortunately has not always been done. It differs from repression in the following respects: (a) it abolishes the activity of an enzyme already formed; (b) it is practically instantaneous; (c) it is reversible; (d) it can be shown with the purified enzyme, and (e) it affects only the first enzyme of the chain exclusively leading to the inhibiting end-product, not all the enzymes in the chain. The last point, however, is based on a rather small number of cases, and may not be generally valid.

Repression may be thought of as a relatively slow controlling mechanism, adjusting the general level of metabolism over a period of time, since its speed of action is limited by the rate at which the enzyme can be synthesized. Feedback inhibition, on the other hand, acts rapidly, and can cope with momentary metabolic fluctuations. Of course inhibition of the first enzyme of a sequence will suffice to inhibit the whole chain, even if the later enzymes are unaffected, unless intermediates are artificially supplied.

The first enzyme may be controlled by the end-product by repression alone, by feedback inhibition alone, or by both. Of the aspartate kinases of *Esch. coli* mentioned above, the first is subject both to repression and to feedback inhibition by lysine, while the second is subject to feedback inhibition by threonine, but not to repression. In Fig. XI.7, the enzyme catalysing reaction *a* is competitively inhibited by isoleucine, but not by valine or other aminoacids (except for leucine, which has an effect about 1 per cent as strong as isoleucine). On the other hand, valine inhibits the enzyme catalysing reaction *f*. In the histidine-synthesizing series in *Salmonella typhimurium*, the first enzyme, which forms N-1-(5'-phosphoribosyl)-ATP from ATP and phosphoribosyl pyrophosphate, has been purified by MARTIN *et al.* (1738), and found to be inhibited 50 per cent by 3×10^{-5} M histidine, whereas even 10^{-3} M histidine has no effect on the next four enzymes in the series. All these enzymes are represented in one operon, and all are repressed by histidine.

In Fig. XI.6, the enzyme catalysing reaction *g* is inhibited by CMP (although not by uracil or UMP) and the CMP competes with the carbamoyl phosphate and to a smaller extent with the aspartate. This enzyme, as already mentioned, is repressed by UMP, which might be converted into CMP in the cells but not in extracts, so that CMP may be responsible for both effects.

The first enzyme exclusively concerned in the synthesis of purine nucleotides is that which catalyses reaction c of Table XII.18 below; this enzyme, as isolated from pigeon liver, is inhibited by ATP, ADP, AMP, GDP, GMP or IMP, which compete with the phosphoribosyl pyrophosphate, but not with the glutamine (2922). A number of other cases are mentioned by UMBARGER (*2695*), who discusses the whole phenomenon.

The inhibiting product often bears little or no chemical resemblance to the substrate of the enzyme affected, and has no obvious connection with the kind of reaction which it catalyses. In view of this, it is very remarkable that these enzymes should have developed two specific centres in their molecules, one the active centre, specific for the substrate, and the other an inhibiting centre, specific for the product of the particular line of metabolism started by the enzyme. These centres may or may not overlap to some extent; if they do, the inhibition is competitive. In some cases it is possible to render the inhibitor centre inoperative by chemical means, without any effect on the catalytic activity of the enzyme. Moreover the same effect can arise as the result of a mutation. Certain analogues of aminoacid products act as bacteriostatic agents, since they inhibit the formation of the aminoacid but cannot be used in its place for growth. The mutants are resistant to such agents, which have no longer the power of inhibiting the aminoacid formation (*1888*).

The study of biological control through the regulation of enzymes is still in its infancy, but there is little doubt that it will become a subject of the greatest importance. Such control may play a large part, not only in enabling micro-organisms to adapt their metabolism to the composition of the surrounding medium, but in higher organisms in the differentiation of tissues, and even, by differential control of growth rates, in the development of form. As will be pointed out in Chapter XIII (p. 650), the essential feature of tumours from the point of view of enzymology is that their cells have escaped from the normal organizing control operating in the tissue of origin.

The structures of both the specific centres in an enzyme which is subject to feedback inhibition are determined by its structural gene. The genes indeed display an astonishing amount of 'knowledge' about the sequence of chemical processes in metabolism. One may well ask how the gene forming enzyme 2.4.2.14 'knows' that phosphoribosyl pyrophosphate will be converted by the consecutive action of ten or more different enzymes into a purine nucleotide (see Table XII.18), or how the gene for the first enzyme of histidine biosynthesis, which acts on the same compound, 'knows' that its product will be converted into histidine by a different series of enzymes. Even with this information, how do these genes 'know' what aminoacid sequences in their enzymes will act as specific centres combining with purine nucleotides or histidine respectively?

Evidently there must be some mechanism whereby information derived from the metabolic processes themselves is transmitted back to the genes, and there incorporated in the form of polynucleotide sequences. The manner in which control was established in the first place, and the nature and mode of action of this mechanism, is one of the most fascinating and fundamental questions in biology.

Certain proteolytic enzymes concerned in digestion have the special feature that they are produced as inactive proteins, which are subsequently converted into the active enzymes. For instance, pepsin, rennin, trypsin, chymotrypsin and carboxypeptidase A are secreted as pepsinogen, prorennin, trypsinogen, chymotrypsinogen and procarboxypeptidase A respectively. This is no doubt a protective mechanism, preventing the autodigestion of the tissues which produce them. With the exception of prorennin and procarboxypeptidase A, these precursors have all been obtained as pure crystalline proteins. An account of their purification and properties has been given by NORTHROP, KUNITZ and HERRIOTT (*1996*). Certain other enzymes are also probably formed as inactive proteins, for example, those connected with blood clotting, but it appears that all the enzymes which are produced in this way are proteolytic enzymes

Conversion of the precursors into the active enzymes is brought about by catalysis, either by enzymes or by hydrogen ions. For instance, pepsinogen and prorennin are activated by hydrogen ions; pepsinogen by hydrogen ions or by pepsin itself, chymotrypsinogen and procarboxypeptidase A by trypsin, trypsinogen by trypsin or by enteropeptidase. A striking feature of the activation of pepsinogen and trypsinogen is that the activation is brought about by the actual enzyme which is produced thereby; thus the process is autocatalytic, proceeding at a velocity which increases rapidly as the activation proceeds.

A great deal of work has been done on the mechanism of these activations; in all the cases on which information is available, the process appears to consist of the breaking of peptide links, with or without the removal of free peptides.

Elucidation of the mechanism of activation, and of the differences between the precursor and the corresponding active enzyme, may yield results of far-reaching importance on the nature and situation of active centres in enzymes. The activation process appears to involve an unmasking of the active centre, and if the difference between the two very similar proteins can be determined it will give an important clue to the nature of the structures necessary for the enzymatic activity. We shall now consider each case in detail.

The activation of pepsinogen

The nature of this process has not yet been completely cleared up; the observed changes are somewhat complicated, and it is not clear how far they are associated with the activation itself and how far with subsequent digestion processes. Pig pepsinogen and pepsin were both crystallized by NORTHROP *et al.* Pepsinogen has a molecular weight of 42,000, pepsin one of approximately 35,000 (*303*). Pepsin is a much more highly acidic protein than pepsinogen, migrating as a negative ion at least as far down as pH 1, whereas pepsinogen has an isoelectric point of $3 \cdot 7$. Thus the activation involves the removal of nearly one-fifth of the molecule, the part removed being predominantly basic.

The kinetics of the activation of pig pepsinogen have been studied by HERRIOTT (*1081*). The activation may be started by acidification or by addition of pepsin, and below pH 5 it proceeds autocatalytically. The curves agree with the equation

$$\text{XI.3} \qquad \frac{d[\text{pepsin}]}{dt} = k[\text{pepsinogen}][\text{pepsin}]$$

which gives on integration

$$\text{XI.4} \qquad kt = \frac{2 \cdot 3}{[\text{pepsin}]_\infty} \log \frac{[\text{pepsin}]_t \cdot [\text{pepsinogen}]_0}{[\text{pepsin}]_0 \cdot [\text{pepsinogen}]_t}$$

The overall process has a maximum rate at pH 2.

Titration shows that the formation of active pepsin from pepsinogen is accompanied by the breaking of up to nine peptide bonds per molecule. Six small peptides are produced during the activation process; the largest of these (the 'pepsin inhibitor') remains attached to the pepsin above pH $5 \cdot 4$, so that under these conditions the process is not autocatalytic. At lower pHs the inhibitor dissociates reversibly from the enzyme. This equilibrium between enzyme and inhibitor is responsible for the so-called 'Schütz law', since both are usually present in crude preparations (see Chapter IV, section (A)(*f*)). The pig pepsin inhibitor has been purified and crystallized by HERRIOTT (*1082*), who studied the equilibrium between pepsin and inhibitor; the combination is reversible and strongly affected by pH. The inhibitor was originally stated to have a molecular weight of between 4,000 and 10,000 and to be a basic polypeptide having a high content of arginine but no tryptophan or tyrosine. Later work by VAN VUNAKIS and HERRIOTT (*2723*), however, has modified these statements; the molecular weight has now been shown to be 3,240 by Sanger's method and the molecule contains 29 aminoacid residues including only one arginine residue, but also one tyrosine and four lysines. It also contains acidic groups; four aspartic and two glutamic residues were found.

The same workers also studied the other products produced together with the inhibitor during the activation of pepsinogen. Five neutral peptides were formed, with an average size of 10 aminoacid residues and an aggregate molecular weight of about 4,000. These five peptides, with the inhibitor, account for the difference in molecular weight between pepsinogen and pepsin, and the formation of these products accounts for six of the nine peptide bonds known to be broken in the process.

End-group assay shows that pepsinogen and pepsin each consist of only one peptide chain. The sequence of aminoacids at the carboxyl end has been shown by degradation with carboxypeptidase to be the same in both, namely, R–valyl-leucyl-alanine (2722). Thus it seems very probable that pepsin constitutes the C-terminal part of the pepsinogen molecule. Theoretically, therefore, pepsinogen could be converted into pepsin merely by hydrolysing the one peptide bond which unites this segment with the rest of the chain. Whether the other eight bonds are broken before or after the hydrolysis of this bond is not known. It is known, however, that further hydrolysis of the other products by pepsin can take place; in particular, on standing, the inhibitor is itself hydrolysed by pepsin to small peptides, the optimum for this process being at pH 3·5. Thus the whole process of the formation of pepsin from pig pepsinogen can be represented as

XI.5   Pepsinogen $\xrightarrow{\text{Pepsin}}$ pepsin-inhibitor complex + 5 peptides

XI.6   Pepsin-inhibitor complex $\underset{\text{pH}>5\cdot4}{\overset{\text{pH}<5\cdot4}{\rightleftharpoons}}$ pepsin + inhibitor

XI.7   Inhibitor $\xrightarrow{\text{Pepsin}}$ 4 peptides

VAN VUNAKIS and HERRIOTT (2724) have also determined the aminoacid sequences at the amino end of the chain in pepsinogen, inhibitor and pepsin, and found them to be leucyl-isoleucyl-R', leucyl-glutamyl-R'' and isoleucyl-glycyl-R''' respectively. This shows that the inhibitor does not occupy a terminal position in pepsinogen. The sequence of the six aminoacids at the N-terminal end of pepsin has been determined by WILLIAMSON and PASSMANN (2874). The information available about the pepsinogen chain may be represented as in Fig. XI.8, where the terminal NH_3^+- and $-COO^-$ groups are indicated by + and − signs respectively.

Pig and ox pepsins appear to be identical proteins by all ordinary tests, namely, crystalline form, solubility, physical properties, enzyme activity on several different substrates and even immunological tests. Too much importance, however, must not be attached to the immunological tests, since the precipitin tests were carried out with denatured enzyme. There is one test, however, which appears to indicate that they are different proteins. Although they both have the same solubility, each dissolves independently of the other, so that a mixture of the two is twice as soluble as either separately. Fowl pepsin can be distinguished from pig pepsin by its lower rate of inactivation at pH 9. This fact has been used in the study of the activation of pepsinogen from one species of animal by pepsin from another. Pig pepsinogen activated by fowl pepsin was found to produce the characteristic pig pepsin and vice versa. The action of pepsin inhibitors also shows some species specificity; inhibitor from pig pepsinogen inhibits pig and ox pepsins equally,

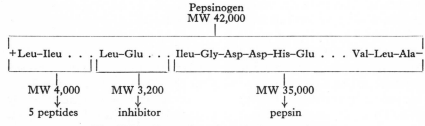

Fig. XI.8. *Formation of pepsin from pepsinogen.*

but does not inhibit fowl pepsin; the fowl peptide also inhibits pig and ox pepsins, but strangely enough not fowl pepsin. Thus the difference in behaviour towards pepsin inhibitors appears to lie in the pepsins rather than in the inhibitors; pig and ox pepsins are inhibited and fowl pepsin is not, whatever the source of the inhibitor.

The activation of prorennin

The existence of prorennin was demonstrated in 1932 by KLEINER and TAUBER (*1396*), but neither they nor subsequent workers have obtained it in the pure state. The activation has been studied by these workers and also by EGE and LUNDSTEEN (*677*) in 1934, but we are not aware of any later studies. Little appears to be known about the nature of the process, except that it is catalysed by acid; it is negligible at pH 5 but very rapid below pH 3. It is not known whether the activation can be brought about enzymatically; some of the progress curves of Ege and Lundsteen (experimental points as distinct from the curves drawn) show a fairly marked autocatalysis, suggesting that the rennin formed might have an activating effect, and the same authors claimed that the pro-rennin was activated by 'pancreatin' at pH 5·5, where no acid activation was possible.

The activation of trypsinogen

Trypsinogen, not trypsin, is produced by the pancreas and secreted in the pancreatic juice. Purification of trypsinogen and trypsin, and study of the kinetics of conversion, have largely been carried out by members of NORTHROP's school (see *1996*). Crystalline trypsinogen can be activated by trypsin itself (cf. pepsinogen), so that under appropriate conditions the process will be autocatalytic. It can also be activated by enteropeptidase, a proteolytic enzyme present in the intestinal secretion, as well as by similar enzymes prepared from other sources, such as the 'kinase' of *Penicillium* sp. studied by KUNITZ (*1488*). The same trypsin is produced in all cases.

The autocatalysis is complicated by an alternative reaction converting the trypsinogen into an inactive protein and not into trypsin (Mc-DONALD and KUNITZ, *1655*). The formation of active trypsin and the formation of inactive protein are competing reactions; the partition of the trypsinogen between the two reactions depends on the pH and the presence of certain ions. Calcium ions in particular accelerate the former reaction and suppress the latter, so that in the presence of 0·02 M $CaCl_2$ the reaction, once it is started by a small amount of enteropeptidase, proceeds as a pure autocatalysis. The partition determines the yield of active enzyme; a high yield is favoured by calcium and also by low pH (less than 4) at which, however, the rate of activation is less. Thus the addition of calcium enables a high yield to be obtained at a reasonable rate.

Mould 'kinase' differs markedly from the other 'kinases' in acting in acid solution (optimum pH 3·5) in which trypsin is inactive; therefore in this case the activation is not autocatalytic, but follows a unimolecular law. Enteropeptidase acts best in the pH range 6–8, but since trypsin itself is active in this range and catalyses the conversion of trypsinogen into both trypsin and inactive protein, it is difficult to say with certainty how much of the activation is due to the trypsin and how much to the enteropeptidase. An approximation to activation by enteropeptidase alone, which follows first order kinetics, can be obtained by taking a small amount of trypsinogen and a relatively large amount of enteropeptidase, more especially at a pH below 6. Conversely, an approximation to activation by trypsin alone, and therefore a pure autocatalysis, may be obtained by taking a larger amount of trypsinogen with only a trace of enteropeptidase.

The molecular weights of ox trypsinogen and trypsin are identical within experimental error, both being about 24,000. There are, however, slight differences in ultraviolet absorption and aminoacid analysis which indicate that there is a small loss on transforming trypsinogen into trypsin. Both consist of a single peptide chain; one α-amino group can be detected (*2262*), but no free C-terminal end can be found with carboxypeptidase, which has led to the suggestion of a cyclic structure at this end of the molecule, although this may merely be due to steric inaccessibility to the peptidase. The N-terminal group in ox trypsin is not the same as that of trypsinogen; the former is isoleucine, while the latter

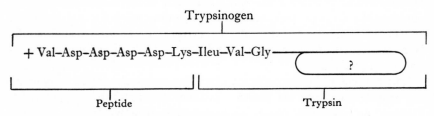

Fig. XI.9. *Formation of trypsin from ox trypsinogen.*

is valine, as shown by ROVERY, FABRE and DESNUELLE(*2262*). This again suggests that a small peptide is split off from the N-terminal end of the chain, and in fact this peptide has been isolated by DAVIE and NEURATH (*553*) and shown to be a hexapeptide. Thus the process of activation of trypsinogen by trypsin is similar in character to that of pepsinogen, consisting of the removal of a portion of the N-terminal end of the chain, although in this case the process is simpler and the part removed is very much smaller. Similar results have been obtained for the activation of trypsinogen by enteropeptidase (*2935, 2937*).

The two alternative processes can therefore be written as

XI.8   Trypsinogen $\xrightarrow[\text{or 'kinases'}]{\text{Trypsin}}$ trypsin $+$ a hexapeptide

XI.9   Trypsinogen $\xrightarrow{\text{Trypsin}}$ inactive protein $+$?

Knowledge of the aminoacid sequences in ox trypsinogen, trypsin, and the hexapeptide led to a fairly clear chemical picture of the activation process; this process (*596, 1957*) is shown diagrammatically in Fig. XI.9. Thus the activation consists in the breaking of a single peptide bond between lysine and isoleucine. In this process, or as a result of it, the active centre becomes unmasked; this unmasking can be shown chemically, since trypsin, unlike trypsinogen, can take up one molecule of di-isopropyl phosphorofluoridate per protein molecule.

More recently ROVERY and DESNUELLE (2260) have examined trypsinogen from pig pancreas. The N-terminal residue is in this case phenylalanine, and the autocatalytic activation of this trypsinogen involves the breaking of a single peptide bond and the liberation of an octapeptide Phe–(Thr, Pro, Asp_4)–Lys. C-terminal sequences can be readily detected in both trypsinogen and trypsin from this species, in contrast to the results discussed above for the ox. The C-terminal aminoacid sequence, which is not affected by the conversion of trypsinogen to trypsin, is either Ileu–Ala–Asp(NH_2) or Ileu–Ala–Glu(NH_2).

The activation of chymotrypsinogen

A special feature of the chymotrypsinogen-chymotrypsin system is the large number of different active forms, most of which have been obtained in the crystalline state. The commonly obtained pancreatic chymotrypsinogen, which was crystallized by KUNITZ and NORTHROP (1494), is known variously as chymotrypsinogen, chymotrypsinogen A (which we prefer), chymotrypsinogen α, or α-chymotrypsinogen. A second chymotrypsinogen from pancreas, chymotrypsinogen B, was crystallized by LASKOWSKI et al. (342). Chymotrypsinogen B is more difficult to crystallize and was at first thought to be a minor constituent of pancreatic juice, but DESNUELLE (596) has shown that chymotrypsinogens A and B are present in ox pancreatic juice in roughly equal amounts. Both chymotrypsinogens are activated by trypsin, but not by chymotrypsin, although chymotrypsin may participate in the subsequent changes. The process is therefore not autocatalytic. From chymotrypsinogen A on activation are formed (though not in this order) α-, β-, γ-, δ- and π-chymotrypsins; α-, β- and γ-chymotrypsins have been crystallized as such and δ-chymotrypsin as a di-isopropylphosphoryl derivative. Chymotrypsinogen B gives rise to chymotrypsin B on activation; this also has been crystallized.

The probable course of the transformations of chymotrypsinogen A under various conditions may be represented as in Fig. XI.10, where Chg is written for chymotrypsinogen, Ch for chymotrypsin, and Tr for trypsin.

If chymotrypsinogen A is activated by small amounts of trypsin, so that the process is comparatively slow, the rate of activation is proportional to the amount of trypsin added and follows unimolecular kinetics. Under these conditions predominantly α-chymotrypsin is produced; this has been crystallized by KUNITZ and NORTHROP (1494), but not more

than 50 per cent of the chymotrypsin activity produced can be obtained
in this form. KUNITZ (*1487*) showed that on standing for some days
crystals of a different form can be obtained from the mother liquor, and
that these were mixed crystals of two further chymotrypsins, β- and
γ-chymotrypsins, with some inactive protein. By recrystallization at a
different pH, the γ-enzyme may be obtained in the pure state. At a
higher salt concentration, mixed crystals of the β-enzyme with the inactive protein may be obtained after the removal of the γ-enzyme, and
when a solution of these crystals is kept at 35° at pH 8, the β-enzyme
digests the inactive protein and can then be obtained in the pure state

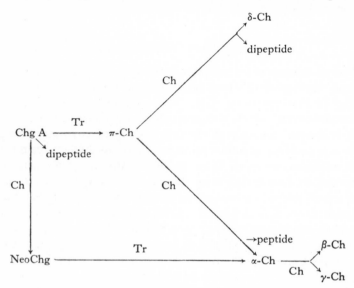

Fig. XI.10. *Interrelationships in the chymotrypsin system.*

by crystallization. The β- and γ-enzymes seem undoubtedly to be produced from the α-enzyme, since either can be obtained on allowing
solutions of recrystallized α-enzyme to stand under appropriate conditions. Formation of the γ-enzyme is favoured by incubation for a short
time at higher pHs and higher temperatures, and conversely for the
β-enzyme. By suitably adjusting the conditions, the α-enzyme can be
converted almost completely into either the β- or the γ-enzyme at
will, as judged by enzymatic activity, although up to 35 per cent of the
α-enzyme protein is lost during the conversion. Once obtained, solutions
of the β- and γ-enzymes can be recrystallized without change and it is
clear that these enzymes are not interconvertible, nor can they be converted back into the α-enzyme.

Enzymatically, α-, β- and γ-chymotrypsins are indistinguishable; they have the same specificity and their activities with a number of different substrates are of the same order. Immunologically they are also indistinguishable. However, their protein properties show some differences; their solubilities, rates of inactivation and molecular weights differ quite definitely. The interpretation of molecular weight differences is complicated by the fact that the α-enzyme at least exists mainly as a dimer.

If the activation of chymotrypsinogen A is carried out with larger amounts of trypsin and at 0°, the kinetics become more complicated. From an extensive kinetic study, JACOBSEN (1227) deduced that the process takes a different course, producing first a very active and very unstable chymotrypsin, which he termed π-chymotrypsin, by the hydrolysis of one peptide bond. The activity of this component was deduced to be 2·5 times that of α-chymotrypsin. The π-chymotrypsin is rapidly converted by the hydrolysis of a second peptide bond into another enzyme, δ-chymotrypsin, with an activity 1·5 times that of α-chymotrypsin. Alternatively, the π-enzyme can be converted into the α-enzyme by the hydrolysis of probably three peptide bonds, but with rapid activation the yield of α-chymotrypsin is only a fraction of one per cent. These deductions were confirmed by BETTELHEIM and NEURATH (242), who actually isolated the π- and δ-enzymes as inactive di-isopropyl-phosphoryl derivatives in the practically pure state; the latter was also obtained in the form of impure crystals. In order to obtain the π-enzyme, it was necessary to inhibit the action of chymotrypsin by the addition of the specific inhibitor β-phenylpropionate; on these and other grounds they concluded that the conversion of the π- into the δ- and α-enzymes is due to chymotrypsin itself, contrary to Jacobsen's views. They found the activity of the π- and δ-enzymes to be approximately the same. The δ-enzyme has not only a higher V but also a higher affinity for synthetic substrates than the α-enzyme, showing that the difference is not merely a question of the number of active centres (2350).

The nature of the changes during activation of chymotrypsinogen was largely cleared up by the determination of the end-groups in the various forms, particularly by the schools of DESNUELLE and of NEURATH (see 241–2, 596, 1957). No end-groups can be detected in chymotrypsinogen A by the normal methods, and the molecule was at first supposed to contain a closed chain. However, BETTELHEIM (241) showed that after oxidation an N-terminal cysteic group is present and he concluded that chymotrypsinogen contains a half-cystine N-terminal residue. Similarly although no C-terminal group can be detected when native chymotrypsinogen is exposed to carboxypeptidase, a C-terminal asparagine residue becomes available after reduction of the disulphide bonds or even after denaturation by urea (*1777, 2263*). No change in molecular weight is brought about by breaking the disulphide bonds of chymotrypsinogen A, which must therefore be a single open chain beginning with half-cystine and ending with asparagine. The chain contains approximately 240 aminoacid residues, and considerable progress has been made towards the elucidation of the complete sequence (see HARTLEY, *1012*). The tertiary structure is presumably such that the terminal groups are inaccessible to chemical reagents or enzymatic attack.

The conversions during the activation process, set out in Fig. XI. 10, are accompanied by the appearance of new end-groups; these are set out in Table XI.8.

TABLE XI.8

TERMINAL GROUPS OF CHYMOTRYPSINS

Form	N-terminal	C-terminal
Chymotrypsinogen A	Half-cystine	Asparagine
Neochymotrypsinogen	Half-cystine alanine	Asparagine tyrosine
π-chymotrypsin	Half-cystine isoleucine	Asparagine arginine
δ-chymotrypsin	Half-cystine isoleucine	Asparagine leucine
α-, β-, γ-chymotrypsins	Half-cystine isoleucine alanine	Asparagine leucine tyrosine

The conversion of π-chymotrypsin into δ-chymotrypsin is associated with the liberation of a dipeptide, identified as seryl–arginine by DREYER and NEURATH (*654*), while the conversion of chymotrypsinogen A to neochymotrypsinogen by chymotrypsin itself is accompanied by the liberation of a second dipeptide, threonyl–asparagine (*2264*). These results, together with those in Table XI. 8, suggest that all the activation processes can be attributed to the hydrolytic splitting of four peptide bonds, namely, tyrosyl–threonine, asparaginyl–alanine, leucyl–serine and arginyl–isoleucine. The probable structures of the various forms are set out in Fig. XI. 11.

It will be seen that the single chain of chymotrypsinogen is broken into three open chains in α-chymotrypsin. These are held together by di-sulphide bridges, but can be obtained as separate peptides by oxidizing these bridges with performic acid (MEEDOM, *1776*). Since the chymotrypsin-catalysed hydrolyses occur near the C-terminus and the trypsin-catalysed hydrolyses near the N-terminus of the chymotrypsinogen

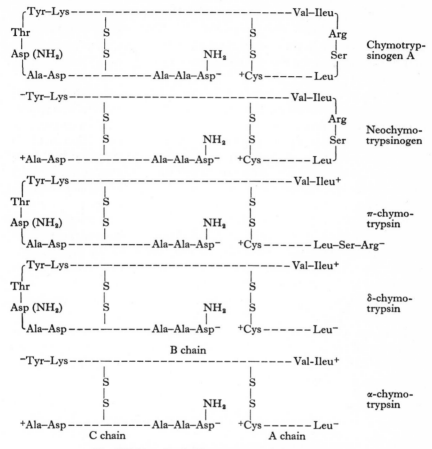

Fig. XI.11. *Probable structures of chymotrypsins.*

It should be noted that a consequence of writing the structure in a cyclic form is that the top line, contrary to the usual convention, has the N-terminal end on the right. Thus the right-hand termination is to be read as isoleucyl-valyl- and not -valyl-isoleucine.

chain, the three chains of α-chymotrypsin (the A, B and C chains of Meedom) are of very unequal length. The A chain has 13 aminoacid residues with N-terminal half-cystine and C-terminal leucine; the C chain has about 50 residues with N-terminal alanine and C-terminal asparagine. The B-chain, with about 180 residues, forms the major part of the molecule and includes the essential histidine, although the DFP-sensitive serine is probably in the C-chain (*1012*).

The changes in the right-hand portions of the structures shown in Fig. XI.11, which are brought about by trypsin, are responsible for the unmasking or creation of the active centre. Drastic changes in the tertiary structure of the protein seem to occur during these conversions, as shown by a large decrease in the optical rotation (*1958*). Activation may be due to different parts of the chain which form part of the active centre being brought closer together (*596*).

The changes on the left-hand side of Fig. XI.11 are due to chymotrypsin itself; they are not essential to the activation process and indeed appear to lower the specific activity. The two sets of proteolytic changes can take place in either order, depending on the activator present. High yields of the most active form, π-chymotrypsin, can only be obtained by 'rapid activation' with a high concentration of trypsin, to minimize autolysis by the chymotrypsin formed. On the other hand the action of a relatively high amount of pure α-chymotrypsin on pure chymotrypsinogen A produces three neochymotrypsinogens (*2264–5*), which are themselves inactive but can be activated to α-chymotrypsin. These neochymotrypsinogens are produced by the splitting of the tyrosyl–threonine and asparaginyl–alanine bonds taking place before activation proper. During 'slow activation' of chymotrypsinogen A by low concentrations of trypsin both sets of hydrolyses are proceeding simultaneously and the major product is therefore α-chymotrypsin.

Little is known about the structure of chymotrypsinogen B or of the chemistry of its conversion to chymotrypsin B by trypsin. It has been reported (*1312*) that a C-terminal arginine appears during the activation, as in the case of chymotrypsinogen A.

The activation of procarboxypeptidases

The existence of a precursor of carboxypeptidase A in pancreatic juice was shown by Anson (*77*), who partially purified it. More recently it has been obtained completely pure by Keller, Cohen and Neurath (*1352–3*), who compared its physical properties with those of carboxypeptidase. The differences between precursor and enzyme are very much greater than those found in other cases. The isoelectric point of procarboxypeptidase is below $4·5$, while that of carboxypeptidase is $6·0$; the sedimentation constants are $5·87$ and $3·07$ respectively, and the molecular weights calculated from light-scattering data are 96,000 and 34,300 respectively. Correspondingly, the enzyme activity obtained by activating 1 mg of procarboxypeptidase A is only one-third of the activity of 1 mg of carboxypeptidase A. Thus it would appear that during the activation of procarboxypeptidase two-thirds of the molecule is lost.

The activation of procarboxypeptidase A is a more complex process than the activations previously considered, and involves the splitting of many peptide bonds. It is brought about by the combined action of trypsin and an endopeptidase which is also derived from procarboxypeptidase A (*1353*). The sequence of events is probably

$$\text{Procarboxypeptidase A} \xrightarrow{\text{Trypsin}} \text{Endopeptidase} \xrightarrow[\text{endopeptidase}]{\text{Trypsin} +} \text{Carboxy-peptidase A}$$

Carboxypeptidase A has an N-terminal sequence asparaginyl–serine and a C-terminal asparagine (*70, 2643*), but it is not known whether both of these are formed during activation.

Carboxypeptidase B (3.4.2.2) also exists as an inactive precursor in pancreatic juice, and this is also activated by trypsin. The activated enzyme has a single peptide chain with N-terminal threonyl–serine and C-terminal asparaginyl–threonine (*756*).

Activation of the pancreatic complex

We have now considered separately the activation of the precursors of the proteolytic enzymes of the pancreatic juice. In the digestive system, however, these processes are not independent of one another, for one of the precursors (trypsinogen) forms an enzyme which activates all the precursors. The juice remains inactive until it meets a reasonably high concentration of enteropeptidase; there is then a rapid activation of all the precursors which appears to be autocatalytic. However, this is due to the fact that the production of trypsin is autocatalytic, because trypsin converts trypsinogen into trypsin; the activations of the other precursors are not in themselves autocatalytic, but they are brought about by a rapidly increasing amount of trypsin.

It would be expected that a few molecules of enteropeptidase would be able to set off the whole activation, by producing a small amount of trypsin, which would then not only activate the remaining trypsinogen but would also convert the chymotrypsinogen into π-chymotrypsin and the procarbhxypeptidases into carboxypeptidases. If this were the case, however, the system would be unduly sensitive to activation, which might occur before the juice reaches the intestine. In fact, it is found that the addition of only a small amount of enteropeptidase fails to activate the juice. This is due to the presence in pancreatic juice of an inhibitor of trypsin; this is of peptide nature, with a molecular weight of about 10,000, and acts by combining with trypsin to form an inactive complex.

Both the inhibitor and the trypsin-inhibitor complex were crystallized by KUNITZ and NORTHROP (*1495*). The combination is not instantaneous, but takes up to 30 min for completion. A consequence of this is that if trypsin is added gradually in small amounts to pancreatic juice activation does not occur, while if the same amount of trypsin is added instantaneously the whole mechanism is set off. The same in-inhibitor also inhibits chymotrypsin to some extent. Other trypsin inhibitors, of higher molecular weight, have been purified from human plasma (*359*) and ox plasma (*2921*); many other peptide inhibitors of trypsin have been studied (see *1524*).

Other precursors and their activation

In addition to the well-characterized systems discussed above, other enzymes probably exist as inactive precursors which can be activated by a limited proteolysis. Evidence has been given for the existence in pancreas of a proesterase (*844*), but nothing is known about the nature of its activation.

The exceedingly complicated system involved in the formation and subsequent lysis of a blood clot contains a number of factors which appear to have proteolytic properties, and most of these factors occur physio-logically as inactive precursors. Few of them have been isolated and in some cases they are little more than names, but it seems probable that some, at any rate, of the activation steps are due to hydrolytic splitting of peptide bonds (see *2, 1398, 2801*).

XII

ENZYME SYSTEMS

THE BIOLOGICAL IMPORTANCE OF SYSTEMS OF ENZYMES

ENZYMES ARE highly efficient catalysts, but they are also very restricted in their action, owing to their high specificity. That is to say, a given enzyme can usually bring about only one reaction and can account for only one step in a metabolic chain of reactions. Each line of metabolism therefore requires a co-ordinated system of several enzymes to bring it about, and the number of enzymes in the system is determined by the number of successive steps involved in the whole process.

It may be truly said that metabolism as a whole is brought about by one great multi-enzyme system, since the different lines or chains of reactions are interlinked, but in practice it is convenient to consider separately the different lines of metabolism, such as urea formation or fat breakdown, with the corresponding enzyme systems.

In order to act, such a system must contain a number of enzymes whose specificities form an unbroken chain, such that the product formed by each enzyme falls within the range of specificity of one of the other enzymes present. In this way the substrate molecule can be acted on successively by all the enzymes in a definite sequence, each enzyme effecting a definite change in its structure before it passes on to the next, until ultimately the whole process is completed. This is what is meant by a metabolic process.

It is essential that the chain should be complete and unbroken. If any one of the enzymes is missing or poisoned, the process is blocked at that point and the whole system becomes inoperative.

A group of enzymes taken haphazard is very unlikely to form such a system, as may be seen by selecting a dozen enzymes at random from the list. It is possible, however, to build up chains link by link. Starting with a given substrate, we look in the table for an enzyme which acts upon it and we find the nature of the product. Then we search in the table for another enzyme which will act upon this product, and so on. It is an interesting pastime to build up chains on paper in this way, although it will not necessarily lead to the correct metabolic sequence of reactions, since it is easy to overlook more important alternative reactions.

Nevertheless it may not be without biological significance; it has something in common with STANIER'S (2504) process of 'sequential induction', mentioned in the previous chapter. The latter process, however, is kept within bounds by being under the control of the genetic system of the cell, which determines what enzymes can be formed by adaptive processes in any given kind of cell.

Once a functional chain of enzymes has been formed, it will tend to be maintained, as long as there is a supply of the first substrate; if a partial deficiency of any one of the enzymes develops, this deficiency will cause an accumulation of the substrate of the particular enzyme, and this accumulation in turn will evoke the adaptive formation of more of this enzyme to restore the balance.

The genetic system thus controls, through the enzyme systems, the direction which the metabolic processes shall take, for the transformations which a given organic substance will undergo depend not so much on its chemical properties as on what enzymes are present and in what relative amounts they are present. This directive function of enzyme systems is of the greatest importance.

The co-ordination and organization of enzyme systems is brought about by two main factors. In systems of soluble enzymes, where the enzymes are mixed together in solution, so that there is complete mutual accessibility, we have what has been called 'organization by specificity' (618, p. 19). Here the specificities of the constituent enzymes are so adjusted that the product formed by each enzyme falls within the specificity range of one of the other enzymes present, which is therefore capable of continuing the process and directing the substrate a further step down the right path. This is not an organization by cellular structural factors, but by purely *chemical* specificity, which alone is sufficient to account for the orderly functioning of the system.

In other systems, however, notably those of mitochondrial particles, many of the enzymes are not free to move about, but are held attached to an insoluble structure in definite relative positions, so that accessibility is restricted. The topographical organization then imposes a further control on the reaction sequence, over and above that imposed by the specificity of the components. Such structurally organized systems will be discussed later.

LINKING OF ENZYMES

Each enzyme in a chain may be regarded as being linked with the next enzyme in the series by means of a common substrate. This may not be immediately obvious until it is remembered that enzymes catalyse both directions of their reactions, so that the product of the forward reaction is also the substrate of the back reaction of the enzyme. Thus in the series of successive reactions

$$A \xrightarrow[E_1]{} B \xrightarrow[E_2]{} C \xrightarrow[E_3]{} D \ldots$$

the substance B which is the substrate of enzyme E_2, may also be regarded as a substrate of enzyme E_1, falling within its specificity range. The two enzymes E_1 and E_2 may therefore be said to be linked together functionally by the common substrate B. If two enzymes have no common substrate, they cannot be linked together in this way to form a system.

Now let us consider a two-enzyme system, linked by a common substrate. Two fundamentally different cases may be distinguished. The first is that of which we have been speaking, namely, that in which the second enzyme transforms the substance B, formed by the first, into a new substance C. In this case the linking substance B is a metabolite, proceeding along its path by a series of successive transformations, as, for instance, in Table XII.1.

The other case arises when the action of the first enzyme on the substance is reversed by the second. That is to say, instead of transforming B into C, the second enzyme converts B back into A (naturally by a different reaction, since the two enzymes are not the same). For instance, if the first enzyme phosphorylates A to give B, the second enzyme dephosphorylates B, giving A once more; if the first enzyme reduces it, the second reoxidizes it, and so on. Two examples of this can be seen in Table XII.6; here the first enzyme reduces NAD while the second reoxidizes it, similarly the second enzyme reduces the glyoxylate to glycollate while the third reoxidizes the glycollate to glyoxylate.

The distinction between the two types is a fundamental one. In the first type the linking substance is part of the material being metabolized, and passes on, whereas in the second type the linking substance is part of the catalytic mechanism, a coenzyme in fact, and it remains behind as a more or less permanent part of the system.

The reactions involved in the second type usually consist of the addition or removal of some group, e.g. a phosphate group, and each is a bimolecular reaction in which a second substance acts as donor or acceptor of the group. Obviously they cannot be unimolecular reactions because, if they were, the conversion of B back to A would simply be the back reaction of the initial conversion of A to B, and the two enzymes would be identical.

Thus it becomes clear that what we are dealing with in a system of the second type is a transport mechanism, in which some group is transferred from molecule to molecule by successive reactions and the linking substance acts as a 'carrier' of the group. Table XII.6 is an example of a hydrogen-transport system, in which the two H-atoms are handed on from the initial substrate to O_2 by three successive transfers, by way of two intermediate hydrogen-carriers.

With this type, like the first type, fairly long chains are met with, particularly in hydrogen-transport systems. In some respiration systems, for instance, four or five successive carriers may be involved, and the hydrogen is handed on from one to another by a series of consecutive enzyme reactions before it finally reacts with oxygen. It is customary to represent such chains of reactions by the same type of diagram as that already used for the first type of system, namely

$$A \xrightarrow[E_1]{} B \xrightarrow[E_2]{} C \xrightarrow[E_3]{} D \ . \ . \ .$$

but here the arrows have a different significance. In the former diagram the symbol $A \rightarrow B$ meant 'A is converted into B'; here it means 'A reduces (or phosphorylates, or methylates, as the case may be) B', and the arrows show the direction of hydrogen (or phosphate, or methyl) transfer.

The most important type of cell-respiration system may probably be written in simplified form in this notation as follows:

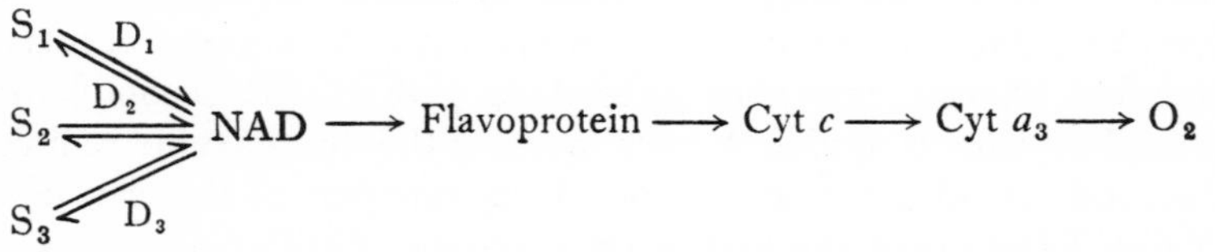

Here S_1, S_2, S_3 represent various substances undergoing oxidation by NAD in the presence of their respective dehydrogenases D_1, D_2, D_3. As NAD reacts with many different dehydrogenases (probably 70 or more), it collects hydrogen from many different biological oxidation processes, and forwards it through a flavoprotein enzyme ($NADH_2$ cytochrome c reductase (1.6.2.1)) to reduce cytochrome c. This in turn reduces cytochrome a_3 (cytochrome oxidase (1.9.3.1)), which reduces O_2 to water, thus terminating the chain of reactions. NADP acts in the same way as NAD, but with a different group of dehydrogenases and with a different cytochrome c reductase (1.6.2.3). This chain has been discussed in relation to cytochrome in Chapter IX.

COENZYME-LINKED DEHYDROGENASE SYSTEMS

In the absence of O_2 the reduced coenzyme cannot be reoxidized through this chain of carriers. In that case reactions occur between the various dehydrogenases through the coenzyme; the coenzyme is reduced by one dehydrogenase and then reoxidized by the reverse reaction of another dehydrogenase. In this way the various fermentations are catalysed. Such a system of two dehydrogenases and the coenzyme is known as a coenzyme-linked dehydrogenase system and is perhaps the most important type of two-enzyme system. It may be represented diagrammatically as follows:

$$S_1^r \xrightarrow[D_1]{} Co \xrightarrow[D_2]{} S_2^o$$

Here the reduced form of the substrate of the first dehydrogenase passes two hydrogen atoms to the coenzyme, and the second dehydrogenase transfers two hydrogen atoms from the reduced coenzyme to the oxidized form of its own substrate.

A great many examples of such reactions could be quoted. The two best known, both of which involve glyceraldehydephosphate dehydrogenase, are involved in glycolysis (reactions XII.1.h–i and n) and in alcoholic fermentation (reactions XII.1.h–i and q) respectively. They can be represented diagrammatically thus

Glyceraldehyde phosphate $\xrightarrow[\substack{\text{glyceraldehyde-}\\\text{phosphate}\\\text{dehydrogenase}\\(1.2.1.12)}]{}$ NAD $\xrightarrow[\substack{\text{lactate}\\\text{dehydrogenase}\\(1.1.1.27)}]{}$ pyruvate
$+$phosphate

and

Glyceraldehyde phosphate $\xrightarrow[\substack{\text{glyceraldehyde-}\\\text{phosphate}\\\text{dehydrogenase}\\(1.2.1.12)}]{}$ NAD $\xrightarrow[\substack{\text{alcohol}\\\text{dehydrogenase}\\(1.1.1.1)}]{}$ acetaldehyde
$+$phosphate

The products are diphosphoglycerate and lactate or alcohol respectively.

A few other less familiar cases may be mentioned in order to illustrate the possibilities of linked dehydrogenase systems. In a number of cases the production of a molecule of some kind by the first dehydrogenase is balanced by the consumption of a molecule of the same kind by the second. For example, in the system

isocitrate $\xrightarrow[\substack{\text{isocitrate de-}\\\text{hydrogenase}\\(1.1.1.42)}]{}$ NADP $\xrightarrow[\substack{\text{malate de-}\\\text{hydrogenase}\\(1.1.1.40)}]{}$ pyruvate $+ CO_2$

the isocitrate is oxidized to 2-oxoglutarate$+CO_2$, and this CO_2 production is balanced by the CO_2 consumption by the malate dehydrogenase so that the CO_2 cancels out and does not appear in the overall reaction, which may be written as

$$\text{isocitrate} + \text{pyruvate} = \text{2-oxoglutarate} + \text{malate}$$

In the system

isocitrate ⎯⎯⎯⎯⎯→ NADP ⎯⎯⎯⎯⎯→ 2-oxoglutarate + NH_3
        isocitrate de-   glutamate
        hydrogenase   dehydrogenase
        (1.1.1.42)   (1.4.1.3)

the isocitrate is oxidized to 2-oxoglutarate+CO_2, and the formation of 2-oxoglutarate by the first enzyme is balanced by the consumption by the second, so that the overall reaction is

$$\text{isocitrate} + NH_3 = \text{glutamate} + CO_2$$

In such cases, although the reactant which cancels out must be added before the reaction will proceed, it remains constant in amount throughout the process and is to be regarded as a part of the catalytic mechanism. The 2-oxoglutarate in the last-mentioned system, and the CO_2 in the preceding one, are just as truly coenzymes for these systems as is glucose diphosphate for phosphoglucomutase (2.7.5.1).

A number of cases are known in which the two dehydrogenases catalyse successive steps in the oxidation of a substance, for instance, alcohol dehydrogenase oxidizes alcohols to aldehydes and aldehyde dehydrogenase oxidizes aldehydes to acids. Thus the intermediate form (aldehyde) acts as both the oxidized form of the substrate of one enzyme and the reduced form of that of the other. Then if the two enzymes are linked by a hydrogen carrier the system will catalyse a dismutation, thus

Aldehyde + H_2O ⎯⎯⎯⎯⎯→ NAD ⎯⎯⎯⎯⎯→ aldehyde
        aldehyde de-   alcohol de-
        hydrogenase   hydrogenase
        (1.2.1.3)   (1.1.1.1)

where the overall reaction is

$$\text{2 aldehyde} = \text{acid} + \text{alcohol}$$

(see RACKER, 2147). This system was formerly thought to be a single enzyme 'aldehyde mutase' (616, 628).

In some cases an additional molecule is involved on one side or both, so that the reaction should perhaps not be called a dismutation in the strictest sense; indeed even in the dismutation of aldehydes a water molecule is involved on one side. Phosphate is involved in the dismutation of triose phosphate, a reaction which is important in glycerol fermentation

Glyceraldehyde phosphate $\xrightarrow[\substack{\text{glyceraldehyde-}\\\text{phosphate}\\\text{dehydrogenase}\\(1.2.1.12)}]{}$ NAD $\xrightarrow[\substack{\text{glycerol-}\\\text{phosphate}\\\text{dehydrogenase}\\(1.1.1.8)}]{}$ dihydroxy-acetone phosphate
+phosphate

This may not appear to be a dismutation until it is remembered that glyceraldehyde phosphate and dihydroxyacetone phosphate are two forms of triose phosphate, readily convertible into one another by triosephosphate isomerase (5.3.1.1); the overall reaction can thus be written

$$2 \text{ triose phosphate}+\text{phosphate} = \text{diphosphoglycerate}+\text{glycerol phosphate}.$$

Coenzyme A is involved in the dismutation of pyruvate (reactions XII.1.r–u and n) and of 2-oxoglutarate (reactions XII.2.g–h, 1.u and 14.a); the latter also involves ammonia. Both systems, however, involve an additional hydrogen carrier, lipoate, as well as additional enzymes.

Pyruvate $\xrightarrow[\substack{\text{pyruvate}\\\text{dehydrogenase}\\(1.2.4.1)+\\\text{lipoate acetyl-}\\\text{transferase}\\(2.3.1.12)}]{}$ lipoate $\xrightarrow[\substack{\text{lipoamide}\\\text{dehydrogenase}\\(1.6.4.3)}]{}$ NAD $\xrightarrow[\substack{\text{lactate}\\\text{dehydrogenase}\\(1.1.1.27)}]{}$ pyruvate
+CoA

The overall reaction here is

$$2 \text{ pyruvate}+\text{CoA} = \text{acetyl-CoA}+\text{lactate}+CO_2$$

In the case of the 2-oxoglutarate system

2-oxo-glutarate $\xrightarrow[\substack{\text{oxoglutarate}\\\text{dehydrogenase}\\(1.2.4.2)+\\\text{lipoate acetyl-}\\\text{transferase}\\(2.3.1.12)?}]{}$ lipoate $\xrightarrow[\substack{\text{lipoamide}\\\text{dehydrogenase}\\(1.6.4.3)}]{}$ NAD $\xrightarrow[\substack{\text{glutamate}\\\text{dehydrogenase}\\1.4.1.2)}]{}$ 2-oxo-glutarate
+CoA +NH$_3$

the overall reaction is

$$2 \text{ 2-oxoglutarate}+\text{CoA}+NH_3 = \text{succinyl-CoA}+\text{glutamate}+CO_2$$

A further possibility arises when two dehydrogenases oxidize different optical isomers of the same substance, giving the same oxidation product. For instance, the system

$$\text{L-lactate} \xrightarrow[\substack{\text{lactate de-}\\ \text{hydrogenase}\\ (1.1.1.27)}]{} \text{NAD} \xrightarrow[\substack{\text{D-lactate de-}\\ \text{hydrogenase}\\ (1.1.1.28)}]{} \text{pyruvate}$$

acts as a racemase (*593*), catalysing the overall reaction

$$\text{L-lactate} = \text{D-lactate}$$

Here the L-lactate is oxidized to pyruvate and the pyruvate is reduced to D-lactate, the pyruvate therefore cancels out and acts as a coenzyme in the way described above.

The number of possible coenzyme-linked dehydrogenase systems which can be formed from the known dehydrogenases is very large. From n different dehydrogenases, $\frac{1}{2}n(n-1)$ different systems may be formed. The Table of Enzymes contains over 70 different dehydrogenases reacting with NAD, which could form over 2,400 coenzyme-linked systems, as well as over 40 reacting with NADP, which could form over 700 more. If, in addition, NAD-specific dehydrogenases could be linked with NADP-specific dehydrogenases, the number of possibilities is very greatly increased and over 5,000 different systems could be formed. The number of systems naturally occurring, however, is very much smaller than this, as the dehydrogenases are never found all together in the same living cell.

If a NAD-specific dehydrogenase is linked with a NADP-specific one, a system is formed in which the two coenzymes act as successive hydrogen carriers in the chain. Such a system could be formed by an enzyme capable of linking the two coenzymes together. One obvious possibility is provided by NAD(P) transhydrogenase (1.6.1.1), which should be capable of bringing about the following type of process:

$$\text{S}_1^r \xrightarrow[\text{D}_1]{} \text{NADP} \xrightarrow[\substack{\text{NAD(P)}\\ \text{transhydro-}\\ \text{genase}\\ (1.6.1.1)}]{} \text{NAD} \xrightarrow[\text{D}_2]{} \text{S}_2^o$$

There is evidence that the oxidation of isocitrate in mitochondria is brought about in such a way (*2127*);

$$\text{Isocitrate} \xrightarrow[\substack{\text{isocitrate de-}\\ \text{hydrogenase}\\ (1.1.1.42)}]{} \text{NADP} \xrightarrow[\substack{\text{NAD(P)}\\ \text{transhydro-}\\ \text{genase}\\ (1.6.1.1)}]{} \text{NAD} \xrightarrow[\substack{\text{NADH}_2\\ \text{oxidase}\\ \text{system}}]{} \text{O}_2$$

Both coenzymes are required, and the rate of each of the separate reactions has been shown to be adequate, while the oxidation of isocitrate by NAD and of $NADPH_2$ by O_2 were both found to proceed at negligible rates.

Another possibility is that the linking might take place through a dehydrogenase which can react with both coenzymes, e.g. glutamate dehydrogenase, thus

$$S_1^r \xrightarrow{\quad D_1 \quad} NADP \xrightarrow[\substack{\text{glutamate} \\ \text{dehydro-} \\ \text{genase} \\ (1.4.1.3)}]{\quad} \substack{\text{2-oxo} \\ \text{glutarate} \\ + NH_3} \xrightarrow[\substack{\text{glutamate} \\ \text{dehydro-} \\ \text{genase} \\ (1.4.1.3)}]{\quad} NAD \xrightarrow{\quad D_2 \quad} S_2^o$$

In this hypothetical system the glutamate acts as a hydrogen carrier, undergoing alternate oxidation and reduction, and thus acting in much the same way as the coenzymes.

Other possibilities of linking exist between those dehydrogenases which do not react with the coenzymes. A few such reactions have been found in tissue preparations, though the mechanism has not been clearly shown. In these cases other substances presumably act instead of the coenzymes. Any reversibly reducible molecule capable of reacting with two different dehydrogenases should theoretically be able to act as a link, provided that its redox potential lies in the right region.

DISTRIBUTIVE FUNCTION OF TRANSFERRING ENZYMES

We have been considering reactions between the substrates of two dehydrogenases only. When many dehydrogenases are present, all capable of reacting with the same coenzyme, the latter will act in such a way as to distribute the available hydrogen among the various substrates in accordance with the equilibrium constants of the separate reactions. This distributive function is not restricted to hydrogen-transferring enzyme systems. The same thing is seen with phosphate transfer, ammonia transfer, methyl-transfer, acyl-transfer, and probably with other types of transfer also. In each type there is one substance which acts as a kind of central depot of active groups of the type involved and in this way links all the enzymes of the class together, not in series but in parallel. For H-transfer the enzymes involved are the dehydrogenases, and $NADH_2$ (or, for a second group of enzymes, $NADPH_2$) acts as the central depot of active hydrogen. For phosphate transfer the enzymes involved are the kinases and ATP forms the central depot of active phosphate groups. For ammonia (amino-groups) aminotransferases are concerned and L-glutamate is the amino-group carrier. For the acyl-transferases acyl-CoA acts as the clearing house, and for the methyl-transferases adenosylmethionine acts as the common carrier. For transfer

T

of formaldehyde (hydroxymethyl groups) or formyl groups, tetrahydro-folate acts as the carrier.

Thus coenzyme-linked dehydrogenase systems, important as they are, form only one example of a much more general phenomenon, which is of great biochemical importance. Thus we may speak of ATP-linked kinase systems, CoA-linked acyltransferase systems, and so on. It is to be noted that in each case the central substance has coenzyme-like functions and forms an indispensable part of the catalytic system. It may further be pointed out that it is only after these substances are discovered that it becomes possible to isolate and study the separate enzymes which act with them. It seems probable that more of these substances will be discovered in the future.

TRANSIT TIME

In a two-enzyme system, such as a coenzyme-linked dehydrogenase system, in which the linking coenzyme has to migrate from one enzyme to the other and back again in order to complete the catalytic cycle, it is obvious that the overall velocity will be a function not only of the velocities of the two separate enzyme reactions, but also of the transit time, that is to say, the time taken by the coenzyme in travelling between the two enzymes. Even if the two enzyme reactions were infinitely fast, the overall velocity would not become infinite, but would then be determined solely by the reciprocal of the transit time.

This introduces a new factor into the kinetics of the system, the effect of which will depend markedly on whether the system is a 'soluble' one, with the components in free solution, or an 'insoluble' or particulate one, in which the components are bound together by attachment to an insoluble structure or otherwise prevented from separating.

In the former case, as the enzyme system is progressively diluted the distance between the two enzyme molecules increases, and the transit time becomes more and more important. The efficiency of the carrier increases with the total concentration of the system, up to a limiting value which is reached when the transit time is negligible. With an 'insoluble' system, on the other hand, the distance between the two enzyme molecules does not change with dilution, and the efficiency of the carrier remains constant.

STRUCTURALLY ORGANIZED ENZYME SYSTEMS

The limiting effect of the transit time will become more important the higher the molecular weight of the linking substance in a soluble system, since the rate of diffusion bears an inverse relation to the molecular weight. It should therefore be particularly marked in systems involving such high-molecular carriers as cytochrome c. This is probably one of the main reasons why the cytochrome system is not found distributed throughout the cytoplasm, but is concentrated in intracellular particles, in the mitochondria of animal and plant tissues and the analogous particles in other cells. The enzymes involved are thus kept close to one another, reducing transit time effects to a minimum. In this case even the carrier cytochrome c is bound to particular sites in the system. By careful extraction of mitochondria with dilute KCl solutions, practically all the cytochrome c can be removed without great damage to the oxidizing and phosphorylating enzymes. The system then no longer takes up O_2 with succinate or related substrates, but on adding cytochrome c the activity is restored. The rate of O_2 uptake is proportional to the amount of cytochrome c added until this amount is equal to the amount extracted, at which point there is a sharp break in the curve and further additions of cytochrome have no effect. All the cytochrome added up to this point has become firmly bound and cannot be washed out by sucrose solutions. In fact it is possible actually to titrate the cytochrome c binding sites in the particles with cytochrome (1226).

A considerable volume of work has shown that many of the complex enzyme systems involved in oxidative metabolism are localized in the mitochondria. In addition to the cytochrome system and other hydrogen carriers, these particles contain many of the enzymes of the citric cycle (Table XII.2), of fatty acid metabolism (Table XII.4) and of oxidative phosphorylation. Whether because the particles are surrounded by a membrane, or because they are largely lipid in nature and may have an emulsion-like structure with a dispersed aqueous phase, or because of definite chemical combination, mitochondria when carefully prepared also contain many substances of lower molecular weight, normally regarded as soluble, e.g. the coenzymes involved in these systems. These components are unable to diffuse out of the particles to any significant extent so long as the mitochondrial structure is unimpaired. Thus the particulate system remains active, even when suspended in large volumes of the appropriate medium, and the particles can be washed at the centrifuge with this medium without loss of activity. The mitochondria, however, are sensitive to changes in the medium, and under abnormal conditions, for instance, after treatment with pure water, some of the components such as cytochrome c and coenzymes can be washed out (2337). The distribution of enzymes among intracellular particles is discussed in Chapter XIII.

A very large amount of work has been done on the effect of various media in the preparation of mitochondria. The best results, so far as enzyme activity is concerned, seem to be given by $0 \cdot 25$ M sucrose, although the microscopic appearance is most normal with $0 \cdot 88$ M sucrose. For details of the preparation of active mitochondria see *52, 1126, 2112*.

The complete disruption of the mitochondrial system can be brought about step by step in several stages. The mitochodria can be broken up by the Waring blendor, by grinding with sand, by sonic vibrations, or in other ways, releasing many of the soluble components but also leaving many of the enzymes associated together in smaller insoluble particles (*813*). These particles can be obtained in a clean state by centrifugal procedures.† The classical preparation of such particles is the cytochrome oxidase preparation of KEILIN and HARTREE (*1340, 1342a*) called more recently by GREEN 'the electron-transport particle or ETP'.

These particles have been used as the starting material for a very large amount of work on the respiratory system. They are believed to be derived from the membranes or cristae of the mitochondria on disruption. In the case of liver mitochondria, mechanical disruption has been shown (*813*) to form fragments of a wide range of particle weights, but all having the same specific enzymatic activities, which suggests a rather uniform distribution of the components in the membranes. Particles obtained by mechanical disruption retain the fully active cytochrome system, but have lost the power of oxidative phosphorylation, but when the disruption is produced by digitonin treatment the particles still retain this power. The mechanism of catalysis of oxidative phosphorylation is discussed in more detail in Chapter XIII.

It is possible to break up the Keilin–Hartree particles into fractions, and in this way to effect an actual physical separation of different segments of the respiratory chain of catalysts. WAINIO, using cholate treatment, separated two main fractions, one containing succinate dehydrogenase and cytochrome b, the other containing the a cytochromes, cytochrome oxidase and copper, and this work has been confirmed and extended by

† There has been a tendency on the part of some workers to apply to such particles the terminology of purified enzymes, for instance to give them names ending in '-ase' and to speak of them as 'highly purified'. 'Succinic oxidase', for example, contains succinate dehydrogenase and cytochrome oxidase, as well as ubiquinone and a number of intermediate cytochromes. 'DPNH-cytochrome c reductase' is spoken of as 'the enzyme' although it contains a flavoprotein, cytochromes b and c_1, ubiquinone and other components. This practice has led to some misunderstandings, and the Commission on Enzymes has recommended that 'names purporting to be names of enzymes, especially those ending in "-ase", should only be used for single enzymes. When it is desired to name a system containing more than one enzyme on the basis of the overall reaction catalysed by it, the word "system" should be included in the name, e.g. "the succinate oxidase system"'.

a number of other workers (see *1252*). HATEFI *et al.* (*1026*) have succeeded in separating the system into four sections, catalysing respectively the reaction between succinate and ubiquinone, $NADH_2$ and ubiquinone, ubiquinone and cytochrome c, and cytochrome c and O_2, as already mentioned in Chapter IX, and these can be recombined with ubiquinone and cytochrome c acting as links.

Recently the process has been carried much further, with the development of methods for breaking lipoprotein associations and improvements in the use of surface-active substances, deoxycholate, etc. As already mentioned, all the cytochrome components have now been separated and purified, as well as a number of the enzymes concerned. Moreover, GREEN *et al.* (*906*) have isolated the 'structural protein' of the mitochondria which apparently functions as the insoluble framework on which the cytochromes are held. This is a colourless protein, insoluble in water but soluble at pH $10\cdot5$ and then having a molecular weight of about 25,000. It has an unusually high proportion of non-polar side-chains, and has the property of specifically binding cytochromes a, b and c_1 (but not c) and also lipid. The cytochromes are bound as monomers, which means that the protein has a depolymerizing effect on them. It forms about one-third of the total protein of the mitochondria. If the cytochromes are indeed arranged physically in the order in which they function in the respiratory chain, it may well be a reflection of specific aminoacid sequences in this protein.

The degree of structural organization of the enzymes within intracellular particles has been much discussed ever since the first suggestion in 1940 of KEILIN and HARTREE (*1342*), who said, referring to the succinate-dehydrogenase-cytochrome system, 'The activity of this system depends not only on the properties of the individual components but also on those of the colloidal protein particles to which they are more or less intimately bound. It is conceivable that each of the colloidal particles acts as a support for the complete system and thus assures the mutual accessibility of its components.'

Much later, this suggestion, which only implies that the components are held close together, was extended, principally by GREEN, into the concept of a physical positioning of the enzymes in the order of their reaction sequence. Referring to the mitochondrial system, Green says, 'We were convinced that we were dealing with an organized mosaic of enzymes in which each of the large number of component enzymes was uniquely located to permit of efficient implementation of consecutive reaction sequences'.

We do not feel that the evidence at present available makes it necessary to go quite as far as this. It seems to us that all that is necessary for efficient working of the system is that the components should be held sufficiently near together to make the transit time small. The exact degree of structural organization must be determined by further evidence. The idea of an arrangement of units in a fixed sequence is of course not unfamiliar in biology; for instance, the arrangement of the genes in a fixed order in the chromosomes is well established.

The confinement of systems of enzymes within intracellular particles, though favourable for reactions between the components of the systems, may hinder reactions between them and the extra-particulate systems in the cytoplasm, for the membrane surrounding the particle may not be freely permeable. This is particularly important in the case of mitochondria, for although their membranes are fairly permeable to a number of substrates, they are not so to $NADH_2$ if intact. NAD-reducing enzymes occur both inside and outside the mitochondria, but the cytochrome oxidase system is confined to the inside. While there is no difficulty in the oxidation of internally-produced $NADH_2$ through cytochrome, it is not immediately obvious how $NADH_2$ produced by the cytoplasmic enzymes can be oxidized. BOXER and DEVLIN (304) have recently discussed this question in detail. Intact liver mitochondria are unable to oxidize added $NADH_2$; heart mitochondria, on the other hand, oxidize it readily, as will liver mitochondria after the permeability of their membranes has been altered by treatment with water. Evidence is accumulating that in liver mitochondria there are separate paths for the oxidation of internal and external $NADH_2$; the internal one being coupled with phosphorylation and sensitive to antimycin A and amytal, while the external one is not associated with phosphorylation and not inhibited by these substances. There is also evidence that external $NADH_2$ can be linked with the internal path by various 'shuttle' mechanisms, and it has been suggested that the substance acting as the shuttle may be mitochondrial cytochrome b_5 (2186-7), the acetoacetate-D-3-hydroxybutyrate pair (1536), or glycerol phosphate (304), in each case the substance being reduced on the outside of the membrane and oxidized on the inside. It is possible also that the changes in permeability which the mitochondrial membranes readily undergo may provide a controlling mechanism in biological oxidations.

SOME PROPERTIES OF MULTI-ENZYME SYSTEMS

In a metabolic system, consisting of a number of enzymes catalysing a series of consecutive reactions, it is clear that after the system has settled down to a steady state all the reactions must proceed at the same rate. If not, the concentrations of the intermediates will change, and they will change in such a way as to bring this condition about. For instance, in a series

$$A \xrightarrow[E_1]{} B \xrightarrow[E_2]{} C \xrightarrow[E_3]{} D \xrightarrow[E_4]{}$$

if at some time the reaction catalysed by enzyme E_3 should be slower than that of E_1 and E_2, C will obviously accumulate. The increase in the concentration of C will tend to increase the velocity of E_3, in accordance with the Michaelis equation. It will also tend to reduce the apparent velocity of E_2 by increasing the rate of the back reaction. This

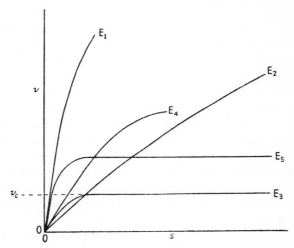

Fig. XII.1. *Michaelis curves of the component enzymes of a system, showing the limiting steady-state conditions.*

equalization process (which is independent of any change in enzyme concentration due to adaptation) will continue until the rates are the same, and then the concentration of C will remain constant.

Now the different enzymes of the system will have different substrate concentration curves, depending on their Michaelis constants, their maximum velocities and the amount of each enzyme present, somewhat as shown in Fig. XII.1. These curves represent the velocities given by the different enzymes in the amounts in which they are present in the system, all plotted on the same velocity scale. s is the concentration of the particular substrate in each case. The height of a given curve will depend on the amount of the corresponding enzyme present; if one enzyme, say E_3, is only present in small amount (or has a low maximum velocity), it is clear that no matter how much the substrate concentration may be increased, its velocity cannot rise above the horizontal part of its curve (v_c). It then becomes the limiting factor in the system and it will determine the rate of the whole chain of reactions. The enzyme whose curve has the lowest horizontal part will always become the limiting enzyme of any system of consecutive enzyme reactions. v_c will then become the velocity of all the other enzyme reactions in the chain and the substrate concentration of each enzyme will adjust itself to that point on its curve which gives this rate. In other words, the point at which each curve cuts the v_c line gives the substrate concentration of the corresponding enzyme in the steady state.

Certain long-term effects might be expected to follow *in vivo* from this principle. There will tend to be an inverse ratio between the amounts of the enzymes and the amounts of the corresponding substrates; if there is a very large amount of one enzyme the concentration of its substrate will be extremely small, and vice versa. One would expect this fact to have an equalizing effect for, as already mentioned, if any one enzyme in a chain is deficient, the concentration of its substrate will be high and the process of inductive formation should in due course produce more of that enzyme. Conversely, the substrate concentrations of the most active enzymes will be very low and there will be less stimulus to evoke their formation. Thus in time induction should operate to remove bottlenecks and to adjust the amounts of the different enzymes in any chain so as to equalize the maximum velocities of the different reactions.

This effect may be reinforced by enzyme repression, which will tend to reduce the amount of any enzymes present in excess.

If one of the enzymes in a chain is inhibited by the use of a specific poison, its substrate will accumulate until it may be possible to detect it by chemical means or even to isolate it, even though normally it may be present in much too small quantities to detect. This principle has proved very valuable in elucidating the intermediate steps in metabolic processes, as also has the study of mutants in which one or other of the enzymes is deficient.

From what has just been said, it would be expected that the poisoning of one of the enzymes would stimulate the inductive formation of more of that enzyme, an effect which is probably important in the development of resistance to drugs.

An effect which is of considerable biological importance is that if a rather slow enzyme is followed by a very active one, the lifetime of the intermediate substrate molecules is very short, as they are utilized by the second enzyme as soon as they are produced by the first. This makes possible the effective utilization of highly unstable intermediates which would otherwise undergo rapid spontaneous decomposition. For example, if B in the following system is unstable, there will be a competition between the spontaneous decomposition and the conversion to

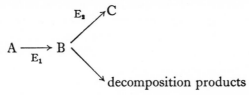

C catalysed by E_2. The greater the amount of the enzyme E_2 present, the less the fraction of B which is lost by decomposition, and by sufficiently increasing the amount of E_2 the loss may be made negligible. This effect is especially important in connection with the biological utilization of the free energy of certain metabolic reactions, since this depends on the utilization of 'energy-rich' intermediates which are by their nature unstable.

A somewhat similar point is that by sufficiently increasing the amount of the relevant enzyme it is possible to make effective use of intermediates which, because of equilibrium considerations, can only be present in vanishingly small concentrations. For instance, in the system

$$A \rightleftharpoons_{E_1} B \xrightarrow{E_2} C$$

the equilibrium of the first reaction may be so far over to the left that only very small amounts of B can be present at any instant. Nevertheless, if the amount of E_2 is sufficiently increased the conversion of even these small amounts of B to C will proceed with adequate velocity; the amounts of B thus used up will be at once replaced by E_1, so that the conversion of A to C will readily proceed. This effect may be very important in metabolic reaction chains.

Competition between enzyme reactions becomes important in connection with the directive function of enzymes, referred to at the beginning of this chapter, when there is the possibility of a branching-point in a metabolic chain. If, for example, the substance B can be acted on by two different enzymes E_2 and E_3 to form C or D respectively, and each of these substances may undergo its own line of metabolism, it is clear

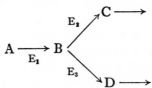

that the relative amounts (and activities) of E_2 and E_3 will determine the partition between the two lines and hence the whole course of A's metabolism.

The relative amounts of the enzymes, however, may not be the sole factor which determines the partition. Other reactants may be concerned in one or other of the competing reactions. For instance, the conversion of B into C may be a dehydrogenation for which a hydrogen acceptor is necessary, and the availability of the acceptor may play a large part in directing the metabolism into one or other of the paths.

An important case of this kind is shown in Table XII.1, in which no less than three enzyme reactions compete for the pyruvate formed by reaction XII.1.m, and the further course of the metabolism is determined both by the amounts of the three enzymes and by the conditions of metabolism. Anaerobically, $NADH_2$ will be available to act as a hydrogen donor in the conversion of pyruvate into lactate by the muscle lactate dehydrogenase (reaction XII.1.n). Aerobically this will not be the case, and the pyruvate dehydrogenase causes the pyruvate to react with lipoate as shown in reactions XII.1.r–t, so directing it into the citric cycle (Table XII.2). Muscle is deficient in pyruvate decarboxylase, but yeast contains sufficiently large amounts to compete effectively with the other reactions, so that anaerobically the pyruvate is decarboxylated as shown in reactions XII.1.o–p and is ultimately converted into alcohol.

COMMENTS ON TABLES

We may now consider in more detail some of the more important multi-enzyme systems.

Table XII.1 sets out the separate reactions involved in glycolysis, together with the enzymes responsible and the numbers by which they may be found in the table of enzymes. Starting with glycogen, the first step is the transfer of the terminal glucose residues from the ends of the polysaccharide chains to phosphate. The second step is the transfer of a phosphate group from the 1-position of the diphosphate to the 6-position of the glucose 1-phosphate. This interesting reaction results both in the disappearance and in the formation of one molecule of the diphosphate; these therefore cancel out, and the net result is the apparent conversion of a molecule of glucose 1-phosphate into one of glucose 6-phosphate.

Alternatively, if we start with glucose, glucose 6-phosphate arises directly by the transfer of a phosphate group from ATP. Thus in both cases glucose 6-phosphate is formed, and this is then converted into fructose-phosphate by an intramolecular transfer of two hydrogen atoms from C_2 to C_1. This is followed by the transfer of another phosphate group from ATP to the 1-position. The molecule is then split into two halves by aldolase, giving two molecules of triose phosphate, one in the aldose and one in the ketose form. The ketose is converted by an isomerase into the aldose by another intramolecular transfer of two hydrogen atoms, this time from C_1 to C_2, so that two molecules of glyceraldehyde phosphate are produced. The aldehyde group of this then combines with an –SH group in the dehydrogenase and two hydrogen atoms are transferred from the resulting complex to NAD, giving a thiolester compound of the enzyme containing an energy-rich bond. The phosphoglyceryl group is then transferred from the –SH group of the enzyme to phosphate, giving a compound with an energy-rich mixed anhydride bond, diphosphoglyceric acid. The kinase which follows then transfers the phosphate from this to ADP, giving ATP and 3-phosphoglycerate. In this way the oxidation is coupled with ATP synthesis.

The phosphoglycerate then undergoes a reaction which is analogous to the phosphoglucomutase reaction (XII.1.b), namely, the transfer of a phosphate group from the 3-position of the diphosphate to the 2-position of the monophosphate. This results in the disappearance of a molecule of 3-phosphoglycerate and the appearance of one of 2-phosphoglycerate, while the amount of the diphosphate remains unchanged. Water is then removed from the 2-phosphoglycerate, giving the enol form of phosphopyruvate. This unusual reaction has the effect of rendering the phosphate bond energy-rich, so that the phosphate can then be transferred to ADP by the pyruvate kinase forming ATP.

The resulting pyruvate may now follow one of three alternative paths, according to circumstances. In muscle, in the absence of oxygen, the reduced coenzyme from reaction XII.1h. reduces it to lactate by means of lactate dehydrogenase. In yeast, where the lactate dehydrogenase is of a different type, not reacting with the coenzyme, the pyruvate in the presence of its decarboxylase becomes attached to thiamine pyrophosphate with elimination of CO_2, as described on p. 413. The compound then breaks down directly to free acetaldehyde, which is then reduced to alcohol by the $NADH_2$ in the presence of alcohol dehydrogenase.

In the presence of oxygen, on the other hand, the pyruvate is oxidized by pyruvate dehydrogenase. With this enzyme the pyruvate and thiamine pyrophosphate form the same compound as before, but now the compound reacts with the oxidized form of lipoate, which acts both as a hydrogen acceptor and an acyl acceptor (reaction XII.1.s). This may occur in a single step as written, with the transfer of a $CH_3 . CHO$ group, or in two successive steps, namely a hydrogen transfer with the formation of acetyl-thiamine pyrophosphate and dihydrolipoate, and then an acetyl-transfer from the thiamine pyrophosphate to the reduced lipoate. Lipoate acetyltransferase next transfers the acetyl group from the lipoate to the –SH group of coenzyme A. The reduced lipoate is reoxidized by NAD with lipoamide dehydrogenase, and the $NADH_2$, like that from reaction XII.1.h, is reoxidized through the cytochrome system. The acetyl-CoA is further metabolized as shown in Table XII.2 or in other ways.

It will be noted that this system illustrates what was said earlier in this chapter about the appearance of coenzyme-linked dehydrogenase reactions when the supply of O_2 is cut off. The glyceraldehydephosphate and lactate dehydrogenases (reactions XII.1.h and n) form such a linked system anaerobically in muscle, and the glyceraldehydephosphate and alcohol dehydrogenases (reactions XII.1.h and q) in yeast.

It will be noted also that of all the reactions involved in this system, all but three are transfer reactions; these exceptions are reactions XII.1.f, l and p.

Table XII.2 shows how the acetyl-CoA is further oxidized by the citric cycle. The first reaction is a transfer of the acetyl group from coenzyme A to oxaloacetate, forming citrate. This is converted into isocitrate by aconitate hydratase, the process involving removal of a molecule of water and replacement in a reversed position. The isocitrate is then oxidized by NADP by means of the appropriate dehydrogenase and the oxalosuccinate formed is decarboxylated by the same enzyme to give 2-oxoglutarate. This is then oxidized by a mechanism very similar to that which oxidizes pyruvate in Table XII.1, involving lipoate. The product in this case is succinyl-CoA, which may break down in two different ways. It may undergo simple hydrolysis by the hydrolase to coenzyme A and succinate (reaction XII.2.i), or its breakdown may be linked with the synthesis of a molecule of ATP from ADP by the reactions XII.2.m–n. The significance of these alternative paths is not yet properly understood. In either case succinate is produced; this is oxidized to fumarate by its dehydrogenase by means of O_2 through the cytochrome system and the fumarate is converted into malate by fumarate hydratase. Finally, the malate is oxidized by its dehydrogenase to oxaloacetate, which replaces that used up in the first reaction, so completing the cycle.

Table XII.3 shows the glyoxylate cycle, which occurs in micro-organisms and plants (see *192, 1442*). It may be regarded as a modification of the citrate cycle in which reactions XII.2.d–k (including the CO_2-producing steps) are by-passed. The citrate cycle is essentially a mechanism for the oxidative breakdown of acetate to CO_2, and while C_4-acids are intermediates in the process there is no net formation which could be used for biosynthetic processes. The glyoxylate cycle, on the other hand is essentially a mechanism for converting two acetyl groups into a C_4-acid, which is available for biosyntheses.

Reactions XII.3.a–c are the same as reactions XII.2.a–c, but in the next step a molecule of succinate is removed from the isocitrate by a lyase reaction, leaving a molecule of glyoxylate. This then reacts with a second molecule of acetyl-CoA to form malate, by a reaction very similar to the initial formation of citrate. The malate is oxidized to oxaloacetate, which completes the cycle. The succinate which is produced by the cycle can be metabolized in various ways for the biosynthesis of a wide variety of substances, and the system plays an important part in micro-organisms growing on acetate. It is also believed to be important in the conversion of fat into carbohydrate, e.g. in germinating seeds, the fat giving acetyl-CoA (see Table XII.4), which is converted by the cycle into succinate, and then by way of oxaloacetate and phosphoenolpyruvate to sugar by the reversal of reactions XII.1.1–c.

Table XII.4 shows, in the first part, how fatty acids are oxidatively broken down to acetyl-CoA, and, in the second part, how long-chain fatty acids may be built up from acetyl-CoA.

The first step in the breakdown is the formation of a thiolester link between the carboxyl group of the fatty acid and the –SH group of coenzyme A by a synthetase; the necessary energy is provided by the breakdown of a pyrophosphate bond in ATP. The next three steps closely resemble a part of the citric cycle (reactions XII.2.j–l), but with different enzymes and with the important distinction that here we are dealing with coenzyme A compounds and with monocarboxylic instead of dicarboxylic acids. The final reaction consists in a transfer of the R.CO– group from its combination with acetyl-CoA to another molecule of coenzyme A, giving an acyl-CoA compound of chain length shorter by two carbon atoms than the original compound. This product can then undergo a similar series of reactions, and this repetition can continue as many times as are necessary to break the whole chain down into 2-carbon fragments, that is into acetyl-CoA. It will be noted that, although no phosphorylation is involved, the oxidation is coupled with the formation of energy-rich bonds in the shape of acyl-CoA thiolester links, one being formed for each C–C bond broken.

Since the separate reactions are reversible under appropriate conditions, it might be thought that the synthesis of long-chain fatty acids from acetyl-CoA would be brought about by a reversal of this cycle. The main synthetic pathway, however, differs from this in a number of important respects (see LYNEN, *1635*). The first step is the carboxylation of acetyl-CoA by a biotin-containing ligase to form malonyl-CoA (WAKIL, *2753*).

The remaining reactions (XII.4.g–l) are carried out by a complex of enzymes, unresolved as yet, which has been extensively purified from yeast and from pigeon liver (LYNEN, *1635*; BRESSLER and WAKIL, *326–7*), and behaves as a particle of molecular weight about 2 million. The reactions in the Table are those given by Lynen, who points out that there are several important differences between this process and a synthesis by the reversal of reactions XII.4.b–e. (*a*) Malonyl-CoA takes the place of acetyl-CoA; the decarboxyiation involved (reaction XII.4.h) shifts the equilibrium in the direction of synthesis. (*b*) In the breakdown the substances are throughout in the form of thiolesters of CoA, whereas in the synthesis they are in the form of thiolesters with an –SH group in the enzyme; if they had been CoA compounds, the acetoacetyl-CoA formed during the first revolution of the cycle (R $=$ CH$_3$–) would have been destroyed by enzyme 2.3.1.9, which would prevent the synthesis from continuing. (*c*) The synthesis involves NADP (reactions XII.4.i and k), whereas the breakdown involves NAD (reaction XII.4.d). (*d*) The hydroxyacid involved in reactions XII.4.i–j is the D-form, whereas the enzymes catalysing reactions XII.4.c–d are specific for the L-form. (*e*) Reaction XII.4.k involves FMN, whereas reaction XII.4.b involves FAD.

Reaction XII.4.1 seems hardly consistent with the fact that no fatty acid compounds of intermediate chain length can be detected, and Lynen suggests that the short- and medium-chain-length acids are transferred, not to CoA, but to another enzyme –SH group for the next repetition of reaction XII.4.h. He has investigated the chain-length specificity of the enzyme catalysing reaction XII.4.1 by isotopic exchange methods, and finds a marked optimum with acyl groups containing 16 or 18 C atoms, so that the cycle operates until this chain length is reached, and it is only then that the product is released. No doubt it is to this that the prevalence of palmitic and stearic acids in nature is due.

BRESSLER and WAKIL (*327*) have recently put forward objections to some features of the scheme, though not to its main outline. For instance they maintain that the product is free palmitic acid and not palmitoyl-CoA.

Table XII.5 shows an extremely interesting series of enzyme reactions occurring in a number of cells, including several animal tissues (*607*), whereby glucose 6-phosphate undergoes oxidation to CO$_2$ by means of NADP. It is sometimes known as the 'glucose-phosphate shunt', since in a sense reactions XII.5.a–h provide a path parallel with reactions XII.1.d–g. It must be remembered, however, that the paths are only parallel for a part of the way, that the glycolytic path is dependent on ATP breakdown, whereas here ATP is not required, that here the oxidation product is CO_2, that here NADP is involved and not NAD, and that for the most part the two systems depend on different enzymes.

In this system a molecule of ribose 5-phosphate, which may itself arise from reactions a–c through i, acts in a catalytic capacity in a remarkable way; as the transformations are somewhat difficult to visualize, the carbon atoms of this catalytic ribose phosphate molecule are shown in heavier type.

The first step is a simple oxidation to the lactone of phosphogluconic acid, which is then opened by a lactonase. The phosphogluconate is then again oxidized and decarboxylated, probably by one enzyme, as in the very similar NADP-specific malate and isocitrate dehydrogenases, giving ribulose phosphate, which is converted to xylulose phosphate by its epimerase. The first two carbons of this are then transferred by transketolase to the catalytic ribose phosphate molecule, forming sedoheptulose 7-phosphate, and the *three* end-carbons of this are transferred back to the residual glyceraldehyde phosphate by transaldolase, giving fructose phosphate and erythrose phosphate. The result of this is that the pentose, which was formed when the terminal carbon of the hexose was removed as CO_2, is now once more converted into a hexose, in which carbon atom 3 is derived from the catalytic ribose phosphate molecule. The isomerase now converts the fructose phosphate into glucose phosphate, which goes back to the beginning and undergoes the oxidation and decarboxylation reactions in the same way as the original glucose phosphate molecule. For the sake of clarity, these reactions, when occurring for the second time, are distinguished as reactions XII.5.a′–d′; they may be thought of as identical with reactions XII.5.a–d, except that carbon 3 is in heavy type. Transketolase next transfers the two end-carbons of the resulting xylulose phosphate to the erythrose phosphate left over from the transaldolase reaction, giving a molecule of glyceraldehyde phosphate and once again one of fructose phosphate. The latter, after conversion into glucose phosphate, undergoes oxidation and decarboxylation as before (reactions XII.5.a″–c″, which may be thought of as identical with reactions XII.5.a–c, but with carbon atoms 2–6 in heavy type). It will be seen that the resulting ribulose phosphate now contains all the five carbon atoms of the original catalytic ribose phosphate molecule; its isomerase finally converts it back into the original molecule, ready to repeat the whole process.

The net result of these reactions is the oxidation of a molecule of glucose phosphate into 3 molecules of CO_2 and 1 of glyceraldehyde phosphate. If we start with two molecules of glucose phosphate, we obtain two molecules of glyceraldehyde phosphate and these can unite to form one of glucose 6-phosphate by reactions XII.5.j–m, which are the reverse of reactions XII.1.g,f,d, with an interpolated hydrolysis of one phosphate ester bond by a phosphatase. Thus, starting with two molecules of glucose phosphate, we find that one of these is cancelled out by the formation of one glucose phosphate molecule, so that the net process is the complete oxidation of one molecule to CO_2 and inorganic phosphate.

Table XII.6 shows a simple system which has been found to be responsible for up to 50 per cent of the respiration of certain plants (*2966*). It illustrates a straightforward hydrogen-transport mechanism in which both NAD and glyoxylate act as coenzymes or hydrogen carriers. Since the last enzyme is a flavoprotein, whose action involves the reduction and reoxidation of its flavin group, this group also acts as a hydrogen carrier; thus the hydrogen from the substrate is passed to O_2 through three successive carriers.

Table XII.7 shows the metabolism of tyrosine. Starting with phenylalanine, the first step is the insertion of an –OH group in the *p*-position of the ring to form tyrosine. The nature of the hydrogen acceptor used by this enzyme is not yet quite certain. The tyrosine is converted into *p*-hydroxyphenylpyruvate by transamination with 2-oxoglutarate. The oxidase reaction which follows is of an unusual type, in which the side-chain undergoes oxidative decarboxylation and at the same time migrates to the adjacent position in the ring, leaving an –OH group in its place. The mechanism of this reaction has not yet been satisfactorily cleared up. The homogentisate thus formed is then oxidized by an oxygenase reaction, that is to say by the insertion of an O_2 molecule in place of one of the double bonds of the ring. This reaction forms maleylacetoacetate, which is then converted by an isomerase into fumarylacetoacetate. Glutathione is a cofactor in this reaction, and it is possible that the isomerization takes place by way of an intermediate formed by the combination of the –SH group of glutathione with the double bond of the maleyl group. The product of the reaction is then hydrolysed into fumarate (which enters the citric cycle) and acetoacetate. The latter is converted into its coenzyme A derivative by a transferase which transfers coenzyme A from succinyl-CoA arising from the citric cycle. Finally, a transacetylase transfers an acetyl group from the acetoacetyl-CoA to another molecule of coenzyme A, forming two molecules of acetyl-CoA, which are oxidized in the normal way by the citric cycle.

Table XII.8 shows the glyoxalase system, previously thought to be a single enzyme, but now resolved into two. The first step could be regarded as taking place by the addition of the –SH group of glutathione across the C=C double bond of the enol form of methylglyoxal, a typical lyase reaction. The S-lactoylglutathione thus formed is hydrolysed by the second enzyme to give free lactic acid and glutathione.

Table XII.9 shows the mechanism of the enzymatic interconversion of glucose and galactose by an inversion at C_4. The epimerase which catalyses this conversion acts only upon the uridinediphosphate derivatives of the sugars, so that the first requirement is to convert the sugars into these derivatives. This is shown in part (*a*) of the table. It is not necessary, however, to convert the whole of the sugar at first into the UDP derivative, because the enzyme 2.7.7.12 can transfer the uridinemonophosphate group from the sugar which has reacted to molecules which are still awaiting reaction, as shown in part (*b*). Thus the UMP group can be regarded as a kind of circulating vehicle carrying sugar-phosphate molecules through the inversion process. The system thus involves not so much a true coenzyme as a 'coenzyme', rather in the sense of the phosphoglucomutase reaction (XII.1.b). The first step in its formation is the phosphorylation of the two reactants to UTP and galactose phosphate, by phosphate-transfer from ATP by the appropriate kinases. The two products are then combined by a typical pyrophosphorylase reaction, with the liberation of inorganic pyrophosphate. The reaction may be represented diagrammatically thus:

$$
\text{XII.1} \qquad
\begin{array}{c}
\text{Ur–R–P–P–P} \\
+ \\
\text{Gal–P}
\end{array}
=
\begin{array}{c}
\text{Ur–R–P} \;+\; \text{P–P} \\
| \\
\text{Gal–P}
\end{array}
$$

where Ur represents uracil. In the reverse reaction glucose takes the place of galactose. Reaction XII.9.f can be represented as follows:

$$
\text{XII.2} \qquad
\begin{array}{c}
\text{Gal–P} \\
+ \\
\text{Ur–R–P} \\
| \\
\text{G–P}
\end{array}
=
\begin{array}{c}
\text{Gal–P} \\
| \\
\text{Ur–R–P} \\
+ \\
\text{G–P}
\end{array}
$$

In mammary gland and brain, uridylyltransferase is missing (*1768*), so that the cyclical process shown in part (*b*) cannot occur.

Table XII.10 shows some reactions involved in the metabolism of methionine. The first enzyme transfers an adenosine group from its combination with the triphosphate group in ATP to the S atom of the methionine. The methyl group is then removed by transfer to some acceptor by one or other of the methyltransferases, and the product remaining is hydrolysed to give homocysteine and adenosine, which is rephosphorylated. L-serine dehydratase then catalyses the combination of the homocysteine with a serine molecule, probably by removing a molecule of water from the latter and adding the –SH group of the homocysteine across the double bond thus formed. The resulting cysta-thionine is broken down by homoserine dehydratase, with the removal of cysteine; probably the first product is vinyl-glycine, which rearranges to give 2-iminobutyrate, which decomposes to the oxo-acid and ammonia. The oxobutyrate can be metabolized in various ways, e.g. by amination to aminobutyrate, a known product of methionine metabolism in animal tissues, or by decarboxylation to propionate.

Table XII.11 illustrates the utilization of ATP energy for the synthesis of a polysaccharide. The process proceeds through the formation of UDPglucose, and the glucose is transferred from the UPD to the end of the polysaccharide chain. The last enzyme requires the presence of glucose 6-phosphate, possibly to provide the branching points of the glycogen chains. As two ATP bonds are broken for the formation of one glucosidic link, the equilibrium point is strongly on the side of synthesis.

Table XII.12 sets out the interconversions of a number of pentoses brought about in bacteria by the co-operation of kinases, ketol-isomerases and epimerases. Since D-xylulose 5-phosphate can be converted into D-ribulose phosphate by a 3-epimerase and into L-ribulose phosphate by a 4-epimerase, as well as being formed by xylulokinase and broken down by phosphoketolase, it forms the key point through which interconver-sions occur. Its formation from D-ribose, D-xylose and L-arabinose involves in each case a kinase and a ketol-isomerase, but whereas with D-xylose and L-arabinose the ketol-isomerase precedes the kinase, in the case of D-ribose the kinase comes first. D-ribose and L-arabinose also require an epimerase, but xylose does not.

Table XII.13 shows the system of enzymes concerned in the synthesis of isoprenoid compounds, a system which is not only of great biological importance, but one which involves a number of enzyme reactions of unusual interest. The first reaction is the transfer of an acetyl group from CoA to the methyl group of a second molecule of acetyl-CoA. A third molecule of acetyl-CoA then reacts with the acetoacetyl-CoA in a way very similar to the synthesis of citrate (reaction XII.2.a), that is to say the methyl group of the acetyl-CoA is added by a lyase reaction to the $C=O$ double bond while at the same time the CoA is released from the other end of the molecule. Then the –CO.CoA group of the hydroxy-methylglutaryl-CoA undergoes a two-stage reduction by $NADPH_2$, apparently by a single enzyme and without the intermediate formation of the aldehyde, at any rate in the free state. It is an important feature of reactions a–c that in each case a CoA molecule is released, and it is the dissolution of the high-energy thiolester bond that causes the equilibrium of all three to be strongly on the side of synthesis. For example, $NADPH_2$

is not normally capable of reducing a carboxyl group to an aldehyde, and it is the release of the CoA that causes the reduction to go essentially to completion.

The mevalonate thus formed has its primary alcohol group pyrophosphorylated by ATP, but in two successive stages, catalysed by two different enzymes. The product undergoes a unique type of enzyme reaction, in which ATP brings about the removal of CO_2 and water. This might possibly be regarded as the converse of a synthetase reaction; with a synthetase, the breakdown of ATP causes the linking together of two molecules, as for instance with the carboxylases of sub-group 6.4.1, but here it is the decarboxylation that is dependent on the breakdown of ATP. The isopentenyl pyrophosphate then undergoes an isomerization to the dimethylallyl form, and there follows a condensation between the two forms, in which the dimethylallyl group is transferred from pyrophosphate to a molecule of isopentenyl pyrophosphate. This condensation is accompanied by a shift of the double bond, so that the resulting geranyl pyrophosphate can be regarded as a substituted dimethylallyl pyrophosphate, and the geranyl group can itself be transferred to a further molecule of isopentenyl pyrophosphate by the dimethylallyl-transferase. In this way long isoprenoid chains can be built up. A molecule of dimethylallyl pyrophosphate is always required to start the process.

In steroid synthesis this type of condensation does not proceed beyond the farnesyl stage, but instead two molecules of farnesyl pyrophosphate join together with the elimination of both pyrophosphate groups under the influence of an enzyme which is not yet fully characterized. This 'tail-to-tail' linking produces squalene, the point of linking being indicated by the arrow in the table under reaction k. O_2 with $NADPH_2$ then brings about a hydroxylation accompanied by an extensive cyclization apparently in a single reaction catalysed by a single hydroxylase, forming lanosterol, from which other steroids are derived. The hydroxylase reaction is a coupled oxidation in which one oxygen atom from the O_2 molecule oxidizes the squalene (appearing in the hydroxyl group) and the other oxidizes the $NADPH_2$.

Table XII.14 shows the system by which urea is formed in liver. The enzyme reactions 14.a–c are concerned with the entry of the first nitrogen atom. In the first reaction the nitrogen is assumed to come from ammonia, in the second (alternative) reaction from aminoacids. In either case glutamate is formed and passes on the ammonia by further transamination to form aspartate. The function of the glutamate is thus to act as an ammonia-carrier. Reactions 14.d–e are concerned with the entry of the second nitrogen atom and the carbon atom. The mechanism of the animal carbamate kinase, its absolute dependence on a cofactor (acetylglutamate), and the requirement for two molecules of ATP, are still not understood. The corresponding bacterial enzyme requires only one molecule of ATP and is independent of acetyl-glutamate. The carbamoyl-transferase transfers the carbamoyl group from the phosphate to the amino group of ornithine, which comes from the final reaction of the cycle. The citrulline thus formed is now combined by a synthetase reaction with the aspartate formed in reaction 14.c, using ATP energy for the bond-formation. The resulting argininosuccinate is split by the next enzyme into arginine and fumarate, which is metabolized as previously described. The arginine is hydrolysed by arginase into ornithine, which supplies reaction 14.e, and urea, the final product. Thus we may regard the 2-oxo-glutarate and the oxaloacetate as two successive carriers of ammonia and the ornithine as a carbamoyl carrier. These three compounds act in a coenzyme-like capacity as part of the catalytic mechanism.

An alternative pathway, instead of reaction 14.j, is shown in reactions 14.k–l. Here the amidine group of the arginine is removed not by hydro-lysis but by transfer to glycine, forming guanidinoacetate, which is then methylated to give creatine.

Table XII.15 gives one path by which lecithin may be synthesized, using ATP energy. To glycerol are added successively one phosphate and two acyl groups. The phosphate is then removed by hydrolysis, leaving a 1,2-diglyceride. Meanwhile choline is phosphorylated and the choline phosphate reacts with CTP, thus:

XII.3
$$
\begin{array}{ccc}
\text{Cy–R–P–P–P} & & \text{Cy–R–P} + \text{P–P} \\
+ & = & | \\
\text{Ch–P} & & \text{Ch–P}
\end{array}
$$

where Cy represents cytosine and Ch represents choline. The last en-zyme then transfers the phosphocholine residue from combination with CMP to the free –OH group of the diglyceride, forming lecithin.

Table XII.16 shows first how NAD and NADP are synthesized. Ribose is first phosphorylated by ATP and then a pyrophosphate group is trans-ferred from ATP to its reducing group. In most cells it appears that the next step is the transfer of the phosphoribosyl group from the pyro-phosphate to nicotinate (reaction c), although in some cells the transfer is to nicotinamide to form NMN (reaction g). In both cases enzyme 2.7.7.1 then transfers an adenylyl group from ATP to the mono-nucleotide, forming NAD or deamido-NAD. The latter is amidated to NAD by a synthetase using glutamine as donor. Finally NAD is phos-phorylated by ATP to NADP. It is interesting that in this system ATP acts as (*a*) a phosphate donor, (*b*) a pyrophosphate donor, (*c*) an adenylyl donor, and (*d*) a synthetase substrate.

The hydrolytic breakdown of NADP may involve any or all of four different links (apart from the breakdown of AMP itself), and the order of hydrolysis may vary with circumstances; the table shows two likely sequences.

Table XII.17 sets out the reactions by which the enzymatic synthesis of coenzyme A is accomplished. β-alanine and pantoate are first joined by an ATP-dependent synthetase reaction, and the resulting pantothenate is phosphorylated on its primary alcohol group by a specific kinase. Cysteine is then added to the carboxyl group by another synthetase, and the cysteine residue is decarboxylated. An adenylyl group from ATP is then added to the pantetheine phosphate by a transferase reaction resembling that which forms NAD. Finally an additional phosphate group is added to the adenylyl residue by another specific kinase.

Table XII.18 shows the sequence of enzyme reactions by which purines and pyrimidines are built up, and forms a most interesting illustration of the way in which enzymes may collaborate in long chains directed to a single end. Part (*a*), dealing with purine synthesis, involves the cooperation of fifteen different enzymes, and part (*b*), concerned with pyrimidines, involves nine more.

Purines are built up, not in the free state, but attached to a phosphoribosyl group, the product being a purine nucleotide. The first two reactions are the same as the first two of Table XII.16, but in the next step the phosphoribosyl group is transferred from pyrophosphate to an $-NH_2$ group from glutamine. It is interesting that during the transfer the ribosyl group undergoes an inversion, the pyrophosphate being attached by an α-link and the $-NH_2$ group by the β-link which is characteristic of the natural nucleotides. A molecule of glycine is then attached to the amino group by an ATP-dependent synthetase, and a formyl group transferred to the amino group of the glycine from tetrahydrofolate. In writing reaction e, only the two nitrogen atoms in positions 5 and 10 of tetrahydrofolate are shown, the former being uppermost.

The next step is the replacement of the oxygen atom of the glycine CO group by an $=NH$ group, glutamine being the donor in this ATP-dependent synthetase reaction. Yet another synthetase then closes the imidazole ring. The building of the other ring continues with the direct addition of CO_2, and the resulting carboxyl group is amidated by the addition of aspartate by a synthetase followed by the removal of fumarate by a lyase. A further formyl group is then transferred from tetrahydrofolate, though not this time from the methenyl form as in reaction e. Finally the purine structure is completed by closure of the ring, in this case without the participation of ATP.

The remaining reactions show the formation of other nucleotides from the IMP. AMP is formed by reactions m and n, which resemble reactions i and j, except that GTP is used instead of ATP. Alternatively, GMP may be formed by way of XMP by reactions o and p.

The important part played by synthetases, and the frequency with which the breakdown of ATP enters, will be noted; the formation of one adenine molecule involves the breakdown of nine pyrophosphate bonds of ATP, making allowance for the fact that the provision of glutamine and GTP depends on ATP breakdown.

The similarities between purines and pyrimidines might suggest that pyrimidines are also built up while attached to a phosphoribosyl group, but this is not the case. The pyrimidine ring is formed first, and only then attached to the phosphoribosyl group to form the nucleotide. The first step is the formation of carbamoyl-phosphate by an enzyme reaction already considered under Table XII.14. The carbamoyl group is then transferred from phosphate to aspartate, and ring closure of the carbamoyl-aspartate (ureidosuccinate) gives dihydro-orotate. This is oxidized by NAD to orotate, and only then is the phosphoribosyl group attached. Decarboxylation yields UMP, and after this has been converted into UTP it can be aminated by a synthetase to give CTP.

The reactions discussed above bring about the synthesis of purine and pyrimidine nucleotides from the beginning, but nucleotides can also be resynthesized from breakdown products, i.e. products containing preformed purines or pyrimidines. This is brought about by other enzymes. The various nucleotides can also be interconverted by enzymatic transfer reactions, by which one base is substituted for another.

Table XII.19 shows, in parts (b) and (c), the enzyme reactions involved in the synthesis of sucrose from CO_2. This chain of reactions is dependent on a supply of ATP and $NADPH_2$. These may be supplied artificially, but in nature they are provided by the photosynthetic mechanism (part (a)) (see *383*). Reaction XII.19.a has recently been shown to involve not only chlorophyll but also ferredoxin, an iron-protein (*544*) with an unusually negative redox potential, and a flavoprotein NADP reductase (*2597*). In the light, the chlorophyll brings about the reduction of the ferredoxin with the liberation of O_2 from water, and the flavoprotein enzyme catalyses the reduction of NADP by the reduced ferredoxin. The mechanism of reaction b is not yet certain, but is believed (*87, 1098*) to be due to a cyclic process involving chlorophyll and the chloroplast cytochromes.

In part (b), reaction c is that in which CO_2 is taken up; it becomes added to the centre of a molecule of ribulose diphosphate (produced later in reaction o), which splits with an intramolecular hydrogen transfer into two molecules of phosphoglycerate. The latter then retraces the path by which phosphoglycerate is formed in glycolysis. Reactions XII.19.d–g are the reverse of reactions XII.1.j–f respectively, and the same enzymes are involved, except for the use of NADP instead of NAD by the plant leaf enzyme. Fructose diphosphate is thereby produced, the reduction being carried out by the $NADPH_2$ supplied by the photochemical reaction. One phosphate group is then removed by hydrolysis by a specific phosphatase, and the fructose 6-phosphate with transketolase transfers its two terminal carbons to glyceraldehyde phosphate formed by reaction e to give erythrose phosphate and xylulose phosphate. The latter, after conversion to ribulose phosphate (reaction n) and phosphorylation (reaction o), supplies the ribulose diphosphate for reaction c. The erythrose phosphate combines with dihydroxyacetone phosphate (formed by reaction f) under the influence of aldolase to give sedoheptulose diphosphate. Phosphatase removes the 1-phosphate from this, and the monophosphate then undergoes the reverse of the transketolase reaction XII.5.e, using another molecule of glyceraldehyde phosphate. This reaction produces another molecule of xylulose phosphate, which is dealt with as before, and one of ribose phosphate, which is converted by its isomerase into yet another ribulose phosphate molecule, so completing the cycle. Since, in order to sum the reactions, h is multiplied by 3 and i only by 2, one molecule of fructose 6-phosphate remains.

In part (c) of the table it is shown how this fructose phosphate can then be converted into sucrose. After conversion by its isomerase into glucose 6-phosphate and by the phosphomutase into glucose 1-phosphate (reverse of reactions XII.1.d and b), it is converted into the UDP derivative by uridylyl-transfer from UTP. Another molecule of fructose phosphate is dephosphorylated by phosphatase, and the glucose is transferred to this fructose molecule from combination with UDP by the glucosyltransferase, forming a molecule of sucrose. Finally, the UTP is regenerated at the expense of ATP. It will be noted that the photosynthetic formation of a sucrose molecule from CO_2 and water requires the provision of 37 molecules of ATP by reaction b, and 24 molecules of $NADPH_2$ by reaction a.

Table XII.1

THE GLYCOLYSIS SYSTEM

XII.1.a   α-glucan phosphorylase (2.4.1.1)

Glycogen $+n$ H_3PO_4 $= n$ glucose 1-phosphate

XII.1.b   Phosphoglucomutase (2.7.5.1)

Glucose 1-phosphate $+$ glucose 1,6-diphosphate
$=$ glucose 1,6-diphosphate $+$ glucose 6-phosphate

Alternatively, starting with glucose, XII.1.a–b are replaced by XII.1.c:

XII.1.c   Hexokinase (2.7.1.1)

Glucose $+$ ATP $=$ glucose 6-phosphate $+$ ADP

XII.1.d   Glucosephosphate isomerase (5.3.1.9)

Glucose 6-phosphate $=$ fructose 6-phosphate

XII.1.e   Phosphofructokinase (2.7.1.11)

Fructose 6-phosphate $+$ ATP $=$ fructose 1,6-diphosphate $+$ ADP

XII.1.f   Aldolase (4.1.2.b)

$$
\begin{array}{ccc}
CH_2 \cdot O \cdot H_2PO_3 & & CH_2 \cdot O \cdot H_2PO_3 \\
| & & | \\
CO & & CO \\
| & & | \\
HOCH & = & CH_2OH \\
| & & \\
HCOH & & + \\
| & & \\
HCOH & & CHO \\
| & & | \\
CH_2 \cdot O \cdot H_2PO_3 & & CHOH \\
& & | \\
& & CH_2 \cdot O \cdot H_2PO_3
\end{array}
$$

Fructose 1,6-   dihydroxyacetone
diphosphate   phosphate $+$
                           D-glyceraldehyde
                           3-phosphate

XII.1.g   Triosephosphate isomerase (5.3.1.1)

$$
\begin{array}{ccc}
CH_2 \cdot O \cdot H_2PO_3 & & CH_2 \cdot O \cdot H_2PO_3 \\
| & & | \\
CO & = & CHOH \\
| & & | \\
CH_2OH & & CHO
\end{array}
$$

Dihydroxyacetone   D-glyceraldehyde
phosphate   3-phosphate

XII.1.h   Glyceraldehydephosphate dehydrogenase (1.2.1.12)

$$CH_2.O.H_2PO_3$$
$$CHOH$$
$$CHO$$
$$+ \text{HS.enzyme}$$
$$+ NAD =$$

$$CH_2.O.H_2PO_3$$
$$CHOH \quad + NADH_2$$
$$CO$$
$$S.\text{enzyme}$$

D-glyceraldehyde
3-phosphate +
dehydrogenase

3-phospho-D-glyceric
acid — enzyme
complex

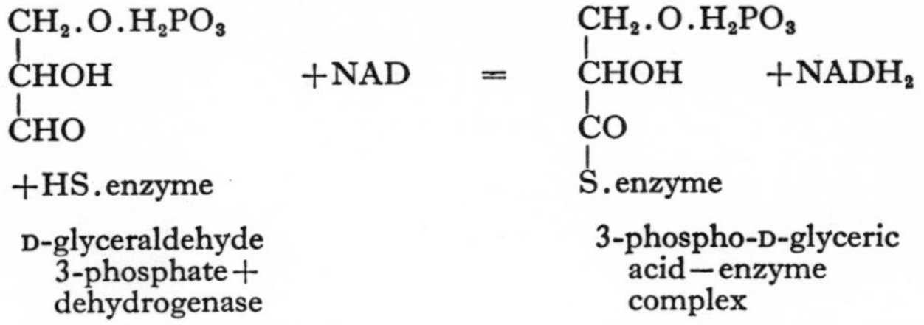

XII.1.i   Glyceraldehydephosphate dehydrogenase (1.2.1.12)

$$CH_2.O.H_2PO_3$$
$$CHOH$$
$$CO \quad + H_3PO_4$$
$$S.\text{Enzyme}$$
$$=$$

$$CH_2.O.H_2PO_3$$
$$CHOH$$
$$CO.O.H_2PO_3$$
$$+ \text{HS.Enzyme}$$

1,3-diphospho-D-glycerate

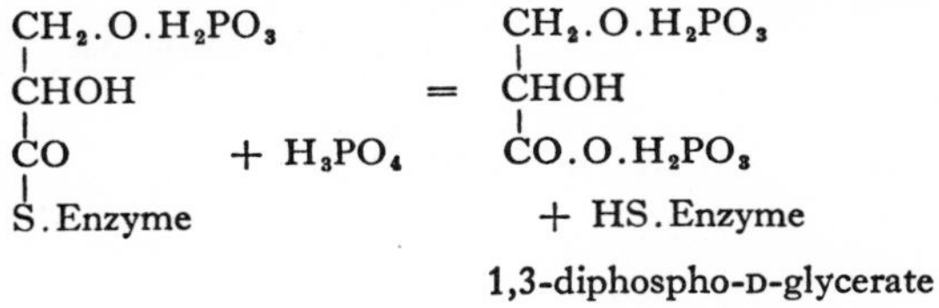

XII.1.j   Phosphoglycerate kinase (2.7.2.3)

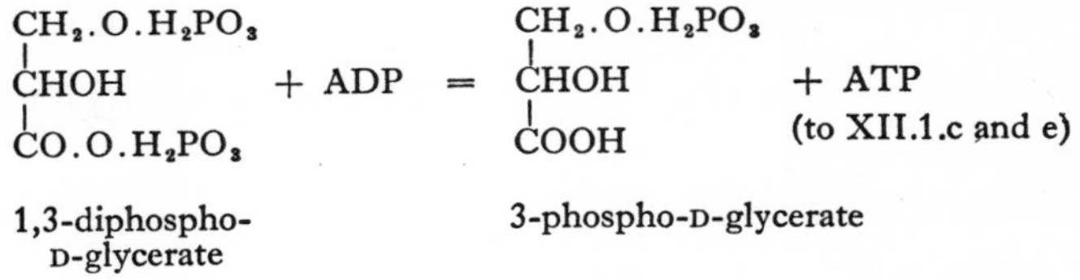

$$CH_2.O.H_2PO_3$$
$$CHOH \quad + ADP =$$
$$CO.O.H_2PO_3$$

$$CH_2.O.H_2PO_3$$
$$CHOH \qquad + ATP$$
$$COOH \qquad \text{(to XII.1.c and e)}$$

1,3-diphospho-
D-glycerate

3-phospho-D-glycerate

XII.1.k   Phosphoglyceromutase (2.7.5.3)

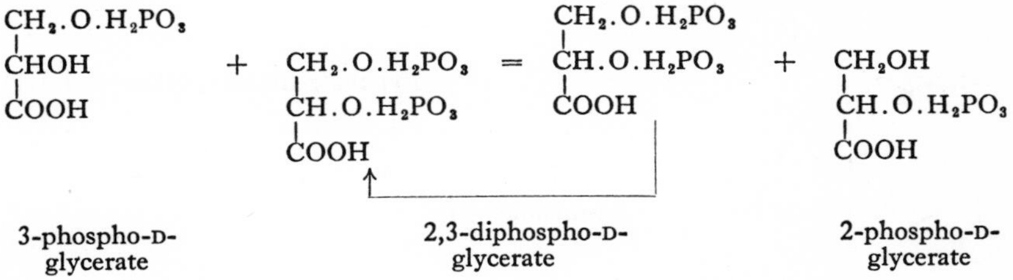

$$CH_2.O.H_2PO_3$$
$$CHOH \qquad +$$
$$COOH$$

$$CH_2.O.H_2PO_3$$
$$CH.O.H_2PO_3 \quad =$$
$$COOH$$

$$CH_2.O.H_2PO_3$$
$$CH.O.H_2PO_3 \qquad +$$
$$COOH$$

$$CH_2OH$$
$$CH.O.H_2PO_3$$
$$COOH$$

3-phospho-D-
glycerate

2,3-diphospho-D-
glycerate

2-phospho-D-
glycerate

XII.1.l   Phosphopyruvate hydratase (4.2.1.11)

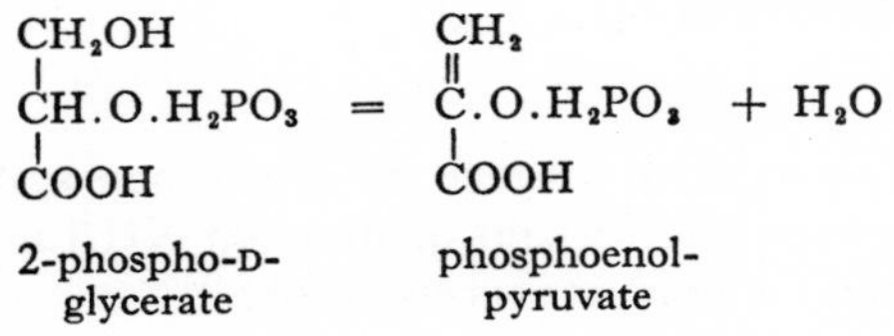

$$CH_2OH$$
$$CH.O.H_2PO_3 \quad =$$
$$COOH$$

$$CH_2$$
$$C.O.H_2PO_3 \quad + H_2O$$
$$COOH$$

2-phospho-D-
glycerate

phosphoenol-
pyruvate

XII.1.m   Pyruvate kinase (2.7.1.40)

$$\begin{array}{l} CH_2 \\ \| \\ C.O.H_2PO_3 \\ | \\ COOH \end{array} + ADP = \begin{array}{l} CH_3 \\ | \\ CO \\ | \\ COOH \end{array} + ATP$$

Phosphoenol-   pyruvate
pyruvate

If O_2 is absent, the $NADH_2$ from XII.1.h is oxidized in muscle by XII.1.n and the end-product is lactate:

XII.1.n   Lactate dehydrogenase (1.1.1.27)

$$\begin{array}{l} CH_3 \\ | \\ CO \\ | \\ COOH \end{array} + NADH_2 = \begin{array}{l} CH_3 \\ | \\ CHOH \\ | \\ COOH \end{array} + NAD$$

Pyruvate   L-lactate

In yeast the end-product is alcohol:

XII.1.o   Pyruvate decarboxylase (4.1.1.1)

$$\begin{array}{l} CH_3 \\ | \\ CO.COOH \\ \\ +thiamine\text{-}PP \end{array} = \begin{array}{l} CH_3 \\ | \\ CHOH \\ | \\ thiamine\text{-}PP \end{array} + CO_2$$

Pyruvate+   α-hydroxyethyl-
   thiamine   thiamine
   pyrophosphate   pyrophosphate

XII.1.p   Pyruvate decarboxylase (4.1.1.1)

$$\begin{array}{l} CH_3 \\ | \\ CHOH \\ | \\ thiamine\text{-}PP \end{array} = \begin{array}{l} CH_3 \\ | \\ CHO \\ \\ +thiamine\text{-}PP \end{array}$$

XII.1.q   Alcohol dehydrogenase (1.1.1.1)

$$\begin{array}{l} CH_3 \\ | \\ CHO \end{array} + NADH_2 = \begin{array}{l} CH_3 \\ | \\ CH_2OH \end{array} + NAD$$

If O_2 is present, the $NADH_2$ is oxidized through the cytochrome system and is not available for reactions XII.1.n and q. Reaction XII.1.m is then followed by XII.1.r–v and the product is acetyl-CoA:

XII.1.r Pyruvate dehydrogenase (1.2.4.1)

$$
\begin{array}{l}
CH_3 \\
| \\
CO.COOH \\
+ \text{ thiamine-PP}
\end{array}
\quad = \quad
\begin{array}{l}
CH_3 \\
| \\
CHOH + CO_2 \\
| \\
\text{thiamine-PP}
\end{array}
$$

Pyruvate +   α-hydroxyethyl-
  thiamine   thiamine
  pyrophosphate   pyrophosphate

XII.1.s Pyruvate dehydrogenase (1.2.4.1)

$$
\begin{array}{l}
CH_3 \\
| \\
CHOH \\
| \\
\text{thiamine-PP}
\end{array}
+
\begin{array}{l}
S.CH_2 \\
| \quad | \\
\quad CH_2 \\
S.CH \\
(CH_2)_4 \\
| \\
COOH
\end{array}
=
\begin{array}{l}
HS.CH_2 \\
| \\
CH_3 \quad CH_2 \\
| \quad\quad | \\
CO-S.CH \\
(CH_2)_4 \\
| \\
COOH
\end{array}
+ \text{ thiamine-PP}
$$

α-hydroxy-   oxidized   6-S-acetylhydro-
ethyl-   lipoate   lipoate
thiamine
pyrophosphate

XII.1.t Lipoate acetyltransferase (2.3.1.12)

$$
\begin{array}{l}
HS.CH_2 \\
| \\
CH_3 \quad CH_2 \\
| \quad\quad\quad | \\
CO-\!-\!-S.CH \\
(CH_2)_4 \\
| \\
COOH
\end{array}
+ CoA
\quad = \quad CH_3.CO.CoA +
\begin{array}{l}
HS.CH_2 \\
| \\
CH_2 \\
| \\
HS.CH \\
(CH_2)_4 \\
| \\
COOH
\end{array}
$$

6-S-acetylhydro-   acetyl-CoA   dihydrolipoate
lipoate

XII.1.u Lipoamide dehydrogenase (1.6.4.3)

$$
\begin{array}{l}
HS.CH_2 \\
| \\
CH_2 + NAD \\
HS.CH \\
| \\
(CH_2)_4 \\
| \\
COOH
\end{array}
=
\begin{array}{l}
S.CH_2 \\
| \quad | \\
\quad CH_2 + NADH_2 \\
S.CH \\
| \\
(CH_2)_4 \\
| \\
COOH
\end{array}
$$

Dihydro-   oxidized
lipoate   lipoate

XII.1.v NADH₂ cytochrome *c* reductase (1.6.2.1)
and cytochrome oxidase (1.9.3.1)

$$NADH_2 + \tfrac{1}{2}O_2 = NAD + H_2O$$

Sum of reactions XII.1.c–n:

$$\text{glucose} + 2ADP + 2H_3PO_4 = 2 \text{ lactic acid} + 2ATP + 2H_2O$$

Sum of reactions XII.1.c–m and o–q:

$$\text{glucose} + 2ADP + 2H_3PO_4 = 2 \text{ alcohol} + 2CO_2 + 2ATP + 2H_2O$$

Sum of reactions XII.1.c–m and r–v:

$$\text{glucose} + 2ADP + 2H_3PO_4 + 2O_2 + 2CoA$$
$$= 2 \text{ acetyl–CoA} + 2CO_2 + 2ATP + 6H_2O$$

Note.—In adding the reactions it is necessary to remember that reactions XII.1.h onwards must be multiplied by 2, since 2 triose phosphate molecules are produced from one glucose molecule (reaction XII.1.f). For this reason XII.1.j produces enough ATP to supply XII.1.c and 1.e and the ATP produced in XII.1.m is an excess, available for other purposes. XII.1.v must be multiplied by 4, to allow for the $NADH_2$ produced in XII.1.h and 1.u.

When arsenate is added, XII.1.i–j are replaced by XII.1.w–x:

XII.1.w   Glyceraldehydephosphate dehydrogenase (1.2.1.12)

$$
\begin{array}{l}
CH_2.O.H_2PO_3 \\
|\\
CHOH \\
| \qquad\qquad\qquad + H_3AsO_4 \\
CO \\
| \\
S.Enzyme
\end{array}
\quad = \quad
\begin{array}{l}
CH_2.O.H_2PO_3 \\
| \\
CHOH \\
| \\
CO.O.H_2AsO_3 \\
\\
+ HS.Enzyme
\end{array}
$$

XII.1.x   (Rapid, spontaneous)

$$
\begin{array}{l}
CH_2.O.H_2PO_3 \\
| \\
CHOH \\
| \qquad\qquad + H_2O \\
CO.O.H_2AsO_3
\end{array}
\quad = \quad
\begin{array}{l}
CH_2.O.H_2PO_3 \\
| \\
CHOH \\
| \qquad\qquad + H_3AsO_4 \\
COOH
\end{array}
$$

The coupled phosphorylation of ADP is therefore abolished.

TABLE XII.2

THE CITRIC CYCLE

This is essentially a mechanism for the oxidation of acetyl-CoA which may arise from carbohydrate (reaction XII.1.t), from fat (reaction XII.4.e) or in other ways during metabolism.

XII.2.a   Citrate synthase (4.1.3.7)

$CH_3.CO.CoA$

$+ H_2O +$ $CH_2.COOH$

$CO.COOH$ $=$ $\overset{|}{C}(OH).COOH$ $+ CoA$

$\overset{|}{C}H_2.COOH$ $\overset{|}{C}H_2.COOH$

(from XII.2.l)

Acetyl-CoA   citrate
+oxaloacetate

XII.2.b   Aconitate hydratase (4.2.1.3)

$CH_2.COOH$ $CH_2.COOH$

$\overset{|}{C}(OH).COOH$ $=$ $\overset{|}{C}.COOH$ $+ H_2O$

$\overset{|}{C}H_2.COOH$ $\overset{||}{C}H.COOH$

Citrate   cis-aconitate

XII.2.c   Aconitate hydratase (4.2.1.3)

$CH_2.COOH$ $CH_2.COOH$

$\overset{|}{C}.COOH$ $+ H_2O$ $=$ $\overset{|}{C}H.COOH$

$\overset{||}{C}H.COOH$ $\overset{|}{C}HOH.COOH$

cis-aconitate L_s-isocitrate

XII.2.d   Isocitrate dehydrogenase (1.1.1.42)

$CH_2.COOH$ $CH_2.COOH$

$\overset{|}{C}H.COOH + NADP$ $=$ $\overset{|}{C}H.COOH$ $+ NADPH_2$

$\overset{|}{C}HOH.COOH$ $\overset{|}{C}O.COOH$

L_s-isocitrate   oxalosuccinate

XII.2.e $NADPH_2$ cytochrome c reductase (1.6,2.3)
                                                and cytochrome oxidase (1.9.3.1)

$NADPH_2 + \tfrac{1}{2}O_2 = NADP + H_2O$

XII.2.f   Isocitrate dehydrogenase (1.1.1.42)

$CH_2.COOH$ $CH_2.COOH$

$\overset{|}{C}H.COOH$ $=$ $\overset{|}{C}H_2$ $+ CO_2$

$\overset{|}{C}O.COOH$ $\overset{|}{C}O.COOH$

Oxalosuccinate   2-oxoglutarate

XII.2.g   Oxoglutarate dehydrogenase (1.2.4.2)
with thiamine pyrophosphate

$$
\begin{array}{l}
CH_2.COOH \\
| \\
CH_2 \\
| \\
CO.COOH
\end{array}
+
\begin{array}{l}
S.CH_2 \\
| \quad | \\
\; \; CH_2 \\
| \\
S.CH \\
\; (CH_2)_4.COOH
\end{array}
=
\begin{array}{l}
CH_2.COOH \quad HS.CH_2 \\
| \qquad\qquad\quad | \\
CH_2 \qquad\qquad\quad CH_2 \\
| \qquad\qquad\qquad | \\
CO\text{------------}S.CH + CO_2 \\
\qquad\qquad\qquad (CH_2)_4.COOH
\end{array}
$$

2-oxoglutarate   oxidized lipoate   6-S-succinyl-hydro-
lipoate

XII.2.h   Lipoate acetyltransferase (2.3.1.12) ?

$$
\begin{array}{l}
CH_2.COOH \quad HS.CH_2 \\
| \qquad\qquad\qquad | \\
CH_2 \qquad\qquad\quad CH_2 \\
| \qquad\qquad\qquad | \\
CO\text{------------}S.CH \\
\qquad\qquad\qquad (CH_2)_4 \\
+ CoA \qquad\qquad COOH
\end{array}
=
\begin{array}{l}
CH_2.COOH \\
| \\
CH_2 \\
| \\
CO.CoA
\end{array}
+
\begin{array}{l}
HS.CH_2 \\
| \\
CH_2 \\
| \\
HS.CH \\
| \\
(CH_2)_4 \\
| \\
COOH \\
(to\ XII.1.u)
\end{array}
$$

6-S-succinyl-hydro-   succinyl-CoA   dihydrolipoate   lipoate

XII.2.i   Succinyl-CoA hydrolase (3.1.2.3)

$$
\begin{array}{l}
CH_2.COOH \\
| \\
CH_2.CO.CoA
\end{array}
+ H_2O =
\begin{array}{l}
CH_2.COOH \\
| \\
CH_2.COOH
\end{array}
+ CoA
$$

Succinyl-CoA   succinate

XII.2.j   Succinate dehydrogenase (1.3.99.1) and cytochrome oxidase (1.9.3.1)

$$
\begin{array}{l}
CH_2.COOH \\
| \\
CH_2.COOH
\end{array}
+ \tfrac{1}{2}O_2 =
\begin{array}{l}
CH.COOH \\
\| \\
CH.COOH
\end{array}
+ H_2O
$$

Succinate   fumarate

XII.2.k   Fumarate hydratase (4.2.1.2)

$$
\begin{array}{l}
CH.COOH \\
\| \\
CH.COOH
\end{array}
+ H_2O =
\begin{array}{l}
CH_2.COOH \\
| \\
CHOH.COOH
\end{array}
$$

Fumarate   L-malate

XII.2.l   Malate dehydrogenase (1.1.1.37)

$$
\begin{array}{l}
CH_2.COOH \\
| \\
CHOH.COOH
\end{array}
+ NAD =
\begin{array}{l}
CH_2.COOH \\
| \\
CO.COOH
\end{array}
+
\begin{array}{l}
NADH_2 \\
(to\ XII.1.v)
\end{array}
$$

L-malate   oxaloacetate
(to XII.2.a)

Sum of reactions:

$$\text{Acetyl-CoA} + 2O_2 = 2CO_2 + H_2O + CoA$$

This system may involve the formation of ATP from ADP if reaction XII.2.i is replaced by the following:

XII.2.m Succinyl-CoA synthetase (6.2.1.4)

$$\begin{array}{c} CH_2.COOH \\ | \\ CH_2.CO.CoA \end{array} + GDP + H_3PO_4 = \begin{array}{c} CH_2.COOH \\ | \\ CH_2.COOH \end{array} + GTP + CoA$$

Succinyl-CoA   succinate

XII.2.n Nucleosidediphosphate kinase (2.7.4.6)

$$GTP + ADP = GDP + ATP$$

Acetyl-CoA can also react in other ways, e.g.

(a) conversion into fat, see Table XII.4;
(b) acetylation reactions by any of the enzymes 2.3.1.1–16, including formation of acetyl-phosphate by phosphate acetyltransferase (2.3.1.8) in bacteria;
(c) simple hydrolysis to acetate and CoA by acetyl-CoA hydrolase (3.1.2.1);
(d) formation of ATP from AMP and pyrophosphate by acetyl-CoA synthetase (6.2.1.1);
(e) conversion into mevalonate, and hence into the numerous isoprenoid compounds, see Table XII.13;
(f) conversion by the glyoxylate cycle into C_4-dicarboxylic acids, used for biosyntheses, see Table XII.3.

TABLE XII.3

THE GLYOXYLATE CYCLE IN PLANTS AND MICRO-ORGANISMS

XII.3.a Citrate synthase (4.1.3.7)

$$\begin{array}{l} CH_3.CO.CoA \\ \quad +H_2O+ \\ CO.COOH \\ | \\ CH_2.COOH \end{array} = \begin{array}{l} CH_2.COOH \\ | \\ C(OH).COOH \\ | \\ CH_2.COOH \end{array} + CoA$$

(from XII.3.f)
Acetyl-CoA+ oxaloacetate — citrate

XII.3.b Aconitate hydratase (4.2.1.3)

$$\begin{array}{l} CH_2.COOH \\ | \\ C(OH).COOH \\ | \\ CH_2.COOH \end{array} = \begin{array}{l} CH_2.COOH \\ | \\ C.COOH \\ \| \\ CH.COOH \end{array} + H_2O$$

Citrate — *cis*-aconitate

XII.3.c Aconitate hydratase (4.2.1.3)

$$\begin{array}{l} CH_2.COOH \\ | \\ C.COOH \\ \| \\ CH.COOH \end{array} + H_2O = \begin{array}{l} CH_2.COOH \\ | \\ CH.COOH \\ | \\ CHOH.COOH \end{array}$$

cis-aconitate — L_s-isocitrate

XII.3.d Isocitrate lyase (4.1.3.1)

$$\begin{array}{l} CH_2.COOH \\ | \\ CH.COOH \\ | \\ CHOH.COOH \end{array} = \begin{array}{l} CH_2.COOH \\ | \\ CH_2.COOH \\ \quad + \\ CHO.COOH \end{array}$$

L_s-isocitrate — succinate+ glyoxylate

XII.3.e Malate synthase (4.1.3.2)

$$\begin{array}{l} CH_3.CO.CoA \\ \quad + H_2O + \\ CHO.COOH \end{array} = \begin{array}{l} CH_2.COOH + CoA \\ | \\ CHOH.COOH \end{array}$$

Acetyl-CoA+ glyoxylate — L-malate

XII.3.f Malate dehydrogenase (1.1.1.37)

$$\begin{array}{l} CH_2.COOH \\ | \\ CHOH.COOH \end{array} + NAD = \begin{array}{l} CH_2.COOH \\ | \\ CO.COOH \end{array} + NADH_2$$

(to XII.1.v)

L-malate — oxaloacetate (to XII.3.a)

Sum of reactions:

$$2\ \text{acetyl-CoA} + H_2O + \tfrac{1}{2}O_2 = \text{succinate} + 2\ \text{CoA}$$

Table XII.4

FATTY ACID BREAKDOWN AND SYNTHESIS

(a) *Breakdown*

XII.4.a Acyl-CoA synthetase (6.2.1.2 or 3)

$$R.CH_2.CH_2.COOH + CoA + ATP$$
$$= R.CH_2.CH_2.CO.CoA + AMP + \text{pyrophosphate}$$

XII.4.b Acyl-CoA dehydrogenase (1.3.2.2) and cytochrome oxidase (1.9.3.1)

$$R.CH_2.CH_2.CO.CoA + \tfrac{1}{2}O_2 = R.CH{=}CH.CO.CoA + H_2O$$

XII.4.c Enoyl-CoA hydratase (4.2.1.17)

$$R.CH{=}CH.CO.CoA + H_2O = R.CHOH.CH_2.CO.CoA$$

XII.4.d 3-hydroxyacyl-CoA dehydrogenase (1.1.1.35)

$$R.CHOH.CH_2.CO.CoA + NAD = R.CO.CH_2.CO.CoA + NADH_2$$

XII.4.e Acetyl-CoA acyltransferase (2.3.1.16)

$$R.CO.CH_2.CO.CoA + CoA = R.CO.CoA + CH_3.CO.CoA$$

The result of these reactions is a shortening of the fatty acid chain by two carbon atoms. By successive repetitions of reactions XII.3.b–e complete breakdown to acetyl-CoA may be brought about. In the later stages enzymes 1.3.2.2 and 2.3.1.16 are replaced by 1.3.2.1 and 2.3.1.9 respectively.

(b) *Synthesis* (according to Lynen, *1635*)

XII.4.f Acetyl-CoA carboxylase (6.4.1.2)

$$CO_2 + CH_3.CO.CoA + H_2O + ATP = \begin{array}{l} COOH \\ | \\ CH_2.CO.CoA \end{array} + ADP + H_3PO_4$$

XII.4.g Enzyme complex

$$\begin{array}{l} COOH \\ | \\ CH_2.CO.CoA \end{array} + HS.\text{enzyme} = \begin{array}{l} COOH \\ | \\ CH_2.CO.S.\text{enzyme} \end{array} + CoA$$

XII.4.h Enzyme complex

$$R.CO.CoA + \begin{array}{l} COOH \\ | \\ CH_2.CO.S.\text{enzyme} \end{array}$$
$$= R.CO.CH_2.CO.S.\text{enzyme} + CO_2 + CoA$$

XII.4.i Enzyme complex

$$R.CO.CH_2.CO.S.\text{enzyme} + NADPH_2$$
$$= R.CHOH.CH_2.CO.S.\text{enzyme} + NADP$$

XII.4.j   Enzyme complex

$$R.CHOH.CH_2.CO.S.enzyme = R.CH=CH.CO.S.enzyme + H_2O$$

XII.4.k   Enzyme complex

$$R.CH=CH.CO.S.enzyme + NADPH_2$$
$$= R.CH_2.CH_2.CO.S.enzyme + NADP$$

XII.4.l   Enzyme complex

$$R.CH_2.CH_2.CO.S.enzyme + CoA$$
$$= R.CH_2.CH_2.CO.CoA + HS.enzyme$$

By successive repetitions of reactions XII.4.h–l, long-chain acids may be built up from malonyl-CoA.

TABLE XII.5

THE GLUCOSE 6-PHOSPHATE OXIDATION SYSTEM

XII.5.a   Glucose-6-phosphate dehydrogenase (1.1.1.49)

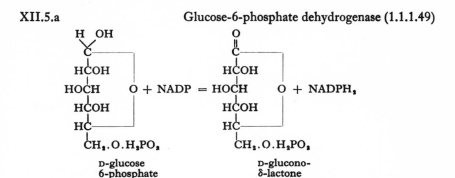

$$
\begin{array}{cccc}
\text{H\ \ OH} & & \text{O} & \\
\diagdown\text{C}\diagup & & \parallel & \\
\text{C} & & \text{C} & \\
| & & | & \\
\text{HCOH} & & \text{HCOH} & \\
| & & | & \\
\text{HOCH} & \text{O + NADP} = \text{HOCH} & \text{O + NADPH}_2 \\
| & & | & \\
\text{HCOH} & & \text{HCOH} & \\
| & & | & \\
\text{HC} & & \text{HC} & \\
| & & | & \\
\text{CH}_2.\text{O}.\text{H}_2\text{PO}_3 & & \text{CH}_2.\text{O}.\text{H}_2\text{PO}_3 &
\end{array}
$$

D-glucose 6-phosphate   D-glucono-δ-lactone 6-phosphate

XII.5.b   Gluconolactonase (3.1.1.17)

$$
\begin{array}{cc}
\text{O} & \\
\parallel & \\
\text{C} & \text{COOH} \\
| & | \\
\text{HCOH} & \text{HCOH} \\
| & | \\
\text{HOCH} \quad \text{O + H}_2\text{O} = \text{HOCH} \\
| & | \\
\text{HCOH} & \text{HCOH} \\
| & | \\
\text{HC} & \text{HCOH} \\
| & | \\
\text{CH}_2.\text{O}.\text{H}_2\text{PO}_3 & \text{CH}_2.\text{O}.\text{H}_2\text{PO}_3
\end{array}
$$

D-glucono-δ-lactone 6-phosphate   6-phospho-D-gluconate

XII.5.c   Phosphogluconate dehydrogenase (1.1.1.44)

$$
\begin{array}{cc}
\text{COOH} & +\text{CO}_2 \\
| & \\
\text{HCOH} & \text{CH}_2\text{OH} \\
| & | \\
\text{HOCH + NADP} = & \text{CO} \quad + \text{NADPH}_2 \\
| & | \\
\text{HCOH} & \text{HCOH} \\
| & | \\
\text{HCOH} & \text{HCOH} \\
| & | \\
\text{CH}_2.\text{O}.\text{H}_2\text{PO}_3 & \text{CH}_2.\text{O}.\text{H}_2\text{PO}_3
\end{array}
$$

6-phospho-D-gluconate   D-ribulose 5-phosphate

XII.5.d   Ribulosephosphate 3-epimerase (5.1.3.1)

$$
\begin{array}{ccc}
CH_2OH & & CH_2OH \\
| & & | \\
CO & & CO \\
| & & | \\
HCOH & = & HOCH \\
| & & | \\
HCOH & & HCOH \\
| & & | \\
CH_2.O.H_2PO_3 & & CH_2.O.H_2PO_3
\end{array}
$$

D-ribulose   D-xylulose
5-phosphate   5-phosphate

XII.5.e   Transketolase (2.2.1.1)

$$
\begin{array}{ccccccc}
CH_2OH & & & & & & CH_2OH \\
| & & & & & & | \\
CO & & & & & & CO \\
| & & | & & | & & | \\
HOCH & + & CHO & & CHO & + & HOCH \\
| & & | & & | & & | \\
HCOH & & HCOH & = & HCOH & & HCOH \\
| & & | & & | & & | \\
CH_2.O.H_2PO_3 & & HCOH & & CH_2.O.H_2PO_3 & & HCOH \\
& & | & & & & | \\
& & HCOH & & & & HCOH \\
& & | & & & & | \\
& & CH_2.O.H_2PO_3 & & & & CH_2.O.H_2PO \\
\end{array}
$$

(from XII.5.i)

D-xylulose   D-ribose   D-glyceraldehyde   D-sedoheptulose
5-phosphate   5-phosphate   3-phosphate   7-phosphate

XII.5.f   Transaldolase (2.2.1.2)

$$
\begin{array}{ccccccc}
 & & CH_2OH & & CH_2OH & & \\
 & & | & & | & & \\
 & & CO & & CO & & \\
 & & | & & | & & \\
 & & HOCH & & HOCH & & \\
| & & | & & | & & | \\
CHO & + & HCOH & = & HCOH & + & CHO \\
| & & | & & | & & | \\
HCOH & & HCOH & & HCOH & & HCOH \\
| & & | & & | & & | \\
CH_2.O.H_2PO_3 & & HCOH & & CH_2.O.H_2PO_3 & & HCOH \\
& & | & & & & | \\
& & CH_2.O.H_2PO_3 & & & & CH_2.O.H_2PO \\
\end{array}
$$

D-glyceraldehyde   D-sedoheptulose   D-fructose   D-erythrose
3-phosphate   7-phosphate   6-phosphate   4-phosphate

XII.5.g — Glucosephosphate isomerase (5.3.1.9)

```
   CH₂OH              CHO               H  OH
    |                  |                 C————
    CO                HCOH              HCOH    |
    |                  |                 |      |
  HOCH       =       HOCH     or       HOCH    O
    |                  |                 |      |
   HCOH               HCOH             HCOH     |
    |                  |                 |      |
   HCOH               HCOH              HC——————
    |                  |                 |
   CH₂.O.H₂PO₃        CH₂.O.H₂PO₃       CH₂.O.H₂PO₃
                                        (to XII.5.a′–d′)

 D-fructose          D-glucose
 6-phosphate         6-phosphate
```

XII.5.h — Transketolase (2.2.1.1)

```
  CH₂OH                                               CH₂OH
   |                                                   |
   CO                                                  CO
   |                                                   |
 HOCH        +      CHO          =      CHO      +    HOCH
   |                 |                    |             |
  HCOH              HCOH                 HCOH          HCOH
   |                 |                    |             |
  CH₂.O.H₂PO₃       HCOH                 CH₂.O.H₂PO₃   HCOH
  (from XII.5.d′)    |                                  |
                    CH₂.O.H₂PO₃                         CH₂.O.H₂PO₃
                    (from XII.5.f)                      (to XII.5.g″–c″)

 D-xylulose         D-erythrose          D-glyceraldehyde   D-fructose
 5-phosphate        4-phosphate          3-phosphate        6-phosphate
```

XII.5.i — Ribosephosphate isomerase (5.3.1.6)

```
   CH₂OH              CHO
    |                  |
    CO                HCOH
    |                  |
   HCOH       =       HCOH
    |                  |
   HCOH               HCOH
    |                  |
   CH₂.O.H₂PO₃        CH₂.O.H₂PO₃
   (from XII.5.c″)    (to XII.5.e)

 D-ribulose          D-ribose
 5-phosphate         5-phosphate
```

XII.5.j — Triosephosphate isomerase (5.3.1.1)

```
   CHO                CH₂OH
    |                  |
   HCOH       =        CO
    |                  |
   CH₂.O.H₂PO₃        CH₂.O.H₂PO₃
   (from XII.5.h)

 D-glyceraldehyde    dihydroxyacetone
 3-phosphate         phosphate
```

XII.5.k   Aldolase (4.1.2.b)

$$
\begin{array}{ccc}
CH_2.O.H_2PO_3 & & CH_2.O.H_2PO_3 \\
| & & | \\
CO & & CO \\
| & & | \\
CH_2OH & & HOCH \\
+ & = & HCOH \\
& & | \\
CHO & & HCOH \\
| & & | \\
HCOH & & CH_2.O.H_2PO_3 \\
| & & \\
CH_2.O.H_2PO_3 & & \\
\text{(from XII.5.h)} & &
\end{array}
$$

Dihydroxyacetone   D-fructose
phosphate + D-glyceraldehyde   1,6-diphosphate
3-phosphate

XII.5.l   Hexosediphosphatase (3.1.3.11)

$$
\begin{array}{ccc}
CH_2.O.H_2PO_3 & & CH_2OH \quad + \; H_3PO_4 \\
| & & | \\
CO & + H_2O & CO \\
| & & | \\
HOCH & = & HOCH \\
| & & | \\
HCOH & & HCOH \\
| & & | \\
HCOH & & HCOH \\
| & & | \\
CH_2.O.H_2PO_3 & & CH_2.O.H_2PO_3
\end{array}
$$

D-fructose   D-fructose
1,6-diphosphate   6-phosphate

XII.5.m   Glucosephosphate isomerase (5.3.1.9)

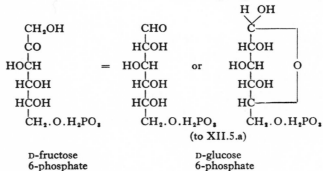

$$
\begin{array}{ccccc}
CH_2OH & & CHO & & \overset{H \; OH}{\underset{|}{C}} \\
| & & | & & | \\
CO & & HCOH & & HCOH \\
| & & | & & | \\
HOCH & = & HOCH & or & HOCH \qquad O \\
| & & | & & | \\
HCOH & & HCOH & & HCOH \\
| & & | & & | \\
HCOH & & HCOH & & HC \\
| & & | & & | \\
CH_2.O.H_2PO_3 & & CH_2.O.H_2PO_3 & & CH_2.O.H_2PO_3
\end{array}
$$

                                        (to XII.5.a)

D-fructose   D-glucose
6-phosphate   6-phosphate

Sum of reactions:

glucose 6-phosphate + 12NADP + 7H$_2$O = 6CO$_2$ + 12NADPH$_2$ + H$_3$PO$_4$

TABLE XII.6

A HYDROGEN-TRANSPORT SYSTEM IN PLANTS (*2964*)

XII.6.a   Dehydrogenases

$$AH_2 + NAD = A + NADH_2$$

XII.6.b   Glyoxylate reductase (1.1.1.26)

$$NADH_2 \; + \; \begin{matrix} COOH \\ | \\ CHO \end{matrix} \; = \; NAD \; + \; \begin{matrix} COOH \\ | \\ CH_2OH \end{matrix}$$

           Glyoxylate   glycollate

XII.6.c   Glycollate oxidase (1.1.3.1)

$$\begin{matrix} COOH \\ | \\ CH_2OH \end{matrix} + O_2 \; = \; \begin{matrix} COOH \\ | \\ CHO \end{matrix} + H_2O_2$$

   Glycollate   glyoxylate

Sum of reactions:

$$AH_2 + O_2 = A + H_2O_2$$

AH_2 represents various substrates of NAD-specific dehydrogenases. There is evidence that this system plays an important part in plant respiration.

TABLE XII.7

PHENYLALANINE OXIDATION SYSTEM

XII.7.a   Phenylalanine 4-hydroxylase (1.99.1.2)

$$
\begin{array}{l}
C_6H_5 \\
|\\
CH_2 \\
|\\
CH.NH_2 \\
|\\
COOH
\end{array}
\quad + \tfrac{1}{2}O_2 \qquad
\begin{array}{l}
C_6H_4OH \\
|\\
CH_2 \\
|\\
CH.NH_2 \\
|\\
COOH
\end{array}
$$

$=$

L-phenyl-
alanine   L-tyrosine

XII.7.b   Tyrosine aminotransferase (2.6.1.5)

$$
\begin{array}{l}
C_6H_4OH \\
|\\
CH_2 \\
|\\
CH.NH_2 \\
|\\
COOH
\end{array}
\; + \;
\begin{array}{l}
CH_2.COOH \\
|\\
CH_2 \\
|\\
CO.COOH \\
\text{(from XII.2.f)}
\end{array}
\; = \;
\begin{array}{l}
C_6H_4OH \\
|\\
CH_2 \\
|\\
CO \\
|\\
COOH
\end{array}
\; + \;
\begin{array}{l}
CH_2.COOH \\
|\\
CH_2 \\
|\\
CH.NH_2 \\
|\\
COOH
\end{array}
$$

L-tyrosine   2-oxoglutarate   p-hydroxyphenyl-   L-glutamate
                             pyruvate

XII.7.c   p-hydroxyphenylpyruvate hydroxylase (1.99.1.14)

p-hydroxyphenyl-
pyruvate   homogentisate

XII.7.d   Homogentisate oxygenase (1.99.2.5)

Homogentisate   4-maleylacetoacetate

XII.7.e   Maleylacetoacetate isomerase (5.2.1.2)

$$
\begin{array}{ccc}
\text{HC.COOH} & & \text{HOOC.CH} \\
\| & & \| \\
\text{HC.CO} & & \text{HC.CO} \\
| & & | \\
\text{CH}_2 & = & \text{CH}_2 \\
| & & | \\
\text{CO} & & \text{CO} \\
| & & | \\
\text{CH}_2.\text{COOH} & & \text{CH}_2.\text{COOH}
\end{array}
$$

4-maleylaceto-   4-fumarylacetoacetate
acetate

XII.7.f   Fumarylacetoacetase (3.7.1.2)

$$
\begin{array}{ccc}
\text{HOOC.CH} & & \text{HOOC.CH} \\
\| & & \| \\
\text{HC.CO} & & \text{HC.COOH} \quad \text{(to XII.2.k)} \\
| & & \\
\text{CH}_2 + \text{H}_2\text{O} = & & + \\
| & & \\
\text{CO} & & \text{CH}_3 \\
| & & | \\
\text{CH}_2.\text{COOH} & & \text{CO} \\
& & | \\
& & \text{CH}_2.\text{COOH}
\end{array}
$$

4-fumarylacetoacetate   fumarate+acetoacetate

XII.7.g   3-ketoacid CoA-transferase (2.8.3.5)

$$
\begin{array}{cccc}
\text{CO.CH}_3 & \text{HOOC.CH}_2 & \text{CO.CH}_3 & \text{HOOC.CH}_2 \\
| \quad + & | & = \quad | \quad + & | \\
\text{CH}_2.\text{COOH} & \text{CoA.OC.CH}_2 & \text{CH}_2.\text{CO.CoA} & \text{HOOC.CH}_2 \\
& \text{(from XII.2.h)} & & \text{(to XII.2.j)}
\end{array}
$$

Acetoacetate   succinyl-CoA   acetoacetyl-CoA   succinate

XII.7.h   Acetyl-CoA acetyltransferase (2.3.1.9)

$$
\begin{array}{cc}
\text{CH}_3 & \text{CH}_3 \\
| & | \\
\text{CO} + \text{CoA} & \text{CO.CoA} \\
| & \\
\text{CH}_2 & = \quad + \\
| & \\
\text{CO.CoA} & \text{CH}_3 \\
& | \\
& \text{CO.CoA}
\end{array}
$$

Acetoacetyl-CoA   2 acetyl-CoA
                        (to XII.2.a)

TABLE XII.8

THE GLYOXALASE SYSTEM

XII.8.a   Lactoyl-glutathione lyase (4.4.1.5)

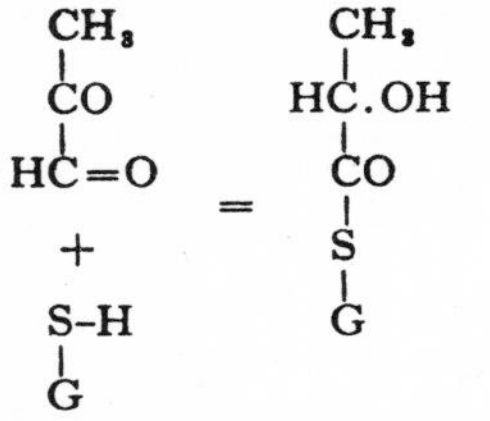

```
  CH₃              CH₃
  |                |
  CO               HC.OH
  |                |
  HC=O      =      CO
                   |
  +                S
                   |
  S-H              G
  |
  G
```

Methylglyoxal +   S-lactoyl-
reduced   glutathione
glutathione

XII.8.b   Hydroxyacylglutathione hydrolase (3.1.2.6)

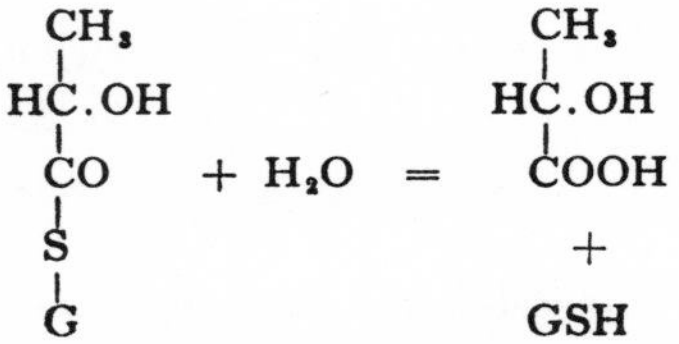

```
  CH₃                        CH₃
  |                          |
  HC.OH                      HC.OH
  |                          |
  CO    + H₂O     =          COOH
  |
  S                          +
  |
  G                          GSH
```

S-lactoyl-   lactate +
glutathione   glutathione

TABLE XII.9

THE GALACTOSE-INVERTING SYSTEM

(a) Formation of the 'coenzyme'

XII.9.a   Nucleosidediphosphate kinase (2.7.4.6)

$\quad$ UDP+ATP = UTP+ADP

XII.9.b   Galactokinase (2.7.1.6)

$\quad$ D-galactose+ATP = α-D-galactose 1-phosphate+ADP

XII.9.c   Galactose-1-phosphate uridylyltransferase (2.7.7.10)

$\quad$ α-D-galactose 1-phosphate+UTP = UDPgalactose+pyrophosphate

Alternatively, when the system is catalysing the reverse reaction,

XII.9.d   Glucose-1-phosphate uridylyltransferase (2.7.7.9)

$\quad$ α-D-glucose 1-phosphate+UTP = UDPglucose+pyrophosphate

(b) Inversion of the sugar

When once the 'coenzyme' is formed, the process can proceed continuously by the following mechanism:

XII.9.e   UDPglucose epimerase (5.1.3.2)+NAD

$\quad$ UDPgalactose ⇌ UDPglucose

XII.9.f   Hexose-1-phosphate uridylyltransferase (2.7.7.12)

$\quad$ UDPglucose+α-D-galactose 1-phosphate ⇌
$\qquad\qquad\qquad$ UDPgalactose+α-D-glucose 1-phosphate

TABLE XII.10

METHIONINE METABOLISM

XII.10.a   Methionine adenosyltransferase (2.4.2.13)

$$\text{L-methionine} + \text{ATP} + H_2O =$$

$$
CH_3 . \overset{+}{S}
\begin{array}{l}
\text{---------} CH_2 \\
| \quad\quad\quad | \\
CH_2 \quad\quad HC\text{----} \\
| \quad\quad\quad | \\
CH_2 \quad\quad HCOH \\
| \quad\quad\quad | \quad\quad O \\
CH.NH_2 \quad HCOH \\
| \quad\quad\quad | \\
COOH \quad\quad HC\text{----} \\
\quad\quad\quad\quad | \\
\quad\quad\quad Adenine
\end{array}
\quad + \text{phosphate} \\
\quad + \text{pyrophosphate}
$$

S-adenosylmethionine

XII.10.b   Methyltransferases (2.1.1.a, etc.)

$$
X + CH_3.\overset{+}{S}\text{---------}CH_2 \;\cdots\; =\; CH_3.\overset{+}{X} + S\text{---------}CH_2 \;\cdots
$$

S-adenosylmethionine   S-adenosylhomocysteine

X represents a variety of methyl acceptors, e.g. nicotinamide.

XII.10.c   Adenosylhomocysteinase (3.3.1.1)

$$
\begin{array}{l}
S\text{---------}CH_2 \\
| \quad\quad\quad | \\
CH_2 \quad\quad HC\text{----} \\
| \quad\quad\quad | \\
CH_2 \quad\quad HCOH \\
| \quad\quad\quad | \quad\quad O \\
CH.NH_2 \quad HCOH \\
| \quad\quad\quad | \\
COOH \quad\quad HC\text{----} \\
\quad\quad\quad\quad | \\
\quad\quad\quad Adenine
\end{array}
+ H_2O =
\begin{array}{l}
SH \\
| \\
CH_2 \\
| \\
CH_2 \\
| \\
CH.NH_2 \\
| \\
COOH
\end{array}
+ \text{adenosine}
$$

S-adenosylhomocysteine   L-homocysteine

XII.10.d   L-serine dehydratase (4.2.1.13)

$$
\begin{array}{l}
SH \\
| \\
CH_2 \\
| \\
CH_2 \\
| \\
CH.NH_2 \\
| \\
COOH
\end{array}
+
\begin{array}{l}
HO.CH_2 \\
| \\
CH.NH_2 \\
| \\
COOH
\end{array}
=
\begin{array}{l}
CH_2\text{---}S\text{---}CH_2 \\
| \quad\quad\quad\quad | \\
CH_2 \quad\quad CH.NH_2 \\
| \quad\quad\quad\quad | \\
CH.NH_2 \quad COOH \\
| \\
COOH
\end{array}
+ H_2O
$$

L-homocysteine   L-serine   cystathionine

XII.10.e   Homoserine dehydratase (4.2.1.15)

$$\begin{array}{ll}
CH_2\!-\!\!-S\!-\!\!-CH_2 & \\
| \qquad\qquad | & \\
CH_2 \qquad\quad CH.NH_2 & \\
| \qquad\qquad | & +H_2O \\
CH.NH_2 \quad\;\; COOH & \\
| & \\
COOH &
\end{array}
=
\begin{array}{ll}
CH_3 \qquad\quad CH_2SH & \\
| \qquad\qquad | & \\
CH_2 \qquad\quad CH.NH_2 & \\
| \qquad\qquad | & \\
CO + NH_3 + COOH & \\
| & \\
COOH &
\end{array}$$

          Cystathionine   2-oxobutyrate   L-cysteine

TABLE XII.11

GLYCOGEN SYNTHESIS

XII.11.a   Glucokinase (2.7.1.2)

Glucose+ATP = glucose 6-phosphate+ADP

XII.11.b   Phosphoglucomutase (2.7.5.1)

Glucose 6-phosphate+glucose 1,6-diphosphate =
glucose 1,6-diphosphate+glucose 1-phosphate

XII.11.c   Nucleosidediphosphate kinase (2.7.4.6)

UDP+ATP = UTP+ADP

XII.11.d   Glucose-1-phosphate uridylyltransferase (2.7.7.9)

Glucose 1-phosphate+UTP = pyrophosphate+UDPglucose

XII.11.e   UDPglucose-glycogen glucosyltransferase (2.4.1.11)

UDPglucose+(glycogen)$_n$ = UDP+(glycogen)$_{n+1}$
where n denotes the number of glucose units in the molecule.

TABLE XII.12

INTERCONVERSION OF PENTOSES IN LACTOBACILLUS (1047)

(a) *From D-ribose*

XII.12.a   Ribokinase (2.7.1.15)

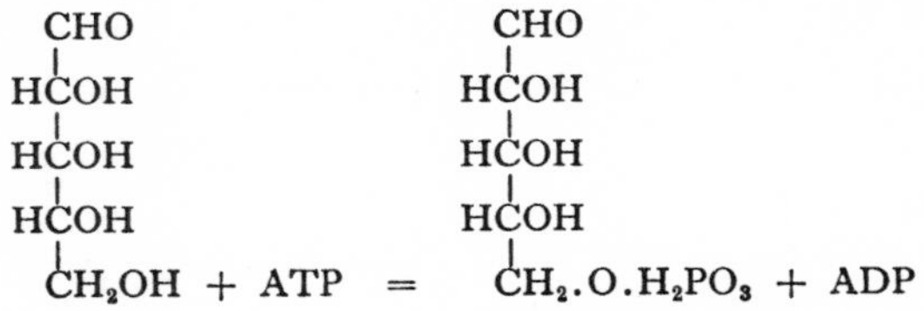

```
    CHO                    CHO
    |                      |
   HCOH                   HCOH
    |                      |
   HCOH                   HCOH
    |                      |
   HCOH                   HCOH
    |                      |
   CH₂OH + ATP   =        CH₂.O.H₂PO₃ + ADP

  D-ribose              D-ribose 5-phosphate
```

$$
\begin{array}{cc}
CHO & CHO \\
HCOH & HCOH \\
HCOH & HCOH \\
HCOH & HCOH \\
CH_2OH + ATP = & CH_2.O.H_2PO_3 + ADP
\end{array}
$$

D-ribose   D-ribose 5-phosphate

XII.12.b   Ribosephosphate isomerase (5.3.1.6)

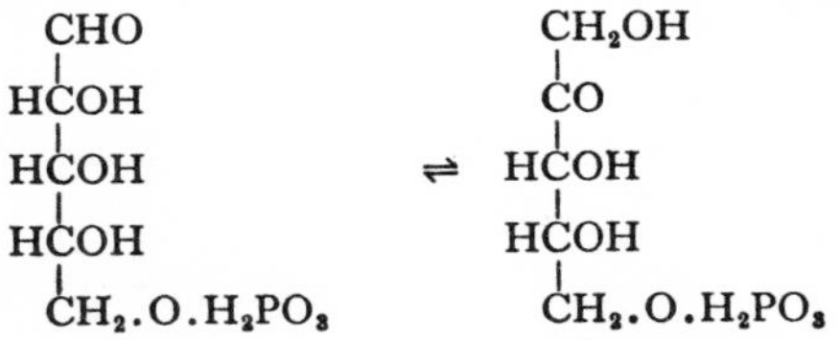

```
    CHO                    CH₂OH
    |                      |
   HCOH                    CO
    |                      |
   HCOH          ⇌        HCOH
    |                      |
   HCOH                   HCOH
    |                      |
   CH₂.O.H₂PO₃            CH₂.O.H₂PO₃

  D-ribose               D-ribulose
  5-phosphate            5-phosphate
```

XII.12.c   Ribulosephosphate 3-epimerase (5.1.3.1)

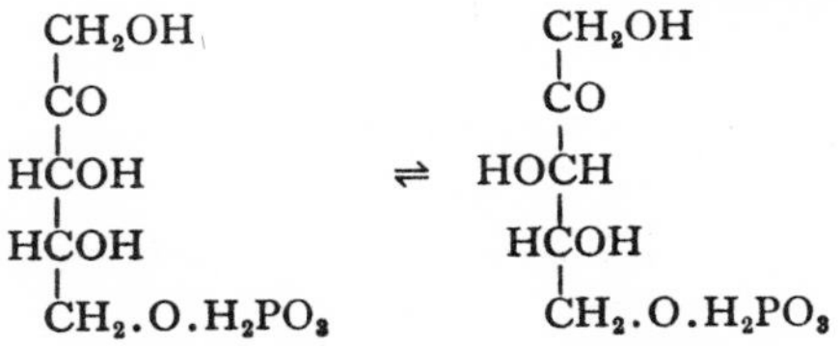

```
    CH₂OH                  CH₂OH
    |                      |
    CO                     CO
    |                      |
   HCOH          ⇌        HOCH
    |                      |
   HCOH                   HCOH
    |                      |
   CH₂.O.H₂PO₃            CH₂.O.H₂PO₃

  D-ribulose             D-xylulose
  5-phosphate            5-phosphate
```

(b) *From D-xylose*

XII.12.d   Xylose isomerase (5.3.1.5)

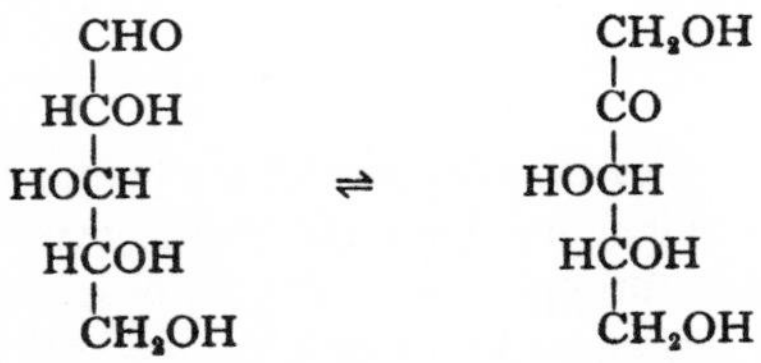

```
    CHO                    CH₂OH
    |                      |
   HCOH                    CO
    |                      |
   HOCH          ⇌        HOCH
    |                      |
   HCOH                   HCOH
    |                      |
   CH₂OH                  CH₂OH

  D-xylose               D-xylulose
```

XII.12.e   Xylulokinase (2.7.1.17)

$$\begin{array}{ccc}
\text{CH}_2\text{OH} & & \text{CH}_2\text{OH} \\
| & & | \\
\text{CO} & & \text{CO} \\
| & & | \\
\text{HOCH} & = & \text{HOCH} \\
| & & | \\
\text{HCOH} & & \text{HCOH} \\
| & & | \\
\text{CH}_2\text{OH} + \text{ATP} & & \text{CH}_2.\text{O}.\text{H}_2\text{PO}_3 + \text{ADP}
\end{array}$$

D-xylulose   D-xylulose 5-phosphate

(c) *From* L-*arabinose*

XII.12.f   Arabinose isomerase (5.3.1.4)

$$\begin{array}{ccc}
\text{CHO} & & \text{CH}_2\text{OH} \\
| & & | \\
\text{HCOH} & & \text{CO} \\
| & & | \\
\text{HOCH} & \rightleftharpoons & \text{HOCH} \\
| & & | \\
\text{HOCH} & & \text{HOCH} \\
| & & | \\
\text{CH}_2\text{OH} & & \text{CH}_2\text{OH}
\end{array}$$

L-arabinose   L-ribulose

XII.12.g   Ribulokinase (2.7.1.16)

$$\begin{array}{ccc}
\text{CH}_2\text{OH} & & \text{CH}_2\text{OH} \\
| & & | \\
\text{CO} & & \text{CO} \\
| & & | \\
\text{HOCH} & = & \text{HOCH} \\
| & & | \\
\text{HOCH} & & \text{HOCH} \\
| & & | \\
\text{CH}_2\text{OH} + \text{ATP} & & \text{CH}_2.\text{O}.\text{H}_2\text{PO}_3 + \text{ADP}
\end{array}$$

L-ribulose   L-ribulose 5-phosphate

XII.12.h   Ribulosephosphate 4-epimerase (5.1.3.a)

$$\begin{array}{ccc}
\text{CH}_2\text{OH} & & \text{CH}_2\text{OH} \\
| & & | \\
\text{CO} & & \text{CO} \\
| & & | \\
\text{HOCH} & \rightleftharpoons & \text{HOCH} \\
| & & | \\
\text{HOCH} & & \text{HCOH} \\
| & & | \\
\text{CH}_2.\text{O}.\text{H}_2\text{PO}_3 & & \text{CH}_2.\text{O}.\text{H}_2\text{PO}_3
\end{array}$$

L-ribulose   D-xylulose
5-phosphate   5-phosphate

Since D-xylulose 5-phosphate is formed in all cases, and all the reactions (with the exception of the kinase reactions) are freely reversible, many of the above sugars are interconvertible through D-xylulose 5-phosphate. It is also the key intermediate in the fermentative breakdown of all the sugars, thus:

(d) *Breakdown*

XII.12.i   Phosphoketolase (4.1.2.9)

$$\begin{array}{c} CH_2OH \\ | \\ CO \\ | \\ HOCH \\ | \\ HCOH \\ | \\ CH_2.O.H_2PO_3 \end{array} + H_3PO_4 \quad = \quad \begin{array}{c} CH_3 \\ | \\ CO.O.H_2PO_3 \\ + \\ CHO \\ | \\ HCOH \quad \text{(to XII.1.h)} \\ | \\ CH_2.O.H_2PO_3 \end{array} \quad + H_2O$$

D-xylulose   acetylphosphate +
5-phosphate   D-glyceraldehyde
                              3-phosphate

XII.12.j   Acetate kinase (2.7.2.1)

$$\begin{array}{c} CH_3 \\ | \\ CO.O.H_2PO_3 \end{array} + ADP \quad = \quad \begin{array}{c} CH_3 \\ | \\ COOH \end{array} + ATP$$

TABLE XII.13

SYNTHESIS OF ISOPRENOID COMPOUNDS (*1637, 2902*)

XII.13.a   Acetyl-CoA acetyltransferase (2.3.1.9)

$$
\begin{array}{l}
CH_3 \\
| \\
CO.CoA \\
\quad + \\
CH_3 \\
| \\
CO.CoA
\end{array}
\quad = \quad
\begin{array}{l}
CH_3 \\
| \\
CO \; + \; CoA \\
| \\
CH_2 \\
| \\
CO.CoA
\end{array}
$$

2 acetyl-CoA   acetoacetyl-CoA

XII.13.b   Hydroxymethylglutaryl-CoA synthase (4.1.3.5)

$$
\begin{array}{l}
CO.CoA \; + \; H_2O \\
| \\
CH_3 \\
\quad + \\
CH_3.CO \\
| \\
CH_2 \\
| \\
CO.CoA
\end{array}
\quad = \quad
\begin{array}{l}
COOH \; + \; CoA \\
| \\
CH_2 \\
| \\
CH_3.C.OH \\
| \\
CH_2 \\
| \\
CO.CoA
\end{array}
$$

Acetyl-CoA +   3-hydroxy-3-
 acetoacetyl-CoA   methylglutaryl-CoA

XII.13.c   Hydroxymethylglutaryl-CoA reductase (1.1.1.34)

$$
\begin{array}{l}
COOH \\
| \\
CH_2 \\
| \\
CH_3.C.OH \\
| \\
CH_2 \quad + \; 2NADPH_2 \\
| \\
CO.CoA
\end{array}
\quad = \quad
\begin{array}{l}
COOH \\
| \\
CH_2 \\
| \\
CH_3.C.OH \\
| \\
CH_2 \quad + \; 2NADP \\
| \\
CH_2OH \; + \; CoA
\end{array}
$$

3-hydroxy-3-   mevalonate
 methylglutaryl-
 CoA

XII.13.d   Mevalonate kinase (2.7.1.36)

$$
\begin{array}{l}
COOH \\
| \\
CH_2 \\
| \\
CH_3.C.OH \\
| \\
CH_2 \\
| \\
CH_2OH \; + \; ATP
\end{array}
\quad = \quad
\begin{array}{l}
COOH \\
| \\
CH_2 \\
| \\
CH_3.C.OH \\
| \\
CH_2 \\
| \\
CH_2.O.H_2PO_3 \; + \; ADP
\end{array}
$$

Mevalonate   5-phosphomevalonate

XII.13.e   Phosphomevalonate kinase (2.7.4.2)

$$
\begin{array}{c}
COOH \\
| \\
CH_2 \\
| \\
CH_3.C.OH \\
| \\
CH_2 \quad + ATP \\
| \\
CH_2.O.H_2PO_3
\end{array}
=
\begin{array}{c}
COOH \\
| \\
CH_2 \\
| \\
CH_3.C.OH \\
| \\
CH_2 \quad\quad + ADP \\
| \\
CH_2.O.H_3P_2O_6
\end{array}
$$

5-phosphomevalonate   5-pyrophosphomevalonate

XII.13.f   Pyrophosphomevalonate decarboxylase (4.1.1.33)

$$
\begin{array}{c}
\\
COOH \\
| \\
CH_2 \\
| \\
CH_3.C.OH \quad +ATP \\
| \\
CH_2 \\
| \\
CH_2.O.H_3P_2O_6
\end{array}
=
\begin{array}{c}
CO_2 \\
+ \\
CH_2 \\
\| \\
CH_3.C \quad\quad + ADP + H_3PO_4 \\
| \\
CH_2 \\
| \\
CH_2.O.H_3P_2O_6
\end{array}
$$

5-pyrophospho-   isopentenyl pyrophosphate
mevalonate

XII.13.g   Isopentenylpyrophosphate isomerase (5.3.3.2)

$$
\begin{array}{c}
CH_3.C=CH_2 \\
| \\
CH_2 \\
| \\
CH_2.O.H_3P_2O_6
\end{array}
=
\begin{array}{c}
CH_3.C.CH_3 \\
\| \\
CH \\
| \\
CH_2.O.H_3P_2O_6
\end{array}
$$

Isopentenyl   dimethylallyl
pyrophosphate   pyrophosphate

XII.13.h   Dimethylallyl transferase (2.5.1.1)

$$
\begin{array}{c}
CH_3.C.CH_3 \\
\| \\
CH \\
| \\
CH_2.O.H_3P_2O_6 \\
+ \\
CH_2 \\
\| \\
CH_3.C \\
| \\
CH_2 \\
| \\
CH_2.O.H_3P_2O_6
\end{array}
=
\begin{array}{c}
CH_3.C.CH_3 \\
\| \\
CH \\
| \\
CH_2 \quad\quad + pyrophosphate \\
| \\
CH_2 \\
| \\
CH_3.C \\
\| \\
CH \\
| \\
CH_2.O.H_3P_2O_6
\end{array}
$$

Dimethylallyl   geranyl pyrophosphate
pyrophosphate +
isopentenyl
pyrophosphate

XII.13.i   Dimethylallyl transferase (2.5.1.1)

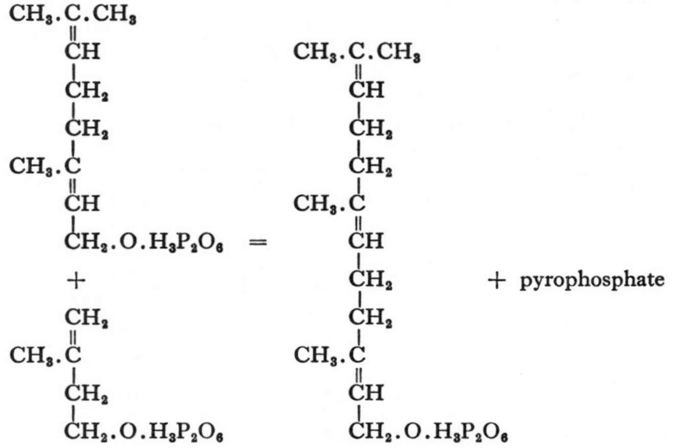

$$CH_3.C.CH_3$$
$$\overset{\|}{C}H$$
$$CH_2$$
$$CH_2$$
$$CH_3.\overset{|}{C}$$
$$\overset{\|}{C}H$$
$$CH_2.O.H_3P_2O_6$$
$$+$$
$$\overset{CH_2}{\underset{}{\|}}$$
$$CH_3.\overset{}{C}$$
$$\overset{|}{C}H_2$$
$$CH_2.O.H_3P_2O_6$$

$=$

$$CH_3.C.CH_3$$
$$\overset{\|}{C}H$$
$$CH_2$$
$$CH_2$$
$$CH_3.\overset{|}{C}$$
$$\overset{\|}{C}H$$
$$CH_2$$
$$CH_2$$
$$CH_3.\overset{|}{C}$$
$$\overset{\|}{C}H$$
$$CH_2.O.H_3P_2O_6$$

$+$ pyrophosphate

Geranyl   farnesyl pyrophosphate
pyrophosphate +
isopentenyl
pyrophosphate

From this point the enzymes are not well characterized. Divergent paths lead to a great variety of products. There are three main possibilities. (*a*) Hydrolytic removal of the pyrophosphate terminal group yields through geraniol or farnesol numerous cyclic or acyclic terpenes. (*b*) A continuation of the 'head-to-tail' addition of C_5-units, as in reactions XII.13.h–i, yields long isoprenoid chains, such as are found in ubiquinone, gutta percha and rubber or (in a saturated form) in phytol, tocopherol and vitamin K or (in a more unsaturated form) in the carotenoids. (*c*) A 'tail-to-tail' linking of two farnesyl pyrophosphate molecules leads through squalene to steroids, thus:

XII.13.j   A microsomal enzyme

2 farnesyl pyrophosphate + $NADPH_2$ =
        squalene + NADP + 2 pyrophosphate

XII.13.k   Squalene cyclohydroxylase (1.99.1.13)

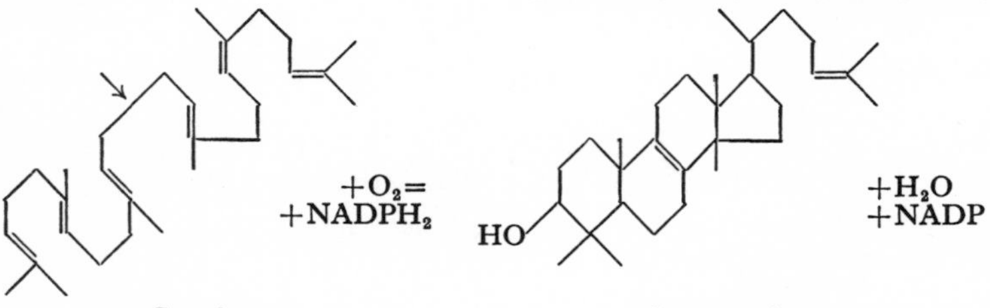

$+O_2=$
$+NADPH_2$

$+H_2O$
$+NADP$

Squalene   lanosterol

TABLE XII.14

UREA FORMATION IN LIVER

XII.14.a   Glutamate dehydrogenase (1.4.1.3)

$$NH_3 \; + \; \begin{array}{c} COOH \\ | \\ (CH_2)_2 \\ | \\ CO \\ | \\ COOH \end{array} \; + \; NADH_2 \;\; = \;\; \begin{array}{c} COOH \\ | \\ (CH_2)_2 \\ | \\ CH.NH_2 \\ | \\ COOH \end{array} \; + \; NAD$$

(from XII.14.c)

2-oxoglutarate   L-glutamate

or

XII.14.b   Aminotransferases (2.6.1.2–8)

$$\textbf{amino-}\text{acids} \; + \; \begin{array}{c} COOH \\ | \\ (CH_2)_2 \\ | \\ CO \\ | \\ COOH \end{array} \; = \; \begin{array}{c} \text{2-keto-}\\ \text{acids} \end{array} \; + \; \begin{array}{c} COOH \\ | \\ (CH_2)_2 \\ | \\ CH.NH_2 \\ | \\ COOH \end{array}$$

2-oxoglutarate   L-glutamate

XII.14.c   Aspartate aminotransferase (2.6.1.1)

$$\begin{array}{c} COOH \\ | \\ (CH_2)_2 \\ | \\ CH.NH_2 \\ | \\ COOH \end{array} \; + \; \begin{array}{c} COOH \\ | \\ CH_2 \\ | \\ CO \\ | \\ COOH \end{array} \; = \; \begin{array}{c} COOH \\ | \\ (CH_2)_2 \\ | \\ CO \\ | \\ COOH \end{array} \; + \; \begin{array}{c} COOH \\ | \\ CH_2 \\ | \\ CH.NH_2 \\ | \\ COOH \end{array}$$

                 (from XII.14.i)   (to XII.14.a)   (to XII.14.f)

L-glutamate   oxalo-   2-oxo-   L-aspartate
                 acetate   glutarate

XII.14.d   Carbamate kinase (2.7.2.a) with
                                             acetyl-glutamate

$$NH_3 + CO_2 + 2ATP + H_2O = H_2N.CO.O.H_2PO_3 + 2ADP + H_3PO_4$$

carbamoyl-
phosphate

XII.14.e   Ornithine carbamoyltransferase (2.1.3.3)

$$\begin{array}{c} NH_2 \\ | \\ (CH_2)_3 \\ | \\ CH.NH_2 \\ | \\ COOH \end{array} \; + \; \begin{array}{c} \textbf{CO.NH} \\ | \\ O.H_2PO_3 \end{array} \; = \; \begin{array}{c} NH.CO.NH_2 \\ | \\ (CH_2)_3 \\ | \\ CH.NH_2 \\ | \\ COOH \end{array} \; + \; H_3PO_4$$

(from XII.14.j)

L-ornithine   carbamoyl-   L-citrulline
            phosphate

XII.14.f   Argininosuccinate synthetase (6.3.4.5)

$$
\begin{array}{ccc}
\text{NH} & \text{COOH} & \text{NH} \quad\quad \text{COOH}\\
\|\ & | & \|\ \quad\quad |\\
\text{C.OH} & \text{H}_2\text{N.CH} & \text{C}\!-\!\!-\!\text{NH}\!-\!\!-\!\text{CH}\\
| & | & | \quad\quad\quad |\\
\text{NH} & \text{CH}_2 & \text{NH} \quad\quad \text{CH}_2\\
| & | & | \quad\quad\quad |\\
(\text{CH}_2)_3 & \text{COOH} & (\text{CH}_2)_3 \quad \text{COOH}\\
| & & |\\
\text{CH.NH}_2 & & \text{CH.NH}_2\\
| & +\text{ATP} & |\\
\text{COOH} & & \text{COOH} \quad +\text{ AMP }+\text{ H}_4\text{P}_2\text{O}_7
\end{array}
$$

L-citrulline   L-aspartate   L-arginino-
                                               succinate

XII.14.g   Argininosuccinate lyase (4.3.2.1)

$$
\begin{array}{ccc}
\text{NH} \quad\quad \text{COOH} & \text{NH} & \text{COOH}\\
\|\ \quad\quad\quad | & \|\ & |\\
\text{C}\!-\!\!-\!\text{NH}\!-\!\!-\!\text{CH} & \text{C.NH}_2 & \text{CH}\\
| \quad\quad\quad | & | & \|\\
\text{NH} \quad\quad \text{CH}_2 & \text{NH} & \text{CH}\\
| \quad\quad\quad | & | & |\\
(\text{CH}_2)_3 \quad \text{COOH} & (\text{CH}_2)_3 & \text{COOH}\\
| & |\\
\text{CH.NH}_2 & \text{CH.NH}_2\\
| & |\\
\text{COOH} & \text{COOH}
\end{array}
$$

L-arginino-   L-arginine   fumarate
succinate

XII.14.h   Fumarate hydratase (4.2.1.2)

$$
\begin{array}{cc}
\text{CH.COOH} & \text{CH}_2.\text{COOH}\\
\|\quad\quad +\text{ H}_2\text{O} = & |\\
\text{CH.COOH} & \text{CHOH.COOH}
\end{array}
$$

Fumarate   L-malate

XII.14.i   Malate dehydrogenase (1.1.1.37)

$$
\begin{array}{cc}
\text{CH}_2.\text{COOH} & \text{CH}_2.\text{COOH}\\
|\quad\quad\quad +\text{ NAD} = & |\quad\quad\quad +\text{ NADH}_2\\
\text{CHOH.COOH} & \text{CO.COOH} \quad \text{(to XII.14.a)}\\
& \text{(to XII.14.c)}
\end{array}
$$

L-malate   oxaloacetate

XII.14.j   Arginase (3.5.3.1)

$$
\begin{array}{cc}
\text{NH} & \quad\quad\quad \text{NH}_2\\
\|\ & +\quad |\\
\text{C.NH}_2 & \quad\quad \text{OC.NH}_2\\
| \quad +\text{ H}_2\text{O} & \\
\text{NH} & \text{NH}_2\\
| & |\\
(\text{CH}_2)_3 \quad = & (\text{CH}_2)_3\\
| & |\\
\text{CH.NH}_2 & \text{CH.NH}_2\\
| & |\\
\text{COOH} & \text{COOH}\\
& \text{(to XII.14.e)}
\end{array}
$$

L-arginine   L-ornithine + urea

Sum of reactions (excluding XII.14.b):

$$2NH_3 + CO_2 + 3ATP + 2H_2O = urea + AMP + 2ADP + 2H_3PO_4 + H_4P_2O_7$$

The two N atoms of urea enter the system by different paths, one by reactions XII.14.a–c, the other by reactions XII.14.d–e. They are first brought together in the same molecule by XII.14.f. The synthesis of urea requires energy, which is supplied by the breakdown of ATP, which in turn is supplied by the oxidative processes (e.g. Tables XII.1–2).

XII.14.b is an alternative mechanism whereby the amino groups of aminoacids can enter the system without passing through the stage of free ammonia, but in that case the reduced coenzyme from XII.14.i must be oxidized in some other way, e.g. by the respiratory system.

The carbon and two nitrogen atoms which will eventually appear in the urea molecule are shown throughout in heavy type.

An alternative pathway from reaction XII.14.g onwards, resulting in the formation of creatine instead of urea, is as follows:

XII.14.k Glycine amidinotransferase (2.6.2.1)

$$
\begin{array}{ccccccc}
NH & & & & & & NH \\
\| & & & & & & \| \\
C.NH_2 & & & & & & C.NH_2 \\
| & & & & & & | \\
NH & & NH_2 & & NH_2 & & NH \\
| & & | & & | & & | \\
(CH_2)_3 & + & CH_2 & = & (CH_2)_3 & + & CH_2 \\
| & & | & & | & & | \\
CH.NH_2 & & COOH & & CH.NH_2 & & COOH \\
| & & & & | & & \\
COOH & & & & COOH & & \\
\end{array}
$$

(from XII.14.g)   (to XII.14.e)

L-arginine   glycine   L-orni·hine   guanidino-
                                             acetate

XII.14.l Guanidinoacetate methyltransferase (2.1.1.2)

$$
\begin{array}{ccccc}
NH & & NH \\
\| & & \| \\
C.NH_2 & S\text{-adenosyl-} & C.NH_2 & S\text{-adenosyl-} \\
| & \text{methionine} & | & \text{homocysteine} \\
NH & + & N.CH_3 & + \\
| & \text{(from XII.10.a)} & | & \text{(to XII.10.c)} \\
CH_2 & & CH_2 \\
| & & | \\
COOH & & COOH \\
\end{array}
$$

guanidino-   creatine
acetate

TABLE XII.15

PHOSPHATIDE SYNTHESIS

XII.15.a   Glycerol kinase (2.7.1.30)

Glycerol+ATP = L-glycerol 3-phosphate+ADP

XII.15.b   Glycerolphosphate acyltransferase (2.3.1.15)

L-glycerol 3-phosphate+2 acyl-CoA =
L-1,2-diglyceride 3-phosphate+2CoA

XII.15.c   Phosphatidate phosphatase (3.1.3.4)

L-1,2-diglyceride 3-phosphate+H_2O =L-1,2-diglyceride+phosphate
(to XII.15.h)

XII.15.d   Choline kinase (2.7.1.32)

Choline+ATP = choline phosphate+ADP

XII.15.e   Nucleosidemonophosphate kinase (2.7.4.4)

CMP+ATP = CDP+ADP

XII.15.f   Nucelosidediphosphate kinase (2.7.4.6)

CDP+ATP = CTP+ADP

XII.15.g   Cholinephosphate cytidylyltransferase (2.7.7.15)

Choline phosphate+CTP = CDPcholine+pyrophosphate

XII.15.h   Cholinephosphotransferase (2.7.8.2)

L-1,2-diglyceride+CDPcholine = lecithin+CMP

Sum of reactions:

choline+glycerol+2acyl-CoA+4ATP+H_2O =
lecithin+2CoA+4ADP+phosphate+pyrophosphate

Note: For the diglyceride, we use the prefix L-1,2- rather than D-2,3- (which represents
the same configuration) in order to avoid any suggestion that optical inversions occur
during the process. The incorrect form D-1,2- also occurs in the literature, resulting
from a misinterpretation of the prefix D-α,β-. The α,β-system is ambiguous, as α- is used
for both the 1- and the 3-positions.

TABLE XII.16

SYNTHESIS AND BREAKDOWN OF NAD AND NADP

(a) Synthesis

XII.16.a   Ribokinase (2.7.1.15)
    D-ribose+ATP = D-ribose 5-phosphate+ADP

XII.16.b   Ribosephosphate pyrophosphokinase (2.7.6.1)
    D-ribose 5-phosphate+ATP =
                5-phospho-α-D-ribosyl-pyrophosphate+AMP

XII.16.c   Nicotinate phosphoribosyltransferase (2.4.2.11)
    Nicotinate+5-phospho-α-D-ribosyl-pyrophosphate =
                        nicotinate ribonucleotide+pyrophosphate

XII.16.d   NMN adenylyltransferase (2.7.7.1)
    Nicotinate ribonucleotide+ATP = deamido-NAD+pyrophosphate

XII.16.e   NAD synthetase (6.3.5.1)
    Deamido-NAD+ATP+L-glutamine + H_2O =
                NAD+AMP+pyrophosphate+L-glutamate

XII.16.f   NAD kinase (2.7.1.23)
    NAD+ATP = NADP+ADP

In some animal tissues reactions XII.16.c–e are replaced to a variable extent
    by the following:

XII.16.g   Nicotinamide phosphoribosyltransferase (2.4.2.12)
    Nicotinamide+5-phospho-α-D-ribosyl-pyrophosphate =
                                NMN+pyrophosphate

XII.16.h   NMN adenylyltransferase (2.7.7.1)
    NMN+ATP = NAD+pyrophosphate

(b) Breakdown

XII.16.i   Alkaline phosphatase (3.1.3.1)
    NADP+H_2O = NAD+phosphate

XII.16.j   Nucleotide pyrophosphatase (3.6.1.9)
    NAD+H_2O = NMN+AMP

XII.16.k   5-nucleotidase (3.1.3.5)
    NMN+H_2O = nicotinamide nucleoside+phosphate

XII.16.l $\hspace{5cm}$ Nucleosidase (3.2.2.1)

Nicotinamide nucleoside $+H_2O$ = nicotinamide $+$ D-ribose

Also, instead of reactions XII.16.j–l, the following may occur:

XII.16.m $\hspace{5cm}$ NAD nucleosidase (3.2.2.5)

$NAD+H_2O$ = nicotinamide $+$ ADPribose

XII.16.n $\hspace{4cm}$ Nucleotide pyrophosphatase (3.6.1.9)

ADPribose $+H_2O$ = AMP $+$ D-ribose 5-phosphate

XII.16.o $\hspace{5cm}$ Alkaline phosphatase (3.1.3.1)

D-ribose 5-phosphate $+H_2O$ = D-ribose $+$ phosphate

Sum of reactions XII.16.a–f:

ribose $+$ nicotinate $+5ATP+$ glutamine $= NADP+2ADP+2AMP$
$$+3 \text{ pyrophosphate} + \text{glutamate}$$

Sum of reactions XII.16.i–l or XII.16.i $+$ m–o:

$NADP+4H_2O$ = nicotinamide $+$ ribose $+2$ phosphate $+AMP$

TABLE XII.17
COENZYME A SYNTHESIS (339)

XII.17.a   Pantothenate synthetase (6.3.2.1)

$$
\begin{array}{ccc}
\text{COOH} & \text{CH}_2\text{OH} & \\
| & | & \\
\text{CH}_2 & \text{CH}_3.\text{C}.\text{CH}_3 & \\
| & + \quad | \quad + \text{ATP} = \\
\text{CH}_2.\text{NH}_2 & \text{HOCH} & \\
& | & \\
& \text{COOH} &
\end{array}
\qquad
\begin{array}{c}
\text{CH}_2\text{OH} \\
| \\
\text{COOH} \quad \text{CH}_3.\text{C}.\text{CH}_3 \\
| \qquad\qquad | \\
\text{CH}_2 \qquad\quad \text{HOCH} \\
| \qquad\qquad\quad | \\
\text{CH}_2.\text{NH}\text{———}\text{CO}
\end{array}
$$

+ AMP + pyrophosphate

β-alanine   L-pantoate   L-pantothenate

XII.17.b   Pantothenate kinase (2.7.1.33)

$$
\begin{array}{c}
\text{CH}_2\text{OH} + \text{ATP} \\
| \\
\text{COOH} \quad \text{CH}_3.\text{C}.\text{CH}_3 \\
| \qquad\qquad | \\
\text{CH}_2 \qquad\quad \text{HOCH} \\
| \qquad\qquad\quad | \\
\text{CH}_2.\text{NH}\text{———}\text{CO}
\end{array}
=
\begin{array}{c}
\text{CH}_2.\text{O}.\text{H}_2\text{PO}_3 \\
| \\
\text{COOH} \quad \text{CH}_3.\text{C}.\text{CH}_3 \quad + \text{ADP} \\
| \qquad\qquad | \\
\text{CH}_2 \qquad\quad \text{HOCH} \\
| \qquad\qquad\quad | \\
\text{CH}_2.\text{NH}\text{———}\text{CO}
\end{array}
$$

L-pantothenate   4′-phosphopanto-
thenate

XII.17.c   Phosphopantothenoylcysteine synthetase (6.3.2.5)

$$
\begin{array}{c}
\text{CH}_2\text{SH} \\
| \\
\text{CH}.\text{COOH} \\
| \\
\text{NH}_2 \\
\\
\quad + \qquad \text{CH}_2.\text{O}.\text{H}_2\text{PO}_3 \\
\qquad\qquad\qquad | \\
\text{COOH} \quad \text{CH}_3.\text{C}.\text{CH}_3 \\
| \qquad\qquad | \\
\text{CH}_2 \qquad\quad \text{HOCH} + \text{ATP} \\
| \qquad\qquad\quad | \\
\text{CH}_2.\text{NH}\text{———}\text{CO}
\end{array}
=
\begin{array}{c}
\text{CH}_2\text{SH} \\
| \\
\text{CH}.\text{COOH} \\
| \\
\text{NH} \qquad\qquad \text{CH}_2.\text{O}.\text{H}_2\text{PO}_3 \\
| \qquad\qquad\qquad | \\
\text{CO} \qquad \text{CH}_3.\text{C}.\text{CH}_3 \\
| \qquad\qquad\quad | \\
\text{CH}_2 \qquad\quad \text{HOCH} \\
| \qquad\qquad\quad | \\
\text{CH}_2.\text{NH}\text{———}\text{CO}
\end{array}
$$

(+ADP+phosphate ?)

L-cysteine +   4′-phospho-L-panto-
4′-phospho-L-   thenoyl-L-cysteine
pantothenate

(The bacterial enzyme uses CTP instead of ATP, the animal enzyme uses either)

XII.17.d   Phosphopantothenoylcysteine decarboxylase (4.1.1.c)

$$
\begin{array}{c}
\text{CH}_2\text{SH} \\
| \\
\text{CH}.\text{COOH} \\
| \\
\text{NH} \qquad\qquad \text{CH}_2.\text{O}.\text{H}_2\text{PO}_3 \\
| \qquad\qquad\qquad | \\
\text{CO} \qquad \text{CH}_3.\text{C}.\text{CH}_3 \\
| \qquad\qquad\quad | \\
\text{CH}_2 \qquad\quad \text{HOCH} \\
| \qquad\qquad\quad | \\
\text{CH}_2.\text{NH}\text{———}\text{CO}
\end{array}
=
\begin{array}{c}
\text{CH}_2\text{SH} \qquad\qquad + \text{CO}_2 \\
| \\
\text{CH}_2 \\
| \\
\text{NH} \qquad\qquad \text{CH}_2.\text{O}.\text{H}_2\text{PO}_3 \\
| \qquad\qquad\qquad | \\
\text{CO} \qquad \text{CH}_3.\text{C}.\text{CH}_3 \\
| \qquad\qquad\quad | \\
\text{CH}_2 \qquad\quad \text{HOCH} \\
| \qquad\qquad\quad | \\
\text{CH}_2.\text{NH}\text{———}\text{CO}
\end{array}
$$

4′-phospho-L-panto-   pantetheine 4′-phosphate
thenoyl-L-cysteine

XII.17.e   Pantetheinephosphate adenylyltransferase (2.7.7.3)

```
CH₂.O.H₂PO₃        O.HPO₂.O                        O   O
                                                   ‖   ‖
CH₃.C.CH₃          CH₂  HOPO              CH₂.O.P.O . P.O
                                                CH₃.C.CH₃  OH HO CH₂
HOCH              HC ──┐    O.H₂PO₃        HOCH              HC ──┐
                                                              
CO                HCOH      ┐ O            CO                HCOH   ┐ O
                                                              
NH                HCOH                     NH                HCOH
                                                              
CH₂        +      HC ──┘              =    CH₂                HC ──┘
                      │  /CH=N                                    │  /CH=N
CH₂                   N                    CH₂                   N
                        \C=C                                      \C=C
CO                   N      \C.NH₂         CO                   N      \C.NH₂
                      \CH-N/                                     \CH-N/
NH                                         NH
                                                              
CH₂                                        CH₂
                                                              
CH₂SH                                      CH₂SH

                                                  +   pyrophosphate

   Pantetheine          ATP                    dephospho-CoA
   4'-phosphate
```

XII.17.f   Dephospho-CoA kinase (2.7.1.24)

```
        O   O                                  O   O
        ‖   ‖                                  ‖   ‖
CH₂.O.P.O . P.O                        CH₂.O.P.O . P.O
CH₃.C.CH₃  OH HO CH₂                   CH₃.C.CH₃  OH HO CH₂   + ADP
HOCH              HC ──┐                HOCH              HC ──┐
CO                HCOH   ┐ O            CO                HC.O.H₂PO₃  ┐ O
NH                HCOH      + ATP  =    NH                HCOH
CH₂               HC ──┘                CH₂               HC ──┘
    │  /CH=N                                │  /CH=N
CH₂ N                                  CH₂ N
      \C=C                                    \C=C
CO   N      \C.NH₂                      CO   N      \C.NH₂
      \CH-N/                                  \CH-N/
NH                                     NH
CH₂                                    CH₂
CH₂SH                                  CH₂SH

   Dephospho-CoA                              CoA
```

Sum of reactions:

   cysteine+pantoate+β-alanine+5ATP = coenzyme A+3ADP+
                              AMP+2 pyrophosphate+phosphate+CO₂

TABLE XII.18

NUCLEOTIDE SYNTHESIS

(a) Purine synthesis (353)

XII.18.a   Ribokinase (2.7.1.15)

D-ribose $+$ ATP $=$ D-ribose 5-phosphate $+$ ADP

XII.18.b   Ribosephosphate pyrophosphokinase (2.7.6.1)

D-ribose 5-phosphate $+$ ATP $=$
5-phospho-α-D-ribosyl-pyrophosphate $+$ AMP

XII.18.c   Amidophosphoribosyltransferase (2.4.2.14)

L-glutamine $+$ 5-phospho-α-D-ribosyl-pyrophosphate $+$ H_2O $=$
L-glutamate $+$ β-D-ribosylamine 5-phosphate (NH$_2$–R–P) $+$ pyrophosphate

($-$R–P denotes the 5-phospho-β-D-ribosyl group)

XII.18.d   Phosphoribosyl-glycineamide synthetase (6.3.1.3)

$NH_2.CH_2.COOH + NH_2$–R–P $+$ ATP $=$
$NH_2.CH_2.CO.NH$–R–P $+$ ADP $+$ H_3PO_4

Glycine   ribosyl-glycineamide 5'-phosphate

XII.18.e   Phosphoribosyl-glycineamide formyltransferase (2.1.2.2)

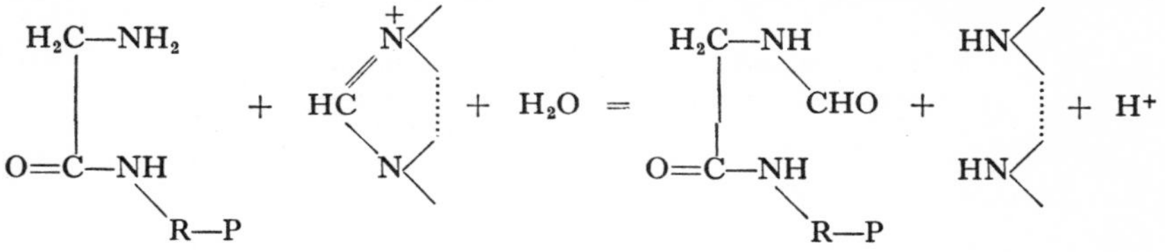

ribosyl-
glycine-
amide
5'-phosphate

5,10-methenyl-
tetrahydro-
folate

5'-phospho-
ribosyl-
N-formyl-
glycine-
amide

tetra-
hydro-
folate

XII.18.f   Phosphoribosyl-formylglycineamidine synthetase (6.3.5.3)

L-glutamine $+$

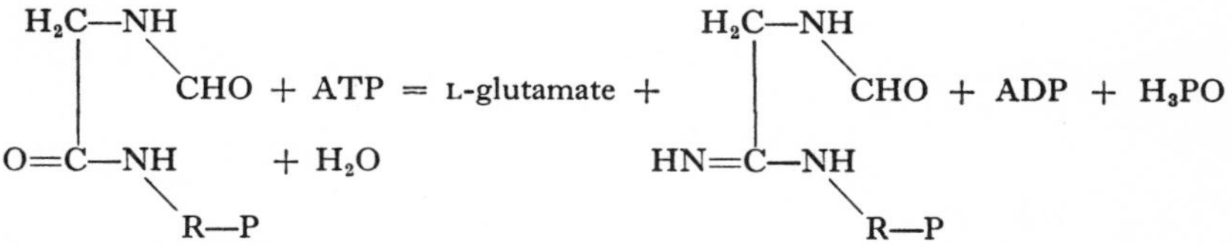

5'-phospho-
ribosyl-
N-formyl-
glycine-
amide

5'-phospho-
ribosyl-
formyl-
glycine-
amidine

XII.18.g   Phosphoribosyl-aminoimidazole synthetase (6.3.3.1)

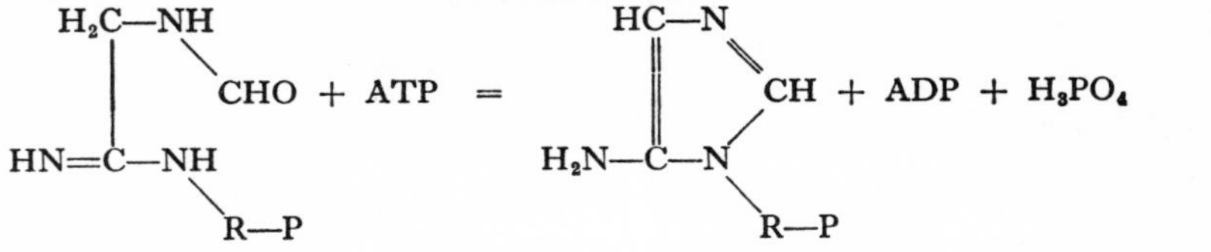

5'-phosphoribosyl-
formylglycine-
amidine

5'-phosphoribosyl-
5-aminoimidazole

XII.18.h   Phosphoribosyl-aminoimidazole carboxylase (4.1.1.21)

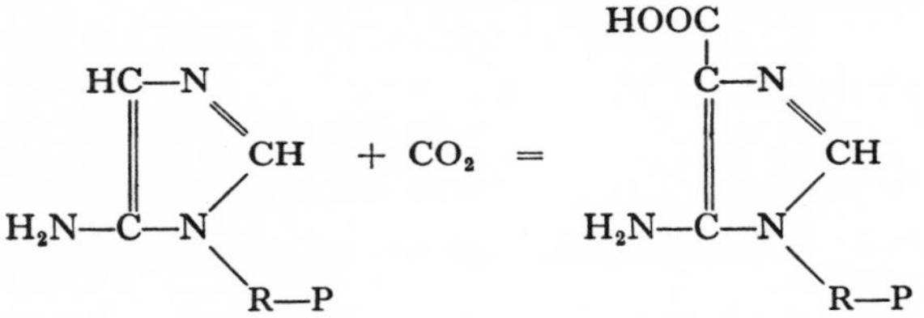

5'-phosphoribosyl-
5-aminoimidazole

5'-phosphoribosyl-
5-amino-4-
imidazole carboxylate

XII.18.i   Phosphoribosyl-aminoimidazole-succinocarboxamide
synthetase (6.3.2.6)

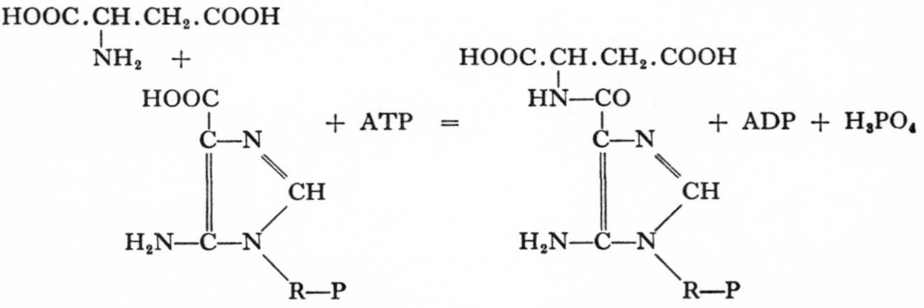

L-aspartate + 5'-phosphoribosyl-5-
amino-4-imidazole-
carboxylate

5'-phosphoribosyl-4-(N-succinocarboxamide)-5-aminoimidazole

XII.18.j

Adenylosuccinate lyase (4.3.2.2)

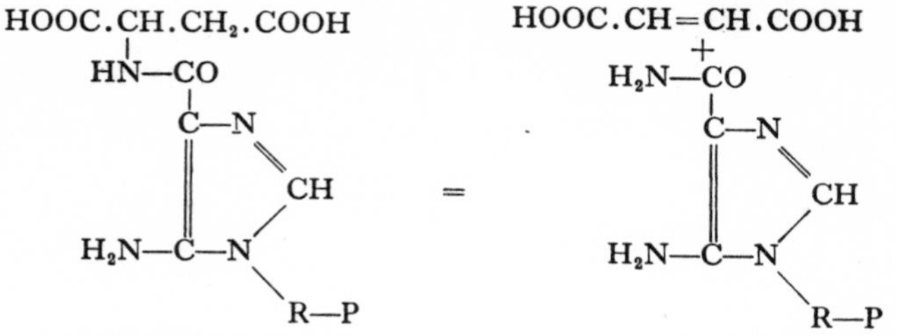

HOOC.CH.CH$_2$.COOH

HN—CO

C—N

CH

H$_2$N—C—N

R—P

5'-phosphoribosyl-4-
(N-succinocarboxamide)-
5-aminoimidazole

=

HOOC.CH=CH.COOH

+

H$_2$N—CO

C—N

CH

H$_2$N—C—N

R—P

5'-phosphoribosyl-5-amino-
4-imidazolecarboxamide
+fumarate

XII.18.k

Phosphoribosyl-aminoimidazolecarboxamide
formyltransferase (2.1.2.3)

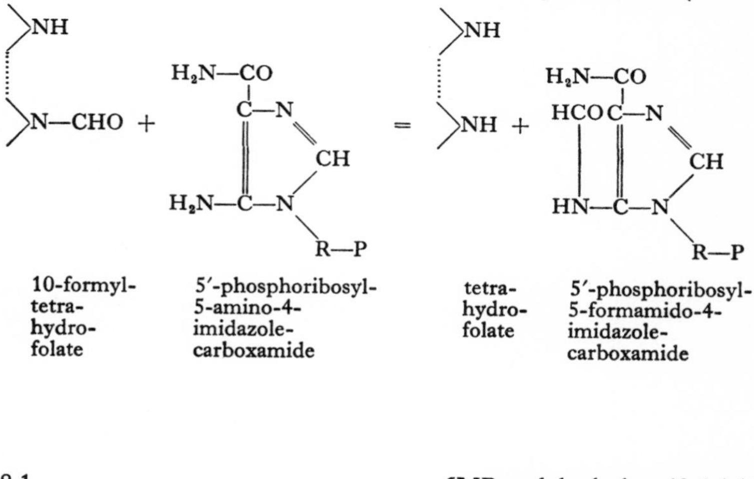

NH

N—CHO +

H$_2$N—CO

C—N

CH

H$_2$N—C—N

R—P

=

NH

NH +

H$_2$N—CO

HCOC—N

CH

HN—C—N

R—P

10-formyl-
tetra-
hydro-
folate

5'-phosphoribosyl-
5-amino-4-
imidazole-
carboxamide

tetra-
hydro-
folate

5'-phosphoribosyl-
5-formamido-4-
imidazole-
carboxamide

XII.18.1

IMP cyclohydrolase (3.5.4.10)

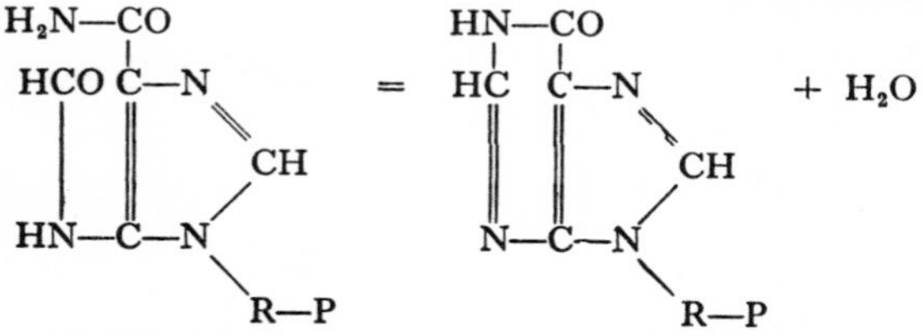

H$_2$N—CO

HCO C—N

CH

HN—C—N

R—P

5'-phosphoribosyl-
5-formamido-4-
imidazole-
carboxamide

=

HN—CO

HC C—N

CH

N—C—N

R—P

IMP

+ H$_2$O

XII.18.m   Adenylosuccinate synthetase (6.3.4.4)

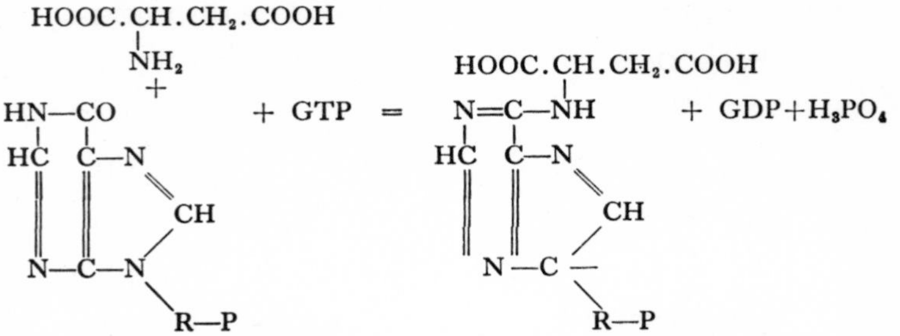

$$HOOC.CH.CH_2.COOH$$

IMP + L-aspartate + GTP = adenylosuccinate + GDP + H_3PO_4

IMP + L-aspartate   adenylosuccinate

XII.18.n   Adenylosuccinate lyase (4.3.2.2)

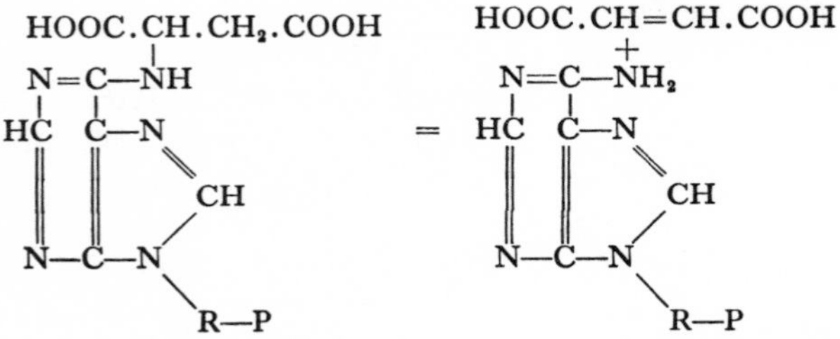

$$HOOC.CH.CH_2.COOH$$

$$HOOC.CH=CH.COOH$$

Adenylosuccinate = fumarate + AMP

Adenylosuccinate   fumarate + AMP

Or, instead of XII.18.m–n

XII.18.o   IMP dehydrogenase (1.2.1.14)

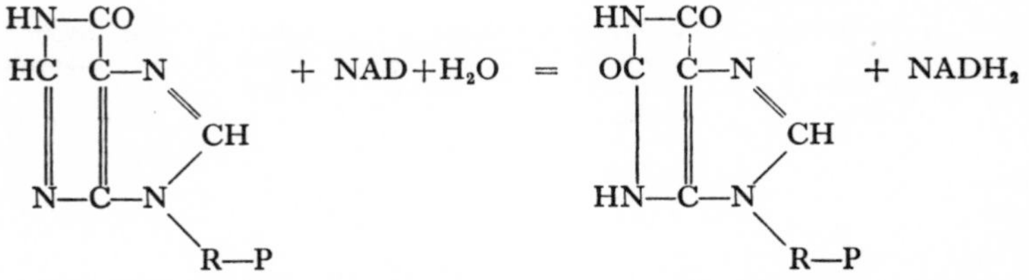

IMP + NAD + H_2O = XMP + $NADH_2$

IMP   XMP

XII.18.p   GMP synthetase (6.3.4.1)

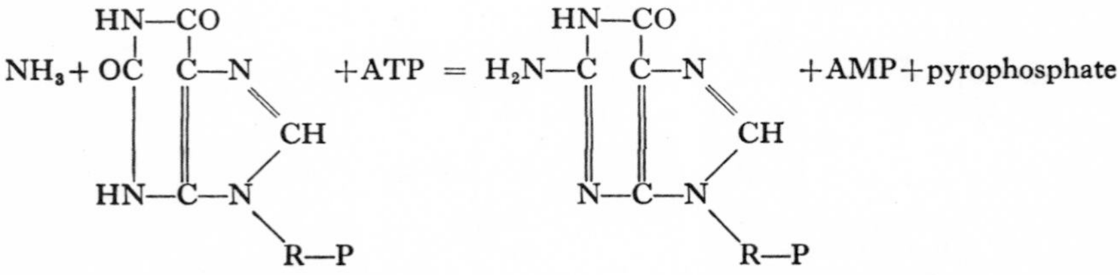

NH_3 + XMP + ATP = GMP + AMP + pyrophosphate

XMP   GMP

(b) *Pyrimidine synthesis (2202)*

XII.18.q   Carbamate kinase (2.7.2.a) with acetyl-glutamate

$$NH_3 + CO_2 + 2ATP + H_2O = H_2N.CO.O.H_2PO_3 + 2ADP + H_3PO_4$$

carbamoyl-
phosphate

XII.18.r   Aspartate carbamoyltransferase (2.1.3.2)

L-aspartate   carbamoyl-phosphate   N-carbamoyl-L-aspartate

XII.18.s   Dihydro-orotase (3.5.2.3)

N-carbamoyl-L-aspartate   L-4,5-dihydro-orotate

XII.18.t   Dihydro-orotate dehydrogenase (1.3.3.1)

L-4,5-dihydro-orotate   orotate

XII.18.u   Orotate phosphoribosyltransferase (2.4.2.10)

Orotate   5-phospho-α-D-ribosyl pyrophosphate   orotidine 5'-phosphate + pyrophosphate

x

XII.18.v   Orotidine-5'-phosphate decarboxylase (4.1.1.23)

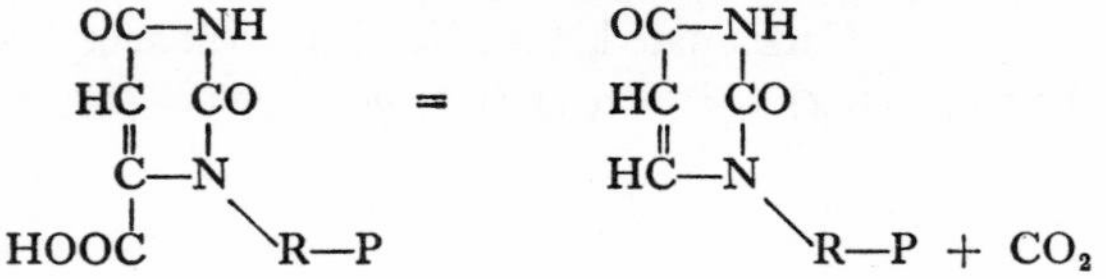

Orotidine
5'-phosphate

uridine
5'-phosphate
(UMP)

XII.18.w   Nucleosidemonophosphate kinase (2.7.4.4)

$UMP + ATP = UDP + ADP$

XII.18.x   Nucleosidediphosphate kinase (2.7.4.6)

$UDP + ATP = UTP + ADP$

XII.18.y   CTP synthetase (6.3.4.2)

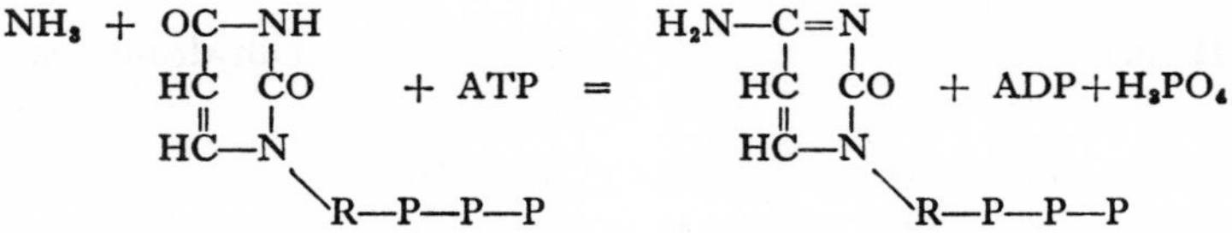

UTP   CTP

TABLE XII.19

FORMATION OF SUCROSE IN PHOTOSYNTHESIS

Part (a)

In illuminated chloroplasts a supply of $NADPH_2$ and of ATP is maintained by photochemical processes, thus:

XII.19.a

$$NADP + H_2O \xrightarrow{\text{Light}} NADPH_2 + \tfrac{1}{2}O_2$$

XII.19.b

$$ADP + H_3PO_4 \xrightarrow{\text{Light}} ATP + H_2O$$

Soluble enzymes then bring about parts (b) and (c), which also occur in the dark if $NADPH_2$ and ATP are added.

Part (b)

XII.19.c   Ribulosediphosphate carboxylase (4.1.1.f)

$$
\begin{array}{l}
CH_2.O.H_2PO_3 \\
|\\
CO \\
|\\
HCOH \\
|\\
HCOH \\
|\\
CH_2.O.H_2PO_3 \\
\text{(from XII.19.o)}
\end{array}
\; + \; CO_2 + H_2O \; = \;
\begin{array}{l}
CH_2.O.H_2PO_3 \\
|\\
HOCH \\
|\\
COOH \\
\\
+ \\
\\
COOH \\
|\\
HCOH \\
|\\
CH_2.O.H_2PO_3
\end{array}
$$

D-ribulose   2 3-phospho-
1,5-diphosphate   D-glycerate

XII.19.d   Phosphoglycerate kinase (2.7.2.3)

$$
\begin{array}{l}
CH_2.O.H_2PO_3 \\
|\\
CHOH \\
|\\
COOH
\end{array}
\; + \; ATP \; = \;
\begin{array}{l}
CH_2.O.H_2PO_3 \\
|\\
CHOH \\
|\\
CO.O.H_2PO_3
\end{array}
\; + \; ADP
$$

3-phospho-   1,3-diphospho-
D-glycerate   D-glyceric acid

XII.19.e   Glyceraldehydephosphate dehydrogenase (1.2.1.13)

$$
\begin{array}{l}
CH_2.O.H_2PO_3 \\
|\\
CHOH \\
|\\
CO.O.H_2PO_3
\end{array}
\; + \; NADPH_2 \; = \;
\begin{array}{l}
CH_2.O.H_2PO_3 \\
|\\
CHOH \\
|\\
CHO
\end{array}
\; + \; NADP + H_3PO_4
$$

1,3-diphospho-   D-glyceraldehyde
D-glyceric acid   3-phosphate

XII.19.f   Triosephosphate isomerase (5.3.1.1)

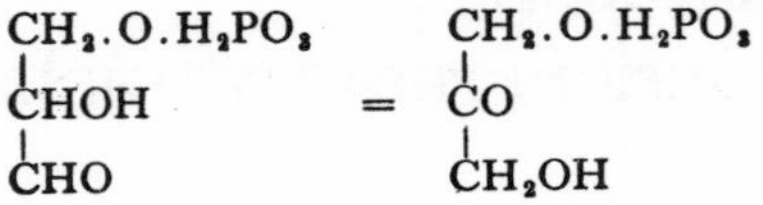

$$CH_2.O.H_2PO_3 \qquad CH_2.O.H_2PO_3$$
$$CHOH \qquad = \qquad CO$$
$$CHO \qquad CH_2OH$$

D-glycer-   dihydroxy-
aldehyde   acetone
3-phosphate   phosphate

XII.19.g   Aldolase (4.1.2.b)

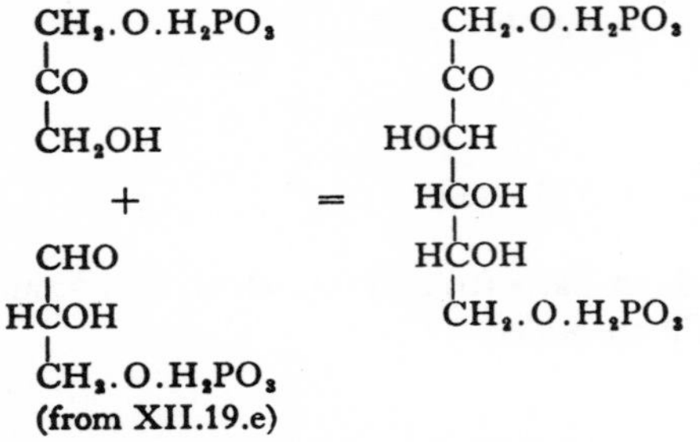

$$CH_2.O.H_2PO_3 \qquad\qquad CH_2.O.H_2PO_3$$
$$CO \qquad\qquad CO$$
$$CH_2OH \qquad\qquad HOCH$$
$$+ \qquad = \qquad HCOH$$
$$CHO \qquad\qquad HCOH$$
$$HCOH \qquad\qquad CH_2.O.H_2PO_3$$
$$CH_2.O.H_2PO_3$$
(from XII.19.e)

Dihydroxy-   D-fructose
acetone   1,6-diphosphate
phosphate
+D-glycer-
aldehyde
3-phosphate

XII.19.h   Hexosediphosphatase (3.1.3.11)

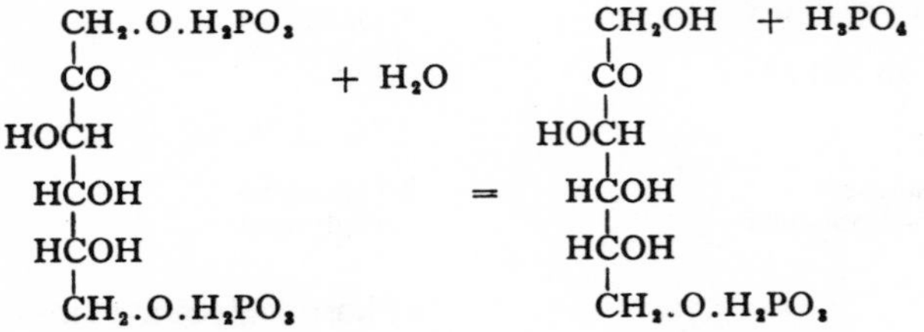

$$CH_2.O.H_2PO_3 \qquad\qquad CH_2OH \quad + \; H_3PO_4$$
$$CO \qquad\qquad\qquad CO$$
$$HOCH \qquad + \; H_2O \qquad HOCH$$
$$HCOH \qquad\qquad\qquad HCOH$$
$$HCOH \qquad = \qquad HCOH$$
$$CH_2.O.H_2PO_3 \qquad\qquad CH_2.O.H_2PO_3$$

D-fructose   D-fructose
1,6-diphosphate   6-phosphate

XII.19.i   Transketolase (2.2.1.1)

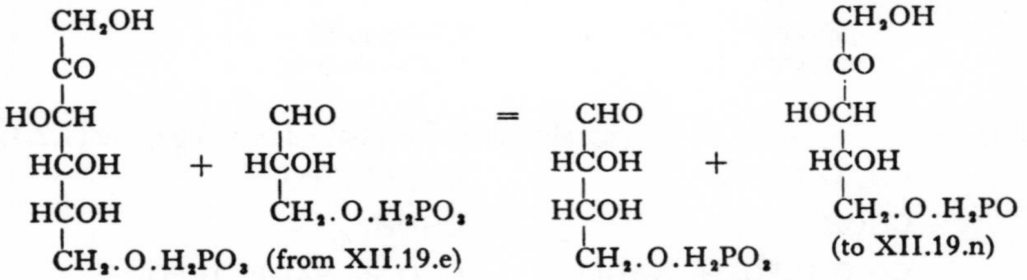

$$CH_2OH \qquad\qquad\qquad\qquad\qquad CH_2OH$$
$$CO \qquad\qquad\qquad\qquad\qquad\qquad CO$$
$$HOCH \qquad CHO \qquad = \qquad CHO \qquad HOCH$$
$$HCOH \; + \; HCOH \qquad\qquad HCOH \; + \; HCOH$$
$$HCOH \qquad CH_2.O.H_2PO_3 \qquad HCOH \qquad CH_2.O.H_2PO$$
$$CH_2.O.H_2PO_3 \quad \text{(from XII.19.e)} \qquad CH_2.O.H_2PO_3 \qquad \text{(to XII.19.n)}$$

D-fructose   D-glycer-   D-erythrose   D-xylulose
6-phosphate   aldehyde   4-phosphate   5-phosphate
                    3-phosphate

XII.19.j   Aldolase (4.1.2.b)

(from XII.19.f)

$$
\begin{array}{l}
CH_2.O.H_2PO_3 \\
|\\
CO \\
|\\
CH_2OH
\end{array}
+
\begin{array}{l}
CHO \\
|\\
HCOH \\
|\\
HCOH \\
|\\
CH_2.O.H_2PO_3
\end{array}
=
\begin{array}{l}
CH_2.O.H_2PO_3 \\
|\\
CO \\
|\\
HOCH \\
|\\
HCOH \\
|\\
HCOH \\
|\\
HCOH \\
|\\
CH_2.O.H_2PO_3
\end{array}
$$

Dihydroxyacetone phosphate + D-erythrose 4-phosphate   D-sedoheptulose 1,7-diphosphate

XII.19.k   Acid phosphatase (3.1.3.2)

$$
\begin{array}{l}
CH_2.O.H_2PO_3 \\
|\\
CO \\
|\\
HOCH \\
|\\
HCOH \\
|\\
HCOH \\
|\\
HCOH \\
|\\
CH_2.O.H_2PO_3
\end{array}
+ H_2O
=
\begin{array}{l}
CH_2OH \\
|\\
CO \\
|\\
HOCH \\
|\\
HCOH \\
|\\
HCOH \\
|\\
HCOH \\
|\\
CH_2.O.H_2PO_4
\end{array}
+ H_3PO_4
$$

D-sedoheptulose 1,7-diphosphate   D-sedoheptulose 7-phosphate

XII.19.l   Transketolase (2.2.1.1)

$$
\begin{array}{l}
CH_2OH \\
|\\
CO \\
|\\
HOCH \\
|\\
HCOH \\
|\\
HCOH \\
|\\
HCOH \\
|\\
CH_2.O.H_2PO_3
\end{array}
+
\begin{array}{l}
CHO \\
|\\
HCOH \\
|\\
CH_2.O.H_2PO_3
\end{array}
=
\begin{array}{l}
CHO \\
|\\
HCOH \\
|\\
HCOH \\
|\\
HCOH \\
|\\
CH_2.O.H_2PO_3
\end{array}
+
\begin{array}{l}
CH_2OH \\
|\\
CO \\
|\\
HOCH \\
|\\
HCOH \\
|\\
CH_2.O.H_2PO_3
\end{array}
$$

(from XII.19.e)   (to XII.19.n)

D-sedoheptulose 7-phosphate   D-glyceraldehyde 3-phosphate   D-ribose 5-phosphate   D-xylulose 5-phosphate

XII.19.m   Ribosephosphate isomerase (5.3.1.6)

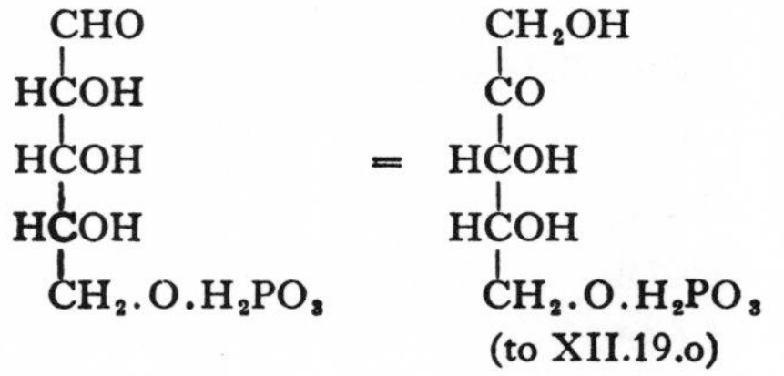

$$
\begin{array}{ccc}
\text{CHO} & & \text{CH}_2\text{OH} \\
\text{HCOH} & & \text{CO} \\
\text{HCOH} & = & \text{HCOH} \\
\text{HCOH} & & \text{HCOH} \\
\text{CH}_2.\text{O}.\text{H}_2\text{PO}_3 & & \text{CH}_2.\text{O}.\text{H}_2\text{PO}_3
\end{array}
$$

(to XII.19.o)

D-ribose   D-ribulose
5-phosphate   5-phosphate

XII.19.n   Ribulosephosphate 3-epimerase (5.1.3.1)

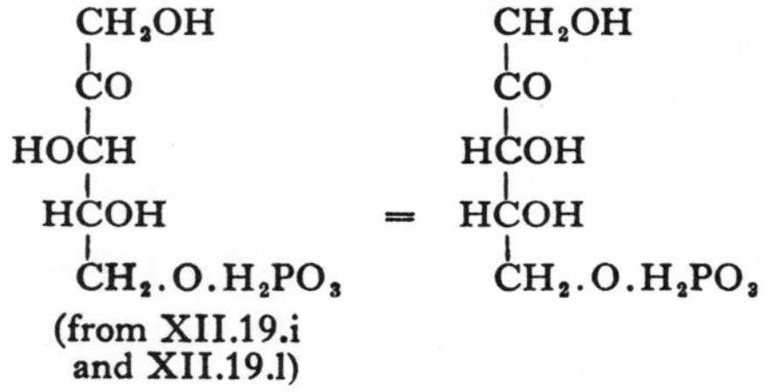

$$
\begin{array}{ccc}
\text{CH}_2\text{OH} & & \text{CH}_2\text{OH} \\
\text{CO} & & \text{CO} \\
\text{HOCH} & & \text{HCOH} \\
\text{HCOH} & = & \text{HCOH} \\
\text{CH}_2.\text{O}.\text{H}_2\text{PO}_3 & & \text{CH}_2.\text{O}.\text{H}_2\text{PO}_3
\end{array}
$$

(from XII.19.i
and XII.19.l)

D-xylulose   D-ribulose
5-phosphate   5-phosphate

XII.19.o   Phosphoribulokinase (2.7.1.19)

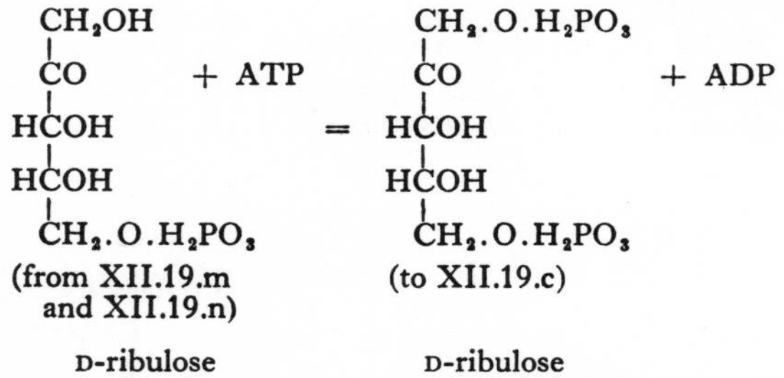

$$
\begin{array}{ccccc}
\text{CH}_2\text{OH} & & & \text{CH}_2.\text{O}.\text{H}_2\text{PO}_3 & \\
\text{CO} & + \text{ATP} & & \text{CO} & + \text{ADP} \\
\text{HCOH} & & = & \text{HCOH} & \\
\text{HCOH} & & & \text{HCOH} & \\
\text{CH}_2.\text{O}.\text{H}_2\text{PO}_3 & & & \text{CH}_2.\text{O}.\text{H}_2\text{PO}_3 &
\end{array}
$$

(from XII.19.m   (to XII.19.c)
and XII.19.n)

D-ribulose   D-ribulose
5-phosphate   1,5-diphosphate

Sum of reactions XII.19.a–o:

$$6CO_2 + H_3PO_4 + 5H_2O = \text{fructose 6-phosphate} + 6O_2$$

Note.—In adding the reactions it must be remembered that for the production of one molecule of fructose 6-phosphate reactions i–m must be multiplied by 2, reactions g–h by 3, reaction n by 4, reaction f by 5, reactions c and o by 6, reactions a, d and e by 12, and reaction b by 18. Thus the synthesis of one molecule of fructose 6-phosphate requires the provision of 12 molecules of $NADPH_2$ and 18 molecules of ATP.

Part (c)

The fructose phosphate can be converted into sucrose as follows:

XII.19.p   Glucosephosphate isomerase (5.3.1.9)

```
                                                        OH
                                                        |
CH₂OH                    CHO                    HC
|                        |                      |
CO                       HCOH                   HCOH
|                        |           or         |
HOCH          =          HOCH                   HOCH        O
|                        |                      |
HCOH                     HCOH                   HC
|                        |                      |
HCOH                     HCOH                   HC─────
|                        |                      |
CH₂.O.H₂PO₃              CH₂.O.H₂PO₃            CH₂.O H₂PO₃
(from XII.19.h)
```

Fructose   glucose 6-phosphate
6-phosphate

XII.19.q   Phosphoglucomutase (2.7.5.1)

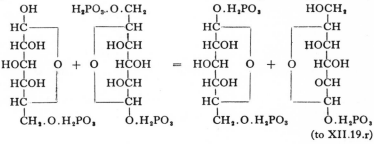

Glucose   glucose   glucose   glucose
6-phosphate   1,6-diphosphate   1,6-diphosphate   1-phosphate

XII.19.r   Glucose-1-phosphate uridylyltransferase (2.7.7.9)

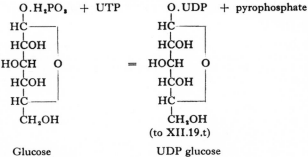

Glucose   UDP glucose
1-phosphate

XII.19.s Acid phosphatase (3.1.3.2)

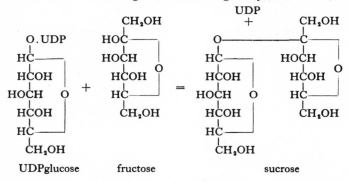

Fructose 6-phosphate   fructose

(from XII.19.h)

XII.19.t UDPglucose-fructose glucosyltransferase (2.4.1.13)

UDPglucose   fructose   sucrose

XII.19.u Nucleosidediphosphate kinase (2.7.4.6)

$$UDP + ATP = UTP + ADP$$

XII.19.v Inorganic pyrophosphatase (3.6.1.1)

$$Pyrophosphate + H_2O = 2H_3PO_4$$

Sum of reactions:

$$2\ \text{fructose 6-phosphate} + ATP + 2H_2O = \text{sucrose} + ADP + 3H_3PO_4$$

Grand total of reactions for photosynthesis of sucrose ((a) + (b) + (c)):

$$12CO_2 + 11H_2O = \text{sucrose} + 12O_2$$

Note.—In adding the reactions part (b) must be multiplied by 2 and added to parts (a) and (c), since two fructose phosphate molecules are used in part (c). Thus the synthesis of one molecule of sucrose requires the provision of 24 molecules of $NADPH_2$ and 37 molecules of ATP.

XIII

ENZYME BIOLOGY

THROUGHOUT THIS BOOK we have been considering the properties of enzymes as chemical catalysts or simply as chemical substances. Those phenomena which a physical chemist (HAMMETT, *988*) has referred to as 'the startling and specific catalytic effects produced by enzymes' present many points of unique interest. The primary and overriding interest of enzymes, however, is their connection with life. Of all the multitudinous chemical processes in the living cell on which its life depends, there is scarcely one which is not due to enzyme catalysis; there can be no life without enzymes. Under the heading of 'enzyme biology' we consider enzymes in relation to the living cell and to life itself.

ENZYMES AS THE BASIS OF LIFE

The most fundamental requirement of living matter, which must be met if life is to exist at all, is that it should contain a mechanism whereby free energy from such chemical reactions as the oxidation of foodstuffs is made available for carrying out energy-requiring reactions and processes, instead of being lost as heat. Examples of processes for which energy is required are biosynthetic reactions, necessary for the formation of new living matter in growth and reproduction, osmotic work in absorption and secretion, mechanical work in movement, particularly as developed in the higher animals, as well as such special processes as bioluminescence in fireflies or generation of electricity in the electric eel.

Living matter contains and is dependent upon a number of unstable substances which are continually breaking down and having to be replenished by synthesis, so that a continuous supply of energy is necessary even to keep the system in a steady state. Even normally stable substances, such as proteins, break down under intracellular conditions, owing to the presence of autolytic enzymes, so that the replenishment of these substances also will need energy. If the energy supply is cut off, the whole system runs down by breakdown of the unstable essential substances and by the predominance of catabolic enzyme processes, thus leading to autolysis of the cell. When this process has gone sufficiently far it becomes irreversible, for the synthetic reactions cannot be resumed in the absence of the essential catalysts. This is what is really meant by the death of the cell.

The essential features of the enzymatic system linking energy-producing processes with energy-utilizing processes are as follows. By a series of enzymatic transformations, the substance serving as the initial source of energy is first converted into a form which can then undergo a breakdown reaction coupled with the formation of an 'energy-rich bond', that is a bond with a standard free energy of hydrolysis of the order of 10,000 cal/mole,† which may be an acid anhydride bond (acyl-phosphate or pyrophosphate), a phosphoamide bond, or a thiolester bond. Examples of such processes are the formation of diphosphoglycerate by the oxidation of glyceraldehyde phosphate (forming an acyl-phosphate bond), the formation of acetyl- or succinyl-hydrolipoate by the oxidation of pyruvate or 2-oxoglutarate (forming a thiolester bond), and the process of oxidative phosphorylation (forming pyrophosphate bonds by reactions not clearly understood).

The components of the system bringing about oxidative phosphorylation in the mitochondria are gradually being unravelled by the use of a variety of experimental approaches. Particulate preparations can be made from disintegrated mitochondria which, although they have active oxidation systems, do not bring about the phosphorylation of ADP (see p. 548). The ability to phosphorylate can be restored to some of these preparations by soluble 'coupling factors'. RACKER and his group (2068, 2124) showed that mechanically disrupted mitochondria could be separated by centrifugation into a particulate preparation and a soluble 'coupling factor' which they partially purified, and showed to be identical with the cold-labile, dinitrophenol-stimulated ATP-ase which is released from the mitochondria on their disruption. They postulated that this enzyme also catalyses some step in the coupled phosphorylation sequence. More recently (2157) they have shown that a second coupling factor is also concerned with the phosphorylation of ADP, and a third factor is required to restore the isotope exchange between P^{32}-labelled inorganic phosphate and ATP in trypsin-treated submitochondrial particles. Although not yet directly proven, it seems probable that this third factor is also part of the phosphorylation system.

---

† The standard free energy of hydrolysis of ATP into ADP and phosphate has been taken until recently to be about —12,000 cal/mole. The actual value depends on the pH, and recent reliable determinations have given —7,700 cal/mole at pH 7 and 30° (2225a), —8,900 cal/mole at pH 7·5 and 25° (369) and —9,300 cal/mole at pH 7·5 and 37° (210). In the presence of magnesium salts, the standard free energy of hydrolysis of $MgATP^{--}$ to $MgADP^{-}$ is —7,000 cal/mole at pH 7 and 37° (210). The value for the thiolester bond of acetyl-CoA is —8,200 at pH 7 and 25° (369).

LEHNINGER's group have also studied mitochondrial factors obtained in a somewhat different type of experiment (see *1944*). Mitochondria swell on treatment with glutathione (as well as other substances) and under suitable conditions ATP can bring about the contraction of the swollen mitochondria. The presence of certain soluble substances ('C-factors') obtained from mitochondria is necessary for this ATP-linked contraction of glutathione-swollen mitochondria; these factors also stimulate coupled phosphorylation in digitonin-treated submito-chondrial particles. On chromatography on DEAE-cellulose three separate C-factors can be obtained from these soluble preparations; one has been identified as glutathione peroxidase (1.11.1.a) and another as catalase (1.11.1.6). The third factor, which appears to be a heat-stable small molecule, has not been identified. The enzymatic factors do not owe their action simply to removal of toxic amounts of H_2O_2 formed during oxidation of substrates, since added peroxide does not stimulate swelling or inhibit ATP-linked contraction.

Other lines of evidence suggest that lipids may be associated with these processes. WOJTCZAK and LEHNINGER showed that during the swelling of mitochondria which occurs spontaneously, or is induced by calcium salts or thyroxine, a heat-stable 'uncoupling' agent is formed inside the mitochondria; this factor is of lipid nature and is probably removed by oxidation during ATP-stimulated contraction of the swollen mitochondria (*2892*). A lipid peroxide is formed during the glutathione-induced swelling of mitochondria or when mitochondria are incubated aerobically in presence of Fe^{++} and ascorbate (*1120*), and the peroxidases which act as coupling factors may use this as their substrates.

The action of 'uncoupling agents', such as dinitrophenol, which inhibit phosphorylation without affecting respiration, has been widely studied. Much of this work supports the idea that dinitrophenol can replace inorganic phosphate to bring about the breakdown of some antecedent, energy-rich compound not formed from inorganic phosphate.

Numerous hypothetical reaction schemes for oxidative phosphory-lation have been put forward which are compatible with the known facts; they are reviewed in *1534*. BORST and SLATER (*296*) believe that their studies on the action of dinitrophenol support the scheme:

XIII.1 $\qquad AH_2 + B + I \rightleftharpoons BH_2 + A \sim I$

XIII.2 $\qquad A \sim I + X \rightleftharpoons A + X \sim I$

XIII.3 $\qquad X \sim I + P_i \rightleftharpoons X \sim P + I$

XIII.4 $\qquad X \sim P + ADP \rightleftharpoons X + ATP$

where A and B are members of the respiratory chain, and X and I are hypothetical intermediates.

According to their scheme, dinitrophenol brings about the rapid hydrolysis of $X \sim I$ and thus suppresses reactions XIII.3 and 4. Racker (*2157*) postulates that the ATPase coupling factor catalyses reaction XIII.4; the other factors are presumably concerned with earlier stages of the sequence. Whatever the details of the process or the nature of X and I turn out to be, it seems clear that oxidation gives rise to a labile intermediate which is subsequently cleaved by inorganic phosphate to give a high energy phosphate, which then reacts with ADP. Two labile phospho-compounds which have actually been shown to be formed during the process are the phosphorylated form of NAD referred to on p. 368 (*931a*), and a phosphorylated form of histidine (*304a*).

The chemical energy of the bonds formed by any of the processes discussed above may be temporarily stored (especially in muscle, where large sudden demands for mechanical work may be made at any moment), or used immediately for biosynthesis. The two main forms in which the energy is stored are as pyrophosphate bonds in nucleoside triphosphates (especially ATP) or as phosphoamide bonds in creatine or arginine phosphates. If the initial reaction has produced an acyl-phosphate, the labile phosphate is transferred by a kinase to ADP to form ATP, or from this to creatine by a further kinase. If the initial energy-rich compound is a thiolester, the thiolester bond energy has to be converted into phosphate bond energy. This may be achieved by means of a synthetase after transacylation from one thiol group to another (reactions XII.2.h, m and n). Alternatively, in bacteria the conversion may be achieved (in the case of pyruvate oxidation) by phosphate acetyltransferase (2.3.1.8) giving acetylphosphate, which then undergoes a kinase reaction to form ATP.

The content of phosphate acceptors which can act as energy stores varies considerably in different tissues. Skeletal muscle differs from most other tissues in having a fairly large adenosine phosphate content and a still larger content of creatine (in vertebrates) or arginine (in most invertebrates). Both creatine and adenosine phosphates are present in other tissues, but in much smaller amounts; other nucleoside triphosphates (GTP, UTP, etc.) are also present in amounts of about the same order. By no means all the creatine present in vertebrate tissues is normally present in the form of creatine phosphate, in fact, the fraction phosphorylated, which does not vary greatly from one tissue to another, is usually only about 20 per cent (*700*).

Most of the energy-utilizing processes are driven by the breakdown of ATP. Biosynthetic reactions making use of this energy may be brought about by two main mechanisms. By means of synthetase re-actions biosynthesis may be directly coupled to the breakdown of one or other of the pyrophosphate bonds of ATP. Alternatively, a kinase and a phosphorylase may co-operate to bring about a similar result; the kinase transfers a phosphate group from ATP to the first reactant, and the latter is then transferred from the phosphate to the second reactant by the phosphorylase, leaving orthophosphate. Muscular contraction depends on the breakdown of ATP which is brought about by the calcium-acti-vated adenosinetriphosphatase of the myofibril, but the details of the mechanism connecting the ATP breakdown with the actual contraction have still to be worked out. Osmotic work (e.g. in the secretion of gastric juice and the transport of K^+ ions across cell membranes), biolumines-cence, and the development of high voltages have also been shown to be connected with ATP breakdown.

All these processes are brought about by integrated systems of en-zymes, many of which have been discussed in the last chapter. Thus Tables XII.1, XII.2, XII.4(b) and XII.5 represent important energy-producing systems, while Tables XII.11 and 13–19 show various biosyntheses which use the energy produced.

As well as the other components of the cell, the catalysts themselves (enzymes and coenzymes) must be produced by biosynthesis, especially during growth. The general considerations outlined above must apply also to these syntheses, which are therefore dependent on the system of reactions catalysed by the products of the synthesis. In the case of the enzymes, which are proteins, the mechanism of synthesis involves an RNA template (see Chapter XI), but the components for both protein and template must be synthesized enzymatically, and the energy for the formation of the large number of bonds contained in the enzyme proteins must come from catabolic enzyme reactions. Thus the whole system is self-maintaining or even self-propagating, which is one of the most fundamental properties of living matter.

ENZYMES AND CELL-STRUCTURE

Although systems of many enzymes, no less than single enzymes, work perfectly well in simple solution, a living cell is certainly far from being a 'bag of enzymes' in homogeneous solution. In fact, a living cell has an elaborate structure, knowledge of which has been greatly extended recently by electron microscopy. We have seen in the last chapter that certain enzymes are specifically situated in particular intracellular parti-ticles, and an important part of enzyme biology is the study of the relationship between these structures and enzyme systems.

Intracellular structures

A typical cell is bounded by a cell membrane, which is permeable only to certain substances and which, in the cells of plants and bacteria, is mechanically strengthened by a surrounding porous cell-wall which determines the shape of the cell but takes no part in the cell metabolism. The cell contents are traditionally divided into cytoplasm and nucleus. The cytoplasm is not homogeneous, but contains particulate structures of various kinds, among which may be mentioned mitochondria, lysosomes, microsomes, 'dense bodies', chromaffin granules, Nissl granules, chloroplasts, 'secretory granules', Golgi apparatus, centrosome, myofibrils, basal granules of cilia or flagellæ, '200 Å granules' of bacteria, phagocytic inclusions, volutin granules, pancreatic zymogen granules, fat droplets, and granules of various metabolic products such as glycogen, starch, sulphur, poly-3-hydroxybutyric acid, calcium oxalate, etc., as well as the 'endoplasmic reticulum'. Not all these structures occur in every cell. Many are not simple particles, but have a highly organized structure. This is especially true of animal mitochondria and chloroplasts. Typical mitochondria are somewhat elongated bodies, which may be 1μ or more in length, surrounded by a characteristic double membrane and containing internal structures consisting of double lamellæ or tubes projecting inwards and bearing numerous small dense particles 10–15 mμ in diameter. The endoplasmic reticulum shows in parts a somewhat similar structure, with rounded or flattened vesicles which in certain 'rough surfaced' regions bear numerous dense particles, or ribosomes, on their outer faces (2043). This network appears to be continuous in places with the nuclear membrane and the cell membrane, and often lies close up against the mitochondria. It has been suggested that the microsomes which can be separated from tissue homogenates by centrifugation (see below) are formed from the endoplasmic reticulum by a 'pinching off' process in the form of vesicles bearing the ribosomes on their outer surfaces (2044). It should be noted that intracellular membranes are not observed in bacteria (307).

The Golgi apparatus consists of a region of parallel smooth membranes, somewhat thicker than those of the endoplasmic reticulum, and often associated with vesicles and vacuoles; its structure resembles in some ways both that of the endoplasmic reticulum and the internal structure of mitochondria (2100).

The structure of the nucleus is very different in dividing and non-dividing cells. In the non-dividing cell it is surrounded (except in bacteria) by a double membrane with numerous pores, usually arranged in a regular pattern and apparently closed by a very thin diaphragm or with other material. The nuclear membrane completely disappears during cell division and reforms round each of the daughter nuclei. The non-dividing nucleus usually presents a homogeneous appearance, although uniformly granular in the electron microscope. Normally the only visible intranuclear structure is the nucleolus (sometimes more than one), a dense body which in electron micrographs is seen to consist of a reticulum containing tightly packed granules. During cell division the nucleolus becomes much smaller and less prominent; and at the same time a number of threadlike bodies, the chromosomes, appear within the nucleus, and after thickening pass through the well known mitotic or meiotic figures. During the process the space originally occupied by the nucleus becomes occupied by a structure known as the spindle, containing protein threads to which the chromosomes become attached and by which they are drawn apart. The chromosomes themselves have a very highly organized internal structure associated with the linear arrangement of a large number of different genes in a definite order.

Until recently the bacterial cell was thought to lack most of the structures seen in animal and plant cells, but here again the electron microscope has given information about internal structure (see, for example, *1834, 2485*). Definite nuclear material is always present; this may be collected into a small spherical 'nucleus' (though without a nuclear membrane), as in many cocci, or it may ramify widely throughout the cell, as in many bacilli. Under the electron microscope the bacterial nucleus appears to contain fibrous material. Outside the nucleus the cell is filled with a granular cytoplasm, the particles being about 10–20 mμ in diameter. Apart from the cell membrane which underlies the cell wall ('the protoplast membrane'), no membranous structures have been observed in bacterial cells.

Thus the living cell is by no means a simple sac, but is in reality a very highly organized system, containing many complex visible structures; furthermore, centrifugation of living cells shows that even the clear particle-free cytoplasm can be separated into at least three layers of different density (*1141*). A knowledge of the localization of the various enzymes within the cell in relation to these structures is highly important for the understanding of the functioning of the cell. The mere extraction of enzymes from a minced tissue gives little indication of their intracellular origin.

Intracellular localization of enzymes

The question of intracellular localization has been studied by two main methods: (*a*) microhistochemical methods, and (*b*) separation of particulate fractions from disintegrated cells, e.g. by differential centrifugation.

The histochemical methods may be regarded as developments from the staining techniques of classical histology, since they depend on the liberation of a staining substance in tissue sections as a result of the enzyme action, followed by microscopic examination of the stained tissue. It is of course necessary to establish that the colour produced remains at the point of formation and does not stain other structures as a result of diffusion. Satisfactory conditions are extremely difficult to achieve, especially if the tissue has been fixed by conventional methods, which destroy most enzymes and may in any case cause their redistribution within the cell by destroying cell structures. Thus the method is only applicable to a few enzymes, notably phosphatase (*1138, 2064*).

The histochemical method has, however, been valuable in locating non-enzymatic constituents such as fat and the nucleic acids. In the latter case enzymes can be used as specific reagents in conjunction with ultraviolet microscopy (*538*). Nucleic acids absorb ultraviolet light of wavelength about 260 mμ very strongly, and as the mercury lamp gives a strong line near this wavelength which can be isolated by a monochromator, it can be used as a light source for microscopy of tissue sections in order to show the location of nucleic acid. By photometric measurements the nucleic acid in various parts of the cell can be roughly estimated. Treatment of the tissue section with peptidase-free ribonuclease will specifically dissolve out the RNA, and comparison of the ultraviolet microphotographs of the treated and untreated sections will then show which parts of the absorption were due to RNA. Similar experiments with deoxyribonuclease will reveal the location of the DNA. In this way it has been shown that DNA is located in the bands of the chromosomes and both RNA and DNA in the resting nucleolus.

A number of intracellular structures can be separated under physiological conditions by centrifuging whole cells suspended in a medium of graded density. The cells take up an equilibrium position and the cell contents (in *Amoeba*) separate into nine distinct layers. Provided that the process is not carried too far, it is completely reversible and the cell is not damaged. If a sufficiently large cell is used, it can be removed (after chilling) and divided into two parts by microdissection, and the amounts of each enzyme in the two parts can be determined separately by micromethods. The point of division is varied in different cells, and the partition of the enzyme between the two parts is compared with the partition of the different cell components. Some results obtained by this method have been presented by HOLTER (*1141*); for example, the succinate dehydrogenase was located in the mitochondria, while dipeptidase was shown to be uniformly distributed.

Nearly all our knowledge of the intracellular localization of enzymes has been the result of the study of preparations of particular cell structures obtained by differential centrifugation. By subjecting cell suspensions to conditions of high shear, it is possible to disrupt the cell membrane without destroying the integrity of the nucleus or cytoplasmic

TABLE XIII.1

APPROXIMATE DIAMETERS OF STRUCTURES OBTAINED FROM LIVER HOMOGENATES

	Diameter ($m\mu$)
Whole cells	20,000
Nuclei	6,000
Nucleoli	1,000
Mitochondria	750*
Lysosomes	200–800
Microsomes	10–150
Glycogen granules	100
Sub-mitochondrial particles	50–100
Ribosomes	10–15
Thickness of membrane around Golgi apparatus	20
Thickness of membranes from endoplasmic reticulum	5
Typical globular protein	5
For comparison:	
Chloroplasts of higher plants	3,000–10,000
Typical bacillus cell	2,000
Typical coccus cell	500
Photosynthetic grana	300–1,700
Bacterial cytoplasmic granules	10–20

* Up to 7,000 mμ long.

particles. The various structural components of such a homogenate then sediment in the centrifuge at different rates, primarily owing to their difference in size (see Table XIII.1), and can be separated by a series of runs, usually at increasing speeds. By resuspending the centrifuged pellets and centrifuging again, a number of fairly homogeneous fractions can be obtained. Differences in density are also important and centrifugation in a density gradient may be employed. These fractions can be obtained in reasonable quantity, and the enzymes present in them can then be determined by the usual methods.

In order to obtain undamaged preparations, homogenization must be carried out in special media. The use of sucrose solutions has enabled preparations of nuclei and mitochondria to be made which appear normal under the microscope and are highly active enzymatically. Hypertonic (0·88 M) sucrose was first used, as this was found to conserve the morphological characteristics with the least possible damage, but it was later found that many of the enzymes of mitochondria were better conserved in isotonic sucrose (0·25 M for mammalian tissues). A number of modifications of this medium have been suggested from time to time for the preparation of tissue components for special purposes; for example buffering at pHs other than neutrality, or the addition of various stabilizing substances to the sucrose medium. Nuclei have also been prepared by centrifugation in non-aqueous media. The methods available for isolating sub-cellular components have been well reviewed by ALLFREY (52).

As the result of the work of SCHNEIDER, CLAUDE, HOGEBOOM, DOUNCE and others, a more or less standard scheme of fractionation has been adopted; this gives the following fractions: intact cells with tissue debris, nuclei, mitochondria (usually including the lysosomes, discussed below), microsomes, supernatant. These fractions differ considerably in their gross chemical composition. The DNA of the cell is almost entirely in the nucleus, while a very large part of the RNA is present in the microsomes, some being present also in both mitochondria and nucleus. Both mitochondria and microsomes are remarkable for their high lipid content (30 to 40 per cent of their dry weight), largely in the form of phospholipids complexed with protein. The water content of normal mitochondria is about 70 per cent (2840).

A mass of data on the distribution of enzymes between such fractions has been obtained, and has been reviewed by a number of authors (see, for example, 456, 581, 1127, 1140). Some of these results are presented schematically in Table XIII.2, where the symbols represent not the specific activities but the total amount of enzyme present in the whole of each fraction. Four + signs represent the activity of the whole unfractionated homogenate, and each + sign represents about a quarter of this. Where, as sometimes happens, different authors disagree, we have given what seems to us to be the best value, taking into consideration the experimental conditions. The results are approximate only; they are affected by various factors and do not necessarily add up to exactly 100 per cent.

The results show clearly that some enzymes are situated entirely in particular fractions, but great care must be taken in interpreting the figures, especially for small activities. There is a possibility of mutual contamination of the different fractions and indeed, since the number of fractions is much smaller than the number of different cell structures, some of them must contain several different kinds of structures. The degree of mutual contamination will vary with the methods used, so that results from different workers are not necessarily strictly comparable; contamination may be due to adsorption, to adhesion, to aggregation of

TABLE XIII.2

LOCATION OF ENZYMES IN INTRACELLULAR STRUCTURES IN RODENT LIVER

The fractions are designated as follows: N, nuclei; Mt. mitochondria; Ms, microsomes; S, supernatant.

	N	Mt	Ms	S
A. *Enzymes present mainly in the nucleus*				
NMN adenylyltransferase (2.7.7.1)	+++	−		+
B. *Enzymes present mainly in the mitochondria*				
D-3-hydroxybutyrate dehydrogenase (1.1.1.30)	+	++++	−	−
Isocitrate dehydrogenase (1.1.1.41)	−	++++	−	−
Succinate dehydrogenase (1.3.99.1	−	++++	−	−
Glutamate dehydrogenase (1.4.1.3)	−	++++		
Urate oxidase (1.7.3.3)	±	+++	±	−
Cytochrome oxidase (1.9.3.1)	−	++++	−	−
Acetyl-CoA acyltransferase (2.3.1.16)		++++		
Adenylate kinase (2.7.4.3)	±	+++	−	−
Ribonuclease (2.7.7.16)	−	+++	+	+
Thiosulphate sulphurtransferase (2.8.1.1)	+	+++	−	−
Acid phosphatase (3.1.3.2)	−	+++	+	±
Deoxyribonuclease II (3.1.4.6)	±	+++	±	+
Arylsulphatases A and B (3.1.6.1)	±	+++	+	+
β-galactosidase (3.2.1.23)	±	++	+	+
β-acetylaminodeoxyglucosidase (3.2.1.30)	+	+++	+	±
C. *Enzymes present mainly in the microsomes*				
Aryl 4-hydroxylase (1.99.1.1)	−	−	+++	−
Carboxylesterase (3.1.1.1)	−	+	++	+
Acetylcholinesterase (3.1.1.7)	±	+	++	−
Cholinesterase (3.1.1.8)	±	±	++	−
Vitamin A esterase (3.1.1.12)	−	−	++++	−
Cholesterol esterase (3.1.1.13)	+	−	++++	−
Alkaline phosphatase (3.1.3.1)	±	±	++++	±
Glucose-6-phosphatase (3.1.3.9)	−	+	+++	−
Arylsulphatase C (3.1.6.1)	±	±	+++	−
Choloyl-CoA synthetase (6.2.1.7)	−	−	++++	−
D. *Soluble enzymes, present mainly in the supernatant*				
Lactate dehydrogenase (1.1.1.27)	−	−	−	++++
Isocitrate dehydrogenase (1.1.1.42)	−	±	−	+++
Glucose-6-phosphate dehydrogenase (1.1.1.49)	−	−	−	++++
Xanthine oxidase (1.2.3.2)	−	−	−	++++
Glutathione reductase (1.6.4.2)	−	−	++++	
α-glucan phosphorylase (2.4.1.1)	±		−	+++
Purine nucleoside phosphorylase (2.4.2.1)				++++
Aspartate aminotransferase (2.6.1.1)	−	+		++++
Glucokinase (2.7.1.2)				+++
Ketohexokinase (2.7.1.3)				+++
Phosphoglucomutase (2.7.5.1)	−	−	−	++++
FMN adenylyltransferase (2.7.7.2)	−	−	−	++++
Hexosediphosphatase (3.1.3.11)	−	−	−	++++
Leucine aminopeptidase (3.4.1.1)	−	±	±	+++
Adenosine deaminase (3.5.4.4)				++++
Aldolase (4.1.2.7)	+	−	−	++++
Aconitate hydratase (4.2.1.3)	±	+	−	++++
E. *Enzymes not present mainly in one fraction*				
Malate dehydrogenase (1.1.1.37)	−	+	+++	
NADPH$_2$ cytochrome *c* reductase (1.6.2.3)	±	++	+	±
Catalase (1.11.1.6)	−	++	−	++
5-nucleotidase (3.1.3.5)	++	+	++	±
β-glucuronidase (3.2.1.31)	−	++	+	−
NAD(P) nucleosidase (3.2.2.6)	++	−	++	++
Arginase (3.5.3.1)	++	±	++	−
ATPase (3.6.1.3)	+	++	+	−
ATPase (3.6.1.4)	+	+++	+	−
Fumarate hydratase (4.2.1.2)	±	++	+	±

smaller particles (giving clumps which appear among the larger particles), to autolysis or the extraction of components, or to other factors.

A further difficulty, which probably invalidates some of the earlier results published, is that the enzyme in the particulate fraction may not be available to substrate in the suspension medium, so that spurious low values are obtained for these fractions. For example, GREVILLE and CHAPPELL (930) showed that the thiosulphate sulphurtransferase (2.8.1.1) of rat liver homogenates prepared in 0·44M sucrose was 'latent', but the activity appeared if the mitochondria from such homogenates were treated in such a way as to induce swelling, for example, by treatment with detergents, phosphate or L-thyroxine. With 3-hydroxybutyrate dehydrogenase (1.1.1.30), on the other hand, which is also latent in rat liver mitochondria, chemical treatments only cause a small degree of unmasking, and drastic treatment such as sonic disruption is required in order to make the enzyme available (1536). The activation of latent mitocondrial dehydrogenases was compared with the activation of lysosomal enzymes by BENDALL and DE DUVE (203) who concluded that two types of activation are involved. The permeability of the mitochondrial membrane may be increased so that substrate molecules can penetrate, without allowing enzyme to leak out; such activations are usually reversible. In other cases the permeability may increase sufficiently to allow the enzyme to pass out into solution, and such activations are clearly irreversible.

It has commonly been assumed that the four fractions listed in Table XIII.2 contain respectively only nuclei, mitochondria, microsomes or cell sap. DE DUVE (187, 580; see also 1481) has shown that the mitocondrial fraction contains, in addition to true mitochondria, particles of a second kind to which the name 'lysosomes' has been given, and these may contain up to 20 per cent of the total nitrogen of the preparation. The two kinds of particle can be partially separated by differential centrifugation, the lysosomes, which are smaller but denser, sedimenting more slowly. More definite evidence can be obtained by centrifuging mitochondrial preparations in a density gradient (187). At equilibrium the particles take up a position in the gradient corresponding to their own density, and if the activity of a particular enzyme in the sample is determined for various positions in the centrifuge tube, a characteristic distribution curve is obtained. These curves fall into two distinct groups. The similar curves obtained for cytochrome oxidase, glutamate dehydrogenase, malate dehydrogenase and deoxyribonuclease are taken to show the distribution of true mitochondria; quite different curves are given by some hydrolytic enzymes, including acid phosphatase, β-glucuronidase and ribonuclease, which are therefore assumed to be lysosomal enzymes. This latter group are shown in italics in Table XIII.2. On the other hand the lysosomes seem to be much less enzymatically homogeneous than the true mitochondria. Urate oxidase, in particular, has a distribution in a density gradient markedly different from that of the hydrolases of the lysosomes, and may occur in quite distinct particles.

Most of the tissue fractionation studies reported in the literature relate to liver. The distribution of enzymes in other tissues may be quite different. For example, ALDRIDGE and JOHNSON (47) showed that in brain only about one third of the cholinesterase and carboxylesterase activities could be accounted for by the microsomal fraction, the rest being distributed throughout the other fractions, whereas in liver the major part of these enzymes is in the microsomes. Thiosulphate sulphur-transferase and adenylate kinase, which are present predominantly in the mitochondria in liver, are completely absent from the mitochondria of heart muscle, being there present mainly in the supernatant fraction (458, 1891). Aconitate hydratase is mainly in the cell sap in liver, but in brain it is exclusively in the mitochondria (2382).

In a recent review, DE DUVE et al. (581) survey the enzymes in the Enzyme List of the Report of the Enzyme Commission, giving a summary of the information available as to their intracellular distribution in various tissues.

Enzyme localization and cell physiology

One of the most striking results which has come from studies on the intracellular localization of enzymes has been that in many of the important metabolic systems all the enzymes and coenzymes concerned are present in the same particle. For example, all the components of the oxidative chain associated with the standard cytochrome system are present in intramitochondrial particles; in contrast, the enzymes of glycolysis are almost entirely in the supernatant fraction.

However, this idea appears to have been over-stressed in the past. Particular importance has been attributed to the mitochondrion as the 'power house of the cell', in which the aerobic energy-producing processes of the cell were thought to take place. In particular, impure preparations of mitochondria (with suitable supplements) had been shown to catalyse the citric cycle, and it was believed that all the enzymes involved in the cycle (Table XII.2) were localized entirely in the mitochondria. However, a glance at Table XIII.2 will show that this is not entirely true, for a number of the essential enzymes of the cycle have been shown to be mainly localized in other fractions, and only two of the enzymes have been definitely shown to be localized entirely in the mitochondria. Other oxidation systems which have been shown to occur in mitochondria are β-oxidation of fatty acids (although the reductive synthesis of fatty acids takes place in the cell sap, and their incorporation into fats in the microsomes), oxidation of succinate, oxidation of reduced NAD and NADP by O_2, and oxidative phosphorylation. The proteolytic systems of liver are also localized largely in the mitochondria, except for glycyl-glycine dipeptidase and aminotripeptidase which are completely in the supernantant fraction (2159). Protein synthesis involves enzymes in the nucleus and cell sap as well as the template system in the ribosomes.

However, the localization of a complete group of metabolic reactions in a particular particle gives no reliable indication that any of the enzymes concerned are mainly situated in that particle; it merely indicates that only in that particle are all the enzymes present together. For instance, in the case of a system depending on four enzymes A, B, C and D, if A and B are situated mainly in the microsomes while C and D are situated mainly in the supernatant, and small amounts of all four enzymes are in the mitochondria, it is only in the mitochondria that the system will be detected. In the intact cell, however, sections of the metabolic sequence may take place elsewhere. Thus in liver the capacity of extramitochondrial enzymes to catalyse the conversion of acetate to 2-oxoglutarate is equal to or greater than the normal rate of oxidative metabolism of whole tissue (1620). This portion of the citric cycle might largely take place outside the mitochondrion, where it plays an important role in maintaining the high ratio of $NADPH_2$ to NADP.

It is interesting to note that many of the essential coenzymes are largely concentrated in the mitochondria (2336). For example, over 50 per cent of the total liver CoA, 65 per cent of the FAD, a very large part of the cytochrome c, and all of the cytochromes a, b and c_1, are in the mitochondria; on the other hand, although NAD is present in mitochondria, the main part is present in the supernatant. The soluble coenzymes when present in the mitochondrion do not readily exchange with those in the external medium, largely because the mitochondrion is surrounded by a membrane impermeable to such molecules.

The distribution of metals in rat liver cells has been studied by THIERS and VALLEE (2639). Mitochondria contain a high concentration of Mg, Mn and Ca relative to the other fractions, while the cell-sap is relatively high in alkali metals. Mitochondria normally contain a high concentration of potassium, for the maintenance of which the occurrence of oxidative phosphorylation is necessary. Anything which inhibits the latter process causes a rapid loss of the excess potassium. When KCl is added to the medium, actively metabolizing mitochondria can draw in extra potassium against a concentration gradient. They also contain fairly high concentrations of sodium, magnesium and calcium. The passage of ions into, and of water out of, the mitochondrion may normally be an active process dependent on metabolism, but the results obtained differ from one ion to another and are not always easy to interpret. The swelling of muscle mitochondria in hypotonic solutions is prevented or even reversed by the addition of ATP or ITP (*432*). It appears that ions can pass passively across the mitochondrial membrane, but that their concentration within the mitochondrion is due to the active accumulation of a 'bound' form which remains fixed in the interior (*2840*).

With regard to the lysosomes, DE DUVE has suggested that these particles are connected with hydrolytic processes, hence the name. The microsomes also might be considered as hydrolytic particles since, of the ten enzymes shown in section C of the table as present mainly in them, eight are esterases. They also contain other hydrolysing enzymes which are shown in section E. In addition, the microsomes contain the greater part of the $NADH_2$ cytochrome c reductase activity of the cell; this is not due to the presence of enzyme 1.6.2.1, but to cytochrome b_5 and its reductase 1.6.2.2. Cytochrome b_5 is the characteristic pigment of animal microsomes.

Many enzyme systems are present not in particles but in a soluble form in the ground plasm of the cell. As well as the enzymes of glycolysis and the other enzymes shown in section D of the table, systems synthesizing glutamine, arginine and FAD are also largely in the supernatant.

Although nuclei can be prepared in the microscopically normal state and free from other particles, it has proved remarkably difficult to decide what enzymatic activities, if any, are associated with the nucleus. Apart from the single enzyme shown in section A of the table, only relatively low enzyme activities are found in nuclear fractions. It is then necessary to be certain that these activities were originally present in the nuclei isolated. In at least some cases the observed activity is due to contamination with other particles; this is always the case for cytochrome oxidase and succinate dehydrogenase (ROODYN, *2244*). Nuclei may adsorb cytoplasmic material during the preparative procedures, especially in aqueous media, or material may pass into or out of the nucleus through the pores of the nuclear membrane. In the case of aldolase, ROODYN (*2245*) showed that about 10 per cent of the activity is definitely in the nucleus, but the amount found in nuclear preparations is often greater than this and varies with the conditions of isolation, particularly with respect to pH and time.

Much effort has been devoted to the development of preparative procedures for isolated nuclei which minimize these redistributions between the cell components. Most workers have used centrifugation in aqueous media (e.g. *2084*), but BEHRENS (*194*) developed a technique of isolation of dehydrated nuclei in non-aqueous media such as cyclohexane and carbon tetrachloride, and this technique has been used with great success by SIEBERT, who showed that with it the redistribution of even small molecules such as lactate could be kept very low. It now seems clear that although complete oxidative systems are lacking in nuclei, many other metabolic systems are present (for reviews see *1832, 2400, 2404*). It has been claimed (*54*) that nuclei possess an oxidative phosphorylation system, producing ATP, which is different from that in the mitochondria; in particular, it is dependent on nuclear DNA or other polynucleotides. The energy thus made available can be utilized for protein synthesis by a mechanism similar to that discussed in Chapter XI (*53*). The nucleus also contains small amounts of many other enzymes, including hydrolases, aminotransferases, and the enzymes of glycolysis and the pentose phosphate cycle.

Where an enzyme occurs in more than one fraction, it is sometimes found that its properties in the two fractions are somewhat different. This is true for example of β-glucuronidase (different pH curves (*580*)), alkaline phosphatase (different metal activation (*694*)) arylsulphatase (different specificity (*640*)), cytochrome reductase (different acceptor), isocitrate dehydrogenase (different acceptor (*706*)), malate dehydrogenase (different physical properties (*2651*)); see also p. 656.

In the green parts of plants the chlorophyll and the photosynthetic enzymes are located in the chloroplasts, together with two cytochrome components which are associated with photosynthesis, namely, cytochromes b_6 and f, and a number of other enzymes (for a review see *2418*). Plant cells contain mitochondria which are, in general, morphologically and enzymatically equivalent to those of animal tissues, containing the normal cytochromes a, a_3, b, c and c_1 (*285, 1735–6*); in the spadix of *Arum* the mitochondria possess an extremely active respiratory system depending on a special cytochrome (cytochrome b_7) (*202*). Plant cells also yield microsomes which are apparently homologous with those of animal tissues with respect to chemical and enzymatic composition, except for the substitution of cytochrome b_3 for cytochrome b_5 (*1736*). In plants, as in animals, intracellular enzyme distribution is not invariant. Catechol oxidase is present in the chloroplasts of tea leaves, but is absent from the chloroplasts of spinach leaves, where it is situated in the cytoplasm (*1581*).

Normal mitochondria can be observed in yeast, with a fine structure similar to that in animal mitochondria (YOTSUYANGI, *2952*). From aerobic yeast, spherical particles 200–300 mμ in diameter capable of active respiration can be obtained (*1601*). However, it should be noted that apparently normal mitochondria are observed in 'petite' mutants which are completely lacking in cytochrome oxidase and other respiratory enzymes.

The bacterial cell differs in several respects from those of higher organisms, particularly in the absence of membranous structures within the cell. One of the more obvious features of the bacterial cell is the cell wall, to which the protoplast membrane is closely pressed. The cell wall appears to have little or no enzymatic activity. It can be removed by various means, and provided that the external osmotic pressure is kept sufficiently high the resulting protoplasts have an unimpaired metabolism, except for the processes connected with cell wall synthesis (*1671*). It appears to be porous, with 'pores' of an effective diameter of around 1 mμ. Nucleotides and coenzymes, but not proteins, can pass freely through the cell wall (*1834*).

It has proved possible to homogenize bacteria and to separate particulate fractions by differential centrifugation, but the results differ in important respects from those obtained with animal cells. Nothing corresponding to the 'nuclear' and 'mitochondrial' fractions of animal and plant homogenates is obtained. The nucleus, which is not bounded by a membrane, disperses and the DNA is found in the supernatant. A particulate fraction consisting of spherical particles about 15 mμ in diameter is obtained (*2320*); these particles contain almost all the RNA of the cell. Such particles, obtained from *Aerobacter* or *Azotobacter*, contain the major part of the succinoxidase system of the cells, as well as the cytochrome system of these cells (*2657*). The particles from *Azotobacter* have been shown to carry out oxidative phosphorylation associated with succinate oxidation, although the efficiency is low unless some of the supernatant is also added (*2661*). Thus biochemically these particles might be considered to be homologous with mitochondria, although in size and RNA content they resemble animal and plant microsomes more closely.

MITCHELL and MOYLE have claimed that the protoplast membrane of *Staphylococcus aureus*, isolated by lysis of the protoplast in distilled water followed by centrifugation, is similar in chemical and enzymatic composition to the small particle fraction obtained after mechanical disintegration of these cells (see *1834–5*). Furthermore, on washing the isolated protoplast membranes with distilled water, they were found to disintegrate into small particles. These authors suggest that the small particles of bacterial homogenates are artifacts, and that the enzymes they contain (including the cytochrome system, many dehydrogenases and acid phosphatase) are normally present in the cell membrane in the intact cell, possibly in actual contact with the external medium. On the other hand, electron micrographs of bacteria, including *Staph. aureus*, show the whole cytoplasm to be densely packed with small granules (*307*) and these might be contaminants of the preparations of Mitchell and Moyle.

Intraparticulate organization

One of the interesting recent developments in the field of biochemical cytology has been the discovery of both morphological and enzymatic differentiation within the particles described above.

We have already mentioned (p. 622) that the electron microscope has revealed a complex internal structure in mitochondria, consisting of tubules or lamellæ bearing numerous electron-dense granules. On rupture of the mitochondrial membrane by mechanical means, or osmotically by suspension in pure water, more than half the dry weight of liver mitochondria appears in solution, including the entire mitochondrial content of a number of enzymes such as glutamate dehydrogenase and fumarate hydratase, as well as nucleotide coenzymes. About a quarter of the dry weight remains in the form of small particles which can be centrifuged down at high speeds. These contain nearly all the RNA of the mitochondria, a great deal of the lipid, and all of the succinate-cytochrome system. Small oxidative particles of this kind, derived from heart mitochondria or 'sarcosomes' (see *431*), had been made empirically many years before any studies on isolated mitochondria had been carried out; the classical Keilin–Hartree preparation consists of such particles. These particles do not usually catalyse oxidative phosphorylation coupled with succinate oxidation. Particulate preparations from disintegrated mitochondria which are capable of catalysing oxidative phosphorylation have, however, been prepared from both heart and liver, especially by the schools of LEHNINGER and GREEN (*498, 899, 905*). Green believes that these phosphorylating particles have a double-layer structure resembling the cristae of the mitochondria, from which they are derived, while the non-phosphorylating oxidative particles (ETP, see p. 548) are vesicles with only a single layer of membrane. The particles are regarded as the basic metabolic units of the mitochondria, each containing one enzyme for each step of the metabolic cycle, and GREEN and ODA (*905*) calculated that there are about 18,000 such units per mitochondrion. The enzymes in each unit are held together by lipid and structural protein.

Lysosomes appear to consist of a sac enclosing a solution of all the enzymes present. So long as this sac remains intact, no enzyme activity can be observed, but the preparation can be 'activated' by a variety of membrane-rupturing procedures, including mechanical rupture, freezing and thawing, exposure to hypotonic media or to a detergent (*825, 2800*), or by incubation under mild conditions with lecithinase, trypsin, or chymotrypsin (but not ribonuclease or muramidase) (*188*). The release of the enzymes in a soluble form is sudden and complete, and occurs simultaneously with all the enzymes of the lysosomes. It is thought to be due to the disruption of a lipoprotein barrier. In fractionations of liver from animals treated with liver poisons, or of livers rendered ischaemic, an increasing proportion of the microsomal enzymes is found in non-sedimentable form; it is suggested that opening of lysosomes plays an important part in autolytic or necrotic phenomena (*189*).

The microsomes are seen under the electron microscope to be vesicles or tubules with electron-dense particles 10–15 mμ in diameter on their outer surface; their probable derivation from the endoplasmic reticulum has already been mentioned. They swell without bursting in hypotonic media, but the structure can be disrupted by treatment with deoxycholate. The ribosomes can then be isolated by high-speed centrifugation (*2044*). They contain almost all the microsomal RNA, but only 20 per cent of the protein, very little of the phospholipid, and none of the cytochrome reductase system or the cytochrome b_5. This oxidation system must therefore be located either in the microsomal membrane or the internal contents. On the other hand, the importance of the ribosomes in protein synthesis has already been discussed in detail in Chapter XI.

Little can be said about the location of enzymes within the nucleus, because most of the enzymes which have been found are only present in small amounts. It has been possible by centrifugation methods to obtain preparations of isolated chromosomes (although starting from whole cells and not from isolated nuclei) (*1831*) and of nucleoli (*1852*). Both have a high content of DNA. Spindle threads have been isolated from dividing sea-urchin eggs and shown to be protein rich in –SH groups (*1771*). Few enzyme tests have been carried out with preparations of nuclear structures, but it is known that aldolase is present in much higher concentration in nucleoli than in whole nuclei, while the reverse is true for arginase and catalase. It has also been reported that the isolated chromosomes are rich in alkaline phosphatase.

The chloroplasts, which contain the chlorophyll of green plants, are highly organized structures. They appear to contain smaller particles, the grana, which may be around 600 mμ in diameter, arranged (in higher plants) in stacks; these grana can be isolated from mechanically disrupted chloroplasts. Each granum is itself a stack of disc-like double lamellae, 7 mμ in thickness. The lamellae are probably continuous throughout the chloroplast, but are more numerous and closely packed in the areas which give rise to grana. The chlorophyll is thought to be located in these lamellae (*1100*).

A great deal remains to be done in this rapidly developing field, but it is already clear that the catalytic organization within the cell has a fine structure which extends down to molecular dimensions, paralleling the intricate morphological fine structure which has been revealed within the last decade.

COMPARATIVE ENZYME BIOCHEMISTRY

Although a great deal has been written about comparative biochemistry little or no attempt has been made to develop comparative enzyme biochemistry as a separate subject. Yet many of the differences between one species and another, as well as the differences between the various tissues of a given organism, no doubt rest on enzymatic differences, and this seems to us to be a subject which is capable of great and fruitful development.

We use the term 'comparative enzyme biochemistry' to include two distinct fields of study, namely, on the one hand the comparison of the enzymatic equipment of different organs and species, and on the other hand the comparison of pure preparations of a given enzyme obtained from different sources. We shall deal with these two fields separately.

(a) *Comparison of tissues*

A comparison of a variety of cells of widely different types shows remarkable similarities in the pattern of enzymes they contain. The same basic metabolic pattern seems to be used throughout living organisms; any differences in metabolic end-products result from the addition or deletion of an enzyme here and there rather than from a change in the whole pattern. The complicated systems of enzymes, coenzymes and carriers involved in carbohydrate metabolism, as set out in the first few tables in Chapter XII, form with only minor modifications the main energy-producing mechanism in animals, plants, moulds, yeast and most other micro-organisms.

There are, however, undoubted differences in metabolism, chemical composition and structure between different tissues and different organisms. The differences in metabolism clearly reflect differences in the complement of enzymes present; the differences in chemical composition are also the result of differences in the enzymes present, especially of the biosynthetic enzymes. It is by no means improbable that the more obvious differences of structure and form may also be referred to differences in enzymatic make-up. Structure and form are known to be controlled by genes, and genes control the production of enzymes, so that unless genes act in two quite different ways it seems likely that structural differences may be mediated through a control of the enzymes present. The form of organs, largely influenced by neighbouring tissues, is no doubt controlled by morphogenetic substances or 'evocators' (see particularly the monograph by NEEDHAM, *1934*), but these are themselves presumably made by enzymes. In any case the whole process is known to be very largely under genic control (see *2746*).

The greatest enzymatic differences between organisms are probably to be found by comparing animals, plants and bacteria. Metabolically, animals show a fairly standard pattern, but plants and moulds, and to some extent bacteria, produce in addition a vast array of specialized metabolic products, for example, the various pigments, alkaloids and other heterocyclic compounds. The extraordinary variety of complex ring compounds produced by moulds has been particularly studied by RAISTRICK (*2162*). Many of these compounds are restricted to one or two species. Little is known of the enzymes involved in their synthesis. As the enzymatic steps become identified, a comparative study may help to relate these special end-products to the physiology of the cells concerned.

The main distribution studies on enzymes relate to animal tissues and to some extent to bacteria. Even these studies, however, are all too fragmentary. About twenty-five years ago it was common practice to include in studies of particular enzymes a rough survey of their distribution, but this practice has largely fallen into desuetude, although more recently a fair volume of data has been accumulated for normal tissues, particularly of the rat and mouse, for the purpose of comparison with tumours. A rough idea of the occurrence of the various enzymes is given in column seven of the Enzyme List, but these data should be treated with caution as they do not necessarily imply that the enzyme is absent from tissues other than those mentioned. This is particularly true of many of the more recently discovered enzymes, which have only been prepared from one source, without any attempt to investigate other sources, or at any rate to report the amounts occurring elsewhere.

Many of the well known enzymes such as the enzymes of glycolysis are very widely distributed and, so far as animals are concerned, occur in all organs of all species, although different tissues may contain very different amounts. Other enzymes, perhaps particularly those concerned in nitrogen metabolism, have a curiously scattered distribution, being often completely absent from some tissues (though present in the same tissues in other species) and present in large amounts in others of the same organism. A good example of the latter type is xanthine oxidase (1.2.3.2), the occurrence of which in a number of animal tissues was reported by MORGAN (*1855*).

In Table XIII.3 we have collected such quantitative information as is known to us about the distribution of enzymes in animal tissues. Where possible, we have expressed the results for each enzyme on a

TABLE XIII.3

DISTRIBUTION OF SOME ENZYMES IN ANIMAL TISSUES

For each enzyme all the activities are expressed with reference to the most active tissue, taken as 100. In a few cases, two independent blocks of data are given. The figures within any one block can be compared with one another, but different blocks, whether for different enzymes or for the same enzyme, are on different scales and cannot be compared. Not all the values in the literature agree with one another. We have given what we consider to be the best value in each case. In any case there are considerable individual variations in enzyme content; the figures are not to be taken as accurate values, but merely as showing the general pattern of distribution.

Enzyme	Species	Liver	Kidney	Spleen	Heart	Skeletal muscle	Lung	Gastric mucosa	Small intestine	Large intestine	Pancreas	Brain	Adrenal	Thymus	Thyroid	Testis	Blood	References
3-hydroxypropionate dehydrogenase (1.1.1.f)	Pig	89	100		100	20						0						592
	Chicken																	
Lactate dehydrogenase (1.1.1.27)	Rabbit	1	8		14	27	3					29						900
	Rat		71		100	25	1					66						
	Pigeon	2	3		4	6						0·4						
Lactate dehydrogenase (1.1.1.27)	Rat	43	20		62	100	9	20	75		16	23		20		20		1781, 2839
	Mouse		38	15	30													
3-hydroxybutyrate dehydrogenase (1.1.1.30)	Monkey	27																1536
	Dog	22																
	Cat	28																
	Rabbit	18																
	Guinea pig	6																
	Rat	100	12	2	8	2					2·5	5	8		0	2		
	Mouse	70																
	Frog	14																
Malate dehydrogenase (1.1.1.37)	Rabbit	13	10		26	2						25						897
	Rat	19	5		100	38						28						
	Pigeon	28	57		86	80						33						
Isocitrate dehydrogenase (1.1.1.42)	Rat	17	100		85													2839
	Mouse					24												
Glycerolphosphate dehydrogenase (1.1.2.1)	Rabbit	70	63		21	71	38		23			100						896
D-aminoacid oxidase (1.4.3.3)	Horse	0·5	0·5															1463
	Sheep	26	100															
	Pig	6	24															
	Dog	12	22															
	Jackal	5	15															
	Cat	0·5	13															
	Guinea pig	0·2	1	0	0	0			0		0	0				0		
	Rat		2															
	Hedgehog	0·2	0·2															

Comparative enzyme distribution table (values are percentages; numbers at head of each block are literature reference numbers).

Enzyme (EC No.)	Ref.	Species	Value 1	Value 2	Other recorded values
Monoamine oxidase (1.4.3.4)	2968	Man	40	100	5, 13, 2, 15, 53, 9, 52
		Sheep	53	59	8, 7, 0·5, 1, 17
		Pig	43	24	3, 0, 28, 24
Diamine oxidase (1.4.3.6)	2969	Man	27	22	30, 9
		Horse	70	20	8, 1
		Ox	100	18	3
		Sheep	54	23	
		Pig	100	17	
		Guinea pig	17	17	
		Rat	±	18	
		Pigeon	15	33	
Pyrroline-2-carboxylate reductase (1.5.1.1)	1787	Rat	100	25	60, 12, 5, 7, 17, 4
NAD(P) transhydrogenase (1.6.1.1)	1299	Ox	19	0	100, 0, 0, 0
		Pig	41	54	54, 0, 0, 0
		Rabbit	10	15	10, 4, 0, 0
		Pigeon			2·5
Cytochrome oxidase (1.9.3.1)	923, 925	Man	9	7	1, 20, 6, 10
		Rabbit	12	7	2, 24, 5
		Guinea pig	13	10	2·5, 2, 11, 24, 4, 10
		Rat	35	30	100, 16, 100, 32, 16, 10
		Mouse	27	20	3, 46, 5, 24, 7
Cytochrome oxidase (1.9.3.1)	1949	Rat	69	65	10, 2, 36, 100, 67, 14, 15
Catalase (1.11.1.6)	924	Rat	12	25	5, 0, 0·1, 3, 1, 0·1
		Mouse	40	100	0·1, 5, 0·1, 0·1
Peroxidases (1.11.1.7)	1949	Rat	2·5	0	75, 100, 37, 40, 1·5, 1, 2, 48
Homogentisate oxygenase (1.99.2.5)	511	Rat	50	100	0, 0, 0, 0, 0, 0
Catechol methyltransferase (2.1.1.a)	115	Rat	30	100	4, 4, 3, 89, 0, 3, 7
Histamine methyltransferase (2.1.1.c)	334	Cat	<5	56	65, <5, 64, 15, 49
		Guinea pig	63	21	92, 74, 85, 46, 50, 78
		Rabbit	55	62	0, 13, 40, 25, 32
		Rat	46	0	0, 29, 0, <5, <5
		Mouse	73	47	44, 69, 25, 36, 50
Dimethylthetin homocysteine methyltransferase (2.1.1.3)	1764	Dog	9	52	72, 0
		Rabbit	16	60	100, 0
		Guinea pig	3	33	52
		Rat		48	22
		Mouse		100	62
		Pigeon		29	
		Eel		92	
		Tortoise		10	

Enzyme	Species	Liver	Kidney	Spleen	Heart	Skeletal muscle	Lung	Gastric mucosa	Small intestine	Large intestine	Pancreas	Brain	Adrenal	Thymus	Thyroid	Testis	Blood	References
Thiaminase I (2.5.1.2) ..	Carp	10	5	100	100	0						0·8						2746
Aspartate aminotransferase (2.6.1.1) ..	Rat	66	53		100	85						85						464
Glutamine-fructose-6-phosphate aminotransferase (2.6.1.16) ..	Ox	4	35				38		2									2098
	Rabbit	0					10		32									
	Rat	100							10									
	Pigeon	0																
Phosphoglyceromutase (2.7.5.3) ..	Ox	11	18	30	55	55						43						2240
	Sheep	7	25	23	93	100						38						
Ribonuclease (2.7.7.16) ..	Rabbit	2	7·5		2	2					14						0·5	141, 2972
	Rat				5	9					100						0·75	
Ribonuclease (2.7.7.16) ..	Mouse	15	10	36			6	35	87		100	23		15				924
Carboxylesterase (3.1.1.1) ..	Rat	17	4	4	0·7	0·2	8	3			87	0·4		0·2			0·2	923
	Mouse	23	6	6		0·7	4		53		100							
Phospholipase B (3.1.1.5)	Rat	43	10	70	3	7	75		100		38	2·5				9		1727
Acetylcholinesterase (3.1.1.7) ..	Man	7															1·3† (80)	97, 557 2031
	Horse	0·05															2·5† (12)	
	Ox																1† (18)	
	Sheep																2† (15)	
	Dog	4		7	2			9		25		13					2† (11)	
	Cat	35	3			4	1·5		21	23							3† (2)	
	Guinea pig	6	2·5										24				12† (19)	
	Rabbit	55	6				4	7				100					3† (5)	
	Rat	23	1	25	15	4			14			43					6† (10)	
	Fowl	2				10			19			7					11† (0·7)	
	Labrus								11								1† (0)	
	Scyllium																2† (0)	
	Helix																75	
Cholinesterases (3.1.1.8 + 9, using benzoylcholine ..	Man	9															94† (1·6)	97, 557 2031
	Horse	4										15					100† (1·6)	
	Ox																0·5† (0·5)	
	Sheep																2·5† (1)	
	Dog	28	25			24		19	5	5		17	1·5				68†	
	Cat	43	36	3	12	0·5		15	30								14† (0)	
	Guinea pig	16	24			7	10		9	62		9					57† (1)	
	Rabbit	50	5						100			4					34† (0)	
	Rat	10	2	20	100												7† (0)	
	Fowl	4															2† (0·5)	
	Labrus																1† (1)	
	Scyllium																1† (0)	
	Helix																16	

Enzyme (EC number)	Species	Values (left → right across tissue columns)	References
Tropinesterase (3.1.1.10), using atropine	Horse	0, 22, 10, 27, 6, 55, 0, 11, 0†, 0†	854
	Guinea pig	100, 0†	
	Rabbit (+)	60, 100† (0)	
	Rabbit (−)	0	
	Frog	0	
Alkaline phosphatase (3.1.3.1), using glycerol phosphate	Man	0·7, 4, 0·8, 0·2, 0·1, 10	1324, 1658
	Dog	2, 10, 3, 0·3, 0·1, 100, 0·5, 1, 3, 0·3	
	Cat	0·6, 12, 0·8, 0·2, 65, 0·7, 0·6	
	Rabbit	0·3, 2, 2, 0·4, 0·1, 10, 1, 1, 0·5	
	Guinea pig	0·4, 7, 0·4, 0·6, 20, 2, 0·3	
	Rat	0·5, 5, 0·4, 0·3, 0·5	
	Mouse	23, 1, 3, 3	
Alkaline phosphatase (3.1.3.1), using phenyl phosphate	Rabbit	0·1, 54, 1, 0·5, 0·1, 0·3, 100, 0·3†	915
	Rat	0·1, 39, 0·6, 0·05, 16	
	Mouse	0·1	
Acid phosphatase (3.1.3.2), using phenyl phosphate	Rat	39, 35, 100, 9, 4, 57, 1, 0·3, 23, 17	316
Acid phosphatase (3.1.3.2), using phenyl phosphate	Rabbit	15, 100, 45, 17, 19, 28, 35, 0·4†	915, 923–4
	Rat	26, 16, 77, 32, 20, 10	
	Mouse	13, 34	
Phosphatidate phosphatase (3.1.3.4)	Rat	71, 100, 100, 34, 60, 36	2456
5-nucleotidase (3.1.3.5)	Horse	2, 4, 1, 2, 0·5, 1, 18, 100	2204
	Ox	0, 0, 0, 0·1, 1, 6, 19	
	Dog	0·1, 0, 0·1, 0·6, 0·7	
	Rabbit	0, 0·1, 1·5, 1·5	
	Rat	2·5, 3, 6, 1, 3	
	Pigeon	0, 0, 0, 0·1	
Glucose-6-phosphatase (3.1.3.9)	Man	100, 1, 0·8, 0·8, 0·4, 0·4, 0·1† (0·1)	1087
	Rat	31, 18, 50, 75, 55, 25, 38, 94	
Deoxyribonucleotidase (3.1.4.5)	Rabbit	65, 63, 100, 55, 75, 31, 94, 19	916, 924
	Rat	41, 50, 38, 25, 5	
	Mouse	89, 10	
β-galactosidase (3.2.1.23)	Man	42, 17, 72, 2, 0, 10, 13, 29, 17	488
	Rat	13, 100, 45, 4, 3, 10, 32, 26	
	Mouse	32	
α-mannosidase (3.2.1.24)	Man	54, 32, 22, 3, 0·7, 77, 0, 18, 0·5	488
	Rat	68, 100, 36, 5, 77, 9, 50	
	Mouse	99, 8, 8	
β-acetylaminodeoxy-glucosidase (3.2.1.30)	Man	32, 100, 17, 4, 10, 16	488
	Rat	25, 60, 9, 10	
	Mouse	34, 10	

Enzyme	Species	Liver	Kidney	Spleen	Heart	Skeletal muscle	Lung	Gastric mucosa	Small intestine	Large intestine	Pancreas	Brain	Adrenal	Thymus	Thyroid	Testis	Blood	References
β-glucuronidase (3.2.1.31)	Man	100	11									0·6				2		488
	Rat	16	21													3		
	Mouse		10															
β-glucuronidase (3.2.1.31)	Rat	63	21	100		0·4	20				5		18		26	0·4		2607
Leucine aminopeptidase (3.4.1.1) ..	Man	2	3	2·5		3		1·5	3	2·5	1·5	3		0·8		2·5	0·1†	909
	Rat	13	100	12	10	10	14		59		11	8						
Arginase (3.5.3.1) ..	Dog	65	0·4	0	0						0				0	0·5	0	671, 920, 923-4
	Cat	48	0·4	0	0				0		0				0	0·2	0	
	Rabbit	46	2	0	0				0		0				0	0·02	0	
	Guinea pig	72	0·4	4	0				0		0				0	0·02	0	
	Rat	70	10	1	3	3		2	0		2	1		1	0	0·3	0	
	Mouse	100	10	0		1			32		3	1						
	Fowl	0·01	0·6		0	0					0							
Guanine deaminase (3.5.4.3) ..	Rat	80	76	92	11	0	20	7	92		57	100	38			65	15	919
	Mouse	82	86	96								76		96				
Adenosine deaminase (3.5.4.4) ..	Rabbit	9	19	100	0·5	2	0·5	0·2	60	25	32	21	1		21	1·5	1	494
AMP deaminase (3.5.4.6) ..	Rabbit	0·2	0·5	1	100	100			1		0·3	1						494
AMP deaminase (3.5.4.6)	Rat	80	96	100	0	0	80		100		72	0		80				919
	Mouse	80	84	100	0	0						70						
ATPase (3.6.1.3) (Ca-activated) ..	Rat	47	75	48	100	82					42	25						2113
Histidine decarboxylase (4.1.1.22) ..	Man	0	0		0		0					0						2841, 2843
	Horse		0															
	Ox		0															
	Sheep		0															
	Pig		0															
	Dog	17	0															
	Cat		0	0				0	0									
	Rabbit	15	90	0				0	0									
	Guinea pig	18	100						75									
Aldolases (4.1.2.7 + b) ..	Rabbit	6	5	2	6	100						7				4	0·3	1809
	Rat					100											0·3	

												References
Citrate synthase (4.1.3.7)												
Pig	8	22	73	34								⎱ 2490
Dog	6	21	67	2								
Rabbit	2	13	47	6								
Rat	6	13	80	6								
Pigeon	2	13	63	100								
Carbonic anhydrase (4.2.1.1)												
Man	0·6‡	1‡		0·5‡		0·8				10		⎱ 89,515; 1791; 2376; 2718
Whale										25		
Horse						0·7				11		
Ox										20		
Goat						1				24		
Dog	0·6‡	12				1				30		
Cat	0·6‡	21								21		
Rabbit	0‡	0·2‡	±	±						100		
Guinea pig	16	3‡			0	1	16	0	76	30	4	
Rat	0·2‡	2‡	±	±		5				100		
Rat	13	37				0·6				45		
Mouse												
Fowl												
Fumarate hydratase (4.2.1.2)												
Rat	50	47	73									⎱ 2839
Mouse	100											
Aconitate hydratase (4.2.1.3)												
Rat	35	70	100	17								⎱ 2746; 2839
Mouse	46					6						
Glutamine synthetase (6.3.1.2)												
Rat	51	2	6	2·5	0·2	61	1	1·5	2	0·2	80	⎱ 1562
Mouse	53	1	0·2	0·7		100					23	
Cytochrome c												
Man	3	3	30	5	2	3	2		2		2	⎱ 653,925; 1279
Horse	2	6	36	14	1	2						
Ox	3		43	14								
Pig		14	55	21				4				
Dog		14		11								
Rabbit		16				10						
Rat	7	80	100	22		18						
Mouse	50	67				23						
Pigeon			100	100						0·3 (0·6)		

† Plasma or serum (values for erythrocytes in parentheses).
‡ Corrected for blood in tissue.

common scale, so as to bring out the differences between the different tissues in one species of animal as well as those between corresponding tissues in different species. For each enzyme the standard of reference is the most active tissue, which is taken as 100; thus the figures do not indicate absolute activities, and different enzymes cannot be compared with one another. The figures are only relative, so that low figures may merely indicate the existence of one tissue with an exceptionally high activity.

The table has been compiled from data scattered throughout the literature; not all of the determinations are equally reliable and some of the older results were obtained with rather unspecific methods. The accurate determination of enzymes in tissues is not an easy matter, owing to the possible presence of interfering enzymes and substances. However, the general pattern of distribution shown in the table may be taken as fairly correct.

The table shows surprisingly large differences, both between tissues and between species. A number of enzymes, for example, D-aminoacid oxidase, xanthine oxidase and catalase are present predominantly in liver and kidney, but are practically absent from muscle; of these enzymes, some are more active in the liver and others in the kidney. In some cases indeed (e.g. arginase) the enzyme is located almost entirely in the liver and the kidney activities in most species are extremely low. Consequently, aminoacid metabolism and urea formation take place largely in the liver, although some urea synthesis does take place in brain. On the other hand aspartate aminotransferase is more active in heart than in liver or kidney, while more glutamine synthetase is found in brain than in liver and scarcely any in other tissues.

High activity of a number of enzymes appears to be characteristically associated with particular organs. For example, alkaline phosphatase with intestinal mucosa, acid phosphatase with kidney and spleen (and even more with prostate, not shown in the table), 5-nucleotidase with testis, β-galactosidase, α-mannosidase and β-acetylaminodeoxyglucosidase with epididymis (not shown in the table), ribonuclease with pancreas (although other tissues contain appreciable amounts), acetylcholinesterase and glutamine synthetase with brain, cholinesterase and carbonic anhydrase with blood. As more information becomes available, these differences will probably be seen to be a part of a general pattern of metabolic specialization. Some use has been made of the concept of 'organ-specific enzymes' in clinical diagnosis (see *348*); for example, high values for serum acid phosphatase are observed in cases of cancer of the prostate. A more valuable approach has made use of the isoenzyme pattern of plasma enzymes (p. 657).

Equally striking species differences can be seen, although the number of different species hitherto studied is extremely limited. There is here an enormous and almost untouched field, the study of which, although laborious, would probably produce results of great interest to the zoologist. Some enzymes seem to be confined to certain species, for example, histidine decarboxylase is active in the kidneys of rabbit and guinea pig but is absent from those of man, horse, ox, sheep, dog and cat. Another enzyme which shows important species differences is arginase. CLEMENTI long ago claimed that arginase is present in the livers of animals which excrete urea and absent from those of animals which excrete uric acid. In the latter case, however, it may be present in the kidney (cf. the fowl). Exceptions to this rule have recently been found; arginase is present in lizard and snake liver (341). In the case of elasmobranch fishes, which synthesize urea throughout the body, arginase is present in large amounts in other tissues, for example, in heart. Another enzyme connected with nitrogen excretion which occurs in some species and not at all in others is urate oxidase, which is present in most mammals, apart from man and the other primates, and is absent from birds. Consequently, the end-product of purine metabolism is uric acid in the primates and allantoin in other mammals; birds in any case produce uric acid as the main nitrogenous end-product. In a detailed study of the distribution of the enzymes of the urea cycle (341), it was shown that carbamate kinase was present in the liver of all amphibians and mammals studied; the specific activity increased in parallel with the degree of amphibian development.

Other striking species differences are shown by NAD(P) transhydrogenase, which is present in the livers of pig and rabbit but absent from that of the ox, and monoamine oxidase, which is active in human heart but present only in traces in sheep and pig heart. Apart from such all-or-none differences, there are usually large differences in the *amounts* of the various enzymes present between one species and another. These differences often seem to be correlated with the size of the animal: the rat and the mouse, which have a high metabolic rate, contain larger amounts of many enzymes per unit weight of tissue than larger animals, though this is by no means an invariable rule. Sheep kidney is by far the best source of D-aminoacid oxidase, being 50 times better than rat kidney, although L-aminoacid oxidase has only been prepared from rat kidney, being barely detectable in kidneys of other species. Such differences are not solely determined by the size of the animal, for the horse is even more deficient in D-aminoacid oxidase than the rat. These figures bring out the practical importance of preliminary studies of this type, before selecting a tissue of a particular species as a source for the isolation of an enzyme (see p. 33).

Most animal tissues include more than one type of cell, and these might well differ in enzyme content. Experiments with the whole tissue will merely give an average of all the cell types present. In many cases attempts have been made to subdivide the tissue by dissection; for example, enzyme determinations have often been made on intestinal mucosa instead of whole intestine, on kidney cortex and medulla instead of whole kidney, on grey and white matter instead of whole brain, and on auricular and ventricular muscle instead of whole heart. When the retina of the eye was subdivided into layers, marked enzyme localizations were found (*1624*). Hexokinase within the first neuron is almost entirely confined to the inner segments of rods and cones, while phosphogluco-mutase, glucosephosphate isomerase and phosphofructokinase are concentrated at the opposite end of the cell. The first neuron is very rich in glucosephosphate dehydrogenase, the concentration being 10–30 times that in the rest of the retina.

Different types of cells are often intimately associated and cannot be separated in this way. This is particularly true of liver, in which the parenchymatous and reticulo-endothelial cells are fairly uniformly distributed throughout the tissue. WATTIAUX *et al.* (*2799*) have made use of the phagocytic properties of the latter cells in order to separate the two kinds of cells. Rats were injected with a suspension of 3 μ iron particles; after these had been taken up by the reticulo-endothelial system, the perfused livers were homogenized and the iron-loaded reticulo-endothelial cells were separated from the parenchymatous cells by means of a magnet. No marked differences were in fact found.

It is by no means certain that even cells which are histologically of the same type have the same enzymatic composition. It has until recently been assumed that all the cells in an organism have the same chromosomes, but it is now known that this is by no means the case in mammals (see BEATTY, *186*). Counts on a number of growing tissues have shown that the chromosome number in different cells in the same tissue may vary widely on either side of the normal. For example, a count of 1,000 cells from normal human uterine endometrium gave a range of chromosome number of from 4 to 104, with peaks at the haploid and diploid numbers (24 and 48). Since there are many cells with less than the haploid number of chromosomes, these cells must presumably lack some of the genes responsible for the formation of enzymes, and it would be interesting to know whether such cells actually lack the corresponding enzymes. If not, either the effect of the gene persists in daughter cells after it is lost, or the gene must be able to act on neighbouring cells across the cell walls. Unfortunately, no information on the enzymatic homogeneity of tissues is available.

In micro-organisms many species differences have been found, and in fact metabolic differences, due to differences in the enzymes present, have been used by bacteriologists for the identification and classification of bacteria. Even with a group of closely related enzymes such differences are found, as is illustrated by the inducible aminoacid decarboxylases (Table XIII.4, from GALE, *806*).

TABLE XIII.4

DISTRIBUTION OF AMINOACID DECARBOXYLASES
IN MICRO-ORGANISMS

	Esch. coli	*Str. faecalis*	*Cl. welchii*	*Cl. fallax*	*Proteus vulgaris*	*Rhizobium trifolium*	*Lactobacillus spp.*
Aspartate decarboxylase (4.1.1.11)	+	−	+	−	−	+	−
Glutamate decarboxylase (4.1.1.15)	+	−	+	−	+	−	+
Ornithine decarboxylase (4.1.1.17)	+	−	−	−	+	−	+
Lysine decarboxylase (4.1.1.18)	+	−	−	−	−	−	+
Arginine decarboxylase (4.1.1.19)	+	−	−	−	−	−	+
Histidine decarboxylase (4.1.1.22)	+	−	+	+	−	−	+
Tyrosine decarboxylase (4.1.1.25)	+	+	−	−	−	−	−
Tryptophan decarboxylase (4.1.1.27)	−	−	−	−	−	−	−
'Phenylalanine decarboxylase'†	−	+	−	−	−	−	−

† This enzyme is hypothetical, and any observed activity may be indirect.

Enzymology of development

It is well known that the metabolic activity of tissues varies with their age, as well as with the other factors which we have been discussing. During the development of the adult organism from the fertilized ovum the enzyme systems have to be synthesized, and unless they are synthesized simultaneously the enzyme pattern will change with age. Such differences might be particularly apparent during the embryonic stages, especially as the different tissues with their characteristic enzyme patterns become differentiated. Unfortunately, the amount of reliable data on this topic is very small. The older work has been collected and discussed by NEEDHAM (*1933*); more recent work will be found in the review by GUSTAFSON (*955*) and the book by WAGNER and MITCHELL (*2746*).

Some enzymes seem to be absent from, or at any rate undetectable in, the early embryo, and to appear rather suddenly at a definite stage of development. Furthermore, they may appear in different organs at different times. For example, MORGAN (*1856*) could detect no xanthine oxidase in the chick embryo up to the 15th day of incubation, when it appeared in the kidney. It was, however, absent from the liver until the 21st day, when the eggs hatched and the enzyme suddenly appeared. The enzymes of the urea cycle all increase markedly at the onset of metamorphosis in the frog (*340*). Acetylcholinesterase, which cannot be detected in the larva of the sea-urchin, appears shortly before hatching, at the same time as the first appearance of co-ordinated nervous activity (*98*). In the chick embryo, there are sharp changes in the specific activity of glutamate, lactate and malate dehydrogenases (*2467-8*), which appear to be associated with differentiation. In the mammal, there are often distinct discontinuities in the development of enzymes at birth. Glucosephosphate dehydrogenase, which is absent from the guinea-pig foetus, appears very rapidly after birth (*1938*) as does tryptophan oxygenase (*1940*); nucleotide pyrophosphatase, which is low in foetal liver, rises towards the end of gestation to adult values just before birth (*1941*). The amount of $NADPH_2$ rises rapidly over the same period.

Changes in the relative proportions of different enzymes during development may result in changes in the metabolic pattern. KRAHL (*1456*) has produced isotopic evidence that in the first 24 hours of development of a fertilized sea-urchin egg, there is a switch of glucose metabolism from a predominantly pentose phosphate pathway to dependence on the citric cycle.

The enzyme activities of mitochondria from developing chick embryos were studied independently by CAREY and GREVILLE (*407*) and by BRAND and MAHLER (*310*). From 5-day embryos mitochondria are obtained which are normal in appearance and in oxidative metabolism of carbohydrate, but which are unable to oxidize 3-hydroxybutyrate. Fat oxidation begins to appear about the 17th day.

The absence of particular enzymes from certain tissues of organisms which contain them elsewhere raises the question of the reason for their absence in spite of the fact that clearly the animal must possess the necessary genes for their formation. When an enzyme suddenly appears in a tissue, as in the cases mentioned above, its previous absence could not have been due to the absence of the necessary gene. It might, however, have been due to a metabolite-controlled repression of its formation by the mechanism described on pp. 498-520. It was suggested, in the case of the cholinesterase, that the appearance of the enzyme was an adaptive response to the formation of acetylcholine at the newly developed nerve endings.

In one case evidence has been offered for the importance of induction;

addition of succinate accelerates the production of succinate dehydrogenase in *Amblyostoma* (*281*). On the other hand the increase of tryptophan oxygenase at birth in the guinea pig, mentioned earlier, cannot be induced by injection of tryptophan (*1939*). Furthermore, if gestation is artificially shortened or lengthened, the rise in the enzyme still occurs promptly on delivery.

Most sudies of the enzymology of development have been concerned with the total quantity of enzyme. MARKERT and MØLLER (*1719*) suggested that there might be a change in the character of a particular enzyme during development, and KAPLAN and CIOTTI (*1303*) confirmed this for lactate dehydrogenase. Specificity studies with four NAD analogues showed significant differences between the enzymes from new-born and adult human hearts, and the enzymes could also be distinguished immunologically (see under 'isoenzymes,' p. 656).

Tumour enzymology

A large volume of work has been done on the comparison of the metabolism and enzyme content of tumours with those of normal tissues, in the hope that this may throw light on the causation and prevention of cancer. The greater part of this has been described and discussed by GREENSTEIN in his book on the subject (*917*). The following brief summary of the results which have been obtained is based largely on his account.

Tumours contain qualitatively much the same enzymes as normal tissues and have much the same overall metabolism. No new or abnormal enzymes have been found; on the other hand, certain enzymes may be absent in tumours although present in the tissues from which they were derived. In general, marked quantitative differences in the enzyme content are found between tumours and normal tissues. The enzyme pattern of a tumour is largely independent of its age, its growth rate, the species and strain of the animal producing it, and the tissue from which it originates. In fact, tumours differ from one another far less than they do from normal tissues or than normal tissues do from one another. Primary tumours may retain some of the enzymatic characters of the parent tissue, but after several transplant generations they approach a uniform pattern, in which all specialized functions characteristic of the initial tissue are lost. For example, the urea-forming system of liver is absent from hepatomas, the pepsinogen-forming system of gastric mucosa is absent from gastric adenocarcinomas, the high alkaline phosphatase and esterase activity of intestinal mucosa drops to a very low level in intestinal adenocarcinoma.

It appears to be generally true that the activity of every enzyme in a tumour, although frequently different from that in the tissue from which it was derived, does not lie outside the range met with in normal tissues. Greenstein has grouped enzymes into three categories, according to whether their activities in tumours are in the upper, middle or lower range of normal tissue activities (though not necessarily those of the tissue from which they were derived). This grouping is shown for a number of enzymes in Table XIII.5.

The enzyme systems which are retained in the cancer cells are those basal systems necessary for the production of energy and for their growth and reproduction. Metabolically, in fact, the tumour approaches closely to the early embryonic tissue before differentiation has begun.

TABLE XIII.5

ACTIVITY OF ENZYMES IN RODENT TUMOURS
COMPARED WITH NORMAL TISSUES
(from *917*)

Enzymes in the upper normal range	*Enzymes in the middle of the normal range*	*Enzymes in the lower normal range*
Xanthine oxidase (1.2.3.2)	Ribonuclease (2.7.7.16)	Cytochrome oxidase (1.9.3.1)
Glycyl-glycine dipeptidase (3.4.3.1)	Acid phosphatase (3.1.3.2)	Catalase (1.11.1.6)
Enzymes hydrolyzing Bz-Arg-NH$_2$	Deoxyribonuclease (3.1.4.5–6)	Carboxylesterase (3.1.1.1)
	Arginase (3.5.3.1)	Alkaline phosphatase (3.1.3.1)
		Aminoacylase I (3.5.1.b)
		Homoserine dehydratase (4.2.1.15).

The parallel may be quite close; for example, normal lymphatic tissue metabolizes glucose almost entirely through the glycolysis-citrate-cycle pathway, whereas in lymphosarcoma cells, like the early embryo, the pathway through phosphogluconate also plays an important part (*2735*). The activity of the NMN adenylyltransferase (2.7.7.1) in the nuclei of mammary tumours is only about a quarter of that in the nuclei of normal mammary tissue; this activity is also low in embryonic liver nuclei and increases with development (*311*).

From the enzymatic point of view, the essential feature of a tumour is that the cells have escaped from the normal organizing control which determines the specialized character of the tissue of origin and its differentiation under the influence of substances diffusing from neighbouring tissues; they have returned in fact to a state resembling that before evocator control began to operate, except that they are no longer responsive to such control. Thus more information about chemical embryology and about the control of enzyme formation by repression in animal tissues might contribute greatly to our understanding of the aetiology of cancer.

The development of a tumour in a host may have a marked effect on the metabolism and enzymatic activity of other tissues in the body. Some of these effects might be due merely to competition for essential metabolites between the cancer and the other tissues, but others are more direct. For example, the catalase of the liver is greatly lowered in activity, and this has been shown to be due to an inhibitory substance produced by the tumour and carried by the blood stream (*1005*). This substance has been purified to some extent and found to be a substance of low molecular weight, stable to acids and alkalis, which inhibits haemoprotein enzymes *in vitro* by combining with the haem prosthetic group, but its nature has not so far been determined. A similar catalase inhibitor has been obtained from embryo extract (*955*). The existence of such inhibitors means that where a fall of activity is shown in Table XIII.5 there has not necessarily been a corresponding fall in enzyme content, since the effect may be due merely to the presence of an inhibitor.

(b) *Comparison of enzymes*

Species differences

We now turn to the other aspect of comparative enzyme biochemistry, namely, comparisons of preparations of a given enzyme obtained from different sources, in other words, the question whether the properties of an enzyme depend in any way on the species and tissue of origin.

We have hitherto assumed that where an enzyme catalysing a particular chemical reaction can be obtained from a number of sources it should be regarded as a single entity unless there are clear-cut differences with respect to such factors as specificity, activator, etc. Slight differences in physical properties such as solubility, crystalline form and electrophoretic mobility have not been regarded as justifying their treatment as separate enzymes. It is a remarkable fact that in general the catalytic properties, specificity, activity, affinities, etc., of a given enzyme vary little with the source. Although there may be slight physical differences in a given enzyme when it is produced by different cells, they are usually unimportant, and the enzyme remains essentially the same enzyme. This is in fact a commonplace of enzymology; for all practical purposes the source of an enzyme is usually regarded as a somewhat secondary matter, rat liver, rabbit muscle, pig heart or baker's yeast often being used indiscriminately for the preparation of a required enzyme. The results obtained with enzymes from such diverse sources are generally the same, and the enzymes are used interchangeably as components of model systems.

The first question is what is meant by saying that preparations of an enzyme from different sources are identical. Does it mean identity merely of the active centre and its immediate surroundings, so that the name of an enzyme is merely the name of a particular active centre, which may be attached to different proteins? Or does it mean that the whole protein is identical? Studies of the catalytic properties only cannot answer this question; one must have recourse to studies of the protein itself, and in particular the aminoacid composition and sequence.

An enzyme may exhibit differences of crystalline form when derived from different species, but this does not necessarily show that there is any difference in the protein, since by different procedures different crystalline forms are frequently obtained, even from the same preparation. Examples of both these points can be seen in the atlas at the end of the book. Differences in other properties (solubility, electrophoretic mobility, sedimentation constant, immunological properties) under comparable conditions indicate that there is a difference, possibly slight, in the structure or state of the peptide chain(s); however, there may be differences which escape detection by such methods. For example, the crystalline pepsins of ox and pig are extraordinarily similar; they have the same catalytic properties, crystalline form and solubility, and can scarcely be distinguished by immunological methods. However, they cannot be completely identical, since although they have the same solubility, each will dissolve in a saturated solution of the other (see p. 526). Immunological methods are capable of detecting very small differences between proteins, and some differences between enzyme preparations from all but closely related species are often found. For example, the ureases of soy bean and jack bean are sufficiently similar proteins to give immunological cross-reactions, but there are large quantitative precipitation differences; a similar situation exists with horse and ox liver catalase (1729) and with alcohol dehydrogenase from bakers' and brewers' yeast (81). On the other hand, muscle phosphorylases from human and rabbit appear to be identical (2953), as do the carbamate kinases of many species, including ox, goat, rat, rabbit, frog and turtle (1731).

The variations in structure of an enzyme molecule from one species to another may in some cases be sufficient to produce significant differences in the kinetics or specificity of the enzyme reaction. KAPLAN (1301) examined the specificity of lactate dehydrogenases from various species towards a number of NAD analogues, and showed such differences, especially with the heart enzyme; for example, that from the flat fishes is clearly distinguished from that for other teleost fishes, the ratio of activity towards one pair of analogues being $0 \cdot 34$ for the tuna heart lactate dehydrogenase and $11 \cdot 2$ for that from flounder heart.

Some of these differences may be due merely to a difference in the manner of folding of the peptide chains, but others may be due to actual chemical differences which would be revealed by comparative studies on aminoacid composition and sequence. Although aminoacid analyses of a number of enzymes have been carried out (see Table X.2), very few species comparisons have been made. The only clear-cut example (where the analyses have been carried out by the same workers using the same methods) is that of the glyceraldehydephosphate dehydrogenases from yeast and rabbit muscle; the analyses are identical within experimental error. The number of chains and the N-terminal aminoacids (valine) are also identical. Thus it is not merely that the active centres are identical in the two enzymes, but that the whole protein molecule must be extremely similar in yeast and rabbit muscle. Nevertheless, they are not quite identical; the muscle enzyme has three of its thiol groups associated with the activity whereas the yeast enzyme has only two, and there are differences in the affinity for the coenzyme and in the dependence of electrophoretic mobility on pH and ionic strength.

The table shows analyses for four α-amylases from different sources. Here there are clearly real differences in aminoacid composition, although there is a certain similarity in general pattern, which is particularly strong between the two animal enzymes. The α-amylase from a thermophilic bacterium contains less basic aminoacids, but much more proline and acidic aminoacids than that from *B. subtilis*; it is also a smaller molecule (*389*). The table also includes figures for the muramidases of egg white and rabbit spleen, but these are clearly different proteins, with marked differences in the content of certain aminoacids, especially tryotophan and glutamic acid.

In the last few years a large amount of data has been obtained about species differences in the aminoacid sequences of non-enzyme proteins; these have been recently reviewed by Šorm (*2476*). Usually most of the chain is invariant, but in certain positions there is a replacement of one aminoacid by another, often closely related, aminoacid. The type of result obtained can be well illustrated by the structure of insulin from a number of species (Fig. XIII.1). The B-chain is completely identical in all these species, as is also the A-chain except for the residues shown as X, Y and Z in the figure.

In the case of cytochrome *c*, Paléus and Tuppy showed that the haem prosthetic group is always attached to two cysteine residues separated by two other aminoacid residues at about the same position in the peptide

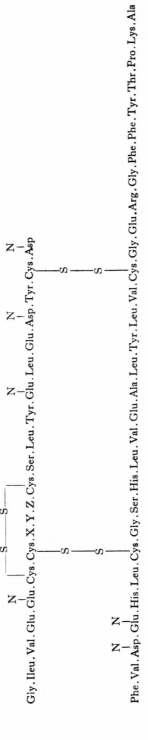

Fig. XIII.1. *Structure of insulins of different species (1009, 1217).*

chain. Within this pattern, however, certain aminoacids can be replaced by others, as shown in Fig. XIII.2. The important histidine residue is always present adjacent to one of the cysteine groups.

Ox ⎫
Horse ⎬   –Val–Glu(NH₂)–Lys–Cys–Ala–Glu(NH₂)–Cys–His–Thr–Val–Glu
Pig ⎪
Salmon ⎭

Fowl   –Val–Glu(NH₂)–Lys–Cys–Ser–Glu(NH₂)–Cys–His–Thr–Val–Glu

Silkworm   –Val–Glu(NH₂)–Arg–Cys–Ala–Glu(NH₂)–Cys–His–Thr–Val–Glu

Yeast   –Lys——Thr—–Arg–Cys–Glu——Leu——Cys–His–Thr–Val–Glu

Rhodospirillum   –Cys–Leu——Ala——Cys–His–Thr–Phe–Asp
rubrum

Cytochrome C
(551, Pseudomonas)   –Cys–Val——Ala——Cys–

Fig. XIII.2. *Haem-binding peptide sequence in cytochrome c from different species*
(after *2047*; *Pseudomonas* cytochrome structure from *58*).

The interchanges of aminoacids in individual proteins from one species to another are limited in number. Table XIII.6 shows the commonly occurring interchanges; it will be seen that many of them involve meta-bolically related aminoacids.

TABLE XIII.6

FREQUENTLY OCCURRING AMINOACID
INTERCHANGES IN PROTEINS (after *2476*)

Aminoacid pair	*Homologous proteins in which found*
Glycine-serine	Insulin, haemoglobin
Glycine-aspartic acid	Corticotropin
Glycine-glutamic acid	Haemoglobin
Alanine-threonine	Insulin, serum albumin
Alanine-serine	Cytochrome *c*
Valine-isoleucine	Insulin, hypertensin
Serine-threonine	Haemoglobin
Serine-aspartic acid	Corticotropin
Serine-glutamic acid	Melanotropin
Glutamic acid-lysine	Haemoglobin
Aspartic acid–glutamic acid	Haemoglobin

It might be expected that differences in enzymes between different species will be attributable to similar interchanges. Detailed information is available in one case: ANFINSEN *et al.* (*75*) compared ovine and

bovine ribonuclease. The chains are identical apart from three interchanges: threonine at residue 3 in ox is replaced by serine in sheep; lysine
at residue 37 in ox is replaced by glutamic acid in sheep; the third
exchange between residues 99 and 104 has not been identified.

Tissue differences

It is surpising to find that in some cases a particular enzyme prepared
from different tissues of the same species or even the same individual can
be distinguished. Immunological methods have been used to distinguish
phosphorylase from dog liver and dog heart (1063); alkaline phosphatase
from human intestine and human bone (2329); α-amylase from pig liver
and pig serum and pancreas (1659); lactate dehydrogenase from various
rabbit tissues (1978) and also from various human tissues (1979).

Muscle and liver phosphorylases show a number of differences in
properties, especially in the details of the inactivation and reactivation
processes (p. 456). Furthermore metabolic abnormalities exist in which
the muscle enzyme is lacking while the liver enzyme is normal (1847,
2334). It would seem probable, therefore, that these are distinct enzymes
produced under the influence of different genes.

Similar conclusions have been drawn for the lactate dehydrogenases
of heart and skeletal muscle by KAPLAN and his co-workers (380). The
specificity differences between heart lactate dehydrogenases of various
species of fish mentioned above (p. 652) are not paralleled by any differences in the skeletal muscle enzyme. With amphibians, too, differences
can be found in the heart enzyme among species with identical skeletal
muscle dehydrogenases. The bull frog (Rana clamitans) has a heart
lactate dehydrogenase which differs sufficiently from other amphibian
lactate dehydrogenases in catalytic, physical and immunological properties to be regarded as a mutant enzyme, yet its skeletal muscle enzyme
is normal. The two tissues must therefore have enzymes controlled by
different genes.

The number of enzymes examined for tissue differences is quite small
and it is not possible to say whether such multiplicity of genetic control
is general or somewhat exceptional.

Isoenzymes

One of the most interesting developments in this field which has taken
place since the first edition of this work has been the demonstration of
multiple molecular forms of an enzyme in a single tissue. This has been
greatly facilitated by improvements in the technique of zone electrophoresis, especially on starch or agar gels. VESELL and BEARN (2733) and
MARKERT and MØLLER (1719) showed that on electrophoresis of normal

human serum the lactate dehydrogenase activity was distributed in five peaks. Markert and Møller suggested the term 'isozyme' for such multiple forms; 'iso-enzyme' and 'isoenzyme' have also been widely used. The present authors prefer the term 'isoenzyme' which by analogy with 'isotope' clearly conveys the intended meaning. Isoenzymes have now been demonstrated for a number of enzymes, including isocitrate and malate dehydrogenases, aspartate ammonia-lyase and ribonuclease.

The isoenzyme forms of a given enzyme may differ in their intracellular distribution. THORNE (2651) showed that two malate dehydrogenases could be separated from rat liver preparations by chromatography on DEAE-cellulose; both enzymes catalyse the same reactions, although they can be distinguished enzymatically by their specificity toward NAD analogues and by differences in susceptibility to inhibition by oxaloacetate. One of these enzymes is of mitochondrial origin, and resembles the enzyme from pig heart mitochondria, the other comes from the supernatant fraction.

Isoenzymes have been demonstrated in higher plants as well as in animals. Turnip peroxidase can be separated electrophoretically into four forms, differing slightly in the pK of dissociation of active centre groups (1170, 2295). In plants also there are sometimes differences in intracellular localization of isoenzymes; peas have been shown to have a mitochondrial and a cell sap malate dehydrogenase, separable on DEAE-cellulose although with identical specificity (554).

The distribution of enzyme activity among enzyme forms may differ from tissue to tissue, and this has become very important in clinical diagnosis. Fig. XIII.3 shows electrophoretograms of lactate dehydrogenase obtained on starch gel by WRÓBLEWSKI (2092). It will be seen that the patterns are characteristic of particular tissues; heart has predominantly isoenzymes 1 and 2, while liver has almost entirely isoenzyme 5. In diseases leading to a leakage of enzyme from a damaged tissue the isoenzyme pattern of the plasma may change from the normal towards that of the particular tissue involved. Thus by preparing an electrophoretogram of plasma and measuring the lactate dehydrogenase distribution it is possible, for example, to distinguish between myocardial infarction and liver disease.

In one case an explanation of the chemical relationship between isoenzymes is available. CAHN et al. (380) studied the lactate dehydrogenases of the fowl, in which, as in some other species, there are definite differences between the heart and the skeletal muscle enzyme (p. 656). These workers prepared 'antienzymes' (see p. 358) by injecting the enzymes into rabbits, and showed that there were quantitative differences in the reaction of the two enzymes with an antienzyme produced in

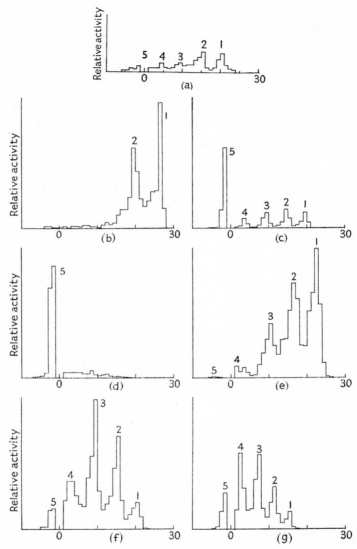

FIG. XIII.3. *Isoenzymes of lactate dehydrogenase in human tissues.*
(*a*) Plasma, (b) heart, (c) skeletal muscle, (d) liver, (e) kidney,
(f) spleen, (g) lung. The isoenzymes were separated by electrophoresis on starch gel; abscissae represent gel fractions, numbered
from the origin. Numbers on the figures show the isoenzyme peaks.

(after *2092*)

response to one of them. They observed that during embryological development the enzyme in breast muscle gradually changed from the heart type to the sketetal muscle type; during the transition three forms are present which are intermediate in both electrophoretic and immunological properties between the heart and muscle types. Since no more than 5 isoenzymes of lactate dehydrogenase are ever observed, and since also both heart and muscle lactate dehydrogenases can be dissociated in guanidine and mercaptoethanol into 4 sub-units of equal molecular weight, Cahn *et al.* suggest that the intermediate forms of the enzyme are in fact hybrids containing both heart and muscle type sub-units. Representing the sub-units of the heart and skeletal muscle enzymes by H and M respectively, 5 forms of the enzyme are possible: HHHH, HHHM, HHMM, HMMM and MMMM. Formation of H and M sub-units are probably controlled by different genes. Thus in this case the existence of 5 isoenzymes is due to the operation of two genes in a single cell.

THE ENZYMOLOGY OF GENETICS

As stated in Chapter XI, the nature of the enzymes which can be formed in a given organism is determined by the genes present in its chromosomes. Genes are not permanently invariant entities, but may undergo sudden changes (mutations) and are thereafter reproduced in the changed form. Gene mutations are recognized by changes in the characteristics of the organism (its 'phenotype'). Different forms of the same gene, occupying the same position in a chromosome, are referred to as 'alleles'. The presence of the various alleles is recognized by changes of form, appearance or function of the organism or parts thereof. Many such characters have been separately recognized, especially in *Drosophila melanogaster*, and given names such as 'vermilion', 'hairy wing', 'scute-1', 'forked', 'bithoraxoid', 'star' and 'spineless'. Most of these characters are presumably due to local changes of pigmentation or cell growth, and it is not improbable that most if not all of them will ultimately be explained by simple changes in single steps in metabolic reaction chains. In other cases, particularly in work with *Neurospora* mutants, the definitive characters are indeed the presence or absence of individual metabolic steps; these are discussed in more detail below. HALDANE suggested in 1920 (see *980*) that each gene 'makes a particular chemical species of enzyme'. This idea has been more recently developed by a number of workers, especially by BEADLE and his co-workers (*181*) as a result of extensive work on *Neurospora* and other moulds. For a general discussion of the biochemical basis of genetics, see the books by

HALDANE (*980*), WAGNER and MITCHELL (*2746*), CATCHESIDE (*416*) and HARRIS (*1008*); the mechanism of the effects has been discussed in Chapter XI. Although this is potentially one of the most important branches of enzymology and is already extremely interesting, we can only deal with it very briefly in the space available.

In the typical diploid cell there are two sets of chromosomes, one derived from the father and the other from the mother. There are thus two genes corresponding to each locus; these are either identical or a pair of alleles. According to the main principle of Mendelian genetics, three forms are possible for each pair of alleles. If we denote the two allelic forms of the gene in question by the letters *A* and *a*, these forms may be written as *AA*, *aa* and *Aa*. One might expect these three combinations to produce three different phenotypes, but this is not always so. In many cases *AA* and *Aa* produce the same phenotype; in this case *A* is said to be dominant and *a* is said to be recessive. Very often the recessive character which appears in the form *aa* is merely the absence of some quality which is present in the other two forms, e.g. pigmentation; thus albinism (the absence of pigment) is a recessive character. This led BATESON and PUNNET to suggest the 'presence-absence theory', namely, that the dominant character is due to the presence of the gene, whereas the recessive character results from its absence. However, in the light of more recent knowledge, particularly about back mutations, the facts are more easily explained by assuming that the recessive character is due not to the absence of the gene but to its inactivity, in other words, that the allele *A* produces something (e.g. an active enzyme) while the allele *a* does not.

All these facts are compatible with the idea, discussed in Chapter XI, that the gene forms a template for the production of a particular protein. If *a* represents *A* which has been modified in such a way that it does not produce active enzyme (though possibly producing a related inactive protein instead), the enzyme will be present in *AA* and *Aa* but absent from *aa*. One would expect more of the enzyme to be produced in cells with two active genes (i.e. *AA*) than in cells with only one (i.e. *Aa*). So far as the effect of this on the development of the character is concerned, two cases must be distinguished, according to whether the enzyme in question is a limiting factor in the relevant metabolic chain or whether it is present in excess. In the latter case the rate of the overall process will be independent of the amount of the enzyme over a wide range, so that the final effect produced by one *A* gene will be the same as that produced by two, and the forms *AA* and *Aa* will appear to be identical. Thus typical Mendelian dominance results. In the former case, although the process can still occur in the heterozygote *Aa*, it will be quantitatively reduced because the amount of the limiting enzyme is much less. This will lead to an intermediate form and incomplete dominance, e.g. to grey pigmentation instead of black.

This idea is well illustrated in rabbits by tropinesterase (acting on atropine). SAWIN and GLICK (*2311*) showed that the enzyme is not present in the serum of all rabbits, but that its possession is inherited as a single Mendelian character. Lack of the enzyme is recessive, so that the form *aa* does not contain it; the heterozygote *Aa* contains about half as much of the enzyme as the dominant homozygote *AA*. Thus each dominant gene *A* acts nearly or quite independently.

The effects of mutations

Most of the earlier work on the enzymology of genetics was based on the idea that the normal gene brought about the formation of an enzyme, and mutations could bring about the inactivation of the gene so that no enzyme was produced. This is quite compatible with the concept that the gene determines the template on which the protein is produced; a mutation would then be a change in the gene, altering the template so that a protein

Haemoglobin	Variant peptide sequence in β-chain
A (normal)	Val–His–Leu–Thr–Pro–Glu–Glu–Lys
S (sickle cell	Val–His–Leu–Thr–Pro–Val–Glu–Lys
C	Val–His–Leu–Thr–Pro–Lys–Glu–Lys
G	Val–His–Leu–Thr–Pro–Glu–Gly–Lys

Fig. XIII.4. *Anomalous peptides obtained from mutant haemoglobins* (from *1103, 1213*).

sufficiently different to be enzymatically inactive results. Some light on the nature of the differences in protein structure due to gene modifications is given by our knowledge of species differences in protein structure, discussed on pp. 651–6 above.

Investigations of the structure of haemoglobins, especially by INGRAM, illustrate the changes that can be produced in a protein in a single species by mutations. The smallest possible change is clearly the replacement of a single aminoacid, but this can produce profound changes in the tertiary structure and overall properties of a protein molecule. Sickle-cell anaemia is due to one such change. Individuals having this condition produce a modified haemoglobin (haemoglobin S) due to the possession of a recessive gene; heterozygotes, possessing both genes, produce both normal and sickle-cell haemoglobins, although there is no anaemia as there is in the recessive homozygote.

Normal and sickle-cell haemoglobins are identical in aminoacid sequence except for a sequence near the N-terminus of the β-chain; the respective sequences are shown in Fig. XIII.4, together with those for two other mutant haemoglobins. It will be seen that sickle-cell haemoglobin differs from normal only in the replacement of two glutamic acid residues by valines (since the complete molecule contains two β-chains). This change of two charges per molecule has a great effect on the physical properties of the haemoglobin, including its solubility. A number of other mutant haemoglobins are known, some of which have variations in the α-chains (1214). Present evidence suggests that the four peptide chains of haemoglobin are controlled by four different genes.

If gene mutations produce their effects in this way, the result on an enzyme will depend in part where in the protein the substitution takes place. If the change only affects part of the protein remote from the active centre, it will presumably not affect the catalytic activity, and in the normal course of events would not be noticed. If on the other hand, the change occurs in the active centre itself, it will probably result in a complete absence of enzymatic activity. Between these extremes there is the possibility that changes in the enzyme protein produced by mutations may result in definite changes in the catalytic properties without complete loss of activity; a number of such cases are now known, and have been reviewed by FINCHAM (730).

The first case to be noticed was that of pantothenate synthetase (6.3.2.1) of *Esch. coli* (1646). A mutant possessed a form of this enzyme which was extremely heat-sensitive, losing 90 per cent of its activity in 25 minutes at 35°C; it differed also in having an abnormally low affinity for pantoate.

Mutation of the glutamate dehydrogenase of *Neurospara crassa* has been studied by FINCHAM (729, 731). If a mutant which is completely lacking in glutamate dehydrogenase is exposed to ultraviolet light, some back-mutations take place. Some of these have reverted to production of normal enzyme, but others produce a low activity due to an enzyme which is distinctly different; this enzyme is readily activated by warming or incubating with substrate. Still another mutant has a variant glutamate dehydrogenase with extremely high K_m values for all substances, up to 30 times those for the normal enzyme.

An allelic variation of the same kind in humans came to light when it was found that a small number of individuals who were abnormally sensitive to a muscle relaxant, suxamethonium, had a very low serum cholinesterase activity. A careful survey of the Canadian population by KALOW and his colleagues (1296) showed that around 1 in 5000 individuals possessed a modified serum cholinesterase, with low specific activity, low substrate affinity and reduced susceptibility to certain competitive inhibitors. About 3 per cent of the population had sera with properties intermediate between the other two groups; inhibition experiments

suggest that these contain a mixture of the normal and modified cholinesterases. Familial studies showed that these individuals are heterozygotes, possessing both normal and modified genes which apparently
produce enzyme independently of one another.

In rare instances alterations in enzyme proteins due to gene variation
may lead to new enzymatic activities. VAN ASPEREN and OPPENOORTH
(*2029–30, 2715*) have investigated the appearance of an enzyme
hydrolysing organophosphorus compounds in mutant houseflies which
have become resistant to this type of insecticide. These mutants have a
very low carboxylesterase activity measured with methyl butyrate as
substrate, and it appears that a single gene mutation has altered the
carboxylesterase to a new enzyme which has extremely low activity
towards methyl butyrate, relative insensitivity towards organophosphorus
inhibitors, but which is able to hydrolyse them at an appreciable rate.
Once again heterozygotes are intermediate in behaviour and appear to
possess both normal and modified enzyme.

The use of mutations in elucidating metabolic patterns

A mutation in a higher organism, resulting in the loss of any one
enzyme reaction in an essential metabolic chain, will normally be lethal,
that is to say, the animal never develops and therefore the mutation is
not observed. Such mutations as are observed bring about relatively
unimportant changes, including the so-called 'inborn errors of metabolism' (GARROD, *816*), such as albinism, porphyrias, alkaptonuria,
tyrosinosis, galactosæmia, phenylketonuria and cystinuria.

In micro-organisms, however, such mutations need not necessarily
be lethal, as the substance normally formed by the missing enzyme can
be artificially supplied by addition to the medium. It has now become
an essential 'growth factor'. This makes it possible to use mutant
micro-organisms to work out the intermediate steps in important
metabolic chains by studying the growth requirements of the various
mutants. In this way it has been possible to elucidate whole lines of
metabolism, even before the individual enzymes have been discovered.
By exhaustive studies of this sort it is often possible to arrive at the
number of enzymes involved even while some of the intermediates are
unknown, since in those cases which have been most studied practically
every step has been found to be blocked by a separate mutation.

A very large amount of work has been done with such organisms as
Neurospora, Penicillium, Esch. coli. A number of charts showing the
sections of intermediary metabolism which have been investigated in
detail in this way are given in the books already cited (*980, 2746*). As an
example, we reproduce in Fig. XIII.5 part of the chart relating to

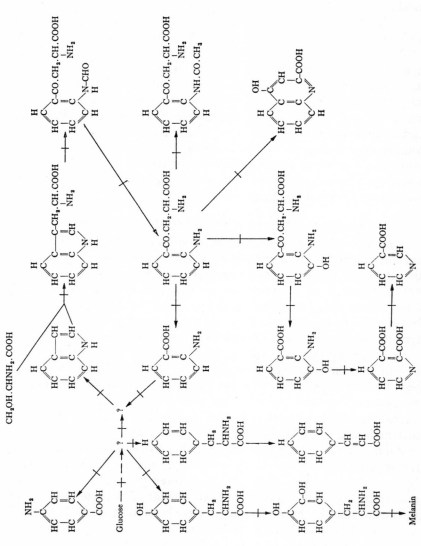

Fig. XIII.5. *Biosynthesis of some aromatic compounds in Neurospora as shown by genetic blocks (after 2746).*

aromatic compounds given in *2746*. In this diagram each arrow may represent either a single step or several consecutive steps, and a cross-bar on the arrow indicates the existence of a mutant in which the corresponding transformation is blocked; each cross-bar represents a separate and distinct mutation. Diagrams of this kind can provide valuable pointers in the search for new enzymes.

THE ORIGIN OF ENZYMES

In this concluding section we should like to discuss a subject which is frankly speculative, but nevertheless extremely important. The association between enzymes and life is so intimate that the problem of the origin of life itself is largely that of the origin of enzymes. This is one of the most difficult scientific problems, and the difficulties appear to have been greatly underestimated. To say airily, as some do, that whenever the conditions are suitable for life to exist, life will inevitably emerge, is to betray a complete ignorance of the problems involved. Without going into any of the philosophical implications of this question, it will be salutary to look at some of these difficulties.

In our experience enzymes are now formed only by living matter, or by highly complex systems obtained directly from living cells. We are beginning to see how this process may take place, and we have discussed it briefly in Chapter XI. The formation of every enzyme molecule depends on the pre-existence of a whole series of enzymes. These are needed to form the aminoacids from which the enzyme protein is built, to form the various components of the nucleic acids which are involved in the synthesis, and to provide the energy for synthesis, either by the breakdown of organic molecules or by photosynthesis. Given pre-existing enzymes, the formation of other enzymes is understandable; but the difficulty arises: if enzymes are formed only by enzymes, how were the first enzymes formed?

Any theory of the origin of life must take account of the extraordinary biochemical similarity of all living matter. Not only are all living cells made of much the same type of material, but one finds the same complex cofactors and prosthetic groups, and essentially the same enzymes, in the most diverse organisms, as we have pointed out earlier in this chapter. The essential unity of the living world extends even to stereochemistry. The same optical isomers of intermediates are involved in metabolism throughout the living world, with one or two exceptions; one does not, for example, find some species using D-glucose and others using L-glucose. This is of course a reflection of the constant stereospecificity of enzymes. Stereochemical enzyme specificity is presumably related to the asymmetry of the active centre. This asymmetry is related to the fact that enzymes are built up from optically active units, namely, exclusively from L-aminoacids so far as we know.

The essential asymmetry of living matter has generally been regarded as a difficulty in accounting for its origin by normal chemical processes, since such processes produce racemic mixtures from symmetrical reactants. Various devices have been invoked to overcome this difficulty, such as the action on photochemical reactions of circularly polarized light (perhaps produced by passing through quartz crystals), origin from one single molecule (which must have either one configuration or the other), separate crystallization of the two isomers from a solution of a racemic mixture, or sterically selective adsorption on an optically active crystal of quartz. The fact that only one pattern of asymmetry is found in life strongly suggests a common origin for all existing living matter. If life had originated otherwise than on one single and unique occasion, one would have expected that sometimes one asymmetric form and sometimes the other would be produced. Thus the event which produced living matter must at all times have been highly improbable, even under primordial conditions.

A number of writers (e.g. OPARIN, *2027*; BERNAL, *232*; BLUM, *276*) have speculated about the nature of these conditions and the events leading up to the origin of life, and an international symposium (*2028*) has recently been held on the subject. It has been assumed, in order to account for the initial formation of aminoacids and similar compounds, that the atmosphere at this time contained no oxygen, but consisted of a mixture of hydrogen and various hydrides, of which water, ammonia and hydrocarbons are particularly important for this discussion. By passing high voltage electric sparks continuously for a week through a mixture of CH_4, NH_3, H_2O and H_2 at the temperature of boiling water, MILLER (*1823-4*) was able to show the formation of small amounts of glycine, alanine, aspartate, glutamate, aminobutyrate, lactate, etc., although presumably these were racemic mixtures. The suggestion is that similar reactions might have been brought about by lightning discharges, the products being dissolved in pools of aqueous ammonia solution kept at high temperatures, possibly by volcanic activity.

Assuming that an aqueous solution of aminoacids has been formed, the next problem is how they could be built up into complex proteins or enzymes. Let us first see whether this could take place purely as a result of mass action. For simplicity of calculation let us assume that we have equal amounts of all the aminoacids, and that all peptide links have the same free energy of hydrolysis. Taking this as 1,400 calories per link,† the hydrolytic dissociation constant of each bond is 10. The equilibrium concentration of a peptide containing n aminoacid residues per molecule is given by

XIII.5 $$[P_n] = c^n K^{-(n-1)}$$

where c is the equilibrium concentration of each free aminoacid, and K is the equilibrium constant for peptide bond hydrolysis. Assuming that the concentration of each free aminoacid is kept at $1\,\text{M}$, the equilibrium concentration of a protein with 100 residues (MW about 12,000) would be $10^{-99}\,\text{M}$, which represents 1 molecule in a volume 10^{50} times the volume of the earth !

This appears to rule out the possibility of the formation of any protein by mass action, even in the presence of a catalyst to bring the system into equilibrium. However, the concentration given by equation XIII.5 is that of each separate molecular species of n-peptide. When only one kind of aminoacid is present, this will indeed be the total concentration of protein containing n residues per molecule, but when a number of different aminoacids are involved there will be many different molecular species of n-peptide, and the total concentration of n-peptide will be the sum of all these.

When the number of different aminoacids present is a, the number of possible n-peptides which can be formed from them is a^n. Thus the total concentration of n-peptide at equilibrium will be given by

XIII.6 $$\sum [P_n] = a^n c^n K^{-(n-1)} = \left(\frac{ac}{K}\right)^n K$$

When ac/K is less than 1, the equilibrium system will contain almost entirely free aminoacids with traces of small peptides; but if ac/K is greater than 1, $\sum [P_n]$ actually *increases* with n, so that the equilibrium system will consist almost entirely of high-molecular proteins. This is connected with the enormous number of possible permutations which can exist when n is large. If 20 aminoacids are present and K is taken as 10, protein synthesis could take place if c is maintained at $\text{M}/2$.

The consequence of this is that, providing that a high concentration of free aminoacids is maintained, the probability of protein being formed is appreciable, although of course the probability of any particular protein being formed is vanishingly small. The above calculation is of course unreal, since the assumed conditions could never have been

---

† This is almost certainly too low; $-\varDelta\text{F}^0$ at 37° varies in different peptides from small values up to 4,000, being commonly about 3,500 for the hydrolysis of dipeptides (BORSOOK, *294*). We have taken 1,400 purely for convenience in calculation.

attained (for instance, the amount of matter in the earth is insufficient to form even one molecule of each of the possible proteins†) and the actual conditions at any moment would be more of a steady state than an equilibrium.

Various factors have been invoked to increase the probability of the spontaneous formation of enzymes or other proteins. Local concentration of aminoacids by evaporation of a pool of solution or by adsorption at the surface of mud particles (232), or removal of the product by various means (adsorption, insolubility, mutual precipitation of proteins, possibly as coacervates), would all tend to increase the amount of protein formed. The equilibrium might also be displaced by the absorption of photochemical energy. The units from which protein was formed were not necessarily simple free aminoacids, but might well have been energy-rich derivatives (e.g. amides) which might have been produced instead of free aminoacids in the intense ultraviolet irradiation in the absence of an oxygen atmosphere. However, irradiation often has a destructive rather than a constructive effect on molecules, and indeed enzymes are usually inactivated by ultraviolet irradiation.

Let us now suppose that in some way proteins did come into existence; even if they had enzymatic properties there is no reason why their activities should be related, and it is highly improbable that they would form a continuous chain such as we have seen is necessary for the trapping of energy and its utilization for the biosynthetic reactions which constitute life. Yet the occurrence of a single gap would prevent the development of the system. It is possible of course that a chain may grow out by a successive induction process, but this presupposes a 'going concern' with a whole complex system for the inductive synthesis of enzymes already operative.

The inherent instability of the vital mechanism is also a difficulty, since it requires a continuous supply of available energy to maintain it. Until a complete functional system is produced, capable of producing the energy for its own maintenance, it might have a strong tendency to disintegrate, as do living cells as we now know them when the energy supply is cut off.

A further difficulty is that of holding the components of the system together until a cell membrane is formed, assuming life to have begun in the ocean. Unless the ocean contained throughout a fairly high concentration of the components (thus being itself one gigantic living cell!),

† An amount of protein of MW 60,000 equal in weight to the earth would contain 6×10^{46} molecules. The number of possible proteins of this MW is 10^{650}. Therefore at any instant not more than 1 in 10^{603} of the possible proteins could exist at all. Thus the simultaneous formation of two or more molecules of any given enzyme purely by chance is extremely improbable.

the components would rapidly disperse, as happens now when a cell membrane is ruptured. The system would then perish by 'lethal dilution'. But the formation of a cell membrane implies a system which already has a high degree of organization.

Thus the whole subject of the origin of enzymes, like that of the origin of life, which is essentially the same thing, bristles with difficulties. We may surely say of the advent of enzymes, as HOPKINS (*1156*) said of the advent of life, that it was

> *'the most improbable and the most significant event in the history of the Universe'.*

TABLE OF ENZYMES

(including most of those known at the middle of 1962)

Column 1 shows the Enzyme Commission number, except in those cases for which these have not yet been allotted, when a provisional number, ending in a letter, is given. The names in column 2, except those in italics, are the systematic names authorized by the Enzyme Commission; the names in italics have been invented or modified by the present authors, in accordance with the rules for naming enzymes given in the Report of the Enzyme Commission and set out on pp. 174–83. Column 3 gives the trivial name which is used throughout this book. Column 4 shows the nature of the prosthetic group (F denoting that the enzyme is a flavoprotein, H that it is a haemoprotein, Bt that it contais bound biotin, Cu, Zn, Fe, etc., that the enzyme contains these metals, and M that it contains an unspecified metal) and in square brackets the cofactors which have to be added (writing Asc for ascorbate, S for a sulphydryl compound, G for reduced glutathione, Py for pyridoxal phosphate, P for phosphate, PP for pyrophosphate, T for thiamine pyrophosphate, B_{12} for coenzyme B_{12}; M^{++} shows that the enzyme is activated by several different divalent metal ions, A that it is activated by a number of anions). The enzyme number is repeated on the right-hand page; the next column shows the reaction on which the systematic name is based. The seventh column shows briefly the sources from which the enzyme has been obtained and gives some notes on the main features of the enzyme's specificity, etc. The last column gives a selected list of papers on the enzyme; it is not intended as a complete bibliography, but as a help to those who wish to obtain further information about the particular enzyme. If the enzyme has been crystallized, this is indicated by a **C** under the enzyme number; in most cases (but not all) a photograph of the crystals will be found in the Atlas following this Table.

EC No.	Systematic name	Trivial name	Active groups and [cofactors]
1 OXIDOREDUCTASES			
1.1 Acting on the CHOH group of donors			
1.1.1 With NAD or NADP as acceptor			
1.1.1.1 C	Alcohol:NAD oxidoreductase	Alcohol dehydrogenase	Zn
1.1.1.2	Alcohol:NADP oxidoreductase	Alcohol dehydrogenase	
1.1.1.a	*Allyl-alcohol:NADP oxidoreductase*	Allyl alcohol dehydrogenase	
1.1.1.3	L-homoserine:NAD oxidoreductase	Homoserine dehydrogenase	
1.1.1.4	2,3-butyleneglycol:NAD oxidoreductase	Butyleneglycol dehydrogenase	
1.1.1.5	Acetoin:NAD oxidoreductase	Acetoin dehydrogenase	
1.1.1.b	*1,2-propanediol:NADP oxidoreductase*	Lactaldehyde reductase	
1.1.1.6	Glycerol:NAD oxidoreductase	Glycerol dehydrogenase	
1.1.1.7	1,2-propanediol-1-phosphate:NAD oxidoreductase	Propanediolphosphate dehydrogenase	
1.1.1.8 C	L-glycerol-3-phosphate:NAD oxidoreductase	Glycerolphosphate dehydrogenase	
1.1.1.c	*Ribitol:NAD oxidoreductase*	Ribitol dehydrogenase	
1.1.1.9	Xylitol:NAD oxidoreductase (D-xylulose-forming)	D-xylulose reductase	
1.1.1.10	Xylitol:NADP oxidoreductase (L-xylulose-forming)	L-xylulose reductase	
1.1.1.11	D-arabitol:NAD oxidoreductase	D-arabitol dehydrogenase	
1.1.1.12	L-arabitol:NAD oxidoreductase (L-xylulose-forming)	L-arabitol dehydrogenase	
1.1.1.13	L-arabitol:NAD oxidoreductase (L-ribulose-forming)	L-arabitol dehydrogenase	
1.1.1.14	L-iditol:NAD oxidoreductase	L-iditol dehydrogenase	

Reaction	Sources, comments on specificity, etc.	References
1.1.1.1	Alcohol + NAD = aldehyde or ketone + NADH$_2$	Yeast, some animal tissues. Acts on primary or secondary alcohols or semiacetals; the animal enzyme acts also on cyclic alcohols; the yeast enzyme acts also on D-lactate	288, 535–6, 1044, 1357, 1800, 1935, 2013, 2149, 2629, 2716
1.1.1.2	Alcohol + NADP = aldehyde + NADPH$_2$	Bacteria. Acts on primary alcohols only	590, 2612
1.1.1.a	Allyl alcohol + NADP = acrolein + NADPH$_2$	Bacteria. Acts slowly on saturated primary alcohols	2037
1.1.1.3	L-homoserine + NAD = L-aspartate-β-semialdehyde + NADH$_2$	Yeast, moulds. NADP also acts, more slowly; the *Neurospora* enzyme also acts on higher homologues of homoserine	256, 2955
1.1.1.4	2,3-butyleneglycol + NAD = acetoin + NADH$_2$	Bacteria	2550
1.1.1.5	Acetoin + NAD = diacetyl + NADH$_2$	Bacteria	2550
1.1.1.b	1,2-propanediol + NADP = L-lactaldehyde + NADPH$_2$	Animal tissues	954
1.1.1.6	Glycerol + NAD = dihydroxyacetone + NADH$_2$	Bacteria. Also acts on 1,2-propanediol	94, 370, 1593
1.1.1.7	1,2-propanediol 1-phosphate + NAD = acetol phosphate + NADH$_2$	Animal tissues	2370
1.1.1.8	L-glycerol 3-phosphate + NAD = dihydroxyacetone phosphate + NADH$_2$	Animal tissues. Also acts on propanediol phosphate	159, 1821
1.1.1.c	Ribitol + NAD = D-ribulose + NADH$_2$	Bacteria	1136, 1987, 2913
1.1.1.9	Xylitol + NAD = D-xylulose + NADH$_2$	Animal tissues, moulds, bacteria. Also acts as an L-erythrulose reductase	444, 1093, 1237
1.1.1.10	Xylitol + NADP = L-xylulose + NADPH$_2$	Animal tissues, moulds	444, 1093, 1136, 2672
1.1.1.11	D-arabitol + NAD = D-xylulose + NADH$_2$	Bacteria	1592, 2913
1.1.1.12	L-arabitol + NAD = L-xylulose + NADH$_2$	Moulds	444–5
1.1.1.13	L-arabitol + NAD = L-ribulose + NADH$_2$	Moulds	445
1.1.1.14	L-iditol + NAD = L-sorbose + NADH$_2$	Animal tissues, bacteria. Also acts on D-glucitol (giving D-fructose) and other closely related sugar alcohols	258, 673, 1649, 2663, 2872

z

EC No.	Systematic name	Trivial name	Active groups and [cofactors]
1.1.1.15	D-iditol: NAD oxidoreductase	D-iditol dehydrogenase	
1.1.1.16	Galactitol: NAD oxidoreductase	Galactitol dehydrogenase	
1.1.1.17	D-mannitol-1-phosphate: NAD oxidoreductase	Mannitol-1-phosphate dehydrogenase	
1.1.1.18	meso-inositol: NAD oxidoreductase	Inositol dehydrogenase	
1.1.1.19	L-gulonate: NADP oxidoreductase	Glucuronate reductase	
1.1.1.20	L-gulono-γ-lactone: NADP oxidoreductase	Glucuronolactone reductase	
1.1.1.d	D-mannonate: NAD oxidoreductase	Fructuronate reductase	
1.1.1.e	D-altronate: NAD oxidoreductase	Tagaturonate reductase	
1.1.1.21	Polyol: NADP oxidoreductase	Aldose reductase	
1.1.1.22	UDPglucose: NAD oxidoreductase	UDPG dehydrogenase	
1.1.1.23	L-Histidinol: NAD oxidoreductase	Histidinol dehydrogenase	
1.1.1.24	Quinate: NAD oxidoreductase	Quinate dehydrogenase	
1.1.1.25	Shikimate: NADP oxidoreductase	Shikimate dehydrogenase	
1.1.1.26 C	Glycollate: NAD oxidoreductase	Glyoxylate reductase	[A]
1.1.1.27 C	L-lactate: NAD oxidoreductase	Lactate dehydrogenase	Zn
1.1.1.28	D-lactate: NAD oxidoreductase	D-lactate dehydrogenase	
1.1.1.f	3-hydroxypropionate: NAD oxidoreductase	3-hydroxypropionate dehydrogenase	
1.1.1.29	D-glycerate: NAD oxidoreductase	Glycerate dehydrogenase	

Reaction	Sources, comments on specificity, etc.	References
1.1.1.15 D-iditol + NAD = D-sorbose + NADH$_2$	Bacteria Also converts xylitol to L-xylulose and L-glucitol to L-fructose	2381
1.1.1.16 Galactitol + NAD = D-tagatose + NADH$_2$	Bacteria Also converts other polyols containing an L-*threo* configuration adjacent to a primary alcohol group to the corresponding sugars	2381
1.1.1.17 D-mannitol 1-phosphate + NAD = D-fructose 6-phosphate + NADH$_2$	Bacteria, yeast	1726, 2898–9
1.1.1.18 *meso*-inositol + NAD = 2-oxo-*myo*-inositol + NADH$_2$	Bacteria	865, 1520
1.1.1.19 L-gulonate + NADP = D-glucuronate + NADPH$_2$	Liver, yeast Also reduces D-galacturonate	2421, 2950
1.1.1.20 L-gulono-γ-lactone + NADP = D-glucurono-γ-lactone + NADPH$_2$	Animal tissues	2576
1.1.1.d D-mannonate + NAD = D-fructuronate + NADH$_2$	Bacteria Also reduces D-tagaturonate	1094, 1379
1.1.1.e D-altronate + NAD = D-tagaturonate + NADH$_2$	Bacteria	1094
1.1.1.21 Polyol + NADP = aldose + NADPH$_2$	Seminal vesicles, placenta Wide specificity	1086
1.1.1.22 UDPglucose + 2NAD + H$_2$O = UDPglucuronate + 2NADH$_2$	Liver	1769, 2559–60
1.1.1.23 L-histidinol + 2NAD = L-histidine + 2NADH$_2$	Moulds, yeast, bacteria Also oxidizes L-histidinal	8–9
1.1.1.24 Quinate + NAD = 5-dehydroquinate + NADH$_2$	Bacteria	1840
1.1.1.25 Shikimate + NADP = 5-dehydroshikimate + NADPH$_2$	Plants, yeast, bacteria	144, 1840, 2941
1.1.1.26 Glycollate + NAD = glyoxylate + NADH$_2$	Plants Reduces glyoxylate to glycollate or hydroxypyruvate to D-glycerate	2964–5
1.1.1.27 L-lactate + NAD = pyruvate + NADH$_2$	Animal tissues, bacteria Also oxidizes other L-2-hydroxymonocarboxylic acids; NADP also acts, more slowly	593, 829, 1476, 1780, 2544, 2712
1.1.1.28 D-lactate + NAD = pyruvate + NADH$_2$	Bacteria	593
1.1.1.f 3-hydroxypropionate + NAD = malonate semialdehyde + NADH$_2$	Animal tissues, bacteria	592
1.1.1.29 D-glycerate + NAD = hydroxypyruvate + NADH$_2$	Higher plants	1148, 2502

EC No.	Systematic name	Trivial name	Active groups and [cofactors]
1.1.1.g C	D-*glycerate: NAD(P) oxidoreductase*	Tartronate semialdehyde reductase	
1.1.1.30	D-3-hydroxybutyrate : NAD oxidoreductase	3-hydroxybutyrate dehydrogenase	[S. Lecithin]
1.1.1.31	3-hydroxyisobutyrate : NAD oxidoreductase	3-hydroxyisobutyrate dehydrogenase	
1.1.1.h	*4-hydroxybutyrate: NAD oxidoreductase*	4-hydroxybutyrate dehydrogenase	
1.1.1.32	Mevalonate : NAD oxidoreductase	Mevaldate reductase	
1.1.1.33	Mevalonate : NADP oxidoreductase	Mevaldate reductase	
1.1.1.34	Mevalonate : NADP oxidoreductase (acylating CoA)	Hydroxymethylglutaryl-CoA reductase	
1.1.1.35 C	L-3-hydroxyacyl-CoA : NAD oxidoreductase	3-hydroxyacyl-CoA dehydrogenase	
1.1.1.36	D-3-hydroxyacyl-CoA : NADP oxidoreductase	Acetoacetyl-CoA reductase	
1.1.1.37 C	L-malate : NAD oxidoreductase	Malate dehydrogenase	
1.1.1.38	L-malate : NAD oxidoreductase (decarboxylating)	Malate dehydrogenase (decarboxylating) (Originally known as 'malic' enzyme)	[$Mn^{++}.K^+$]
1.1.1.39	L-malate : NAD oxidoreductase (decarboxylating)	Malate dehydrogenase (decarboxylating) (Originally known as 'malic' enzyme)	[M^{++}]
1.1.1.40	L-malate : NADP oxidoreductase (decarboxylating)	Malate dehydrogenase (decarboxylating) (Originally known as 'malic' enzyme)	[Mn^{++}]
1.1.1.41	L$_s$-isocitrate : NAD oxidoreductase (decarboxylating)	Isocitrate dehydrogenase	[Mn^{++}
1.1.1.42	L$_s$-isocitrate : NADP oxidoreductase (decarboxylating)	Isocitrate dehydrogenase	[Mn^{++}

	Reaction	Sources, comments on specificity, etc.	References
1.1.1.g	D-glycerate + NAD(P) = tartronate semialdehyde + NAD(P)H$_2$	*Pseudomonas*	*875*
1.1.1.30	D-3-hydroxybutyrate + NAD = acetoacetate + NADH$_2$	Animal tissues, bacteria Also oxidizes other 3-hydroxy-monocarboxylic acids	*901, 1536, 2365*
1.1.1.31	3-hydroxyisobutyrate + NAD = methylmalonate semialdehyde + NADH$_2$	Animal tissues, moulds, bacteria	*2234*
1.1.1.h	4-hydroxybutyrate + NAD = succinate semialdehyde + NADH$_2$	Bacteria	*1970*
1.1.1.32	Mevalonate + NAD = mevaldate + NADH$_2$	Liver	*2330*
1.1.1.33	Mevalonate + NADP = mevaldate + NADPH$_2$	Animal tissues, yeast	*497*
1.1.1.34	Mevalonate + CoA + 2NADP = 3-hydroxy-3-methylglutaryl-CoA + 2NADPH$_2$	Yeast	*355, 661, 1403*
1.1.1.35	L-3-hydroxyacyl-CoA + NAD = 3-oxo-acyl-CoA + NADH$_2$	Animal tissues Also oxidizes S-3-hydroxy-acyl-N-acylthioethanol-amine and S-3-hydroxy-acylhydrolipoate; the heart enzyme will also act, slowly, with NADP	*1535, 1641, 2515, 2755*
1.1.1.36	D-3-hydroxyacyl-CoA + NADP = 3-oxo-acyl-CoA + NADPH$_2$	Liver	*2754*
1.1.1.37	L-malate + NAD = oxaloacetate + NADH$_2$	Animal tissues, plants, yeast, bacteria Also oxidizes some other 2-hydroxydicarboxylic acids	*555, 697, 2546, 2651-2, 2895*
1.1.1.38	L-malate + NAD = pyruvate + CO$_2$ + NADH$_2$	Bacteria Also decarboxylates added oxaloacetate	*1320*
1.1.1.39	L-malate + NAD = pyruvate + CO$_2$ + NADH$_2$	*Ascaris* Does not decarboxylate added oxaloacetate	*2315*
1.1.1.40	L-malate + NADP = pyruvate + CO$_2$ + NADPH$_2$	Animal tissues, plants Also decarboxylates added oxaloacetate	*1000, 2010, 2279, 2531, 2763*
1.1.1.41	L$_s$-isocitrate + NAD = 2-oxoglutarate + CO$_2$ + NADH$_2$	Animal tissues, moulds, yeast Does not decarboxylate added oxalosuccinate	*1436, 2096, 2165*
1.1.1.42	L$_s$-isocitrate + NADP = 2-oxoglutarate + CO$_2$ + NADPH$_2$	Widely distributed Also decarboxylates added oxalosuccinate	*23, 1890, 1892-3, 2165, 2401-2*

EC No.	*Systematic name*	*Trivial name*	*Active groups and [cofactors]*
1.1.1.43	6-phospho-D-gluconate:NAD(P) oxidoreductase	Phosphogluconate dehydrogenase	
1.1.1.44 C	6-phospho-D-gluconate:NADP oxidoreductase (decarboxylating)	Phosphogluconate dehydrogenase (decarboxylating)	
1.1.1.45	L-*3-hydroxyacid:NAD oxidoreductase*	3-hydroxyacid dehydrogenase (Originally known as L-gulonate dehydrogenase)	
1.1.1.46	L-arabinose:NAD oxidoreductase	L-arabinose dehydrogenase	
1.1.1.47	β-D-glucose:NAD(P) oxidoreductase	Glucose dehydrogenase	
1.1.1.48	D-galactose:NAD oxidoreductase	Galactose dehydrogenase	
1.1.1.49 C	D-glucose-6-phosphate:NADP oxidoreductase	Glucose-6-phosphate dehydrogenase	
1.1.1.50	3-α-hydroxysteroid:NAD(P) oxidoreductase	3-α-hydroxysteroid dehydrogenase	
1.1.1.i	*Oestradiol:NAD 17-β-oxidoreductase*	Oestradiol 17-β-dehydrogenase	
1.1.1.j	*17-β-hydroxysteroid:NAD 17-β-oxidoreductase*	Testosterone 17-β-dehydrogenase	
1.1.1.k	*17-β-hydroxysteroid:NADP 17-β-oxidoreductase*	Testosterone 17-β-dehydrogenase	
1.1.1.51	3(or 17)-β-hydroxysteroid:NAD(P) oxidoreductase	β-hydroxysteroid dehydrogenase	
1.1.1.52	3-α-hydroxycholanate:NAD oxidoreductase	α-hydroxycholanate dehydrogenase	
1.1.1.53 C	*20-dihydrocortisone:NAD oxidoreductase*	Cortisone reductase	
1.1.1.l	*Pyridoxin:NADP oxidoreductase*	Pyridoxin dehydrogenase	
1.1.1.m	*10-hydroxydecanoate:NAD oxidoreductase*	ω-hydroxydecanoate dehydrogenase	

	Reaction	Sources, comments on specificity, etc.	References
1.1.1.43	6-phospho-D-gluconate + NAD(P) = 6-phospho-2-oxo-D-gluconate + NAD(P)H₂	Bacteria	768
1.1.1.44	6-phospho-D-gluconate + NADP = D-ribulose 5-phosphate + CO₂ + NADPH₂	Animal tissues, plants, yeast, bacteria	607, 2105, 2356–7
1.1.1.45	L-gulonate + NAD = 3-oxo-L-gulonate + NADH₂	Kidney	2433
1.1.1.46	L-arabinose + NAD = L-arabono-γ-lactone + NADH₂	Bacteria	2825
1.1.1.47	β-D-glucose + NAD(P) = D-glucono-δ-lactone + NAD(P)H₂	Liver Also oxidizes D-xylose	330, 2551
1.1.1.48	D-galactose + NAD = D-galactono-γ-lactone + NADH₂	Bacteria	588
1.1.1.49	D-glucose 6-phosphate + NADP = D-glucono-δ-lactone 6-phosphate + NADPH₂	Animal tissues, plants, yeast, bacteria Certain bacterial preparations also reduce NAD as well as NADP	849, 1276, 1725, 1986, 2356
1.1.1.50	Androsterone + NAD(P) = androstane-3,17-dione + NAD(P)H₂	Liver, bacteria Also acts on other 3-α-hydroxysteroids	1414, 1713, 2608, 2666
1.1.1.i	Oestradiol + NAD = oestrone + NADH₂	Animal tissues	1514
1.1.1.j	Testosterone + NAD = Δ⁵-androstene-3,17-dione + NADH₂	Animal tissues	695, 1414, 2582, 2736
1.1.1.k	Testosterone + NADP = Δ⁵-androstene-3,17-dione + NADPH₂	Animal tissues	695, 1414, 2582, 2736
1.1.1.51	Testosterone + NAD(P) = Δ⁵-androstene-3,17-dione + NAD(P)H₂	Yeast, bacteria Also acts on other 3-β- or 17-β-hydroxysteroids	1642, 1712–3, 2606, 2608–9
1.1.1.52	3-α-hydroxycholanate + NAD = 3-oxocholanate + NADH₂	Bacteria Also acts on other 3-α-hydroxysteroids with an acidic side-chain	1039
1.1.1.53	20-dihydrocortisone + NAD = cortisone + NADH₂	Animal tissues Also acts on other 17,20,21-trihydroxysteroids	413, 1179, 1642, 2193, 2862
1.1.1.l	Pyridoxin + NADP = pyridoxal + NADPH₂	Yeast Also oxidizes pyridoxin phosphate	1150
1.1.1.m	10-hydroxydecanoate + NAD = 10-oxodecanoate + NADH₂	Animal tissues Also acts, more slowly, on 9-hydroxynonanoate and 11-hydroxyundecanoate	1841

EC No.	Systematic name	Trivial name	Active groups and [cofactors]
	1.1.2 With a cytochrome as an acceptor		
1.1.2.1	L-glycerol-3-phosphate : cytochrome c oxidoreductase	Glycerolphosphate dehydrogenase	
1.1.2.2	D-mannitol : cytochrome oxidoreductase	Mannitol dehydrogenase	
1.1.2.3 C	L-lactate : cytochrome c oxidoreductase	Lactate dehydrogenase (Cytochrome b_2)	F.H
1.1.2.4	*D-lactate : cytochrome* c *oxidoreductase*	D-lactate dehydrogenase	F.Zn
	1.1.3 With O_2 as acceptor		
1.1.3.1 C	Glycollate : O_2 oxidoreductase	Glycollate oxidase	F
1.1.3.2 C	L-lactate : O_2 oxidoreductase (decarboxylating)	Lactate oxidase	F
1.1.3.3	L-malate : O_2 oxidoreductase	Malate oxidase	
1.1.3.a	*Aryl-alcohol : O_2 oxidoreductase*	Aryl-alcohol oxidase	
1.1.3.b	*L-gulono-γ-lactone : O_2 oxidoreductase*	L-gulonolactone oxidase	
1.1.3.4 C	β-D-glucose : O_2 oxidoreductase	Glucose oxidase (Notatin)	F
1.1.3.5	D-hexose : O_2 oxidoreductase	Hexose oxidase	F
1.1.3.c	*D-galactose : O_2 oxidoreductase*	Galactose oxidase	Zn
1.1.3.6	Cholesterol : O_2 oxidoreductase	Cholesterol oxidase	
	1.1.99 With other acceptors		
1.1.99.1	Choline : (acceptor) oxidoreductase	Choline dehydrogenase	F ?
1.1.99.2	L-2-hydroxyglutarate : (acceptor) oxidoreductase	2-hydroxyglutarate dehydrogenase	

Reaction	Sources, comments on specificity, etc.	References
1.1.2.1 L-glycerol 3-phosphate + oxidized cytochrome c = dihydroxyacetone phosphate + reduced cytochrome c	Animal tissues	2224
1.1.2.2 D-mannitol + oxidized cytochrome = D-fructose + reduced cytochrome	Bacteria Also oxidizes erythritol, D-sorbitol, D-arabitol, and ribitol	86
1.1.2.3 L-lactate + oxidized cytochrome c = pyruvate + reduced cytochrome c	Yeast, bacteria	82–3, 119, 1880–1
1.1.2.4 D-lactate + oxidized cytochrome c = pyruvate + reduced cytochrome c	Yeast	927–9, 2001
1.1.3.1 Glycollate + O_2 = glyoxylate + H_2O_2	Liver, plants Also oxidizes L-lactate and glyoxylate, more slowly	788, 1486, 2216, 2967
1.1.3.2 L-lactate + O_2 = acetate + CO_2 + H_2O_2	Bacteria	2574
1.1.3.3 L-malate + O_2 = oxaloacetate + (?)	Bacteria	468
1.1.3.a An aromatic primary alcohol + O_2 = an aromatic aldehyde + H_2O_2	White rot fungi Oxidizes many primary alcohols containing an aromatic ring; best substrates were β-naphthyl carbinol and 3-methoxy-benzyl alcohol	714
1.1.3.b L-gulono-γ-lactone + O_2 = L-*xylo*hexulonolactone + H_2O_2	Animal tissues The product spontaneously isomerizes to L-ascorbate	442, 1216
1.1.3.4 β-D-glucose + O_2 = D-glucono-δ-lactone + H_2O_2	Moulds	508, 1343–4
1.1.3.5 β-D-glucose + O_2 = D-glucono-δ-lactone + H_2O_2	Plants Also oxidizes D-galactose, D-mannose, maltose, lactose, and cellobiose	184–5
1.1.3.c D-galactose + O_2 = D-*galacto*-hexodialdose + H_2O_2	Moulds Oxidizes at the 6-position of D-galactose	103, 500
1.1.3.6 Cholesterol + O_2 = Δ^4-cholestene-3-one + (?)	Bacteria	2500
1.1.99.1 Choline + acceptor = betaine aldehyde + reduced acceptor	Liver Uses indophenol as acceptor	668, 2211
1.1.99.2 L-2-hydroxyglutarate + acceptor = 2-oxoglutarate + reduced acceptor	Heart Uses pyocyanine and phenazines as acceptors	2821

EC No.	*Systematic name*	*Trivial name*	*Active groups and [cofactors]*
1.1.99.3	D-gluconate:(acceptor) oxidoreductase	Gluconate dehydrogenase	
1.1.99.4	2-oxo-D-gluconate:(acceptor) oxidoreductase	Oxogluconate dehydrogenase	
1.1.99.a	*D-2-hydroxyacid:(acceptor) oxidoreductase*	D-2-hydroxyacid dehydrogenase	F.Zn

1.2 Acting on the aldehyde or keto-group of donors
1.2.1 With NAD or NADP as acceptor

EC No.	Systematic name	Trivial name	cofactors
1.2.1.1	Formaldehyde:NAD oxidoreductase	Formaldehyde dehydrogenase	[G]
1.2.1.2	Formate:NAD oxidoreductase	Formate dehydrogenase	
1.2.1.3	Aldehyde:NAD oxidoreductase	Aldehyde dehydrogenase	
1.2.1.4	Aldehyde:NADP oxidoreductase	Aldehyde dehydrogenase	[M^{++}]
1.2.1.5	Aldehyde:NAD(P) oxidoreductase	Aldehyde dehydrogenase	[K$^+$] (yeast) [P] (bacteria)
1.2.1.6	Benzaldehyde:NAD oxidoreductase	Benzaldehyde dehydrogenase	
1.2.1.7	Benzaldehyde:NADP oxidoreductase	Benzaldehyde dehydrogenase	
1.2.1.8	Betaine-aldehyde:NAD oxidoreductase	Betaine aldehyde dehydrogenase	[S]
1.2.1.9	D-glyceraldehyde-3-phosphate:NADP oxidoreductase	Glyceraldehydephosphate dehydrogenase, triosephosphate dehydrogenase	
1.2.1.a	*Malonate-semialdehyde:NAD(P) oxidoreductase*	Malonate semialdehyde dehydrogenase	
1.2.1.b	*Succinate-semialdehyde:NAD(P) oxidoreductase*	Succinate semialdehyde dehydrogenase	
1.2.1.10	Aldehyde:NAD oxidoreductase (acylating CoA)	Aldehyde dehydrogenase	
1.2.1.c	*Glyoxylate:NADP oxidoreductase (acylating CoA)*	Glyoxylate dehydrogenase	
1.2.1.d	*Malonate-semialdehyde:NAD(P) oxidoreductase (acetylating CoA)*	Malonate semialdehyde dehydrogenase	

	Reaction	Sources, comments on specificity, etc.	References
1.1.99.3	D-gluconate + acceptor = 2-oxo-D-gluconate + reduced acceptor	Bacteria Uses pyocyanine as acceptor	2166
1.1.99.4	2-oxo-D-gluconate + acceptor = 2,5-dioxo-D-gluconate + reduced acceptor	*Acetobacter* Uses phenazines and indophenol as acceptors	539
1.1.99.a	D-lactate + acceptor = pyruvate + reduced acceptor	Animal tissues, yeast Acts on a variety of D-2-hydroxyacids; uses ferricyanide, methylene blue, etc., as acceptors	282, 929, 1689, 2001, 2685
1.2.1.1	Formaldehyde + NAD + H_2O = formate + $NADH_2$	Liver	2555
1.2.1.2	Formate + NAD = CO_2 + $NADH_2$	Plants	568
1.2.1.3	Aldehyde + NAD + H_2O = acid + $NADH_2$	Animal tissues Wide specificity	2147
1.2.1.4	Aldehyde + NADP + H_2O = acid + $NADPH_2$	Yeast, bacteria	1924, 2360
1.2.1.5	Aldehyde + NAD(P) + H_2O = acid + NAD(P)H_2	Yeast, bacteria	253, 1233, 1385, 2612
1.2.1.6	Benzaldehyde + NAD + H_2O = benzoate + $NADH_2$	Bacteria Wide specificity	951
1.2.1.7	Benzaldehyde + NADP + H_2O = benzoate + $NADPH_2$	Bacteria	951
1.2.1.8	Betaine aldehyde + NAD + H_2O = betaine + $NADH_2$	Animal tissues	2255
1.2.1.9	D-glyceraldehyde 3-phosphate + NADP + H_2O = 3-phospho-D-glycerate + $NADPH_2$	Green plant leaves	2252
1.2.1.a	Malonate semialdehyde + NAD(P) = malonate + NAD(P)H_2	Bacteria	1922
1.2.1.b	Succinate semialdehyde + NAD(P) = succinate + NAD(P)H_2	Brain, bacteria The brain enzyme is specific for NAD	29, 1239, 1970
1.2.1.10	Aldehyde + CoA + NAD = acyl-CoA + $NADH_2$	Bacteria	372
1.2.1.c	Glyoxylate + CoA + NADP = oxalyl-CoA + $NADPH_2$	*Pseudomonas oxalaticus*	2136
1.2.1.d	Malonate semialdehyde + CoA + NAD(P) = acetyl-CoA + CO_2 + NAD(P)H_2	Bacteria	1037, 2927

EC No.	*Systematic name*	*Trivial name*	*Active groups and [cofactors]*
1.2.1.11	L-aspartate-β-semialdehyde : NADP oxidoreductase (phosphorylating)	Aspartate semialdehyde dehydrogenase	
1.2.1.12 C	D-glyceraldehyde-3-phosphate : NAD oxidoreductase (phosphorylating)	Glyceraldehydephosphate dehydrogenase, triosephosphate dehydrogenase	Zn
1.2.1.13	D-glyceraldehyde-3-phosphate : NADP oxidoreductase (phosphorylating)	Glyceraldehydephosphate dehydrogenase, triosephosphate dehydrogenase	
1.2.1.14	IMP : NAD oxidoreductase	IMP dehydrogenase	
1.2.1.e	*4-aminobutyraldehyde : NAD oxidoreductase*	Aminobutyraldehyde dehydrogenase	
1.2.1.f	*Glutarate-semialdehyde : NAD oxidoreductase*	Glutarate semialdehyde dehydrogenase	

1.2.2   With a cytochrome as an acceptor

1.2.2.1	Formate : cytochrome b_1 oxidoreductase	Formate dehydrogenase	
1.2.2.2 C	*Pyruvate : cytochrome b_1 oxidoreductase*	Pyruvate dehydrogenase	F[T]

1.2.3   With O_2 as acceptor

1.2.3.1	Aldehyde : O_2 oxidoreductase	Aldehyde oxidase	F.Mo.H?
1.2.3.2 C	Xanthine : O_2 oxidoreductase	Xanthine oxidase	F.Mo.Fe
1.2.3.3	Pyruvate : O_2 oxidoreductase	Pyruvate oxidase	F[T.M^{++}]
1.2.3.4	Oxalate : O_2 oxidoreductase	Oxalate oxidase	F

1.2.4   With lipoate as acceptor

1.2.4.1	Pyruvate : lipoate oxidoreductase (acceptor-acetylating)	Pyruvate dehydrogenase	[T]
1.2.4.2	2-oxoglutarate : lipoate oxidoreductase (acceptor-acylating)	Oxoglutarate dehydrogenase	[T]

1.2.99   With other acceptors

1.2.99.1	Uracil : (acceptor) oxidoreductase	Uracil dehydrogenase	

	Reaction	Sources, comments on specificity, etc.	References
1.2.1.11	L-aspartate β-semialdehyde + phosphate + NADP = L-β-aspartylphosphate + NADPH$_2$	Yeast	255
1.2.1.12	D-glyceraldehyde 3-phosphate + phosphate + NAD = 1,3-diphospho-D-glyceric acid + NADH$_2$	Widely distributed. Also acts very slowly on D-glyceraldehyde and some other aldehydes; mercaptans can replace phosphate	400, 505, 966, 1461, 2726, 2787
1.2.1.13	D-glyceraldehyde 3-phosphate + phosphate + NADP = 1,3-diphospho-D-glyceric acid + NADPH$_2$	Green plant leaves, *Alcaligenes*	324, 826, 2252
1.2.1.14	IMP + NAD + H$_2$O = xanthosine 5′-phosphate + NADH$_2$	Plants, bacteria	1677, 2690
1.2.1.e	4-aminobutyraldehyde + NAD = 4-aminobutyrate + NADH$_2$	*Pseudomonas*. Nature of substrate not finally proved; $\varDelta^1$-pyrroline was used	1236
1.2.1.f	Glutarate semialdehyde + NAD = glutarate + NADH$_2$	*Pseudomonas*	1204
1.2.2.1	Formate + oxidized cytochrome b_1 = CO$_2$ + reduced cytochrome b_1	Bacteria	805
1.2.2.2	Pyruvate + oxidized cytochrome b_1 = acetate + CO$_2$ + reduced cytochrome b_1	Bacteria	2868
1.2.3.1	Aldehyde + H$_2$O + O$_2$ = acid + H$_2$O$_2$	Liver. Also oxidizes quinoline and pyridine derivatives	871, 1407, 1686
1.2.3.2	Xanthine + H$_2$O + O$_2$ = urate + H$_2$O$_2$	Animal tissues, milk, bacteria. Also oxidizes hypoxanthine, some other purines and pterins and aldehydes	105, 594, 610, 615, 645, 1124, 1665, 1859, 2208, 2737
1.2.3.3	Pyruvate + phosphate + O$_2$ = acetylphosphate + CO$_2$ + H$_2$O$_2$	*Lactobacillus*	967
1.2.3.4	Oxalate + O$_2$ = 2CO$_2$ + H$_2$O$_2$	Mosses	540
1.2.4.1	Pyruvate + oxidized lipoate = 6-S-acetylhydrolipoate + CO$_2$	Animal tissues, bacteria. Possibly a system	2007, 2359
1.2.4.2	2-oxoglutarate + oxidized lipoate = 6-S-succinylhydrolipoate + CO$_2$	Animal tissues, bacteria. Possibly a system	1750, 2007, 2295
1.2.99.1	Uracil + acceptor = barbiturate + reduced acceptor	Bacteria. Also oxidizes thymine; uses methylene blue as acceptor	1035

EC No.	Systematic name	Trivial name	Active groups and [cofactors]
1.3	**Acting on the CH-CH group of donors**		
	1.3.1 With NAD or NADP as acceptor		
1.3.1.1	4,5-dihydro-uracil:NAD oxidoreductase	Dihydro-uracil dehydrogenase	
1.3.1.2	4,5-dihydro-uracil:NADP oxidoreductase	Dihydro-uracil dehydrogenase	
1.3.1.3	*4,5-β-dihydrocortisone:NADP Δ⁴-oxidoreductase*	Cortisone reductase	
1.3.1.a	*4,5-α-dihydrocortisone:NADP Δ⁴-oxidoreductase*	Cortisone reductase	
1.3.1.b	*3,5-cyclohexadiene-1,2-diol:NADP oxidoreductase*	Cyclohexadienediol dehydrogenase	
	1.3.2 With a cytochrome as an acceptor		
1.3.2.1	Butyryl-CoA:cytochrome *c* oxidoreductase	Butyryl-CoA dehydrogenase	F
1.3.2.2	Acyl-CoA:cytochrome *c* oxidoreductase	Acyl-CoA dehydrogenase	F.Fe
1.3.2.3	L-galactono-γ-lactone:cytochrome *c* oxidoreductase	Galactonolactone dehydrogenase	
	1.3.3 With O₂ as acceptor		
1.3.3.1 C	L-4,5-dihydro-orotate:O₂ oxidoreductase	Dihydro-orotate dehydrogenase	F.Fe
	1.3.99 With other acceptors		
1.3.99.1	Succinate:(acceptor) oxidoreductase	Succinate dehydrogenase	F.Fe.[P]
1.3.99.a	*3-ketosteroid:(acceptor) Δ¹-oxidoreductase*	3-ketosteroid Δ¹-dehydrogenase	F ?
1.3.99.b	*3-ketosteroid:(acceptor) Δ⁴-oxidoreductase*	3-ketosteroid Δ⁴-dehydrogenase	F ?
1.4	**Acting on the CH-NH₂ group of donors**		
	1.4.1 With NAD or NADP as acceptor		
1.4.1.1	L-alanine:NAD oxidoreductase (deaminating)	Alanine dehydrogenase	
1.4.1.2	L-glutamate:NAD oxidoreductase (deaminating)	Glutamate dehydrogenase	

	Reaction	Sources, comments on specificity, etc.	References
1.3.1.1	4,5-dihydro-uracil + NAD = uracil + NADH$_2$	Bacteria	387
1.3.1.2	4,5-dihydro-uracil + NADP = uracil + NADPH$_2$	Liver Also acts on dihydrothymine	789, 934
1.3.1.3	4,5-β-dihydrocortisone + NADP = cortisone + NADPH$_2$	Liver	344, 1574, 2667
1.3.1.a	4,5-α-dihydrocortisone + NADP = cortisone + NADPH$_2$	Liver microsomes	1662
1.3.1 b	3,5-cyclohexadiene-1,2-diol + NADP = catechol + NADPH$_2$	Liver	117
1.3.2.1	Butyryl-CoA + oxidized cytochrome c = crotonoyl-CoA + reduced cytochrome c	Animal tissues Also acts (with decreasing activity) on CoA compounds of acids up to C$_8$	903, 1028, 1680
1.3.2.2	Acyl-CoA + oxidized cytochrome c = 2,3-dehydroacyl-CoA + reduced cytochrome c	Animal tissues Acts best on higher members of the series	514, 1028
1.3.2.3	L-galactono-γ-lactone + oxidized cytochrome c = L-ascorbate + reduced cytochrome c	Plants	1709, 1711
1.3.3.1	L-4,5-dihydro-orotate + O$_2$ = orotate + H$_2$O$_2$ (?)	Bacteria NAD can replace O$_2$; NADH$_2$ can replace dihydro-orotate	786
1.3.99.1	Succinate + acceptor = fumarate + reduced acceptor	Animal tissues, yeast, bacteria Uses phenazine alkylsulphate as an acceptor	740, 1328, 1330, 1754, 2413, 2415, 2781, 2793–4
1.3.99.a	A 3-ketosteroid + acceptor = a Δ^1-3-ketosteroid + reduced acceptor	*Pseudomonas* Uses phenazine alkylsulphate as an acceptor	1575
1.3.99.b	A 3-ketosteroid + acceptor = a Δ^4-3-ketosteroid + reduced acceptor	*Pseudomonas* Uses phenazine alkylsulphate as an acceptor	1575
1.4.1.1	L-alanine + H$_2$O + NAD = pyruvate + NH$_3$ + NADH$_2$	Bacteria	2013, 2085
1.4.1.2	L-glutamate + H$_2$O + NAD = 2-oxoglutarate + NH$_3$ + NADH$_2$	Animal tissues, plants, bacteria	162, 357, 709, 1976

EC No.	Systematic name	Trivial name	Active groups and [cofactors]
1.4.1.3 C	L-glutamate: NAD(P) oxidoreductase (deaminating)	Glutamate dehydrogenase	Zn
1.4.1.4	L-glutamate: NADP oxidoreductase (deaminating)	Glutamate dehydrogenase	
1.4.1.5	L-aminoacid: NAD oxidoreductase (deaminating)	L-aminoacid dehydrogenase	[P]
1.4.1.6	5-aminovalerate: NAD oxidoreductase (cyclizing)	D-proline reductase	[M++

1.4.3   With O₂ as acceptor

EC No.	Systematic name	Trivial name	Active groups and [cofactors]
1.4.3.1	D-aspartate: O₂ oxidoreductase (deaminating)	D-aspartate oxidase	F
1.4.3.2 C	L-aminoacid: O₂ oxidoreductase (deaminating)	L-aminoacid oxidase	F
1.4.3.3 C	D-aminoacid: O₂ oxidoreductase (deaminating)	D-aminoacid oxidase	F
1.4.3.4 C	Monoamine: O₂ oxidoreductase (deaminating)	Monoamine oxidase (Originally known as tyraminase)	Cu
1.4.3.5	*Pyridoxaminephosphate: O₂ oxidoreductase (deaminating)*	Pyridoxaminephosphate oxidase	F
1.4.3.6	Diamine: O₂ oxidoreductase (deaminating)	Diamine oxidase, histaminase	[Py]

1.5   Acting on the C–NH group of donors
1.5.1   With NAD or NADP as acceptor

EC No.	Systematic name	Trivial name	Active groups and [cofactors]
1.5.1.1	L-proline: NAD(P) 2-oxidoreductase	Pyrroline-2-carboxylate reductase	
1.5.1.2	L-proline: NAD(P) 5-oxidoreductase	Pyrroline-5-carboxylate reductase	
1.5.1.3	5,6,7,8-tetrahydrofolate: NADP oxidoreductase	Tetrahydrofolate dehydrogenase	
1 5.1.4	7,8-dihydrofolate: NADP oxidoreductase	Dihydrofolate dehydrogenase	

	Reaction	Sources, comments on specificity, etc.	References
1.4.1.3	L-glutamate + H_2O + NAD(P) = 2-oxoglutarate + NH_3 + NAD(P)H_2	Liver	*2023, 2461, 2549, 2709*
1.4.1.4	L-glutamate + H_2O + NADP = 2-oxoglutarate + NH_3 + NADPH_2	Moulds, yeast, bacteria	*18–19, 2743*
1.4.1.5	An L-aminoacid + H_2O + NAD = a 2-oxo-acid + NH_3 + NADH_2	*Clostridia* Acts on aliphatic aminoacids	*1977*
1.4.1.6	5-aminovalerate + NAD = D-proline + NADH_2	Bacteria	*2499, 2501*
1.4.3.1	D-aspartate + H_2O + O_2 = oxaloacetate + NH_3 + H_2O_2	Kidney	*2533–4*
1.4.3.2	An L-aminoacid + H_2O + O_2 = a 2-oxo-acid + NH_3 + H_2O_2	Liver, kidney, snake venom, moulds, bacteria The enzyme from liver and kidney also oxidizes 2-hydroxy acids; that from snake venom does not	*264–6, 299, 368, 1463, 2411, 2838*
1.4.3.3	A D-aminoacid + H_2O + O_2 = a 2-oxo-acid + NH_3 + H_2O_2	Liver, kidney, moulds, bacteria Wide specificity for D-aminoacids	*1463, 1753*
1.4.3.4	A monoamine + H_2O + O_2 = an aldehyde + NH_3 + H_2O_2	Animal tissues, plants Acts on primary, secondary and tertiary amines	*1152, 2593, 2834, 2928–9, 2968*
1.4.3.5	Pyridoxamine phosphate + H_2O + O_2 = pyridoxal phosphate + NH_3 + H_2O_2	Animal tissues, yeast, bacteria Also oxidizes pyridoxin 5-phosphate and pyridoxin	*2744*
1.4.3.6	A diamine + H_2O + O_2 = an aminoaldehyde + NH_3 + H_2O_2	Animal tissues, plants, bacteria Also oxidizes histamine	*1705, 2700, 2968*
1.5.1.1	L-proline + NAD(P) = Δ^1-pyrroline-2-carboxylate + NAD(P)H_2	Animal tissues, plants, moulds Reduces Δ^1-pyrroline-2-carboxylate to L-proline or Δ^1-piperidine-2-carboxylate to L-pipecolate	*1787*
1.5.1.2	L-proline + NAD(P) = Δ^1-pyrroline-5-carboxylate + NAD(P)H_2	Liver, moulds Also reduces Δ^1-pyrroline-3-hydroxy-5-carboxylate to L-hydroxyproline	*13, 1787, 2453, 2954*
1.5.1.3	5,6,7,8-tetrahydrofolate + NADP = 7,8-dihydrofolate + NADPH_2	Liver Also slowly oxidizes 7,8-dihydrofolate to folate	*2957*
1.5.1.4	7,8-dihydrofolate + NADP = folate + NADPH_2	Bacteria	*263*

EC No.	Systematic name	Trivial name	Active groups and [cofactors]
1.5.1.5	*5,10-methylenetetrahydro-folate:NADP oxidoreductase*	Methylenetetrahydro-folate dehydrogenase	
	1.5.3 With O_2 as acceptor		
1.5.3.1	Sarcosine:O_2 oxidoreductase (demethylating)	Sarcosine oxidase	
1.5.3.2	N-methyl-L-aminoacid:O_2 oxidoreductase (demethylating)	N-methyl-aminoacid oxidase	F
1.5.3.3	Spermine:O_2 oxidoreductase (donor-cleaving)	Spermine oxidase	

1.6   Acting on $NADH_2$ or $NADPH_2$ as donor
   1.6.1   With NAD or NADP as acceptor

1.6.1.1	$NADPH_2$:NAD oxidoreductase	NAD(P) transhydrogenase	
	1.6.2 With a cytochrome as an acceptor		
1.6.2.1	$NADH_2$:cytochrome c oxidoreductase	$NADH_2$ cytochrome c reductase	F
1.6.2.2	$NADH_2$:cytochrome b_5 oxidoreductase	$NADH_2$ cytochrome b_5 reductase	F.Mg
1.6.2.3	$NADPH_2$:cytochrome c oxidoreductase	$NADPH_2$ cytochrome c reductase	F
	1.6.4 With a disulphide compound as acceptor		
1.6.4.1	$NADH_2$:L-cystine oxidoreductase	Cystine reductase	
1.6.4.2	$NAD(P)H_2$:glutathione oxidoreductase	Glutathione reductase	F
1.6.4.3	$NADH_2$:lipoamide oxidoreductase	Lipoamide dehydrogenase (Originally known as diaphorase)	F
	1.6.5 With a quinone or related compound as acceptor		
1.6.5.1	$NAD(P)H_2$:quinone oxidoreductase	Quinone reductase	F
1.6.5.2	$NAD(P)H_2$:2-methyl-1,4-naphthoquinone oxidoreductase	Menadione reductase	F
1.6.5.3	$NAD(P)H_2$:ubiquinone oxidoreductase	Ubiquinone reductase	F
1.6.5.4	$NAD(P)H_2$:oxidized-ascorbate oxidoreductase	Oxidized ascorbate reductase	

	Reaction	*Sources, comments on specificity, etc.*	*References*
1.5.1.5	5,10-methylenetetrahydro-folate $+ H^+ + NADP =$ 5,10-methenyltetrahydro-folate $+ H_2O + NADPH_2$	Liver	*1027, 2034*
1.5.3.1	Sarcosine $+ H_2O + O_2 =$ glycine $+ H.CHO + H_2O_2$ (?)	Liver	*995*
1.5.3.2	An N-methyl-L-aminoacid $+ H_2O + O_2 =$ an L-aminoacid $+ H.CHO + H_2O_2$	Kidney	*1864–5*
1.5.3.3	Spermine $+ H_2O + O_2 =$ $H_2N.(CH_2)_3.NH.(CH_2)_3.CHO + H_2N.(CH_2)_3.NH_2 + H_2O_2$	Bacteria Also oxidizes spermidine	*2802*
1.6.1.1	$NADPH_2 + NAD =$ $NADP + NADH_2$	Animal tissues, yeast, bacteria Also acts with deamino-coenzymes	*482, 1189, 1306–7*
1.6.2.1	$NADH_2 + 2$ oxidized cyto-chrome $c =$ $NAD + 2$ reduced cytochrome c	Animal tissues, bacteria	*331, 576, 778, 1682, 1688*
1.6.2.2	$NADH_2 + 2$ oxidized cyto-chrome $b_5 =$ $NAD + 2$ reduced cytochrome b_5	Liver microsomes	*1687, 2557*
1.6.2.3	$NADPH_2 + 2$ oxidized cyto-chrome $c =$ $NADP + 2$ reduced cytochrome c	Animal tissues, yeast	*961–2, 1159, 1510*
1.6.4.1	$NADH_2 + $ L-cystine $=$ $NAD + 2$ L-cysteine	Plants, yeast	*2243*
1.6.4.2	$NAD(P)H_2 + $ oxidized glutathione $=$ $NAD(P) + 2$ reduced glutathione	Animal tissues, plants, yeast, bacteria	*1710, 2153, 2163, 2575, 2719*
1.6.4.3	$NADH_2 + $ oxidized lipoamide $=$ $NAD + $ dihydro-lipoamide	Animal tissues, plants, yeast, bacteria	*178, 527, 968, 1419, 1749, 1752, 2310, 2543*
1.6.5.1	$NAD(P)H_2 + $ a quinone $=$ $NAD(P) + $ a diphenol	Plants, yeast, bacteria	*648, 2917–8*
1.6.5.2	$NAD(P)H_2 + $ 2-methyl-1,4-naphthoquinone $=$ $NAD(P) + $ 2-methyl-naphthohydroquinone	Animal tissues, plants, bacteria Also acts on other 1,4-naphthoquinones	*843, 1722, 2916*
1.6.5.3	$NAD(P)H_2 + $ ubiquinone $=$ $NAD(P) + $ dihydro-ubiquinone	Animal tissues Possibly a system	*1026*
1.6.5.4	$NAD(P)H_2 + $ oxidized ascorbate $=$ $NAD(P) + $ ascorbate	Plants, yeast, bacteria	*1365, 1927*

EC No.	Systematic name	Trivial name	Active groups and [cofactors]
	1.6.6 With a nitrogenous group as acceptor		
1.6.6.1	NADH$_2$:nitrate oxidoreductase	NADH$_2$ nitrate reductase	F.M
1.6.6.2	NAD(P)H$_2$:nitrate oxidoreductase	Nitrate reductase	F
1.6.6.3	NADPH$_2$:nitrate oxidoreductase	NADPH$_2$ nitrate reductase	F.Mo[P]
1.6.6.4	NAD(P)H$_2$:nitrite oxidoreductase	Nitrite reductase	F.M
1.6.6.6	NADH$_2$:hyponitrite oxidoreductase	Hyponitrite reductase	F?.M
1.6.6.7	NADPH$_2$:dimethylaminoazobenzene oxidoreductase	Azobenzene reductase	
1.6.6.a	*NADPH$_2$:GMP oxidoreductase (deaminating)*	GMP reductase	[S]
	1.6.99 With other acceptors		
1.6.99.1 C	NADPH$_2$:(acceptor) oxidoreductase	NADPH$_2$ diaphorase (The yeast enzyme was originally known as 'old yellow enzyme')	F
1.7	**Acting on other nitrogenous compounds as donors**		
	1.7.3 With O$_2$ as acceptor		
1.7.3.1	Nitroethane:O$_2$ oxidoreductase	Nitroethane oxidase	
1.7.3.2	N-acetylindoxyl:O$_2$ oxidoreductase	Acetylindoxyl oxidase	
1.7.3.3	Urate:O$_2$ oxidoreductase	Urate oxidase (Originally known as uricase)	Cu
	1.7.99 With other acceptors		
1.7.99.1	Ammonia:(acceptor) oxidoreductase	Hydroxylamine reductase	F.Mn
1.7.99.2	Nitrogen:(acceptor) oxidoreductase	Nitric oxide reductase	F.Fe
1.7.99.a	*Nitric oxide:(acceptor) oxidoreductase*	Nitrite reductase	F.Cu
1.8	**Acting on sulphur groups of donors**		
	1.8.1 With NAD or NADP as acceptor		
1.8.1.1	Cysteamine:NAD oxidoreductase	Cysteamine dehydrogenase	

	Reaction	*Sources, comments on specificity, etc.*	*References*
1.6.6.1	$NADH_2$ + nitrate = NAD + nitrite + H_2O	Plants, moulds, bacteria	*726, 1963, 2481*
1.6.6.2	$NAD(P)H_2$ + nitrate = $NAD(P)$ + nitrite + H_2O	Plants	*1964*
1.6.6.3	$NADPH_2$ + nitrate = $NADP$ + nitrite + H_2O	Plants, moulds	*1926, 1962, 2615*
1.6.6.4	$3 NAD(P)H_2$ + nitrite = $3 NAD(P)$ + NH_4OH + H_2O	Plants, moulds, bacteria	*1527, 1961, 2615*
1.6.6.6	$NADH_2$ + hyponitrite = NAD + NH_2OH	Moulds	*1774*
1.6.6.7	$NADPH_2$ + dimethylamino-azobenzene = $NADP$ + dimethyl-*p*-phenylene-diamine + aniline	Animal tissues	*1897*
1.6.6.a	$NADPH_2$ + GMP = $NADP$ + IMP + NH_3	Bacteria	*1678*
1.6.99.1	$NADPH_2$ + acceptor = $NADP$ + reduced acceptor	Plants, yeast Reacts with methylene blue as acceptor (and slowly with oxygen)	*107, 567, 1351 2625, 2632*
1.7.3.1	$C_2H_5 . NO_2 + H_2O + O_2$ = $CH_3CHO + HNO_2 + H_2O_2$	Moulds Acts on some other aliphatic nitro-compounds	*1606*
1.7.3.2	N-acetylindoxyl + O_2 = N-acetylisatin + (?)	Plants	*193*
1.7.3.3	Urate + O_2 = unidentified products	Animal tissues, adapted yeast	*1180, 1552, 1613, 1685, 2226, 2257*
1.7.99.1	Ammonia + acceptor = hydroxylamine + reduced acceptor	Plants, moulds, bacteria Reduced pyocyanine, methylene blue or flavins act as donor for reduction of hydroxylamine	*2614–5, 2765*
1.7.99.2	N_2 + acceptor = $2NO$ + reduced acceptor	Bacteria Reduced pyocyanine acts as donor for the reduction of NO	*455, 725*
1.7.99.a	$2NO + 2H_2O$ + acceptor = 2 nitrite + reduced acceptor	Bacteria Reduced pyocyanine, flavins, etc., act as donor for the reduction of nitrite	*454, 2764*
1.8.1.1	Cysteamine + $3 NAD + 2 H_2O$ = cystamine disulphoxide + $3 NADH_2$	Liver	*2293*

EC No.	Systematic name	Trivial name	Active groups and [cofactors]
1.8.1.2	H₂S:NADP oxidoreductase	Sulphite reductase	
	See also 1.6.4.1–3		
	1.8.3 With O₂ as acceptor		
1.8.3.1	Sulphite:O₂ oxidoreductase	Sulphite oxidase	H
1.8.3.2	Thiol:O₂ oxidoreductase	Thiol oxidase	
	1.8.4 With a disulphide compound as acceptor		
1.8.4.1	Glutathione:homocystine oxidoreductase	Glutathione-homocystine transhydrogenase	
	1.8.5 With a quinone or related compound as acceptor		
1.8.5.1	Glutathione:dehydroascorbate oxidoreductase	Glutathione dehydrogenase	
	1.8.6 With a nitrogenous group as acceptor		
1.8.6.1	Glutathione:polyolnitrate oxidoreductase	Nitrate ester reductase	
	1.9 Acting on haem groups of donors		
	1.9.3 With O₂ as acceptor		
1.9.3.1 C	Cytochrome c:O₂ oxidoreductase	Cytochrome oxidase (cytochrome a₃)	H.Cu
1.9.3.a C	*Cytochrome (c₄,c₅):O₂ oxidoreductase*	*Pseudomonas* cytochrome oxidase (a cytochrome CD)	H
	1.9.6 With a nitrogenous group as acceptor		
1.9.6.1	Cytochrome:nitrate oxidoreductase	Nitrate reductase	
	1.10 Acting on diphenols and related substances as donors		
	1.10.3 With O₂ as acceptor		
1.10.3.1	o-diphenol:O₂ oxidoreductase	Catechol oxidase	Cu
1.10.3.2	p-diphenol:O₂ oxidoreductase	p-diphenol oxidase	Cu
1.10.3.3	L-ascorbate:O₂ oxidoreductase	Ascorbate oxidase	Cu

	Reaction	Sources, comments on specificity, etc.	References
1.8.1.2	$H_2S + 3NADP + 3H_2O =$ sulphite $+ 3NADPH_2$	Yeast	1105
1.8.3.1	Sulphite $+ O_2 + H_2O =$ sulphate $+ H_2O_2$	Animal tissues, plants, bacteria	1668, 2600
1.8.3.2	$4R:CR'.SH + O_2 =$ $2R:CR'.S.S.CR':R + 2H_2O$	Fungi. R may be $=S$ or $=O$, or a variety of other groups; the enzyme is not specific for R'	1948
1.8.4.1	2 reduced glutathione + homocystine = oxidized glutathione + 2 homocysteine	Liver	2154
1.8.5.1	2 reduced glutathione + dehydroascorbate = oxidized glutathione + ascorbate	Higher plants, yeast	520
1.8.6.1	2 reduced glutathione + polyolnitrate = oxidized glutathione + nitrite + unidentified product	Liver	1066
1.9.3.1	4 reduced cytochrome c + $O_2 =$ 4 oxidized cytochrome c + $2H_2O$	Widely distributed	933, 1340–1, 2424, 2452, 2749, 2948–9
1.9.3.a	4 reduced cytochrome c_4 (or c_5) + $O_2 =$ 4 oxidized cytochrome + $2H_2O$	Pseudomonas	1167, 2451, 2656, 2934
1.9.6.1	A reduced cytochrome + nitrate = oxidized cytochrome + nitrite	Bacteria	2286
1.10.3.1	2 o-diphenol + $O_2 =$ 2 o-quinone + $2H_2O$	Plants, fungi, some animal tissues. Acts on various o-diphenols; monophenols also undergo oxidation in the system	337, 533, 570, 680, 1348, 1367, 1473, 1741
1.10.3.2	2 p-diphenol + $O_2 =$ 2 p-quinone + $2H_2O$	Plants, fungi. Acts on various p-diphenols and p-phenylenediamines	926, 1349, 1741, 1923
1.10.3.3	2 L-ascorbate + $O_2 =$ 2 dehydroascorbate + $2H_2O$	Plants	570

EC No.	Systematic name	Trivial name	Active groups and [cofactors]
1.11	**Acting on H$_2$O$_2$ as acceptor**		
1.11.1.1	NADH$_2$:H$_2$O$_2$ oxidoreductase	NAD peroxidase	F
1.11.1.2	NADPH$_2$:H$_2$O$_2$ oxidoreductase	NADP peroxidase	
1.11.1.3	Palmitate:H$_2$O$_2$ oxidoreductase	Fatty acid peroxidase	
1.11.1.5	Cytochrome c:H$_2$O$_2$ oxidoreductase	Cytochrome peroxidase	H
1.11.1.a	*Glutathione:H$_2$O$_2$ oxidoreductase*	Glutathione peroxidase	
1.11.1.6 C	H$_2$O$_2$:H$_2$O$_2$ oxidoreductase	Catalase	H
1.11.1.7 C	Donor:H$_2$O$_2$ oxidoreductase	Peroxidase	H
1.11.1.8	Iodide:H$_2$O$_2$ oxidoreductase	Iodinase	H ?
1.98	**Enzymes using H$_2$ as reductant**		
1.98.1.1	*H$_2$: ferredoxin oxidoreductase*	Hydrogenase	Fe
1.99	**Other enzymes using O$_2$ as oxidant** (Reaction not yet fully understood; no systematic names recommended)		
	1.99.1 Hydroxylases		
1.99.1.1		Aryl 4-hydroxylase	
1.99.1.2		Phenylalanine 4-hydroxylase	
1.99.1.3		Nicotinate 6-hydroxylase	
1.99.1.4		Tryptophan 5-hydroxylase	
1.99.1.5		Kynurenine 3-hydroxylase	
1.99.1.a		Steroid 2-hydroxylase	

Reaction	Sources, comments on specificity, etc.	References
1.11.1.1	$NADH_2 + H_2O_2 =$ $NAD + 2H_2O$	Bacteria Ferricyanide, quinones, etc., can replace H_2O_2	646–7, 1843
1.11.1.2	$NADPH_2 + H_2O_2 =$ $NADP + 2H_2O$	Plants	489
1.11.1.3	Palmitic acid $+ 2H_2O_2 =$ 1-pentadecanal $+ CO_2 + 3H_2O$	Plants Acts on long chain fatty acids from lauric to stearic acid	1739
1.11.1.5	2 reduced cytochrome $c +$ $H_2O_2 =$ 2 oxidized cytochrome $c +$ $2H_2O$	Moulds, yeast, bacteria	56, 1550
1.11.1.a	2 reduced glutathione $+$ $H_2O_2 =$ oxidized glutathione $+$ $2H_2O$	Animal tissues	1826
1.11.1.6	$H_2O_2 + H_2O_2 =$ $O_2 + 2H_2O$	Widely distributed Several organic substances, especially ethanol, can act as hydrogen donor	1077–8, 1336, 2119, 2567, 2628
1.11.1.7	Donor $+ H_2O_2 =$ oxidized donor $+ 2H_2O$	Animal tissues, plants	22, 420, 1170–1, 1364, 1734, 1861, 1870, 2308, 2599, 2626
1.11.1.8	Iodide $+ H_2O_2 =$ iodine $+ 2H_2O$	Animal tissues	523, 1173–4, 2374
1.98.1.1	$H_2 + 2$ ferredoxin $=$ 2 reduced ferredoxin	Bacteria Uses molecular hydrogen for the reduction of a variety of substances	1871, 2039, 2066, 2221, 2287, 2393, 2597, 2705

1.99.1.1	Liver Hydroxylates aniline and other aromatic compounds; $NADPH_2$ · is one of the reactants	290, 1837
1.99.1.2	Liver Hydroxylates L-phenylalanine to L-tyrosine; a reduced pteridine is one of the reactants	1317, 1321, 1836, 2693
1.99.1.3	*Pseudomonas* Hydroxylates nicotinate to 6-hydroxynicotinate	195, 1190
1.99.1.4	Liver, Bacteria Hydroxylates L-tryptophan to 5-hydroxytryptophan	1838, 2211a
1.99.1.5	Liver Hydroxylates L-kynurenine to 3-hydroxykynurenine; $NADPH_2$ is one of the reactants	577, 2289
1.99.1.a	Liver Hydroxylates oestriol to 2-hydroxy-oestriol; $NAD(P)H_2$ is one of the reactants	1384

EC No.	Systematic name	Trivial name	Active groups and [cofactors]
1.99.1.6		Steroid 11-α-hydroxylase	
1.99.1.7		Steroid 11-β-hydroxylase	
1.99.1.8		Steroid 6-β-hydroxylase	
1.99.1.9		Steroid 17-α-hydroxylase	
1.99.1.10		Steroid 19-hydroxylase	
1.99.1.11		Steroid 21-hydroxylase	
1.99.1.12		Alkoxyaryl hydroxylase	
1.99.1.13		Squalene cyclohydroxylase	
1.99.1.14		p-hydroxyphenylpyruvate hydroxylase	

1.99.2 Oxygenases

EC No.	Systematic name	Trivial name	Active groups and [cofactors]
1.99.2.1 C		Lipoxygenase (Originally known as lipoxidase)	
1.99.2.2		Catechol 1,2-oxygenase	[Fe^{++}]
1.99.2.a		Catechol 2,3-oxygenase	
1.99.2.3		Protocatechuate oxygenase	[Fe^{++}]
1.99.2.4		Gentisate oxygenase	[Fe^{++}]
1.99.2.5		Homogentisate oxygenase	[Fe^{++}]
1.99.2.b		3-hydroxyanthranilate oxygenase	
1.99.2.6		meso-inositol oxygenase	[Fe^{++}]
1.99.2.c		Tryptophan oxygenase	H

Reaction	Sources, comments on specificity, etc.	References
1.99.1.6	Moulds	1700, 2079
Hydroxylates steroids to 11-α-hydroxysteroids		
1.99.1.7	Animal tissues	885, 1043, 2581, 2668
Hydroxylates steroids to 11-β-hydroxysteroids; NADPH$_2$ is one of the reactants		
1.99.1.8	Adrenal	977
Hydroxylates steroids to 6-β-hydroxysteroids		
1.99.1.9	Adrenal, testis, *Cephalothecium*	1642, 1790
Hydroxylates steroids to 17-α-hydroxysteroids; NADPH$_2$ is one of the reactants		
1.99.1.10	Adrenal	1804
Hydroxylates 11-deoxycorticosterone to 19-hydroxy-11-deoxy-corticosterone		
1.99.1.11	Adrenal	1042, 2093, 2281
Hydroxylates steroids to 21-hydroxysteroids; NADPH$_2$ is one of the reactants		
1.99.1.12	Liver	109
Converts $R.CH_2.O.C_6H_4.R'$ into $R.CHO$ and $HO.C_6H_4.R'$; NADPH$_2$ is one of the reactants		
1.99.1.13	Liver	2623
Converts squalene into lanosterol; NADPH$_2$ is one of the reactants		
1.99.1.14	Liver	969, 1501
Converts p-hydroxyphenylpyruvate into homogentisate and CO_2		
1.99.2.1	Unsaturated fat $+ O_2 =$ a peroxide of the unsaturated fat	Plants	2617, 2634, 2670
1.99.2.2	Catechol $+ O_2 =$ *cis-cis*-muconate	*Pseudomonas*	1034, 2419
1.99.2.a	Catechol $+ O_2 =$ 2-hydroxy-muconate semialdehyde	Bacteria	1420
1.99.2 3	Protocatechuate $+ O_2 =$ 3-carboxy-*cis-cis*-muconate	*Pseudomonas*, moulds	936, 2506
1.99.2.4	Gentisate $+ O_2 =$ maleylpyruvate	*Pseudomonas*	2563
1.99.2.5	Homogentisate $+ O_2 =$ 4-maleylacetoacetate	Liver, kidney, bacteria	512, 1409, 2183, 2665
1.99.2.b	3-hydroxyanthranilate $+ O_2 =$ 2-amino-3-carboxy-muconate semialdehyde	Liver, kidney	578
1.99.2.6	*meso*-inositol $+ O_2 =$ D-glucuronate	Kidney	435
1.99.2.c	L-tryptophan $+ O_2 =$ formyl-kynurenine	Animal tissues, bacteria	1038, 2611

EC No.	Systematic name	Trivial name	Active groups and [cofactors]

2   TRANSFERASES

   2.1   Transferring one-carbon groups

   2.1.1   Methyltransferases
   (For the trivial name, 'methyltransferase' may be replaced by 'transmethylase')

2.1.1.a	*S-adenosylmethionine: catechol O-methyltransferase*	Catechol methyltransferase	[M++]
2.1.1.b	*S-adenosylmethionine: nicotinate N-methyltransferase*	Nicotinate methyltransferase	
2.1.1.1	S-adenosylmethionine: nicotinamide N-methyltransferase	Nicotinamide methyltransferase	
2.1.1.c	*S-adenosylmethionine: histamine N-methyltransferase*	Histamine methyltransferase	
2.1.1.2	S-adenosylmethionine: guanidino-acetate N-methyltransferase	Guanidinoacetate methyltransferase	
2.1.1.d	*S-adenosylmethionine: thiol S-methyltransferase*	Thiol methyltransferase	
2.1.1.e	*S-adenosylmethionine: L-homocysteine S-methyltransferase*	Homocysteine methyltransferase	
2.1.1.3	Dimethylthetin: L-homocysteine S-methyltransferase	Dimethylthetin homocysteine methyltransferase	
2.1.1.4	S-adenosylmethionine: N-acetyl-serotonin O-methyltransferase	Acetylserotonin methyltransferase	
2.1.1.5	Betaine: L-homocysteine S-methyltransferase	Betaine homocysteine methyltransferase	

   2.1.2   Hydroxymethyl-, formyl- and related transferases
   (For the trivial name, 'hydroxymethyltransferase', 'formyltransferase', 'formiminotransferase' may be replaced by 'transhydroxymethylase', 'transformylase' and 'transformiminase' respectively)

| 2.1.2.1 | *L-serine: tetrahydrofolate 5,10-hydroxymethyltransferase* | Serine hydroxymethyltransferase | [Py.Mn++] |

Reaction	Sources, comments on specificity, etc.	References
2.1.1.a	S-adenosylmethionine + catechol = S-adenosylhomocysteine + guiacol	Animal tissues	115
2.1.1.b	S-adenosylmethionine + nicotinate = S-adenosylhomocysteine + N-methylnicotinate	Plants	1269
2.1.1.1	S-adenosylmethionine + nicotinamide = S-adenosylhomocysteine + N-methylnicotinamide	Liver	393
2.1.1.c	S-adenosylmethionine + histamine = S-adenosylhomocysteine + 1-methylhistamine	Animal tissues	334
2.1.1.2	S-adenosylmethionine + guanidinoacetate = S-adenosylhomocysteine + creatine	Liver	397–8
2.1.1.d	S-adenosylmethionine + a thiol = S-adenosylhomocysteine + a thioether	Animal tissues A variety of thiols and hydroxythiols can act as acceptor	323
2.1.1.e	S-adenosylmethionine + L-homocysteine = S-adenosylhomocysteine + methionine	Yeast, bacteria	2379–80
2.1.1.3	Dimethylthetin + L-homocysteine = S-methylthioglycollate + L-methionine	Liver	660, 1394, 1762–3
2.1.1.4	S-adenosylmethionine + N-acetylserotonin = S-adenosylhomocysteine + N-acetyl-5-methoxytryptamine	Pineal body	116
2.1.1.5	Betaine + L-homocysteine = dimethylglycine + L-methionine	Liver	1394
2.1.2.1	L-serine + tetrahydrofolate = glycine + 5,10-methylene-tetrahydrofolate	Liver	261, 1182, 1390

EC No.	Systematic name	Trivial name	Active groups and [cofactors]
2.1.2.2	5′-phosphoribosyl-N-formylglycine-amide : tetrahydrofolate 5,10-formyltransferase	Phosphoribosyl-glycineamide formyltransferase	
2.1.2.3	5′-phosphoribosyl-5-formamido-4-imidazolecarboxamide : tetrahydro-folate 10-formyltransferase	Phosphoribosylamino-imidazolecarboxamide formyltransferase	[K⁺]
2.1.2.a	*N-formyl-L-glutamate : tetrahydro-folate 5-formyltransferase*	Formylglutamate formyltransferase	
2.1.2.4	N-formiminoglycine : tetrahydro-folate 5-formiminotransferase	Glycine formiminotransferase	
2.1.2.5	N-formimino-L-glutamate : tetra-hydrofolate 5-formimino-transferase	Glutamate formiminotransferase	

2.1.3 Carboxyl- and carbamoyltransferases
(For the trivial name. 'carboxyltransferase' and 'carbamoyltransferase' may be replaced by 'transcarboxylase' and 'transcarbamoylase' respectively)

EC No.	Systematic name	Trivial name	Active groups and [cofactors]
2.1.3.1	Methylmalonyl-CoA : pyruvate carboxyltransferase	Methylmalonyl-CoA carboxytransferase	Bt
2.1.3.2 C	Carbamoylphosphate : L-aspartate carbamoyltransferase	Aspartate carbamoyltransferase	
2.1.3.3	Carbamoylphosphate : L-ornithine carbamoyltransferase	Ornithine carbamoyltransferase	

2.2 Transferring aldehydic or ketonic residues

EC No.	Systematic name	Trivial name	Active groups and [cofactors]
2.2.1.1 C	D-sedoheptulose-7-phosphate : D-glyceraldehyde-3-phosphate glycolaldehydetransferase	Transketolase, 1-glycolaldehydetransferase	[Mg⁺⁺.T]
2.2.1.2 C	D-sedoheptulose-7-phosphate : D-glyceraldehyde-3-phosphate dihydroxyacetonetransferase	Transaldolase, dihydroxyacetonetransferase	

	Reaction	Sources, comments on specificity, etc.	References
2.1.2.2	5'-phosphoribosyl-N-formyl-glycineamide + tetrahydro-folate = 5'-phosphoribosyl-glycine-amide + 5,10-methenyltetra-hydrofolate + H_2O	Liver	1017, 2792
2.1.2.3	5'-phosphoribosyl-5-formamido-4-imidazole-carboxamide + tetrahydro-folate = 5'-phosphoribosyl-5-amino-4-imidazolecarboxamide + 10-formyltetrahydrofolate	Liver	1017
2.1.2.a	N-formyl-L-glutamate + tetrahydrofolate = L-glutamate + 5-formyltetrahydrofolate	Liver	2405
2.1.2.4	N-formiminoglycine + tetrahydrofolate = glycine + 5-formiminotetra-hydrofolate	Bacteria	2141, 2143, 2288
2.1.2.5	N-formimino-L-glutamate + tetrahydrofolate = L-glutamate + 5-formimino-tetrahydrofolate	Liver	1817, 2596
2.1.3.1	Methylmalonyl-CoA + pyruvate = propionyl-CoA + oxaloacetate	Bacteria	2588, 2909
2.1.3.2	Carbamoylphosphate + L-aspartate = orthophosphate + N-carbamoyl-L-aspartate	Animal tissues, bacteria	1621, 2203, 2383
2.1.3.3	Carbamoylphosphate + L-ornithine = orthophosphate + L-citrulline	Animal tissues, bacteria	364, 1266, 1406, 2184, 2201
2.2.1.1	D-sedoheptulose 7-phosphate + D-glyceraldehyde 3-phos-phate = D-ribose 5-phosphate + D-xylulose 5-phosphate	Plants, yeast, bacteria Wide specificity for both reactants, e.g. converts hydroxypyruvate and R.CHO into CO_2 and R.CHOH.CO.CH_2OH	587, 1162, 1164, 2156
2.2.1.2	D-sedoheptulose 7-phosphate + D-glyceraldehyde 3-phos-phate = D-erythrose 4-phosphate + D-fructose 6-phosphate	Liver, plants, yeast	1163, 2731

EC No.	Systematic name	Trivial name	Active groups and [cofactors]

2.3 Acyltransferases

2.3.1 Acyltransferases
(For the trivial name, 'acetyltransferase', etc., may be replaced by 'transacetylase', etc.)

2.3.1.a	*Acetyl-CoA : L-aspartate N-acetyltransferase*	Aspartate acetyltransferase	[A]
2.3.1.1	Acetyl-CoA : L-glutamate N-acetyltransferase	Aminoacid acetyltransferase	[HCN]
2.3.1.2	Acetyl-CoA : imidazole N-acetyltransferase	Imidazole acetyltransferase	
2.3.1.3	Acetyl-CoA : 2-amino-2-deoxy-D-glucose N-acetyltransferase	Aminodeoxyglucose acetyltransferase	
2.3.1.4	Acetyl-CoA : 2-amino-2-deoxy-D-glucose-6-phosphate N-acetyltransferase	Aminodeoxyglucosephosphate acetyltransferase	
2.3.1.5	Acetyl-CoA : arylamine N-acetyltransferase	Arylamine acetyltransferase	
2.3.1.6	Acetyl-CoA : choline O-acetyltransferase	Choline acetyltransferase	
2.3.1.7	Acetyl-CoA : carnitine O-acetyltransferase	Carnitine acetyltransferase	
2.3.1.b	*Acetyl-CoA : galactoside 6-0-acetyltransferase*	Galactoside acetyltransferase	
2.3.1.8	Acetyl-CoA : orthophosphate acetyltransferase	Phosphate acetyltransferase	[K⁺]
2.3.1.9	Acetyl-CoA : acetyl-CoA C-acetyltransferase	Acetyl-CoA acetyltransferase, acetoacetyl-CoA thiolase	
2.3.1.10	Acetyl-CoA : H₂S S-acetyltransferase	H₂S acetyltransferase	
2.3.1.11	Acetyl-CoA : thioethanolamine S-acetyltransferase	Thioethanolamine acetyltransferase (Originally known as thioltransacetylase B)	
2.3.1.12	Acetyl-CoA : dihydrolipoate S-acetyltransferase	Lipoate acetyltransferase (Originally known as thioltransacetylase A)	

Reaction	Sources, comments on specificity, etc.	References
2.3.1.a	Acetyl-CoA + L-aspartate = CoA + N-acetyl-L-aspartate	Brain	863
2.3.1.1.	Acetyl-CoA + L-glutamate = CoA + N-acetyl-L-glutamate	Bacteria Also acts with L-aspartate and, more slowly, with some other aminoacids	1647
2.3.1.2	Acetyl-CoA + imidazole = CoA + N-acetylimidazole	*Clostridium* Also acts with propionyl-CoA	1387
2.3.1.3	Acetyl-CoA + 2-amino-2-deoxy-D-glucose = CoA + 2-acetylamino-2-deoxy-D-glucose	Liver	452
2.3.1.4	Acetyl-CoA + 2-amino-2-deoxy-D-glucose 6-phosphate = CoA + 2-acetylamino-2-deoxy-D-glucose 6-phosphate	Animal tissues, moulds, yeast, bacteria	336, 549
2.3.1.5	Acetyl-CoA + arylamine = CoA + N-acetylarylamine	Animal tissues Wide specificity for aromatic amines, including serotonin; also catalyses acetyl-transfer between aryl-amines without CoA	240, 451, 2595, 2833
2.3.1.6	Acetyl-CoA + choline = CoA + O-acetylcholine	Nervous tissue Propionyl-CoA can act, more slowly, in place of acetyl-CoA	231, 237
2.3.1.7	Acetyl-CoA + carnitine = CoA + O-acetylcarnitine	Liver	785
2.3.1.b	Acetyl-CoA + a β-D-galactoside = CoA + a 6-acetyl-β-D-galactoside	*Esch. coli* Best acceptors are thiogalactosides	2956
2.3.1.8	Acetyl-CoA + orthophosphate = CoA + acetylphosphate	Bacteria	2497
2.3.1.9	Acetyl-CoA + acetyl-CoA = CoA + acetoacetyl-CoA	Animal tissues	1639a, 2523
2.3.1.10	Acetyl-CoA + H_2S = CoA + thioacetate	Liver, bacteria	309
2.3.1.11	Acetyl-CoA + thioethanolamine = CoA + S-acetyl-thioethanolamine	Liver, bacteria	309, 947
2.3.1.12	Acetyl-CoA + dihydrolipoate = CoA + 6-S-acetylhydrolipoate	Liver, bacteria Also acetylates monothioglycol	309, 947–8

2A

EC No.	Systematic name	Trivial name	Active groups and [cofactors]
2.3.1.c	*Butyryl-CoA : orthophosphate butyryltransferase*	Phosphate butyryltransferase	
2.3.1.13	Acyl-CoA : glycine N-acyltransferase	Glycine acyltransferase	
2.3.1.14	Phenylacetyl-CoA : L-glutamine α-N-phenylacetyltransferase	Glutamine phenylacetyltransferase	
2.3.1.15	Acyl-CoA : L-glycerol-3-phosphate O-acyltransferase	Glycerolphosphate acyltransferase	[S]
2.3.1.d	*Acyl-CoA : 1,2-diglyceride O-acyltransferase*	Diglyceride acyltransferase	
2.3.1.16	Acyl-CoA : acetyl-CoA C-acyltransferase	Acetyl-CoA acyltransferase, 3-ketoacyl-CoA thiolase	

2.3.2   Aminoacyltransferases

2.3.2.1	Glutamine : D-glutamyl glutamyltransferase	D-glutamyltransferase	

2.4   Glycosyltransferases

(For the trivial name, 'glucosyltransferase', 'fructosyltransferase', etc., may be replaced by 'transglucosylase', 'transfructosylase', etc.)

2.4.1   Hexosyltransferases

2.4.1.1 C	α-1,4-glucan : orthophosphate glucosyltransferase	α-glucan phosphorylase	Py (mammalian enzyme)
2.4.1.2	Dextrin : α-1,6-glucan 6-glucosyltransferase	Dextrin 6-glucosyltransferase	
2.4.1.3	α-1,4-glucan : D-glucose 4-glucosyltransferase	Maltose 4-glucosyltransferase, amylomaltase	
2.4.1.4	α-1,4-glucan : D-fructose 2-glucosyltransferase	Sucrose glucosyltransferase, amylosucrase	
2.4.1.5	α-1,6-glucan : D-fructose 2-glucosyltransferase	Sucrose 6-glucosyltransferase, dextransucrase	
2.4.1.6	Maltose : D-glucose 3-glucosyltransferase	Maltose 3-glucosyltransferase	
2.4.1.7	Disaccharide glucosyltransferase (non-specific)	Sucrose glucosyltransferase (Originally known as sucrose phosphorylase)	

	Reaction	Sources, comments on specificity, etc.	References
2.3.1.c	Butyryl-CoA + orthophosphate = CoA + butyrylphosphate	Bacteria	2706
2.3.1.13	Acyl-CoA + glycine = CoA + N-acylglycine	Animal tissues Acts with the CoA derivatives of a number of aliphatic and aromatic acids	2321
2.3.1.14	Phenylacetyl-CoA + L-glutamine = CoA + α-N-phenylacetyl-L-glutamine	Animal tissues	1846
2.3.1.15	Acyl-CoA + L-glycerol-3-phosphate = CoA + monoglyceride phosphate	Liver Acts only with CoA derivatives of fatty acids of chain length above C_{10}; also forms diglyceride phosphates	1440
2.3.1.d	Acyl-CoA + a 1,2-diglyceride = CoA + a triglyceride	Liver, adipose tissue	861, 2828
2.3.1.16	Acyl-CoA + acetyl-CoA = CoA + 3-oxoacyl-CoA	Animal tissues, bacteria	199, 860, 2517, 2524
2.3.2.1	L (or D)-glutamine + D-glutamyl-R = NH_3 + 5-glutamyl-D-glutamyl-R	Bacteria	2871
2.4.1.1	(α-1,4-glucosyl)$_n$ + orthophosphate = (α-1,4-glucosyl)$_{n-1}$ + α-D-glucose 1-phosphate	Widely distributed Acts on starch, glycogen, etc.	179, 501, 509, 893, 997–8, 2164, 2566, 2573
2.4.1.2	(α-1,4-glucosyl)$_n$ + (α-1,6-glucosyl)$_m$ = (α-1,4-glucosyl)$_{n-1}$ + (α-1,6-glucosyl)$_{m+1}$	Bacteria Transforms dextrins into 1,6-glucans	1050–2
2.4.1.3	(α-1,4-glucosyl)$_n$ + D-glucose = (α-1,4-glucosyl)$_{n-1}$ + maltose	Blood plasma, bacteria Converts maltose into a 1,4-glucan and glucose	165, 651, 1050, 1819, 1851
2.4.1.4	(α-1,4-glucosyl)$_n$ + D-fructose = (α-1,4-glucosyl)$_{n-1}$ + sucrose	Bacteria Converts sucrose into a 1,4-glucan and fructose	720, 1050, 1053
2.4.1.5	(α-1,6-glucosyl)$_n$ + D-fructose = (α-1,6-glucosyl)$_{n-1}$ + sucrose	*Leuconostoc, Streptococcus* Converts sucrose into a 1,6-glucan and fructose	139, 762, 870, 1049–50, 2538
2.4.1.6	Maltose + D-glucose = D-glucose + α-1,3-glucosyl-glucose	Moulds	168, 2061
2.4.1.7	α-D-glucosyl-1-R + R′ = α-D-glucosyl-1-R′ + R	Bacteria R and R′ may represent various ketoses, L-arabinose, phosphate or arsenate	1021, 1023

EC No.	Systematic name	Trivial name	Active groups and [cofactors]
2.4.1.8	Maltose : orthophosphate glucosyltransferase	Maltose phosphorylase	
2.4.1.a	*Cellobiose : orthophosphate glucosyltransferase*	Cellobiose phosphorylase	
2.4.1.9	β-1,2-fructan : D-glucose 1-fructosyltransferase	Sucrose 1-fructosyltransferase, inulosucrase	
2.4.1.10	β-2,6-fructan : D-glucose 6-fructosyltransferase	Sucrose 6-fructosyltransferase, levansucrase	
2.4.1.11	*UDPglucose : glycogen α-4-glucosyltransferase*	UDPglucose-glycogen glucosyltransferase, glycogen-UDP glucosyltransferase	[Mg^{++}.S]
2.4.1.b	*UDPglucose : α-1,4-glucan α-4-glucosyltransferase*	UDPglucose-starch glucosyltransferase	
2.4.1.12	UDPglucose : β-1,4-glucan β-4-glucosyltransferase	UDPglucose-β-glucan glucosyltransferase, UDPglucose-cellulose glucosyltransferase, β-glucan-UDP glucosyltransferase	
2.4.1.13	UDPglucose : D-fructose 2-glucosyltransferase	UDPglucose-fructose glucosyltransferase, sucrose-UDP glucosyltransferase	
2.4.1.14	UDPglucose : D-fructose-6-phosphate 2-glucosyltransferase	UDPglucose-fructose-phosphate glucosyltransferase, sucrose-phosphate-UDP glucosyltransferase	
2.4.1.15	UDPglucose : D-glucose-6-phosphate 1-glucosyltransferase	UDPglucose-glucose-phosphate glucosyltransferase, trehalosephosphate-UDP glucosyltransferase	
2.4.1.16	UDP-2-acetylamino-2-deoxy-D-glucose : chitin acetylamino-deoxyglucosyltransferase	Chitin-UDP acetylamino-deoxyglucosyltransferase	
2.4.1.c	*UDPgalactose : D-glucose 1-galactosyltransferase*	UDPgalactose-glucose galactosyltransferase	

Reaction	Sources, comments on specificity, etc.	References
2.4.1.8	Maltose + orthophosphate = β-D-glucose 1-phosphate + D-glucose	Bacteria	746, 2128, 2908
2.4.1.a	Cellobiose + orthophosphate = α-D-glucose 1-phosphate + D-glucose	Bacteria	118
2.4.1.9	(β-1,2-fructosyl)$_n$ + D-glucose = (β-1,2-fructosyl)$_{n-1}$ + sucrose	Plants Converts sucrose into inulin and glucose	243, 579, 670
2.4.1.10	(β-2,6-fructosyl)$_n$ + D-glucose = (β-2,6-fructosyl)$_{n-1}$ + sucrose	Bacteria Converts sucrose into fructan and glucose; some other sugars can act as fructosyl acceptors	104, 719–20, 1050, 1090
2.4.1.11	UDPglucose + (glycogen)$_n$ = UDP + (glycogen)$_{n+1}$	Animal tissues, yeast, bacteria Converts UDPglucose into glycogen and UDP; activated by D-glucose 6-phosphate and other hexose phosphates	49, 177, 1543, 1545, 2230, 2734
2.4.1.b	UDPglucose + (α-1,4-glucosyl)$_n$ = UDP + (α-1,4-glucosyl)$_{n+1}$	Plants Starch, 1,4-linked oligosaccharides or maltose can act as acceptor	1541
2.4.1.12	UDPglucose + (β-1,4-glucosyl)$_n$ = UDP + (β-1,4-glucosyl)$_{n+1}$	Bacteria Converts UDPglucose into cellulose and UDP	846
2.4.1.13	UDPglucose + D-fructose = UDP + sucrose	Plants	406
2.4.1.14	UDPglucose + D-fructose 6-phosphate = UDP + sucrose 6-phosphate	Plants	1796
2.4.1.15	UDPglucose + D-glucose 6-phosphate = UDP + trehalose 6-phosphate	Insect tissues, yeast	378, 390
2.4.1.16	UDP-2-acetylamino-2-deoxy-D-glucose + (β-1,4-(2-acetyl-amino-2-deoxy-D-glucosyl))$_n$ = UDP + (β-1,4-(2-acetylamino-2-deoxy-D-glucosyl))$_{n+1}$	Moulds Converts UDP-2-acetyl-amino-2-deoxy-D-glucose into chitin and UDP	850
2.4.1.c	UDPgalactose + D-glucose = UDP + lactose	Mammary gland	2796

EC No.	Systematic name	Trivial name	Active groups and [cofactors]
2.4.1.d	*UDPgalactose:sphingosine O-galactosyltransferase*	UDPgalactose-sphingosine galactosyltransferase, psychosine-UDP galactosyltransferase	
2.4.1.17	UDPglucuronate glucuronyl-transferase (acceptor-unspecific)	UDP glucuronyltransferase	
2.4.1.18 C	α-1,4-glucan:α-1,4-glucan 6-glycosyltransferase	α-glucan-branching glycosyltransferase (Originally known as Q-enzyme or branching factor)	
2.4.1.e	*α-1,4-glucan:α-1,4-oligoglucan 6-glycosyltransferase*	Oligoglucan-branching glycosyltransferase (Originally called T-enzyme in plants)	
2.4.1.f	*α-1,4-glucan:α-1,4-glucan 4-glycosyltransferase*	Dextrin glycosyltransferase (Originally known as D-enzyme or disproportionating enzyme)	
2.4.1.19	α-1,4-glucan 4-glycosyl-transferase (cyclizing)	Cyclodextrin glycosyl-transferase	
2.4.1.g	*UDPglucose:DNA α-glucosyltransferase*	UDPglucose-DNA α-glucosyltransferase	
2.4.1.h	*UDPglucose:DNA β-glucosyltransferase*	UDPglucose-DNA β-glucosyltransferase	
2.4.1.i	*UDPglucose:*glycosyl-*DNA β-glucosyltransferase*	UDPglucose-gylcosyl-DNA β-glucosyltransferase	

2.4.2 Pentosyltransferases

EC No.	Systematic name	Trivial name	Active groups and [cofactors]
2.4.2.1	Purine nucleoside:orthophosphate ribosyltransferase	Purine nucleoside phosphorylase	
2.4.2.a	*Guanosine:orthophosphate ribosyltransferase*	Guanosine phosphorylase	
2.4.2.3	Uridine:orthophosphate ribosyltransferase	Uridine phosphorylase	
2.4.2.4	Thymidine:orthophosphate deoxyribosyltransferase	Thymidine phosphorylase	
2.4.2.5	Nucleoside:purine (pyrimidine) ribosyltransferase	Nucleoside ribosyltransferase	

	Reaction	Sources, comments on specificity, etc.	References
2.4.1.d	UDPgalactose + sphingosine = UDP + psychosine	Brain	*457*
2.4.1.17	UDPglucuronate + acceptor = UDP + acceptor-glucuronide	Liver A wide range of phenols, alcohols, amines and fatty acids can act as acceptor	*112, 662, 1219, 2541*
2.4.1.18	Transfers part of a 1,4-glucan chain from a 4- to a 6-position	Widely distributed Converts amylose into amylopectin	*166–7, 179, 502, 835, 1050, 1053*
2.4.1.e	Transfer part of a 1,4-glucan chain from a 4- to a 6-position	Plants, moulds Acts on short-chain 1,4-glucans	*1, 168, 2305*
2.4.1.f	Transfers part of 1,4-glucan chain to a new 4-position	Liver, plants Can convert maltodextrins into amylose and glucose	*1631, 2065, 2526, 2766*
2.4.1.19	Transfers part of a 1,4-glucan chain to its own non-reducing end	*B. macerans* Forms cyclic dextrins	*166, 774, 1050, 2352*
2.4.1.g	Transfers an α-glucosyl residue from UDPglucose to a hydroxymethylcytosine residue in DNA	Phage-infected bacteria Different enzymes are produced by different phages; in each case the DNA from the infecting phage cannot act as acceptor	*1445*
2.4.1.h	Transfers a β-glucosyl residue from UDPglucose to a hydroxymethylcytosine residue in DNA	T_4-phage-infected bacteria The DNA from the infecting phage cannot act as acceptor	*1445*
2.4.1.i	Transfers a β-glucosyl residue from UDPglucose to a glucosyl-hydroxymethyl-cytosine residue in DNA	T_6-phage-infected bacteria	*1445*
2.4.2.1	Purine nucleoside + orthophosphate = α-D-ribose 1-phosphate + purine	Animal tissues, yeast, bacteria Specificity not completely determined	*1069, 1184, 1287, 1289, 1422, 2139, 2266, 2681*
2.4.2.a	Guanosine + orthophosphate = guanine + D-ribose 1-phosphate	Bone marrow Also acts on deoxy-guanosine	*2925*
2.4.2.3	Uridine + orthophosphate = uracil + D-ribose 1-phosphate	Animal tissues, *Esch. coli*	*391, 2040, 2104*
2.4.2.4	Thymidine + orthophosphate = thymine + 2-deoxy-D-ribose 1-phosphate	Animal tissues	*784*
2.4.2.5	D-ribosyl-R + R′ = D-ribosyl-R′ + R	*Esch. coli* R and R′ represent various purines and pyrimidines	*1413*

EC No.	Systematic name	Trivial name	Active groups and [cofactors]
2.4.2.6	Nucleoside: purine (pyrimidine) deoxyribosyltransferase	Nucleoside deoxyribosyltransferase	
2.4.2.7	AMP: pyrophosphate phosphoribosyltransferase	Adenine phosphoribosyltransferase, AMP pyrophosphorylase	[Mg^{++}]
2.4.2.8	IMP: pyrophosphate phosphoribosyltransferase	Hypoxanthine phosphoribosyltransferase, IMP pyrophosphorylase	[Mg^{++}]
2.4.2.9	UMP: pyrophosphate phosphoribosyltransferase	Uracil phosphoribosyltransferase, UMP pyrophosphorylase	
2.4.2.10	Orotidine-5'-phosphate: pyrophosphate phosphoribosyltransferase	Orotate phosphoribosyltransferase, orotidine-5'-phosphate pyrophosphorylase	[Mg^{++}]
2.4.2.11	Nicotinatenucleotide: pyrophosphate phosphoribosyltransferase	Nicotinate phosphoribosyltransferase	[Mg^{++}]
2.4.2.12	Nicotinamidenucleotide: pyrophosphate phosphoribosyltransferase	Nicotinamide phosphoribosyltransferase, NMN pyrophosphorylase	
2.4.2.13	ATP: L-methionine S-adenosyltransferase	Methionine adenosyltransferase	[$Mg^{++}.M^{+}.S$]
2.4.2.14	Ribosylamine-5-phosphate: pyrophosphate phosphoribosyltransferase (glutamate-amidating)	Amidophosphoribosyltransferase, phosphoribosylpyrophosphate amidotransferase	

2.5   Transferring alkyl or related groups

EC No.	Systematic name	Trivial name	Active groups and [cofactors]
2.5.1.1	Dimethylallylpyrophosphate: isopentenylpyrophosphate dimethylallyltransferase	Dimethylallyltransferase, prenyltransferase (Originally known as farnesyl-pyrophosphate synthetase)	
2.5.1.a	*2-methyl-4-amino-5-hydroxymethyl-pyrimidine-pyrophosphate: 4-methyl-5-(2'-phospho-ethyl)-thiazole 2-methyl-4-aminopyrimidine-5-methenyltransferase*	Thiaminephosphate pyrophosphorylase	[Mg^{++}]
2.5.1.2	Thiamine: base 2-methyl-4-amino-pyrimidine-5-methenyltransferase	Thiaminase I	

	Reaction	*Sources, comments on specificity, etc.*	*References*
2.4.2.6	2-deoxy-D-ribosyl-R + R′ = 2-deoxy-D-ribosyl-R′ + R	Bacteria R and R′ represent various purines and pyrimidines	*1291, 1670, 2256*
2.4.2.7	AMP + pyrophosphate = adenine + 5-phospho-α-D-ribosyl-pyrophosphate	Liver, yeast 5-amino-4-imidazole-carboxamide can replace adenine	*747, 1433, 1630*
2.4.2.8	IMP + pyrophosphate = hypoxanthine + 5-phospho-α-D-ribosyl-pyrophosphate	Liver, yeast Guanine and 6-mercapto-purine can replace hypoxanthine	*1433, 1630, 2207*
2.4.2.9	UMP + pyrophosphate = uracil + 5-phospho-α-D-ribosyl-pyrophosphate	Bacteria	*515*
2.4.2.10	Orotidine-5′-phosphate + pyrophosphate = orotate + 5-phospho-α-D-ribosyl-pyrophosphate	Liver, yeast	*1432, 1589*
2.4.2.11	Nicotinate ribonucleotide + pyrophosphate = nicotinate + 5-phospho-α-D-ribosyl-pyrophosphate	Erythrocytes, yeast, bacteria	*1208–9*
2.4.2.12	Nicotinamide ribonucleotide + pyrophosphate = nicotinamide + 5-phospho-α-D-ribosyl-pyrophosphate	Erythrocytes	*2116*
2.4.2.13	ATP + L-methionine + H_2O = orthophosphate + pyrophosphate + S-adenosyl-methionine	Liver, yeast	*394, 396, 1896*
2.4.2.14	β-D-ribosylamine 5-phosphate + pyrophosphate + L-glutamate = L-glutamine + 5-phospho-α-D-ribosyl-pyrophosphate + H_2O	Liver	*866, 1015–6, 2922*
2.5.1.1	Dimethylallyl pyrophosphate + isopentenyl pyrophosphate = pyrophosphate + geranyl pyrophosphate	Yeast Also transfers geranyl and farnesyl residues	*1636*
2.5.1.a	2-methyl-4-amino-5-hydroxy-methyl-pyrimidine pyro-phosphate + 4-methyl-5-(2′-phospho-ethyl)-thiazole = pyrophosphate + thiamine monophosphate	Yeast	*385, 1529*
2.5.1.2	Thiamine + pyridine = heteropyrithiamine + a thiazole	Freshwater fish, some invertebrates, plants Various bases and thiol compounds can act instead of pyridine	*797–801, 1363, 2194*

EC No.	Systematic name	Trivial name	Active groups and [cofactors]
2.5.1.b	*S-adenosylmethionine alkyltransferase (cyclizing)*	Adenosylmethionine cyclotransferase	
2.5.1.c	*Galactose-6-sulphate alkyltransferase (cyclizing)*	Galactose-6-sulphatase, porphyran sulphatase	

2.6 Transferring nitrogenous groups

2.6.1 Aminotransferases
(For the trivial name, 'aminotransferase' may be replaced by 'transaminase')

2.6.1.1	L-aspartate: 2-oxoglutarate aminotransferase	Aspartate aminotransferase (Formerly known as glutamic-oxaloacetic transaminase)	[Py]
2.6.1.2	L-alanine: 2-oxoglutarate aminotransferase	Alanine aminotransferase (Formerly known as glutamic-pyruvic transaminase)	[Py]
2.6.1.3	L-cysteine: 2-oxoglutarate aminotransferase	Cysteine aminotransferase	[Py]
2.6.1.4	Glycine: 2-oxoglutarate aminotransferase	Glycine aminotransferase	[Py]
2.6.1.5	L-tyrosine: 2-oxoglutarate aminotransferase	Tyrosine aminotransferase	[Py]
2.6.1.6	L-leucine: 2-oxoglutarate aminotransferase	Leucine aminotransferase	[Py]
2.6.1.7	L-kynurenine: 2-oxoglutarate aminotransferase	Kynurenine aminotransferase	[Py]
2.6.1.8	2,5-diaminovalerate: 2-oxoglutarate aminotransferase	Diaminoacid aminotransferase	
2.6.1.9	L-histidinolphosphate: 2-**oxog**lutarate aminotransferase	Histidinolphosphate aminotransferase	[Py]
2.6.1.10	D-aspartate: 2-oxoglutarate aminotransferase	D-aspartate aminotransferase	[Py]
2.6.1.11	α-N-acetyl-L-ornithine: 2-oxo-glutarate aminotransferase	Acetylornithine aminotransferase	[Py]
2.6.1.a	*N-succinyl-L-2,6-diaminopimelate: 2-oxo-glutarate aminotransferase*	Succinyl-diaminopimelate aminotransferase	[Py]

	Reaction	*Sources,* *comments on specificity, etc.*	*References*
2.5.1.b	S-adenosyl-methionine = 5′-(methylthio)-adenosine + 2-amino-γ-butyrolactone	Yeast, bacteria	*1894–5*
2.5.1.c	Eliminates sulphate from the galactose 6-sulphate residues of porphyran, producing 3,6-anhydrogalactose residues	Seaweeds	*2197–8*
2.6.1.1	L-aspartate + 2-oxoglutarate = oxaloacetate + L-glutamate	Animal tissues, plants, bacteria	*158, 463–4,* *692, 864, 1254,* *2877*
2.6.1.2	L-alanine + 2-oxoglutarate = pyruvate + L-glutamate	Animal tissues, plants 2-aminobutyrate acts slowly instead of alanine	*902a, 2877*
2.6.1.3	L-cysteine + 2-oxoglutarate = mercaptopyruvate + L-glutamate	Liver	*439*
2.6.1.4	Glycine + 2-oxoglutarate = glyoxylate + L-glutamate	Plants	*2307, 2877*
2.6.1.5	L-tyrosine + 2-oxoglutarate = p-hydroxyphenylpyruvate + L-glutamate	Animal tissues, yeast Phenylalanine can act instead of tyrosine	*392, 1108,* *1361, 1410,* *2267, 2373*
2.6.1.6	L-leucine + 2-oxoglutarate = 2-oxoisocaproate + L-glutamate	Animal tissues, plants, bacteria	*463, 2267,* *2613*
2.6.1.7	L-kynurenine + 2-oxoglutarate = o-aminobenzoylpyruvate + L-glutamate	Kidney moulds, bacteria	*1234, 1742*
2.6.1.8	2,5-diaminovalerate + 2-oxoglutarate = 2-oxo-5-aminovalerate + L-glutamate	Animal tissues, moulds, bacteria 2,5-diaminoglutarate can act instead of diaminovalerate	*2232*
2.6.1.9	L-histidinolphosphate + 2-oxoglutarate = imidazoleacetolphosphate + L-glutamate	Moulds	*63*
2.6.1.10	D-aspartate + 2-oxoglutarate = oxaloacetate + D-glutamate	Bacteria Pyruvate can replace either ketoacid	*2648–50*
2.6.1.11	α-N-acetyl-L-ornithine + 2-oxoglutarate = N-acetyl-L-glutamate γ-semi- aldehyde + L-glutamate	Bacteria	*2739*
2.6.1.a	N-succinyl-L-diaminopimel- ate + 2-oxoglutarate = N-succinyl-2-amino-6-oxo- L-pimelate + L-glutamate	Bacteria	*2075*

EC No.	Systematic name	Trivial name	Active groups and [cofactors]
2.6.1.12	L-alanine:2-oxoacid aminotransferase	Alanine-ketoacid aminotransferase	[Py]
2.6.1.13	L-ornithine:2-oxoacid aminotransferase	Ornithine-ketoacid aminotransferase	[Py]
2.6.1.14	L-asparagine:2-oxoacid aminotransferase	Asparagine-ketoacid aminotransferase	[Py]
2.6.1.15	L-glutamine:2-oxoacid aminotransferase	Glutamine-ketoacid aminotransferase	[Py]
2.6.1.16	L-glutamine:D-fructose-6-phosphate aminotransferase	Glutamine-fructose-6-phosphate aminotransferase, hexosephosphate aminotransferase	
2.6.1.b	*L-alanine:malonate-semialdehyde aminotransferase*	β-alanine aminotransferase	
2.6.1.c	*4-aminobutyrate:2-oxoglutarate aminotransferase*	Aminobutyrate aminotransferase	

2.6.2 Amidinotransferases
(For the trivial name, 'amidinotransferase' may be replaced by 'transamidinase').

2.6.2.1	L-arginine:glycine amidinotransferase	Glycine amidinotransferase	

2.6.3 Oximinotransferases

2.6.3.1	Pyruvateoxime:acetone oximinotransferase	Oximinotransferase, transoximinase	

2.7 Transferring phosphorus-containing groups

2.7.1 Phosphotransferases with an alcohol group as acceptor

2.7.1.1 C	ATP:D-hexose 6-phosphotransferase	Hexokinase	[Mg^{++}]
2.7.1.2	ATP:D-glucose 6-phosphotransferase	Glucokinase	[Mg^{++}]
2.7.1.a	*ATP:D-glucuronate 1-phosphotransferase*	Glucuronokinase	[M^{++}]
2.7.1.3	ATP:D-fructose 1-phosphotransferase	Ketohexokinase	[Mg^{++}.K$^+$]
2.7.1.4	ATP:D-fructose 6-phosphotransferase	Fructokinase	[Mg^{++}]

	Reaction	Sources, comments on specificity, etc.	References
2.6.1.12	L-alanine + a 2-oxo-acid = pyruvate + an L-aminoacid	Animal tissues, plants, bacteria	55, 2268, 2292, 2877
2.6.1.13	L-ornithine + a 2-oxo-acid = L-glutamate γ-semialdehyde + an L-aminoacid	Liver, moulds	728, 1782, 2133
2.6.1.14	L-asparagine + a 2-oxo-acid = 2-oxosuccinamate + an aminoacid	Liver	1784
2.6.1.15	L-glutamine + a 2-oxo-acid = 2-oxoglutaramate + an aminoacid	Liver, kidney L-glutamine can be replaced by a few closely related compounds	1783
2.6.1.16	L-glutamine + D-fructose 6-phosphate = 2-amino-2-deoxy-D-glucose 6-phosphate + L-glutamate	Liver, moulds	824, 941, 1539
2.6.1.b	L-alanine + malonate semialdehyde = pyruvate + β-alanine	Bacteria	1037
2.6.1.c	4-aminobutyrate + 2-oxoglutarate = succinate semialdehyde + L-glutamate	Animal tissues, bacteria	2358
2.6.2.1	L-arginine + glycine = L-ornithine + guanidinoacetate	Kidney, plants Canavanine can act instead of arginine	295, 2181–2, 2769–70
2.6.3.1	Pyruvateoxime + acetone = pyruvate + acetoxime	Silkworm tissues, algae Acetaldehyde can act instead of acetone: D-glucoseoxime can act instead of pyruvateoxime	2930–2
2.7.1.1	ATP + D-hexose = ADP + D-hexose 6-phosphate	Animal tissues, moulds, yeast D-glucose, D-mannose, D-fructose and 2-amino-2-deoxy-D-glucose can act as acceptor; ITP and deoxy-ATP can act as donor	138, 218, 548, 1493, 1991, 1996
2.7.1.2	ATP + D-glucose = ADP + D-glucose 6-phosphate	Liver, bacteria	356, 403
2.7.1.a	ATP + D-glucuronate = ADP + α-D-glucuronate 1-phosphate	Plants	1945
2.7.1.3	ATP + D-fructose = ADP + D-fructose 1-phosphate	Liver, muscle, bacteria D-sorbose and D-tagatose can also act as acceptor	504, 1085, 1087, 1555, 2055
2.7.1.4	ATP + D-fructose = ADP + D-fructose 6-phosphate	Plants, Schistosoma	356, 1775

EC No.	Systematic name	Trivial name	Active groups and [cofactors]
2.7.1.5	ATP:L-rhamnulose 1-phosphotransferase	Rhamnulokinase	
2.7.1.6	ATP:D-galactose 1-phosphotransferase	Galactokinase	$[Mg^{++}]$
2.7.1.b	*ATP:D-galacturonate 1-phosphotransferase*	Galacturonokinase	$[M^{++}]$
2.7.1.7	ATP:D-mannose 6-phosphotransferase	Mannokinase	$[Mg^{++}]$
2.7.1.8	ATP:2-amino-2-deoxy-D-glucose phosphotransferase	Aminodeoxyglucose kinase	$[Mg^{++}]$
2.7.1.10	ATP:D-glucose-1-phosphate 6-phosphotransferase	Phosphoglucokinase	$[Mg^{++}]$
2.7.1.11	ATP:D-fructose-6-phosphate 1-phosphotransferase	Phosphofructokinase	$[Mg^{++}]$
2.7.1.12	ATP:D-gluconate 6-phosphotransferase	Gluconokinase	$[Mg^{++}]$
2.7.1.13	ATP:2-oxo-D-gluconate 6-phosphotransferase	Oxogluconokinase	$[Mg^{++}]$
2.7.1.c	*ATP:2-oxo-3-deoxy-D-gluconate 6-phosphotransferase*	Oxodeoxygluconokinase	$[Mg^{++}]$
2.7.1.14	ATP:D-sedoheptulose 7-phosphotransferase	Sedoheptulokinase	$[Mg^{++}]$
2.7.1.d	*ATP:L-arabinose 1-phosphotransferase*	Arabinokinase	$[M^{++}]$
2.7.1.15	ATP:D-ribose 5-phosphotransferase	Ribokinase	$[Mg^{++}]$
2.7.1.e	*ATP:D-ribulose 5-phosphotransferase*	D-ribulokinase	$[M^{++}]$
2.7.1.16	ATP:L(or D)-ribulose 5-phosphotransferase	Ribulokinase	$[Mg^{++}]$
2.7.1.17	ATP:D-xylulose 5-phosphotransferase	Xylulokinase	$[Mg^{++}]$
2.7.1.18	ATP:D-ribose-5-phosphate 1-phosphotransferase	Phosphoribokinase	

	Reaction	Sources, comments on specificity, etc.	References
2.7.1.5	ATP+L-rhamnulose = ADP+L-rhamnulose 1-phosphate	Bacteria	2879
2.7.1.6	ATP+D-galactose = ADP+α-D-galactose 1-phosphate	Animal tissues, plants, yeast, bacteria 2-amino-2-deoxy-D-galactose can also act as acceptor	405, 1946, 2677, 2866
2.7.1.b	ATP+D-galacturonate = ADP+α-D-galacturonate 1-phosphate	Plants	1947
2.7.1.7	ATP+D-mannose = ADP+D-mannose 6-phosphate	*Schistosoma*	356
2.7.1.8	ATP+2-amino-2-deoxy-D-glucose = ADP+2-amino-2-deoxy-D-glucose phosphate	*Schistosoma*	356
2.7.1.10	ATP+D-glucose 1-phosphate = ADP+D-glucose 1,6-diphosphate	Muscle, yeast	2045
2.7.1.11	ATP+D-fructose 6-phosphate = ADP+D-fructose 1,6-diphosphate	Animal tissues, plants, yeast D-tagatose 6-phosphate can act as acceptor; UTP, CTP and ITP can act as donor	114, 1598, 1900, 2146
2.7.1.12	ATP+D-gluconate = ADP+6-phospho-D-gluconate	Animal tissues, yeast, bacteria	465, 1528, 1925, 2285
2.7.1.13	ATP+2-oxo-D-gluconate = ADP+2-oxo-6-phospho-D-gluconate	Bacteria	769
2.7.1.c	ATP+2-oxo-3-deoxy-D-gluconate = ADP+2-oxo-3-deoxy-6-phospho-D-gluconate	Bacteria	528
2.7.1.14	ATP+D-sedoheptulose = ADP+D-sedoheptulose 7-phosphate	Bacteria	666
2.7.1.d	ATP+L-arabinose = ADP+β-L-arabinose 1-phosphate	Plants	1946
2.7.1.15	ATP+D-ribose = ADP+D-ribose 5-phosphate	Liver, yeast, bacteria 2-deoxy-D-ribose can also act as acceptor	24, 838, 1045, 1614, 2284
2.7.1.e	ATP+D-ribulose = ADP+D-ribulose 5-phosphate	*Aerobacter*	792
2.7.1.16	ATP+L (or D)-ribulose = ADP+L (or D)-ribulose 5-phosphate	*Lactobacillus* Ribitol and L-arabitol can also act as acceptor	361, 2406
2.7.1.17	ATP+D-xylulose = ADP+D-xylulose 5-phosphate	Liver, bacteria	1092, 2430, 2562
2.7.1.18	ATP+D-ribose 5-phosphate = ADP+D-ribose 1,5-diphosphate	Animal tissues	2316

EC No.	Systematic name	Trivial name	Active groups and [cofactors]
2.7.1.19	ATP:D-ribulose-5-phosphate 1-phosphotransferase	Phosphoribulokinase	[S.Mg^{++}]
2.7.1.20	ATP:adenosine 5'-phosphotransferase	Adenosine kinase	[Mg^{++}]
2.7.1.f	*ATP:uridine 5'-phosphotransferase*	Uridine kinase	[M^{++}]
2.7.1.21	ATP:thymidine 5'-phosphotransferase	Thymidine kinase	
2.7.1.22	ATP:N-ribosylnicotinamide 5'-phosphotransferase	Ribosylnicotinamide kinase	
2.7.1.23	ATP:NAD 2'-phosphotransferase	NAD kinase	[Mg^{++}]
2.7.1.24	ATP:dephospho-CoA 3'-phosphotransferase	Dephospho-CoA kinase	[Mg^{++}]
2.7.1.25	ATP:adenylylsulphate 3'-phosphotransferase	Adenylylsulphate kinase (Originally known as APS-kinase)	[Mg^{++}]
2.7.1.26	ATP:riboflavin 5'-phosphotransferase	Riboflavin kinase (Originally known as flavokinase)	[Mg^{++}]
2.7.1.27	ATP:erythritol phosphotransferase	Erythritol kinase	[M^{++}]
2.7.1.28	ATP:D-glyceraldehyde 3-phosphotransferase	Triokinase	[Mg^{++}]
2.7.1.29	ATP:hydroxyacetone phosphotransferase	Acetol kinase	
2.7.1.30 C	ATP:glycerol phosphotransferase	Glycerol kinase	[Mg^{++}]
2.7.1.31	ATP:D-glycerate 3-phosphotransferase	Glycerate kinase	[Mg^{++}]
2.7.1.32	ATP:choline phosphotransferase	Choline kinase	[Mg^{++}]
2.7.1.33	ATP:pantothenate 4'-phosphotransferase	Pantothenate kinase	

	Reaction	Sources, comments on specificity, etc.	References
2.7.1.19	ATP + D-ribulose 5-phosphate = ADP + D-ribulose 1,5-diphosphate	Plants	1199, 1235
2.7.1.20	ATP + adenosine = ADP + AMP	Animal tissues, yeast 2-amino-adenosine can also act as acceptor	399, 1438
2.7.1.f	ATP + uridine = ADP + UMP	Animal tissues Cytidine can act as acceptor; GTP or ITP can act as donor	2423
2.7.1.21	ATP + thymidine = ADP + thymidine 5'-phosphate	Bacteria	1431
2.7.1.22	ATP + N-ribosylnicotin-amide = ADP + nicotinamideribo-nucleotide	Liver	2266
2.7.1.23	ATP + NAD = ADP + NADP	Animal tissues, yeast	1315, 1427, 2779
2.7.1.24	ATP + dephospho-CoA = ADP + CoA	Animal tissues	1113a, 2779
2.7.1.25	ATP + adenylylsulphate = ADP + 3'-phospho-adenylylsulphate	Animal tissues, yeast	153, 2227
2.7.1.26	ATP + riboflavin = ADP + FMN	Animal tissues, plants, yeast	841, 1327
2.7.1.27	ATP + erythritol = ADP + D-erythritol 4-phosphate	Bacteria	1139
2.7.1.28	ATP + D-glyceraldehyde = ADP + D-glyceraldehyde 3-phosphate	Liver	1088
2.7.1.29	ATP + hydroxyacetone = ADP + hydroxyacetone phosphate	Liver	2369
2.7.1.30	ATP + glycerol = ADP + L-glycerol 3-phosphate	Liver, kidney, yeast Dihydroxyacetone and L-glyceraldehyde can act as acceptor; UTP (and, in the case of the yeast enzyme, ITP and GTP) can act as donor	230, 350, 2860
2.7.1.31	ATP + D-glycerate = ADP + 3-phospho-D-glycerate	Liver, yeast	257, 1203
2.7.1.32	ATP + choline = ADP + choline phosphate	Animal tissues, yeast Ethanolamine and its methyl and ethyl derivatives can also act as acceptor	2890
2.7.1.33	ATP + pantothenate = ADP + 4'-phospho-pantothenate	Bacteria	339, 2086

EC No.	Systematic name	Trivial name	Active groups and [cofactors]
2.7.1.34	ATP:pantetheine 4'-phosphotransferase	Pantetheine kinase	[M++.P]
2.7.1.g	*ATP:2-methyl-4-amino-5-hydroxy-methylpyrimidine 5-phosphotransferase*	Hydroxymethylpyrimidine kinase	
2.7.1.35	ATP:pyridoxal 5-phosphotransferase	Pyridoxal kinase	[M++]
2.7.1.h	*ATP:4-methyl-5-(2'-hydroxyethyl)-thiazole 2'-phosphotransferase*	Hydroxyethylthiazole kinase	[Mg++]
2.7.1.36	ATP:mevalonate 5-phosphotransferase	Mevalonate kinase	[M++]
2.7.1.37	ATP:protein phosphotransferase	Protein kinase	[Mg++]
2.7.1.38	ATP:phosphorylase phosphotransferase	Phosphorylase kinase	[M++]
2.7.1.39	ATP:L-homoserine O-phosphotransferase	Homoserine kinase	[M++]
2.7.1.40 C	ATP:pyruvate phosphotransferase	Pyruvate kinase	[Mg++.K+]
2.7.1.41	D-glucose-1-phosphate:D-glucose-1-phosphate 6-phosphotransferase	Glucose-1-phosphate phosphodismutase	[S]
2.7.1.42	D-glucose-1-phosphate:riboflavin 5'-phosphotransferase	Riboflavin phosphotransferase	

2.7.2 Phosphotransferases with a carboxyl group as acceptor

2.7.2.1	ATP:acetate phosphotransferase	Acetate kinase	[Mg++]
2.7.2.2	ATP:carbamate phosphotransferase	Carbamate kinase	[Mg++]
2.7.2.a	ATP:carbamate phosphotransferase (dephosphorylating)	Carbamate kinase	[Mg++.ace-tylgluta-mate]
2.7.2.3 C	ATP:3-phospho-D-glycerate 1-phosphotransferase	Phosphoglycerate kinase	[Mg++]
2.7.2.4	ATP:L-aspartate 4-phosphotransferase	Aspartate kinase	[M++]

	Reaction	Sources, comments on specificity, etc.	References
2.7.1.34	ATP + pantetheine = ADP + pantetheine 4'-phosphate	Animal tissues	1998
2.7.1.g	ATP + 2-methyl-4-amino-5-hydroxymethyl-pyrimidine = ADP + 2-methyl-4-amino-5-phosphomethyl-pyrimidine	Yeast CTP, UTP and GTP can act as donor	1577
2.7.1.35	ATP + pyridoxal = ADP + pyridoxal 5-phosphate	Animal tissues, yeast, bacteria Pyridoxin, pyridoxamine and various derivatives can also act as acceptor	1193, 1650, 2678
2.7.1.h	ATP + 4-methyl-5-(2'-hydroxyethyl)-thiazole = ADP + 4-methyl-5-(2'-phospho-ethyl)-thiazole	Yeast	385
2.7.1.36	ATP + mevalonate = ADP + 5-phospho-mevalonate	Liver, plants, yeast GTP, CTP, or UTP can also act as donor	1059, 1573, 1723, 2622
2.7.1.37	ATP + a protein = ADP + a phosphoprotein	Animal tissues	174, 365, 2145
2.7.1.38	4 ATP + 2 phosphorylase b = 4 ADP + phosphorylase a	Animal tissues	1459–60, 2164
2.7.1.39	ATP + L-homoserine = ADP + O-phospho-homoserine	Yeast	750, 2795
2.7.1.40	ATP + pyruvate = ADP + phosphoenolpyruvate	Animal tissues UTP, GTP, CTP, ITP and deoxy-ATP can also act as donor. Also phosphorylates hydroxylamine and fluoride in the presence of CO_2	1438, 1477, 2558, 2654
2.7.1.41	D-glucose 1-phosphate + D-glucose 1-phosphate = D-glucose 1,6-diphosphate + D-glucose	Muscle, bacteria	1546, 2399
2.7.1.42	D-glucose 1-phosphate + riboflavin = D-glucose + FMN	Bacteria	1313
2.7.2.1	ATP + acetate = ADP + acetylphosphate	Bacteria, yeast Propionate also acts as acceptor, but more slowly	2246, 2524
2.7.2.2	ATP + NH_3 + CO_2 = ADP + carbamoylphosphate	Bacteria	852, 1266
2.7.2.a	2 ATP + NH_3 + CO_2 + H_2O = 2 ADP + phosphate + carbamoylphosphate	Animal tissues May be a system	1265, 1732–3
2.7.2.3	ATP + 3-phospho-D-glycerate = ADP + 1,3-diphospho-D-glyceric acid	Animal tissues, plants, yeast	110, 354, 2169
2.7.2.4	ATP + L-aspartate = ADP + 4-phospho-L-aspartate	Yeast, bacteria	254

EC No.	*Systematic name*	*Trivial name*	*Active groups and [cofactors]*
	2.7.3 Phosphotransferases with a nitrogenous group as acceptor		
2.7.3.1	ATP: guanidinoacetate phosphotransferase	Guanidinoacetate kinase	
2.7.3.a	*ATP: taurocyamine phosphotransferase*	Taurocyamine kinase	
2.7.3.2 C	ATP: creatine phosphotransferase	Creatine kinase	[Mg++]
2.7.3.3 C	ATP: L-arginine phosphotransferase	Arginine kinase	[Mg++]
2.7.3.b	*ATP: lombricine phosphotransferase*	Lombricine kinase	
	2.7.4 Phosphotransferases with a phospho-group as acceptor		
2.7.4.1	ATP: polyphosphate phosphotransferase	Polyphosphate kinase	[Mg++]
2.7.4.2	ATP: 5-phosphomevalonate phosphotransferase	Phosphomevalonate kinase	[Mg++]
2.7.4.a	*ATP: 2-methyl-4-amino-5-phospho-methylpyrimidine phosphotransferase*	Phosphomethylpyrimidine kinase	[Mg++]
2.7.4.3 C	ATP: AMP phosphotransferase	Adenylate kinase	[Mg++]
2.7.4.4	ATP: nucleosidemonophosphate phosphotransferase	Nucleosidemonophosphate kinase	[Mg++]
2.7.4.b	*ATP: GMP phosphotransferase*	Guanylate kinase	
2.7.4.5	ATP: deoxy-CMP phosphotransferase	Deoxycytidylate kinase	[Mg++]
2.7.4.c	*ATP: thymidinemonophosphate phosphotransferase*	Thymidinemonophosphate kinase	[Mg++]
2.7.4.6	ATP: nucleosidediphosphate phosphotransferase	Nucleosidediphosphate kinase	[M++]
2.7.4.d	*GTP: AMP phosphotransferase*	GTP-adenylate kinase	[Mg++]

	Reaction	Sources, comments on specificity, etc.	References
2.7.3.1	ATP + guanidinoacetate = ADP + phosphoguanidino-acetate	Some annelid worms	1114, 2640
2.7.3.a	ATP + taurocyamine = ADP + phosphotaurocyamine	Some annelid worms	1114, 2640
2.7.3.2	ATP + creatine = ADP + phosphocreatine	Animal tissues. Negmine can also act as acceptor	93, 701, 1479
2.7.3.3	ATP + L-arginine = ADP + L-phosphoarginine	Invertebrate muscle	143, 693, 932, 1868, 2592
2.7.3.b	ATP + lombricine = ADP + phospholombricine	Earthworms	2051
2.7.4.1	ATP + (phosphate)$_n$ = ADP + (phosphate)$_{n+1}$	Yeast, bacteria	1119, 1430, 1898
2.7.4.2	ATP + 5-phospho-mevalonate = ADP + 5-pyrophospho-mevalonate	Animal tissues, yeast	274, 1059, 1064, 1573
2.7.4.a	ATP + 2-methyl-4-amino-5-phosphomethyl-pyrimidine = ADP + 2-methyl-4-amino-5-pyrophosphomethyl-pyrimidine	Yeast	1577
2.7.4.3	ATP + AMP = ADP + ADP	Animal tissues, plants, yeast, bacteria. Inorganic triphosphate can also act as donor	447, 1583, 1980–1, 2021
2.7.4.4	ATP + a nucleoside monophosphate = ADP + a nucleoside diphosphate	Animal tissues, yeast. Many nucleotides can act as acceptor; other nucleoside triphosphates can act instead of ATP	828, 1072, 1590
2.7.4.b	ATP + GMP = ADP + GDP	Ascaris	702
2.7.4.5	ATP + deoxy-CMP = ADP + deoxy-CDP	Bacteria. CMP can also act as acceptor	1195
2.7.4.c	ATP + thymidine monophosphate = ADP + thymidine diphosphate	Bacteria	1195
2.7.4.6	ATP + a nucleoside diphosphate = ADP + a nucleoside triphosphate	Animal tissues, plants, yeast. Many nucleoside diphosphates can act as acceptor	216, 828, 1389, 1464
2.7.4.d	GTP + AMP = GDP + ADP	Animal tissues. ITP can act instead of GTP	448

EC No.	Systematic name	Trivial name	Active groups and [cofactors]
	2.7.5 Phosphotransferases with regeneration of donors (apparently catalysing intramolecular transfers)		
2.7.5.1 C	α-D-glucose-1,6-diphosphate : α-D-glucose-1-phosphate phosphotransferase	Phosphoglucomutase, glucose phosphomutase	[M++]
2.7.5.2	2-acetylamino-2-deoxy-D-glucose-1,6-diphosphate : 2-acetylamino-2-deoxy-D-glucose-1-phosphate phosphotransferase	Acetylaminodeoxyglucose phosphomutase	[Mg++]
2.7.5.3 C	2,3-diphospho-D-glycerate : 2-phospho-D-glycerate phosphotransferase	Phosphoglyceromutase, Glycerate phosphomutase	
2.7.5.4	1,3-diphospho-D-glyceric acid : 3-phospho-D-glycerate phosphotransferase	Diphosphoglyceromutase, Glycerate phosphomutase	
	2.7.6 Pyrophosphotransferases		
2.7.6.1	ATP : D-ribose-5-phosphate pyrophosphotransferase	Ribosephosphate pyrophosphokinase	[Mg++]
2.7.6.2	ATP : thiamine pyrophosphotransferase	Thiamine pyrophosphokinase	[Mg++]
	2.7.7 Nucleotidyltransferases		
2.7.7.1	ATP : NMN adenylyltransferase	NMN adenylyltransferase, NAD pyrophosphorylase	[Mg++]
2.7.7.a	*ATP : nicotinatemononucleotide adenylyltransferase*	Nicotinatemononucleotide adenylyltransferase, deamido-NAD pyrophosphorylase	[Mg++]
2.7.7.2	ATP : FMN adenylyltransferase	FMN adenylyltransferase, FAD pyrophosphorylase	[Mg++]
2.7.7.3	ATP : pantetheine-4'-phosphate adenylyltransferase	Pantetheinephosphate adenylyltransferase, dephospho-CoA pyrophosphorylase	[Mg++]
2.7.7.4	ATP : sulphate adenylyltransferase	Sulphate adenylyltransferase	[Mg++]
2.7.7.5	ADP : sulphate adenylyltransferase	Sulphate adenylyltransferase	
2.7.7.b	*ATP : polynucleotide adenylyltransferase*	Polyadenylate nucleotidyltransferase	

	Reaction	Sources, comments on specificity, etc.	References
2.7.5.1	α-D-glucose 1,6-diphosphate + α-D-glucose 1-phosphate = D-glucose 6-phosphate + α-D-glucose 1,6-diphosphate	Widely distributed	335, 1651, 1829, 1920, 2109, 2530, 2571
2.7.5.2	2-acetylamino-2-deoxy-D-glucose 1,6-diphosphate + 2-acetylamino-2-deoxy-D-glucose 1-phosphate = 2-acetylamino-2-deoxy-D-glucose 6-phosphate + 2-acetylamino-2-deoxy-D-glucose 1,6-diphosphate	Animal tissues, moulds	1540, 2205
2.7.5.3	2,3-diphospho-D-glycerate + 2-phospho-D-glycerate = 3-phospho-D-glycerate + 2,3-diphospho-D-glycerate	Widely distributed	510, 2239–40, 2572
2.7.5.4	1,3-diphospho-D-glyceric acid + 3-phospho-D-glycerate = 3-phospho-D-glycerate + 2,3-diphospho-D-glycerate	Animal tissues	1273, 2175
2.7.6.1	ATP + D-ribose 5-phosphate = AMP + 5-phospho-α-D-ribosyl-pyrophosphate	Liver	1192, 1432, 2207
2.7.6.2	ATP + thiamine = AMP + thiamine pyrophosphate	Animal tissues, yeast	1554, 2391, 2529, 2822
2.7.7.1	ATP + nicotinamide ribonucleotide = pyrophosphate + NAD	Animal tissues, yeast Nicotinate nucleotide can also act as acceptor	95, 1426, 1437
2.7.7.a	ATP + nicotinate ribonucleotide = pyrophosphate + deamido-NAD	Bacteria	1208
2.7.7.2	ATP + FMN = pyrophosphate + FAD	Liver, plants, yeast, bacteria	842, 2342
2.7.7.3	ATP + pantetheine 4′-phosphate = pyrophosphate + dephospho-CoA	Animal tissues	113a, 1998
2.7.7.4	ATP + sulphate = pyrophosphate + adenylylsulphate	Liver, yeast, moulds	153, 1107, 2228–9
2.7.7.5	ADP + sulphate = orthophosphate + adenylylsulphate	Animal tissues, yeast	2227–8
2.7.7.b	ATP + (adenylate)$_n$ = pyrophosphate + (adenylate)$_{n+1}$	Thymus nuclei Also acts slowly with CTP	672

EC No.	Systematic name	Trivial name	Active groups and [cofactors]
2.7.7.c	*ATP:RNA adenylyltransferase*	RNA adenylyltransferase	
2.7.7.d	*CTP:RNA cytidylyltransferase*	RNA cytidylyltransferase	
2.7.7.6	Nucleosidetriphosphate:RNA nucleotidyltransferase	RNA nucleotidyltransferase	
2.7.7.7	Deoxynucleosidetriphosphate:DNA deoxynucleotidyltransferase	DNA nucleotidyltransferase	[Mg^{++}]
2.7.7.8	Nucleosidediphosphate:poly-nucleotide nucleotidyltransferase	Polynucleotide nucleotidyltransferase, polynucleotide phosphorylase	[Mg^{++}]
2.7.7.e	*GDP:D-mannose-1-phosphate guanylyltransferase*	Mannose-1-phosphate guanylyltransferase, GDPmannose phosphorylase	
2.7.7.9	UTP:α-D-glucose-1-phosphate uridylyltransferase	Glucose-1-phosphate uridylyltransferase, UDPG pyrophosphorylase	[M^{++}]
2.7.7.f	*UTP:2-acetylamino-2-deoxy-α-D-glucose-1-phosphate uridylyltransferase*	UDPaminodeoxyglucose pyrophosphorylase	[M^{++}]
2.7.7.10	UTP:α-D-galactose-1-phosphate uridylyltransferase	Galactose-1-phosphate uridylyltransferase	[Mg^{++}]
2.7.7.11	UTP:α-D-xylose-1-phosphate uridylyltransferase	Xylose-1-phosphate uridylyltransferase	
2.7.7.12	UDPglucose:α-D-galactose-1-phosphate uridylyltransferase	Hexose-1-phosphate uridylyltransferase	[Mg^{++}]
2.7.7.g	*Deoxy-TTP:α-D-glucose-1-phosphate thymidylyltransferase*	Glucose-1-phosphate thymidylyltransferase	
2.7.7.13	GTP:α-D-mannose-1-phosphate guanylyltransferase	Mannose-1-phosphate guanylyltransferase	
2.7.7.14	CTP:ethanolaminephosphate cytidylyltransferase	Ethanolaminephosphate cytidylyltransferase	
2.7.7.15	CTP:cholinephosphate cytidylyltransferase	Cholinephosphate cytidylyltransferase	[Mg^{++}]

Reaction	Sources, comments on specificity, etc.	References
2.7.7.c	$ATP + RNA_n =$ pyrophosphate $+ RNA_{n+1}$ (RNA_n denotes an RNA chain of n nucleotide units)	Bacteria Also incorporates a CMP residue from CTP	803
2.7.7.d	$CTP + RNA_n =$ pyrophosphate $+ RNA_{n+1}$	Thymus	1196
2.7.7.6	m nucleoside triphosphate $+ RNA_n =$ m pyrophosphate $+ RNA_{n+m}$	Animal tissues, bacteria Needs DNA as primer	2827
2.7.7.7	n deoxynucleoside triphosphate $+ DNA_n =$ n pyrophosphate $+ 2DNA_n$	Animal tissues, bacteria A DNA chain acts as a primer, and the enzyme forms a complementary chain	239, 283, 1532, 2319
2.7.7.8	A nucleoside diphosphate $+ RNA_n =$ orthophosphate $+ RNA_{n+1}$	Animal sperm, plants, moulds, yeast, bacteria ADP, IDP, GDP, UDP and CDP can act as donor	940, 978, 1605, 2008, 2011
2.7.7.e	$GDP + $ D-mannose 1-phosphate $=$ orthophosphate $+$ GDPmannose	Yeast	408
2.7.7.9	$UTP + \alpha$-D-glucose 1-phosphate $=$ pyrophosphate $+$ UDPglucose	Mammary gland, plants, yeast	839, 1289, 2435
2.7.7.f	$UTP + $ 2-acetylamino-2-deoxy-D-glucose 1-phosphate $=$ pyrophosphate $+$ UDP-2-acetylamino-2-deoxy-D-glucose	Animal tissues, bacteria	2056, 2561
2.7.7.10	$UTP + \alpha$-D-galactose 1-phosphate $=$ pyrophosphate $+$ UDPgalactose	Animal tissues, yeast	1218, 1289
2.7.7.11	$UTP + \alpha$-D-xylose 1-phosphate $=$ pyrophosphate $+$ UDPxylose	Plants	840
2.7.7.12	UDPglucose $+ \alpha$-D-galactose 1-phosphate $=$ α-D-glucose 1-phosphate $+$ UDPgalactose	Animal tissues, yeast, bacteria	1290, 1498, 2435
2.7.7.g	Deoxy-TTP $+ \alpha$-D-glucose 1-phosphate $=$ pyrophosphate $+$ deoxy-TDPglucose	Bacteria	1446, 2062
2.7.7.13	$GTP + \alpha$-D-mannose 1-phosphate $=$ pyrophosphate $+$ GDPmannose	Yeast	1899
2.7.7.14	$CTP + $ ethanolamine phosphate $=$ pyrophosphate $+$ CDPethanolamine	Animal tissues, plants, yeast	1360
2.7.7.15	$CTP + $ choline phosphate $=$ pyrophosphate $+$ CDPcholine	Animal tissues, plants, yeast	292, 1360, 2873

EC No.	Systematic name	Trivial name	Active groups and [cofactors]
2.7.7.16 C	Polyribonucleotide 2-oligo-nucleotidotransferase (cyclizing)	Ribonuclease	
2.7.7.h	*Polyribonucleotide 2-oligonucleotido-transferase (cyclizing)*	Ribonuclease	

2.7.8 Transferases for other substituted phospho-groups

2.7.8.1	CDPethanolamine:1,2-diglyceride ethanolaminephosphotransferase	Ethanolaminephospho-transferase	
2.7.8.2	CDPcholine:1,2-diglyceride cholinephosphotransferase	Cholinephosphotransferase	[Mg^{++}]
2.7.8.a	*CDPcholine:ceramide cholinephosphotransferase*	Ceramide cholinephosphotransferase	

2.8 Transferring sulphur-containing groups

2.8.1 Sulphurtransferases

2.8.1.1 C	Thiosulphate:cyanide sulphurtransferase	Thiosulphate sulphurtransferase (Originally known as rhodanese)	
2.8.1.2	3-mercaptopyruvate:cyanide sulphurtransferase	3-mercaptopyruvate sulphurtransferase	

2.8.2 Sulphotransferases

2.8.2.1	3'-phosphoadenylylsulphate:phenol sulphotransferase	Aryl sulphotransferase	[Mg^{++}]
2.8.2.a	*3'-phosphoadenylylsulphate:arylamine sulphotransferase*	Arylamine sulphotransferase	[Mg^{++}]
2.8.2.2	3'-phosphoadenylylsulphate:3-β-hydroxysteroid sulphotransferase	3-β-hydroxysteroid sulphotransferase	
2.8.2.b	*3'-phosphoadenylylsulphate:oestrone sulphotransferase*	Oestrone sulphotransferase	

Reaction	Sources, comments on specificity, etc.	References
2.7.7.16	Transfers the 3'-phosphate of a pyrimidine nucleotide residue of a polynucleotide from the 5'-position of the adjoining nucleotide to the 2'-position of the pyrimidine nucleotide itself, forming a cyclic nucleotide	Animal tissues, especially pancreas. Also catalyses the transfer of the phosphate group from the 2'-position in the cyclic phosphate to water; the overall reaction brings about the depolymerization of RNA	*1074, 1109, 1308, 1654, 1720, 2479*
2.7.7.h	Acts on polyribonucleotides similarly to 2.7.7.16, but transfers purine nucleotide residues as well as pyrimidine nucleotide residues	Plant leaves, bacteria. Brings about the depolymerization of RNA	*1132, 1721, 2480, 2691*
2.7.8.1	CDPethanolamine + 1,2-diglyceride = CMP + a phosphatidylethanolamine	Liver, yeast	*1360*
2.7.8.2	CDPcholine + 1,2-diglyceride = CMP + a phosphatidylcholine	Liver, yeast	*1360, 2830*
2.7.8.a	CDPcholine + ceramide = CMP + sphingomyelin	Liver	*2493*
2.8.1.1	Thiosulphate + cyanide = sulphite + thiocyanate	Animal tissues. A few other sulphur compounds can act as donor	*2472–3, 2847*
2.8.1.2	3-mercaptopyruvate + cyanide = pyruvate + thiocyanate	Animal tissues. Sulphite, sulphinates, mercaptoethanol and mercaptopyruvate can also act as acceptor	*727, 1202, 2474*
2.8.2.1	3'-phosphoadenylylsulphate + a phenol = adenosine 3',5'-diphosphate + an arylsulphate	Animal tissues	*347, 1107, 1997, 2228*
2.8.2.a	3'-phosphoadenylylsulphate + an arylamine = adenosine 3',5'-diphosphate + an arylsulphamate	Liver	*2273*
2.8.2.2	3'-phosphoadenylylsulphate + a 3-β-hydroxysteroid = adenosine 3',5'-diphosphate + a steroid 3-β-sulphate	Liver	*1997*
2.8.2.b	3'-phosphoadenylylsulphate + oestrone = adenosine 3',5'-diphosphate + oestrone 3-sulphate	Liver	*1997*

EC No.	Systematic name	Trivial name	Active groups and [cofactors]
2.8.2.c	3'-phosphoadenylylsulphate:chondroitin sulphotransferase	Chondroitin sulphotransferase	

2.8.3 CoA-transferases

2.8.3.1	Acetyl-CoA:propionate CoA-transferase	Propionate CoA-transferase	
2.8.3.2	*Succinyl-CoA:oxalate CoA-transferase*	Oxalate CoA-transferase	
2.8.3.3	Acetyl-CoA:malonate CoA-transferase	Malonate CoA-transferase	
2.8.3.5	Succinyl-CoA:3-oxo-acid CoA-transferase	3-ketoacid CoA-transferase	
2.8.3.6	Succinyl-CoA:3-oxo-adipate CoA-transferase	3-oxo-adipate CoA-transferase	

3   HYDROLASES
3.1   Acting on ester bonds
3.1.1   Carboxylic ester hydrolases

3.1.1.1	Carboxylic ester hydrolase	Carboxylesterase (Formerly known as ali-esterase or B-esterase)	
3.1.1.2	Aryl ester hydrolase	Arylesterase (Formerly known as A-esterase, or, in one case, as paraoxonase)	
3.1.1.3	Glycerol ester hydrolase	Lipase	$[Ca^{++}]$
3.1.1.4 C	Phosphatide acyl-hydrolase	Phospholipase A	$[Ca^{++}]$
3.1.1.5 C	Lysolecithin acyl-hydrolase	Lysophospholipase, Phospholipase B	

Reaction	Sources, comments on specificity, etc.	References
2.8.2.c	3'-phosphoadenylylsulphate + chondroitin = adenosine 3',5'-diphosphate + chondroitin 4-sulphate	Animal tissues Oligo- and poly-saccharides containing 2-acetylamino-2-deoxy-D-galactose can act as acceptor	550, 2577
2.8.3.1	Acetyl-CoA + propionate = acetate + propionyl-CoA	*Clostridia* Butyrate and lactate can also act as acceptor	2496
2.8.3.2	Succinyl-CoA + oxalate = succinate + oxalyl-CoA	*Pseudomonas oxalaticus*	2135
2.8.3.3	Acetyl-CoA + malonate = acetate + malonyl-CoA	Bacteria	1032
2.8.3.5	Succinyl-CoA + a 3-oxo-acid = succinate + a 3-oxoacyl-CoA	Animal tissues, bacteria Acetoacetate and, more slowly, 3-oxovalerate, 3-oxo-iso-caproate and 3-oxo-caproate, can act as acceptor; malonyl-CoA can act instead of succinyl-CoA	1639a, 2518
2.8.3.6	Succinyl-CoA + 3-oxo-adipate = succinate + 3-oxo-adipyl-CoA	*Pseudomonas*	1314
3.1.1.1	A carboxylic ester + H_2O = an alcohol + a carboxylic acid	Animal tissues, plants, moulds, yeast Wide specificity	17, 42–3, 360, 490, 2714
3.1.1.2	A phenyl acetate + H_2O = a phenol + acetic acid	Animal tissues Acts on many phenolic esters; the enzyme from sheep serum also hydrolyses paraoxon	42, 100, 1691–2
3.1.1.3	A triglyceride + H_2O = a diglyceride + a fatty acid	Animal tissues, especially pancreas, plants, moulds, bacteria The pancreatic enzyme acts only at an ester–water interface; the outer ester links are preferentially hydrolysed	1425, 1643, 1737, 1760, 2302–3, 2410
3.1.1.4	A lecithin + H_2O = a lysolecithin + an unsaturated fatty acid	Venoms of snakes, scorpions, wasps, etc., bacteria Also acts on phosphatidyl-ethanolamine, choline plas-malogen and phosphatidates removing the fatty acid attached to the 2-position	574, 642, 770, 965, 991, 1616, 2223
3.1.1.5	A lysolecithin + H_2O = glycerolphosphocholine + a fatty acid	Animal tissues, wasp venom, plants, moulds	492, 572–3, 713, 2378

EC No.	Systematic name	Trivial name	Active groups and [cofactors]
3.1.1.6	Acetic ester acetyl-hydrolase	Acetylesterase (The animal enzyme has been known as C-esterase)	
3.1.1.7	Acetylcholine acetyl-hydrolase	Acetylcholinesterase (Formerly known as 'true cholinesterase')	
3.1.1.8	Acylcholine acyl-hydrolase	Cholinesterase (Formerly known as 'pseudo-cholinesterase')	
3.1.1.9	Benzoylcholine hydrolase	Benzoylcholinesterase	
3.1.1.10	Atropine acyl-hydrolase	Tropinesterase	
3.1.1.11	Pectin pectyl-hydrolase	Pectinesterase	[M⁺⁺]
3.1.1.12	Vitamin A acetate hydrolase	Vitamin A esterase	
3.1.1.13	Sterol ester hydrolase	Cholesterol esterase	
3.1.1.14	Chlorophyll chlorophyllido-hydrolase	Chlorophyllase	
3.1.1.15	L-arabono-γ-lactone hydrolase	Arabonolactonase	
3.1.1.16	4-carboxymethyl-4-hydroxy-isocrotonolactone hydrolase	4-carboxymethyl-4-hydroxy-isocrotonolactonase	
3.1.1.17	D-glucono-δ-lactone hydrolase	Gluconolactonase	[M⁺⁺]
3.1.1.18	D(or L)-gulono-γ-lactone hydrolase	Aldonolactonase	
3.1.1.19	D-glucurono-δ-lactone hydrolase	Uronolactonase	
3.1.1.20	Tannin acyl-hydrolase	Tannase	

3.1.2   Thiolester hydrolases

3.1.2.1	Acetyl-CoA hydrolase	Acetyl-CoA hydrolase	

Reaction	*Sources, comments on specificity, etc.*	*References*
3.1.1.6 An acetic ester $+ H_2O =$ an alcohol $+$ acetic acid	Animal tissues, citrus fruits, moulds	*42, 224, 227, 375, 1243–4*
3.1.1.7 Acetylcholine $+ H_2O =$ choline $+$ acetic acid	Animal tissues, snake venom Acts on a variety of acetic esters; also catalyses transacetylations	*97, 225, 541, 556, 1618, 1794, 1918, 2032, 2882, 2971*
3.1.1.8 An acylcholine $+ H_2O =$ choline $+$ an acid	Animal tissues, blood Acts on a variety of choline esters and a few other compounds	*97, 100, 556, 559, 1793–4, 1918, 2552*
3.1.1.9 Benzoylcholine $+ H_2O =$ choline $+$ benzoic acid	Animal tissues	*1418, 2312*
3.1.1.10 Atropine $+ H_2O =$ tropine $+$ tropic acid	Some rabbits Also acts on cocaine and other tropine esters	*855*
3.1.1.11 Pectin $+ n\ H_2O =$ n methanol $+$ pectic acid	Plants, moulds, bacteria	*600, 1597, 1828*
3.1.1.12 Vitamin A acetate $+ H_2O =$ vitamin A $+$ acetic acid	Animal tissues	*1661, 1679*
3.1.1.13 A cholesterol ester $+ H_2O =$ cholesterol $+$ an acid	Pancreatic juice, liver, dog serum Also acts on esters of cholestanol and some other sterols	*376, 1079, 1447, 1967, 2583–4*
3.1.1.14 Chlorophyll $+ H_2O =$ phytol $+$ chlorophyllide	Plants, photosynthetic bacteria Also catalyses chlorophyllide transfer, e.g. converts chlorophyll in methanol into methyl-chlorophyllide	*1131, 1395*
3.1.1.15 L-arabono-γ-lactone $+ H_2O =$ L-arabonic acid	Bacteria	*2825*
3.1.1.16 4-carboxymethyl-4-hydroxyiso- crotonolactone $+ H_2O =$ 3-oxo-adipic acid	Bacteria	*2419*
3.1.1.17 D-glucono-δ-lactone $+ H_2O =$ D-gluconic acid	Animal tissues, yeast, bacteria Also acts on D-glucono-δ- lactone 6-phosphate	*332, 682*
3.1.1.18 D (or L)-gulono-γ-lactone $+$ $H_2O =$ gulonic acid	Animal tissues	*352, 441*
3.1.1.19 D-glucurono-δ-lactone $+$ $H_2O =$ D-glucuronic acid	Animal tissues	*2889*
3.1.1.20 Digallate $+ H_2O =$ gallate $+$ gallic acid	Moulds Also hydrolyses ester links in other tannins	*663*
3.1.2.1 Acetyl-CoA $+ H_2O =$ CoA $+$ acetic acid	Heart	*823*

EC No.	Systematic name	Trivial name	Active groups and [cofactors]
3.1.2.2	Palmitoyl-CoA hydrolase	Palmitoyl-CoA hydrolase	
3.1.2.3	Succinyl-CoA hydrolase	Succinyl-CoA hydrolase	
3.1.2.4	3-hydroxyisobutyryl-CoA hydrolase	3-hydroxyisobutyryl-CoA hydrolase	
3.1.2.5	3-hydroxy-3-methylglutaryl-CoA hydrolase	Hydroxymethylglutaryl-CoA hydrolase	
3.1.2.6	S-2-hydroxyacylglutathione hydrolase	Hydroxyacylglutathione hydrolase (Originally known as glyoxalase II)	
3.1.2.7	S-acylglutathione hydrolase	Glutathione thiolesterase	
3.1.2.8	S-acetoacetylglutathione hydrolase	Acetoacetylglutathione hydrolase	

3.1.3 Phosphoric monoester hydrolases

EC No.	Systematic name	Trivial name	Active groups and [cofactors]
3.1.3.1	Orthophosphoric monoester phosphohydrolase	Alkaline phosphatase	[M^{++}]
3.1.3.2	Orthophosphoric monoester phosphohydrolase	Acid phosphatase	
3.1.3.a	*Phosphoglycollate phosphohydrolase*	Phosphoglycollate phosphatase	[M^{++}]
3.1.3.3	Phosphoserine phosphohydrolase	Phosphoserine phosphatase	[M^{++}]
3.1.3.b	*2-phosphoglycerol phosphohydrolase*	Glycerolphosphatase	[Fe^{+++}]
3.1.3.4	L-α-phosphatidate phosphohydrolase	Phosphatidate phosphatase	
3.1.3.5	5′-ribonucleotide phosphohydrolase	5-nucleotidase	[Mg^{++}]
3.1.3.6	3′-ribonucleotide phosphohydrolase	3-nucleotidase	
3.1.3.7	Adenosine-3′,5′-diphosphate 3′-phosphohydrolase	Phosphoadenylate 3-nucleotidase	[Mg^{++}]

Reaction	Sources, comments on specificity, etc.	References
3.1.2.2	Palmitoyl-CoA + H_2O = CoA + palmitic acid	Animal tissues, yeast	2107, 2492
3.1.2.3	Succinyl-CoA + H_2O = CoA + succinic acid	Heart	823
3.1.2.4	3-hydroxyisobutyryl-CoA + H_2O = CoA + 3-hydroxyisobutyric acid	Animal tissues, moulds, bacteria. Also hydrolyses 3-hydroxy-propionyl-CoA	2210
3.1.2.5	3-hydroxy-3-methylglutaryl-CoA + H_2O = CoA + 3-hydroxy-3-methyl-glutaric acid	Animal tissues, moulds, bacteria	585
3.1.2.6	S-2-hydroxyacylglutathione + H_2O = reduced glutathione + a 2-hydroxy-acid	Animal tissues	2150
3.1.2.7	S-acylglutathione + H_2O = reduced glutathione + an acid	Animal tissues	1375
3.1.2.8	S-acetoacetylglutathione + H_2O = reduced glutathione + acetoacetic acid	Liver	2522
3.1.3.1	An orthophosphoric mono-ester + H_2O = an alcohol + H_3PO_4	Animal tissues, milk. Wide specificity; also catalyses transphosphoryl-ations	57, 699, 1873–6, 2676
3.1.3.2	An orthophosphoric mono ester + H_2O = an alcohol + H_3PO_4	Animal tissues, plants, yeast, bacteria. Wide specificity; also catalyses transphosphorylations	868, 1274, 1496, 1612, 2680, 2683
3.1.3.a	Phosphoglycollate + H_2O = glycollate + H_3PO_4	Plants	2217
3.1.3.3	L (or D)-phosphoserine + H_2O = L (or D)-serine + H_3PO_4	Liver, yeast, bacteria	293, 1951
3.1.2.b	2-phosphoglycerol + H_2O = glycerol + H_3PO_4	Plants	2171
3.1.3.4	An L-α-phosphatidate + H_2O = a D-2,3(or L-1,2)-diglyceride + H_3PO_4	Animal tissues	2456
3.1.3.5	A 5'-ribonucleotide + H_2O = a ribonucleoside + H_3PO_4	Animal tissues, snake venom, bacteria. Wide specificity for 5'-nucleotides	946, 1067, 2362
3.1.3.6	A 3'-ribonucleotide + H_2O = a ribonucleoside + H_3PO_4	Plants. Wide specificity for 3'-nucleotides	2397
3.1.3.7	Adenosine 3',5'-diphosphate + H_2O = AMP + H_3PO_4	Liver. Also acts on 3'-phospho-adenylylsulphate	347

EC No.	Systematic name	Trivial name	Active groups and [cofactors]
3.1.3.8	*meso*-inositol-hexaphosphate phosphohydrolase	Phytase	[Mg^{++}]
3.1.3.9	D-glucose-6-phosphate phosphohydrolase	Glucose-6-phosphatase	
3.1.3.10	D-glucose-1-phosphate phosphohydrolase	Glucose-1-phosphatase	
3.1.3.11	D-fructose-1,6-diphosphate 1-phosphohydrolase	Hexosediphosphatase	[Mg^{++}]
3.1.3.12	Trehalose-6-phosphate phosphohydrolase	Trehalosephosphatase	[Mg^{++}]
3.1.3.13	2,3-diphospho-D-glycerate 2-phosphohydrolase	Diphosphoglycerate phosphatase	
3.1.3.14	Methylthio-3-phospho-D-glycerate phosphohydrolase	Methylthiophosphoglycerate phosphatase	
3.1.3.15	L-histidinolphosphate phosphohydrolase	Histidinolphosphatase	
3.1.3.16	Phosphoprotein phosphohydrolase	Phosphoprotein phosphatase	
3.1.3.17	Phosphorylase phosphohydrolase	Phosphorylase phosphatase (Originally known as PR-enzyme)	
3.1.4 Phosphoric diester hydrolases			
3.1.4.1	Orthophosphoric diester phosphohydrolase	Phosphodiesterase	[Mg^{++}]
3.1.4.2	L-3-glycerylphosphorylcholine glycerophosphohydrolase	Glycerophosphorylcholine diesterase	
3.1.4.3	Phosphatidylcholine cholinephosphohydrolase	Phospholipase C (*Clostridium welchii* α-toxin; *Cl. oedematiens* β- and γ-toxins)	[Ca^{++}]
3 1 4.4	Phosphatidylcholine phosphatidohydrolase	Phospholipase D	[Ca^{++}]

	Reaction	Sources, comments on specificity, etc.	References
3.1.3.8	*meso*-inositol hexaphosphate + 6 H_2O = *meso*-inositol + 6H_3PO_4	Plants, moulds	*752, 1648, 2067*
3.1.3.9	D-glucose 6-phosphate + H_2O = D-glucose + H_3PO_4	Liver Also acts on 2-amino-2-deoxy-D-glucose 6-phosphate	*1087, 1512, 1694, 2579*
3.1.3.10	D-glucose 1-phosphate + H_2O = D-glucose + H_3PO_4	Silkworm blood, plants Also acts, more slowly, on D-galactose 1-phosphate	*716, 2688*
3.1.3.11	D-fructose 1,6-diphosphate + H_2O = D-fructose 6-phosphate + H_3PO_4	Animal tissues	*867, 1844*
3.1.3.12	Trehalose 6-phosphate + H_2O = trehalose + H_3PO_4	Insect tissues, yeast	*378, 390*
3.1.3.13	2,3-diphospho-D-glycerate + H_2O = 3-phospho-D-glycerate + H_3PO_4	Animal tissues, yeast	*1272, 2174*
3.1.3.14	Methylthio-3-phospho-D-glycerate + H_2O = methylthio-D-glycerate + H_3PO_4	Yeast	*257*
3.1.3.15	L-histidinol phosphate + H_2O = L-histidinol + H_3PO_4	Moulds	*60*
3.1.3.16	A phosphoprotein + n H_2O = a protein + n H_3PO_4	Animal tissues Acts on casein and other phosphoproteins; the spleen enzyme also acts on phenolic phosphates and phosphoamides	*2041, 2249, 2568*
3.1.3.17	Phosphorylase a + 4 H_2O = 2 phosphorylase b + 4 H_3PO_4	Animal tissues	*890, 1355, 2164, 2919*
3.1.4.1	A phosphoric diester + H_2O = a phosphoric monoester + an alcohol	Widely distributed Wide specificity, varying with source; the spleen enzyme forms 3′-nucleotides, and the venom enzyme 5′-nucleotides, from polynucleotides	*28, 561, 582, 945, 1104, 1678, 2190–2, 2856, 2867*
3.1.4.2	L-3-glycerylphosphoryl-choline + H_2O = choline + glycerol 1-phosphate	Animal tissues, bacteria Also acts on L-3-glyceryl-phosphorylethanolamine	*571, 1033, 1036, 2814*
3.1.4.3	A phosphatidylcholine + H_2O = a 1,2-diglyceride + choline phosphate	Brain, bacterial toxins, snake venoms Also acts on sphingomyelin	*321, 655, 994, 1615, 1656–7*
3.1.4.4	A phosphatidylcholine + H_2O = choline + a phosphatidic acid	Plants Also acts on other phosphatides	*681, 992–3, 2669*

EC No.	Systematic name	Trivial name	Active groups and [cofactors]
3.1.4.5 C	Deoxyribonucleate oligonucleotido-hydrolase	Deoxyribonuclease	[Mg++]
3.1.4.6	Deoxyribonucleate 3'-nucleotidohydrolase	Deoxyribonuclease II	
3.1.4.7		Micrococcal nuclease	
3.1.4.a		*Azotobacter* nuclease	
3.1.4.8	Ribonucleate 3'-guanylohydrolase	*Aspergillus oryzae* ribonuclease	
3.1.5	**Triphosphoric monoester hydrolases**		
3.1.5.1	Deoxy-GTP triphosphohydrolase	DeoxyGTPase	
3.1.6	**Sulphuric ester hydrolases**		
3.1.6.1	Aryl-sulphate sulphohydrolase	Arylsulphatase	[Cl⁻] in some cases
3.1.6.a	*Choline-sulphate sulphohydrolase*	Cholinesulphatase	
3.1.6.2	Sterol-sulphate sulphohydrolase	Sterol sulphatase	
3.1.6.3	Sugar-sulphate sulphohydrolase	Glycosulphatase	
3.1.6.4	Chondroitin-sulphate sulphohydrolase	Chondrosulphatase	
3.1.6.b	*Cellulose-sulphate sulphohydrolase*	Cellulose polysulphatase	
3.2	**Acting on glycosyl compounds**		
3.2.1	**Glycoside hydrolases**		
3.2.1.1 C	α-1,4-glucan 4-glucanohydrolase	α-amylase	Ca.[A]

Reaction	Sources, comments on specificity, etc.	References
3.1.4.5	$DNA + (n-1) H_2O =$ n oligodeoxyribonucleotides	Animal tissues, especially pancreas	*583, 1492,* *2403*
3.1.4.6	Forms 3'-nucleotides from DNA	Animal tissues, bacteria	*524, 583, 771,* *1416, 1452,* *2403*
3.1.4.7	Attacks RNA and DNA, forming 3'-nucleotides; DNA is attacked with preference for the adenine-thymine nucleotide pair	*Micrococcus*	*48*
3.1.4.a	Attacks RNA and DNA, forming 5'-nucleotides	*Azotobacter*	*2528*
3.1.4.8	Attacks RNA, forming 3'-guanylate or oligonucleotides with guanylate end groups	*Aspergillus*	*2602*
3.1.5.1	Deoxy-GTP + H_2O = deoxyguanosine + triphosphate	Bacteria Also acts on GTP	*1443*
3.1.6.1	A phenol sulphate + H_2O = a phenol + H_2SO_4	Animal tissues, plants, moulds, bacteria A group of enzymes with rather similar specificities	*637–8, 641,* *2269, 2271–2,* *2809*
3.1.6.a	Choline sulphate + H_2O = choline + H_2SO_4	*Pseudomonas*	*2605*
3.1.6.2	Dehydro*epi*androsterone 3-sulphate + H_2O = dehydro*epi*androsterone + H_2SO_4	Various invertebrates Also acts on some related sterol sulphates	*2270, 2272,* *2535*
3.1.6.3	D-glucose 6-sulphate + H_2O = D-glucose + H_2SO_4	Various invertebrates, bacteria Also acts on other sulphates of mono- and disaccharides and on adenosine 5'-sulphate	*635, 676, 790,* *2272*
3.1.6.4	Hydrolytically removes the 6-sulphate groups of the 2-acetylamino-2-deoxy-D-galactose 6-sulphate units of chondroitin sulphate	Molluscs, moulds, bacteria	*636, 639,* *1942, 2089*
3.1.6.b	Hydrolytically removes the 2- and 3-sulphate groups of the polysulphates of cellulose and charonin	Marine invertebrates	*2603*
3.2.1.1	Hydrolyses α-1,4-glucan links in polysaccharides containing three or more α-1,4-linked D-glucose units	Animal tissues, saliva, plants, moulds, bacteria Acts on starch, glycogen and related polysaccharides and oligosaccharides in random manner	*27, 333, 739,* *1707–8, 1724,* *2353, 2699*

EC No.	Systematic name	Trivial name	Active groups and [cofactors]
3.2.1.2 C	α-1,4-glucan maltohydrolase	β-amylase	
3.2.1.3	α-1,4-glucan glucohydrolase	Glucoamylase	
3.2.1.4 C	β-1,4-glucan 4-glucanohydrolase	Cellulase	
3.2.1.6	*β-1,3(4)-glucan glucanohydrolase*	Laminarinase	
3.2.1.7	Inulin 1-fructanohydrolase	Inulase	
3.2.1.8 C	Xylan 4-xylanohydrolase	Xylanase	
3.2.1.a	*Xylan 3-xylanohydrolase*	1,3-xylanase	
3.2.1.9	*Amylopectin 6-glucanohydrolase*	Amylopectin-1,6-glucosidase (Originally known as R-enzyme)	
3.2.1.b	*Dextrin 6-glucanohydrolase*	Dextrin-1,6-glucosidase (Originally known as amylo-1,6-glucosidase)	
3.2.1.10 C	*Oligodextrin 6-glucanohydrolase*	Oligo-1,6-glucosidase (Formerly known as limit dextrinase)	
3.2.1.11	α-1,6-glucan 6-glucanohydrolase	Dextranase	
3.2.1.12	Cycloheptaglucan 4-glucanohydrolase	Cycloheptaglucanase	[Ca++]
3.2.1.13	Cyclohexaglucan 4-glucanohydrolase	Cyclohexaglucanase	[Ca++]
3.2.1.14	Chitin glycanohydrolase	Chitinase	
3.2.1.15	Polygalacturonide glycanohydrolase	Polygalacturonase (Formerly known as pectinase)	
3.2.1.16	Alginate glycanohydrolase	Alginase	

	Reaction	Sources, comments on specificity, etc.	References
3.2.1.2	Hydrolyses α-1,4-glucan links in polysaccharides so as to remove successive maltose units from the non-reducing ends of the chains	Plants Acts on starch, glycogen and related polysaccharides and oligosaccharides, producing β-maltose by an inversion	*148, 772, 1707, 1807*
3.2.1.3	Hydrolyses α-1,4-glucan links in polysaccharides so as to remove successive glucose units from the non-reducing ends of the chains	Blood, moulds, bacteria Acts on starch, glycogen, and related polysaccharides and oligosaccharides	*773, 1366, 1818, 2083*
3.2.1.4	Hydrolyses β-1,4-glucan links in cellulose	*Helix*, plants, fungi, bacteria The fungal enzyme also catalyses transcellobio-sylation	*983, 1909, 1974–5, 2542, 2851–2*
3.2.1.6	Hydrolyses either β-1,3- or β-1,4-glucan links adjacent to a β-1,3-link	Plants, algae, fungi Hydrolyses laminarin; also hydrolyses lichenin to β-1,3-cellobiosyl-D-glucose	*526, 659, 1866, 1904, 2199*
3.2.1.7	Hydrolyses β-1,2-fructan links in inulin	Yeast	*16*
3.2.1.8	Hydrolyses β-1,4-xylan links	Invertebrates, plants, moulds, bacteria	*889, 1175, 1210, 2850*
3.2.1.a	Hydrolyses β-1,3-xylan links		*802*
3.2.1.9	Hydrolyses α-1,6-glucan links in amylopectin	Plants	*1115, 1673, 1707*
3.2.1.b	Hydrolyses α-1,6-glucan links in dextrins containing short 1,6-linked side chains	Animal tissues, yeast	*503, 1522, 1707*
3.2.1.10	Hydrolyses α-1,6-glucan links in isomaltose, panose and dextrins produced from starch and glycogen by α-amylase	Intestine, plants, moulds	*1519, 1521, 1673, 2699*
3.2.1.11	Hydrolyses α-1,6-glucan links	Animal tissues, moulds, bacteria	*21, 140, 531, 738, 1188, 2275*
3.2.1.12	Hydrolyses one α-1,4-glucan link in cycloheptaglucan, producing the linear heptaglucan	Moulds Produces no inversion	*206, 1405*
3.2.1.13	Hydrolyses one α-1,4-glucan link in cyclohexaglucan, producing the linear hexaglucan	Moulds Produces an inversion, giving a terminal β-configuration	*206, 1405*
3.2.1.14	Hydrolyses α-1,4-acetylamino-2-deoxy-D-glucoside links in chitin and chitodextrin	Invertebrates, plants, moulds	*1255–7, 2674, 2962–3*
3.2.1.15	Hydrolyses α-1,4-D-galact-uronide links in pectate and other polygalacturonides	Snails, a few plants, fungi, yeast, bacteria	*600, 1597, 1628, 1652, 1816, 2082*
3.2.1.16	Hydrolyses β-1,4-mannuronide links in alginate	Bacteria	*1421, 2758*

EC No.	Systematic name	Trivial name	Active groups and [cofactors]
3.2.1.17 C	N-acetylmuramide glycanohydrolase	Muramidase (Formerly known as lysozyme)	
3.2.1.18	N-acetyl-neuraminate glycohydrolase	Neuraminidase	
3.2.1.c	*Chondroitinsulphate glycanohydrolase*	Chondroitinase	
3.2.1.d	*Hyaluronate glycanohydrolase*	Hyaluronidase	
3.2.1.e	*Hyaluronate glycanohydrolase*	Hyaluronidase	
3.2.1.19	Heparin glycanohydrolase	Heparinase	
3.2.1.20	α-D-glucoside glucohydrolase	α-glucosidase	
3.2.1.21	β-D-glucoside glucohydrolase	β-glucosidase	
3.2.1.22	α-L galactoside galactohydrolase	α-galactosidase	
3.2.1.23 C	β-D-galactoside galactohydrolase	β-galactosidase	
3.2.1.24	α-D-mannoside mannohydrolase	α-mannosidase	
3.2.1.25	β-D-mannoside mannohydrolase	β-mannosidase	

	Reaction	*Sources, comments on specificity, etc.*	*References*
3.2.1.17	Probably hydrolyses β-1,4-links between N-acetylmuramic acid and 2-acetylamino-2-deoxy-D-glucose residues in a mucopolysaccharide or mucopeptide	Spleen, egg-white, nasal mucus, plant latex Dissolves the wall substance of certain bacteria; also acts slowly on chitin	*3, 40, 345, 1260–1, 1805, 2446*
3.2.1.18	Probably hydrolyses terminal α-2,6-links between N-acetylneuraminic acid and 2-acetylamino-2-deoxy-D-galactose residues in various mucopolysaccharides	Certain pathogenic bacteria and myxo-viruses	*880–2*
3.2.1.c	Hydrolyses β-1,4-links between 2-acetylamino-2-deoxy-D-galactose sulphate and D-glucuronate residues in chondroitin sulphate	Bacteria Also hydrolyses hyaluronate	*1740*
3.2.1.d	Hydrolyses links between 2-acetylamino-2-deoxy-D-glucose and D-glucuronate residues in hyaluronate	Testis, snake venom Also acts on chondroitin and mucoitin sulphates; can catalyse transglycosylation	*1806, 2176, 2836*
3.2.1.e	Hydrolyses β-1,3-links between D-glucuronate and 2-acetyl-amino-2-deoxy-D-glucose residues in hyaluronate	Leech	*1600*
3.2.1.19	Hydrolyses α-1,4-links between 2-amino-2-deoxy-D-glucose and D-glucuronic acid residues in heparin	Liver, kidney	*1249–50, 1423–4*
3.2.1.20	An α-D-glucoside + H_2O = an alcohol + D-glucose	Widely distributed Wide specificity for α-D-glucopyranoside, varying with source; also catalyses glucotransferase reactions	*182, 1517, 1586, 2274, 2854*
3.2.1.21	A β-D-glucoside + H_2O = an alcohol + D-glucose	Animal tissues, plants, moulds, bacteria Wide specificity for β-D-glucopyranosides; possibly acts also on β-D-galactosides Also catalyses glucotransferase reactions	*486, 522, 532, 1091, 1517, 1928*
3.2.1.22	An α-D-galactoside + H_2O = an alcohol + D-galactose	Plants, yeast, bacteria	*1128, 2725*
3.2.1.23	A β-D-galactoside + H_2O = an alcohol + D-galactose	Plants, moulds, bacteria Also catalyses galactotrans-ferase reactions	*488, 1478, 1508, 2775–7*
3.2.1.24	An α-D-mannoside + H_2O = an alcohol + D-mannose	Animal tissues, plants, actinomycetes	*487, 1117, 2725*
3.2.1.25	A β-D-mannoside + H_2O = an alcohol + D-mannose	Yeast Substrates include mannan gums	*16, 599*

EC No.	Systematic name	Trivial name	Active groups and [cofactors]
3.2.1.f	*β-D-xyloside xylohydrolase*	β-xylosidase, xylobiase	
3.2.1.26	β-D-fructofuranoside fructohydrolase	β-fructofuranosidase (Formerly known as invertase, saccharase, sucrase, etc.)	
3.2.1.27	Nigerose 3-glucohydrolase	α-1,3-glucosidase	
3.2.1.28	Trehalose 1-glucohydrolase	Trehalase	
3.2.1.29	Chitobiose acetylaminodeoxyglucohydrolase	Chitobiase	
3.2.1.30	β-2-acetylamino-2-deoxy-D-glucoside acetylaminodeoxyglucohydrolase	β-acetylaminodeoxy-glucosidase	
3.2.1.31	β-D-glucuronide glucuronohydrolase	β-glucuronidase	

3.2.2 Hydrolyzing N-glycosyl compounds

3.2.2.1	N-ribosyl-purine ribohydrolase	Nucleosidase	
3.2.2.2	Inosine ribohydrolase	Inosinase	
3.2.2.3	Uridine ribohydrolase	Uridine nucleosidase	
3.2.2.4	AMP phosphoribohydrolase	AMP nucleosidase	[PP.M^{++}]
3.2.2.5	NAD glycohydrolase	NAD nucleosidase	
3.2.2.6	NAD(P) glycohydrolase	NAD(P) nucleosidase	

3.2.3 Hydrolysing S-glycosyl compounds

3.2.3.1	*Thioglucoside glucohydrolase*	Thioglucosidase	

3.3 Acting on ether bonds

3.3.1 Thioether hydrolases

3.3.1.1	S-adenosyl-L-homocysteine hydrolase	Adenosylhomocysteinase	

	Reaction	Sources, comments on specificity, etc.	References
3.2.1.f	A β-D-xyloside + H_2O = an alcohol + D-xylose	Bacteria Removes single xylose residues from a β-1,4-xylan; also hydrolyses xylobiose	1175
3.2.1.26	A β-D-fructofuranoside + H_2O = an alcohol + D-fructose	Plants, moulds, yeast Substrates include sucrose; also catalyses fructotransferase reactions	124, 182–3, 1061, 1915, 1943
3.2.1.27	Nigerose + H_2O = 2 D-glucose	Intestinal mucosa Acts also on other α-1,3-D-glucosides	1518
3.2.1.28	Trehalose + H_2O = 2 D-glucose	Insects, moulds, yeast Acts also on 6-substituted trehalose derivatives	1292, 1917
3.2.1.29	Chitobiose + H_2O = 2 2-acetylamino-2-deoxy-D-glucose	Invertebrates, plants, moulds	2962–3
3.2.1.30	β-phenyl-2-acetylamino-2-deoxy-D-glucoside + H_2O = phenol + 2-acetylamino-2-deoxy-D-glucose	Animal tissues, plants, moulds	732, 2121, 2915, 2962–3
3.2.1.31	A β-D-glucuronide + H_2O = an alcohol + D-glucuronic acid	Animal tissues, plants, bacteria Also catalyses glucuronotransferase reactions	652, 743–4, 1564–6, 1730, 1827, 2434, 2750
3.2.2.1	An N-ribosyl-purine + H_2O = a purine + D-ribose	Fish muscle, plants, yeast, bacteria	1069, 1288, 1507, 2115, 2231, 2601, 2618
3.2.2.2	Inosine + H_2O = hypoxanthine + D-ribose	Fish muscle, bacteria	1413, 2618
3.2.2.3	Uridine + H_2O = uracil + D-ribose	Yeast	411
3.2.2.4	AMP + H_2O = adenine + D-ribose 5-phosphate	Bacteria	1197
3.2.2.5	NAD + H_2O = nicotinamide + R	Erythrocytes R-nicotinamide represents NAD	1121
3.2.2.6	NAD(P) + H_2O = nicotinamide + (P)R	Animal tissues, moulds, bacteria Also catalyses R-transferase reactions	50, 2959–60
3.2.3.1	A thioglycoside + H_2O = a thiol + a sugar	Animal tissues, plants Has a wide specificity for thioglycosides	507, 869, 2088
3.3.1.1	S-adenosyl-L-homocysteine + H_2O = adenosine + L-homocysteine	Liver	586

EC No.	Systematic name	Trivial name	Active groups and [cofactors]
3.4	**Acting on peptide bonds (peptide hydrolases)** Few systematic names are possible in this section		
	3.4.1 α-aminopeptide aminoacidohydrolases		
3.4.1.1		Leucine aminopeptidase	[M⁺⁺]
3.4.1.2		Aminopeptidase	
3.4.1.3		Aminotripeptidase	
3.4.1.a		Proline iminopeptidase	
	3.4.2 α-carboxypeptide aminoacidohydrolases		
3.4.2.1 C		Carboxypeptidase A	Zn
3.4.2.2		Carboxypeptidase B (Formerly known as protaminase)	Zn
3.4.2.3		Yeast carboxypeptidase	
	3.4.3 Dipeptide hydrolases		
3.4.3.1	Glycyl-glycine hydrolase	Glycyl-glycine dipeptidase	[Co⁺⁺]
3.4.3.2	Glycyl-L-leucine hydrolase	Glycyl-leucine dipeptidase	[M⁺⁺]
3.4.3.3	Aminoacyl-L-histidine hydrolase	Aminoacyl-histidine dipeptidase, carnosinase	[M⁺⁺]
3.4.3.4	Aminoacyl-1-methyl-L-histidine hydrolase	Aminoacyl-methylhistidine dipeptidase, Anserinase	[Zn⁺⁺]
3.4.3.5	L-cysteinyl-glycine hydrolase	Cysteinyl-glycine dipeptidase	[M⁺⁺]
3.4.3.6		Iminodipeptidase	[M⁺⁺]
3.4.3.7		Imidodipeptidase, Prolidase	[Mn⁺⁺]

	Reaction	Sources, comments on specificity, etc.	References
3.4.1.1	Hydrolyses L-peptides, splitting off N-terminal residues with a free α-amino group, especially when the N-terminal residue is leucine or a related amino-acid	Animal tissues, intestinal secretion, yeast	1101, 2438, 2444, 2478
3.4.1.2	Hydrolyses dipeptides and tripeptides, splitting off the N-terminal residue	Semen	1634
3.4.1.3	Hydrolyses tripeptides containing neutral amino-acid residues, splitting off the N-terminal residue	Animal tissues	11, 26, 691, 2682
3.4.1.a	Hydrolyses L-peptides, splitting off the N-terminal L-proline residues	Bacteria	2304
3.4.2.1	Hydrolyses peptides, splitting off the C-terminal L-amino-acid residue unless this is a basic residue or proline	Pancreatic juice Formed from pro-carboxy-peptidase A	76, 1956, 1996, 2438, 2710
3.4.2.2	Hydrolyses peptides having a C-terminal lysine or arginine residue, splitting off this residue	Pancreatic juice	758, 1956
3.4.2.3	Hydrolyses peptides having a C-terminal glycine or leucine residue, splitting off this residue	Yeast	722
3.4.3.1	Hydrolyses glycyl-glycine and sarcosyl-glycine	Animal tissues, plants	613, 2436
3.4.3.2	Hydrolyses glycyl-L-leucine	Animal tissues	2437
3.4.3.3	Hydrolyses dipeptides of L-histidine and their amides	Animal tissues	999, 2251, 2438
3.4.3.4	Anserine $+ H_2O =$ β-alanine $+$ 1-methyl-L-histidine	Fish muscle	1267
3.4.3.5	Hydrolyses L-cysteinyl-glycine	Animal tissues	248, 2372
3.4.3.6	Hydrolyses dipeptides or amides in which a proline residue provides an α-imino end group	Animal tissues	564, 1952, 2438
3.4.3.7	Hydrolyses dipeptides in which a proline residue is bound by its imino group	Animal tissues	12, 14, 565

EC No.	Systematic name	Trivial name	Active groups and [cofactors]
	3.4.4 Peptide Peptidohydrolases		
3.4.4.1 C		Pepsin	
3.4.4.2		Pepsin B (Formerly known as parapepsin)	
3.4.4.a C		Gastricsin	
3.4.4.3 C		Rennin	
3.4.4.4 C		Trypsin	
3.4.4.5 C		Chymotrypsin	
3.4.4.6 C		Chymotrypsin B	
3.4.4.7 C		Pancreatopeptidase E (Formerly known as elastase)	
3.4.4.8		Enteropeptidase (Formerly known as enterokinase)	
3.4.4.9		Cathepsin C	[S]
3.4.4.b		Cathepsin D	
3.4.4.10 C		Papain	[S]
3.4.4.11 C		Chymopapain	[S]

	Reaction	*Sources,* *comments on specificity, etc.*	*References*
3.4.4.1	Hydrolyses peptides, including those with bonds adjacent to aromatic or dicarboxylic L-amino-acid residues	Gastric juice Formed from pepsinogen	*303, 1083,* *1988, 1990–1,* *1996, 2621*
3.4.4.2	Hydrolyses peptides; the specificity is similar to that of 3.4.4.1	Gastric juice Formed from pepsinogen B	*2282*
3.4.4.a	Hydrolyses peptides	Human gastric juice Optimum pH when acting on haemoglobin is 3, higher than that for 3.4.4.1	*2616*
3.4.4.3	Hydrolyses peptides; specificity may be similar to that of 3.4.4.1	Gastric juice of young animals Formed from prorennin	*235–6, 741*
3.4.4.4	Hydrolyses peptides, amides, esters, etc., at bonds involving the carboxyl groups of L-arginine or L-lysine	Pancreatic juice Formed from trypsinogen	*597, 1495,* *1994, 1996,* *2569*
3.4.4.5	Hydrolyses peptides, amides, esters, etc., especially at bonds involving the carboxyl groups of aromatic L-amino-acids	Pancreatic juice Formed from chymotrypsinogen; a number of chymotrypsins are formed, according to the number of bonds hydrolysed in the precursor	*596, 643, 1487,* *1494, 1955,* *1996*
3.4.4.6	Specificity similar to 3.4.4.5	Pancreatic juice Formed from chymotrypsinogen B	*342*
3.4.4.7	Hydrolyses peptides, especially at bonds adjacent to neutral amino-acid residues	Pancreas	*154, 886, 982,* *1579–80, 1703,* *1930*
3.4.4.8	Hydrolyses peptides; converts trypsinogen into trypsin	Intestinal secretion	*1489, 1996,* *2936*
3.4.4.9	Hydrolyses peptides, especially at bonds involving an aromatic amino-acid adjacent to a free α-amino group	Animal tissues	*794, 2610*
3.4.4.b	Hydrolyses peptides; its specificity is somewhat similar to 3.4.4.1, but more restricted	Spleen	*1516, 2117*
3.4.4.10	Hydrolyses peptides, amides and esters, especially at bonds involving basic amino-acids, or leucine or glycine	*Carica papaya* latex	*147, 1259,* *1380–1, 2445*
3.4.4.11	Hydrolyses peptides, etc.; its specificity is similar to that of 3.4.4.10	*Carica papaya* latex	*1240*

EC No.	Systematic name	Trivial name	Active groups and [cofactors]
3.4.4.12 C		Ficin	[S]
3.4.4.c		Bromelain	[S]
3.4.4.13		Thrombin	[Ca++]
3.4.4.14		Plasmin (Formerly known as fibrinolysin)	
3.4.4.15		Renin	
3.4.4.16 C		Subtilopeptidase A (Formerly known as subtilisin)	
3.4.4.17 C		Aspergillopeptidase A	
3.4.4.18 C		*Streptococcus* peptidase A	
3.4.4.19		Clostridiopeptidase A (Formerly known as collagenase)	[M++]
3.4.4.20		Clostridiopeptidase B	

Many peptidases other than those listed above undoubtedly exist. Many of these have mexicanain, tabermontanain, euphorbain, solanain, bacterial proteinase, yeast

3.5   Acting on C–N bonds, other than peptide bonds

3.5.1   In linear amides

3.5.1.1	L-asparagine amidohydrolase	Asparaginase	
3.5.1.2	L-glutamine amidohydrolase	Glutaminase	[A]
3.5.1.3	ω-amidodicarboxylate amidohydrolase	ω-amidase	
3.5.1.4	Acylamide amidohydrolase	Amidase	
3.5.1.5 C	Urea amidohydrolase	Urease	[P]

Reaction	Sources, comments on specificity, etc.	References
3.4.4.12 Hydrolyses peptides, amides and esters; its specificity is similar to that of 3.4.4.10	Latex of *Ficus* sp.	*2445, 2778*
3.4.4.c Hydrolyses peptides, amides and esters; its specificity is somewhat similar to that of 3.4.4.10	Pineapple stems	*1901*
3.4.4.13 Hydrolyses peptides, amides and esters of L-arginine; converts fibrinogen into fibrin	Blood serum Formed from prothrombin	*2386, 2801*
3.4.4.14 Hydrolyses peptides and esters of L-arginine and L-lysine; converts fibrin into soluble products	Blood serum Formed from plasminogen	*2, 245, 2206, 2675*
3.4.4.15 Converts hypertensinogen into hypertensin	Kidney	*963–4*
3.4.4.16 Hydrolyses peptides; converts ovalbumin into plakalbumin	*B. subtilis* Also hydrolyses some simple aliphatic esters	*883, 952–3, 970, 972*
3.4.4.17 Hydrolyses peptides, especially at bonds involving the carboxyl groups of arginine or leucine; converts trypsinogen into trypsin	*Aspergillus saitoi*	*518, 1842*
3.4.4.18 Hydrolyses peptides and amides; shows wide specificity, but does not attack bonds close to a glycine residue	*Streptococcus*	*687*
3.4.4.19 Hydrolyses peptides containing proline, including collagen and gelatin	*Clostridium*	*246, 575, 1415, 1703, 2364*
3.4.4.20 Hydrolyses peptides at bonds involving arginine residues	*Clostridium*	*575, 2015*
been described under such names as cathepsins, asclepain, pinguinain, polypeptidase, etc.		*409, 910, 970, 2439, 2445, 2673, 2738*
3.5.1.1 L-asparagine + H_2O = L-aspartate + NH_3	Plants, yeast, bacteria	*888, 939, 984*
3.5.1.2 L-glutamine + H_2O = L-glutamate + NH_3	Animal tissues, protozoa, bacteria	*85, 1186, 1399 2036*
3.5.1.3 An ω-amido-dicarboxylic acid + H_2O = a dicarboxylic acid + NH_3	Animal tissues Acts on glutaramate, succinamate, and the corresponding α-keto-ω-amido-acids	*1786*
3.5.1.4 A monocarboxylic acid amide + H_2O = a monocarboxylic acid + NH_3	Animal tissues	*318–9*
3.5.1.5 Urea + H_2O = CO_2 + 2 NH_3	Plants, moulds, bacteria	*2565*

EC No.	Systematic name	Trivial name	Active groups and [cofactors]
3.5.1.6	N-carbamoyl-β-alanine amidohydrolase	β-ureidopropionase	
3.5.1.7	N-carbamoyl-L-aspartate amidohydrolase	Ureidosuccinase	[M^{++}.S]
3.5.1.8	N-formyl-aspartate amidohydrolase	Formylaspartate deformylase	[Fe^{++}]
3.5.1.9	Aryl-formylamine amidohydrolase	Formamidase	
3.5.1.a	*Aryl-acylamide amidohydrolase*	Aryl acylamidase	
3.5.1.10	10-formyltetrahydrofolate amidohydrolase	Formyltetrahydrofolate deformylase	
3.5.1.11	Benzylpenicillin amidohydrolase	Penicillin amidase	
3.5.1.12	*p*-biotinylaminobenzoate amidohydrolase	Biotinidase	[M^{++}]
3.5.1.b	*N-acylaminoacid amidohydrolase*	Aminoacylase I (Formerly known as dehydropeptidase II, or hippuricase)	
3.5.1.c	*N-acylaspartate amidohydrolase*	Aspartoacylase (Originally known as aminoacylase II)	
3.5.1.d	*α-N-acetyl-L-ornithine amidohydrolase*	Acetylornithine deacetylase	[Co^{++}]
3.5.1.e	*ε-N-acyl-L-lysine amidohydrolase*	Acyl-lysine deacylase	
3.5.1.f	*N-succinyl-L-2,6-diaminopimelate amidohydrolase*	Succinyldiaminopimelate desuccinylase	

3.5.2 In cyclic amides

3.5.2.1	Barbiturate amidohydrolase	Barbiturase	
3.5 2.2	4,5-dihydropyrimidine amidohydrolase	Dihydropyrimidinase (Originally known as hydantoinase)	[M^{++}]
3.5.2.3	L-4,5-dihydro-orotate amidohydrolase	Dihydro-orotase	
3.5.2.4	L-5-carboxymethylhydantoin amidohydrolase	Carboxymethylhydantoinase	
3.5.2.5	Allantoin amidohydrolase	Allantoinase	

Reaction	Sources, comments on specificity, etc.	References
3.5.1.6	N-carbamoyl-β-alanine + H_2O = β-alanine + CO_2 + NH_3	Liver, bacteria The animal enzyme also acts on β-ureido-isobutyrate	388, 402, 934
3.5.1.7	N-carbamoyl-L-aspartate + H_2O = L-aspartate + CO_2 + NH_3	Bacteria	1588
3.5.1.8	N-formyl-L-aspartate + H_2O = formate + L-aspartate	Bacteria	2018
3.5.1.9	N-formyl-L-kynurenine + H_2O = formate + L-kynurenine	Liver, moulds, bacteria Also acts on other aromatic formylamines	1041, 1232, 1778
3.5.1.a	An N-acyl-anilide + H_2O = a fatty acid + aniline	Chick kidney Also acts on para-substituted acyl-anilides	1969
3.5.1.10	10-formyl-tetrahydrofolate + H_2O = formate + tetrahydrofolate	Liver	1181
3.5.1.11	Benzylpenicillin + H_2O = phenylacetate + penicin	Moulds	2290
3.5.1.12	p-biotinylaminobenzoate + H_2O = biotin + p-aminobenzoate	Animal tissues Also acts on other biotinides	2642
3.5.1.b	An N-acyl-aminoacid + H_2O = a fatty acid + an aminoacid	Animal tissues, fungi, bacteria Wide specificity; also hydrolyses dehydro-peptides	250–1, 759, 918, 2054
3.5.1.c	N-acyl-aspartate + H_2O = a fatty acid + aspartate	Kidney	250–1
3.5.1.d	α-N-acetyl-L-ornithine + H_2O = acetic acid + L-ornithine	Bacteria Also hydrolyses N-acetyl-methionine	2739, 2741
3.5.1.e	ϵ-N-acyl-L-lysine + H_2O = a fatty acid + L-lysine	Animal tissues	2042
3.5.1.f	N-succinyl-L-2,6-diamino-pimelate + H_2O = succinate + L-2,6-diamino-pimelate	Bacteria	1382
3.5.2.1	Barbiturate + $2H_2O$ = malonate + urea	Bacteria	1035
3.5.2.2	4,5-dihydrouracil + H_2O = 3-ureidopropionic acid	Animal tissues, plants Also acts on hydantoin and dihydrothymine	664, 934–5, 2773
3.5.2.3	L-4,5-dihydro-orotate + H_2O = N-carbamoyl-L-aspartate	Liver, bacteria	499, 1587
3.5.2.4	L-5-carboxymethyl-hydantoin + H_2O = N-carbamoyl-L-aspartate	Bacteria	1587
3.5.2.5	Allantoin + H_2O = allantoic acid	Amphibia, certain invertebrates, plants, yeast	346, 754

EC No.	Systematic name	Trivial name	Active groups and [cofactors]
3.5.2.6 C	Penicillin amidohydrolase	Penicillinase	
3.5.2.a	*4-imidazolone-5-propionate amidohydrolase*	Imidazolonepropionase	

3.5.3 In linear amidines

EC No.	Systematic name	Trivial name	Active groups and [cofactors]
3.5.3.1 C	L-arginine ureohydrolase	Arginase	[M^{++}]
3.5.3.2	Guanidinoacetate ureohydrolase	Glycocyaminase	[Mn^{++}]
3.5.3.3	Creatinine ureohydrolase	Creatininase	
3.5.3.4	Allantoate ureohydrolase	Allantoicase	
3.5.3.5	N-formimino-L-aspartate iminohydrolase	Formiminoaspartate deiminase	
3.5.3.6	L-arginine iminohydrolase	Arginine deiminase	

3.5.4 In cyclic amidines

EC No.	Systematic name	Trivial name	Active groups and [cofactors]
3.5.4.1	Cytosine aminohydrolase	Cytosine deaminase	
3.5.4.2	Adenine aminohydrolase	Adenine deaminase (Originally known as adenase)	
3.5.4.3	Guanine aminohydrolase	Guanine deaminase (Originally known as guanase)	
3.5.4.a	*Pterin aminohydrolase*	Pterin deaminase	
3.5.4.4	Adenosine aminohydrolase	Adenosine deaminase	
3.5.4.5	Cytidine aminohydrolase	Cytidine deaminase	
3.5.4.6 C	AMP aminohydrolase	AMP deaminase	
3.5.4.b	*Deoxy-CMP aminohydrolase*	Deoxy-CMP deaminase	
3.5.4.7	ADP aminohydrolase	ADP deaminase	
3.5.4.8	4-aminoimidazole aminohydrolase	Aminoimidazolase	
3.5.4.9	5,10-methenyltetrahydrofolate 5-hydrolase (decyclizing)	Methenyltetrahydrofolate cyclohydrolase	

	Reaction	Sources, comments on specificity, etc.	References
3.5.2.6	Penicillin + H_2O = penicilloic acid	Bacteria	2102
3.5.2.a	4-imidazolone-5-propionate + H_2O = N-formimino-L-glutamate	Animal tissues, bacteria	2168, 2465
3.5.3.1	L-arginine + H_2O = L-ornithine + urea	Animal tissues, plants. Also hydrolyses α-N-substituted L-arginines and canavanine	120–1, 377, 911–2
3.5.3.2	Guanidinoacetate + H_2O = glycine + urea	Bacteria	2237
3.5.3.3	Creatinine + H_2O = sarcosine + urea	Bacteria	2237
3.5.3.4	Allantoate + H_2O = glyoxylate + 2 urea	Amphibia, certain invertebrates	754
3.5.3.5	N-formimino-L-aspartate + H_2O = N-formyl-L-aspartate + NH_3	Bacteria	693
3.5.3.6	L-arginine + H_2O = L-citrulline + NH_3	Animal tissues, yeast, bacteria. Also acts on canavanine	2014, 2081, 2177, 2236
3.5.4.1	Cytosine + H_2O = uracil + NH_3	Animal tissues, yeast, bacteria. Also acts on 5-methyl-cytosine	436, 467, 1035, 1458
3.5.4.2	Adenine + H_2O = hypoxanthine + NH_3	Animal tissues, bacteria	273, 1071
3.5.4.3	Guanine + H_2O = xanthine + NH_3	Animal tissues, adapted yeast, bacteria. Also acts on 1-methylguanine	1112, 1286, 2139
3.5.4.a	A pterin + H_2O = a lumazine + NH_3	Bacteria	1557
3.5.4.4	Adenosine + H_2O = inosine + NH_3	Animal tissues, moulds, bacteria	1285–6, 1305, 2115
3.5.4.5	Cytidine + H_2O = uridine + NH_3	Animal tissues, plants, yeast, bacteria	493, 2231, 2335, 2780
3.5.4.6	AMP + H_2O = IMP + NH_3	Animal tissues, plants	1285–6, 1530, 1797, 1968, 2689, 2823
3.5.4.b	Deoxy-CMP + H_2O = deoxy-UMP + NH_3	Sea-urchin eggs. Also acts on some 5-substituted deoxy-CMPs	2317–8
3.5.4.7	ADP + H_2O = IDP + NH_3	Muscle	601
3.5.4.8	4-aminoimidazole + H_2O = unidentified product + NH_3	Bacteria	2142
3.5.4.9	5,10-methenyltetrahydro-folate + H_2O = 10-formyltetrahydrofolate	Liver, bacteria	2140, 2596

EC No.	Systematic name	Trivial name	Active groups and [cofactors]
3.5.4.10	IMP 1,2-hydrolase (decyclizing)	IMP cyclohydrolase	

3.5.99   In other compounds

3.5.99.1	Riboflavin hydrolase	Riboflavinase	
3.5.99.2 C	Thiamine hydrolase	Thiaminase II	

3.6   Acting on acid anhydride bonds

3.6.1   In phosphoryl-containing anhydrides

3.6.1.1 C	Pyrophosphate phosphohydrolase	Inorganic pyrophosphatase	[Mg^{++}]
3.6.1.2	Trimetaphosphate phosphohydrolase	Trimetaphosphatase	[M^{++}]
3.6.1.a	*Pyrophosphate phosphohydrolase*	Pyrophosphatase	
3.6.1.3	ATP phosphohydrolase	ATPase (myosin)	[Ca^{++}]
3.6.1.4	ATP phosphohydrolase	ATPase	[Mg^{++}]
3.6.1.5	ATP diphosphohydrolase	Apyrase	[Ca^{++}]
3.6.1.6	Nucleosidediphosphate phosphohydrolase	Nucleosidediphosphatase	[Mg^{++}]
3.6.1.7	Acylphosphate phosphohydrolase	Acylphosphatase	
3.6.1.8	ATP pyrophosphohydrolase	ATPase	
3.6.1.b	*Deoxy-CTP nucleotidohydrolase*	Deoxy-CTPase	
3.6.1.9	Dinucleotide nucleotidohydrolase	Nucleotide pyrophosphatase	
3.6.1.10	Polyphosphate polyphosphohydrolase	Polyphosphatase	

Reaction	Sources, comments on specificity, etc.	References
3.5.4.10	IMP + H_2O = 5'-phosphoribosyl-5-formamido-4-imidazole-carboxamide	Liver	748
3.5.99.1	Riboflavin + H_2O = ribitol + lumichrome	Bacteria	2940
3.5.99.2	Thiamine + H_2O = 2-methyl-4-amino-5-hydroxy-methyl-pyrimidine + 4-methyl-5-(2'-hydroxy-ethyl)-thiazole	Bacteria	799, 1206
3.6.1.1	Pyrophosphate + H_2O = 2 orthophosphate	Widely distributed	137, 1068, 1491, 1919, 2160
3.6.1.2	Trimetaphosphate + H_2O = triphosphate	Animal tissues, yeast	1444, 1811
3.6.1.a	Pyrophosphate + H_2O = 2 orthophosphate	Plants Low specificity; hydrolyses ATP, ADP and inorganic pyrophosphate at about the same rate	763, 1960
3.6.1.3	ATP + H_2O = ADP + orthophosphate	Muscle Also acts on ITP, CTP, GTP, UTP and triphosphate	787, 931, 1374, 1376, 1932, 2074
3.6.1.4	ATP + H_2O = ADP + orthophosphate	Animal tissues Also acts on ITP, and possibly on ADP	379, 857, 1377, 2072
3.6.1.5	ATP + H_2O = ADP + orthophosphate	Plants Also acts on ADP	1283, 1467
3.6.1.6	A nucleoside diphosphate + H_2O = a nucleotide + orthophosphate	Liver, kidney Acts on IDP, GDP, UDP, and also on D-ribose 5-pyrophosphate	827, 1160, 2095
3.6.1.7	An acylphosphate + H_2O = an acid + orthophosphate	Widely distributed	1603, 2161
3.6.1.8	ATP + H_2O = AMP + pyrophosphate	Animal tissues, snake venom Also acts on ITP	1070, 1258
3.6.1.b	Deoxy-CTP + H_2O = deoxy-CMP + pyrophosphate	Phage-infected bacteria Also hydrolyses deoxy-CDP to deoxy-CMP and orthophosphate	2970
3.6.1.9	A dinucleotide + H_2O = 2 mononucleotides	Animal tissues, snake venom, plants Substrates include NAD, ADP, FAD, CoA and also also ATP and ADP	1228a, 1434, 1999, 2580
3.6.1.10	Polyphosphate + n H_2O = n pentaphosphate	Moulds, yeast	1695

EC No.	*Systematic name*	*Trivial name*	*Active groups and [cofactors]*
3.7	**Acting on C–C bonds**		
	3.7.1 In ketonic substances		
3.7.1.1	Oxaloacetate acetylhydrolase	Oxaloacetase	[Mn++]
3.7.1.2	4-fumarylacetoacetate fumarylhydrolase	Fumarylacetoacetase (Formerly known as β-diketonase)	
3.8	**Acting on halide bonds**		
	3.8.1 In C-halide compounds		
3.8.1.1	Alkyl-halide halidohydrolase	Alkylhalidase	[S]
	3.8.2 In P-halide compounds		
3.8.2.1	Di-isopropylphosphorofluoridate fluorohydrolase	DFPase	[M++]
3.9	**Acting on P–N bonds**		
3.9.1.1	Phosphoamide hydrolase	Phosphoamidase	

4 LYASES

4.1 Carbon-carbon lyases

4.1.1 Carboxy-lyases

EC No.	Systematic name	Trivial name	Active groups
4.1.1.1	2-oxo-acid carboxy-lyase	Pyruvate decarboxylase (Formerly known as α-carboxylase)	[T.M++]
4.1.1.2	Oxalate carboxy-lyase	Oxalate decarboxylase	
4.1.1.3 C	Oxaloacetate carboxy-lyase	Oxaloacetate decarboxylase	[M++]
4.1.1.4	Acetoacetate carboxy-lyase	Acetoacetate decarboxylase	
4.1.1.5	2-acetolactate carboxy-lyase	Acetolactate decarboxylase	[Mn++]
4.1.1.6	*cis*-aconitate carboxy-lyase	Aconitate decarboxylase	
4.1.1.a	*3-oxo-L-gulonate carboxy-lyase*	Oxo-L-gulonate decarboxylase	
4.1.1.7	Benzoylformate carboxy-lyase	Benzoylformate decarboxylase	[T]
4.1.1.8	Oxalyl-CoA carboxy-lyase	Oxalyl-CoA decarboxylase	[T]
4.1.1.9	Malonyl-CoA carboxy-lyase	Malonyl-CoA decarboxylase	
4.1.1.10	Aminomalonate carboxy-lyase	Aminomalonate decarboxylase	
4.1.1.11	L-aspartate 1-carboxy-lyase	Aspartate 1-decarboxylase	[Py]

Reaction	Sources, comments on specificity, etc.	References
3.7.1.1 Oxaloacetate $+ H_2O =$ oxalate $+$ acetate	Moulds	1040
3.7.1.2 4-fumarylacetoacetate $+ H_2O =$ acetoacetate $+$ fumarate	Liver Also acts on other 3,5- and 2,4-diketoacids	491, 674, 1785, 2183
3.8.1.1 $CH_2BrCl + H_2O =$ $H . CHO + HBr + HCl$	Liver	1073
3.8.2.1 Di-isopropyl phosphorofluoridate $+ H_2O =$ di-isopropyl phosphate $+$ HF	Animal tissues, bacteria Acts on other organophosphorus compounds and 'nerve gases'	99, 462, 1883-6
3.9.1.1 Phosphocreatine $+ H_2O =$ creatine $+$ orthophosphate	Animal tissues, snake venom, plants Also acts on phospho-arginine and other phospho-amides	322, 2408, 2568, 2759
4.1.1.1 a 2-oxo-acid $=$ an aldehyde $+ CO_2$	Plants, yeast, bacteria Also catalyses acyloin formation	902, 1147, 2416-7
4.1.1.2 Oxalate $=$ formate $+ CO_2$	Fungi	2389-90
4.1.1.3 Oxaloacetate $=$ pyruvate $+ CO_2$	Animal tissues, bacteria	506, 1075
4.1.1.4 Acetoacetate $=$ acetone $+ CO_2$	*Clostridium*	560
4.1.1.5 $(+)$-2-acetolactate $=$ $(-)$-acetoin $+ CO_2$	Bacteria	1278, 2798
4.1.1.6 *cis*-aconitate $=$ itaconate $+ CO_2$	Moulds	208
4.1.1.a 3-oxo-L-gulonate $=$ L-xylulose $+ CO_2$	Animal tissues	2888
4.1.1.7 Benzoylformate $=$ benzaldehyde $+ CO_2$	Bacteria	951
4.1.1.8 Oxalyl-CoA $=$ formyl-CoA $+ CO_2$	Bacteria	1238, 2135
4.1.1.9 Malonyl-CoA $=$ acetyl-CoA $+ CO_2$	Animal tissues, bacteria	1032
4.1.1.10 Aminomalonate $=$ glycine $+ CO_2$	Animal tissues	2392
4.1.1.11 L-aspartate $=$ β-alanine $+ CO_2$	Bacteria	547, 806

EC No.	Systematic name	Trivial name	Active groups and [cofactors]
4.1.1.12	L-aspartate 4-carboxy-lyase	Aspartate 4-decarboxylase	[Py]
4.1.1.13	N-carbamoyl-L-aspartate 1-carboxy-lyase	Carbamoylaspartate decarboxylase	
4.1.1.14	L-valine carboxy-lyase	Valine decarboxylase	[Py]
4.1.1.15	L-glutamate 1-carboxy-lyase	Glutamate decarboxylase	[Py]
4.1.1.16	3-hydroxy-L-glutamate 1-carboxy-lyase	Hydroxyglutamate decarboxylase	[Py]
4.1.1.17	L-ornithine carboxy-lyase	Ornithine decarboxylase	[Py]
4.1.1.18	L-lysine carboxy-lyase	Lysine decarboxylase	[Py]
4.1.1.19	L-arginine carboxy-lyase	Arginine decarboxylase	[Py]
4.1.1.20	*meso*-2,6-diaminopimelate carboxy-lyase	Diaminopimelate decarboxylase	[Py]
4.1.1.21	5′-phosphoribosyl-5-amino-4-imidazolecarboxylate carboxy-lyase	Phosphoribosyl-amino-imidazole carboxylase	
4.1.1.22	L-histidine carboxy-lyase	Histidine decarboxylase	[Py.M^{++}]
4.1.1.23	Orotidine-5′-phosphate carboxy-lyase	Orotidine-5′-phosphate decarboxylase	
4.1.1.24	Aminobenzoate carboxy-lyase	Aminobenzoate decarboxylase	[Py.M^{++}]
4.1.1.25	L-tyrosine carboxy-lyase	Tyrosine decarboxylase	[Py]
4.1.1.26	3,4-dihydroxy-L-phenylalanine carboxy-lyase	DOPA decarboxylase	[Py]
4.1.1.27	L-tryptophan carboxy-lyase	Tryptophan decarboxylase	
4.1.1.28	5-hydroxy-L-tryptophan carboxy-lyase	Hydroxytryptophan decarboxylase	[Py]
4.1.1.b	*UDPglucuronate carboxy-lyase*	UDPglucuronate decarboxylase	
4.1.1.29	L-cysteinesulphinate carboxy-lyase	Cysteinesulphinate decarboxylase	[Py.S]

	Reaction	Sources, comments on specificity, etc.	References
4.1.1.12	L-aspartate = L-alanine + CO_2	Bacteria	244, 1789
4.1.1.13	N-carbamoyl-L-aspartate = carbamoyl-β-alanine + CO_2	Bacteria	934
4.1.1.14	L-valine = isobutylamine + CO_2	Bacteria. Also acts on L-leucine	1383a
4.1.1.15	L-glutamate = 4-aminobutyrate + CO_2	Brain, plants, yeast, bacteria. The brain enzyme also acts on L-cysteate and L-cysteine-sulphinate	566, 765, 806, 1468, 2324, 2394, 2619
4.1.1.16	3-hydroxy-L-glutamate = 3-hydroxy-4-aminobutyrate + CO_2	Bacteria	2697
4.1.1.17	L-ornithine = putrescine + CO_2	Bacteria	806, 2619
4.1.1.18	L-lysine = cadaverine + CO_2	Bacteria. Also acts on 5-hydroxy-L-lysine	806, 810, 1595, 2384
4.1.1.19	L-arginine = agmatine + CO_2	Bacteria	806, 2385, 2619
4.1.1.20	meso-2,6-diaminopimelate = L-lysine + CO_2	Bacteria	602
4.1.1.21	5′-phosphoribosyl-5-amino-4-imidazolecarboxylate = 5′-phosphoribosyl-5-amino-imidazole + CO_2	Liver	1629
4.1.1.22	L-histidine = histamine + CO_2	Animal tissues, bacteria	703, 806, 1144, 1146, 2832, 2842
4.1.1.23	Orotidine 5′-phosphate = UMP + CO_2	Liver, yeast	517
4.1.1.24	p(or o)-aminobenzoate = aniline + CO_2	Bacteria	1653
4.1.1.25	L-tyrosine = tyramine + CO_2	Animal tissues, bacteria. The bacterial enzyme also acts on 3-hydroxytyrosine and, more slowly, on 3-hydroxy-phenylalanine	806, 1145, 2431
4.1.1.26	3,4-dihydroxy-L-phenyl-alanine = dihydroxyphenylethylamine + CO_2	Animal tissues. Also acts on 2-(or 3-) hydroxyphenylalanine and 3-hydroxyphenylserine	268, 902a, 1018, 1145, 2325, 2477
4.1.1.27	L-tryptophan = tryptamine + CO_2	Animal tissues	2844
4.1.1.28	5-hydroxy-L-tryptophan = 5-hydroxytryptamine + CO_2	Animal tissues	374, 2692
4.1.1.b	UDPglucuronate = UDPxylose + CO_2	Plants	721
4.1.1.29	L-cysteinesulphinate = hypotaurine + CO_2	Liver, kidney	219, 267, 440, 566, 1151, 2475

EC No.	Systematic name	Trivial name	Active groups and [cofactors]
4.1.1.30	N-(L-pantothenoyl)-L-cysteine carboxy-lyase	Pantothenoylcysteine decarboxylase	
4.1.1.c	4'-phospho-N-(L-pantothenoyl)-L cysteine carboxy-lyase	Phosphopantothenoylcysteine decarboxylase	
4.1.1.d	Urophorphyrinogen-III carboxy-lyase	Uroporphyrinogen decarboxylase	
4.1.1.31	Orthophosphate:oxaloacetate carboxy-lyase (phosphorylating)	Phosphopyruvate carboxylase	[Mg++.S]
4.1.1.e	Pyrophosphate:oxaloacetate carboxy-lyase (phosphorylating)	Phosphopyruvate carboxylase	
4.1.1.32	GTP:oxaloacetate carboxy-lyase (transphosphorylating)	Phosphopyruvate carboxylase	[Mn++]
4.1.1.33	ATP:5-pyrophosphomevalonate carboxy-lyase (dehydrating)	Pyrophosphomevalonate decarboxylase	[Mg++]
4.1.1.f	3-phospho-D-glycerate carboxy-lyase (dimerizing)	Ribulosediphosphate carboxylase	[M++]

4.1.2 Aldehyde-lyases

EC No.	Systematic name	Trivial name	Active groups and [cofactors]
4.1.2.1	2-oxo-4-hydroxybutyrate formaldehyde-lyase	Oxohydroxybutyrate aldolase	
4.1.2.a	2-oxo-pantoate formaldehyde-lyase	Ketopantoaldolase	[M++]
4.1.2.2	Erythrulose-1-phosphate formaldehyde-lyase	Ketotetrosealdolase	
4.1.2.3	Ribose-5-phosphate formaldehyde-lyase	Pentosealdolase	
4.1.2.4	2-deoxy-D-ribose-5-phosphate acetaldehyde-lyase	Deoxyriboaldolase	
4.1.2.5	L-threonine acetaldehyde-lyase	Threonine aldolase	[Py]
4.1.2.6	L-allothreonine acetaldehyde-lyase	Allothreonine aldolase	[Py]
4.1.2.7	Ketose-1-phosphate aldehyde-lyase	Aldolase	

C

	Reaction	Sources, comments on specificity, etc.	References
4.1.1.30	N-(L-pantothenoyl)-L-cysteine = pantetheine + CO_2	Liver, bacteria	338–9
4.1.1.c	4'-phospho-N-(L-pantothenoyl)-L-cysteine = pantetheine 4'-phosphate + CO_2	Bacteria	337a
4.1.1.d	Uroporphyrinogen-III = coproporphyrinogen + 4 CO_2	Animal tissues	1761
4.1.1.31	Orthophosphate + oxaloacetate = H_2O + phospho-enolpyruvate + CO_2	Plants	151, 2624
4.1.1.e	Pyrophosphate + oxaloacetate = orthophosphate + phospho-enolpyruvate + CO_2	Bacteria	2420
4.1.1.32	GTP + oxaloacetate = GDP + phospho-enolpyruvate + CO_2	Liver, kidney ITP can also act as phosphate donor	152, 891, 1497, 2532, 2702
4.1.1.33	ATP + 5-pyrophospho-mevalonate = ADP + orthophosphate + isopentenyl pyrophosphate + CO_2	Animal tissues, yeast	274, 1064
4.1.1.f	2 3-phospho-D-glycerate = D-ribulose 1,5-diphosphate + CO_2	Plants	384, 1235, 1770, 2831
4.1.2.1	2-oxo-4-hydroxybutyrate = pyruvate + formaldehyde	Liver Also acts on phenylpyruvate	1095
4.1.2.a	2-oxo-pantoate = 2-oxo-isovalerate + formaldehyde	Bacteria	1663
4.1.2.2	Erythrulose 1-phosphate = dihydroxyacetone phosphate + formaldehyde	Liver	433
4.1.2.3	Ribose 5-phosphate = erythrulose 1-phosphate + formaldehyde	Animal tissues	434
4.1.2.4	2-deoxy-D-ribose 5-phosphate = D-glyceraldehyde 3-phosphate + acetaldehyde	Bacteria	2120, 2151
4.1.2.5	L-threonine = glycine + acetaldehyde	Liver, kidney	312, 1309, 1594
4.1.2.6	L-allothreonine = glycine + acetaldehyde	Liver	312, 1309, 1594
4.1.2.7	A ketose 1-phosphate = dihydroxyacetone phosphate + an aldehyde	Liver Wide specificity	2063, 2280

EC No.	Systematic name	Trivial name	Active groups and [cofactors]
4.1.2.b C	*Fructose-1,6-diphosphate* D-*glyceraldehyde-3-phosphate-lyase*	Aldolase	
4.1.2.8	Indole-3-glycerolphosphate D-glyceraldehyde-3-phosphate-lyase	Indoleglycerolphosphate aldolase	
4.1.2.c	*6-phospho-2-oxo-3-deoxy-*D-*gluconate* D-*glyceraldehyde-3-phosphate-lyase*	Phospho-2-oxo-3-deoxy-gluconate aldolase	
4.1.2.9	D-xylulose-5-phosphate D-glyceraldehyde-3-phosphate-lyase (phosphate-acetylating)	Phosphoketolase	[T.S]
4.1.2.d	*7-phospho-2-oxo-3-deoxy-*D-*arabino-heptonate* D-*erythrose-4-phosphate-lyase* (*pyruvate-phosphorylating*)	Phospho-2-oxo-3-deoxy heptonate aldolase	
4.1.2.e	*8-phospho-2-oxo-3-deoxy-*D-*octonate* D-*arabinose-5-phosphate-lyase* (*pyruvate-phosphorylating*)	Phospho-2-oxo-3-deoxy-octonate aldolase	
4.1.2.10	Mandelonitrile benzaldehyde-lyase	Hydroxynitrile lyase	F
4.1.2.f	p-*hydroxymandelonitrile hydroxybenzaldehyde-lyase*	Hydroxynitrile lyase	

4.1.3   Ketoacid-lyases

EC No.	Systematic name	Trivial name	Active groups and [cofactors]
4.1.3.1	L$_s$-isocitrate glyoxylate-lyase	Isocitrate lyase	[Mg^{++}.S]
4.1.3.2	L-malate glyoxylate-lyase (CoA-acetylating)	Malate synthase (Formerly known as glyoxylate transacetase)	
4.1.3.3	N-acetylneuraminate pyruvate-lyase	N-acetylneuraminate lyase	
4.1.3.4	3-hydroxy-3-methylglutaryl-CoA acetoacetate-lyase	Hydroxymethylglutaryl-CoA lyase	[Mg^{++}.S]
4.1.3.5	3-hydroxy-3-methylglutaryl-CoA acetoacetyl-CoA-lyase (CoA-acetylating)	Hydroxymethylglutaryl-CoA synthase	
4.1.3.6	Citrate oxaloacetate-lyase	Citrate lyase	[Mg^{++}]

	Reaction	Sources, comments on specificity, etc.	References
4.1.2.b	Fructose 1,6-diphosphate = dihydroxyacetone phosphate + D-glyceraldehyde 3-phosphate	Muscle, moulds, yeast	*1231, 2215, 2248, 2280, 2620, 2789*
4.1.2.8	Indole 3-glycerolphosphate = indole + D-glyceraldehyde 3-phosphate	Bacteria	*2944*
4.1.2.c	6-phospho-2-oxo-3-deoxy-D-gluconate = pyruvate + D-glyceraldehyde 3-phosphate	Gram-negative bacteria	*1455*
4.1.2.9	D-xylulose 5-phosphate + orthophosphate = acetylphosphate + H_2O + D-glyceraldehyde 3-phosphate	*Lactobacillus*	*1047*
4.1.2.d	7-phospho-2-oxo-3-deoxy-D-*arabino*heptonate + orthophosphate = phospho-enolpyruvate + D-erythrose 4-phosphate + H_2O	Bacteria	*1559, 2495*
4.1.2.e	8-phospho-2-oxo-3-deoxy-D-octonate + orthophosphate = phospho-enolpyruvate + D-arabinose 5-phosphate + H_2O	Bacteria	*1559*
4.1.2.10	Mandelonitrile = benzaldehyde + HCN	Almonds	*1466, 1664*
4.1.2.f	*p*-hydroxymandelonitrile = *p*-hydroxybenzaldehyde + HCN	Sorghum	*302*
4.1.3.1	L$_s$-isocitrate = succinate + glyoxylate	Plants, moulds, yeast, bacteria	*410, 1441, 2022, 2314, 2454*
4.1.3.2	L-malate + CoA = acetyl-CoA + H_2O + glyoxylate	Plants, yeast, bacteria	*2904, 2933*
4.1.3.3	N-acetylneuraminate = 2-acetylamino-2-deoxy-D-mannose + pyruvate	Bacteria Also acts on N-glycolyl-neuraminate	*485*
4.1.3.4	3-hydroxy-3-methylglutaryl-CoA = acetyl-CoA + acetoacetate	Animal tissues	*123, 355*
4.1.3.5	3-hydroxy-3-methylglutaryl-CoA + CoA = acetyl-CoA + H_2O + acetoacetyl-CoA	Animal tissues, yeast	*355, 723, 2276*
4.1.3.6	Citrate = acetate + oxaloacetate	Bacteria	*530, 2849*

EC No.	Systematic name	Trivial name	*Active groups and [cofactors]*
4.1.3.7 C	Citrate oxaloacetate-lyase (CoA-acetylating)	Citrate synthase (Formerly known as 'citrate condensing enzyme', and oxaloacetate transacetase)	
4.1.3.a	*ATP:citrate oxaloacetate-lyase (CoA-acetylating and ATP-dephosphorylating)*	ATP citrate lyase	[Mg⁺⁺]

4.2 Carbon-oxygen lyases

4.2.1 Hydro-lyases

EC No.	Systematic name	Trivial name	*Active groups and [cofactors]*
4.2.1.1 C	Carbonate hydro-lyase	Carbonate dehydratase, Carbonic anhydrase	Zn
4.2.1.2 C	L-malate hydro-lyase	Fumarate hydratase (Formerly known as fumarase)	
4.2.1.3	Citrate (isocitrate) hydro-lyase	Aconitate hydratase (Formerly known as aconitase)	[Fe⁺⁺.S]
4.2.1.4	Citrate hydro-lyase	Citrate dehydratase	
4.2.1.5	D-arabonate hydro-lyase	Arabonate dehydratase	
4.2.1.a	L-*arabonate hydro-lyase*	L-arabonate dehydratase	
4.2.1.6	D-galactonate hydro-lyase	Galactonate dehydratase	
4.2.1.7	D-altronate hydro-lyase	Altronate dehydratase	[Fe⁺⁺]
4.2.1.8	D-mannonate hydro-lyase	Mannonate dehydratase	
4.2.1.9	2,3-dihydroxyacid hydro-lyase	Dihydroxyacid dehydratase	[M⁺⁺.S]
4.2.1.10	5-dehydroquinate hydro-lyase	5-dehydroquinate dehydratase	
4.2.1.11 C	2-phospho-D-glycerate hydro-lyase	Phosphopyruvate hydratase (Originally known as enolase)	[M⁺⁺]
4.2.1.12	6-phospho-D-gluconate hydro-lyase	Phosphogluconate dehydratase	[M⁺⁺]
4.2.1.13	L-serine hydro-lyase (deaminating)	L-serine dehydratase (Formerly known as serine deaminase, or cystathionine synthetase)	[Py.M⁺]
4.2.1.14	D-serine hydro-lyase (deaminating)	D-serine dehydratase	[Py]

	Reaction	Sources, comments on specificity, etc.	References
4.1.3.7	Citrate + CoA = acetyl-CoA + H_2O + oxaloacetate	Widely distributed	*2012, 2490, 2525*
4.1.3.a	ATP + citrate + CoA = ADP + orthophosphate + acetyl-CoA + oxaloacetate	Widely distributed	*2487–8*
4.2.1.1	H_2CO_3 = $CO_2 + H_2O$	Animal tissues, plants	*626, 2005, 2259, 2355*
4.2.1.2	L-malate = fumarate + H_2O	Widely distributed	*35, 1743*
4.2.1.3	Citrate = *cis*-aconitate + H_2O	Widely distributed. Also converts isocitrate into *cis*-aconitate	*609, 1867*
4.2.1.4	Citrate = *cis*-aconitate + H_2O	*Aspergillus*. Does not act on isocitrate	*1936*
4.2.1.5	D-arabonate = 2-oxo-3-deoxy-D-arabonate + H_2O	Bacteria	*2049*
4.2.1.a	L-arabonate = 2-oxo-3-deoxy-L-arabonate + H_2O	Bacteria	*2824*
4.2.1.6	D-galactonate = 2-oxo-3-deoxy-D-galactonate + H_2O	Bacteria	*588*
4.2.1.7	D-altronate = 2-oxo-3-deoxy-D-gluconate + H_2O	Bacteria	*2432*
4.2.1.8	D-mannonate = 2-oxo-3-deoxy-D-gluconate + H_2O	Bacteria	*2432*
4.2.1.9	2,3-dihydroxyisovalerate = 2-oxoisovalerate + H_2O	Moulds, yeast, bacteria	*1910, 2891*
4.2.1.10	5-dehydroquinate = 5-dehydroshikimate + H_2O	Plants, bacteria	*145, 1839*
4.2.1.11	2-phospho-D-glycerate = phospho-enolpyruvate + H_2O	Widely distributed	*529, 718, 1137 1697, 2788*
4.2.1.12	6-phospho-D-gluconate = 2-oxo-3-deoxy-6-phospho-D-gluconate + H_2O	Bacteria	*1454, 1660, 2049*
4.2.1.13	L-serine + H_2O = pyruvate + $NH_3 + H_2O$	Liver, moulds, bacteria. Also forms cystathionine from L-serine and L-homocysteine	*2368, 2911, 2945*
4.2.1.14	D-serine + H_2O = pyruvate + $NH_3 + H_2O$	Moulds, bacteria. Also acts, slowly, on D-threonine	*1803, 2943*

EC No.	Systematic name	Trivial name	Active groups and [cofactors]
4.2.1.15 C	L-homoserine hydro-lyase (deaminating)	Homoserine dehydratase (Formerly known as cystathionase)	[Py]
4.2.1.16	L-threonine hydro-lyase (deaminating)	Threonine dehydratase	[Py]
4.2.1.b	*2-amino-2-deoxy-D-gluconate hydro-lyase (deaminating)*	Aminodeoxygluconate dehydratase	[Py]
4.2.1.17 C	L-3-hydroxyacyl-CoA hydro-lyase	Enoyl-CoA hydratase (Originally known as crotonase)	
4.2.1.18	3-hydroxy-3-methylglutaryl-CoA hydro-lyase	Methylglutaconyl-CoA hydratase	
4.2.1.19	D-*erythro*-imidazoleglycerolphosphate hydro-lyase	Imidazoleglycerolphosphate dehydratase	[Mn^{++}.S]
4.2.1.20	L-serine hydro-lyase (adding indole)	Tryptophan synthase	[Py]
4.2.1.22	L-serine hydro-lyase (adding H_2S)	Cysteine synthase	[Py]
4.2.1.23	L-serine hydro-lyase (adding methanethiol)	Methylcysteine synthase	[Py]
4.2.1.24	5-aminolaevulinate hydro-lyase (adding 5-aminolaevulinate and cyclizing)	Porphobilinogen synthase, Aminolaevulinate dehydratase	[S]
4.2.1.c	*Malonate-semialdehyde hydro-lyase*	Malonate semialdehyde dehydratase	

4.2.99   Other carbon-oxygen lyases

4.2.99.1	Hyaluronate lyase	Hyaluronate lyase (Formerly known as hyaluronidase; but see also 3.2.1.d, e)	
4.2.99.2	O-phosphohomoserine phospho-lyase (adding H_2O)	Threonine synthase	[Py]

4.3   Carbon-nitrogen lyases

4.3.1   Ammonia lyases

4.3.1.1	L-aspartate ammonia-lyase	Aspartate ammonia-lyase (Originally known as aspartase)	[M^{++}]
4.3.1.2	L-*threo*-3-methylaspartate ammonia-lyase	Methylaspartate ammonia-lyase	
4.3.1.3	L-histidine ammonia-lyase	Histidine ammonia-lyase (Formerly known as histidine α-deaminase)	[S]

	Reaction	*Sources, comments on specificity, etc.*	*References*
4.2.1.15	L-homoserine $+ H_2O =$ 2-oxobutyrate $+ NH_3 + H_2O$	Liver Also converts cystathionine into 2-oxobutyrate, NH_3 and cysteine	*312, 314, 1757–8*
4.2.1.16	L-threonine $+ H_2O =$ 2-oxobutyrate $+ NH_3 + H_2O$	Liver, bacteria	*1972, 2052, 2278*
4.2.1.b	2-amino-2-deoxy- D-gluconate $+ H_2O =$ 2-oxo-3-deoxy-D-gluconate $+$ $NH_3 + H_2O$	Bacteria	*1799*
4.2.1.17	An L-3-hydroxyacyl-CoA $=$ a 2,3- (or 3,4-)*trans*-enoyl- CoA $+ H_2O$	Animal tissues Also acts (in the reverse reaction) on the *cis*-compounds	*2516, 2520–1 2752*
4.2.1.18	3-hydroxy-3-methylglutaryl- CoA $=$ *trans*-3-methylglutaconyl- CoA $+ H_2O$	Animal tissues, plants, bacteria	*1106*
4.2.1.19	D-*erythro*-imidazoleglycerol phosphate $=$ imidazoleacetol phosphate $+$ H_2O	Moulds, bacteria	*61*
4.2.1.20	L-serine $+$ indole $=$ L-tryptophan $+ H_2O$	Plants, moulds, bacteria The bacterial enzyme is a 2-protein system	*516, 2103, 2570, 2942*
4.2.1.22	L-serine $+ H_2S =$ L-cysteine $+ H_2O$	Yeast	*2331–2*
4.2.1.23	L-serine $+$ methanethiol $=$ S-methyl-L-cysteine $+ H_2O$	Yeast	*2896*
4.2.1.24	2 5-aminolaevulinate $=$ porphobilinogen $+ 2 H_2O$	Animal tissues, bacteria	*832, 884*
4.2.1.c	Malonate semialdehyde $=$ acetylene monocarboxylate $+$ H_2O	Bacteria	*2926*
4.2.99.1	Hyaluronate $=$ n 3(β-D-gluco-4,5-en-urono)- 2-acetylamino-2-deoxy- D-glucose	Bacteria	*1599, 1627, 1806*
4.2.99.2	O-phosphohomoserine $+$ $H_2O =$ threonine $+$ phosphate	Fungi	*749–51*
4.3.1.1	L-aspartate $=$ fumarate $+ NH_3$	Some plants, bacteria	*284, 705, 804 2870*
4.3.1.2	L-*threo*-3-methylaspartate $=$ mesaconate $+ NH_3$	Bacteria	*164*
4.3.1.3	L-histidine $=$ urocanate $+ NH_3$	Liver, bacteria	*981, 1205, 2594, 2858*

EC No.	Systematic name	Trivial name	Active groups and [cofactors]
4.3.1.a	L-*phenylalanine ammonia-lyase*	Phenylalanine ammonia-lyase	
4.3.1.4	5-formiminotetrahydrofolate ammonia-lyase (cyclizing)	Formiminotetrahydrofolate cyclodeaminase	
4.3.1.b	*β-alanyl-CoA ammonia-lyase*	β-alanyl-CoA ammonia-lyase	

4.3.2   Amididine-lyases

4.3.2.1	L-argininosuccinate arginine-lyase	Argininosuccinate lyase (Originally known as argininosuccinase)	
4.3.2.2	Adenylosuccinate AMP-lyase	Adenylosuccinate lyase (Originally known as adenylosuccinase)	

4.4   Carbon-sulphur lyases

4.4.1.1	L-cysteine hydrogensulphide-lyase (deaminating)	Cysteine desulphhydrase	[Py]
4.4.1.2	L-homocysteine hydrogensulphide-lyase (deaminating)	Homocysteine desulphhydrase	[Py]
4.4.1.3	S-dimethyl-β-propiothetin dimethylsulphide-lyase	Dimethylpropiothetin dethiomethylase	[S]
4.4.1.4	Alliin allylsulphenate-lyase	Alliin lyase	[Py]
4.4.1.5	S-lactoyl-glutathione methylglyoxal-lyase (isomerizing)	Lactoyl-glutathione lyase (Formerly known as glyoxalase I)	

4.5   Carbon-halide lyases

4.5.1.1	1,1,1-trichloro-2,2-bis-(*p*-chloro-phenyl)-ethane hydrogenchloride-lyase	DDT-dehydrochlorinase	[S]

5   ISOMERASES

5.1   Racemases and epimerases

5.1.1   Acting on aminoacids and derivatives

5.1.1.1	Alanine racemase	Alanine racemase	[Py]
5.1.1.2	Methionine racemase	Methionine racemase	[Py]
5.1.1.3	Glutamate racemase	Glutamate racemase	[Py]
5.1.1.4	Proline racemase	Proline racemase	[S]
5.1.1.5	Lysine racemase	Lysine racemase	
5.1.1.6	Threonine epimerase	Threonine epimerase	

	Reaction	Sources, comments on specificity, etc.	References
4.3.1.a	L-phenylalanine = *trans*-cinnamate + NH₃	Plants	*1453*
4.3.1.4	5-formiminotetrahydro-folate = 5,10-methenyltetrahydro-folate + NH₃	Liver, bacteria	*2141, 2596*
4.3.1.b	β-alanyl-CoA = acrylyl-CoA + NH₃	Bacteria	*2704*
4.3.2.1	L-argininosuccinate = fumarate + L-arginine	Animal tissues, plants, yeast, bacteria	*2177, 2179, 2767–8*
4.3.2.2	Adenylosuccinate = fumarate + AMP	Liver, yeast, bacteria Also acts on 5′-phosphoribosyl-4-(N-succinocarboxamide)-5-aminoimidazole	*412, 1585, 1822*
4.4.1.1	L-cysteine + H₂O = pyruvate + NH₃ + H₂S	Animal tissues, bacteria	*313, 1525, 2459*
4.4.1.2	L-homocysteine + H₂O = 2-oxobutyrate + NH₃ + H₂S	Animal tissues, bacteria	*791, 1293*
4.4.1.3	S-dimethyl-β-propiothetin = acrylate + dimethyl sulphide	Algae	*395*
4.4.1.4	An S-alkyl-L-cysteinesulph-oxide = 2-aminoacrylate + an alkylsulphenate	Garlic	*874, 2540*
4.4.1.5	S-lactoyl-glutathione = glutathione + methylglyoxal	Animal tissues Also acts on 3-phospho-glyceroyl-glutathione	*460, 521, 2150, 2803*
4.5.1.1	1,1,1-trichloro-2,2-bis-(*p*-chlorophenyl)-ethane = 1,1-dichloro-2,2-bis-(*p*-chlorophenyl)-ethylene + HCl	Insects	*1602, 1854*
5.1.1.1	L-alanine = D-alanine	Bacteria	*1728, 2910 2912*
5.1.1.2	L-methionine = D-methionine	Bacteria	*1294*
5.1.1.3	L-glutamate = D-glutamate	Bacteria	*848*
5.1.1.4	L-proline = D-proline	Bacteria	*2501*
5.1.1.5	L-lysine = D-lysine	Bacteria	*1176*
5.1.1.6	L-threonine = D-threonine	Bacteria	*65*

2c•

EC No.	Systematic name	Trivial name	Active groups and [cofactors]
5.1.1.7	2,6-LL-diaminopimelate 2-epimerase	Diaminopimelate epimerase	[S]
5.1.1.a	*Hydroxyproline 2-epimerase*	Hydroxyproline epimerase	

5.1.2   Acting on hydroxyacids and derivatives

5.1.2.1	Lactate racemase	Lactate racemase	
5.1.2.2	Mandelate racemase	Mandelate racemase	
5.1.2.3	3-hydroxybutyryl-CoA 3-epimerase	3-hydroxybutyryl-CoA epimerase	

5.1.3   Acting on carbohydrates and derivatives

5.1.3.1	D-ribulose-5-phosphate 3-epimerase	Ribulosephosphate 3-epimerase	
5.1.3.a	*L-ribulose-5-phosphate 4-epimerase*	Ribulosephosphate 4-epimerase	
5.1.3.2	UDPglucose 4-epimerase	UDPglucose epimerase (Originally known as galactowaldenase)	[NAD.Mg^{++}]
5.1.3.b	*UDParabinose 4-epimerase*	UDParabinose epimerase	
5.1.3.c	*UDPglucuronate 4-epimerase*	UDPglucuronate epimerase	
5.1.3.d	*UDP-2-acetylamino-2-deoxy-D-glucose 4-epimerase*	UDPacetylaminodeoxy-glucose epimerase	[NAD] for the liver enzyme
5.1.3.3	Aldose 1-epimerase	Aldose 1-epimerase, aldose mutarotase	

5.1.99   Acting on other compounds

5.1.99.a	*Methylmalonyl-CoA racemase*	Methylmalonyl-CoA racemase	

5.2   Cis-trans isomerases

5.2.1.1	Maleate *cis-trans*-isomerase	Maleate isomerase	
5.2.1.2	4-maleylacetoacetate *cis-trans*-isomerase	Maleylacetacetate isomerase	[G]
5.2.1.a	*3-maleylpyruvate* cis-trans-*isomerase*	Maleylpyruvate isomerase	[G]
5.2.1.3	All-*trans*-retinene 11-*cis-trans* isomerase	Retinene isomerase	

5.3   Intramolecular oxidoreductases

5.3.1   Interconverting aldoses and ketoses

5.3.1.1 C	D-glyceraldehyde-3-phosphate ketol-isomerase	Triosephosphate isomerase	

Reaction	Sources, comments on specificity, etc.	References
5.1.1.7	2,6-LL-diaminopimelate = *meso*-diaminopimelate	Bacteria	*80*
5.1.1.a	L-hydroxyproline = D-allohydroxyproline	*Pseudomonas* Also interconverts D-hydroxyproline and L-allohydroxyproline	*10*
5.1.2.1	L-lactate = D-lactate	Animal tissues, bacteria	*1183, 1392*
5.1.2.2	L-mandelate = D-mandelate	Bacteria	*951*
5.1.2.3	L-3-hydroxybutyryl-CoA = D-3-hydroxybutyryl-CoA	Liver	*2519, 2751*
5.1.3.1	D-ribulose 5-phosphate = D-xylulose 5-phosphate	Widely distributed	*90, 608, 104 1198, 2489, 2562, 2900*
5.1.3.a	L-ribulose 5-phosphate = D-xylulose 5-phosphate	Bacteria	*362, 2900*
5.1.3.2	UDPglucose = UDPgalactose	Animal tissues, yeast, bacteria	*401, 1537–8, 1765, 1767–8*
5.1.3.b	UDP-L-arabinose = UDP-D-xylose	Plants	*721*
5.1.3.c	UDP-D-glucuronate = UDP-D-galacturonate	Plants	*721*
5.1.3.d	UDP-2-acetylamino-2-deoxy-D-glucose = UDP-2-acetylamino-2-deoxy-D-galactose	Liver, bacteria	*847*
5.1.3.3	α-D-glucose = β-D-glucose	Kidney, moulds Also acts on L-arabinose, D-xylose, D-galactose, maltose and lactose	*207, 1345, 1369, 1567*
5.1.99.a	D-methylmalonyl-CoA = L-methylmalonyl-CoA	Animal tissues, bacteria	*1773, 2038*
5.2.1.1	Maleate = fumarate	Nicotinate-adapted *Pseudomonas*	*195*
5.2.1.2	4-maleylacetoacetate = 4-fumarylacetoacetate	Liver Also acts on maleylpyruvate	*674, 1500*
5.2.1.a	3-maleylpyruvate = 3-fumarylpyruvate	Bacteria	*1500*
5.2.1.3	All-*trans*-retinene = 11-*cis*-retinene	Retina Light shifts the equilibrium towards the *cis*-isomer	*1178*
5.3.1.1	D-glyceraldehyde 3-phosphate = dihydroxyacetone phosphate	Widely distributed	*1808, 1810*

EC No.	*Systematic name*	*Trivial name*	*Active groups and [cofactors]*
5.3.1.2	D-erythrose ketol-isomerase	Erythrose isomerase	
5.3.1.3	D-arabinose ketol-isomerase	Arabinose isomerase	[Mg^{++}]
5.3.1.4	L-arabinose ketol-isomerase	L-arabinose isomerase	
5.3.1.5	D-xylose ketol-isomerase	Xylose isomerase	[Mg^{++}]
5.3.1.6	D-ribose-5-phosphate ketol-isomerase	Ribosephosphate isomerase	
5.3.1.a	D-*arabinose-5-phosphate ketol-isomerase*	Arabinosephosphate isomerase	
5.3.1.7	D-mannose ketol-isomerase	Mannose isomerase	
5.3.1.8	D-mannose-6-phosphate ketol-isomerase	Mannosephosphate isomerase	
5.3.1.b	L-*rhamnose ketol-isomerase*	Rhamnose isomerase	
5.3.1.9	D-glucose-6-phosphate ketol-isomerase	Glucosephosphate isomerase	
5.3.1.10	2-amino-2-deoxy-D-glucose-6-phosphate ketol-isomerase (deaminating)	Aminodeoxyglucose-phosphate isomerase	[M^{++}]
5.3.1.11	2-acetylamino-2-deoxy-D-glucose-6-phosphate ketol-isomerase (deaminating)	Acetylaminodeoxyglucose-phosphate isomerase	
5.3.1.12	D-glucuronate ketol-isomerase	Glucuronate isomerase	

5.3.2 Interconverting keto- and enol-groups

5.3.2.1	Phenylpyruvate keto-enol-isomerase	Phenylpyruvate tautomerase	

5.3.3 Transposing C=C bonds

5.3.3.1 C	3-ketosteroid Δ^4-Δ^5-isomerase	Steroid Δ-isomerase	
5.3.3.2	Isopentenylpyrophosphate Δ^3-Δ^2-isomerase	Isopentenylpyrophosphate isomerase	[Mg^{++}.S]
5.3.3.3	Vinylacetyl-CoA Δ^3-Δ^2-isomerase	Vinylacetyl-CoA isomerase	

$\tilde{k}_i$	bimolecular velocity constant for combination of a particular ionic form of enzyme with I
k_B	Boltzmann constant
K	an equilibrium constant
K	overall equilibrium constant of a reversible enzyme reaction
$K_1\ K_2\ K_3$	equilibrium constants of successive steps in a reversible enzyme reaction
$K_1\ K_2$	molecular ionization constants
$K_1\ K_2$	values of K_m for enzymes E_1 and E_2
$K_{1x}\ K_{1y}$	ionization constants of groups x and y in the first step
$K_{2x}\ K_{2y}$	ionization constants of groups x and y in the second step
K_0	dissociation constant of MS
$K_A\ K'_A$	equilibrium constants for dissociation of M (or activator A) from EM and EMS (or EA and EAS) respectively
$\tilde{K}_A$	equilibrium constant for dissociation of M from a particular ionic species of EM
$K_a\ K_b$	dissociation constants of EA and EB
$K'_a\ K'_b$	equilibrium constants for dissociation of A and B respectively from EAB
K_{Ap}	apparent dissociation constant of EM
K_{AS}	equilibrium constant for dissociation of MS from EMS
$K_e\ K_{es}\ K_{eas}$	ionization constants of E, ES and EMS respectively
K_i	dissociation constant of EI (the inhibitor constant)
K'_i	equilibrium constant for dissociation of I from EIS
K_m	concentration of substrate giving half maximal velocity (the Michaelis constant)
K'_m	value of K_m in presence of excess of inhibitor
K_p	apparent value of K_m
K_s	dissociation constant of ES (the substrate constant)
K'_s	equilibrium constant for dissociation of S from EIS or EMS
K'_S	a solubility constant
$\tilde{K}_s$	dissociation constant of a particular ionic species of ES
$\tilde{K}'_s$	equilibrium constant for dissociation of S from particular ionic species of EIS or EMS
$\tilde{K}_{s^-}$	equilibrium constant for dissociation of S$^-$ from a particular ionic species of ES
K_{sa}	equilibrium constant for dissociation of S combined as activator in ES
K_{sp}	apparent value of K_s
K_t	overall equilibrium constant of a reversible enzyme reaction, in terms of total concentrations of reactants
K^*	equilibrium constant for conversion of reactants into activated complex
mμ	10^{-7} cm

n	number of carbon atoms in a chain
n	total number of binding sites in an enzyme molecule
p	concentration of ES or EMS
p'	concentration of EIS
p_{max}	maximum value of p (at the steady state)
$p_a\ p_b$	concentrations of EA and EB
pH	$-\log_{10} H$
pH_0	optimum pH of an enzyme
pI_{50}	$-\log_{10} I_{50}$
pK etc.	$-\log_{10} K$
pS	$-\log_{10} s$
$q\ r$	concentrations of inactive enzyme complexes
Q_{10}	temperature coefficient for a reaction
Q_x	μl of X produced per hr per mg dry weight (for non-gaseous substances calculated on the basis that 1 μmole $= 22 \cdot 4$ μl)
r	average number of substrate molecules bound by one molecule of an enzyme
r	K_s'/K_s
$\tilde{r}$	$\tilde{K}_s/\tilde{K}_s'$
R	V_b/V_a or k'/k
R	gas constant
s	solubility
s	substrate concentration
s_0	substrate concentration at zero time
s_m	substrate concentration when $p = p_{max}$
t	subscript denoting total concentrations
t	time
T	absolute temperature
U	enzyme unit
v	velocity of a reaction
v_0	velocity of an enzyme reaction with very low substrate concentration
$v_a\ v_b$	velocity of breakdown of A and B respectively by an enzyme
v_c	steady-state velocity in a system of enzymes
v_i	velocity of an enzyme reaction in presence of an inhibitor
v	total velocity of two enzymes acting simultaneously $(v_1 + v_2)$, or of one enzyme catalysing two reactions $(v_a + v_b)$
V	velocity of an enzyme reaction when saturated with substrate
V^b	velocity of an enzyme reaction in presence of an excess of inhibitor and substrate
$V_a\ V$	velocity of a bimolecular enzyme reaction with excess b and fixed a or excess a and fixed b respectively

V_a	velocity of an enzyme reaction with excess activator
V_M	total velocity of breakdown by an enzyme of two substrates A and B, present in equimolar mixture
V_p	apparent value of V in presence of an inhibitor
V_1 V_2	values of V for two enzymes acting on the same substrate
y	amount of substrate changed in time t
z	concentration of product of an enzyme reaction
z_0	value of z at zero time
α	v_i/v
α β ι σ ϕ	relative quantities, equal to a/K_a, b/K_b, i/K_i, s/K_s and v/V respectively
$[\alpha]_D^{1\%}$	specific optical rotation, using sodium light and a 1 per cent solution
β'	a solubility constant
$\Gamma/2$	ionic strength
ΔF	change of free energy
ΔH	change of heat content
ΔS	change of entropy
ΔF^0 ΔH^0 ΔS^0	values of ΔF, ΔH and ΔS for standard conditions, i.e. for unit activities
ΔF^* ΔH^* ΔS^*	values of ΔF^0, ΔH^0 and ΔS^0 for formation of the activated complex
'ΔH^*' $\Delta H^{*\prime}$	apparent values of ΔH^*
ΔH_c	heat of conversion of an enzyme from an active to an inactive form
ΔH	heat of ionization
ϵ	base of natural logarithms
ϵ	extinction coefficient
ι	relative inhibitor concentration, i.e. i/K_i
μ	'micro-' i.e. $\times 10^{-6}$
σ	relative substrate concentration, i.e. s/K_s or s/K_m
τ	lag period in the start of an enzyme reaction
ϕ	relative velocity, i.e. v/V
ϕ_t	relative velocity of an enzyme catalysing two reactions simultaneously, i.e. v_t/V_a
ϕ_o, ϕ_a etc	functions of velocity constants
$[X]$	concentration of X

Abbreviations

A B C D	reactants in an enzyme reaction
A AH_2	oxidized and reduced forms of a hydrogen acceptor
AH_2 AH^- $A^=$	a dibasic acid and its anions
AH_x^- AH_y^-	forms of AH^- produced by ionization of groups x and y in an unsymmetrical acid AH_2
Ac	acetyl

ADP	adenosine diphosphate
Ala	alanine
AmB	amino-n-butyryl
AmiB	amino-isobutyryl
AmCapr	aminocaproyl
AMP	adenosine 5'-phosphate
Arg	arginine
ARPPP	see ATP
As	arsenate
Asp	aspartic acid
ATP	adenosine triphosphate
Bt	biotin
Bz	benzoyl
BzS	benzenesulphonyl
C	denotes a crystalline enzyme
cal	calories
CB	carbobenzoxy
CDP	cytidine diphosphate
Ch	choline
ClAc	chloroacetyl
CMP	cytidine 5'-phosphate
CoA	coenzyme A
CSH	cysteine
CSSC	cystine
Cy	cytosine
Cys	cysteine or 'half-cystine'
CySH	cysteine
D- L-	prefixes for compounds of the D- and L- configurational series
deg	degrees
DFP	di-isopropyl phosphorofluoridate
DNA	deoxyribonucleic acid
DOPA	dihydroxyphenylalanine
e	an electron
E EH	enzyme
EA	complex of enzyme and A
EI	enzyme–inhibitor complex
EIS	enzyme–inhibitor–substrate complex
EM	complex of enzyme and activating metal
EMS	enzyme–activator–substrate complex
ES_I ES_{II}	peroxidase–peroxide complexes
E^n ES^n	E and ES with n negative charges
ES* EX* EZ*	the three activated complexes involved in the conversion of substrate to product by an enzyme
Et	ethyl
F	fructose

F	flavin prosthetic group
FAD	flavin–adenine dinucleotide
FMN	flavin mononucleotide
Form	formyl
g	grams
G	glucose
Gal	galactose
GDP	guanosine diphosphate
Glu	glutamic acid
Gly	glycine
GMP	guanosine 5′-phosphate
GSH	reduced glutathione
GSSG	oxidized glutathione
GTP	guanosine triphosphate
His	histidine
hr	hours
Hx	hypoxanthine
Hypro	hydroxyproline
I	inhibitor
IAA	iodoacetic acid
IDP	inosine diphosphate
Ileu	isoleucine
IMP	inosine 5′-phosphate
ITP	inosine triphosphate
L-	see D-
Leu	leucine
Lys	lysine
M	activating metal ion
Me	methyl
Met	methionine
min	minutes
MS	complex of substrate and activating metal ion
MW	molecular weight
NAD	nicotinamide–adenine dinucleotide
$NADH_2$	reduced NAD
NADHD	monodeutero–$NADH_2$
NADP	nicotinamide–adenine dinucleotide phosphate
$NADPH_2$	reduced NADP
N_o N_r	oxidized and reduced forms of NAD
NMN	nicotinamide mononucleotide
Naph	naphthyl
Nic	nicotinyl
Norleu	norleucine
Norval	norvaline
N.T.P.	normal temperature and pressure
Orn	ornithine

P	phosphate
PG	3-phosphoglycerate
Ph	phosphate
Phe	phenylalanine
Phgly	phenylglycine
PhPyr	phenylpyruvyl
Phth	phthalyl
PP	pyrophosphate
Pro	proline
Py	pyridoxal phosphate
R R' R'' R_1 R_2	various chemical groups
RNA	ribonucleic acid
S	substrate
S^- $S^=$	substrate anions
S_A	substrate combined with enzyme as activator
S_f S_b	substrates in forward and backward reactions
S^o S^r	oxidized and reduced forms of substrate
sec	seconds
Ser	serine
T	thiamine pyrophosphate
Terleu	tertiary leucine
THFA	tetrahydrofolate
Thr	threonine
Try	tryptophan
Ts	toluenesulphonyl
Tyr	tyrosine
UDP	uridine diphosphate
UMP	uridine 5'-phosphate
UQ_n	ubiquinone (containing a side-chain of n isoprene units)
Ur	uracil
UTP	uridine triphosphate
Val	valine
XMP XDP XTP	nucleoside mono- di- and tri-phosphates
YMP YDP YTP	as above
Z	product
*	isotopically labelled or activated

'ATLAS' OF
CRYSTALLINE
ENZYMES

In the following pages we reproduce microphotographs of most of the crystalline enzymes for which illustrations have been published. Below each picture we give the enzyme name, the EC number, source, approximate magnification, and reference. For several enzymes a number of pictures are given, representing either the same enzyme from different sources, or different crystalline forms of the enzyme from a single source.

Alcohol dehydrogenase
(1.1.1.1)
(horse liver)
× 900   from *289*

Alcohol dehydrogenase
(1.1.1.1)
(yeast)
× ?   from *1935*

Glycerolphosphate
dehydrogenase (1.1.1.8)
(rabbit muscle)
× 1000   from *529*

Lactate dehydrogenase
(1.1.1.27)
(ox heart)
× 330   from *2544*

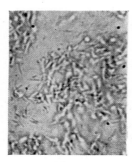

Lactate dehydrogenase
(1.1.1.27)
(rat liver)
× 1500   from *829*

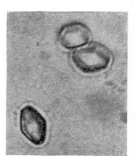

Tartronate semialdehyde
reductase (1.1.1.g)
(*Pseudomonas*)
× 2800   from *875*

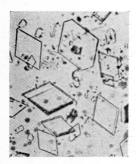

Malate dehydrogenase
(1.1.1.37)
(ox heart supernatant)
× 300   from *697*

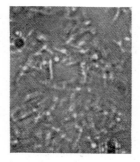

Phosphogluconate dehydro-
genase (decarboxylating)
(1.1.1.44)
(yeast)
× 1700   from *2105*

Glucose-6-phosphate
dehydrogenase (1.1.1.49)
(ox mammary gland)
× 370   from *1276*

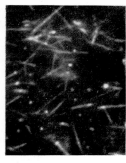

Cortisone reductase
(1.1.1.53)
(*Streptomyces*)
× 1000   from *1179*

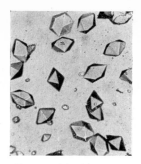

Lactate dehydrogenase
(cytochrome b_2)
(1.1.2.3)
× 42   from *1881*

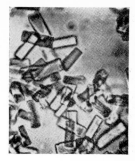

Glycollate oxidase
(1.1.3.1)
(spinach leaves)
× 480   from *788*

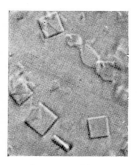

Lactate oxidase
(1.1.3.2)
(*Mycobacterium*)
× 2150   from *2574*

Glucose oxidase
(1.1.3.4)
(*Penicillium*)
× 310   from *1499*

Glyceraldehydephosphate
dehydrogenase (1.2.1.12)
(rabbit muscle)
× 260   from *505*

Glyceraldehydephosphate
dehydrogenase (1.2.1.12)
(yeast)
× 55   from *2787*

Glyceraldehydephosphate
dehydrogenase (1.2.1.12)
('yeast protein 2')
× 130   from *1493*

Pyruvate dehydrogenase
(1.2.2.2)
(*Esch. coli*)
× 250   from *2868*

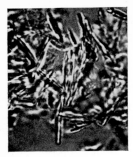

Xanthine oxidase
(1.2.3.2)
(cow's milk)
× 1000   from *105*

Dihydro-orotate dehydro-
genase (1.3.3.1)
(*Zymobacterium*)
× ?   from *786*

Glutamate dehydrogenase
(1.4.1.3)
(human liver)
× 1800   from *1472*

L-aminoacid oxidase
(1.4.3.2)
(snake venom)
× 500   from *2838*

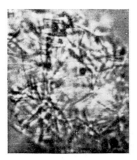

D-aminoacid oxidase
(1.4.3.3)
(pig kidney)
× 545   from *1753*

NADPH$_2$ diaphorase
(1.6.99.1)
(yeast)
× 290   from *2632*

Cytochrome oxidase
(1.9.3.1)
(ox heart)
× 200   from *2949*

Pseudomonas cytochrome
oxidase (1.9.3.a)
× 160   from *2934*

Catalase (1.11.1.6)
(ox liver, 1st form)
× 260   from *2567*

Catalase (1.11.1.6)
(ox liver, 2nd form)
× 265   from *2567*

Catalase (1.11.1.6)
(ox liver, 3rd form)
× 270   from *2567*

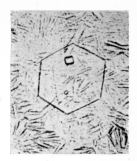

Catalase (1.11.1.6)
(ox liver, 4th form)
× 250   from *2338*

Catalase (1.11.1.6)
(ox liver, 5th form)
× 250   from *2338*

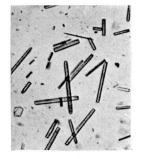

Catalase (1.11.1.6)
(ox liver, 6th form)
× 250   from *2338*

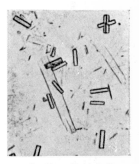

Catalase (1.11.1.6)
(ox liver, 7th form)
× 250   from *2338*

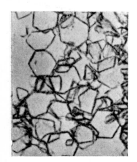

Catalase (1.11.1.6)
(ox liver, 8th form)
× 250   from *2338*

Catalase (1.11.1.6)
(ox liver, 9th form)
× 250   from *2338*

Catalase (1.11.1.6)
(horse erythrocytes)
× 130   from *287*

798

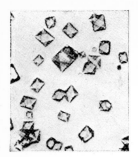

Catalase (1.11.1.6)
(*Micrococcus lysodeikticus*)
× 200   from *1077*

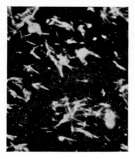

Peroxidase (1.11.1.7)
(horseradish root)
× 680   from *2626*

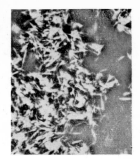

Peroxidase (1.11.1.7)
(turnip)
× 390   from *1170*

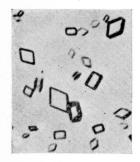

Peroxidase *a* (1.11.1.7)
(Japanese radish, 1st form)
× 350   from *1861*

Peroxidase *a* (1.11.1.7)
(Japanese radish, 2nd form)
× 265   from *1861*

Peroxidase *c* (1.11.1.7)
(Japanese radish)
× 120   from *1863*

Peroxidase (1.11.1.7)
(wheat germ)
× 150   from *2598*

Peroxidase (1.11.1.7)
(cow's milk)
× 700   from *2638b*

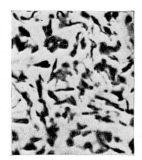

Lipoxygenase (1.99.2.1)
(soy bean)
× 1200   from *2634*

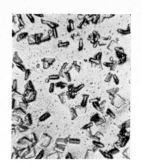

Aspartate carbamoyl-
transferase (2.1.3.2)
(*Esch. coli*)
× ?   from *2383*

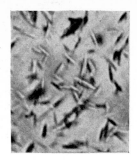

Transketolase (2.2.1.1)
(yeast)
× 1600   from *587*

α-glucan phosphorylase *a*
(2.4.1.1)
(rabbit muscle)
× 90   from *893*

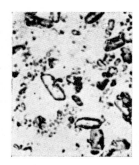

α-glucan phosphorylase *b*
(2.4.1.1)
(rabbit muscle)
× 350   from *501*

α-glucan phosphorylase *b*
(Mg-AMP-dimer)
(rabbit muscle)
× 50   from *735*

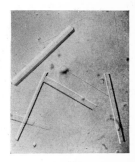

Hexokinase
(2.7.1.1)
(yeast, 1st form)
× 38   from *1493*

Hexokinase
(2.7.1.1)
(yeast, 2nd form)
× 68   from *138*

Glycerol kinase
(2.7.1.30)
(pigeon liver)
× 140   from *2860*

Pyruvate kinase
(2.7.1.40)
(rabbit muscle)
× 600   from *2654*

Phosphoglycerate kinase
(2.7.2.3)
(yeast, 1st form)
× ?   from *354*

Phosphoglycerate kinase
(2.7.2.3)
(yeast, 2nd form)
× ?   from *354*

Creatine kinase
(2.7.3.2)
(rabbit muscle)
× 190   from *1479*

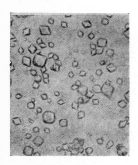

Arginine kinase
(2.7.3.3)
(crab muscle)
× ?   from *2592*

Adenylate kinase
(2.7.4.3)
(rabbit muscle)
× 200   from *1981*

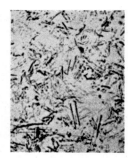

Phosphoglucomutase
(2.7.5.1)
(rabbit muscle)
× 160   from *1920*

Phosphoglyceromutase
(2.7.5.3)
(yeast)
× 300   from *2239*

Luciferase
(firefly)
× 42   from *894*

Ribonuclease
(2.7.7.16)
(ox pancreas, 1st form)
× 190   from *1490*

Ribonuclease
(2.7.7.16)
(ox pancreas, 2nd form)
× 200   from *1490*

Ribonuclease
(2.7.7.16)
(ox pancreas, 3rd form)
× 140   from *1490*

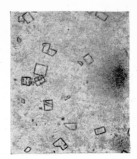

Thiosulphate sulphur-
transferase (2.8.1.1)
(ox liver, 1st form)
× 150   from *2472*

Thiosulphate sulphur-
transferase (2.8.1.1)
(ox liver, 2nd form)
× 300   from *2472*

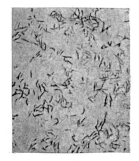

Phospholipase A
(3.1.1.4)
(cobra venom)
× 200   from *574*

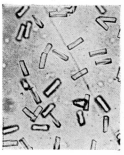

Deoxyribonuclease
(3.1.4.5)
(ox pancreas)
× 250   from *1492*

α-amylase (3.2.1.1)
(human pancreas)
× 730   from *1916a*

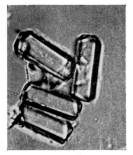

α-amylase (3.2.1.1)
(human saliva, 1st form)
× 550   from *1916a*

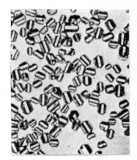

α-amylase (3.2.1.1)
(human saliva, 2nd form)
× 150   from *737*

α-amylase (3.2.1.1)
(pig pancreas)
× 230   from *1916a*

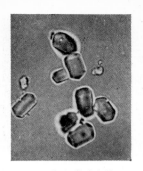

α-amylase (3.2.1.1)
(malt)
× 580   from *2353*

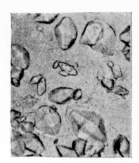

α-amylase (3.2.1.1)
(*Aspergillus*, 1st form)
× 150   from *2699*

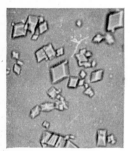

α-amylase (3.2.1.1)
(*Aspergillus*, 2nd form)
× 205   from *736*

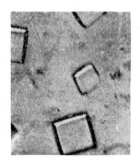

α-amylase (3.2.1.1)
(*Aspergillus*, 3rd form)
× 1000   from *27*

α-amylase (3.2.1.1)
(*B. stearothermophilus*)
× ?   from *1708*

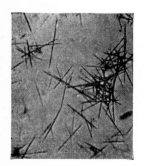

α-amylase (3.2.1.1)
(*B. subtilis*)
× 110   from *1916a*

β-amylase (3.2.1.2)
(sweet potato)
× 200   from *148*

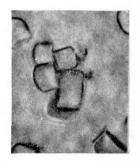

β-amylase (3.2.1.2)
(wheat)
× 940   from *1807*

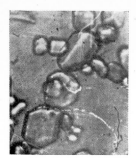

Cellulase (3.2.1.4)
(*Irpex lacteus*)
× 600   from *1974*

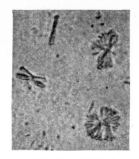

Xylanase (3.2.1.8)
(*Bacillus*)
× 600   from *1210*

Oligo-1,6-glucosidase
(3.2.1.10)
(*Aspergillus*)
× 150   from *2699*

Muramidase (3.2.1.17)
(egg white, 1st form)
× ?   from *3*

Muramidase (3.2.1.17)
(egg white, 2nd form)
× 95   from *40*

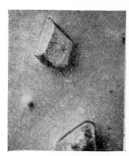

Muramidase (3.2.1.17)
(rabbit spleen, 1st form)
× 75   from *1261*

Muramidase (3.2.1.17)
(rabbit spleen, 2nd form)
× 60   from *1262*

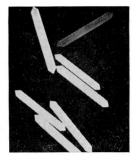

β-galactosidase
(3.2.1.23)
(*Esch. coli*)
× 200   from *2777*

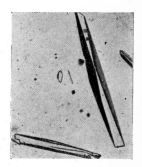

Carboxypeptidase A
(3.4.2.1)
(ox pancreatic juice,
1st form)
× 47   from *76*

Carboxypeptidase A
(3.4.2.1)
(ox pancreatic juice,
2nd form)
× 170   from *2130*

Carboxypeptidase A
(3.4.2.1)
(ox pancreatic juice,
3rd form)
× 170   from *2130*

Pepsin (3.4.4.1)
(pig gastric juice, 1st form)
×60   from *1083*

Pepsin (3.4.4.1)
(pig gastric juice, 2nd form)
×120   from *1993a*

Pepsin (3.4.4.1)
(salmon stomach)
× ?   from *1988*

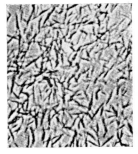

Gastricsin (3.4.4.a)
(human gastric juice)
× 480   from *2616*

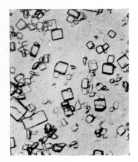

Rennin (3.4.4.3)
(calf stomach)
× 300   from *235*

Trypsin (3.4.4.4)
(ox pancreatic juice)
× 200   from *1495*

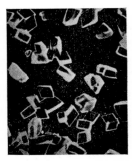

α-chymotrypsin (3.4.4.5)
(ox pancreatic juice,
1st form)
× 120   from *1494*

α-chymotrypsin (3.4.4.5)
(ox pancreatic juice,
2nd form)
× 150   from *1487*

β-chymotrypsin (3.4.4.5)
(ox pancreatic juice)
× 315   from *1487*

γ-chymotrypsin (3.4.4.5)
(ox pancreatic juice)
× 12   from *1487*

Chymotrypsin B (3.4.4.6)
(ox pancreatic juice,
1st form)
× 210   from *342*

Chymotrypsin B (3.4.4.6)
(ox pancreatic juice,
2nd form)
× 210   from *342*

Pancreatopeptidase E
(3.4.4.7)
(pig pancreas)
× 750   from *1579*

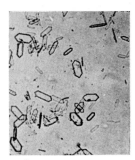

Papain (3.4.4.10)
(*Carica papaya* latex)
× 100   from *147*

Subtilopeptidase A
(3.4.4.16)
(*B. subtilis*)
× 135   from *953*

Subtilopeptidase A
(3.4.4.16)
(*B. subtilis*)
× 200   from *972*

Aspergillopeptidase A
(3.4.4.17)
(*Aspergillus*)
× 300   from *518*

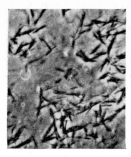

Streptococcus peptidase A
(3.4.4.18)
× 560   from *687*

Tetrahymena peptidase
(Hg salt)
× 40   from *2738*

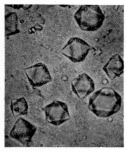

Urease (3.5.1.5)
(jack bean)
× 1300   from *2565*

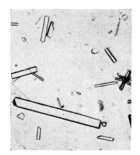

Penicillinase (3.5.2.6)
(*B. cereus*)
× 27   from *2102*

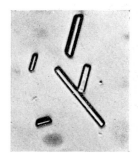

Arginase (3.5.3.1)
(ox liver)
× 340   from *120*

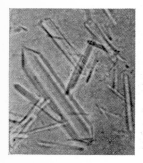

AMP deaminase (3.5.4.6)
(rabbit muscle)
× ?   from *1530*

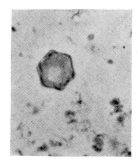

Thiaminase II (3.5.99.2)
(*B. aneurinolyticus*)
× 650   from *1206*

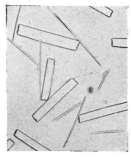

Inorganic pyrophosphatase
(3.6.1.1)
(yeast)
× 110   from *1491*

Aldolase (4.1.2.7)
(ox liver)
× 440   from *2063*

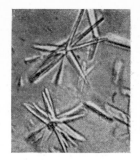

Aldolase (4.1.2.b)
(rat muscle, 1st form)
× ?   from *2789*

Aldolase (4.1.2.b)
(rat muscle, 2nd form)
× 150   from *2620*

Aldolase (4.1.2.b)
(rabbit muscle, 1st form)
× 85   from *2620*

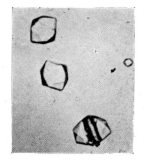

Aldolase (4.1.2.b)
(rabbit muscle, 2nd form)
× 260   from *161*

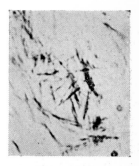

Citrate synthase
(4.1.3.7)
(pig heart)
× 600   from *2012*

Fumarate hydratase
(4.2.1.2)
(pig heart, 1st form)
× 600   from *1743*

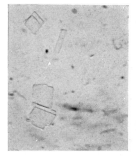

Fumarate hydratase
(4.2.1.2)
(pig heart, 2nd form)
× 400   from *1743*

Fumarate hydratase
(4.2.1.2)
(pig heart, 3rd form)
× ?   from *1751*

Phosphopyruvate hydratase
(4.2.1.11)
(Hg salt)
(yeast)
× 300   from *2788*

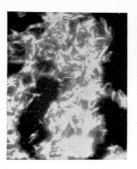

Phosphopyruvate hydratase
(4.2.1.11)
(rabbit muscle)
× 850   from *529*

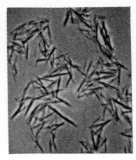

Homoserine dehydratase
(4.2.1.15)
(rat liver)
× 500   from *1757*

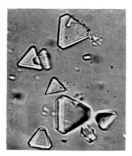

Enoyl-CoA hydratase
(4.2.1.17)
(ox liver)
× 700   from *2521*

Triosephosphate isomerase
(5.3.1.1)
(rabbit muscle, 1st form)
× 200   from *529*

Triosephosphate isomerase
(5.3.1.1)
(rabbit muscle, 2nd form)
× 200   from *529*

Steroid Δ-isomerase
(5.3.3.1)
(*Pseudomonas*)
× 56   from *1323*

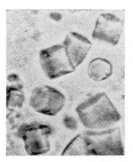

Propionyl-CoA carboxylase
(6.4.1.3)
(pig heart)
× 850   from *1326*

REFERENCES

1. ABDULLAH, M., and WHELAN, W. J. *Biochem. J.* **75**, 12P (1960)
2. ABLONDI, F. B., and HAGAN, J. J., in *The Enzymes*, 2nd edn., ed. P. D. Boyer, H. Lardy and K. Myrbäck (New York, Academic Press, 1960), Vol. 4, p. 175
3. ABRAHAM, E. P., and ROBINSON, R. *Nature, Lond.* **140**, 24 (1937)
4. ABRAMS, R., and BENTLEY, M. *Arch. Biochem. Biophys.* **79**, 91 (1959)
5. ADAMS, D. H. *Biochim. biophys. Acta* **3**, 1 (1949)
6. ADAMS, D. H., and WHITTAKER, V. P. *Biochim. biophys Acta* **3**, 358 (1949)
7. ADAMS, D. H., and WHITTAKER, V. P. *Biochim. biophys. Acta* **4**, 543 (1950)
8. ADAMS, E. *J. biol. Chem.* **209**, 829 (1954)
9. ADAMS, E. *J. biol. Chem.* **217**, 325 (1955)
10. ADAMS, E. *J. biol. Chem.* **234**, 2073 (1959)
11. ADAMS, E., DAVIS, N. C., and SMITH, E. L. *J. biol. Chem.* **199**, 845 (1952)
12. ADAMS, E., DAVIS, N. C., and SMITH, E. L. *J. biol. Chem.* **208**, 573 (1954)
13. ADAMS, E., and GOLDSTONE, A. *J. biol. Chem.* **235**, 3499 (1960)
14. ADAMS, E., and SMITH, E. L. *J. biol. Chem.* **198**, 671 (1952)
15. ADAMS, E. Q. *J. Amer. chem. Soc.* **38**, 1503 (1916)
16. ADAMS, M., RICHTMYER, N. K., and HUDSON, C. S. *J. Amer. chem. Soc.* **65**, 1369 (1943)
17. ADLER, A. J., and KISTIAKOWSKY, G. B. *J. biol. Chem.* **236**, 3240 (1961)
18. ADLER, E., GÜNTHER, G., and EVERETT, J. E. *Z. physiol. Chem.* **255**, 27 (1938)
19. ADLER, E., HELLSTRÖM, V., GÜNTHER, G., and EULER, H. VON. *Z. physiol. Chem.* **255**, 14 (1938)
20. ADRIAN, E. D., FELDBERG, W., and KILBY, B. A. *Brit. J. Pharmacol.* **2**, 56 (1947)
21. ADROUNY, G. A., BLOOM, W. L., and WILHELM, A. E. *Fed. Proc.* **16**, 143 (1957)
22. AGNER, K. *Acta physiol. scand.* **2**, Suppl. VIII (1941)
23. AGOSIN, M. and WEINBACH, E. C. *Biochim. biophys. Acta*, **21**, 117 (1956)
24. AGRANOFF, B. W., and BRADY, R. O. *J. biol. Chem.* **219**, 221 (1956)
25. AGRANOFF, B. W., EGGERER, H., HENNING, U., and LYNEN, F. *J. biol. Chem.* **235**, 326 (1960)
26. ÅGREN, G. *Acta physiol. scand.* **9**, 248, 255 and 269 (1945)
27. AKABORI, S., IKENAKA, T., and HAGIHARA, B. *J. Biochem., Tokyo* **41**, 577 (1954)
28. AKAMATSU, S., and NISHIBORI, O. *Enzymologia* **16**, 273 (1954)
29. ALBERS, R. W., and KOVAL, G. J. *Biochim. biophys. Acta* **52**, 29 (1961)
30. ALBERT, A. *Biochem. J.* **47**, xxvii (1950)
31. ALBERT, A. *Biochem. J.* **54**, 646 (1953)
32. ALBERTY, R. A. *J. Amer. chem. Soc.* **76**, 2494 (1954)
33. ALBERTY, R. A. *Advanc. Enzymol.* **17**, 1 (1956)
34. ALBERTY, R. A. *J. cell. comp. Physiol.* **47**, Suppl. 1, 245 (1956)
35. ALBERTY, R. A., in *The Enzymes*, 2nd edn., ed. P. D. Boyer, H. Lardy and K. Myrbäck (New York, Academic Press, 1961), Vol. 5, p. 531

36. ALBERTY, R. A., and MARVIN, H. H. *J. phys. Chem.* **54,** 47 (1950)
37. ALBERTY, R. A., and MARVIN, H. H. *J. Amer. chem. Soc.* **73,** 3220 (1951)
38. ALBERTY, R. A., and MASSEY, V. *Biochim. biophys. Acta* **13,** 347 (1954)
39. ALBERTY, R. A., MILLER, W. G., and FISHER, H. F. *J. Amer. chem. Soc.* **79,** 3973 (1957)
40. ALDERTON, G., WARD, W. H., and FEVOLD, H. L. *J. biol. chem.* **157,** 43 (1945)
41. ALDRIDGE, W. N. *Biochem. J.* **46,** 451 (1950)
42. ALDRIDGE, W. N. *Biochem. J.* **53,** 110 (1953)
43. ALDRIDGE, W. N. *Biochem. J.* **53,** 117 (1953)
44. ALDRIDGE, W. N. *Biochem. J.* **54,** 442 (1953)
45. ALDRIDGE, W. N., and DAVISON, A. N. *Biochem. J.* **52,** 663 (1952)
46. ALDRIDGE, W. N., and DAVISON, A. N. *Biochem. J.* **55,** 763 (1953)
47. ALDRIDGE, W. N., and JOHNSON, M. K. *Biochem. J.* **73,** 270 (1959)
48. ALEXANDER, M., HEPPEL, L. A., and HURWITZ, J. *J. biol. Chem.* **236,** 3014 (1961)
49. ALGRANATI, I. D., and CABIB, E. *Biochim. biophys. Acta* **43,** 141 (1960)
50. ALIVASATOS, S. G. A., and WOOLLEY, D. W. *J. biol. Chem.* **219,** 823 (1956)
51. ALLEN, E. H., GLASSMAN, E., and SCHWEET, R. S. *J. biol. Chem.* **235,** 1061 (1960)
52. ALLFREY, V. G., in *The Cell*, ed. J. Brachet and A. E. Mirsky (New York, Academic Press. 1959), Vol. 1, p. 193
53. ALLFREY, V. G. *Proceedings of the fifth International Congress of Biochemistry, Moscow*, Symp. No. 2 (Oxford, Pergamon Press, 1963)
54. ALLFREY, V. G., MIRSKY, A. E., and OSAWA, S. *J. gen. Physiol.* **40,** 451 (1957)
55. ALTENBERN, R. A., and HOUSEWRIGHT, R. D. *J. biol. Chem.* **204,** 159 (1953)
56. ALTSCHUL, A. M., ABRAMS, R., and HOGNESS, T. R. *J. biol. Chem.* **136,** 777 (1940)
57. ALVAREZ, E. F., and LORA-TAMAYO, M. *Biochem. J.* **69,** 312 (1958)
58. AMBLER, R. P. *Biochem. J.* **82,** 30P (1962)
59. AMBROSE, J. F., KISTIAKOWSKY, G. B., and KRIDL, A. G. *J. Amer. chem. Soc.* **73,** 1232 (1951)
60. AMES, B. N. *J biol. Chem.* **226,** 583 (1957)
61. AMES, B. N. *J. biol. Chem.* **228,** 131 (1957)
62. AMES, B. N., and GARRY, B. *Proc. nat. Acad. Sci. U.S.* **45,** 1453 (1959)
63. AMES, B. N., and HORECKER, B. L. *J. biol. Chem.* **220,** 113 (1956)
64. AMMON, R. *Pflüg. Arch. ges. Physiol.* **233,** 486 (1934)
65. AMOS, H. *J. Amer. chem. Soc.* **76,** 3858 (1954)
66. ANDERSON, B. M., CIOTTI, C. J., and KAPLAN, N. O. *J. biol. Chem.* **234,** 1219 (1959)
67. ANDERSON, B. M., CORDES, E. H., and JENCKS, W. P. *J. biol. Chem.* **236,** 455 (1961)
68. ANDERSON, B. M., and KAPLAN, N. O. *J. biol. Chem.* **234,** 1226 (1959)
69. ANDERSON, D. G., and VENNESLAND, B. *J. biol. Chem.* **207,** 613 (1954)
70. ANDO, T., FUJIOKA, H., and KAWANISHI, Y. *Biochim. biophys. Acta* **34,** 296 (1959)
71. ANET, F. A. L. *J. Amer. chem. Soc.* **82,** 994 (1960)
72. ANFINSEN, C. B. *C. R. Lab. Carlsberg (Sér. Chim.)* **30,** 13 (1956)
73. ANFINSEN, C. B. *J. biol. Chem.* **221,** 405 (1956)

74. ANFINSEN, C. B. *Proceedings of the fifth International Congress of Biochemistry, Moscow* (Oxford, Pergamon Press, 1963)

75. ANFINSEN, C. B., ÅQVIST, S. E. Q., COOKE, J. P., and JONSSON, B. *J. biol. Chem.* **234**, 1118 (1959)

76. ANSON, M. L. *J. gen. Physiol.* **20**, 663 (1937)

77. ANSON, M. L. *J. gen. Physiol.* **20**, 777 (1937)

78. ANSON, M. L. *J. gen. Physiol.* **22**, 79 (1939)

79. ANSON, M. L., and MIRSKY, A. E. *J. gen. Physiol.* **17**, 393 (1934)

80. ANTIA, M., HOARE, D. S., and WORK, E. *Biochem. J.* **65**, 448 (1957)

81. ANTONI, F., and KELETI, T. *Nature, Lond.* **179**, 1020 (1957)

82. APPLEBY, C. A., and MORTON, R. K. *Biochem. J.* **71**, 492 (1959)

83. APPLEBY, C. A., and MORTON, R. K. *Biochem. J.* **73**, 539 (1959)

84. APPLEBY, C. A., MORTON, R. K., and SIMMONDS, D. H. *Biochem. J.* **75**, 72 (1960)

85. ARCHIBALD, R. M. *J. biol. Chem.* **154**, 657 (1944)

86. ARCUS, A. C., and EDSON, N. L. *Biochem. J.* **64**, 385 (1956)

87. ARNON, D. I., in *Light and Life*, ed. W. D. McElroy and B. Glass (Baltimore, Johns Hopkins Press, 1961), p. 489

88. ARONSSON, T. *Scand. J. clin. lab. Invest.* **9**, 95 (1957)

89. ASHBY, W. *J. biol. Chem.* **151**, 521 (1943)

90. ASHWELL, G., and HICKMAN, J. *J. biol. Chem.* **226**, 65 (1957)

91. ASHWELL, G., WAHBA, A. J., and HICKMAN, J. *J. biol. Chem.* **235**, 1559 (1960)

92. ASKONAS, B. A. *Biochem. J.* **48**, 42 (1951)

93. ASKONAS, B. A. Thesis for Ph.D. Degree, University of Cambridge (1952)

94. ASNIS, R. E., and BRODIE, A. F. *J. biol. Chem.* **203**, 153 (1953)

95. ATKINSON, M. R., JACKSON, J. F., and MORTON, R. K. *Biochem. J.* **80**, 318 (1961)

96. AUERBACH, V. H., WAISMAN, H. A., and WYCKOFF, L. B. *Nature, Lond.* **182**, 871 (1958)

97. AUGUSTINSSON, K.-B. *Acta physiol. scand.* **15**, Suppl. 52 (1948)

98. AUGUSTINSSON, K.-B., and GUSTAFSON, T. *J. cell. comp. Physiol.* **34**, 311 (1949)

99. AUGUSTINSSON, K.-B., and HEIMBÜRGER, G. *Acta chem. scand.* **8**, 753, 762, and 1533 (1954)

100. AUGUSTINSSON, K.-B., and OLSSON, B. *Biochem. J.* **71**, 477 (1959)

101. AULT, R. G., BAIRD, D. K., CARRINGTON, H. C., HAWORTH, W. N., HERBERT, R., HIRST, E. L., PERCIVAL, E. G. V., SMITH, F., and STACEY, M. *J. chem. Soc.* p. 1419 (1933)

102. AVIGAD, G. *J. biol. Chem.* **229**, 121 (1957)

103. AVIGAD, G., AMARAL, D., ASENSIO, C., and HORECKER, B. L. *J. biol. Chem.* **237**, 2736 (1962)

104. AVINERI-SHAPIRO, S., and HESTRIN, S. *Biochem. J.* **39**, 167 (1945)

105. AVIS, P. G., BERGEL, F., and BRAY, R. C. *J. chem. Soc.* p. 1100 (1955)

106. AVIS, P. G., BERGEL, F., and BRAY, R. C. *J. chem. Soc.* p. 1219 (1956)

107. AVRON, M. and JAGENDORF, A. T. *Arch. Biochem. Biophys.* **65**, 475 (1956)

108. AWAD, E. S., NEURATH, H., and HARTLEY, B. S. *J. biol. Chem.* **235**, PC35 (1960)

109. AXELROD, J. *Biochem. J.* **63**, 634 (1956)

110. AXELROD, B., and BANDURSKI, R. S. *J. biol. Chem.* **204**, 939 (1953)

111. AXELROD, A. E., and ELVEHJEM, C. A. *J. biol. Chem.* **140,** 725 (1941)
112. AXELROD, J., INSCOE, J. K., and TOMKINS, G. M. *J. biol. Chem.* **232,** 835 (1958)
113. AXELROD, B., and JANG, R. *J. biol. Chem.* **209,** 847 (1954)
114. AXELROD, B., SALTMAN, P., BANDURSKI, R. S., and BAKER, R. S. *J. biol. Chem.* **197,** 89 (1952)
115. AXELROD, J., and TOMCHICK, R. *J. biol. Chem.* **233,** 702 (1958)
116. AXELROD, J., and WEISSBACH, H. *J. biol. Chem.* **236,** 211 (1961)
117. AYENGAR, P., HAYAISHI, O., NAKAJIMA, M., and TOMIDA, I. *Biochim. biophys. Acta* **33,** 111 (1959)
118. AYERS, W. A. *J. biol. Chem.* **234,** 2819 (1959)
119. BACH, S. J., DIXON, M., and ZERFAS, L. G. *Biochem. J.* **40,** 229 (1946)
120. BACH, S. J., and KILLIP, J. D. *Biochim. biophys. Acta* **29,** 273 (1958)
121. BACH, S. J., and KILLIP, J. D. *Biochim. biophys. Acta* **47,** 336 (1961)
122. BACH, S. J., and WHITEHOUSE, D. B. *Biochem. J.* **57,** xxxi (1954)
123. BACHHAWAT, B. K., ROBINSON, W. G., and COON, M. J. *J. biol. Chem.* **216,** 727 (1955)
124. BACON, J. S. D. *Biochem. J.* **57,** 320 (1954)
125. BACON, J. S. D. Personal communication (1962)
126. BACON, J. S. D., and BELL, D. J. *J. chem. Soc.* p. 3581 (1957)
127. BACQ, Z. M. *Experientia* **2,** 349 and 385 (1946)
128. BADDILEY, J. *Advanc. Enzymol.* **16,** 1 (1955)
129. BADDILEY, J., and GALE, E. F. *Nature, Lond.* **155,** 727 (1945)
130. BADDILEY, J., and HUGHES, N. A. *Advanc. Enzymol.* **22,** 157 (1960)
131. BADDILEY, J., and MATHIAS, A. P. *J. chem. Soc.* p. 2583 (1952)
132. BADDILEY, J., and NEUHAUS, F. C. *Biochem. J.* **75,** 579 (1960)
133. BAICH, A., WOLFE, R. G., and REITHEL, F. J. *J. biol. Chem.* **235,** 3130 (1960)
134. BAILEY, J. M., WHELAN, W. J., and PEAT, S. *J. chem. Soc.* p. 3692 (1950)
135. BAILEY, K. *Biochem. J.* **36,** 121 (1942)
136. BAILEY, K. *Biochem. J.* **43,** 271 (1948)
137. BAILEY, K., and WEBB, E. C. *Biochem. J.* **38,** 394 (1944)
138. BAILEY, K., and WEBB, E. C. *Biochem. J.* **42,** 60 (1948)
139. BAILEY, R. W. *Biochem. J.* **72,** 42 (1959)
140. BAILEY, R. W., and CLARKE, R. T. J. *Biochem. J.* **72,** 49 (1959)
141. BAIN, J. A., and RUSCH, H. P. *J. biol. Chem.* **153,** 659 (1944)
142. BAKER, L. E. *J. biol. Chem.* **193,** 809 (1951)
143. BALDWIN, E., and NEEDHAM, D. M. *Proc. roy. Soc.* B, **122,** 197 (1937)
144. BALINSKY, D., and DAVIES, D. D. *Biochem. J.* **80,** 292 (1961)
145. BALINSKY, D., and DAVIES, D. D. *Biochem. J.* **80,** 300 (1961)
146. BALLS, A. K., and JANSEN, E. F. *Advanc. Enzymol.* **13,** 321 (1952)
147. BALLS, A. K., and LINEWEAVER, H. *J. biol. Chem.* **130,** 669 (1939)
148. BALLS, A. K., WALDEN, M. K., and THOMPSON, R. R. *J. biol. Chem.* **173,** 9 (1948)
149. BALLS, A. K., and WOOD, H. N. *J. biol. Chem.* **219,** 245 (1956)
150. BAMANN, E., and SCHMELLER, M. *Z. physiol. Chem.* **183,** 149 (1929)
151. BANDURSKI, R. S. *J. biol. Chem.* **217,** 137 (1955)
152. BANDURSKI, R. S., and LIPMANN, F. *J. biol. Chem.* **219,** 741 (1956)
153. BANDURSKI, R. S., WILSON, L. G., and SQUIRES, C. L. *J. Amer. chem. Soc.* **78,** 6408 (1956)
154. BANGA, I. *Acta physiol. hung.* **3,** 317 (1952)

155. BANGHAM, A. D., and DAWSON, R. M. C. *Biochem. J.* **72,** 486 (1959)
156. BANGHAM, A. D., and DAWSON, R. M. C. *Biochem. J.* **75,** 133 (1960)
157. BANKS, B. E. C., DIAMANTIS, A. A., and VERNON, C. A. *J. chem. Soc.* p. 4235 (1961)
158. BANKS, B. E. C., and VERNON, C . A. *J. chem. Soc.* p. 1698 (1961)
159. BARANOWSKI, T. *J. biol. Chem.* **180,** 535 (1949)
160. BARANOWSKI, T., ILLINGSWORTH, B., BROWN, D. H., and CORI, C. F. *Biochim. biophys. Acta* **25,** 16 (1957)
161. BARANOWSKI, T., and NIEDERLAND, T. R. *J. biol. Chem.* **180,** 543 (1949)
162. BARBAN, S. *J. Bact.* **68,** 493 (1954)
163. BARKER, H. A. *Fed. Proc.* **20,** 956 (1961)
164. BARKER, H. A., SMYTH, R. D., WILSON, R. M., and WEISSBACH, H. *J. biol. Chem.* **234,** 320 (1959)
165. BARKER, S. A., and BOURNE, E. J. *J. chem. Soc.* p. 209 (1952)
166. BARKER, S. A., and BOURNE, E. J. *Quart. Rev. chem. Soc., Lond.* **7,** 56 (1953)
167. BARKER, S. A., BOURNE, E., and PEAT, S. *J. chem. Soc.* p. 1705 (1949)
168. BARKER, S. A., and CARRINGTON, T. R. *J. chem. Soc.,* p. 3588 (1953)
169. BARNARD, E. A., and STEIN, W. D. *Advanc. Enzymol.* **20,** 51 (1958)
170. BARNARD, E. A., and STEIN, W. D. *J. mol. Biol.* **1,** 339 (1959)
171. BARNARD, M. L., and LAIDLER, K. J. *J. Amer. chem. Soc.* **74,** 6099 (1952)
172. BARRETT, J. *Biochem. J.* **64,** 626 (1956)
173. BARRON, E. S. G. *Advanc. Enzymol.* **11,** 201 (1951)
174. BARTH, L. G., and JAEGER, L. *J. cell. comp. Physiol.* **35,** 413 (1950)
175. BARTSCH, R. G., and KAMEN, M. D. *J. biol. Chem.* **230,** 41 (1958)
176. BARTSCH, R. G., and KAMEN, M. D. *J. biol. Chem.* **235,** 825 (1960)
177. BASU, D. K., and BACHHAWAT, B. K. *Biochim. biophys. Acta* **50,** 123 (1961)
178. BASU, D. K., and BURMA, D. P. *J. biol. Chem.* **235,** 509 (1960)
179. BAUM, H., and GILBERT, G. A. *Nature, Lond.* **171,** 983 (1953)
180. BAYLISS, B. J., and TODRICK, A. *Biochem. J.* **62,** 62 (1956)
181. BEADLE, G. W. *Chem. Rev.* **37,** 15 (1945)
182. BEALING, F. J. *Biochem. J.* **55,** 93 (1953)
183. BEALING, F. J., and BACON, J. S. D. *Biochem. J.* **53,** 277 (1953)
184. BEAN, R. C., and HASSID, W. Z. *J. biol. Chem.* **218,** 425 (1956)
185. BEAN, R. C., PORTER, G. G., and STEINBERG, B. M. *J. biol. Chem.* **236,** 1235 (1961)
186. BEATTY, R. A. *Int. Rev. Cytol.* **3,** 177 (1954)
187. BEAUFAY, H., BENDALL, D. S., BAUDHUIN, P., WATTIAUX, R., and DE DUVE, C. *Biochem. J.* **73,** 628 (1959)
188. BEAUFAY, H., and DE DUVE, C. *Biochem. J.* **73,** 604 (1959)
189. BEAUFAY, H., VAN CAMPENHOUT, E., and DE DUVE, C. *Biochem. J.* **73,** 617 (1959)
190. BECK, W. S., FLAVIN, M., and OCHOA, S. *J. biol. Chem.* **229,** 997 (1957)
191. BECK, W. S., and OCHOA, S. *J. biol. Chem.* **232,** 931 (1958)
192. BEEVERS, H. *Nature, Lond.* **191,** 433 (1961)
193. BEEVERS, H., and FRENCH, R. C. *Arch. Biochem. Biophys.* **50,** 427 (1954)
194. BEHRENS, M. *Z. physiol. Chem.* **209,** 59 (1932)
195. BEHRMAN, E. J., and STANIER, R. Y. *J. biol. Chem.* **228,** 923 (1957)
196. BEINERT, H. *Biochim. biophys. Acta* **20,** 588 (1956)
197. BEINERT, H. *J. Amer. chem. Soc.* **78,** 5323 (1956)

198. BEINERT, H., in *The Enzymes*, 2nd edn., ed. P. D. Boyer, H. Lardy and K. Myrbäck (New York, Academic Press, 1960), Vol. 2, p. 339

199. BEINERT, H., BOCK, R. M., GOLDMAN, D. S., GREEN, D. E., MAHLER, H. R., MII, S., STANSLY, P. G., and WAKIL, S. J. *J. Amer. chem. Soc.* **75,** 4111 (1953)

200. BEISENHERZ, G., BOLTZE, H. J., BÜCHER, T., CZOK, R., GARBADE, K. H., MEYER-ARENDT, E., and PFLEIDERER, G. *Z. Naturf.* **8b,** 555 (1953)

201. BELLAMY, W. D., and GUNSALUS, I. C. *J. Bact.* **48,** 191 (1944)

202. BENDALL, D. S. *Biochem. J.* **70,** 381 (1958)

203. BENDALL, D. S., and DE DUVE, C. *Biochem. J.* **74,** 444 (1960)

204. BENDALL, D. S., and HILL, R. *New Phytol.* **55,** 206 (1956)

204a. BENDER, A. E., and KREBS, H. A. *Biochem. J.* **46,** 210 (1950)

205. BENESCH, R. E., and BENESCH, R. *J. Amer. chem. Soc.* **77,** 5877 (1955)

206. BEN-GERSHOM, E. *Nature, Lond.* **175,** 593 (1955)

207. BENTLEY, R., and BHATE, D. S. *J. biol. Chem.* **235,** 1219 and 1225 (1960)

208. BENTLEY, R., and THIESSEN, C. P. *J. biol. Chem.* **226,** 703 (1957)

209. BENZER, S., and WEISBLUM, B. *Proc. nat. Acad. Sci. U.S.* **47,** 1149 (1961)

210. BENZINGER, T., KITZINGER, C., HEMS, R., and BURTON, K. *Biochem. J.* **71,** 400 (1959)

211. BERENDS, F., POSTHUMUS, C. H., SLUYS, I. V. D., and DEIERKAUF, F. A. *Biochim. biophys. Acta* **34,** 576 (1959)

212. BERG, P. *J. biol. Chem.* **222,** 991 (1956)

213. BERG, P. *J. biol. Chem.* **222,** 1015 (1956)

214. BERG, P. *J. biol. Chem.* **222,** 1025 (1956)

215. BERG, P., BERGMANN, F. H., OFENGAND, E. J., and DIECKMANN, M. *J. biol. Chem.* **236,** 1726 (1961)

216. BERG, P., and JOKLIK, W. K. *J. biol. Chem.* **210,** 657 (1954)

217. BERG, P., and OFENGAND, E. J. *Proc. nat. Acad. Sci. U.S.* **44,** 78 (1958)

218. BERGER, L., SLEIN, M. W., COLOWICK, S. P., and CORI, C. F. *J. gen. Physiol.* **29,** 379 (1946)

219. BERGERET, B., CHATAGNER, F., and FROMAGEOT, C. *Biochim. biophys. Acta* **22,** 329 (1956)

220. BERGMANN, F. H., BERG, P., and DIECKMANN, M. *J. biol. Chem.* **236,** 1735 (1961)

220a. BERGMANN, M. *Advanc. Enzymol.* **2,** 49 (1942)

221. BERGMANN, M., and FRUTON, J. S. *J. biol. Chem.* **118,** 405 (1937)

222. BERGMANN, M., and FRUTON, J. S. *J. biol. Chem.* **124,** 321 (1938)

223. BERGMANN, M., and FRUTON, J. S. *Advanc. Enzymol.* **1,** 63 (1941)

224. BERGMANN, F., and RIMON, S. *Biochem. J.* **77,** 209 (1960)

225. BERGMANN, F., RIMON, S., and SEGAL, R. *Biochem. J.* **68,** 493 (1958)

226. BERGMANN, F., and SEGAL, R. *Biochem. J.* **58,** 692 (1954)

227. BERGMANN, F., SEGAL, R., and RIMON, S. *Biochem. J.* **67,** 481 (1957)

228. BERGMANN, F., SEGAL, R., SHIMONI, A., and WURZEL, M. *Biochem. J.* **63,** 684 (1956)

229. BERGMANN, F., WURZEL, M., and SHIMONI, E. *Biochem. J.* **55,** 888 (1953)

230. BERGMEYER, H.-U., HOLZ, G., KAUDER, E. M., MÖLLERING, H., and WIELAND, O. *Biochem. Z.* **333,** 471 (1961)

231. BERMAN, R., WILSON, I. B., and NACHMANSOHN, D. *Biochim. biophys. Acta* **12,** 315 (1953)

REFERENCES   815

232. BERNAL, J. D. *The Physical Basis of Life* (London, Routledge & Kegan Paul, 1951)
233. BERNHARD, S. A. *Biochem. J.* **59,** 506 (1955)
234. BERNHARD, S. A., and GUTFREUND, H. *Biochem. J.* **63,** 61 (1956)
235. BERRIDGE, N. J. *Biochem. J.* **39,** 179 (1945)
236. BERRIDGE, N. J. *Advanc. Enzymol.* **15,** 423 (1954)
237. BERRY, J. F., and WHITTAKER, V. P. *Biochem. J.* **73,** 447 (1959)
238. BERSIN, T. *Biochem. Z.* **248,** 3 (1932)
239. BESSMAN, M. J., LEHMAN, I. R., SIMMS, E. S., and KORNBERG, A. *J. biol. Chem.* **233,** 171 (1958)
240. BESSMAN, S. P., and LIPMANN, F. *Arch. Biochem. Biophys.* **46,** 252 (1953)
241. BETTELHEIM, F. R. *J. biol. Chem.* **212,** 235 (1955)
242. BETTELHEIM, F. R., and NEURATH, H. *J. biol. Chem.* **212,** 241 (1955)
243. BHATIA, I. S., SATYANARAYANA, M. N., and SRINIVASAN, M. *Biochem. J.* **61,** 171 (1955)
244. BHEEMESWAR, B. *Nature, Lond.* **176,** 555 (1955)
245. BIDWELL, E. *Biochem. J.* **55,** 497 (1953)
246. BIDWELL, E., and VAN HEYNINGEN, W. E. *Biochem. J.* **42,** 140 (1948)
247. BIER, M., in *Methods in Enzymology,* ed. S. P. Colowick and N. O. Kaplan (New York, Academic Press, 1962) Vol. 5, p. 33
248. BINKLEY, F. *Nature, Lond.* **167,** 888 (1951)
249. BIRK, Y., SILVER, W. S., and HEIM, A. H. *Biochim. biophys. Acta* **25,** 227 (1957)
250. BIRNBAUM, S. M., in *Methods in Enzymology,* ed. S. P. Colowick and N. O. Kaplan (New York, Academic Press, 1955), Vol. 2, p. 115
251. BIRNBAUM, S. M., LEVINGTOW, L., KINGSLEY, R. B., and GREENSTEIN, J. P. *J. biol. Chem.* **194,** 455 (1952)
252. BISHOP, J., LEAHY, J., and SCHWEET, R. *Proc. nat. Acad. Sci. U.S.* **46,** 1030 (1960)
253. BLACK, S. *Arch. Biochem. Biophys.* **34,** 86 (1951)
254. BLACK, S., and WRIGHT, N. G. *J. biol. Chem.* **213,** 27 (1955)
255. BLACK, S., and WRIGHT, N. G. *J. biol. Chem.* **213,** 39 (1955)
256. BLACK, S., and WRIGHT, N. G. *J. biol. Chem.* **213,** 51 (1955)
257. BLACK, S., and WRIGHT, N. G. *J. biol. Chem.* **221,** 171 (1956)
258. BLAKLEY, R. L. *Biochem. J.* **49,** 257 (1951)
259. BLAKLEY, R. L. *Biochem. J.* **58,** 448 (1954)
260. BLAKLEY, R. L. *Biochem. J.* **61,** 315 (1955)
261. BLAKLEY, R. L. *Biochem. J.* **77,** 459 (1960)
262. BLAKLEY, E. R., and BOYER, P. D. *Biochim. biophys. Acta* **16,** 576 (1955)
263. BLAKLEY, R. L., and McDOUGALL, B. M. *J. biol. Chem.* **236,** 1163 (1961)
264. BLANCHARD, M., GREEN, D. E., NOCITO, V., and RATNER, S. *J. biol. Chem.* **155,** 421 (1944)
265. BLANCHARD, M., GREEN, D. E., NOCITO, V., and RATNER, S. *J. biol. Chem.* **161,** 583 (1945)
266. BLANCHARD, M., GREEN, D. E., NOCITO-CARROLL, V., and RATNER, S. *J. biol. Chem.* **163,** 137 (1946)
267. BLASCHKO, H. *Biochem. J.* **36,** 571 (1942)
268. BLASCHKO, H. *Biochem. J.* **44,** 268 (1949)
269. BLASCHKO, H., and DUTHIE, R. *Biochem. J.* **39,** 347 (1945)
270. BLASCHKO, H., and DUTHIE, R. *Biochem. J.* **39,** 478 (1945)

271. BLASCHKO, H., FASTIER, F. N., and WAJDA, I. *Biochem. J.* **49,** 250 (1951)
272. BLASCHKO, H., RICHTER, D., and SCHLOSSMANN, H. *Biochem. J.* **31,** 2187 (1937)
273. BLAUCH, M., KOCH, F. C., and HANE, M. E. *J. biol. Chem.* **130,** 471 (1939)
274. BLOCH, K., CHAYKIN, S., PHILLIPS, A. H., and DE WAARD, A. *J. biol. Chem.* **234,** 2595 (1959)
275. BLOCH-FRANKENTHAL, L. *Biochem. J.* **57,** 87 (1954)
276. BLUM, H. F. *Time's Arrow and Evol⋅tion* (Princeton University Press, 1951)
277. BOARDMAN, N. K., and PARTRIDGE, S. M. *Biochem. J.* **59,** 543 (1955)
278. BOCK, R. M., and LING, N.-S. *Anal. Chem.* **26,** 1543 (1954)
279. BODO, G. *Nature, Lond.* **176,** 829 (1955)
280. BODO, G. *Biochim. biophys. Acta* **25,** 428 (1957)
281. BOELL, E. J. *Anat. Rec.* **105,** 600 (1949)
282. BOERI, E., CREMONA, T., and SINGER, T. P. *Biochem. biophys. res. Comm.* **2,** 298 (1960)
283. BOLLUM, F. J. *J. biol. Chem.* **235,** 2399 (1960)
284. BOMSTEIN, R., GOLDBERGER, R., and TISDALE, H. *Biochim. biophys. Acta* **50,** 527 (1961)
285. BONNER, W. D. *Proceedings of the fifth International Congress of Biochemistry, Moscow,* Symp. No. 2 (Oxford, Pergamon Press, 1963)
286. BONNICHSEN, R. *Acta chem. scand.* **1,** 114 (1947)
287. BONNICHSEN, R. K. *Arch. Biochem.* **12,** 83 (1947)
288. BONNICHSEN, R. K. *Acta chem. scand.* **4,** 715 (1950)
289. BONNICHSEN, R. K., and WASSÉN, A. M. *Arch. Biochem.* **18,** 361 (1948)
290. BOOTH, J., and BOYLAND, E. *Biochem. J.* **66,** 73 (1957)
291. BORGSTRØM, B., and WHEELDON, L. W. *Biochim. biophys. Acta* **50,** 171 (1961)
292. BORKENHAGEN, L. F., and KENNEDY, E. P. *J. biol. Chem.* **227,** 951 (1957)
293. BORKENHAGEN, L. F., and KENNEDY, E. P. *J. biol. Chem.* **234,** 849 (1959)
294. BORSOOK, H. *Advanc. Protein Chem.* **8,** 127 (1953)
295. BORSOOK, H., and DUBNOFF, J. W. *J. biol. Chem.* **138,** 389 (1941)
296. BORST, P., and SLATER, E. C. *Biochim. biophys. Acta* **48,** 362 (1961)
297. BOTTS, J. *Trans. Faraday Soc.* **54,** 593 (1958)
298. BOTTS, J., and MORALES, M. *Trans. Faraday Soc.* **49,** 696 (1953)
299. BOULANGER, P., and OSTEUX, R. *Biochim. biophys. Acta* **21,** 552 (1956)
300. BOURSNELL, J. C., in *Symposium on the biochemical Reactions of Chemical Warfare Agents,* ed. R. T. Williams, Biochem. Soc. Symposium, No. 2, p. 8 (Cambridge University Press. 1948)
301. BOURSNELL, J. C., and WEBB, E. C. *Nature, Lond.* **164,** 875 (1949)
302. BOVÉ, C., and CONN, E. E. *J. biol. Chem.* **236,** 207 (1961)
303. BOVEY, F. A., and YANARI, S. S., in *The Enzymes,* 2nd edn., ed. P. D. Boyer, H. Lardy and K. Myrbäck (New York, Academic Press, 1960), Vol. 4, p. 63
304. BOXER, G. E., and DEVLIN, T. M. *Science* **134,** 1495 (1961)
304a. BOYER, P. D., DEHUCA, M., EBNER, K. E., NULTQUIST, D. E., and PETER, J. B. *J. biol. Chem.* **237,** 3306 (1962)
305. BOYER, P. D., and HARRISON, W. H., in *A Symposium on the Mechanism of Enzyme Action,* ed. W. D. McElroy and B. Glass (Baltimore, Johns Hopkins Press, 1954), p. 658

306. Boyer, P. D., Koeppe, O. J., and Luchsinger, W. W. *J. Amer. chem. Soc.* **78,** 356 (1956)

307. Bradfield, J. R. G., in *Symposium on Bacterial Anatomy* (6th Symposium of the Society for General Microbiology), ed. E. T. C. Spooner and B. A. D. Stocker (Cambridge University Press, 1956), p. 296

308. Brady, R. O., Mamoon, A., and Stadtman, E. R. *J. biol. Chem.* **222,** 795 (1956)

309. Brady, R. O., and Stadtman, E. R. *J. biol. Chem.* **211,** 621 (1954)

310. Brand, L., and Mahler, H. R. *J. biol. Chem.* **234,** 1615 (1959)

311. Branster, M. V., and Morton, R. K. *Biochem. J.* **63,** 640 (1956)

312. Braunstein, A. E., in *The Enzymes*, 2nd edn., ed. P. D. Boyer, H. Lardy and K. Myrbäck (New York, Academic Press, 1960), Vol. 2, p. 113

313. Braunstein, A. E., and Azarkh, R. M. *Doklady Akad. Nauk, S.S.S.R.* **71,** 93 (1950)

314. Braunstein, A. E., and Azarkh, R. M. *Doklady Akad. Nauk, S.S.S.R.* **85,** 385 (1952)

315. Braunstein, A. E., and Kritzman, M. G. *Biokhimiya* **8,** 1 (1943)

316. Brawerman, G., and Chargaff, E. *Biochim. biophys. Acta* **16,** 524 (1955)

317. Bray, R. C. *Biochem. J.* **81,** 196 (1961)

318. Bray, H. G., James, S. P., Raffan, I. M., Ryman, B. E., and Thorpe, W. V. *Biochem. J.* **44,** 618 (1949)

319. Bray, H. G., James, S. P., Thorpe, W. V., and Wasdell, M. R. *Biochem. J.* **47,** 294 (1950)

320. Bray, R. C., Pettersson, R., and Ehrenberg, A. *Biochem. J.* **81,** 178 (1961)

321. Breard, J. J. V., and Elias, V. E. *Arch. Farm. Bioquim. Tucuman* **5,** 77 (1950)

322. Bredereck, H., and Geyer, E. *Z. physiol. Chem.* **254,** 223 (1938)

323. Bremer, J., and Greenberg, D. M. *Biochim. biophys. Acta* **46,** 217 (1961)

324. Brenneman, F. N., and Volk, W. A. *J. biol. Chem.* **234,** 2443 (1959)

325. Brenner, M., Müller, H. R., and Pfister, R. W. *Helv. chim. Acta* **33,** 568 (1950)

326. Bressler, R., and Wakil, S. J. *J. biol. Chem.* **236,** 1643 (1961)

327. Bressler, R., and Wakil, S. J. *J. biol. Chem.* **237,** 1441 (1962)

328. Briggs, G. E., and Haldane, J. B. S. *Biochem. J.* **19,** 338 (1925)

329. Brill, A. S., and Williams, R. J. P. *Biochem. J.* **78,** 246 and 253 (1961)

330. Brink, N. G. *Acta chem. scand.* **7,** 1081 (1953)

331. Brodie, A. F., in *Methods in Enzymology*, ed. S. P. Colowick and N. O. Kaplan (New York, Academic Press, 1955), Vol. 2, p. 693

332. Brodie, A. F., and Lipmann, F. *J. biol. Chem.* **212,** 677 (1955)

333. Brosemer, R. W., and Rutter, W. J. *J. biol. Chem.* **236,** 1253 (1961)

334. Brown, D. D., Tomchick, R., and Axelrod, J. *J. biol. Chem.* **234,** 2948 (1959)

335. Brown, D. H. *J. biol. Chem.* **204,** 877 (1953)

336. Brown, D. H. *Biochim. biophys. Acta* **16,** 429 (1955)

337. Brown, F. C., and Ward, D. N. *J. Amer. chem. Soc.* **79,** 2647 (1957)

337a. Brown, G. M. *J. biol. Chem.* **234,** 370 (1959)

338. Brown, G. M. *J. biol. Chem.* **226,** 651 (1957)

339. Brown, G. M. *J. biol. Chem.* **234,** 370 (1959)

340. Brown, G. W., Brown, W. R., and Cohen, P. P. *J. biol. Chem.* **234,** 1775 (1959)

341. BROWN, G. W., and COHEN, P. P. *Biochem. J.* **75,** 82 (1960)

342. BROWN, K. D., SHUPE, R. E., and LASKOWSKI, M. *J. biol. Chem.* **173,** 99 (1948)

343. BROWN, M. S., and MOSHER, H. S. *J. biol. Chem.* **235,** 2145 (1960)

344. BROWN-GRANT, K., FORCHIELLI, E., and DORFMAN, R. I. *J. biol. Chem.* **235,** 1317 (1960)

345. BRUMFITT, W., WARDLAW, A. C., and PARK, J. T. *Nature, Lond.* **181,** 1783 (1958)

346. BRUNEL, A. Thesis, University of Paris (1936), quoted by M. Florkin and G. Duchateau-Bosson, *Enzymologia* **9,** 5 (1940)

347. BRUNGRABER, E. G. *J. biol. Chem.* **233,** 472 (1958)

348. BRUNS, F. H. *Proceedings of the fourth International Congress on Clinical Chemistry, Edinburgh* (Edinburgh, E. & S. Livingstone, 1961), p. 76

349. BRUNS, F. H., NOLTMANN, E., and WILLEMSEN, A. *Biochem. Z.* **330,** 411 (1958)

350. BUBLITZ, C., and KENNEDY, E. P. *J. biol. Chem.* **211,** 951 (1955)

351. BUBLITZ, C., and KENNEDY, E. P. *J. biol. Chem.* **211,** 963 (1955)

352. BUBLITZ, C., and LEHNINGER, A. L. *Biochim. biophys. Acta* **47,** 288 (1961)

353. BUCHANAN, J. M., and HARTMAN, S. C. *Advanc. Enzymol.* **21,** 199 (1959)

354. BÜCHER, T. *Biochim. biophys. Acta* **1,** 292 (1947)

355. BUCHER, N. L. R., OVERATH, P., and LYNEN, F. *Biochim. biophys. Acta* **40,** 491 (1960)

356. BUEDING, E., and MACKINNON, J. A. *J. biol. Chem.* **215,** 495 (1955)

357. BULEN, W. A. *Arch. Biochem. Biophys.* **62,** 173 (1956)

358. BULL, H. B., and CURRIE, B. T. *J. Amer. chem. Soc.* **71,** 2758 (1949)

359. BUNDY, H. F., and MEHL, J. W. *J. biol. Chem.* **234,** 1124 (1959)

360. BURCH, J. *Biochem. J.* **58,** 415 (1954)

361. BURMA, D. P., and HORECKER, B. L. *J. biol. Chem.* **231,** 1039 (1958)

362. BURMA, D. P., and HORECKER, B. L. *J. biol. Chem.* **231,** 1053 (1958)

363. BURMA, D. P., TAKAGI, Y., and SMYRNIOTIS, P. Z. *Fed. Proc.* **16,** 161 (1957)

364. BURNETT, G. H., and COHEN, P. P. *J. biol. Chem.* **229,** 337 (1957)

365. BURNETT, G., and KENNEDY, E. P. *J. biol. Chem.* **211,** 69 (1955)

366. BURT, J. R. *Biochem. J.* **77,** 16P (1960)

367. BURTON, K. *Biochem. J.* **48,** 458 (1951)

368. BURTON, K. *Biochem. J.* **50,** 258 (1951)

369. BURTON, K. *Biochem. J.* **59,** 44 (1955)

370. BURTON, R. M., and KAPLAN, N. O. *J. Amer. chem. Soc.* **75,** 1005 (1953)

371. BURTON, R. M., and KAPLAN, N. O. *Arch. Biochem. Biophys.* **70,** 107 (1957)

372. BURTON, R. M., and STADTMAN, E. R. *J. biol. Chem.* **202,** 873 (1953)

373. BUTTIN, G. *Cold Spring Harbor Symposia on quantitative Biology,* **26,** 213 (1961)

374. BUZARD, J. A., and NYTCH, P. D. *J. biol. Chem.* **227,** 225 (1957)

375. BYRDE, R. J. W., and FIELDING, H. A. *Biochem. J.* **61,** 337 (1955)

376. BYRON, J. E., WOOD, W. A., and TREADWELL, C. R. *J. biol. Chem.* **205,** 483 (1953)

377. CABELLO, J., BASILIO, C., and PRAJOUX, V. *Biochim. biophys. Acta* **48,** 148 (1961)

378. CABIB, E., and LELOIR, L. F. *J. biol. Chem.* **231,** 259 (1958)

379. CAFFREY, R. W., TREMBLAY, R., GABRIO, B. W., and HUENNEKENS, F. M. *J. biol. Chem.* **223,** 1 (1956)

380. Cahn, R., Kaplan, N. O., Levine, L., and Zwilling, E. *Science* **136,** 962 (1962)

381. Callaghan, O. H., and Weber, G. *Biochem. J.* **73,** 473 (1959)

382. Calvin, M. *Fed. Proc.* **13,** 697 (1954)

383. Calvin, M., and Bassham, J. A. *The Photosynthesis of Carbon Compounds* (New York, W. A. Benjamin, 1962)

384. Calvin, M., Quayle, R., Fuller, R. C., Mayaudon, J., Benson, A. A., and Bassham, J. A. *Fed. Proc.* **14,** 188 (1955)

385. Camiener, G. W., and Brown, G. M. *J. biol. Chem.* **235,** 2411 (1960)

386. Campbell, L. L. *J. Amer. chem. Soc.* **76,** 5256 (1954)

387. Campbell, L. L. *J. biol. Chem.* **227,** 693 (1957)

388. Campbell, L. L. *J. biol. Chem.* **235,** 2375 (1960)

389. Campbell, L. L., and Manning, G. B. *J. biol. Chem.* **236,** 2962 (1961)

390. Candy, D. J., and Kilby, B. A. *Biochem. J.* **78,** 531 (1961)

391. Canellakis, E. S. *J. biol. Chem.* **227,** 329 (1957)

392. Canellakis, Z. N., and Cohen, P. P. *J. biol. Chem.* **222,** 53 and 63 (1956)

393. Cantoni, G. L. *J. biol. Chem.* **189,** 203 (1951)

394. Cantoni, G. L. *J. biol. Chem.* **204,** 403 (1953)

395. Cantoni, G. L., and Anderson, D. G. *J. biol. Chem.* **222,** 171 (1956)

396. Cantoni, G. L., and Durell, J. *J. biol. Chem.* **225,** 1033 (1957)

397. Cantoni, G. L., and Scarano, E. *J. Amer. chem. Soc.* **76,** 4744 (1954)

398. Cantoni, G. L., and Vignos, P. J. *J. biol. Chem.* **209,** 647 (1954)

399. Caputto, R. *J. biol. Chem.* **189,** 801 (1951)

400. Caputto, R., and Dixon, M. *Nature, Lond.* **156,** 630 (1945)

401. Caputto, R., and Trucco, R. E. *Nature, Lond.* **169,** 1061 (1952)

402. Caravaca, J., and Grisolia, S. *J. biol. Chem.* **231,** 357 (1958)

403. Cardini, C. E. *Enzymologia* **14,** 362 (1951)

404. Cardini, C. E. *Enzymologia* **15,** 303 (1953)

405. Cardini, C. E., and Leloir, L. F. *Arch. Biochem. Biophys.* **45,** 55 (1953)

406. Cardini, C. E., Leloir, L. F., and Chiriboga, J. *J. biol. Chem.* **214,** 149 (1955)

407. Carey, N. H., and Greville, G. D. *Biochem. J.* **71,** 166 (1959)

408. Carminatti, H., and Cabib, E. *Biochim. biophys. Acta* **53,** 417 (1961)

409. Carpenter, D. C., and Lovelace, F. E. *J. Amer. chem. Soc.* **65,** 2364 (1943)

410. Carpenter, W. D., and Beevers, H. *Plant Physiol.* **34,** 403 (1959)

411. Carter, C. E. *J. Amer. chem. Soc.* **73,** 1508 (1951)

412. Carter, C. E., and Cohen, L. H. *J. biol. Chem.* **222,** 17 (1956)

413. Caspi, E., Lindberg, M. C., Hayano, M., Cohen, J. L., Matsuba, M., Rosenkrantz, H., and Dorfman, R. I. *Arch. Biochem. Biophys.* **61,** 267 (1956)

414. Castor, L. N., and Chance, B. *J. biol. Chem.* **217,** 453 (1955)

415. Castor, L. N., and Chance, B. *J. biol. Chem.* **234,** 1587 (1959)

416. Catcheside, D. G. *The Genetics of Micro-organisms* (London, Pitman, 1949)

417. Chamberlin, M., and Berg, P. *Proc. nat. Acad. Sci. U.S.* **48,** 81 (1962)

418. Chance, B. *J. biol. Chem.* **151,** 553 (1943)

419. Chance, B. *Acta chem. scand.* **1,** 236 (1947)

420. Chance, B., in *Enzymes and Enzyme Systems*, ed. J. T. Edsall (Harvard University Press, 1951), p. 93

421. Chance, B. *Arch. Biochem. Biophys.* **41,** 416 (1952)

422. CHANCE, B. *J. biol. Chem.* **194,** 483 (1952)

423. CHANCE, B. *J. biol. Chem.* **202,** 383 (1953)

424. CHANCE, B., and PAPPENHEIMER, A. M. *J. biol. Chem.* **209,** 931 (1954)

425. CHANCE, B., and REDFEARN, E. R. *Biochem. J.* **80,** 632 (1961)

426. CHANCE, B., and SAGER, R. *Plant Physiol.* **32,** 548 (1957)

427. CHANCE, B., and WILLIAMS, G. R. *J. biol. Chem.* **209,** 945 (1954)

428. CHANCE, B., and WILLIAMS, G. R. *J. biol. Chem.* **217,** 383 (1955)

429. CHAPEVILLE, F., LIPMANN, F., VON EHRENSTEIN, G., WEISBLUM, B., RAY, W. J., and BENZER, S. *Proc. nat. Acad. Sci. U.S.* **48,** 1086 (1962)

430. CHAPPELL, J. B., in *Biological Structure and Function*, ed. T. W. Goodwin and O. Lindberg (New York, Academic Press, 1961), Vol. 2, p. 71

431. CHAPPELL, J. B., and PERRY, S. V. *Biochem. J.* **55,** 586 (1953)

432. CHAPPELL, J. B., and PERRY, S. V. *Nature, Lond.* **173,** 1094 (1954)

433. CHARALAMPOUS, F. C. *J. biol. Chem.* **211,** 249 (1954)

434. CHARALAMPOUS, F. C. *J. Amer. chem. Soc.* **77,** 1391 (1955)

435. CHARALAMPOUS, F. C. *J. biol. Chem.* **234,** 220 (1959)

436. CHARGAFF, E., and KREAM, J. *J. biol. Chem.* **175,** 993 (1948)

437. CHARLWOOD, P. A., PALMER, G., and BENNETT, R. *Biochim. biophys. Acta* **50,** 17 (1961)

438. CHASE, A. M. *Arch. Biochem.* **23,** 385 (1949)

439. CHATAGNER, F., and SAURET-IGNAZI, G. *Bull. Soc. Chim. biol., Paris* **38,** 415 (1956)

440. CHATAGNER, F., TABECHIAN, H., and BERGERET, B. *Biochim. biophys. Acta* **13,** 313 (1954)

441. CHATTERJEE, I. B., CHATTERJEE, G. C., GHOSH, N. C., GHOSH, J. J., and GUHA, B. C. *Biochem. J.* **74,** 193 (1960)

442. CHATTERJEE, I. B., CHATTERJEE, G. C., GHOSH, N. C., GHOSH, J. J., and GUHA, B. C. *Biochem. J.* **76,** 279 (1960)

443. CHAYKIN, S., MEINHART, J. O., and KREBS, E. G. *J. biol. Chem.* **220,** 811 (1956)

444. CHIANG, C., and KNIGHT, S. G. *Biochem. biophys. res. Comm.* **3,** 554 (1960)

445. CHIANG, C., and KNIGHT, S. G. *Biochim. biophys. Acta* **46,** 271 (1961)

446. CHIBNALL, A. C., REES, M. W., and WILLIAMS, E. F. *Biochem. J.* **37,** 354 (1943)

447. CHIGA, M., and PLAUT, G. W. E. *J. biol. Chem.* **235,** 3260 (1960)

448. CHIGA, M., ROGERS, A. E., and PLAUT, G. W. E. *J. biol. Chem.* **236,** 1800 (1961)

449. CHILDS, A. F., DAVIES, D. R., GREEN, A. L., and RUTLAND, J. P. *Brit. J. Pharmacol.* **10,** 462 (1955)

450. CHIN, C. H. Thesis for Ph.D. Degree, University of Cambridge (1952)

451. CHOU, T. C., and LIPMANN, F. *J. biol. Chem.* **196,** 89 (1952)

452. CHOU, T. C., and SOODAK, M. *J. biol. Chem.* **196,** 105 (1952)

453. CHRISTIE, S. M. H., KENNER, G. W., and TODD, A. R. *J. chem. Soc.* p. 46 (1954)

454. CHUNG, C. W., and NAJJAR, V. A. *J. biol. Chem.* **218,** 617 (1956)

455. CHUNG, C. W., and NAJJAR, V. A. *J. biol. Chem.* **218,** 627 (1956)

456. CLAUDE, A. *Proc. roy. Soc.* B, **142,** 177 (1954)

457. CLELAND, W. W., and KENNEDY, E. P. *J. biol. Chem.* **235,** 45 (1960)

458. CLELAND, K. W., and SLATER, E. C. *Biochem. J.* **53,** 547 (1953)

459. CLEZY, P. S., and BARRETT, J. *Biochem. J.* **78,** 798 (1961)
460. CLIFFE, E. E., and WALEY, S. G. *Biochem. J.* **79,** 475 (1961)
461. COHEN, J. A., and WARRINGA, M. G. P. J. *Biochim. biophys. Acta* **11,** 52 (1953)
462. COHEN, J. A., and WARRINGA, M. G. P. J. *Biochim. biophys. Acta* **26,** 29 (1957)
463. COHEN, P. P., in *The Enzymes,* 1st edn., ed. J. B. Sumner and K. Myrbäck (New York, Academic Press, 1951), Vol. 1, p. 1040
464. COHEN, P. P., in *Methods in Enzymology,* ed. S. P. Colowick and N. O. Kaplan (New York, Academic Press, 1955), Vol. 2, p. 178
465. COHEN, S. S. *J. biol. Chem.* **189,** 617 (1951)
466. COHEN, S. S. *J. biol. Chem.* **201,**71 (1953)
467. COHEN, S. S., and BARNER, H. D. *J. biol. Chem.* **226,** 631 (1957)
468. COHN, D. V. *J. biol. Chem.* **233,** 299 (1958)
469. COHN, E. J., and EDSALL, J. T. *Proteins, Amino Acids and Peptides* (New York, Reinhold Publishing Corp., 1943)
470. COHN, E. J., GURD, F. R. N., SURGENOR, D. M., BARNES, B. A., BROWN, R. K., DEROVAUX, G., GILLESPIE, J. M., KAHNT, J. M., LEVER, W. F., LIU, C. H., MITTELMAN, D., MOUTON, R. F., SCHMID, K., and UROMA, E. *J. Amer. chem. Soc.* **72,** 465 (1950)
471. COHN, M. *J. biol. Chem.* **180,** 771 (1949)
472. COHN, M. *J. biol. Chem.* **201,** 735 (1953)
473. COHN, M. *Biochim. biophys. Acta* **20,** 92 (1956)
474. COHN, M. *J. biol. Chem.* **230,** 369 (1958)
475. COHN, M., COHEN, G. N., and MONOD, J. *C. R. Acad. Sci., Paris* **236,** 746 (1953)
476. COHN, M., and CORI, G. T. *J. biol. Chem.* **175,** 89 (1948)
477. COLE, R. D., COOTE, J., and WORK, T. S. *Nature, Lond.* **179,** 199 (1957)
478. COLE, S. W. *J. Physiol.* **30,** 202 (1904)
479. COLEMAN, J. E., and VALLEE, B. L. *J. biol. Chem.* **236,** 2244 (1961)
480. COLOWICK, S. P., and KALCKAR, H. M. *J. biol. Chem.* **137,** 789 (1941)
481. COLOWICK, S. P., and KAPLAN, N. O., eds. *Methods in Enzymology* (New York, Academic Press, 1955–63)
482. COLOWICK, S. P., KAPLAN, N. O., NEUFELD, E. F., and CIOTTI, M. M. *J. biol. Chem.* **195,** 951 (1952)
483. COMB, D. G., and ROSEMAN, S. *Fed. Proc.* **16,** 166 (1957)
484. COMB, D. G., and ROSEMAN, S. *J. biol. Chem.* **232,** 807 (1958)
485. COMB, D. G., and ROSEMAN, S. *J. biol. Chem.* **235,** 2529 (1960)
486. CONCHIE, J. *Biochem. J.* **58,** 552 (1954)
487. CONCHIE, J., FINDLAY, J., and LEVVY, G. A. *Nature, Lond.* **178,** 1469 (1956)
488. CONCHIE, J., FINDLAY, J., and LEVVY, G. A. *Biochem. J.* **71,** 318 (1959)
489. CONN, E. E., KRAEMER, L. M., LIU, P.-N., and VENNESLAND, B. *J. biol. Chem.* **194,** 143 (1952)
490. CONNORS, W. M., PIHL, A., DOUNCE, A. L., and STOTZ, E. *J. biol. Chem.* **184,** 29 (1950)
491. CONNORS, W. M., and STOTZ, E. *J. biol. Chem.* **178,** 881 (1949)
492. CONTARDI, A., and ERCOLI, A. *Biochem. Z.* **261,** 275 (1933)
493. CONWAY, E. J., and COOKE, R. *Biochem. J.* **33,** 457 (1939)
494. CONWAY, E. J., and COOKE, R. *Biochem. J.* **33,** 479 (1939)
495. CONWAY, E. J., and MACDONNELL, E. *Nature, Lond.* **156,** 752 (1945)

822   REFERENCES

496. CONWAY, E. J., and O'MALLEY, E. *Biochem. J.* **54,** 154 (1953)
497. COON, M. J., KUPIECKI, F. P., DEKKER, E. E., SCHLESINGER, M. J., and
     DEL CAMPILLO, A., in *CIBA Symposium on the Biosynthesis of Terpenes
     and Sterols,* ed. G. E. W. Wolstenholme and M. O'Connor (London,
     Churchill, 1959), p. 62
498. COOPER, C., and LEHNINGER, A. L. *J. biol. Chem.* **219,** 489 (1956)
499. COOPER, C., and WILSON, D. W. *Fed. Proc.* **13,** 194 (1954)
500. COOPER, J. A. D., SMITH, W., BACILA, M., and MEDINA, H. *J. biol. Chem.*
     234, 445 (1959)
501. CORI, C. F., and CORI, G. T. *J. biol. Chem.* **158,** 341 (1945)
502. CORI, G. T., and CORI, C. F. *J. biol. Chem.* **151,** 57 (1943)
503. CORI, G. T., and LARNER, J. *J. biol. Chem.* **188,** 17 (1951)
504. CORI, G. T., OCHOA, S., SLEIN, M. W., and CORI, C. F. *Biochim. biophys.
     Acta* **7,** 304 (1951)
505. CORI, G. T., SLEIN, M. W., and CORI, C. F. *J. biol. Chem.* **173,** 605
     (1948)
505a. CORNFORTH, J. W., RYBACK, G., POPJAK, G., DONNINGER, C., and
     SCHROEPFER, G. *Biochem. biophys. res. Comm.* **9,** 371 (1962)
506. CORWIN, L. M. *J. biol. Chem.* **234,** 1338 (1959)
507. COSTA, O. A. *Rev. Quím. Farm., Rio de J.* **2,** 71 (1937)
508. COULTHARD, C. E., MICHAELIS, R., SHORT, W. F., SYKES, G., SKRIMSHIRE,
     G. E. H., STANDFAST, A. F. B., BIRKINSHAW, J. H., and RAISTRICK, H.
     Biochem. J. **39,** 24 (1945)
509. COWGILL, R. W. *J. biol. Chem.* **234,** 3146 (1959)
510. COWGILL, R. W., and PIZER, L. I. *J. biol. Chem.* **223,** 885 (1956)
511. CRANDALL, D. I. *Fed. Proc.* **12,** 192 (1953)
512. CRANDALL, D. I., and HALIKIS, D. N. *J. biol. Chem.* **208,** 629 (1954)
513. CRANE, F. L. *Plant Physiol.* **32,** 619 (1957)
514. CRANE, F. L., MII, S., HAUGE, J. G., GREEN, D. E., and BEINERT, H.
     J. biol. Chem. **218,** 701 (1956)
515. CRAWFORD, I., KORNBERG, A., and SIMMS, E. S. *J. biol. Chem.* **226,** 1093
     (1957)
516. CRAWFORD, I. P., and YANOFSKY, C. *Proc. nat. Acad. Sci. U.S.* **44,** 1161
     (1958)
517. CREASEY, W. A., and HANDSCHUMACHER, R. E. *J. biol. Chem.* **236,** 2058
     (1961)
518. CREWTHER, W. G., and LENNOX, F. G. *Nature, Lond.* **165,** 680 (1950)
519. CRICK, F. H. C., BARNETT, L., BRENNER, S., and WATTS-TOBIN, R. J.
     Nature, Lond. **192,** 1227 (1961)
520. CROOK, E. M. *Biochem. J.* **35,** 226 (1941)
521. CROOK, E. M., and LAW, K. *Biochem. J.* **52,** 492 (1952)
522. CROOK, E. M., and STONE, B. A. *Biochem. J.* **65,** 1 (1956)
523. CUNNINGHAM, B. A., and KIRKWOOD, S. *J. biol. Chem.* **236,** 485 (1961)
524. CUNNINGHAM, L., CATLIN, B. W., and DE GARILHE, M. P. *J. Amer. chem.
     Soc.* **78,** 4642 (1956)
525. CUNNINGHAM, L. W., and BROWN, C. S. *J. biol. Chem.* **221,** 287 (1956)
526. CUNNINGHAM, W. L., and MANNERS, D. J. *Biochem. J.* **80,** 42P (1961)
527. CUTOLO, E. *Arch. Biochem. Biophys.* **64,** 242 (1956)
528. CYNKIN, M. A., and ASHWELL, G. *J. biol. Chem.* **235,** 1576 (1960)
529. CZOK, R., and BÜCHER, T. *Advanc. Protein Chem.* **15,** 315 (1960)

530. DAGLEY, S., and DAWES, E. A. *Biochim. biophys. Acta* **17,** 177 (1955)

531. DAHLQVIST, A. *Biochem. J.* **78,** 282 (1961)

532. DAHLQVIST, A. *Biochim. biophys. Acta* **50,** 55 (1961)

533. DALTON, H. R., and NELSON, J. M. *J. Amer. chem. Soc.* **61,** 2946 (1939)

534. DALZIEL, K. *Acta chem. scand.* **11,** 1706 (1957)

535. DALZIEL, K. *Acta chem. scand.* **12,** 459 (1958)

536. DALZIEL, K. *Biochem. J.* **80,** 440 (1961)

537. DALZIEL, K. *Biochem. J.* **84,** 240 (1962)

538. DANIELLI, J. F., and BROWN, R., eds. *Symposium on Nucleic Acids* (1st Symposium of the Society of Experimental Biology) (Cambridge University Press, 1947)

539. DATTA, A. G., and KATZNELSON, H. *Arch. Biochem. Biophys.* **65,** 576 (1956)

540. DATTA, P. K., MEEUSE, B. J. D., ENGSTROM-HEG, V., and HILAL, S. H. *Biochim. biophys. Acta* **17,** 602 (1955)

541. DAUTERMAN, W. C., TALENS, A., and VAN ASPEREN, K. *J. Ins. Physiol.* **8,** 1 (1962)

542. DAVENPORT, H. E. *Nature, Lond.* **170,** 1112 (1952)

543. DAVENPORT, H. E., and HILL, R. *Proc. roy. Soc.* B, **139,** 327 (1952)

544. DAVENPORT, H. E., and HILL, R. *Biochem. J.* **74,** 493 (1960)

545. DAVENPORT, H. W., and WILHELMI, A. E. *Proc. Soc. exp. Biol., N.Y.* **48,** 53 (1941)

546. DAVEY, C. L. *Nature, Lond.* **183,** 995 (1959)

547. DAVID, W. E., and LICHSTEIN, H. C. *Proc. Soc. exp. Biol., N.Y.* **73,** 216 (1950)

548. DAVIDSON, E. A. *J. biol. Chem.* **235,** 23 (1960)

549. DAVIDSON, E. A., BLUMENTHAL, H. J., and ROSEMAN, F. *J. biol. Chem.* **226,** 125 (1957)

550. DAVIDSON, E. A., and RILEY, J. G. *J. biol. Chem.* **235,** 3367 (1960)

551. DAVIDSON, J. N. *The Biochemistry of the Nucleic Acids,* 4th edn. (London, Methuen, 1960)

552. DAVIE, E. W., KONINGSBERGER, V. V., and LIPMANN, F. *Arch. Biochem. Biophys.* **65,** 21 (1956)

553. DAVIE, E. W., and NEURATH, H. *J. biol. Chem.* **212,** 515 (1955)

554. DAVIES, D. D. *Biochem. J.* **80,** 93 (1961)

555. DAVIES, D. D., and KUN, E. *Biochem. J.* **66,** 307 (1957)

556. DAVIES, D. R. *J. Pharm., Lond.* **6,** 1 (1954)

557. DAVIES, D. R. Personal communication

558. DAVIES, D. R., and GREEN, A. L. *Advanc. Enzymol.* **20,** 283 (1958)

559. DAVIES, D. R., and RUTLAND, J. P. *Nature, Lond.* **178,** 697 (1956)

560. DAVIES, R. *Biochem. J.* **37,** 230 (1943)

561. DAVIS, F. F., and ALLEN, F. W. *Biochim. biophys. Acta* **21,** 14 (1956)

562. DAVIS, N. C. *J. biol. Chem.* **223,** 935 (1956)

563. DAVIS, N. C., and ADAMS, E. *Arch. Biochem. Biophys.* **57,** 301 (1955)

564. DAVIS, N. C., and SMITH, E. L. *J. biol. Chem.* **200,** 373 (1953)

565. DAVIS, N. C., and SMITH, E. L. *J. biol. Chem.* **224,** 261 (1957)

566. DAVISON, A. N. *Biochim. biophys. Acta* **19,** 66 (1956)

567. DAVISON, D. C. *Nature, Lond.* **166,** 265 (1950)

568. DAVISON, D. C. *Biochem. J.* **49,** 520 (1951)

569. DAVOLL, J., LYTHGOE, B., and TODD, A. R. *J. chem. Soc.,* p. 833 (1946)

570. DAWSON, C. R., and TARPLEY, W. B., in *The Enzymes*, 1st edn. ed. J. B. Sumner and K. Myrbäck (New York, Academic Press, 1951), Vol. 2, p. 454

571. DAWSON, R. M. C. *Biochem. J.* **62,** 689 (1956)

572. DAWSON, R. M. C. *Biochem. J.* **64,** 192 (1956)

573. DAWSON, R. M. C. *Biochem. J.* **70,** 559 (1958)

574. DE, S. S. *Ann. Biochem. Exp. Med.* (*India*) **4,** 45 (1944)

575. DEBELLIS, R., MANDL, I., MACLENNAN, J. D., and HOWES, E. L. *Nature, Lond.* **174,** 1191 (1954)

576. DE BERNARD, B. *Biochim. biophys. Acta* **23,** 510 (1957)

577. DE CASTRO, F. T., PRICE, J. M., and BROWN, R. R. *J. Amer. chem. Soc.* **78,** 2904 (1956)

578. DECKER, R. H., KANG, H. H., LEACH, F. R., and HENDERSON, L. M. *J. biol. Chem.* **236,** 3076 (1961)

579. DEDONDER, R. *Bull. Soc. Chim. biol., Paris* **34,** 171 (1952)

580. DE DUVE, C., PRESSMAN, B. C., GIANETTO, R., WATTIAUX, R., and APPELMANS, F. *Biochem. J.* **60,** 604 (1955)

581. DE DUVE, C., WATTIAUX, R., and BAUDHUIN, P. *Advanc. Enzymol.* **24,** 291 (1962)

582. DE GARILHE, M. P., and LASKOWSKI, M. *Biochim. biophys. Acta* **18,** 370 (1955)

583. DE GARILHE, M. P., and LASKOWSKI, M. *J. biol. Chem.* **215,** 269 (1955)

584. DEKKER, C. A., TAYLOR, S. P., and FRUTON, J. S. *J. biol. Chem.* **180,** 155 (1949)

585. DEKKER, E. E., SCHLESINGER, M. J., and COON, M. J. *J. biol. Chem.* **233,** 434 (1958)

586. DE LA HABA, G., and CANTONI, G. L. *J. biol. Chem.* **234,** 603 (1959)

587. DE LA HABA, G., LEDER, I. G., and RACKER, E. *J. biol. Chem.* **214,** 409 (1955)

588. DE LEY, J., and DOUDOROFF, M. *J. biol. Chem.* **227,** 745 (1957)

589. DEMARS, R. *Biochim. biophys. Acta* **27,** 435 (1958)

590. DEMOSS, R. *Bact. Proc.*, p. 81 (1953)

591. DEMPSEY, M. E., and BOYER, P. D. *J. biol. Chem.* **236,** PC6 (1961)

592. DEN, H., ROBINSON, W. G., and COON, M. J. *J. biol. Chem.* **234,** 1666 (1959

593. DENNIS, D., and KAPLAN, N. O. *J. biol. Chem.* **235,** 810 (1960)

594. DE RENZO, E. C. *Advanc. Enzymol.* **17,** 293 (1956)

595. DE RENZO, E. C., KALEITA, E., HEYTLER, P. G., OLESON, J. J., HUTCHINGS, B. L., and WILLIAMS, J. H. *Arch. Biochem. Biophys.* **45,** 247 (1953)

596. DESNUELLE, P., in *The Enzymes*, 2nd edn., ed. P. D. Boyer, H. Lardy and K. Myrbäck (New York, Academic Press, 1960), Vol. 4, p. 93

597. DESNUELLE, P., in *The Enzymes*, 2nd edn., ed. P. D. Boyer, H. Lardy and K. Myrbäck (New York, Academic Press, 1960), Vol. 4, p. 119

598. DESNUELLE, P., ROVERY, M., and BONJOUR, G. *Biochim. biophys. Acta* **5,** 116 (1950)

599. DEUEL, H., LEUENBERGER, R., and HUBER, G. *Helv. chim. Acta* **33,** 942 (1950)

600. DEUEL, H., and STUTZ, E. *Advanc. Enzymol.* **20,** 341 (1958)

601. DEUTSCH, A., and NILSSON, R. *Acta chem. scand.* **8,** 1898 (1954)

602. DEWEY, D. L., HOARE, D. S., and WORK, E. *Biochem. J.* **58,** 523 (1954)

603. DEWEY, V. C. *Proc. Soc. exp. Biol., N.Y.* **46,** 482 (1941)

604. DEWEY, V. C. *Biol. Bull.* **87,** 107 (1944)

605. DI CARLO, F. J., SCHULTZ, A. S., and KENT, A. M. *Arch. Biochem. Biophys.* **44,** 468 (1953)

606. DICKENS, F. *Biochem. J.* **27,** 1141 (1933)

607. DICKENS, F., and GLOCK, G. E. *Biochem. J.* **50,** 81 (1951)

608. DICKENS, F., and WILLIAMSON, D. H. *Biochem. J.* **64,** 567 (1956)

609. DICKMAN, S. R., in *The Enzymes,* 2nd edn., ed. P. D. Boyer, H. Lardy and K. Myrbäck (New York, Academic Press, 1961), Vol. 5, p. 495

610. DIKSTEIN, S., BERGMANN, F., and HENIS, Y. *J. biol. Chem.* **224,** 67 (1957)

610a. DIVEN, W. F., JOHNSTON, R. B., and SCHOLZ, J. J. *Biochim. biophys. Acta* **67,** 161 (1962)

611. DINTZIS, H. M. *Proc. nat. Acad. Sci. U.S.* **47,** 247 (1961)

612. DIXON, G. H., KAUFFMAN, D. L., and NEURATH, H. *J. biol. Chem.* **233,** 1373 (1958)

613. DIXON, G. H., and SMITHIES, O. *Biochim. biophys. Acta* **23,** 198 (1957)

614. DIXON, M. *Nature, Lond.* **140,** 806 (1937)

615. DIXON, M. *Enzymologia* **5,** 198 (1938)

616. DIXON, M. *Ergebn. Enzymforsch.* **8,** 217 (1939)

617. DIXON, M., in *Symposium on the Biochemical Reactions of Chemical Warfare Agents* (Biochem. Soc. Symposium No. 2), ed. R. T. Williams (Cambridge University Press, 1948), p. 39

618. DIXON, M. *Multi-enzyme Systems* (Cambridge University Press, 1949)

619. DIXON, M. *Manometric Methods* (Cambridge University Press, 1951)

620. DIXON, M. *Biochem. J.* **54,** 457 (1953)

621. DIXON, M. *Biochem. J.* **55,** 161 (1953)

622. DIXON, M. *Biochem. J.* **55,** 170 (1953)

623. DIXON, M. *Disc. Faraday Soc.,* No. 20, 'The Physical Chemistry of Enzymes', p. 9 (1955).

624. DIXON, M. *Disc. Faraday Soc.,* No. 20, 'The Physical Chemistry of Enzymes', p. 301, (1955).

625. DIXON, M., and CAPUTTO, R. Unpublished observations

626. DIXON, M., and KEILIN, D. *Proc. roy. Soc.* B, **119,** 159 (1936)

627. DIXON, M., and KODAMA, K. *Biochem. J.* **20,** 1104 (1926)

628. DIXON, M., and LUTWAK-MANN, C. *Biochem. J.* **31,** 1347 (1937)

629. DIXON, M., MASSEY, V., and WEBB, E. C. Unpublished observations

630. DIXON, M., and THURLOW, S. *Biochem. J.* **18,** 976 (1924)

631. DIXON, M., and WEBB, E. C. *Advanc. Protein Chem.* **16,** 197 (1961)

632. DIXON, M., and WEBB, E. C. *Enzymes,* 1st edn. (1958)

633. DIXON, M., and WEBB, E. C. *Nature, Lond.,* **184,** 1298 (1959)

634. DODGSON, K. S. *Enzymologia* **20,** 301 (1959)

635. DODGSON, K. S. *Biochem. J.* **78,** 324 (1961)

636. DODGSON, K. S., and LLOYD, A. G. *Biochem. J.* **68,** 88 (1958)

637. DODGSON, K. S., and POWELL, G. M. *Biochem. J.* **73,** 666 and 672 (1959)

638. DODGSON, K. S., ROSE, F. A., and SPENCER, B. *Biochem. J.* **66,** 357 (1957)

639. DODGSON, K. S., and SPENCER, B. *Biochem. J.* **57,** 310 (1954)

640. DODGSON, K. S., SPENCER, B., and THOMAS, J. *Biochem. J.* **59,** 29 (1955)

640a. DODGSON, K. S., SPENCER, B., and WILLIAMS, K. *Biochem. J.* **61,** 374 (1955)

641. DODGSON, K. S., SPENCER, B., and WILLIAMS, K. *Biochem. J.* **64,** 216 (1956)

642. DOERY, H. M., and PEARSON, J. E. *Biochem. J.* **78,** 820 (1961)

643. DOHERTY, D. G. *J. Amer. chem. Soc.* **77,** 4887 (1955)

644. DOHERTY, D. G., and VASLOW, F. *J. Amer. chem. Soc.* **74,** 931 (1952)

645. DOISY, R. J., RICHERT, D. A., and WESTERFELD, W. W. *J. biol. Chem.* **217,** 307 (1955)

646. DOLIN, M. I. *Arch. Biochem. Biophys.* **46,** 483 (1953)

647. DOLIN, M. I. *J. biol. Chem.* **225,** 557 (1957)

648. DOLIN, M. I., and WOOD, N. P. *J. biol. Chem.* **235,** 1809 (1960)

649. DOTY, P., BOEDTKER, H., FRESCO, J. R., HASELKORN, R., and LITT, M. *Proc. nat. Acad. Sci. U.S.* **45,** 482 (1959)

650. DOUDOROFF, M., BARKER, H. A., and HASSID, W. Z. *J. biol. Chem.* **168,** 725 (1947)

651. DOUDOROFF, M., HASSID, W. Z., PUTMAN, E. W., POTTER, A. L., and LEDERBERG, J. *J. biol. Chem.* **179,** 921 (1949)

652. DOYLE, M. L., KATZMAN, P. A., and DOISY, E. A. *J. biol. Chem.* **217,** 921 (1955)

653. DRABKIN, D. L. *J. biol. Chem.* **182,** 317 (1950)

654. DREYER, W. J., and NEURATH, H. *J. biol. Chem.* **217,** 527 (1955)

655. DRUZHININA, K. V., and KRITZMAN, M. G. *Biokhimiya* **17,** 77 (1952)

656. DRYSDALE, G. R., and COHN, M. *Biochim. biophys. Acta* **21,** 397 (1956)

657. DRYSDALE, G. R., and LARDY, H. A. *J. biol. Chem.* **202,** 119 (1953)

658. DRYSDALE, G. R., SPIEGEL, M. J., and STRITTMATTER, P. *J. biol. Chem.* **236,** 2323 (1961)

659. DUNCAN, W. A. M., MANNERS, D. J., and ROSS, A. G. *Biochem. J.* **63,** 44 (1956)

660. DURELL, J., ANDERSON, D. G., and CANTONI, G. L. *Biochim. biophys. Acta* **26,** 270 (1957)

661. DURR, I. F., and RUDNEY, H. *J. biol. Chem.* **235,** 2572 (1960)

662. DUTTON, G. J. *Biochem. J.* **64,** 693 (1956)

663. DYCKERHOFF, H., and ARMBRUSTER, R. *Z. physiol. Chem.* **219,** 38 (1933)

664. EADIE, G. S., BERNHEIM, F., and BERNHEIM, M. L. C. *J. biol. Chem.* **181,** 449 (1949)

665. EASSON, L. H., and STEDMAN, E. *Proc. roy. Soc.* B, **121,** 142 (1936)

666. EBATA, M., SATO, R., and BAK, T. *J. Biochem., Tokyo* **42,** 715 (1955)

667. EBERSOLE, E. R., GUTTENTAG, C., and WILSON, P. W. *Arch. Biochem.* **3,** 399 (1943)

668. EBISUZAKI, K., and WILLIAMS, J. N. *Biochem. J.* **60,** 644 (1955)

669. EDELHOCH, H., RODWELL, V. W., and GRISOLIA, S. *J. biol. Chem.* **228,** 891 (1957)

670. EDELMAN, J., and BACON, J. S. D. *Biochem. J.* **49,** 529 (1951)

671. EDLBACHER, S., and RÖTHLER, H. *Z. physiol. Chem.* **148,** 273 (1925)

672. EDMONDS, M., and ABRAMS, R. *J. biol. Chem.* **235,** 1142 (1960)

673. EDSON, N. L. *Aust. N.Z. Ass. Adv. Sci. (Rep. 29th meeting, Sydney)* **29,** 281 (1952)

674. EDWARDS, S. W., and KNOX, W. E. *J. biol. Chem.* **220,** 79 (1956)

675. EGAMI, F., ITAHASHI, M., SATO, R., and MORI, T. *J. Biochem., Tokyo* **40,** 527 (1953)

676. EGAMI, F., and TAKAHASHI, N. *Bull. chem. Soc., Japan* **25,** 666 (1955)

677. EGE, R., and LUNDSTEEN, E. *Biochem. Z.* **268,** 164 (1934)

678. EGGERER, H., STADTMAN, E. R., OVERATH, P., and LYNEN, F. *Biochem. Z.* **333,** 1 (1960)

679. EHRENBERG, A., and THEORELL, H. *Acta chem. scand.* **9,** 1193 (1955)
680. EIGER, I. Z., and DAWSON, C. R. *Arch. Biochem. Biophys.* **21,** 194 (1949)
681. EINSET, E., and CLARK, W. L. *J. biol. Chem.* **231,** 703 (1958)
682. EISENBERG, F., and FIELD, J. B. *J. biol. Chem.* **222,** 293 (1956)
683. EISENBERG, M. A. *Biochim. biophys. Acta* **16,** 58 (1955)
684. EISENSTADT, J. M., KAMEYAMA, T., and NOVELLI, G. D. *Proc. nat. Acad. Sci. U.S.* **48,** 652 (1962)
685. ELKINS-KAUFMAN, E., and NEURATH, H. *J. biol. Chem.* **175,** 893 (1948)
686. ELLFOLK, N. *Acta chem. scand.* **8,** 151 (1954)
687. ELLIOTT, S. D. *J. exp. Med.* **92,** 201 (1950)
688. ELLIOTT, W. H. *J. biol. Chem.* **201,** 661 (1953)
689. ELLIOTT, W. H. *Biochem. J.* **62,** 427 (1956)
690. ELLIOTT, W. H. *Biochem. J.* **65,** 315 (1957)
691. ELLIS, D., and FRUTON, J. S. *J. biol. Chem.* **191,** 153 (1951)
692. ELLIS, R. J., and DAVIES, D. D. *Biochem. J.* **78,** 615 (1961)
693. ELÖDI, P., and SZORENYI, E. T. *Acta physiol. Acad. sci. Hung.* **9,** 367 (1956)
694. EMERY, A. J., and DOUNCE, A. L. *J. biophys. biochem. Cytol.* **1,** 315 and 331 (1956)
695. ENDAHL, G. L., KOCHAKIAN, C. D., and HAMM, D. *J. biol. Chem.* **235,** 2792 (1960)
696. ENGLAND, S. *J. biol. Chem.* **235,** 1510 (1960)
697. ENGLARD, S., and BREIGER, H. H. *Biochim. biophys. Acta* **56,** 571 (1962)
698. ENGSTRÖM, L. *Acta Soc. Med. Ups.* **64,** 214 (1959)
699. ENGSTRÖM, L. *Biochim. biophys. Acta* **52,** 36 (1961)
700. ENNOR, A. H., and ROSENBERG, H. *Biochem. J.* **51,** 606 (1952)
701. ENNOR, A. H., ROSENBERG, H., and ARMSTRONG, M. D. *Nature, Lond.* **175,** 120 (1955)
702. ENTNER, N., and GONZALEZ, C. *Biochim. biophys. Acta* **47,** 52 (1961)
703. EPPS, H. M. R. *Biochem. J.* **39,** 42 (1945)
704. EPPS, H. M. R., and GALE, E. F. *Biochem. J.* **36,** 619 (1942)
705. ERKAMA, J., and VIRTANEN, A. I., in *The Enzymes,* 1st edn., ed. J. B. Sumner and K. Myrbäck (New York, Academic Press, 1951), Vol. 1, p. 1244
706. ERNSTER, L., and NAVAZIO, F. *Exp. Cell Res.* **11,** 483 (1956)
707. ESTABROOK, R. W. *J. biol. Chem.* **230,** 735 (1958)
708. ESTABROOK, R. W., and SACKTOR, B. *Arch. Biochem. Biophys.* **76,** 532 (1958)
709. EULER, H. VON, ADLER, E., GUNTHER, G., and DAS, N. B. *Z. physiol. Chem.* **254,** 61 (1938)
710. EULER, H. VON, ALBERS, H., and SCHLENK, F. *Z. physiol. Chem.* **240,** 113 (1936)
711. EYRING, H. *J. chem. Phys.* **3,** 107 (1935)
712. EYSTER, H. C. *Plant Physiol.* **25,** 630 (1950)
713. FAIRBAIRN, D. *J. biol. Chem.* **173,** 705 (1948)
714. FARMER, V. C., HENDERSON, M. E. K., and RUSSELL, J. D. *Biochem. J.* **74,** 257 (1960)
715. FARRAR, T. C., GUTOROWSKY, H. S., ALBERTY, R. A., and MILLER, W. G. *J. Amer. chem. Soc.* **79,** 3978 (1957)
716. FAULKNER, P. *Biochem. J.* **60,** 590 (1955)

717. FAWCETT, C. P., CIOTTI, M. M., and KAPLAN, N. O. *Biochim. biophys. Acta* **54,** 210 (1961)
718. FEDORCHENKO, O. Y. *Ukrain. Biokhim. Zhur.* **30,** 552 (1958)
719. FEINGOLD, D. S., AVIGAD, G., and HESTRIN, S. *Biochem. J.* **64,** 351 (1956)
720. FEINGOLD, D. S., AVIGAD, G., and HESTRIN, S. *J. biol. Chem.* **224,** 295 (1957)
721. FEINGOLD, D. S., NEUFELD, E. F., and HASSID, W. Z. *J. biol. Chem.* **235,** 910 (1960)
722. FÉLIX, F., and LABOUESSE-MERCOUROFF, J. *Biochim. biophys. Acta* **21,** 303 (1956)
723. FERGUSON, J. J., and RUDNEY, H. *J. biol. Chem.* **234,** 1072 (1959)
724. FERNANDEZ, M., and GRISOLIA, S. *J. biol. Chem.* **235,** 2188 (1960)
725. FEWSON, C. A., and NICHOLAS, D. J. D. *Biochem. J.* **78,** 9P (1961)
726. FEWSON, C. A., and NICHOLAS, D. J. D. *Biochim. biophys. Acta* **49,** 335 (1961)
727. FIEDLER, H., and WOOD, J. L. *J. biol. Chem.* **222,** 387 (1956)
728. FINCHAM, J. R. S. *Biochem. J.* **53,** 313 (1953)
729. FINCHAM, J. R. S. *Biochem. J.* **65,** 721 (1957)
730. FINCHAM, J. R. S. *Advanc. Enzymol.* **22,** 1 (1960)
731. FINCHAM, J. R. S., and BOND, P. A. *Biochem. J.* **77,** 96 (1960)
732. FINDLAY, J., and LEVVY, G. A. *Biochem. J.* **77,** 170 (1960)
733. FISCHER, E. *Ber. dtsch. chem. Ges.* **27,** 2985 (1894)
734. FISCHER, E. H., GRAVES, D. J., CRITTENDEN, E. R. S., and KREBS, E. G. *J. biol. Chem.* **234,** 1698 (1959)
735. FISCHER, E. H., and KREBS, E. G. *J. biol. Chem.* **231,** 65 (1958)
736. FISCHER, E. H., and MONTMOLLIN, R. DE. *Helv. chim. Acta* **34,** 1987 (1951)
737. FISCHER, E. H., and STEIN, E. A. *Arch. Sci. Genève* **7,** 131 (1954)
738. FISCHER, E. H., and STEIN, E. A., in *The Enzymes*, 2nd edn., ed. P. D. Boyer, H. Lardy and K. Myrbäck (New York, Academic Press, 1960), Vol. 4, p. 301
739. FISCHER, E. H., and STEIN, E. A., in *The Enzymes*, 2nd edn., ed. P. D. Boyer, H. Lardy and K. Myrbäck (New York, Academic Press, 1960), Vol. 4, p. 313
740. FISCHER, F. G., ROEDIG, A., and RAUCH, K. *Liebigs Ann.* **552,** 203 (1942)
741. FISH, J. C. *Nature, Lond.* **180,** 345 (1957)
742. FISHER, H. F., CONN, E. E., VENNESLAND, B., and WESTHEIMER, F. H. *J. biol. Chem.* **202,** 687 (1953)
743. FISHMAN, W. H. *Advanc. Enzymol.* **16,** 361 (1955)
744. FISHMAN, W. H., and GREEN, S. *J. biol. Chem.* **225,** 435 (1957)
745. FISKE, C. H., and SUBBAROW, Y. *J. biol. Chem.* **66,** 375 (1925)
746. FITTING, C., and DOUDOROFF, M. *J. biol. Chem.* **199,** 153 (1952)
747. FLAKS, J. G., ERWIN, M. J., and BUCHANAN, J. M. *J. biol. Chem.* **228,** 201 (1957)
748. FLAKS, J. G., ERWIN, M. J., and BUCHANAN, J. M. *J. biol. Chem.* **229,** 603 (1957)
749. FLAVIN, M., and KONO, T. *J. biol. Chem.* **235,** 1109 (1960)
750. FLAVIN, M., and SLAUGHTER, C. *J. biol. Chem.* **235,** 1103 (1960)
751. FLAVIN, M., and SLAUGHTER, C. *J. biol. Chem.* **235,** 1112 (1960)
752. FLEURY, P., and COURTOIS, J. *Helv. chim. Acta* **29,** 1297 (1946)
753. FLORINI, J. R., and VESTLING, C. S. *Biochim. biophys. Acta* **25,** 575 (1957)

754. FLORKIN, M., and DUCHATEAU-BOSSON, G. *Enzymologia* **9**, 5 (1940)
755. FLUHARTY, A. L., and BALLOU, C. E. *J. biol. Chem.* **234**, 2517 (1959)
756. FOLK, J. E., BRAUNBERG, R. C., and GLADNER, J. A. *Biochim. biophys. Acta* **47**, 595 (1961)
757. FOLK, J. E., and GLADNER, J. A. *Biochim. biophys. Acta* **48**, 139 (1961)
758. FOLK, J. E., PIEZ, K. A., CARROLL, W. R., and GLADNER, J. A. *J. biol. Chem.* **235**, 2272 (1960)
759. FONES, W. S., and LEE, M. *J. biol. Chem.* **201**, 847 (1953)
760. FORD-MOORE, A. H. *Porton Report* to the Ministry of Supply (1936) quoted in *Symposium on the Biochemical Reactions of Chemical Warfare Agents* (Biochem. Soc. Symposium No. 2), ed. R. T. Williams (Cambridge University Press, 1948), p. 39
761. FORMICA, J. V., and BRADY, R. O. *J. Amer. chem. Soc.* **81**, 752 (1959)
762. FORSYTH, W. G. C., and WEBLEY, D. M. *J. gen. Microbiol.* **4**, 87 (1950)
763. FORTI, G. *Biochim. biophys. Acta* **48**, 200 (1961)
764. FOSTER, R. J., and NIEMANN, C. *J. Amer. chem. Soc.* **77**, 1886 (1955)
765. FOWDEN, L. *J. exp. Bot.* **5**, 28 (1954)
766. FOX, J. B., and DANDLIKER, W. B. *J. biol. Chem.* **221**, 1005 (1956)
767. FOYE, W. O., and LANGE, W. E. *J. Amer. chem. Soc.* **76**, 2199 (1954)
768. FRAMPTON, E. W., and WOOD, W. A. *J. biol. Chem.* **236**, 2571 (1961)
769. FRAMPTON, E. W., and WOOD, W. A. *J. biol. Chem.* **236**, 2578 (1961)
770. FRAENKEL-CONRAT, H., and FRAENKEL-CONRAT, J. *Biochim. biophys. Acta* **5**, 98 (1950)
771. FREDERICQ, E., and OTH, A. *Biochem. J.* **66**, 33P (1957)
772. FRENCH, D., in *The Enzymes*, 2nd edn., ed. P. D. Boyer, H. Lardy and K. Myrbäck (New York, Academic Press, 1960), Vol. 4, p. 345
773. FRENCH, D., and KNAPP, D. W. *J. biol. Chem.* **187**, 463 (1950)
774. FRENCH, D., LEVINE, M. L., NORBERG, E., NORDIN, P., PAZUR, J. H., and WILD, G. M. *J. Amer. chem. Soc.* **76**, 2387 (1954)
775. FRENCH, D., and WILD, G. M. *J. Amer. chem. Soc.* **75**, 4490 (1953)
776. FREUNDLICH, M., BURNS, R. O., and UMBARGER, H. E. *Proc. nat. Acad. Sci. U.S.* **48**, 1804 (1962)
777. FRIEDBERG, F. *Arch. Biochem. Biophys.* **61**, 263 (1956)
778. FRIEDEN, C. *Biochim. biophys. Acta* **24**, 241 (1957)
779. FRIEDEN, C. *J. Amer. chem. Soc.* **79**, 1894 (1957)
780. FRIEDEN, C. *J. biol. Chem.* **234**, 809 and 815 (1959)
781. FRIEDEN, C. *J. biol. Chem.* **234**, 2891 (1959)
782. FRIEDEN, C., and VELICK, S. F. *Biochim. biophys. Acta* **23**, 439 (1957)
783. FRIEDENWALD, J. S., and MAENGWYN-DAVIES, G. D., in *A Symposium on the Mechanism of Enzyme Action*, ed. W. D. McElroy and B. Glass (Baltimore, Johns Hopkins Press, 1954), p. 154
784. FRIEDKIN, M., and ROBERTS, D. *J. biol. Chem.* **207**, 245 (1954)
785. FRIEDMAN, S., and FRAENKEL, G. *Arch. Biochem. Biophys.* **59**, 491 (1955)
786. FRIEDMANN, H. C., and VENNESLAND, B. *J. biol. Chem.* **235**, 1526 (1960)
787. FRIESS, E. T., and MORALES, M. F. *Arch. Biochem. Biophys.* **56**, 326 (1955)
788. FRIGERIO, N. A., and HARBURY, H. A. *J. biol. Chem.* **231**, 135 (1958)
789. FRITZSON, P. *J. biol. Chem.* **235**, 719 (1960)
790. FROMAGEOT, C. *Ergebn. Enzymforsch.* **7**, 50 (1938)
791. FROMAGEOT, C., and DESNUELLE, P. *C. R. Acad. Sci., Paris* **214**, 647 (1942)
792. FROMM, H. J. *J. biol. Chem.* **234**, 3097 (1959)

793. FRUTON, J. S., JOHNSTON, R. B., and FRIED, M. *J. biol. Chem.* **190,** 39 (1950)
794. FRUTON, J. S., and MYCEK, M. J. *Arch. Biochem. Biophys.* **65,** 11 (1956)
795. FRUTON, J. S., SMITH, V. A., and DRISCOLL, P. E. *J. biol. Chem.* **173,** 457 (1948)
796. FRY, B. A. *Biochem. J.* **59,** 579 (1955)
797. FUJITA, A. *Advanc. Enzymol.* **15,** 389 (1954)
798. FUJITA, A., NOSE, Y., KOZUKA, S., TASHIRO, T., UEDA, K., and SAKAMOTO, S. *J. biol. Chem.* **196,** 289 (1952)
799. FUJITA, A., NOSE, Y., and KURATANI, K. *J. Vitaminol.* **1,** 1 (1954)
800. FUJITA, A., NOSE, Y., UEDA, K., and HASEGAWA, E. *J. biol. Chem.* **196,** 297 (1952)
801. FUJITA, A., NOSE, Y., UYEO, S., and KOIZUMI, J. *J. biol. Chem.* **196,** 313 (1952)
802. FUKUI, S., SUZUKI, T., KITAHARA, K., and MIWA, T. *J. gen. appl. Microbiol.* **6,** 270 (1960)
803. FURTH, J. J., HURWITZ, J., KRUG, R., and ALEXANDER, M. *J. biol. Chem.* **236,** 3317 (1961)
804. GALE, E. F. *Biochem. J.* **32,** 1583 (1938)
805. GALE, E. F. *Biochem. J.* **33,** 1012 (1939)
806. GALE, E. F. *Brit. med. Bull.* **9,** 135 (1953)
807. GALE, E. F. *Sci. Amer.* **194,** 41 (1956)
808. GALE, E. F., in *The Bacteria*, ed. I. C. Gunsalus and R. Y. Stanier (London and New York, Academic Press, 1962), Vol. III
809. GALE, E. F., and EPPS, H. M. R. *Nature, Lond.* **152,** 327 (1943)
810. GALE, E. F., and EPPS, H. M. R. *Biochem. J.* **38,** 232 (1944)
811. GALE, E. F., and EPPS, H. M. R. *Biochem. J.* **38,** 250 (1944)
812. GALE, E. F., and FOLKES, J. P. *Biochem. J.* **59,** 675 (1955)
813. GAMBLE, J. L., and LEHNINGER, A. L. *J. biol. Chem.* **223,** 921 (1956)
814. GAREN, A., and ECHOLS, H. *Proc. nat. Acad. Sci. U.S.* **48,** 1398 (1962)
815. GAREN, A., and LEVINTHAL, C. *Biochim. biophys. Acta* **38,** 470 (1960)
816. GARROD, A. E. *Inborn Errors of Metabolism* (Oxford University Press, 1909)
817. GAVRILESCU, N., and PETERS, R. A. *Biochem. J.* **25,** 2150 (1931)
818. GAWRON, O., and FONDY, T. P. *J. Amer. chem. Soc.* **81,** 6333 (1959)
819. GEHRMANN, G., and OKADA, S. *Biochim. biophys. Acta* **23,** 621 (1957)
820. GEIDUSCHEK, E. P., MOOHR, J. W., and WEISS, S. B. *Proc. nat. Acad. Sci. U.S.* **48,** 1078 (1962)
821. GEORGE, P. *Biochem. J.* **54,** 267 (1953)
822. GEORGE, P. *Biochem. J.* **55,** 220 (1953)
823. GERGELY, J., HELE, P., and RAMAKRISHNAN, C. V. *J. biol. Chem.* **198,** 323 (1952)
824. GHOSH, S., BLUMENTHAL, H. J., DAVIDSON, E., and ROSEMAN, S. *J. biol. Chem.* **235,** 1265 (1960)
825. GIANETTO, R., and DE DUVE, C. *Biochem. J.* **59,** 433 (1955)
826. GIBBS, M., in *Methods in Enzymology*, ed. S. P. Colowick and N. O. Kaplan (New York, Academic Press, 1955), Vol. 1, p. 411
827. GIBSON, D. M., AYENGAR, P., and SANADI, D. R. *Biochim. biophys. Acta* **16,** 536 (1955)
828. GIBSON, D. M., AYENGAR, P., and SANADI, D. R. *Biochim. biophys. Acta* **21,** 86 (1956)

829. GIBSON, D. M., DAVISSON, E. O., BACHHAWAT, B. K., RAY, B. R., and VESTLING, C. S. *J. biol. Chem.* **203,** 397 (1953)

830. GIBSON, J. *Biochem. J.* **79,** 151 (1961)

831. GIBSON, K. D. *Biochim. biophys. Acta* **10,** 221 (1953)

832. GIBSON, K. D., NEUBERGER, A., and SCOTT, J. J. *Biochem. J.* **61,** 618 (1955)

833. GIBSON, Q. H., and GREENWOOD, C. *Biochem. J.* **86,** 541 (1963)

834. GILBERT, G. A. *Proc. roy. Soc.* A, **250,** 377 (1959)

835. GILBERT, G. A., and PATRICK, A. P. *Biochem. J.* **51,** 181 (1952)

836. GILBERT, J. B., OTEY, M. C., and PRICE, V. E. *J. biol. Chem.* **190,** 377 (1951)

837. GINOZA, H. S., and ALTENBERN, R. A. *Arch. Biochem. Biophys.* **56,** 537 (1955)

838. GINSBURG, A. *J. biol. Chem.* **234,** 481 (1959)

839. GINSBURG, V. *J. biol. Chem.* **232,** 55 (1958)

840. GINSBURG, V., NEUFELD, E. F., and HASSID, W. Z. *Proc. nat. Acad. Sci. U.S.* **42,** 333 (1956)

841. GIRI, K. V., KRISHNASWAMY, P. R., and RAO, N. A. *Biochem. J.* **70,** 66 (1958)

842. GIRI, K. V., RAO, N. A., CAMA, H. R., and KUMAR, S. A. *Biochem. J.* **75,** 381 (1960)

843. GIUDITTA, A., and STRECKER, H. J. *Biochim. biophys. Acta* **48,** 10 (1961)

844. GJESSING, E. C., EMERY, R., and CLEMENTS, J. P. *J. biol. Chem.* **234,** 1098 (1959)

845. GLADNER, J. A., and LAKI, K. *J. Amer. chem. Soc.* **80,** 1263 (1958)

846. GLASER, L. *J. biol. Chem.* **232,** 627 (1958)

847. GLASER, L. *J. biol. Chem.* **234,** 2801 (1959)

848. GLASER, L. *J. biol. Chem.* **235,** 2095 (1960)

849. GLASER, L., and BROWN, D. H. *J. biol. Chem.* **216,** 67 (1955)

850. GLASER, L., and BROWN, D. H. *J. biol. Chem.* **228,** 729 (1957)

851. GLASSTONE, S. *Text-Book of Physical Chemistry* (London, Macmillan, 1940)

852. GLASZIOU, K. T. *Aust. J. biol. Sci.* **9,** 253 (1956)

853. GLENN, J. L., and CRANE, F. L. *Biochim. biophys. Acta* **22,** 111 (1956)

854. GLICK, D., and GLAUBACH, S. *J. gen. Physiol.* **25,** 197 (1941)

855. GLICK, D., GLAUBACH, S., and MOORE, D. H. *J. biol. Chem.* **144,** 525 (1942)

856. GLOCK, G., and McLEAN, P. *Biochem. J.* **61,** 388 (1955)

857. GOLDBERG, M., and GILMOUR, D. *Arch. Biochem. Biophys.* **51,** 411 (1954)

858. GOLDBERGER, R., SMITH, A. L., TISDALE, H., and BOMSTEIN, R. *J. biol. Chem.* **236,** 2788 (1961)

859. GOLDENBERG, V., GOLDENBERG, H., and McLAREN, A. D. *J. Amer. chem. Soc.* **72,** 5317 (1950)

860. GOLDMAN, D. S. *J. biol. Chem.* **208,** 345 (1954)

861. GOLDMAN, P., and VAGELOS, P. R. *J. biol. Chem.* **236,** 2620 (1961)

862. GOLDSTEIN, A. *J. gen. Physiol.* **27,** 529 (1944)

863. GOLDSTEIN, F. B. *J. biol. Chem.* **234,** 2702 (1959)

864. GOLDSTONE, A., and ADAMS, E. *J. biol. Chem.* **237,** 3476 (1962)

865. GOLDSTONE, J. M., and MAGASANIK, B. *Fed. Proc.* **13,** 218 (1954)

866. GOLDTHWAIT, D. A., PEABODY, R. A., and GREENBERG, G. R. *J. biol. Chem.* **221,** 569 (1956)

867. GOMORI, G. *J. biol. Chem.* **148,** 139 (1943)

868. GOODLAD, G. A. J., and MILLS, G. T. *Biochem. J.* **66,** 346 (1957)

869. GOODMAN, I., FOUTS, J. R., BRESNICK, E., MENEGAS, R., and HITCHINGS, G. H. *Science*, **130,** 450 (1959)

870. GOODMAN, A., WEIL, R. M., and STERN, K. G. *J. biol. Chem.* **217,** 977 (1955)

871. GORDON, A. H., GREEN, D. E., and SUBRAHMANYAN, V. *Biochem. J.* **34,** 764 (1940)

872. GORINI, L., and MAAS, W. K. *Biochim. biophys. Acta* **25,** 208 (1957)

873. GORINI, L., and MAAS, W. K., in *Symposium on the chemical Basis of Development*, ed. W. D. McElroy and B. Glass (Baltimore, Johns Hopkins Press, 1958)

874. GORYACHENKOVA, E. V. *Doklady Akad. Nauk, S.S.S.R.* **87,** 457 (1952)

875. GOTTO, A. M., and KORNBERG, H. L. *Biochem. J.* **81,** 273 (1961)

876. GOTTSCHALK, A. *Aust. J. exp. Biol. med. Sci.* **21,** 133 (1943)

877. GOTTSCHALK, A. *Aust. J. exp. Biol. med. Sci.* **23,** 261 (1945)

878. GOTTSCHALK, A. *Biochem. J.* **41,** 276 (1947)

879. GOTTSCHALK, A. *Advanc. Carbohyd. Chem.* **5,** 49 (1950)

880. GOTTSCHALK, A. *Biochim. biophys. Acta* **23,** 645 (1957)

881. GOTTSCHALK, A. *Advanc. Enzymol.* **20,** 135 (1958)

882. GOTTSCHALK, A., in *The Enzymes*, 2nd edn., ed. P. D. Boyer, H. Lardy and K. Myrbäck (New York, Academic Press, 1960), Vol. 4, p. 461

883. GRAAE, J. *Acta chem. scand.* **8,** 356 (1954)

884. GRANICK, S., and MAUZERALL, D. *J. biol. Chem.* **232,** 1119 (1958)

885. GRANT, J. K., and BROWNIE, A. C. *Biochim. biophys. Acta* **18,** 433 (1955)

886. GRANT, N. H., and ROBBINS, K. C. *J. Amer. chem. Soc.* **78,** 5888 (1956)

887. GRASSMANN, W., and HANNIG, K. *Naturwiss.* **37,** 397 (1950)

888. GRASSMANN, W., and MAYR, O. *Z. physiol. Chem.* **214,** 185 (1933)

889. GRASSMANN, W., STADLER, R., and BENDER, R. *Liebigs Ann.* **503,** 167 (1933)

890. GRAVES, D. J., FISCHER, E. H., and KREBS, E. G. *J. biol. Chem.* **235,** 805 (1960)

891. GRAVES, J. L., VENNESLAND, B., UTTER, M. F., and PENNINGTON, R. J. *J. biol. Chem.* **223,** 551 (1956)

892. GRAZI, E., ROWLEY, P. T., CHENG, T., TCHOLA, O., and HORECKER, B. L. *Biochem. biophys. res. Comm.* **9,** 38 (1962)

893. GREEN, A. A., and CORI, G. T. *J. biol. Chem.* **151,** 21 (1943)

894. GREEN, A. A., and McELROY, W. D. *Biochim. biophys. Acta* **20,** 170 (1956)

895. GREEN, A. L., and NICHOLLS, J. D. *Biochem. J.* **72,** 70 (1959)

896. GREEN, D. E. *Biochem. J.* **30,** 629 (1936)

897. GREEN, D. E. *Biochem. J.* **30,** 2095 (1936)

898. GREEN, D. E. *Proceedings of the Second International Conference on Biochemical Problems of Lipids*, Ghent (London, Butterworths Scientific Publications, 1955), p. 233

899. GREEN, D. E. *Disc. Faraday Soc.* **27,** 206 (1959)

900. GREEN, D. E., and BROSTEAUX, J. *Biochem. J.* **30,** 1489 (1936)

901. GREEN, D. E., DEWAN, J. G., and LELOIR, L. F. *Biochem. J.* **31,** 934 (1937)

902. GREEN, D. E., HERBERT, D., and SUBRAHMANYAN, V. *J. biol. Chem.* **138,** 327 (1941)

902a. GREEN, D. E., LELOIR, L. F., and NOCITO, W. *J. biol. Chem.* **161,** 559 (1945)

903. GREEN, D. E., MII, S., MAHLER, H. R., and BOCK, R. M. *J. biol. Chem.* **206,** 1 (1954)

904. GREEN, D. E., NEEDHAM, D. M., and DEWAN, J. G. *Biochem. J.* **31,** 2327 (1937)
905. GREEN, D. E., and ODA, T. *J. Biochem., Tokyo* **49,** 742 (1961)
906. GREEN, D. E., TISDALE, H. D., CRIDDLE, R. S., CHEN, P. Y., and BOCK, R. M. *Biochem. biophys. res. Comm.* **5,** 109 (1961)
907. GREEN, J. R., and WESTLEY, J. *J. biol. Chem.* **236,** 3047 (1961)
908. GREEN, M., and COHEN, S. S. *J. biol. Chem.* **219,** 557 (1956)
909. GREEN, M. N., TSOU, K.-C., BRESSLER, R., and SELIGMAN, A. M. *Arch. Biochem. Biophys.* **57,** 458 (1955)
910. GREENBERG, D. M., in *Methods in Enzymology*, ed. S. P. Colowick and N. O. Kaplan (New York, Academic Press, 1955), Vol. 2, p. 54
911. GREENBERG, D. M., in *The Enzymes*, 2nd edn., ed. P. D. Boyer, H. Lardy and K. Myrbäck (New York, Academic Press, 1960), Vol. 4, p. 257
912. GREENBERG, D. M., BAGOT, A. E., and ROHOLT, O. A. *Arch. Biochem. Biophys.* **62,** 446 (1956)
913. GREENBERG, D. M., and MOHAMED, M. S. *Arch. Biochem.* **8,** 365 (1945)
914. GREENBERG, G. R., JAENICKE, L., and SILVERMAN, M. *Biochim. biophys. Acta* **17,** 589 (1955)
915. GREENSTEIN, J. P. *J. nat. Cancer Inst.* **2,** 511 (1942)
916. GREENSTEIN, J. P. *J. nat. Cancer Inst.* **4,** 55 (1943)
917. GREENSTEIN, J. P. *Biochemistry of Cancer*, 2nd ed. (New York, Academic Press, 1954)
918. GREENSTEIN, J. P., in *Methods in Enzymology*, ed. S. P. Colowick and N. O. Kaplan (New York, Academic Press, 1955), Vol. 2, p. 109
919. GREENSTEIN, J. P., CARTER, C. E., CHALKLEY, H. W., and LEUTHARDT, F. M. *J. nat. Cancer Inst.* **7,** 9 (1946)
920. GREENSTEIN, J. P., JENRETTE, W. V., MIDER, G. B., and WHITE, J. *J. nat. Cancer Inst.* **1,** 687 (1941)
921. GREENSTEIN, J. P., KLEMPERER, F. W., and WYMAN, J. *J. biol. Chem.* **129,** 681 (1939)
922. GREENSTEIN, J. P., and LEUTHARDT, F. M. *J. nat. Cancer Inst.* **6,** 197 (1946)
923. GREENSTEIN, J. P., and LEUTHARDT, F. M. *J. nat. Cancer Inst.* **6,** 317 (1946)
924. GREENSTEIN, J. P., and THOMPSON, J. W. *J. nat. Cancer Inst.* **4,** 275 (1943)
925. GREENSTEIN, J. P., WERNE, J., ESCHENBRENNER, A. B., and LEUTHARDT, F. M. *J. nat. Cancer Inst.* **5,** 55 (1944)
926. GREGG, D. C., and MILLER, W. H. *J. Amer. chem. Soc.* **62,** 1374 (1940)
927. GREGOLIN, C., and SINGER, T. P. *Biochim. biophys. Acta* **67,** 201 (1963)
928. GREGOLIN, C., and SINGER, T. P. *Biochim. biophys. Acta* **57,** 410 (1962)
929. GREGOLIN, C., SINGER, T. P., KEARNEY, E. B., and BOERI, E. *Ann. N.Y. Acad. Sci.* **94,** 780 (1961)
930. GREVILLE, G. D., and CHAPPELL, J. B. *Biochim. biophys. Acta* **33,** 267 (1959)
931. GREVILLE, G. D., and REICH, E. *Biochim. biophys. Acta* **20,** 440 (1956)
931a. GRIFFITHS, D. E., and CHAPLAIN, R. A. *Biochem. biophys. res. Comm.* **8,** 497 and 501 (1962)
932. GRIFFITHS, D. E., MORRISON, J. F., and ENNOR, A. H. *Biochem. J.* **65,** 153 (1957)
933. GRIFFITHS, D. E., and WHARTON, D. C. *J. biol. Chem.* **236,** 1850 and 1857 (1961)
934. GRISOLIA, S., and CARDOSO, S. *Biochim. biophys. Acta* **25,** 430 (1957)

935. GRISOLIA, S., and WALLACH, D. P. *Biochim. biophys. Acta* **18,** 449 (1955)
936. GROSS, S. R., GAFFORD, R. D., and TATUM, E. L. *J. biol. Chem.* **219,** 781 (1956)
937. GROSSOWICZ, N., and HALPERN, Y. S. *J. biol. Chem.* **228,** 643 (1957)
938. GROSSOWICZ, N., and HALPERN, Y. S. *Nature, Lond.* **177,** 623 (1956)
939. GROVER, C. E., and CHIBNALL, A. C. *Biochem. J.* **21,** 857 (1927)
940. GRUNBERG-MANAGO, M., ORTIZ, P. J., and OCHOA, S. *Biochim. biophys. Acta* **20,** 269 (1956)
941. GRYDER, R. M., and POGELL, B. M. *J. biol. Chem.* **235,** 558 (1960)
942. GUEST, J. R., FRIEDMAN, S., WOODS, D. D., and SMITH, E. L. *Nature, Lond.,* **195,** 340 (1962)
943. GUIDITTA, A., and SINGER, T. P. *J. biol. Chem.* **234,** 666 (1959)
944. GUIRARD, B. M., SNELL, E. E., and WILLIAMS, R. J. *Arch. Biochem.* **9,** 361 (1946)
945. GULLAND, J. M., and JACKSON, E. M. *Biochem. J.* **32,** 590 (1938)
946. GULLAND, J. M., and JACKSON, E. M. *Biochem. J.* **32,** 597 (1938)
947. GUNSALUS, I. C., in *A Symposium on the Mechanism of Enzyme Action,* ed. W. D. McElroy and B. Glass (Baltimore, Johns Hopkins Press, 1954), p. 545
948. GUNSALUS, I. C., BARTON, L. S., and GRUBER, W. *J. Amer. chem. Soc.* **78,** 1763 (1956)
949. GUNSALUS, I. C., and BELLAMY, W. D. *J. biol. Chem.* **155,** 357 (1944)
950. GUNSALUS, I. C., BELLAMY, W. D., and UMBREIT, W. W. *J. biol. Chem.* **155,** 685 (1944)
951. GUNSALUS, C. F., STANIER, R. Y., and GUNSALUS, I. C. *J. Bact.* **66,** 548 (1953)
952. GÜNTELBERG, A. V., and OTTESEN, M. *Nature, Lond.* **170,** 802 (1952)
953. GÜNTELBERG, A. V., and OTTESEN, M. *C. R. Lab. Carlsberg* (Sér. chim) **29,** 36 (1953)
954. GUPTA, N. K., and ROBINSON, W. G. *J. biol. Chem.* **235,** 1609 (1960)
955. GUSTAFSON, T. *Int. Rev. Cytol.* **3,** 277 (1954)
956. GUTFREUND, H. *Disc. Faraday Soc.,* No. 17, 'The Study of Fast Reactions', p. 220, (1954)
957. GUTFREUND, H. *Disc. Faraday Soc.,* No. 20, 'The Physical Chemistry of Enzymes', p. 167 (1955),
958. GUTFREUND, H. *Trans. Faraday Soc.* **51,** 441 (1955)
959. GUTFREUND, H., and HAMMOND, B. R. *Biochem. J.* **73,** 526 (1959)
960. GUTFREUND, H., and STURTEVANT, J. M. *Biochem. J.* **73,** 1 (1959)
961. HAAS, E., HARRER, C. J., and HOGNESS, T. R. *J. biol. Chem.* **143,** 341 (1942)
962. HAAS, E., HORECKER, B. L., and HOGNESS, T. R. *J. biol. Chem.* **136,** 747 (1940)
963. HAAS, E., LAMFROM, H., and GOLDBLATT, H. *Arch. Biochem. Biophys.* **42,** 368 (1953)
964. HAAS, E., LAMFROM, H., and GOLDBLATT, H. *Arch. Biochem. Biophys.* **44,** 63 (1953)
965. HABERMANN, E. *Biochem. J.* **329,** 405 (1957)
966. HAGEMAN, R. H., and ARNON, D. I. *Arch. Biochem. Biophys.* **55,** 162 (1955)
967. HAGER, L. P., GELLER, D. M., and LIPMANN, F. *Fed. Proc.* **13,** 734 (1954)
968. HAGER, L. P., and GUNSALUS, I. C. *J. Amer. chem. Soc.* **75,** 5767 (1953)

969. HAGER, S. E., GREGERMAN, R. I., and KNOX, W. E. *J. biol. Chem.* **225,** 935 (1957)

970. HAGIHARA, B., in *The Enzymes,* 2nd edn., ed. P. D. Boyer, H. Lardy and K. Myrbäck (New York, Academic Press, 1960), Vol. 4, p. 193

971. HAGIHARA, B., HORIO, T., YAMASHITA, J., NOZAKI, M., and OKUNUKI, K. *Nature, Lond.* **178,** 629 (1956)

972. HAGIHARA, B., MATSUBARA, H., NAKAI, M., and OKUNUKI, K. *J. Biochem., Tokyo* **45,** 185 and 251 (1958)

973. HAGIHARA, B., MORIKAWA, I., SEKUZU, I., HORIO, T., and OKUNUKI, K. *Nature, Lond.* **178,** 630 (1956)

974. HAGIHARA, B., SEKUZU, I., TAGAWA, K., YONEDA, M., and OKUNUKI, K. *Nature, Lond.* **181,** 1588 (1958)

975. HAGIHARA, B., TAGAWA, K., NOZAKI, M., MORIKAWA, I., YAMASHITA, J., and OKUNUKI, K. *Nature, Lond.* **179,** 249 (1957)

976. HAGIHARA, B., TAGAWA, K., SEKUZU, I., MORIKAWA, I., and OKUNUKI, K. *J. Biochem., Tokyo* **46,** 11 (1959)

977. HAINES, W. J. *Recent Progr. Hormone Res.* **7,** 255 (1952)

978. HAKIM, A. A. *Nature, Lond.* **183,** 334 (1959)

979. HALDANE, J. B. S. *Enzymes* (London, Longmans, 1930)

980. HALDANE, J. B. S. *The Biochemistry of Genetics* (London, Allen & Unwin, 1954)

981. HALL, D. A. *Biochem. J.* **51,** 499 (1952)

982. HALL, D. A., and CZERKAWSKI, J. W. *Biochem. J.* **73,** 356 (1959)

983. HALLIWELL, G. *Biochem. J.* **79,** 185 (1961)

984. HALPERN, Y. S., and GROSSOWICZ, N. *Biochem. J.* **65,** 716 (1957)

985. HALSEY, Y. D. *J. biol. Chem.* **214,** 589 (1955)

986. HALVORSON, H. O. *Advanc. Enzymol.* **22,** 99 (1960)

987. HALVORSON, H., and ELLIAS, L. *Biochim. biophys. Acta* **30,** 28 (1958)

988. HAMMETT, L. P. *Physical Organic Chemistry* (New York, McGraw-Hill, 1940)

989. HAMMOND, B. R., and GUTFREUND, H. *Biochem. J.* **61,** 187 (1955)

990. HAMMOND, B. R., and GUTFREUND, H. *Biochem. J.* **72,** 349 (1959)

991. HANAHAN, D. J., BROCKERHOFF, H., and BARRON, E. J. *J. biol. Chem.* **235,** 1917 (1960)

992. HANAHAN, D. J., and CHAIKOFF, I. L. *J. biol. Chem.* **169,** 699 (1947)

993. HANAHAN, D. J., and CHAIKOFF, I. L. *J. biol. Chem.* **172,** 191 (1948)

994. HANAHAN, D. J., and VERCAMER, R. *J. Amer. chem. Soc.* **76,** 1804 (1954)

995. HANDLER, P., BERNHEIM, M. L. C., and KLEIN, J. R. *J. biol. Chem.* **138,** 211 (1941)

996. HANES, C. S. *Biochem. J.* **26,** 1406 (1932)

997. HANES, C. S. *Proc. roy. Soc.* B, **128,** 421 (1940)

998. HANES, C. S. *Proc. roy. Soc.* B, **129,** 174 (1940)

999. HANSON, H. T., and SMITH, E. L. *J. biol. Chem.* **179,** 789 (1949)

1000. HARARY, I., KOREY, S. R., and OCHOA, S. *J. biol. Chem.* **203,** 595 (1953)

1001. HARBURY, H. A. *J. Amer. chem. Soc.* **75,** 4625 (1953)

1002. HARDEN, A., and YOUNG, W. J. *Proc. roy. Soc.* B, **77,** 405 (1906)

1003. HARDEN, A., and YOUNG, W. J. *Proc. roy. Soc.* B, **78,** 369 (1906)

1004. HARE, M. L. C. *Biochem. J.* **22,** 968 (1928)

1005. HARGREAVES, A. B., and DEUTSCH, H. F. *Cancer Res.* **12,** 720 (1952)

1006. HARINGTON, C. R., and MEAD, T. H. *Biochem. J.* **29,** 1602 (1935)

1007. HARINGTON, C. R., and RIVERS, R. V. PITT. *Biochem. J.* **38,** 417 (1944)

1008. HARRIS, H. *Human Biochemical Genetics* (Cambridge University Press, 1959)

1009. HARRIS, J. I., SANGER, F., and NAUGHTON, M. A. *Arch. Biochem. Biophys.* **65,** 427 (1956)

1010. HARRIS, R. J. C., ed. *Protein Biosynthesis* (London and New York, Academic Press, 1961)

1011. HARTING, J., and VELICK, S. F. *J. biol. Chem.* **207,** 867 (1954)

1011a. HARTLEY, B. S. *Biochem. J.* **64,** 27P (1956)

1012. HARTLEY, B. S. *Proceedings of the fifth International Congress of Biochemistry, Moscow,* Symp. No. 4 (Oxford, Pergamon Press, 1963)

1013. HARTLEY, B. S., and MASSEY, V. *Biochim. biophys. Acta* **21,** 58 (1956)

1014. HARTMAN, P. E., LOPER, J. C., and ŠERMAN, D. *J. gen. Microbiol.* **22,** 323 (1960)

1015. HARTMAN, S. C., and BUCHANAN, J. M. *J. biol. Chem.* **233,** 451 (1958)

1016. HARTMAN, S. C., and BUCHANAN, J. M. *J. biol. Chem.* **233,** 456 (1958)

1017. HARTMAN, S. C., and BUCHANAN, J. M. *J. biol. Chem.* **234,** 1812 (1959)

1018. HARTMAN, W. J., POGRUND, R. S., DRELL, W., and CLARK, W. G. *J. Amer. chem. Soc.* **77,** 816 (1955)

1019. HASE, E. *J. Biochem., Tokyo* **39,** 259 (1952)

1020. HASS, L. F., BOYER, P. D., and REYNARD, A. M. *J. biol. Chem.* **236,** 2284 (1961)

1021. HASSID, W. Z., and DOUDOROFF, M. *Advanc. Carbohyd. Chem.* **5,** 29 (1950)

1022. HASSID, W. Z., and DOUDOROFF, M. *Advanc. Enzymol.* **10,** 123 (1950)

1023. HASSID, W. Z., DOUDOROFF, M., and BARKER, H. A., in *The Enzymes,* 1st edn., ed. J. B. Sumner and K. Myrbäck (New York, Academic Press, 1951), Vol. 1, p. 1014

1024. HATCH, M. D., and STUMPF, P. K. *J. biol. Chem.* **236,** 2879 (1961)

1025. HATEFI, Y. *Biochim. biophys. Acta* **34,** 183 (1959)

1026. HATEFI, Y. HAAVIK, A. G. and GRIFFITHS, D. E. *Biochem. biophys. res. Comm.* **4,** 441 (1961)

1027. HATEFI, Y., OSBORN, M. J., KAY, L. D., and HUENNEKENS, F. M. *J. biol. Chem.* **227,** 637 (1957)

1028. HAUGE, J. G., CRANE, F. L., and BEINERT, H. *J. biol. Chem.* **219,** 727 (1956)

1029. HAUGHTON, B. G., and KING, H. K. *Boichem. J.* **80,** 268 (1961)

1030. HAWKINS, R. D., and GUNTER, J. M. *Biochem. J.* **40,** 192 (1946)

1031. HAWKINS, R. D., and MENDEL, B. *Biochem. J.* **44,** 260 (1949)

1032. HAYAISHI, O. *J. biol. Chem.* **215,** 125 (1955)

1033. HAYAISHI, O., in *Methods in Enzymology,* ed. S. P. Colowick and N. O. Kaplan (New York, Academic Press, 1955), Vol. 1, p. 668

1034. HAYAISHI, O., KATAGIRI, M., and ROTHBERG, S. *J. biol. Chem.* **229,** 905 (1957)

1035. HAYAISHI, O., and KORNBERG, A. *J. biol. Chem.* **197,** 717 (1952)

1036. HAYAISHI, O., and KORNBERG, A. *J. biol. Chem.* **206,** 647 (1954)

1037. HAYAISHI, O., NISHIZUKA, Y., TATIBANA, M., TAKESHITA, M., and KUNO, S. *J. biol. Chem.* **236,** 781 (1961)

1038. HAYAISHI, O., ROTHBERG, S., MEHLER, A. H., and SAITO, Y. *J. biol. Chem.* **229,** 889 (1957)

1039. HAYAISHI, O., SAITO, Y., JAKOBY, W. B., and STOHLMAN, E. F. *Arch. Biochem. Biophys.* **56,** 554 (1955)

1040. HAYAISHI, O., SHIMAZONO, H., KATAGIRI, M., and SAITO, Y. *J. Amer. chem. Soc.* **78,** 5126 (1956)

1041. HAYAISHI, O., and STANIER, R. Y. *J. Bact.* **62,** 691 (1951)

1042. HAYANO, M., and DORFMAN, R. I. *Arch. Biochem. Biophys.* **36,** 237 (1952)

1043. HAYANO, M., and DORFMAN, R. I. *J. biol. Chem.* **211,** 227 (1954)

1044. HAYES, J. E., and VELICK, S. F. *J. biol. Chem.* **207,** 225 (1954)

1045. HEALD, K., and LONG, C. *Biochem. J.* **59,** 316 (1955)

1046. HEATH, E. C., HORECKER, B. L., SMYRNIOTIS, P. Z., and TAKAGI, Y. *J. biol. Chem.* **231,** 1031 (1958)

1047. HEATH, E. C., HURWITZ, J., HORECKER, B. L., and GINSBURG, A. *J. biol. Chem.* **231,** 1009 (1958)

1048. HECHT, L. I., STEPHENSON, M. L., and ZAMECNIK, P. C. *Proc. nat. Acad. Sci. U.S.* **45,** 505 (1959)

1049. HEHRE, E. J. *Proc. Soc. exp. Biol., N.Y.* **54,** 18 (1943)

1050. HEHRE, E. J. *Advanc. Enzymol.* **11,** 297 (1951)

1051. HEHRE, E. J., and HAMILTON, D. M. *Proc. Soc. exp. Biol., N.Y.* **71,** 336 (1949)

1052. HEHRE, E. J., and HAMILTON, D. M. *J. biol. Chem.* **192,** 161 (1953)

1053. HEHRE, E. J., HAMILTON, D. M., and CARLSON, A. S. *J. biol. Chem.* **177,** 267 (1949)

1054. HEIMBERG, M., and VELICK, S. F. *J. biol. Chem.* **208,** 725 (1954)

1055. HELE, P. *J. biol. Chem.* **206,** 671 (1954)

1056. HELFERICH, B. *Ergebn. Enzymforsch.* **2,** 74 (1933)

1057. HELLERMAN, L., and PERKINS, M. E. *J. biol. Chem.* **112,** 175 (1935)

1058. HELLERMAN, L., and STOCK, C. C. *J. biol. Chem.* **125,** 771 (1938)

1059. HELLIG, H., and POPJÁK, G. *J. Lipid Research* **2,** 235 (1961)

1060. HELLSTRÖM, N. *Z. physik. Chem.* A, **157,** 242 (1931)

1061. HENDERSON, R. W., MORTON, R. K., and RAWLINSON, W. A. *Biochem. J.* **72,** 340 (1959)

1062. HENDERSON, R. W., and RAWLINSON, W. A. *Biochem. J.* **62,** 21 (1956)

1063. HENION, W. F., and SUTHERLAND, E. W. *J. biol. Chem.* **224,** 477 (1957)

1064. HENNING, U., MÖSLEIN, E. M., and LYNEN, F. *Arch. Biochem. Biophys.* **83,** 259 (1959)

1065. HENRI, V. *C. R. Acad. Sci., Paris* **135,** 916 (1902)

1066. HEPPEL, L. A., and HILMOE, R. J. *J. biol. Chem.* **183,** 129 (1950)

1067. HEPPEL, L. A., and HILMOE, R. J. *J. biol. Chem.* **188,** 665 (1951)

1068. HEPPEL, L. A., and HILMOE, R. J. *J. biol. Chem.* **192,** 87 (1951)

1069. HEPPEL, L. A., and HILMOE, R. J. *J. biol. Chem.* **198,** 683 (1952)

1070. HEPPEL, L. A., and HILMOE, R. J. *J. biol. Chem.* **202,** 217 (1953)

1071. HEPPEL, L. A., HURWITZ, J., and HORECKER, B. L. *J. Amer. chem. Soc.* **79,** 630 (1957)

1072. HEPPEL, L. A., STROMINGER, J. L., and MAXWELL, E. S. *Biochim. biophys. Acta* **32,** 422 (1959)

1073. HEPPEL, L. A., and PORTERFIELD, V. T. *J. biol. Chem.* **176,** 763 (1948)

1074. HEPPEL, L. A., WHITFELD, P. R., and MARKHAM, R. *Biochem. J.* **60,** 8 (1955)

1075. HERBERT, D., in *Methods in Enzymology,* ed. S. P. Colowick and N. O. Kaplan (New York, Academic Press, 1955), Vol. 1, p. 753

1076. HERBERT, D., GORDON, H., SUBRAHMANYAN, V., and GREEN, D. E. *Biochem. J.* **34,** 1108 (1940)

1077. HERBERT, D., and PINSENT, J. *Biochem. J.* **43,** 193 (1948)

1078. HERBERT, D., and PINSENT, J. *Biochem. J.* **43,** 203 (1948)

1079. HERNANDEZ, H. H., and CHAIKOFF, I. L. *J. biol. Chem.* **228,** 447 (1957)

1080. HERRIOTT, R. M. *J. gen. Physiol.* **21,** 501 (1938)

1081. HERRIOTT, R. M. *J. gen. Physiol.* **22,** 65 (1938)

1082. HERRIOTT, R. M. *J. gen. Physiol.* **24,** 325 (1941)

1083. HERRIOTT, R. M., and NORTHROP, J. H. *J. gen. Physiol* **18,** 35 (1934)

1084. HERS, H. G. *Biochim. biophys. Acta* **8,** 424 (1952)

1085. HERS, H. G. *Biochim. biophys. Acta* **8,** 416 (1952)

1086. HERS, H. G. *Biochim. biophys. Acta* **37,** 120 (1960)

1087. HERS, H. G. *Le Métabolisme du Fructose* (Brussels, Arscia, 1957)

1088. HERS, H. G., and KUSAKA, T. *Biochim. biophys. Acta* **11,** 427 (1953)

1089. HESTRIN, S. *J. biol. Chem.* **179,** 943 (1949)

1090. HESTRIN, S., FEINGOLD, D. S., and AVIGAD, G. *Biochem. J.* **64,** 340 (1956)

1091. HEYWORTH, R., and WALKER, P. G. *Biochem. J.* **83,** 331 (1962)

1092. HICKMAN, J., and ASHWELL, G. *J. biol. Chem.* **232,** 737 (1958)

1093. HICKMAN, J., and ASHWELL, G. *J. biol. Chem.* **234,** 758 (1959)

1094. HICKMAN, J., and ASHWELL, G. *J. biol. Chem.* **235,** 1566 (1960)

1095. HIFT, H., and MAHLER, H. R. *J. biol. Chem.* **198,** 901 (1952)

1096. HILL, R. *Nature, Lond.* **174,** 501 (1954)

1097. HILL, R. *Proceedings of the third International Congress of Biochemistry, Brussels* (New York, Academic Press, 1955), p. 225

1098. HILL, R., and BENDALL, F. *Nature, Lond.* **186,** 136 (1960)

1099. HILL, R., and SCARISBRICK, R. *New Phytol.* **50,** 98 (1951)

1100. HILL, R., and WHITTINGHAM, C. P. *Photosynthesis* (London, Methuen, 1955)

1101. HILL, R. L., and SMITH, E. L. *J. biol. Chem.* **228,** 577 (1957)

1102. HILL, R. L., and SMITH, E. L. *J. biol. Chem.* **235,** 2332 (1960)

1103. HILL, R. L., SWENSON, R. T., and SCHWARTZ, H. C. *J. biol. Chem.* **235,** 3182 (1960)

1104. HILMOE, R. J. *J. biol. Chem.* **235,** 2117 (1960)

1105. HILZ, H., KITTLER, M., and KNAPE, G. *Biochem. Z.* **332,** 151 (1959)

1106. HILZ, H., KNAPPE, J., RINGELMANN, E., and LYNEN, F. *Biochem. Z.* **329,** 476 (1958)

1107. HILZ, H., and LIPMANN, F. *Proc. nat. Acad. Sci. U.S.* **41,** 880 (1955)

1108. HIRD, F. J. R., and ROWSELL, E. V. *Nature, Lond.* **166,** 517 (1950)

1109. HIRS, C. H. W., MOORE, S., and STEIN, W. H. *J. biol. Chem.* **235,** 633 (1960)

1110. HIRS, C. H. W., STEIN, W. H., and MOORE, S. *J. biol. Chem.* **211,** 941 (1954)

1111. HIRSCHMANN, H. *J. biol. Chem.* **235,** 2762 (1960)

1112. HITCHINGS, G. H., and FALCO, E. A. *Proc. nat. Acad. Sci. U.S.* **30,** 294 (1944)

1113. HJERTÉN, S., and MOSBACH, R. *Anal. Biochem.* **3,** 109 (1962)

1113a. HOAGLAND, M. B., and NOVELLI, G. D. *J. biol. Chem.* **207,** 767 (1954)

1114. HOBSON, G. E., and REES, K. R. *Biochem. J.* **65,** 305 (1957)

1115. HOBSON, P. N., WHELAN, W. J., and PEAT, S. *J. chem. Soc.*, p. 1451 (1951)

1116. HOCHSTER, R. M., and WATSON, R. W. *Arch. Biochem. Biophys.* **48,** 120 (1954)

1117. HOCKENHULL, D. J. D., ASHTON, G. C., FANTES, K. H., and WHITEHEAD, B. K. *Biochem. J.* **57,** 93 (1954)

1118. HOFFMANN-OSTENHOF, O. *Advanc. Enzymol.* **14,** 219 (1953)

1119. HOFFMANN-OSTENHOF, O., KENEDY, J., KECK, K., GABRIEL, O., and SCHÖNFELLINGER, H. W. *Biochim. biophys. Acta* **14,** 285 (1954)

1120. HOFFSTEN, P. E., HUNTER, F. E., GEBICKI, J. M., and WEINSTEIN, J. *Biochem. biophys. res. Comm.* **7,** 276 (1962)

1121. HOFMANN, E. C. G., and RAPOPORT, S. *Biochim. biophys. Acta* **18,** 296 (1955)

1122. HOFMANN, K., and BERGMANN, M. *J. biol. Chem.* **130,** 81 (1939)

1123. HOFMANN, K., and BERGMANN, M. *J. biol. Chem.* **134,** 225 (1940)

1124. HOFSTEE, B. H. J. *J. biol. Chem.* **179,** 633 (1949)

1125. HOFSTEE, B. H. J. *Nature, Lond.* **184,** 1296 (1959)

1126. HOGEBOOM, G. H., in *Methods in Enzymology,* ed. S. P. Colowick and N. O. Kaplan (New York, Academic Press, 1955), Vol. 1, p. 16

1127. HOGEBOOM, G. H., KUFF, E. L., and SCHNEIDER, W. C. *Int. Rev. Cytol.* **6,** 425 (1957)

1128. HOGNESS, D. S., and BATTLEY, E. H. *Fed. Proc.* **16,** 197 (1957)

1129. HOGNESS, D. S., COHN, M., and MONOD, J. *Biochim. biophys. Acta* **16,** 99 (1955)

1130. HOKIN, L. E. *Biochem. J.* **48,** 320 (1951)

1131. HOLDEN, M. *Biochem. J.* **78,** 359 (1961)

1132. HOLDEN, M., and PIRIE, N. W. *Biochem. J.* **60,** 39 (1955)

1133. HOLLANDER, V. *Proc. Soc. exp. Biol., N.Y.* **53,** 179 (1943)

1134. HOLLEY, R. W., BRUNNGRABER, E. F., SAAD, F., and WILLIAMS, H. H. *J. biol. Chem.* **236,** 197 (1961)

1135. HOLLEY, R. W., and GOLDSTEIN, J. *J. biol. Chem.* **234,** 1765 (1959)

1136. HOLLMANN, S., and TOUSTER, O. *J. biol. Chem.* **225,** 87 (1957)

1137. HOLT, A., and WOLD, F. *J. biol. Chem.* **236,** 3227 (1961)

1138. HOLT, S. J. *Proc. roy. Soc.* B, **142,** 160 (1954)

1139. HOLTEN, D., and FROMM, H. J. *J. biol. Chem.* **236,** 2581 (1961)

1140. HOLTER, H. *Advanc. Enzymol.* **13,** 1 (1952)

1141. HOLTER, H. *Proc. roy. Soc.* B, **142,** 140 (1954)

1142. HOLTER, H., and LI, S.-O. *Acta chem. scand.* **4,** 1321 (1950)

1143. HOLTON, F. A., and COLPA-BOONSTRA, J. *Biochem. J.* **76,** 179 (1960)

1144. HOLTZ, P., and CREDNER, K. *Z. physiol. Chem.* **280,** 1 (1944)

1145. HOLTZ, P., CREDNER, K., and WALTER H. *Z. physiol. Chem.* **262,** 111 (1939)

1146. HOLTZ, P., HEISE, R., and SPREYER, W. *Arch. exp. Path. Pharmak.* **188,** 580 (1938)

1147. HOLZER, H., and BEAUCAMP, K. *Biochim. biophys. Acta* **46,** 225 (1961)

1148. HOLZER, H., and HOLLDORF, A. *Biochem. Z.* **329,** 292 (1957)

1149. HOLZER, H., KATTERMANN, R., and BUSCH, D. *Biochem. biophys. res. Comm.* **7,** 167 (1962)

1150. HOLZER, H., and SCHNEIDER, S. *Biochim. biophys. Acta* **48,** 71 (1961)

1151. HOPE, D. B. *Biochem. J.* **59,** 497 (1955)

1152. HOPE, D. B., and SMITH, D. B. *Biochem. J.* **74,** 101 (1960)

1153. HOPKINS, F. G. *Biochem. J.* **15,** 286 (1921)

1154. HOPKINS, F. G. *J. biol. Chem.* **84,** 269 (1929)

1155. HOPKINS, F. G. Presidential Address at the Anniversary Meeting of the Royal Society, *Proc. roy. Soc.* B, **112,** 159 (1932)

1156. HOPKINS, F. G. Presidential Address to the British Association for the Advancement of Science (1933)

1157. HOPKINS, F. G., and MORGAN, E. J. *Biochem. J.* **42,** 23 (1948)

1158. HOPKINS, F. G., MORGAN, E. J., and LUTWAK-MANN, C. *Biochem. J.* **32,** 1829 (1938)

1159. HORECKER, B. L. *J. biol. Chem.* **183,** 593 (1950)

1160. HORECKER, B. L., HURWITZ, J., and HEPPEL, L. A. *J. Amer. chem. Soc.* **79,** 701 (1957)

1161. HORECKER, B. L., HURWITZ, J., and SMYRNIOTIS, P. Z. *J. Amer. chem. Soc.* **78,** 692 (1956)

1162. HORECKER, B. L., and SMYRNIOTIS, P. Z. *J. Amer. chem. Soc.* **75,** 1009 (1953)

1163. HORECKER, B. L., and SMYRNIOTIS, P. Z. *J. biol. Chem.* **212,** 811 (1955)

1164. HORECKER, B. L., SMYRNIOTIS, P. Z., and HURWITZ, J. *J. biol. Chem.* **223,** 1009 (1956)

1165. HORECKER, B. L., SMYRNIOTIS, P. Z., and SEEGMILLER, J. E. *J. biol. Chem.* **193,** 383 (1951)

1166. HORIO, T., HIGASHI, T., SASAGAWA, M., KUSAI, K., NAKAI, M., and OKUNUKI, K. *Biochem. J.* **77,** 194 (1960)

1167. HORIO, T., HIGASHI, T., YAMANAKA, T., MATSUBARA, H., and OKUNUKI, K. *J. biol. Chem.,* **236,** 944 (1961)

1168. HORIO, T., and KAMEN, M. D. *Biochim. biophys. Acta* **48,** 266 (1961)

1169. HORIO, T., YAMASHITA, J., and OKUNUKI, K. *Biochim. biophys. Acta* **32,** 593 (1959)

1170. HOSOYA, T. *J. Biochem., Tokyo* **47,** 369 (1960)

1171. HOSOYA, T. *J. Biochem., Tokyo* **48,** 37 (1960)

1172. HOSOYA, T. *J. Biochem., Tokyo* **48,** 178 (1960)

1173. HOSOYA, T., KONDO, Y., and UI, N. *J. Biochem., Tokyo* **52,** 180 (1962)

1174. HOSOYA, T., and UI, N. *Nature, Lond.* **192,** 4803 (1961)

1175. HOWARD, B. H., JONES, G., and PURDOM, M. R. *Biochem. J.* **74,** 173 (1960)

1176. HUANG, H. T. U.S. Pat. 2944943; *Chem. Abstracts* **54,** 20073 (1960)

1177. HUANG, H. T., and NIEMANN, C. *J. Amer. chem. Soc.* **74,** 4634 (1952)

1178. HUBBARD, R. *J. gen. Physiol.* **39,** 935 (1956)

1179. HÜBENER, H. J., and SAHRHOLZ, F. G. *Biochem. Z.* **333,** 95 (1960)

1180. HÜBSCHER, G., BAUM, H., and MAHLER, H. R. *Biochim. biophys. Acta* **23,** 43 (1957)

1181. HUENNEKENS, F. M. *Fed. Proc.* **16,** 199 (1957)

1182. HUENNEKENS, F. M., HATEFI, Y., and KAY, L. *J. biol. Chem.* **224,** 435 (1957)

1183. HUENNEKENS, F. M., MAHLER, H. R., and NORDMANN, J. *Arch. Biochem.* **30,** 77 (1951)

1184. HUENNEKENS, F. M., NURK, E., and GABRIO, B. W. *J. biol. Chem.* **221,** 971 (1956)

1185. HUENNEKENS, F. M., and OSBORN, M. J. *Advanc. Enzymol.* **21,** 369 (1959)

1186. HUGHES, D. E., and WILLIAMSON, D. H. *Biochem. J.* **51,** 45 (1952)

1187. HUGHES, N. A., KENNER, G. W., and TODD, A. R. *J. chem. Soc.* p. 3733 (1957)

1188. HULTIN, E., and NORDSTRÖM, L. *Acta chem. scand.* **3,** 1405 (1949)

1189. HUMPHREY, G. F. *Biochem. J.* **65,** 546 (1957)

1190. HUNT, A. L. *Biochem. J.* **72,** 1 (1959)

1191. HUNTER, A., and DOWNS, C. E. *J. biol. Chem.* **157,** 427 (1945)

1192. HURLBERT, R. B., and REICHARD, P. *Acta chem. scand.* **9,** 251 (1955)

1193. HURWITZ, J. *J. biol. Chem.* **205,** 935 (1953)

1194. HURWITZ, J. *Fed. Proc.* **15,** 278 (1956)

1195. HURWITZ, J. *J. biol. Chem.* **234,** 2351 (1959)
1196. HURWITZ, J., and BRESLER, A. E. *J. biol. Chem.* **236,** 542 (1961)
1197. HURWITZ, J., HEPPEL, L. A., and HORECKER, B. L. *J. biol. Chem.* **226,** 525 (1957)
1198. HURWITZ, J., and HORECKER, B. L. *J. biol. Chem.* **223,** 993 (1956)
1199. HURWITZ, J., WEISSBACH, A., HORECKER, B. L., and SMYRNIOTIS, P. Z. *J. biol. Chem.* **218,** 769 (1956)
1200. HUTTON, R., and WESTHEIMER, F. *Tetrahedron* **3,** 73 (1958)
1201. HUXLEY, H. E., and ZUBAY, G. *J. mol. Biol.* **2,** 10 (1960)
1202. HYLIN, J. W., and WOOD, J. L. *J. biol. Chem.* **234,** 2141 (1959)
1203. ICHIHARA, A., and GREENBERG, D. M. *J. biol. Chem.* **225,** 949 (1957)
1204. ICHIHARA, A., and ICHIHARA, E. A. *J. Biochem., Tokyo* **49,** 154 (1961)
1205. ICHIHARA, K., UCHIDA, M., MATSUDA, K., KUMAGAI, N., and KIKUOKA, H. *Z. physiol. Chem.* **295,** 220 (1953)
1206. IKEHATA, H. *J. gen. appl. Microbiol.* **6,** 30 (1960)
1207. ILLINGWORTH, B., JANSZ, H. S., BROWN, J. H., and CORI, C. F. *Proc. nat. Acad. Sci. U.S.* **44,** 1180 (1958)
1208. IMSANDE, J. *J. biol. Chem.* **236,** 1494 (1961)
1209. IMSANDE, J., and HANDLER, P. *J. biol. Chem.* **236,** 525 (1961)
1210. INAOKA, M., and SODA, H. *Nature, Lond.* **178,** 202 (1956)
1211. INGOLD, C. K. *Structure and Mechanism in Organic Chemistry* (London, G. Bell, 1953)
1212. INGRAHAM, L. L., and MAKOWER, B. *J. phys. Chem.* **58,** 266 (1954)
1213. INGRAM, V. M. *Nature, Lond.* **183,** 1795 (1959)
1214. INGRAM, V. M. *Proceedings of the fifth International Congress of Biochemistry, Moscow,* Symp. No. 1 (Oxford, Pergamon Press, 1963)
1215. IRVING, G. W., FRUTON, J. S., and BERGMANN, M. *J. biol. Chem.* **138,** 231 (1941)
1216. ISHERWOOD, F. A., MAPSON, L. W., and CHEN, Y. T. *Biochem. J.* **76,** 157 (1960)
1217. ISHIHARA, Y., SAITO, T., ITO, Y., and FUJINO, M. *Nature, Lond.* **181,** 1468 (1958)
1218. ISSELBACHER, K. J. *J. biol. Chem.* **232,** 429 (1958)
1219. ISSELBACHER, K. J., and AXELROD, J. *J. Amer. chem. Soc.* **77,** 1070 (1955)
1220. ITO, E., and STROMINGER, J. L. *J. biol. Chem.* **237,** 2689 (1962)
1221. ITO, E., and STROMINGER, J. L. *J. biol. Chem.* **237,** 2696 (1962)
1222. ITO, N., and GRISOLIA, S. *J. biol. Chem.* **234,** 242 (1959)
1223. IZUMIYA, N., and FRUTON, J. S. *J. biol. Chem.* **218,** 59 (1956)
1224. JACOB, F., and MONOD, J. *Cold Spring Harbor Symposia on quantitative Biology* **26,** 193 (1961)
1225. JACOB, F., and MONOD, J. *J. mol. Biol.* **3,** 318 (1961)
1226. JACOBS, E. E., and SANADI, D. R. *J. biol. Chem.* **235,** 531 (1960)
1227. JACOBSEN, C. F. *C. R. Lab. Carlsberg* (Sér. chim) **25,** 325 (1947)
1228. JACOBSEN, C. F., LÉONIS, J., LINDERSTRØM-LANG, K., and OTTESON, M. *Methods of Biochemical Analysis* **4,** 171 (1957)
1228a. JACOBSON, K. B., and KAPLAN, N. O. *J. biol. Chem.* **226,** 427 (1957)
1229. JAENICKE, L., and BRODE, E. *Biochem. Z.* **334,** 108 (1961)
1230. JAENICKE, L., and LYNEN, F., in *The Enzymes,* 2nd edn., ed. P. D. Boyer, H. Lardy and K. Myrbäck (New York, Academic Press, 1960), Vol. 3, p. 3

1231. JAGANNATHAN, V., SINGH, K., and DAMODARAN, M. *Biochem. J.* **63,** 94 (1956)

1232. JAKOBY, W. B. *J. biol. Chem.* **207,** 657 (1954)

1233. JAKOBY, W. B. *J. biol. Chem.* **232,** 75 (1958)

1234. JAKOBY, W. B., and BONNER, D. M. *J. biol. Chem.* **221,** 689 (1956)

1235. JAKOBY, W. B., BRUMMOND, D. O., and OCHOA, S. *J. biol. Chem.* **218,** 811 (1956)

1236. JAKOBY, W. B., and FREDERICKS, J. *J. biol. Chem.* **234,** 2145 (1959)

1237. JAKOBY, W. B., and FREDERICKS, J. *Biochim. biophys. Acta* **48,** 26 (1961)

1238. JAKOBY, W. B., OHMURA, E., and HAYAISHI, O. *J. biol. Chem.* **222,** 435 (1956)

1239. JAKOBY, W. B., and SCOTT, E. M. *J. biol. Chem.* **234,** 937 (1959)

1240. JANSEN, E. F., and BALLS, A. K. *J. biol. Chem.* **137,** 459 (1941)

1241. JANSEN, E. F., and BALLS, A. K. *J. biol. Chem.* **194,** 721 (1952)

1242. JANSEN, E. F., JANG, R., and BALLS, A. K. *J. biol. Chem.* **196,** 247 (1952)

1243. JANSEN, E. F., JANG, R., and MACDONALD, L. R. *Arch. Biochem.* **15,** 415 (1947)

1244. JANSEN, E. F., NUTTING, M.-D. F., and BALLS, A. K. *J. biol. Chem.* **175,** 975 (1948)

1245. JANSEN, E. F., NUTTING, M.-D. F., and BALLS, A. K. *J. biol. Chem.* **179,** 189 and 201 (1949)

1246. JANSEN, E. F., NUTTING, M.-D. F., JANG, R., and BALLS, A. K. *J. biol. Chem.* **185,** 209 (1950)

1247. JANSZ, H. S., BRONS, D., and WARRINGA, M. G. P. J. *Biochim. biophys. Acta* **34,** 573 (1959)

1248. JANSZ, H. S., POSTHUMUS, C. H., and COHEN, J. A. *Biochim. biophys. Acta* **33,** 387 and 396 (1959)

1249. JAQUES, L. B. *J. biol. Chem.* **133,** 445 (1940)

1250. JAQUES, L. B., and CHO, M. H. *Biochem. J.* **58,** xxv (1954)

1251. JARABAK, J., and TALALAY, P. *J. biol. Chem.* **235,** 2147 (1960)

1252. JÄRNEFELT, J., BASFORD, R. E., TISDALE, H. D., and GREEN, D. E. *Biochim. biophys. Acta* **29,** 123 (1958)

1253. JENKINS, W. T., and SIZER, I. W. *J. biol. Chem.* **235,** 620 (1960)

1254. JENKINS, W. T., YPHANTIS, D. A., and SIZER, I. W. *J. biol. Chem.* **234,** 51 (1959)

1255. JEUNIAUX, C. *Biochem. J.* **66,** 29P (1957)

1256. JEUNIAUX, C. *Arch. Int. Physiol. Biochim.* **67,** 597 (1959)

1257. JEUNIAUX, C. *Arch. Int. Physiol. Biochim.* **68,** 684 (1960)

1258. JOHNSON, M., KAYE, M. A. G., HEMS, R., and KREBS, H. A. *Biochem. J.* **54,** 625 (1953)

1259. JOHNSTON, R. B. *J. biol. Chem.* **221,** 1037 (1956)

1260. JOLLÈS, P., in *The Enzymes,* 2nd edn., ed. P. D. Boyer, H. Lardy and K. Myrbäck (New York, Academic Press, 1960), Vol. 4, p. 431

1261. JOLLÈS, G., and FROMAGEOT, C. *Biochim. biophys. Acta* **11,** 95 (1953)

1262. JOLLÈS, G., and FROMAGEOT, C. *Biochim. biophys. Acta* **14,** 219 (1954)

1263. JOLLÈS, P., and FROMAGEOT, C. *Biochim. biophys. Acta* **19,** 91 (1956)

1264. JONES, M. E., LIPMANN, F. L., HILZ, H., and LYNEN, F. *Amer. chem. Soc.* **75,** 3285 (1953)

1265. JONES, M. E., and SPECTOR, L. *J. biol. Chem.* **235,** 2897 (1960)

1266. JONES, M. E., SPECTOR, L., and LIPMANN, F. *Amer. chem. Soc.* **77,** 819 (1955)

1267. JONES, N. R. *Biochem. J.* **60,** 81 (1955)

1268. JOSEPHSON, K. *Z. physiol. Chem.* **134,** 50 (1924)

1269. JOSHI, J. G., and HANDLER, P. *J. biol. Chem.* **235,** 2981 (1960)

1270. JOSSE, J., KAISER, A., D., and KORNBERG, A. *J. biol. Chem.* **236,** 864 (1961)

1271. JOWETT, M., and QUASTEL, J. H. *Biochem. J.* **27,** 486 (1932)

1272. JOYCE, B. K., and GRISOLIA, S. *J. biol. Chem.* **233,** 350 (1958)

1273. JOYCE, B. K., and GRISOLIA, S. *J. biol. Chem.* **234,** 1330 (1959)

1274. JOYCE, B. K., and GRISOLIA, S. *J. biol. Chem.* **235,** 2278 (1960)

1275. JUKES, T. H. *Proc. nat. Acad. Sci. U.S.* **48,** 1809 (1962)

1276. JULIAN, G. R., WOLFE, R. G., and REITHEL, F. J. *J. biol. Chem.* **236,** 754 (1961)

1277. JUNGE, J. M., STEIN, E. A., NEURATH, H., and FISCHER, E. H. *J. biol. Chem.* **234,** 556 (1959)

1278. JUNI, E. *J. biol. Chem.* **195,** 715 (1952)

1279. JUNOWICZ-KOCHOLATY, R., and HOGNESS, T. R. *J. biol. Chem.* **129,** 569 (1939)

1280. KACSER, H. *Disc. Faraday Soc.*, No. 20, 'The Physical Chemistry of Enzymes', p. 283 (1955)

1281. KÄGI, J. H. R., and VALLEE, B. L. *J. biol. Chem.* **235,** 3188 (1960)

1282. KAHANA, S. E., LOWRY, O. H., SCHULZ, D. W., PASSONNEAU, J. V., and CRAWFORD, E. J. *J. biol. Chem.* **235,** 2178 (1960)

1283. KALCKAR, H. M. *J. biol. Chem.* **153,** 355 (1944)

1284. KALCKAR, H. M. *J. biol. Chem.* **158,** 313 (1945)

1285. KALCKAR, H. M. *J. biol. Chem.* **167,** 445 (1947)

1286. KALCKAR, H. M. *J. biol. Chem.* **167,** 461 (1947)

1287. KALCKAR, H. M. *J. biol. Chem.* **167,** 477 (1947)

1288. KALCKAR, H. M. *Pubbl. Staz. zool. Napoli* **23,** Suppl. 87 (1951)

1289. KALCKAR, H. M. *Biochim. biophys. Acta* **12,** 250 (1953)

1290. KALCKAR, H. M., BRAGANCA, B., and MUNCH-PETERSEN, A. *Nature, Lond.* **172,** 1038 (1953)

1291. KALCKAR, H. M., MACNUTT, W. S., and HOFF-JØRGENSEN, E. *Biochem. J.* **50,** 397 (1952)

1292. KALF, G. F., and RIEDER, S. V. *J. biol. Chem.* **230,** 691 (1958)

1293. KALLIO, R. E. *J. biol. Chem.* **192,** 371 (1951)

1294. KALLIO, R. E., and LARSON, A. D., in *A Symposium on Amino Acid Metabolism*, ed. W. D. McElroy and H. B. Glass (Baltimore, Johns Hopkins Press, 1955), p. 616

1295. KALNITSKY, G., and ANDERSON, E. E. *Biochim. biophys. Acta* **16,** 302 (1955)

1296. KALOW, W., and STARON, N. *Canad. J. Biochem. Physiol.* **35,** 1305 (1957)

1297. KALYANKAR, G. D., and MEISTER, A. *J. biol. Chem.* **234,** 3210 (1959)

1298. KAMEN, M. D., and TAKEDA, Y. *Biochim. biophys. Acta* **21,** 518 (1956)

1299. KAPLAN, N. O., in *Methods in Enzymology*, ed. S. P. Colowick and N. O. Kaplan (New York, Academic Press, 1955), Vol. 2, p. 681

1300. KAPLAN, N. O., in *Methods in Enzymology*, ed. S. P. Colowick and N. O. Kaplan (New York, Academic Press, 1957), Vol. 3, p. 873

1301. KAPLAN, N. O., in *Steric Course of Microbiological Reactions*, CIBA Foundation Study Group No. 2 (London, Churchill, 1959), p. 37

1302. KAPLAN, N. O., in *The Enzymes*, 2nd edn., ed. P. D. Boyer, H. Lardy and K. Myrbäck (New York, Academic Press, 1960), Vol. 3, p. 105

1303. KAPLAN, N. O., and CIOTTI, M. M. *Biochim. biophys. Acta* **49,** 425 (1961)

1304. KAPLAN, N. O., CIOTTI, M. M., STOLZENBACH, F. E., and BACHUR, N. R. *J. Amer. chem. Soc.* **77**, 815 (1955)

1305. KAPLAN, N. O., COLOWICK, S. P., and CIOTTI, M. M. *J. biol. Chem.* **194**, 579 (1952)

1306. KAPLAN, N. O., COLOWICK, S. P., and NEUFELD, E. F. *J. biol. Chem.* **195**, 107 (1952)

1307. KAPLAN, N. O., COLOWICK, S. P., and NEUFELD, E. F. *J. biol. Chem.* **205**, 1 (1953)

1308. KAPLAN, H. S., and HEPPEL, L. A. *J. biol. Chem.* **222**, 907 (1956)

1309. KARASEK, M. A., and GREENBERG, D. M. *J. biol. Chem.* **227**, 191 (1957)

1310. KARRER, P., and KRISHNA, H. *Helv. chim. Acta* **33**, 555 (1950)

1311. KARRER, P., SCHÖPP, K., and BENZ, F. *Helv. chim. Acta* **18**, 426 (1935)

1312. KASSEL, B. *Fed. Proc.* **18**, 257 (1959)

1313. KATAGIRI, H., YAMADA, H., and IMAI, K. *J. Biochem.*, *Tokyo* **46**, 1119 (1959)

1314. KATAGIRI, M., and HAYAISHI, O. *J. biol. Chem.* **226**, 439 (1957)

1315. KATCHMAN, B., BETHEIL, J. J., SCHEPARTZ, A. I., and SANADI, D. R. *Arch. Biochem. Biophys.* **34**, 437 (1951)

1316. KAUFMAN, S. *J. biol. Chem.* **216**, 153 (1955)

1317. KAUFMAN, S. *J. biol. Chem.* **234**, 2677 (1959)

1318. KAUFMAN, S., and ALIVASATOS, S. G. A. *J. biol. Chem.* **216**, 141 (1955)

1319. KAUFMAN, S., GILVARG, C., CORI, O., and OCHOA, S. *J. biol. Chem.* **203**, 869 (1953)

1320. KAUFMAN, S., KORKES, S., and DEL CAMPILLO, A. *J. biol. Chem.* **192**, 301 (1951)

1321. KAUFMAN, S., and LEVENBERG, B. *J. biol. Chem.* **234**, 2683 (1959)

1322. KAUFMAN, S., and NEURATH, H. *Arch. Biochem.* **21**, 437 (1949)

1323. KAWAHARA, F. S., and TALALAY, P. *J. biol. Chem.* **235**, PC1 (1960)

1324. KAY, H. D. *Biochem. J.* **22**, 855 (1928)

1325. KAZIRO, Y., LEONE, E., and OCHOA, S. *Proc. nat. Acad. Sci. U.S.* **46**, 1319 (1960)

1326. KAZIRO, Y., OCHOA, S., WARNER, R. C., and CHEN, J. *J. biol. Chem.* **236**, 1917 (1961)

1327. KEARNEY, E. B. *J. biol. Chem.* **194**, 747 (1952)

1328. KEARNEY, E. B. *J. biol. Chem.* **235**, 865 (1960)

1329. KEARNEY, E. B., and SINGER, T. P. *Arch. Biochem. Biophys.* **33**, 377, 397 and 414 (1951)

1330. KEARNEY, E. B., and SINGER, T. P. *J. biol. Chem.* **219**, 963 (1956)

1331. KEILIN, D. *Proc. roy. Soc.* B, **98**, 312 (1925)

1332. KEILIN, D. *Proc. roy. Soc.* B, **104**, 206 (1929)

1333. KEILIN, D. *Proc. roy. Soc.* B, **106**, 418 (1930)

1334. KEILIN, D. *Ergebn. Enzymforsch.* **2**, 239 (1933)

1335. KEILIN, D. *Nature, Lond.* **133**, 290 (1934)

1336. KEILIN, D., and HARTREE, E. F. *Proc. roy. Soc.* B, **119**, 141 (1936)

1337. KEILIN, D., and HARTREE, E. F. *Proc. roy. Soc.* B, **121**, 173 (1936)

1338. KEILIN, D., and HARTREE, E. F. *Proc. roy. Soc.* B, **122**, 298 (1937)

1339. KEILIN, D., and HARTREE, E. F. *Proc. roy. Soc.* B, **124**, 397 (1938)

1340. KEILIN, D., and HARTREE, E. F. *Proc. roy. Soc.* B, **125**, 171 (1938)

1341. KEILIN, D., and HARTREE, E. F. *Proc. roy. Soc.* B, **127**, 167 (1939)

1342. KEILIN, D., and HARTREE, E. F. *Proc. roy. Soc.* B, **129**, 277 (1940)

1342a. KEILIN, D., and HARTREE, E. F. *Biochem. J.* **41**, 500 (1947)

1343. KEILIN, D., and HARTREE, E. F. *Biochem. J.* **42**, 221 (1948)

1344. KEILIN, D., and HARTREE, E. F. *Biochem. J.* **50**, 331 (1952)

1345. KEILIN, D., and HARTREE, E. F. *Biochem. J.* **50**, 341 (1952)

1346. KEILIN, D., and HARTREE, E. F. *Biochem. J.* **61**, 153 (1955)

1346a. KEILIN, D., and HARTREE, E. F. *Nature, Lond.* **176**, 200 (1955)

1347. KEILIN, D., and MANN, T. *Proc. roy. Soc.* B, **122**, 119 (1937)

1348. KEILIN, D., and MANN, T. *Proc. roy. Soc.* B, **125**, 187 (1938)

1349. KEILIN, D., and MANN, T. *Nature, Lond.* **143**, 23 (1939)

1350. KEILIN, J. *Biochem. J.* **64**, 663 (1956)

1351. KEISTER, D. L., SAN PIETRO, A., and STOLZENBACH, F. E. *J. biol. Chem.* **235**, 2989 (1960)

1352. KELLER, P. J., COHEN, E., and NEURATH, H. *J. biol. Chem.* **223**, 457 (1956)

1353. KELLER, P. J., COHEN, E., and NEURATH, H. *J. biol. Chem.* **230**, 905 (1958)

1354. KELLER, P. J., COHEN, E., and NEURATH, H. *J. biol. Chem.* **233**, 344 (1958)

1355. KELLER, P. J., and CORI, G. T. *J. biol. Chem.* **214**, 127 (1955)

1356. KELLERMAN, G. M. *J. biol. Chem.* **231**, 427 (1958)

1357. KENDAL, L. P., and RAMANATHAN, A. N. *Biochem. J.* **52**, 430 (1952)

1358. KENDALL, E. C., McKENZIE, B. F., and MASON, H. L. *J. biol. Chem.* **84**, 657 (1929)

1359. KENDREW, J. C., WATSON, H. C., STRANDBERG, B. E., DICKERSON, R. E., PHILLIPS, D. C., and SHORE, V. C. *Nature, Lond.* **190**, 666 (1961)

1360. KENNEDY, E. P., and WEISS, S. B. *J. biol. Chem.* **222**, 193 (1956)

1361. KENNEY, F. T. *J. biol. Chem.* **234**, 2707 (1959)

1362. KENT, A. B., KREBS, E. G., and FISCHER, E. H. *J. biol. Chem.* **232**, 549 (1958)

1363. KENTEN, R. H. *Biochem. J.* **67**, 25 (1957)

1364. KENTEN, R. H., and MANN, P. J. G. *Biochem. J.* **57**, 347 (1954)

1365. KERN, M., and RACKER, E. *Arch. Biochem. Biophys.* **48**, 235 (1954)

1366. KERR, R. W., CLEVELAND, F. C., and KATZBECK, W. J. *J. Amer. chem. Soc.* **73**, 3916 (1951)

1367. KERTÉSZ, D., and ZITO, R. *Nature, Lond.* **179**, 1017 (1957)

1368. KESTON, A. S. *Science* **120**, 355 (1954)

1369. KESTON, A. S. *Fed. Proc.* **14**, 234 (1955)

1370. KHORANA, H. G., FERNANDES, J. F., and KORNBERG, A. *J. biol. Chem.* **230**, 941 (1958)

1371. KIDDER, G. W., and DEWEY, V. C. *Arch. Biochem.* **8**, 293 (1945)

1372. KIDDER, G. W., and DEWEY, V. C. *Arch. Biochem.* **20**, 433 (1949)

1373. KIELLEY, R. K. *Fed. Proc.* **14**, 235 (1955)

1374. KIELLEY, W. W., in *The Enzymes*, 2nd edn., ed. P. D. Boyer, H. Lardy and K. Myrbäck (New York, Academic Press, 1961), Vol. 5, p. 159

1375. KIELLEY, W. W., and BRADLEY, L. B. *J. biol. Chem.* **206**, 327 (1954)

1376. KIELLEY, W. W., KALCKAR, H. M., and BRADLEY, L. B. *J. biol. Chem.* **219**, 95 (1956)

1377. KIELLEY, W. W., and MEYERHOF, O. *J. biol. Chem.* **176**, 591 (1948)

1378. KILBY, B. A., and YOUATT, G. *Biochem. J.* **57**, 303 (1954)

1379. KILGORE, W. W., and STARR, M. P. *J. biol. Chem.* **234**, 2227 (1959)

1380. KIMMEL, J. R., and SMITH, E. L. *Advanc. Enzymol.* **19**, 267 (1957)

1381. KIMMEL, J. R., and SMITH, E. L. *J. biol. Chem.* **207**, 515 (1954)

1382. KINDLER, S. H., and GILVARG, C. *J. biol. Chem.* **235**, 3532 (1960)

1383. KING, E. L., and ALTMAN, C. *J. phys. Chem.* **60,** 1375 (1956)

1383a. KING, H. K. *Biochem. J.* **54,** xi (1953)

1384. KING, R. J. B. *Biochem. J.* **79,** 361 (1961)

1385. KING, T. E., and CHELDELIN, V. H. *J. biol. Chem.* **220,** 177 (1956)

1386. KING, T. E., and LEE, C. P. *Biochim. biophys. Acta* **37,** 342 (1960)

1387. KINSKY, S. C. *J. biol. Chem.* **235,** 94 (1960)

1388. KIRK, P. L. *Advanc. Protein Chem.* **3,** 139 (1947)

1389. KIRKLAND, R. J. A., and TURNER, J. F. *Biochem. J.* **72,** 716 (1959)

1390. KISLIUK, R. L., and SAKAMI, W. *J. biol. Chem.* **214,** 47 (1955)

1391. KISTIAKOWSKY, G. B., and LUMRY, R. *J. Amer. chem. Soc.* **71,** 2006 (1949)

1392. KITAHARA, K., ÔBAYASHI, A., and FUKUI, S. *Enzymologia* **15,** 259 (1953)

1393. KLEE, W. A., and RICHARDS, F. M. *J. biol. Chem.* **229,** 489 (1957)

1394. KLEE, W. A., RICHARDS, H. H., and CANTONI, G. L. *Biochim. biophys. Acta* **54,** 157 (1961)

1395. KLEIN, A. O., and VISHNIAC, W. *J. biol. Chem.* **236,** 2544 (1961)

1396. KLEINER, I. S., and TAUBER, H. *J. biol. Chem.* **96,** 755 (1932)

1397. KLENOW, H., and ANDERSEN, B. *Biochim. biophys. Acta* **23,** 92 (1957)

1398. KLINE, D. L., in *Methods in Enzymology,* ed. S. P. Colowick and N. O. Kaplan (New York, Academic Press, 1955), Vol. 2, p. 139

1399. KLINGMAN, J. D., and HANDLER, P. *J. biol. Chem.* **232,** 369 (1958)

1400. KLOTZ, I. M., in *A Symposium on the Mechanism of Enzyme Action,* ed. W. D. McElroy and B. Glass (Baltimore, Johns Hopkins Press, 1954), p. 257

1401. KLOTZ, I. M., and LOH MING, W.-C. *J. Amer. chem. Soc.* **76,** 805 (1954)

1402. KLOTZ, I. M., WALKER, F. M., and PIVAN, R. B. *J. Amer. chem. Soc.* **68,** 1486 (1946)

1403. KNAPPE, J., RINGELMANN, E., and LYNEN, F. *Biochem. Z.* **332,** 195 (1959)

1404. KNAPPE, J., SCHLEGEL, H.-G., and LYNEN, F. *Biochem. Z.* **335,** 101 (1961)

1405. KNEEN, E., and BECKORD, L. D. *Arch. Biochem.* **10,** 41 (1946)

1406. KNIVETT, V. A. *Biochem. J.* **56,** 602 (1954)

1407. KNOX, W. E. *J. biol. Chem.* **163,** 699 (1946)

1408. KNOX, W. E., in *Methods in Enzymology,* ed. S. P. Colowick and N. O. Kaplan (New York, Academic Press, 1955), Vol. 2, p. 289

1409. KNOX, W. E., and EDWARDS, S. W. *J. biol. Chem.* **216,** 479 (1955)

1410. KNOX, W. E., and LE MAY-KNOX, M. *Biochem. J.* **49,** 686 (1951)

1411. KNOX, W. E., and PITT, B. M. *J. biol. Chem.* **225,** 675 (1957)

1412. KOBAYASI, S. *J. Biochem., Tokyo* **33,** 301 (1941)

1413. KOCH, A. L. *J. biol. Chem.* **223,** 535 (1956)

1414. KOCHAKIAN, C. D., CARROLL, B. R., and UHRI, B. *J. biol. Chem.* **224,** 811 (1957)

1415. KOCHOLATY, W., and KREJCI, L. E. *Arch. Biochem.* **18,** 1 (1948)

1416. KOERNER, J. F., and SINSHEIMER, R. L. *J. biol. Chem.* **228,** 1039 and 1049 (1957)

1417. KOELLE, G. B. *J. Pharmacol.* **88,** 232 (1946)

1418. KOELLE, G. B. *Biochem. J.* **53,** 217 (1953)

1419. KOIKE, M., SHAH, P. C., and REED, L. J. *J. biol. Chem.* **235,** 1939 (1960)

1420. KOJIMA, Y., ITADA, N., and HAYAISHI, O. *J. biol. Chem.* **236,** 2223 (1961)

1421. KOOIMAN, P. *Biochim. biophys. Acta* **13,** 338 (1954)

1422. KORN, E. D., and BUCHANAN, J. M. *J. biol. Chem.* **217,** 183 (1955)

1423. KORN, E. D., and PAYZA, A. N. *Biochim. biophys. Acta* **20,** 596 (1956)

1424. KORN, E. D., and PAYZA, A. N. *J. biol. Chem.* **223,** 859 (1956)

1425. KORN, E. D., and QUIGLEY, T. W. *J. biol. Chem.* **226,** 833 (1957)

1426. KORNBERG, A. *J. biol. Chem.* **182,** 779 (1950)

1427. KORNBERG, A. *J. biol. Chem.* **182,** 805 (1950)

1428. KORNBERG, A., in *A Symposium on Phosphorus Metabolism,* ed. W. D. McElroy and B. Glass (Baltimore, Johns Hopkins Press, 1951), Vol. 1, p. 392

1429. KORNBERG, A. *Science* **131,** 1503 (1960)

1430. KORNBERG, A., KORNBERG, S. R., and SIMMS, E. S. *Biochim. biophys. Acta* **20,** 215 (1956)

1431. KORNBERG, A., LEHMAN, I. R., and SIMMS, E. S. *Fed. Proc.* **15,** 291 (1956)

1432. KORNBERG, A., LIEBERMAN, I., and SIMMS, E. S. *J. Amer. chem. Soc.* **76,** 2844 (1954)

1433. KORNBERG, A., LIEBERMAN, I., and SIMMS, E. S. *J. biol. Chem.* **215,** 417 (1955)

1434. KORNBERG, A., and PRICER, W. E. *J. biol. Chem.* **182,** 763 (1950)

1435. KORNBERG, A., and PRICER, W. E. *J. biol. Chem.* **186,** 557 (1950)

1436. KORNBERG, A., and PRICER, W. E. *J. biol. Chem.* **189,** 123 (1951)

1437. KORNBERG, A., and PRICER, W. E. *J. biol. Chem.* **191,** 535 (1951)

1438. KORNBERG, A., and PRICER, W. E. *J. biol. Chem.* **193,** 481 (1951)

1439. KORNBERG, A., and PRICER, W. E. *J. biol. Chem.* **204,** 329 (1953)

1440. KORNBERG, A., and PRICER, W. E. *J. biol. Chem.* **204,** 345 (1953)

1441. KORNBERG, H. L., and BEEVERS, H. *Biochim. biophys. Acta* **26,** 531 (1957)

1442. KORNBERG, H. L., and ELSDEN, S. R. *Advanc. Enzymol.* **23,** 401 (1961)

1443. KORNBERG, S. R., LEHMAN, I. R., BESSMAN, M. J., SIMMS, E. S., and KORNBERG, A. *J. biol. Chem.* **233,** 159 (1958)

1444. KORNBERG, S. R. *J. biol. Chem.* **218,** 23 (1956)

1445. KORNBERG, S. R., ZIMMERMAN, S. B., and KORNBERG, A. *J. biol. Chem.* **236,** 1487 (1961)

1446. KORNFELD, S., and GLASER, L. *J. biol. Chem.* **236,** 1791 (1961)

1447. KORZENOVSKY, M., DILLER, E. R., MARSHALL, A. C., and AUDA, B. M. *Biochem. J.* **76,** 238 (1960)

1448. KOSHLAND, D. E. *Biol. Rev.* **28,** 416 (1953)

1449. KOSHLAND, D. E., and ERWIN, M. J. *J. Amer. chem. Soc.* **79,** 2657 (1957)

1450. KOSHLAND, D. E., RAY, W. J., and ERWIN, M. J. *Fed. Proc.* **17,** 1145 (1958)

1451. KOSHLAND, D. E., and STEIN, S. S. *J. biol. Chem.* **208,** 139 (1954)

1452. KOSZALKA, T. R., FALKENHEIM, R., and ALTMAN, K. I. *Biochim. biophys. Acta* **23,** 647 (1957)

1453. KOUKOL, J., and CONN, E. E. *J. biol. Chem.* **236,** 2692 (1961)

1454. KOVACHEVICH, R., and WOOD, W. A. *J. biol. Chem.* **213,** 745 (1955)

1455. KOVACHEVICH, R., and WOOD, W. A. *J. biol. Chem.* **213,** 757 (1955)

1456. KRAHL, M. E. *Biochim. biophys. Acta* **20,** 27 (1956)

1457. KRAMPITZ, L. O., SUZUKI, I., and GREULL, G. *Fed. Proc.* **20,** 971 (1961)

1457a. KRASNA, A. I. *J. biol. Chem.* **233,** 1010 (1958)

1458. KREAM, J., and CHARGAFF, E. *J. Amer. chem. Soc.* **74,** 5157 (1952)

1459. KREBS, E. G., and FISCHER, E. H. *Biochim. biophys. Acta* **20,** 150 (1956)

1460. KREBS, E. G., KENT, A. B., and FISCHER, E. H. *J. biol. Chem.* **231,** 73 (1958)

1461. KREBS, E. G., RAFTER, G. W., and JUNGE, J. M. *J. biol. Chem.* **200,** 479 (1953)

1462. KREBS, H. A. *Biochem. Z.* **220,** 283 (1930)

1463. KREBS, H. A., in *The Enzymes*, 1st edn., ed. J. B. Sumner and K. Myrbäck (New York, Academic Press, 1951), Vol. 2, p. 499

1464. KREBS, H. A., and HEMS, R. *Biochim. biophys. Acta* **12**, 172 (1953)

1465. KREBS, H. A., and ROUGHTON, F. J. W. *Biochem. J.* **43**, 550 (1948)

1466. KRIEBLE, V. K., and WIELAND, W. A. *J. Amer. chem. Soc.* **43**, 164 (1921)

1467. KRISHNAN, P. S. *Arch. Biochem.* **20**, 272 (1949)

1468. KRISHNASWAMY, P. R., and GIRI, K. V. *Biochem. J.* **62**, 301 (1956)

1469. KRISHNASWAMY, P. R., and MEISTER, A. *J. biol. Chem.* **235**, 408 (1960)

1470. KRUPKA, R. M., and LAIDLER, K. J. *J. Amer. chem. Soc.* **83**, 1445 (1961)

1471. KRUPKA, R. M., and LAIDLER, K. J. *J. Amer. chem. Soc.* **83**, 1448 (1961)

1472. KUBO, H., YAMANO, T., IWATSUBO, M., WATARI, H., SOYAMA, T., SHIRAISHI, J., SAWADA, S., and KAWASHIMA, N. *Proc. Int. Symp. on Enzyme Chemistry, Tokyo and Kyoto* (1957), p. 345

1473. KUBOWITZ, F. *Biochem. Z.* **292**, 221 (1937)

1474. KUBOWITZ, F. *Biochem. Z.* **299**, 32 (1938)

1475. KUBOWITZ, F., and HAAS, E. *Biochem. Z.* **255**, 247 (1932)

1476. KUBOWITZ, F., and OTT, P. *Biochem. Z.* **314**, 94 (1943)

1477. KUBOWITZ, F., and OTT, P. *Biochem. Z.* **317**, 193 (1944)

1478. KUBY, S. A., and LARDY, H. A. *J. Amer. chem. Soc.* **75**, 890 (1953)

1479. KUBY, S. A., NODA, L., and LARDY, H. A. *J. biol. Chem.* **209**, 191 (1954)

1480. KUBY, S. A., NODA, L., and LARDY, H. A. *J. biol. Chem.* **210**, 65 (1954)

1481. KUFF, E. L., HOGEBOOM, G. H., and DALTON, A. J. *J. biophys. biochem. Cytol.* **2**, 33 (1956)

1482. KUHN, R., REINEMUND, K., WEYGAND, F., and STRÖBELE, R. *Ber. dtsch. chem. Ges.* **68**, 1765 (1935)

1483. KUHN, R., and WAGNER-JAUREGG, T. *Ber. dtsch. chem. Ges.* **67**, 361 (1934)

1484. KÜHNAU, J. *Biochem. Z.* **243**, 14 (1931)

1485. KÜHNE, W. *Unters. a. d. physiol. Institut der Univ. Heidelberg* **1**, 291 (1878)

1486. KUN, E. *J. biol. Chem.* **194**, 603 (1952)

1487. KUNITZ, M. *J. gen. Physiol.* **22**, 207 (1938)

1488. KUNITZ, M. *Enzymologia* **7**, 1 (1939)

1489. KUNITZ, M. *J. gen. Physiol.* **22**, 447 (1939)

1490. KUNITZ, M. *J. gen. Physiol.* **24**, 15 (1940)

1491. KUNITZ, M. *J. gen. Physiol.* **35**, 423 (1952)

1492. KUNITZ, M. *Science* **108**, 19 (1948)

1493. KUNITZ, M., and McDONALD, M. R. *J. gen. Physiol.* **29**, 393 (1946)

1494. KUNITZ, M., and NORTHROP, J. H. *J. gen. Physiol.* **18**, 433 (1935)

1495. KUNITZ, M., and NORTHROP, J. H. *J. gen. Physiol.* **19**, 991 (1936)

1496. KUO, M.-H., and BLUMENTHAL, H. J. *Biochim. biophys. Acta* **52**, 13 (1961)

1497. KURAHASHI, K., PENNINGTON, R. J., and UTTER, M. F. *J. biol. Chem.* **226**, 1059 (1957)

1498. KURAHASHI, K., and SUGIMURA, A. *J. biol. Chem.* **235**, 940 (1960)

1499. KUSAI, K., SEKUZU, I., HAGIHARA, B., OKUNUKI, K., YAMAUCHI, S., and NAKAI, M. *Biochim. biophys. Acta* **40**, 555 (1960)

1500. LACK, L. *J. biol. Chem.* **236**, 2835 (1961)

1501. LA DU, B. N., and ZANNONI, V. G. *J. biol. Chem.* **219**, 273 (1956)

1502. LAGERKVIST, U. *J. biol. Chem.* **233**, 143 (1958)

1503. LAIDLER, K. J. *Disc. Faraday Soc.* No. 20, 'The Physical Chemistry of Enzymes', p. 83 (1955)

1504. LAIDLER, K. J. *Trans. Faraday Soc.* **51**, 528 (1955)

1505. LAIDLER, K. J. *Trans. Faraday Soc.* **51,** 550 (1955)

1506. LAJTHA, A., MELA, P., and WAELSCH, H. *J. biol. Chem.* **205,** 553 (1953)

1507. LAMPEN, J. O., and WANG, T. P. *J. biol. Chem.* **198,** 385 (1952)

1508. LANDMAN, O. E. *Biochim. biophys. Acta* **23,** 558 (1957)

1509. LANE, M. D., HALENZ, D. R., KOSOW, D. P., and HEGRE, C. S. *J. biol. Chem.* **235,** 3082 (1960)

1510. LANG, C. A., and NASON, A. *J. biol. Chem.* **234,** 1874 (1959)

1511. LANGDON, R. G. *J. biol Chem.* **226,** 615 (1957)

1512. LANGDON, R. G., and WEAKLEY, D. R. *Fed. Proc.* **16,** 208 (1957)

1513. LANGE, K. *Z. physiol. Chem.* **303,** 272 (1956)

1514. LANGER, L. J., ALEXANDER, J. A., and ENGEL, L. L. *J. biol. Chem.* **234,** 2609 (1959)

1515. LANGMUIR, I. *J. Amer. chem. Soc.* **38,** 2221 (1916)

1516. LAPRESLE, C., and WEBB, T. *Biochem. J.* **76,** 538 (1960)

1517. LARNER, J., in *The Enzymes,* 2nd edn., ed. P. D. Boyer, H. Lardy and K. Myrbäck (New York, Academic Press, 1960), Vol. 4, p. 369

1518. LARNER, J., and GILLESPIE, R. E. *J. Amer. chem. Soc.* **78,** 882 (1956)

1519. LARNER, J., and GILLESPIE, R. E. *J. biol. Chem.* **223,** 709 (1956)

1520. LARNER, J., JACKSON, W. T., GRAVES, D. J., and STAMER, J. R. *Arch. Biochem. Biophys.* **60,** 352 (1956)

1521. LARNER, J., and McNICKLE, C. M. *J. Amer. chem. Soc.* **76,** 4747 (1954)

1522. LARNER, J., and SCHLISELFELD, L. H. *Biochim. biophys. Acta* **20,** 53 (1956)

1523. LARSSON, L., HOLMSTEDT, B., and TJUS, E. *Acta chem. scand.* **8,** 1563 (1954)

1524. LASKOWSKI, M., and LASKOWSKI, M. *Advanc. Protein Chem.* **9,** 203 (1954)

1525. LAWRENCE, J. M., and SMYTHE, C. V. *Arch. Biochem.* **2,** 225 (1943)

1526. LAYNE, E. C., and NASON, A. *J. biol. Chem.* **231,** 889 (1958)

1527. LAZZARINI, R. A., and ATKINSON, D. E. *J. biol. Chem.* **236,** 3330 (1961)

1528. LEDER, I. G. *J. biol. Chem.* **225,** 125 (1957)

1529. LEDER, I. G. *J. biol. Chem.* **236,** 3066 (1961)

1530. LEE, Y. P. *J. biol. Chem.* **227,** 987, 993 and 999 (1957)

1531. LEHMAN, I. R. *J. biol. Chem.* **235,** 1479 (1960)

1532. LEHMAN, I. R., BESSMAN, M. J., SIMMS, E. S., and KORNBERG, A. *J. biol. Chem.* **233,** 163 (1958)

1533. LEHNINGER, A. L. *Physiol. Rev.* **30,** 393 (1950)

1534. LEHNINGER, A. L. *Fed. Proc.* **19,** 952 (1960)

1535. LEHNINGER, A. L., and GREVILLE, G. D. *Biochem. biophys. Acta* **12,** 188 (1953)

1536. LEHNINGER, A. L., SUDDUTH, H. C., and WISE, J. B. *J. biol. Chem.* **235,** 2450 (1960)

1537. LELOIR, L. F. *Arch. Biochem. Biophys.* **33,** 186 (1951)

1538. LELOIR, L. F. *Advanc. Enzymol.* **14,** 193 (1953)

1539. LELOIR, L. F., and CARDINI, C. E. *Biochim. biophys. Acta* **12,** 15 (1953)

1540. LELOIR, L. F., and CARDINI, C. E. *Biochim. biophys. Acta* **20,** 33 (1956)

1541. LELOIR, L. F., DE FEKETE, M. A., and CARDINI, C. E. *J. biol. Chem.* **236,** 636 (1961)

1542. LELOIR, L. F., and DIXON, M. *Enzymologia* **2,** 81 (1937)

1543. LELOIR, L. F., and GOLDEMBERG, S. H. *J. biol. Chem.* **235,** 919 (1960)

1544. LELOIR, L. F., and MUÑOZ, J. M. *Biochem. J.* **32,** 299 (1938)

1545. LELOIR, L. F., OLAVARRÍA, J. M., GOLDEMBERG, S. H., and CARMINATTI, H. *Arch. Biochem. Biophys.* **81,** 508 (1959)

1546. LELOIR, L. F., TRUCCO, R. E., CARDINI, C. E., PALADINI, A. C., and CAPUTTO, R. *Arch. Biochem.* **24,** 65 (1949)

1547. LEMBERG, R. *Advanc. Enzymol.* **23,** 265 (1961)

1548. LEMBERG, R., NEWTON, N., and O'HAGAN, J. E. *Proc. roy. Soc.* B, **155,** 356 (1961)

1549. LENHERT, P. G., and HODGKIN, D. C. *Nature, Lond.* **192,** 937 (1961)

1550. LENHOFF, H. M., and KAPLAN, N. O. *J. biol. Chem.* **220,** 967 (1956)

1551. LENTA, M. P., and RIEHL, M. A. *Cancer Res.* **12,** 498 (1952)

1552. LEONE, E. *Biochem. J.* **54,** 393 (1953)

1553. LESTER, R. L., and FLEISCHER, S. *Biochim. biophys. Acta* **47,** 358 (1961)

1554. LEUTHARDT, F., and NIELSEN, H. *Helv. chim. Acta* **35,** 1196 (1952)

1555. LEUTHARDT, F., and TESTA, E. *Helv. chim. Acta* **34,** 931 (1951)

1556. LEVENBERG, B., and BUCHANAN, J. M. *J. biol. Chem.* **224,** 1005 and 1018 (1957)

1557. LEVENBERG, B., and HAYAISHI, O. *J. biol. Chem.* **234,** 955 (1959)

1558. LEVIN, A. P., and MAGASANIK, B. *J. biol. Chem.* **236,** 184 (1961)

1559. LEVIN, D. H., and RACKER, E. *J. biol. Chem.* **234,** 2532 (1959)

1560. LEVIN, Ö., in *Methods in Enzymology,* ed. S. P. Colowick and N. O. Kaplan (New York, Academic Press, 1962), Vol. 5, p. 27

1561. LEVIN, Y., BERGER, A., and KATCHALSKI, E. *Biochem. J.* **63,** 308 (1956)

1562. LEVINTOW, L. *J. nat. Cancer Inst.* **15,** 347 (1954)

1563. LEVINTOW, L., and MEISTER, A. *Fed. Proc.* **13,** 251 (1954)

1564. LEVVY, G. A. *Brit. med. Bull.* **9,** 126 (1953)

1565. LEVVY, G. A. *Biochem. J.* **58,** 462 (1954)

1566. LEVVY, G. A., and MARSH, C. A. *Biochem. J.* **52,** 690 (1952)

1567. LEVY, G. B., and COOK, E. S. *Biochem. J.* **57,** 50 (1954)

1568. LEVY, H. M., SHARON, N., and KOSHLAND, D. E. *Biochim. biophys. Acta* **33,** 288 (1959)

1569. LEVY, H. M., SHARON, N., and KOSHLAND, D. E. *Proc. nat. Acad. Sci. U.S.* **45,** 785 (1959)

1570. LEVY, H. M., SHARON, N., LINDEMANN, E., and KOSHLAND, D. E. *J. biol. Chem.* **235,** 2628 (1960)

1571. LEVY, H. R., GRAVES, J. L., and VENNESLAND, B. *Fed. Proc.* **15,** 300 (1956)

1572. LEVY, H. R., LOEWUS, F. A., and VENNESLAND, B. *J. Amer. chem. Soc.* **79,** 2949 (1957)

1573. LEVY, H. R., and POPJÁK, G. *Biochem. J.* **75,** 417 (1960)

1574. LEVY, H. R., and TALALAY, P. *J. Amer. chem. Soc.* **79,** 2658 (1957)

1575. LEVY, H. R., and TALALAY, P. *J. biol. Chem.* **234,** 2014 (1959)

1576. LEVY, H. R., and VENNESLAND, B. *J. biol. Chem.* **228,** 85 (1957)

1577. LEWIN, L. M., and BROWN, G. M. *J. biol. Chem.* **236,** 2768 (1961)

1578. LEWIS, J. C., SNELL, N. S., HIRSCHMANN, D. J., and FRAENKEL-CONRAT, H. *J. biol. Chem.* **186,** 23 (1950)

1579. LEWIS, U. J., WILLIAMS, D. E., and BRINK, N. G. *J. biol. Chem.* **222,** 705 (1956)

1580. LEWIS, U. J., WILLIAMS, D. E., and BRINK, N. G. *J. biol. Chem.* **234,** 2304 (1959)

1581. LI, L. P., and BONNER, J. *Biochem. J.* **41,** 105 (1947)

1582. LIDDLE, A. M., MANNERS, D. J., and WRIGHT, A. *Biochem. J.* **80,** 304 (1961)

1583. LIEBERMAN, I. *J. biol. Chem.* **219,** 307 (1956)

1584. LIEBERMAN, I. *J. biol. Chem.* **222,** 765 (1956)

1585. LIEBERMAN, I. *J. biol. Chem.* **223,** 327 (1956)

1586. LIEBERMAN, I., and ETO, W. H. *J. biol. Chem.* **225,** 899 (1957)

1587. LIEBERMAN, I., and KORNBERG, A. *J. biol. Chem.* **207,** 911 (1954)

1588. LIEBERMAN, I., and KORNBERG, A. *J. biol. Chem.* **212,** 909 (1955)

1589. LIEBERMAN, I., KORNBERG, A., and SIMMS, E. S. *J. biol. Chem.* **215,** 403 (1955)

1590. LIEBERMAN, I., KORNBERG, A., and SIMMS, E. S. *J. biol. Chem.* **215,** 429 (1955)

1591. LIGHT, A., and SMITH, E. L. *J. biol. Chem.* **235,** 3144, 3151 and 3159 (1960)

1592. LIN, E. C. C. *J. biol. Chem.* **236,** 31 (1961)

1593. LIN, E. C. C., and MAGASANIK, B. *J. biol. Chem.* **235,** 1820 (1960)

1594. LIN, S.-C. C., and GREENBERG, D. M. *J. gen. Physiol.* **38,** 181 (1954)

1595. LINDSTEDT, S. *Acta chem. scand.* **5,** 486 (1951)

1596. LINEWEAVER, H., and BURK, D. *J. Amer. chem. Soc.* **56,** 658 (1934)

1597. LINEWEAVER, H., and JANSEN, E. F. *Advanc. Enzymol.* **11,** 267 (1951)

1598. LING, K.-H., and LARDY, H. A. *J. Amer. chem. Soc.* **76,** 2842 (1954)

1599. LINKER, A., MEYER, K., and HOFFMAN, P. *J. biol. Chem.* **219,** 13 (1956)

1600. LINKER, A., MEYER, K., and HOFFMAN, P. *J. biol. Chem.* **235,** 924 (1960)

1601. LINNANE, A. W., and STILL, J. L. *Arch. Biochem. Biophys.* **59,** 383 (1955)

1602. LIPKE, H., and KEARNS, C. W. *J. biol. Chem.* **234,** 2123 and 2129 (1959)

1603. LIPMANN, F. *Advanc. Enzymol.* **6,** 231 (1946)

1604. LIPMANN, F., JONES, M. E., BLACK, S., and FLYNN, R. M. *J. cell. comp. Physiol.* **41,** suppl. 1, 109 (1953)

1605. LITTAUER, U. Z., and KORNBERG, A. *J. biol. Chem.* **226,** 1077 (1957)

1606. LITTLE, H. N. *J. biol. Chem.* **193,** 347 (1951)

1607. LOEWUS, F. A., VENNESLAND, B., and HARRIS, D. L. *J. Amer. chem. Soc.* **77,** 3391 (1955)

1608. LOEWUS, F. A., WESTHEIMER, F. H., and VENNESLAND, B. *J. Amer. chem. Soc.* **75,** 5018 (1953)

1609. LOEWUS, M. W., and BRIGGS, D. R. *J. biol. Chem.* **199,** 857 (1952)

1610. LOHMANN, K. *Biochem. Z.* **254,** 332 (1932)

1611. LOHMANN, K., and SCHUSTER, P. *Angew. Chem.* **50,** 221 (1937)

1612. LONDON, M., and HUDSON, P. B. *Arch. Biochem. Biophys.* **46,** 141 (1953)

1613. LONDON, M., and HUDSON, P. B. *Biochim. biophys. Acta* **21,** 290 (1956)

1614. LONG, C. *Biochem. J.* **59,** 322 (1955)

1615. LONG, C., and MAGUIRE, M. F. *Biochem. J.* **57,** 223 (1954)

1616. LONG, C., and PENNY, I. F. *Biochem. J.* **65,** 382 (1957)

1617. LORBER, V., UTTER, M. F., RUDNEY, H., and COOK, M. *J. biol. Chem.* **185,** 689 (1950)

1618. LORD, K. A. *Biochem. J.* **78,** 483 (1961)

1619. LOW, B. W., in *The Proteins*, ed. H. Neurath and K. Bailey (New York, Academic Press, 1953), Vol. 1, p. 235

1620. LOWENSTEIN, J. M. *J. biol. Chem.* **236,** 1217 (1961)

1621. LOWENSTEIN, J. M., and COHEN, P. P. *J. biol. Chem.* **220,** 57 (1956)

1622. LOWRY, O. H., BESSEY, O. A., and CRAWFORD, E. J. *J. biol. Chem.* **180,** 399 (1949)

1623. LOWRY, O. H., PASSONNEAU, J. V., and ROCK, M. K. *J. biol. Chem.* **236,** 2756 (1961)

1624. LOWRY, O. H., ROBERTS, N. R., SCHULZ, D. W., CLOW, J. E., and CLARK, J. R. *J. biol. Chem.* **236,** 2813 (1961)

1625. LOWRY, O. H., ROSEBROUGH, N. J., FARR, A. L., and RANDALL, R. J. *J. biol. Chem.* **193,** 265 (1951)

1626. LUCAS, N., KING, H. K., and BROWN, S. J. *Biochem. J.* **84,** 118 (1962)

1627. LUDOWIEG, J., VENNESLAND, B., and DORFMAN, A. *J. biol. Chem.* **236,** 333 (1961)

1628. LUH, B. S., and PHAFF, H. J. *Arch. Biochem. Biophys.* **48,** 23 (1954)

1629. LUKENS, L. N., and BUCHANAN, J. M. *J. biol. Chem.* **234,** 1799 (1959)

1630. LUKENS, L. N., and HERRINGTON, K. A. *Biochim. biophys. Acta* **24,** 432 (1957)

1631. LUKOMSKAIA, I. S. *Dokl. Akad. Nauk, S.S.S.R.* **129,** 1172 (1959)

1632. LUMRY, R., SMITH, E. L., and GLANTZ, R. R. *J. Amer. chem. Soc.* **73,** 4330 (1951)

1633. LUNDEGÅRDH, H. *Physiol. Plant.* **7,** 375 (1954)

1634. LUNDQUIST, F., THORSTEINSSON, T., and BUUS, O. *Biochem. J.* **59,** 69 (1955)

1635. LYNEN, F. *Fed. Proc.* **20,** 941 (1961)

1636. LYNEN, F., AGRANOFF, B. W., EGGERER, H., HENNING, U., and MÖSLEIN, E. M. *Angew. Chem.* **71,** 657 (1959)

1637. LYNEN, F., and HENNING, U. *Angew. Chem.* **72,** 820 (1960)

1638. LYNEN, F., KNAPPE, J., LORCH, E., JÜTTING, G., and RINGELMANN, E. *Angew. Chem.* **71,** 481 (1959)

1639. LYNEN, F., KNAPPE, J., LORCH, E., JÜTTING, G., RINGELMANN, E., and LACHANCE, J.-P. *Biochem. Z.* **335,** 123 (1961)

1639a. LYNEN, F., and OCHOA, S. *Biochim. biophys. Acta* **12,** 299 (1953)

1640. LYNEN, F., and REICHERT, E. *Angew. Chem.* **63,** 47 (1951)

1641. LYNEN, F., WESSELY, L., WIELAND, O., and RUEFF, L. *Angew. Chem.* **64,** 687 (1952)

1642. LYNN, W. S., and BROWN, R. H. *J. biol. Chem.* **232,** 1015 (1958)

1643. LYNN, W. S., and PERRYMAN, N. C. *J. biol. Chem.* **235,** 1912 (1960)

1644. MAAS, W. K. *J. biol. Chem.* **198,** 23 (1952)

1645. MAAS, W. K. *Fed. Proc.* **15,** 305 (1956)

1646. MAAS, W. K., and DAVIS, B. D. *Proc. nat. Acad. Sci. U.S.* **38,** 785 (1952)

1647. MAAS, W. K., NOVELLI, G. D., and LIPMANN, F. *Proc. nat. Acad. Sci. U.S.* **39,** 1004 (1953)

1648. MCCANCE, R. A., and WIDDOWSON, E. M. *Nature, Lond.* **153,** 650 (1944)

1649. MCCORKINDALE, J., and EDSON, N. L. *Biochem. J.* **57,** 518 (1954)

1650. MCCORMICK, D. B., GREGORY, M. E., and SNELL, E. E. *J. biol Chem.* **236,** 2076 (1961)

1651. MCCOY, E. E., and NAJJAR, V. A. *J. biol. Chem.* **234,** 3017 (1959)

1652. MCCREADY, R. M., and SEEGMILLER, C. G. *Arch. Biochem. Biophys.* **50,** 440 (1954)

1653. MCCULLOUGH, W. G., PILIGIAN, J. T., and DANIEL, I. J. *J. Amer. chem. Soc.* **79,** 628 (1957)

1654. MCDONALD, M. R. *J. gen. Physiol.* **32,** 39 (1948)

1655. MCDONALD, M. R., and KUNITZ, M. *J. gen. Physiol.* **25,** 53 (1941)

1656. MACFARLANE, M. G. *Biochem. J.* **42,** 587 and 590 (1948)

1657. MACFARLANE, M. G. *Biochem. J.* **47,** 270 (1950)

1658. MACFARLANE, M. G., PATTERSON, L. M. B., and ROBISON, R. *Biochem. J.* **28,** 720 (1934)

1659. McGEACHIN, R. L., and REYNOLDS, J. M. *J. biol. Chem.* **234,** 1456 (1959)

1660. MACGEE, J., and DOUDOROFF, M. *J. biol. Chem.* **210,** 617 (1954)

1661. McGUGAN, W. A., and LAUGHLAND, D. H. *Arch. Biochem. Biophys.* **35,** 428 (1952)

1662. McGUIRE, J. S., HOLLIS, V. W., and TOMKINS, G. M. *J. biol. Chem.* **235,** 3112 (1960)

1663. McINTOSH, E. N., PURKO, M., and WOOD, W. A. *J. biol. Chem.* **228,** 499 (1957)

1664. McKENZIE, A. *Ergebn. Enzymforsch.* **5,** 49 (1936)

1665. MACKLER, B., MAHLER, H. R.. and GREEN, D. E. *J. biol. Chem.* **210,** 149 (1954)

1666. MACKWORTH, J. F. *Biochem. J.* **42,** 82 (1948)

1667. MACKWORTH, J. F., and WEBB, E. C. *Biochem. J.* **42,** 91 (1948)

1668. MACLEOD, R. M., FARKAS, W., FRIDOVITCH, I., and HANDLER, P. *J. biol. Chem.* **236,** 1841 (1961)

1669. MACMUNN, C. A. *Phil. Trans.* **177,** 267 (1886)

1670. MACNUTT, W. S. *Biochem. J.* **50,** 384 (1952)

1671. McQUILLEN, K. *Biochim. biophys. Acta* **17,** 382 (1955)

1672. McQUILLEN, K. *Progr. in Biophys.* **12,** 67 (1962)

1673. MACWILLIAM, I. C. *Nature, Lond.* **181,** 1143 (1958)

1674. MADSEN, N. B., and CORI, C. F. *J. biol. Chem.* **223,** 1055 (1956)

1675. MAEHLY, A. C., in *Methods in Enzymology,* ed. S. P. Colowick and N. O. Kaplan (New York, Academic Press, 1955), Vol. 2, p. 808, footnote 41.

1676. MAGASANIK, B. *Cold Spring Harbor Symposia on quantitative Biology* **26,** 249 (1961)

1677. MAGASANIK, B., MOYED, H. S., and GEHRING, L. B. *J. biol. Chem.* **226,** 339 (1957)

1678. MAGER, J., and MAGASANIK, B. *J. biol. Chem.* **235,** 1474 (1960)

1679. MAHADEVAN, S., MURTHY, S. K., KRISHNAMURTHY, S., and GANGULY, J. *Biochem. J.* **79,** 416 (1961)

1680. MAHLER, H. R. *J. biol. Chem.* **206,** 13 (1954)

1681. MAHLER, H. R., and DOUGLAS, J. *J. Amer. chem. Soc.* **79,** 1159 (1957)

1682. MAHLER, H. R., and ELOWE, D. G. *J. biol. Chem.* **210,** 165 (1954)

1683. MAHLER, H. R., and GLENN, J. L., in *Symposium on Inorganic Nitrogen Metabolism,* ed. W. D. McElroy and B. Glass (Baltimore, Johns Hopkins Press, 1956), p. 575

1684. MAHLER, H. R., and GREEN, D. E. *Science* **120,** 7 (1954)

1685. MAHLER, H. R., HÜBSCHER, G., and BAUM, H. *J. biol. Chem.* **216,** 625 (1955)

1686. MAHLER, H. R., MACKLER, B., GREEN, D. E., and BOCK, R. M. *J. biol. Chem.* **210,** 465 (1954)

1687. MAHLER, H. R., RAW, I., MOLINARI, R., and DO AMARAL, D. F. *J. biol. Chem.* **233,** 230 (1958)

1688. MAHLER, H. R., SARKAR, N. K., VERNON, L. P., and ALBERTY, R. A. *J. biol. Chem.* **199,** 585 (1952)

1689. MAHLER, H. R., TOMISEK, A., and HUENNEKENS, F. M. *Exp. Cell Res.* **4,** 208 (1953)

854   REFERENCES

1690. MAHLER, H. R., WAKIL, S. J., and BOCK, R. M. *J. biol. Chem.* **204,** 453 (1953)
1691. MAIN, A. R. *Biochem. J.* **74,** 10 (1960)
1692. MAIN, A. R. *Biochem. J.* **75,** 188 (1960)
1693. MAIN, A. R. *Biochem. J.* **79,** 246 (1961)
1694. MALEY, F., and LARDY, H. A. *J. Amer. chem. Soc.* **78,** 1393 (1956)
1695. MALMGREN, H. *Acta chem. scand.* **6,** 16 (1952)
1696. MALMSTRÖM, B. G. *Biochim. biophys. Acta* **18,** 285 (1955)
1697. MALMSTRÖM, B. G., in *The Enzymes,* 2nd edn., ed. P. D. Boyer, H. Lardy
         and K. Myrbäck (New York, Academic Press, 1961), Vol. 5, p. 471
1698. MALMSTRÖM, B. G., KIMMEL, J. R., and SMITH, E. L. *J. biol. Chem.* **234,**
         1108 (1959)
1699. MALMSTRÖM, B. G., and ROSENBERG, A. *Advanc. Enzymol.* **21,** 131 (1959)
1700. MANCERA, O., ZAFFARONI, A., RUBIN, B. A., SONDHEIMER, F., ROSEN-
         KRANTZ, G., and DJERASSI, C. *J. Amer. chem. Soc.* **74,** 3711 (1952)
1701. MANDELES, S., and BLOCH, K. *J. biol. Chem.* **214,** 639 (1955)
1702. MANDELSTAM, J., and YUDKIN, J. *Biochem. J.* **51,** 681 (1952)
1703. MANDL, I. *Advanc. Enzymol.* **23,** 163 (1961)
1704. MANN, P. J. G. *Biochem. J.* **25,** 918 (1931)
1705. MANN, P. J. G. *Biochem. J.* **79,** 623 (1961)
1706. MANN, P. J. G., and WOOLF, B. *Biochem. J.* **24,** 427 (1930)
1707. MANNERS, D. J. *Advanc. Carbohydrate Chem.* **17,** 371 (1962)
1708. MANNING, G. B., and CAMPBELL, L. L. *J. biol. Chem.* **236,** 2952 (1961)
1709. MAPSON, L. W., and BRESLOW, E. *Biochem. J.* **65,** 29P (1957)
1710. MAPSON, L. W., and GODDARD, D. R. *Biochem. J.* **49,** 593 (1951)
1711. MAPSON, L. W., ISHERWOOD, F. A., and CHEN, Y. T. *Biochem. J.* **56,** 21
         (1954)
1712. MARCUS, P. I., and TALALAY, P. *Proc. roy. Soc.* B, **144,** 116 (1955)
1713. MARCUS, P. I., and TALALAY, P. *J. biol. Chem.* **218,** 661 (1956)
1714. MARCUS, A., VENNESLAND, B., and STERN, J. R. *J. biol. Chem.* **233,** 722
         (1958)
1715. MARGOLIASH, E. Quoted by D. Keilin and E. C. Slater, *Brit. med. Bull.* **9,**
         95 (1953)
1716. MARGOLIASH, E. *Biochem. J.* **56,** 529 and 535 (1954)
1717. MARGOLIASH, E., FROHWIRT, N., and WIENER, E. *Biochem. J.* **71,** 559 (1959)
1718. MARGOLIASH, E., SMITH, E. L., KREIL, G., and TUPPY, H. *Nature, Lond.*
         192, 1125 (1961)
1719. MARKERT, C. L., and MØLLER, F. *Proc. nat. Acad. Sci. U.S.* **45,** 753 (1959)
1720. MARKHAM, R., and SMITH, J. D. *Biochem. J.* **52,** 558 (1952)
1721. MARKHAM, R., and STROMINGER, J. L. *Biochem. J.* **64,** 46P (1956)
1722. MÄRKI, F., and MARTIUS, C. *Biochem. Z.* **333,** 111 (1960)
1723. MARKLEY, K. and SMALLMAN, E. *Biochim. biophys. Acta* **47,** 327 (1961)
1724. MARKOVITZ, A., KLEIN, H. P., and FISCHER, E. H. *Biochim. biophys. Acta*
         19, 267 (1956)
1725. MARKS, P. A., and BANKS, J. *Proc. nat. Acad. Sci. U.S.* **46,** 447 (1960)
1726. MARMUR, J., and HOTCHKISS, R. D. *J. biol. Chem.* **214,** 383 (1955)
1727. MARPLES, E. A., and THOMPSON, R. H. S. *Biochem. J.* **74,** 123 (1960)
1728. MARR, A. G., and WILSON, P. W. *Arch. Biochem. Biophys.* **49,** 424 (1954)
1729. MARRACK, J. R., in *The Enzymes,* 1st edn., ed. J. B. Sumner and K.
         Myrbäck (New York, Academic Press, 1951), Vol. 1, p. 343

1730. MARSH, C. A. *Biochem. J.* **58,** 609 (1954)

1731. MARSHALL, M., and COHEN, P. P. *J. biol. Chem.* **236,** 718 (1961)

1732. MARSHALL, M., METZENBERG, R. L., and COHEN, P. P. *J. biol. Chem.* **233,** 102 (1958)

1733. MARSHALL, M., METZENBERG, R. L., and COHEN, P. P. *J. biol. Chem.* **236,** 2229 (1961)

1734. MARTIN, A. P., NEUFELD, H. A., LUCAS, F. V., and STOTZ, E. *J. biol. Chem.* **233,** 206 (1958)

1735. MARTIN, E. M., and MORTON, R. K. *Biochem. J.* **62,** 696 (1956)

1736. MARTIN, E. M., and MORTON, R. K. *Biochem. J.* **65,** 404 (1957)

1737. MARTIN, H. F., and PEERS, F. G. *Biochem. J.* **55,** 523 (1953)

1738. MARTIN, R. G., AMES, B. N., and GARRY, B. J. *Fed. Proc.* **20,** 225 (1961)

1739. MARTIN, R. O., and STUMPF, P. K. *J. biol. Chem.* **234,** 2548 (1959)

1740. MARTINEZ, R. J., WOLFE, J. B., and NAKADA, H. I. *J. biol. Chem.* **234,** 2236 (1959)

1741. MASON, H. S. *Nature, Lond.* **177,** 79 (1956)

1742. MASON, M. *J. biol. Chem.* **227,** 61 (1957)

1743. MASSEY, V. *Biochem. J.* **51,** 490 (1952)

1744. MASSEY, V. *Biochem. J.* **53,** 67 (1953)

1745. MASSEY, V. *Biochem. J.* **53,** 72 (1953)

1746. MASSEY, V. *Biochem. J.* **55,** 172 (1953)

1747. MASSEY, V. *Biochim. biophys. Acta* **30,** 500 (1958)

1748. MASSEY, V. *Biochim. biophys. Acta* **37,** 310 (1960)

1749. MASSEY, V. *Biochim. biophys. Acta* **37,** 314 (1960)

1750. MASSEY, V. *Biochim. biophys. Acta* **38,** 447 (1960)

1751. MASSEY, V. Personal communication

1751a. MASSEY, V., and ALBERTY, R. A. *Biochim. biophys. Acta* **13,** 354 (1954)

1752. MASSEY, V., GIBSON, Q. H., and VEEGER, C. *Biochem. J.* **77,** 341 (1960)

1753. MASSEY, V., PALMER, G., and BENNETT, R. *Biochim. biophys. Acta* **48,** 1 (1961)

1754. MASSEY, V., and SINGER, T. P. *J. biol. Chem.* **228,** 263 (1957)

1755. MASSEY V., and VEEGER, C. *Biochim. biophys. Acta* **48,** 33 (1961)

1756. MATHEWS, M. B. *J. biol. Chem.* **176,** 229 (1948)

1757. MATSUO, Y., and GREENBERG, D. M. *J. biol. Chem.* **230,** 545 and 561 (1958)

1758. MATSUO, Y., and GREENBERG, D. M. *J. biol. Chem.* **234,** 516 (1959)

1759. MATTHAEI, J. H., JONES, O. W., MARTIN, R. G., and NIRENBERG, M. W. *Proc. nat. Acad. Sci. U.S.* **48,** 666 (1962)

1760. MATTSON, F. H., and BECK, L. W. *J. biol. Chem.* **219,** 735 (1956)

1761. MAUZERALL, D., and GRANICK, S. *J. biol. Chem.* **232,** 1141 (1958)

1762. MAW, G. A. *Biochem. J.* **63,** 116 (1956)

1763. MAW, G. A. *Biochem. J.* **70,** 168 (1958)

1764. MAW, G. A. *Biochem. J.* **72,** 602 (1959)

1765. MAXWELL, E. S. *J. biol. Chem.* **229,** 139 (1957)

1766. MAXWELL, E. S. *Proc. nat. Acad. Sci. U.S.* **48,** 1639 (1962)

1767. MAXWELL, E. S., and DE ROBICHON-SZULMAJSTER, H. *J. biol. Chem.* **235,** 308 (1960)

1768. MAXWELL, E. S., KALCKAR, H. M., and BURTON, R. M. *Biochim. biophys. Acta* **18,** 444 (1955)

1769. MAXWELL, E. S., KALCKAR, H. M., and STROMINGER, J. L. *Arch. Biochem. Biophys.* **65,** 2 (1956)

856   REFERENCES

1770. MAYAUDON, J., BENSON, A. A., and CALVIN, M. *Biochim. biophys. Acta* **23,** 342 (1957)

1771. MAZIA, D., and DAN, K. *Proc. nat. Acad. Sci. U.S.* **38,** 826 (1952)

1772. MAZUMDER, R., SANADI, D. R., and RODWELL, W. V. *J. biol. Chem.* **235,** 2546 (1960)

1773. MAZUMDER, R., SASAKAWA, T., KAZIRO, Y., and OCHOA, S. *J. biol. Chem.* **237,** 3065 (1962)

1774. MEDINA, A., and NICHOLAS, D. J. D. *Nature, Lond.* **179,** 533 (1957)

1775. MEDINA, A., and SOLS, A. *Biochim. biophys. Acta* **19,** 378 (1956)

1776. MEEDOM, B. *Acta chem. scand.* **10,** 150 (1956)

1777. MEEDOM, B. *Biochim. biophys. Acta* **31,** 260 (1959)

1778. MEHLER, A. H., and KNOX, W. E. *J. biol. Chem.* **187,** 431 (1950)

1779. MEINHART, J. O., CHAYKIN, S., and KREBS, E. G. *J. biol. Chem.* **220,** 821 (1956)

1780. MEISTER, A. *J. biol. Chem.* **184,** 117 (1950)

1781. MEISTER, A. *J. nat. Cancer Inst.* **10,** 1263 (1950)

1782. MEISTER, A. *J. biol. Chem.* **206,** 587 (1954)

1783. MEISTER, A. *J. biol. Chem.* **210,** 17 (1954)

1784. MEISTER, A., and FRASER, P. E. *J. biol. Chem.* **210,** 37 (1954)

1785. MEISTER, A., and GREENSTEIN, J. P. *J. biol. Chem.* **175,** 573 (1948)

1786. MEISTER, A., LEVINTOW, L., GREENFIELD, R. E., and ABENDSCHEIN, P. A. *J. biol. Chem.* **215,** 441 (1955)

1787. MEISTER, A., RADHAKRISHNAN, A. N., and BUCKLEY, S. D. *J. biol. Chem.* **229,** 789 (1957)

1788. MEISTER, A., SOBER, H. A., and PETERSON, E. A. *J. biol. Chem.* **206,** 89 (1954)

1789. MEISTER, A., SOBER, H. A., and TICE, S. V. *J. biol. Chem.* **189,** 577 (1951)

1790. MEISTER, P. D., REINECKE, L. M., MEEKS, R. C., MURRAY, H. C., EPPSTEIN, S. H., OSBORN, H. M. L., WEINTRAUB, A., and PETERSON, D. H. *J. Amer. chem. Soc.* **76,** 4050 (1954)

1791. MELDRUM, N. U., and ROUGHTON, F. J. W. *J. Physiol.* **80,** 113 (1933)

1792. MELNICK, I., and BUCHANAN, J. M. *J. biol. Chem.* **225,** 157 (1957)

1793. MENDEL, B., and MUNDELL, D. B. *Biochem. J.* **37,** 64 (1943)

1794. MENDEL, B., MUNDELL, D. B., and RUDNEY, H. *Biochem. J.* **37,** 473 (1943)

1795. MENDEL, B., and RUDNEY, H. *Biochem. J.* **37,** 59 (1943)

1796. MENDICINO, J. *J. biol. Chem.* **235,** 3347 (1960)

1797. MENDICINO, J., and MUNTZ, J. A. *J. biol. Chem.* **233,** 178 (1958)

1798. MENON, C. K. K., FRIEDMAN, D. L., and STERN, J. R. *Biochim. biophys. Acta* **44,** 375 (1960)

1799. MERRICK, J. M., and ROSEMAN, S. *J. biol. Chem.* **235,** 1274 (1960)

1800. MERRITT, A. D., and TOMKINS, G. M. *J. biol. Chem.* **234,** 2778 (1959)

1801. MESELSON, M., and STAHL, F. W. *Proc. nat. Acad. Sci. U.S.* **44,** 671 (1958)

1802. METZLER, D. E., IKAWA, M., and SNELL, E. E. *J. Amer. chem. Soc.* **76,** 648 (1954)

1803. METZLER, D. E., and SNELL, E. E. *J. biol. Chem.* **198,** 363 (1952)

1804. MEYER, A. S. *Experientia* **11,** 99 (1955)

1805. MEYER, K., and HAHNEL, E. *J. biol. Chem.* **163,** 723 (1946)

1806. MEYER, K., and RAPPORT, M. M. *Advanc. Enzymol.* **13,** 199 (1952)

1807. MEYER, K. H., SPAHR, P.-F., and FISCHER, E. H. *Helv. chim. Acta* **36,** 1924 (1953)

1808. MEYER-ARENDT, E., BEISENHERZ, G., and BÜCHER, T. *Naturwiss.* **40,** 59 (1953)

1809. MEYERHOF, O., in *The Enzymes*, 1st edn., ed. J. B. Sumner and K. Myrbäck (New York, Academic Press, 1951), Vol. 2, p. 162

1810. MEYERHOF, O., and BECK, L. V. *J. biol. Chem.* **156,** 109 (1944)

1811. MEYERHOF, O., SHATAS, R., and KAPLAN, A. *Biochim. biophys. Acta* **12,** 121 (1953)

1812. MICHAELIS, L. *Die Wasserstoffionenkonzentration* (Berlin, Springer-Verlag, 1922)

1813. MICHAELIS, L. *Chem. Rev.* **16,** 243 (1935)

1814. MICHAELIS, L., and DAVIDSOHN, H. *Biochem. Z.* **35,** 386 (1911)

1815. MICHAELIS, L., and MENTEN, M. L. *Biochem. Z.* **49,** 333 (1913)

1816. MILL, P. J., and TUTTOBELLO, R. *Biochem. J.* **79,** 57 (1961)

1817. MILLER, A., and WAELSCH, H. *J. biol. Chem.* **228,** 397 (1957)

1818. MILLER, K. D., and COPELAND, W. H. *Biochim. biophys. Acta* **22,** 193 (1956)

1819. MILLER, K. D., and COPELAND, W. H. *J. biol. Chem.* **231,** 997 (1958)

1820. MILLER, K. D., and VAN VUNAKIS, H. *J. biol. Chem.* **223,** 227 (1956)

1821. MILLER, O. N., HUGGINS, C. G., and ARAI, K. *J. biol. Chem.* **202,** 263 (1953)

1822. MILLER, R. W., LUKENS, L. N., and BUCHANAN, J. M. *J. biol. Chem.* **234,** 1806 (1959)

1823. MILLER, S. L. *J. Amer. chem. Soc.* **77,** 2351 (1955)

1824. MILLER, S. L. *Biochim. biophys. Acta* **23,** 480 (1957)

1825. MILLERD, A., and BONNER, J. *Arch. Biochem. Biophys.* **49,** 343 (1954)

1826. MILLS, G. C. *Arch. Biochem. Biophys.* **86,** 1 (1960)

1827. MILLS, G. T., PAUL, J., and SMITH, E. E. B. *Biochem. J.* **53,** 232 (1953)

1828. MILLS, J. B. *Biochem. J.* **44,** 302 (1949)

1829. MILSTEIN, C. *Biochem. J.* **79,** 574, 584 and 591 (1961)

1830. MILSTEIN, C., and SANGER, F. *Biochem. J.* **79,** 456 (1961)

1831. MIRSKY, A. E. *Cold Spring Harbor Symposia on quantitative Biology* **12,** 143 (1947)

1832. MIRSKY, A. E. *Proceedings of the fifth International Congress of Biochemistry, Moscow*, Symp. No. 2 (Oxford, Pergamon Press, 1963)

1833. MIRSKY, A. E., and ANSON, M. L. *J. gen. Physiol.* **18,** 307 (1935)

1834. MITCHELL, P. D. *Ann. Rev. Microbiol.* **13,** 407 (1959)

1835. MITCHELL, P. D., in *Biological Structure and Function*, ed. T. W. Goodwin and O. Lindberg (New York, Academic Press, 1961), Vol. 2, p. 581

1836. MITOMA, C. *Arch. Biochem. Biophys.* **60,** 477 (1956)

1837. MITOMA, C., POSNER, H. S., REITZ, H. C., and UDENFRIEND, S. *Arch. Biochem. Biophys.* **61,** 431 (1956)

1838. MITOMA, C., WEISSBACH, H., and UDENFRIEND, S. *Nature, Lond.* **175,** 994 (1955)

1839. MITSUHASHI, S., and DAVIS, B. D. *Biochim. biophys. Acta* **15,** 54 (1954)

1840. MITSUHASHI, S., and DAVIS, B. D. *Biochim. biophys. Acta* **15,** 268 (1954)

1841. MITZ, M. A., and HEINRIKSON, R. L. *Biochim. biophys. Acta* **46,** 45 (1961)

1842. MIZUNUMA, T., and IGUCHI, N. *Report of the Noda Inst. Scientific Research* **2,** 18 (1958)

1843. MIZUSHIMA, S., and KITAHARA, K. *J. gen. appl. Microbiol.* **8,** 56 (1962)

858   REFERENCES

1844. MOKRASCH, L. C., and McGILVERY, R. N. *J. biol. Chem.* **221,** 909 (1956)
1845. MOLDAVE, K., CASTELFRANCO, P., and MEISTER, A. *J. biol. Chem.* **234,** 841 (1959)
1846. MOLDAVE, K., and MEISTER, A. *J. biol. Chem.* **229,** 463 (1957)
1847. MOMMAERTS, W. F. H. M., ILLINGWORTH, B., PEARSON, C. M., GUILLORY, R. J., and SERAYDARIAN, K. *Proc. nat. Acad. Sci. U.S.* **45,** 791 (1959)
1848. MONOD, J., and COHEN-BAZIRE, G. *C. R. Acad. Sci., Paris,* **236,** 530 (1953)
1849. MONOD, J., COHEN-BAZIRE, G., and COHN, M. *Biochim. biophys. Acta* **7,** 585 (1951)
1850. MONOD, J., and COHN, M. *Advanc. Enzymol.* **13,** 67 (1952)
1851. MONOD, J., and TORRIANI, A.-M. *Ann. Inst. Pasteur* **78,** 65 (1950)
1852. MONTY, K. J., LITT, M., KAY, E. R. M., and DOUNCE, A. L. *J. biophys. biochem. Cytol.* **2,** 127 (1956)
1853. MOORE, B. W., and LEE, R. H. *J. biol. Chem.* **235,** 1359 (1960)
1854. MOOREFIELD, H. H. *Contr. Boyce Thompson Inst.* **18,** 303 (1956)
1855. MORGAN, E. J. *Biochem. J.* **20,** 1282 (1926)
1856. MORGAN, E. J. *Biochem. J.* **24,** 410 (1930)
1857. MORGAN, E. J., and FRIEDMANN, E. *Biochem. J.* **32,** 733 (1938)
1858. MORGAN, E. J., and FRIEDMANN, E. *Biochem. J.* **32,** 862 (1938)
1859. MORGAN, E. J., STEWART, C. P., and HOPKINS, F. G. *Proc. roy. Soc.* B, **94,** 109 (1922)
1860. MORITA, S. *J. Biochem., Tokyo* **48,** 870 (1960)
1861. MORITA, Y., and KAMEDA, K. *Memoirs of the Research Institute for Food Science, Kyoto University* **12,** 14 (1957)
1862. MORITA, Y., and KAMEDA, K. *Bull. agr. chem. Soc., Japan* **23,** 28 (1959)
1863. MORITA, Y., KAMEDA, K., and MIZUNO, M. *Agr. biol. Chem.* **25,** 136 (1961)
1864. MORITANI, M. *Hukuoka Acta Med.* **43,** 651 and 731 (1952)
1865. MORITANI, M., TUNG, T-C., FUJII, S., MITO, H., IZUMIKA, N., KENMOCHI, K., and HIROHATA, R. *J. biol. Chem.* **209,** 485 (1954)
1866. MORRIS, D. L. *J. biol. Chem.* **142,** 881 (1942)
1867. MORRISON, J. F. *Biochem. J.* **56,** 99 (1954)
1868. MORRISON, J. F., GRIFFITHS, D. E., and ENNOR, A. H. *Biochem. J.* **65,** 143 (1957)
1869. MORRISON, J. F., O'SULLIVAN, W. J., and OGSTON, A. G. *Biochim. biophys. Acta* **52,** 82 (1961)
1870. MORRISON, M., HAMILTON, H. B., and STOTZ, E. *J. biol. Chem.* **228,** 767 (1957)
1871. MORTENSON, L. E., VALENTINE, R. C., and CARNAHAN, J. E. *Biochem. biophys. res. Comm.* **7,** 448 (1962)
1872. MORTON, R. A. *Nature, Lond.* **182,** 1764 (1958)
1873. MORTON, R. K. *Biochem. J.* **55,** 786 (1953)
1874. MORTON, R. K. *Biochem. J.* **57,** 595 (1954)
1875. MORTON, R. K. *Biochem. J.* **61,** 232 (1955)
1876. MORTON, R. K. *Biochem. J.* **61,** 240 (1955)
1877. MORTON, R. K., in *Methods in Enzymology,* ed. S. P. Colowick and N. O. Kaplan (New York, Academic Press, 1955), Vol. 1, p. 25
1878. MORTON, R. K. *Biochem. J.* **65,** 674 (1957)
1879. MORTON, R. K. *Biochem. J.* **70,** 139 and 150 (1958)
1880. MORTON, R. K. *Nature, Lond.* **192,** 4804 (1961)
1881. MORTON, R. K., and SHEPLEY, K. *Nature, Lond.* **192,** 639 (1961)

1882. MOUNTER, L. A., ALEXANDER, H. C., TUCK, K. D., and DIEN, L. T. H. *J. biol. Chem.* **226**, 867 (1957)

1883. MOUNTER, L. A., BAXTER, R. F., and CHANUTIN, A. *J. biol. Chem.* **215**, 699 (1955)

1884. MOUNTER, L. A., and DIEN, L. T. H. *J. biol. Chem.* **219**, 685 (1956)

1885. MOUNTER, L. A., DIEN, L. T. H., and CHANUTIN, A. *J. biol. Chem.* **215**, 691 (1955)

1886. MOUNTER, L. A., FLOYD, C. S., and CHANUTIN, A. *J. biol. Chem.* **204**, 221 (1953)

1887. MOUNTER, L. A., and SHIPLEY, B. A. *J. biol. Chem.* **231**, 855 (1958)

1888. MOYED, H. S. *Cold Spring Harbor Symposia on quantitative Biology* **26**, 323 (1961)

1889. MOYED, H. S., and MAGASANIK, B. *J. biol. Chem.* **226**, 351 (1957)

1890. MOYLE, J. *Biochem. J.* **63**, 552 (1956)

1891. MOYLE, J. *Nature, Lond.* **172**, 508 (1953)

1892. MOYLE, J., and DIXON, M. *Biochim. biophys. Acta* **16**, 434 (1955)

1893. MOYLE, J., and DIXON, M. *Biochem. J.* **63**, 548 (1956)

1894. MUDD, S. H. *J. biol. Chem.* **234**, 87 (1959)

1895. MUDD, S. H. *J. biol. Chem.* **234**, 1784 (1959)

1896. MUDD, S. H., and CANTONI, G. L. *J. biol. Chem.* **231**, 481 (1958)

1897. MUELLER, G. C., and MILLER, J. A. *J. biol. Chem.* **180**, 1125 (1949)

1898. MUHAMMED, A. *Biochim. biophys. Acta* **54**, 121 (1961)

1899. MUNCH-PETERSEN, A. *Arch. Biochem. Biophys.* **55**, 592 (1955)

1900. MUNTZ, J. A. *Arch. Biochem. Biophys.* **42**, 435 (1953)

1901. MURACHI, T., and NEURATH, H. *J. biol. Chem.* **235**, 99 (1960)

1902. MURRAY, D. R. P. *Biochem. J.* **24**, 1890 (1930)

1903. MURRAY, D. R. P. Thesis for Ph.D. Degree, University of Cambridge (1933)

1904. MURTI, C. R. K., and STONE, B. A. *Biochem. J.* **78**, 715 (1961)

1905. MUUS, J. *C. R. Lab. Carlsberg* (Sér. chim.) **28**, 317 (1953)

1906. MUUS, J. *J. Amer. chem. Soc.* **76**, 5163 (1954)

1907. MYERS, D. K. *Biochem. J.* **51**, 303 (1952)

1908. MYERS, D. K. *Biochem. J.* **55**, 67 (1953)

1909. MYERS, F. L., and NORTHCOTE, D. H. *Biochem. J.* **71**, 749 (1959)

1910. MYERS, J. W. *J. biol. Chem.* **236**, 1414 (1961)

1911. MYRBÄCK, K. *Z. physiol. Chem.* **158**, 160 (1926)

1912. MYRBÄCK, K. *Z. physiol. Chem.* **159**, 1 (1926)

1913. MYRBÄCK, K. *Acta chem. scand.* **1**, 142 (1947)

1914. MYRBÄCK, K. *Ark. Kemi* **11**, 47 (1957)

1915. MYRBÄCK, K., in *The Enzymes*, 2nd edn., ed. P. D. Boyer, H. Lardy and K. Myrbäck (New York, Academic Press, 1960), Vol. 4, p. 379

1916. MYRBÄCK, K., and BJÖRKLUND, V. *Ark. Kemi* **4**, 567 (1952)

1916a. MYRBÄCK, K., and NEUMÜLLER, G., in *The Enzymes*, 1st edn., ed. J. B. Sumner and K. Myrbäck (New York, Academic Press, 1951) Vol. 1, p. 653

1917. MYRBÄCK, K., and ÖRTENBLAD, B. *Biochem. Z.* **291**, 61 (1937)

1918. NACHMANSOHN, D., and WILSON, I. B. *Advanc. Enzymol.* **12**, 259 (1951)

1919. NAGANNA, B., RAMAN, A., VENUGOPAL, B., and SRIPATHI, C. E. *Biochem. J.* **60**, 215 (1955)

1920. NAJJAR, V. A. *J. biol. Chem.* **175**, 281 (1948)

1921. NAKAMOTO, T., and VENNESLAND, B. *J. biol. Chem.* **235,** 202 (1960)

1922. NAKAMURA, K., and BERNHEIM, F. *Biochim. biophys. Acta* **50,** 147 (1961)

1923. NAKAMURA, T. *Biochim. biophys. Acta* **30,** 44 and 538 (1958)

1924. NAKAYAMA, T. *J. Biochem., Tokyo* **48,** 812 (1960)

1925. NARROD, S. A., and WOOD, W. A. *J. biol. Chem.* **220,** 45 (1956)

1926. NASON, A., and EVANS, H. J. *J. biol. Chem.* **202,** 655 (1953)

1927. NASON, A., WOSILAIT, W. D., and TERRELL, A. J. *Arch. Biochem. Biophys.* **48,** 233 (1954)

1928. NATH, R. L., and RYDON, H. N. *Biochem. J.* **57,** 1 (1954)

1929. NATHANS, D., and LIPMANN, F. *Proc. nat. Acad. Sci. U.S.* **47,** 497 (1961)

1930. NAUGHTON, M. A., and SANGER, F. *Biochem. J.* **78,** 156 (1961)

1931. NAUGHTON, M. A., SANGER, F., HARTLEY, B. S., and SHAW, D. C. *Biochem. J.* **77,** 149 (1960)

1932. NEEDHAM, D. M., and WILLIAMS, J. M. *Biochem. J.* **73,** 171 (1959)

1933. NEEDHAM, J. *Chemical Embryology* (Cambridge University Press, 1931)

1934. NEEDHAM, J. *Biochemistry and Morphogenesis* (Cambridge University Press, 1942)

1935. NEGELEIN, E., and WULFF, H.-J. *Biochem. Z.* **293,** 351 (1937)

1936. NEILSON, N. E. *Biochim. biophys. Acta* **17,** 139 (1955)

1937. NELSON, J. M., and SCHUBERT, M. P. *J. Amer. chem. Soc.* **50,** 2188 (1928)

1938. NEMETH, A. M. *J. biol. Chem.* **208,** 773 (1954)

1939. NEMETH, A. M. *J. biol. Chem.* **234,** 2921 (1959)

1940. NEMETH, A. M. *Biochim. biophys. Acta* **48,** 189 (1961)

1941. NEMETH, A. M., and DICKERMAN, H. *J. biol. Chem.* **235,** 1761 (1960)

1942. NEUBERG, C., and HOFMANN, E. *Naturwissenschaften* **19,** 484 (1931)

1943. NEUBERG, C., and MANDL, I., in *The Enzymes*, 1st edn., ed. J. B. Sumner and K. Myrbäck (New York, Academic Press, 1951), Vol. 1, p. 527

1944. NEUBERT, D., WOJTCZAK, A. B., and LEHNINGER, A. L. *Proc. nat. Acad. Sci. U.S.* **48,** 1651 (1962)

1945. NEUFELD, E. F., FEINGOLD, D. S., and HASSID, W. Z. *Arch. Biochem. Biophys.* **83,** 96 (1959)

1946. NEUFELD, E. F., FEINGOLD, D. S., and HASSID, W. Z. *J. biol. Chem.* **235,** 906 (1960)

1947. NEUFELD, E. F., FEINGOLD, D. S., ILVES, S. M., KESSLER, G., and HASSID, W. Z. *J. biol. Chem.* **236,** 3102 (1961)

1948. NEUFELD, H. A., GREEN, L. F., LATTERELL, F. M., and WEINTRAUB, R. L. *J. biol. Chem.* **232,** 1093 (1958)

1949. NEUFELD, H. A., LEVAY, A. N., LUCAS, F. V., MARTIN, A. P., and STOTZ, E. *J. biol. Chem.* **233,** 209 (1958)

1950. NEUHAUS, F. C. *Fed. Proc.* **21,** 229 (1962)

1951. NEUHAUS, F. C., and BYRNE, W. L. *J. biol. Chem.* **234,** 113 (1959)

1952. NEUMAN, R. E., and SMITH, E. L. *J. biol. Chem.* **193,** 97 (1951)

1953. NEUMANN, H., LEVIN, Y., BERGER, A., and KATCHALSKI, E. *Biochem. J.* **73,** 33 (1959)

1954. NEUMANN, N. P., and BURRIS, R. H. *J. biol. Chem.* **234,** 3286 (1959)

1955. NEURATH, H., in *Modern Trends in Physiology and Biochemistry*, ed. E. S. G. Barron (New York, Academic Press, 1952), p. 453

1956. NEURATH, H., in *The Enzymes*, 2nd edn., ed. P. D. Boyer, H. Lardy and K. Myrbäck (New York, Academic Press, 1960), Vol. 4, p. 11

1957. NEURATH, H., and DREYER, W. J. *Disc. Faraday Soc.*, No. 20, 'The Physical Chemistry of Enzymes', p. 32 (1955)

1958. NEURATH, H., RUPLEY, J. A., and DREYER, W. J. *Arch. Biochem. Biophys.* **65,** 243 (1956)

1959. NEURATH, H., and SCHWERT, G. W. *Chem. Rev.* **46,** 69 (1950)

1960. NEWMARK, M. Z., and WENGER, A. B. *Arch. Biochem. Biophys.* **89,** 110 (1960)

1961. NICHOLAS, D. J. D., MEDINA, A., and JONES, O. T. G. *Biochim. biophys. Acta* **37,** 468 (1960)

1962. NICHOLAS, D. J. D., and NASON, A. *J. biol. Chem.* **207,** 353 (1954)

1963. NICHOLAS, D. J. D., and NASON, A. *J. Bact.* **69,** 580 (1955)

1964. NICHOLAS, D. J. D., and NASON, A. *Plant Physiol.* **30,** 135 (1955)

1965. NICHOLAS, D. J. D., NASON, A., and MCELROY, W. D. *J. biol. Chem.* **207,** 341 (1954)

1966. NICHOLAS, D. J. D., and SCAWIN, J. H. *Nature, Lond.* **178,** 1474 (1956)

1967. NIEFT, M. L. *J. biol. Chem.* **177,** 151 (1949)

1968. NIKIFORUK, G., and COLOWICK, S. P. *J. biol. Chem.* **219,** 119 (1956)

1969. NIMMO-SMITH, R. H. *Biochem. J.* **75,** 284 (1960)

1970. NIRENBERG, M. W., and JAKOBY, W. B. *J. biol. Chem.* **235,** 954 (1960)

1971. NIRENBERG, M. W., and MATTHAEI, J. H. *Proc. nat. Acad. Sci. U.S.* **47,** 1588 (1961)

1972. NISHIMURA, J. S., and GREENBERG, D. M. *J. biol. Chem.* **236,** 2684 (1961)

1973. NISHIMURA, M. *J. Biochem. Tokyo* **46,** 219 (1959)

1974. NISIZAWA, K. *J. Biochem., Tokyo* **42,** 825 (1955)

1975. NISIZAWA, K., and HASHIMOTO, Y. *Arch. Biochem. Biophys.* **81,** 211 (1959)

1976. NISMAN, B. *Bact. Rev.* **18,** 16 (1954)

1977. NISMAN, B., and MAGER, J. *Nature, Lond.* **169,** 243 (1952)

1978. NISSELBAUM, J. S., and BODANSKY, O. *J. biol. Chem.* **234,** 3276 (1959)

1979. NISSELBAUM, J. S., and BODANSKY, O. *J. biol. Chem.* **236,** 401 (1961)

1980. NODA, L. *J. biol. Chem.* **232,** 237 (1958)

1981. NODA, L., and KUBY, S. A. *J. biol. Chem.* **226,** 541 and 551 (1957)

1982. NODA, L., KUBY, S. A., and LARDY, H. A. *J. biol. Chem.* **210,** 83 (1954)

1983. NODA, L., NIHEI, T., and MORALES, M. F. *J. biol. Chem.* **235,** 2830 (1960)

1984. NOLTMANN, E., and BRUNS, F. H. *Biochem. Z.* **330,** 514 (1958)

1985. NOLTMANN, E., and BRUNS, F. H. *Biochem. Z.* **331,** 436 (1959)

1986. NOLTMANN, E. A., GUBLER, C. J., and KUBY, S. A. *J. biol. Chem.* **236,** 1225 (1961)

1987. NORDLIE, R. C., and FROMM, H. J. *J. biol. Chem.* **234,** 2523 (1959)

1988. NORRIS, E. R., and ELAM, D. W. *J. biol. Chem.* **134,** 443 (1940)

1989. NORTHROP, J. H. *J. gen. Physiol.* **2,** 471 (1920)

1990. NORTHROP, J. H. *J. gen. Physiol.* **13,** 739 and 767 (1930)

1991. NORTHROP, J. H. *J. gen. Physiol.* **14,** 713 (1931)

1992. NORTHROP, J. H. *J. gen. Physiol.* **15,** 29 (1931)

1993. NORTHROP, J. H. *Ergebn. Enzymforsch.* **1,** 302 (1932)

1993a. NORTHROP, J. H. *J. gen. Physiol.* **30,** 177 (1946)

1994. NORTHROP, J. H., and KUNITZ, M. *J. gen. Physiol.* **16,** 267 and 295 (1932)

1995. NORTHROP, J. H., and KUNITZ, M. *Ergebn. Enzymforsch.* **2,** 104 (1933)

1996. NORTHROP, J. H., KUNITZ, M., and HERRIOTT, R. M. *Crystalline Enzymes,* 2nd edn (Columbia University Press, 1948)

1997. NOSE, Y., and LIPMANN, F. *J. biol. Chem.* **233,** 1348 (1958)

1998. NOVELLI, G. D. *Fed. Proc.* **12,** 675 (1953)

1999. NOVELLI, G. D., SCHMETZ, F. J., and KAPLAN, N. O. *J. biol. Chem.* **206,** 533 (1954)

2000. NOVICK, A., and HORIUCHI, T. *Cold Spring Harbor Symposia on quantitative Biology* **26,** 239 (1961)

2001. NYGAARD, A. P. *J. biol. Chem.* **236,** 920 (1961)

2002. NYGAARD, A. P., and THEORELL, H. *Acta chem. scand.* **8,** 1489 (1954)

2003. NYGAARD, A. P., and THEORELL, H. *Acta chem. scand.* **9,** 1300 (1955)

2004. NYLANDER, O., and MALMSTRÖM, B. G. *Biochim. biophys. Acta* **34,** 196 (1959)

2005. NYMAN, P. O. *Biochim. biophys. Acta* **52,** 1 (1961)

2006. OCHOA, S. *J. biol. Chem.* **174,** 133 (1948)

2007. OCHOA, S. *Advanc. Enzymol.* **15,** 183 (1954)

2008. OCHOA, S. *Angew. Chem.* **72,** 225 (1960)

2009. OCHOA, S., BURMA, D. P., KRÖGER, H., and WEILL, J. D. *Proc. nat. Acad. Sci. U.S.* **47,** 670 (1961)

2010. OCHOA, S., MEHLER, A. H., and KORNBERG, A. *J. biol. Chem.* **174,** 979 (1948)

2011. OCHOA, S., and MII, S. *J. biol. Chem.* **236,** 3303 (1961)

2012. OCHOA, S., STERN, J. R., and SCHNEIDER, M. C. *J. biol. Chem.* **193,** 691 (1951)

2013. O'CONNOR, R. J., and HALVORSON, H. *Biochim. biophys. Acta* **48,** 47 (1961)

2014. OGINSKY, E. L., and GEHRIG, R. F. *J. biol. Chem.* **198,** 799 (1952)

2015. OGLE, J. D., and TYTELL, A. A. *Arch. Biochem. Biophys.* **42,** 327 (1953)

2016. OGSTON, A. G. *Nature, Lond.* **162,** 963 (1948)

2017. OGSTON, A. G. *Nature, Lond.* **181,** 1462 (1958)

2018. OHMURA, E., and HAYAISHI, O. *J. biol. Chem.* **227,** 181 (1957)

2019. O'KANE, D. J., and GUNSALUS, I. C. *J. Bact.* **56,** 499 (1948)

2020. OKUNUKI, K., SEKUZU, I., YONETANI, T., and TAKEMORI, S. *J. Biochem., Tokyo* **45,** 847 (1958)

2021. OLIVER, I. T., and PEEL, J. L. *Biochim. biophys. Acta* **20,** 390 (1956)

2022. OLSON, J. A. *J. biol. Chem.* **234,** 5 (1959)

2023. OLSON, J. A., and ANFINSEN, C. B. *J. biol. Chem.* **197,** 67 (1952)

2024. OLSSON, U. *Z. physiol. Chem.* **114,** 51 (1921)

2025. OOSTERBAAN, R. A., KUNST, P., VAN ROTTERDAM, J., and COHEN, J. A. *Biochim. biophys. Acta* **27,** 556 (1958)

2026. OOSTERBAAN, R. A., and VAN ADRICHEM, M. E. *Biochim. biophys. Acta* **27,** 423 (1958)

2027. OPARIN, A. I. *The Origin of Life on the Earth,* 3rd edn. (Edinburgh, Oliver & Boyd, 1957)

2028. OPARIN, A. I., ed. *The Origin of Life on the Earth.* Proceedings of the I.U.B. Symposium, Moscow (Oxford, Pergamon Press, 1957)

2029. OPPENOORTH, F. J., and VAN ASPEREN, K. *Ent. exp. & appl.* **4,** 311 (1961)

2030. OPPENOORTH, F. J., and VAN ASPEREN, K. *Science* **132,** 298 (1960)

2031. ORD, M. G., and THOMPSON, R. H. S. *Biochem. J.* **46,** 346 (1950)

2032. ORD, M. G., and THOMPSON, R. H. S. *Biochem. J.* **49,** 191 (1951)

2033. ORMEROD, W. E. *Biochem. J.* **54,** 701 (1953)

2034. OSBORN, M. J., and HUENNEKENS, F. M. *Biochim. biophys. Acta* **26,** 646 (1957)

2035. O'SULLIVAN, W. J., and PERRIN, D. D. *Biochim. biophys. Acta* **52,** 612 (1961)

2036. OTEY, M. C., BIRNBAUM, S. M., and GREENSTEIN, J. P. *Arch. Biochem. Biophys.* **49,** 245 (1954)

2037. OTSUKA, K. *J. gen. appl. Microbiol.* **4,** 211 (1958)

2038. OVERATH, P., KELLERMAN, G. M., and LYNEN, F. *Biochem. Z.* **335,** 500 (1962)

2039. PACKER, L., and VISHNIAC, W. *Biochim. biophys. Acta* **17,** 153 (1955)

2040. PAEGE, L. M., and SCHLENK, F. *Arch. Biochem. Biophys.* **40,** 42 (1952)

2041. PAIGEN, K. *J. biol. Chem.* **233,** 388 (1958)

2042. PAIK, W. K., BLOCH-FRANKENTHAL, L., BIRNBAUM, S. M., WINITZ, M., and GREENSTEIN, J. P. *Arch. Biochem. Biophys.* **69,** 56 (1957)

2043. PALADE, G. E., and PORTER, K. R. *J. exp. Med.* **100,** 641 (1954)

2044. PALADE, G. E., and SIEKEVITZ, S. *J. biophys. biochem. Cytol.* **2,** 171 (1956)

2045. PALADINI, A. C., CAPUTTO, R., LELOIR, L. F., TRUCCO, R. E., and CARDINI, C. E. *Arch. Biochem.* **23,** 55 (1949)

2046. PALÉUS, S., and NEILANDS, J. B. *Acta chem. scand.* **4,** 1024 (1950)

2047. PALÉUS, S., and TUPPY, H. *Acta chem. scand,* **13,** 641 (1959)

2048. PALLERONI, N. J., and DOUDOROFF, M. *J. biol. Chem.* **218,** 535 (1956)

2049. PALLERONI, N. J., and DOUDOROFF, M. *J. biol. Chem.* **223,** 499 (1956)

2050. PALMER, R. F. *Biochem. J.* **78,** 839 (1961)

2051. PANT, R. *Biochem. J.* **73,** 30 (1959)

2052. PARDEE, A., and PRESTIDGE, L. *J. Bact.* **70,** 667 (1955)

2053. PARK, J. H., MERIWETHER, B. P., CLODFELDER, P., and CUNNINGHAM, L. W. *J. biol. Chem.* **236,** 136 (1961)

2054. PARK, R. W., and FOX, S. W. *J. biol. Chem.* **235,** 3193 (1960)

2055. PARKS, R. E., BEN-GERSHOM, E., and LARDY, H. A. *J. biol. Chem.* **227,** 231 (1957)

2056. PATTABIRAMAN, T. N., and BACHHAWAT, B. K. *Biochim. biophys. Acta* **50,** 129 (1961)

2057. PATTABIRAMAN, T. N., and BACHHAWAT, B. K. *Biochim. biophys. Acta* **54,** 273 (1961)

2058. PAUL, K.-G. *Arch. Biochem.* **12,** 441 (1947)

2059. PAULING, L., and COREY, R. B. *Proc. nat. Acad. Sci. U.S.* **37,** 241 (1951)

2060. PAYEN, A., and PERSOZ, J. F. *Ann. Chim. (Phys.)* **53,** 73 (1833)

2061. PAZUR, J. H., BUDOVICH, T., and TIPTON, C. L. *J. Amer. chem. Soc.* **79,** 625 (1957)

2062. PAZUR, J. H., and SHUEY, E. W. *J. biol. Chem.* **236,** 1780 (1961)

2063. PEANASKY, R. J., and LARDY, H. A. *J. biol. Chem.* **233,** 365 (1958)

2064. PEARSE, A. G. E. *Int. Rev. Cytol.* **3,** 329 (1954)

2065. PEAT, S., WHELAN, W. J., and REES, W. R. *J. chem. Soc.* p. 44 (1956)

2066. PECK, H. D., and GEST, H. *Biochim. biophys. Acta* **15,** 587 (1954)

2067. PEERS, F. G. *Biochem. J.* **53,** 102 (1953)

2068. PENEFSKY, H. S., PULLMAN, M. E., DATTA, A., and RACKER, E. *J. biol. Chem.* **235,** 3330 (1960)

2069. PENG, C. H. L. *Biochim. biophys. Acta* **22,** 42 (1956)

2070. PERLMANN, G. E. *Nature, Lond.* **173,** 406 (1954)

2071. PERRIN, D., JACOB, F., and MONOD, J. *C. R. Acad. Sci., Paris* **251,** 155 (1960)

2072. PERRY, S. V. *Bioch. biophys. Acta* **8,** 499 (1952)

2073. PERRY, S. V. *Biochem. J.* **48**, 257 (1951)

2074. PERRY, S. V. *Biochem. J.* **74**, 94 (1960)

2075. PETERKOFSKY, B., and GILVARG, C. *J. biol. Chem.* **236**, 1432 (1961)

2076. PETERS, R. A. *Proc. roy. Soc.* B, **139**, 143 (1952)

2077. PETERS, R. A. *Disc. Faraday Society*, No. 20, 'The Physical Chemistry of Enzymes', p. 189 (1955)

2078. PETERS, R. A. *Johns Hopkins Hosp. Bull.* **97**, 21 (1955)

2079. PETERSON, D. H., and MURRAY, H. C. *J. Amer. chem. Soc.* **74**, 1871 (1952)

2080. PETERSON, E. A., and SOBER, H. A., in *Methods in Enzymology*, ed. S. P. Colowick and N. O. Kaplan (New York, Academic Press, 1962), Vol. 5, p. 3

2081. PETRACK, B., SULLIVAN, L., and RATNER, S. *Arch. Biochem. Biophys.* **69**, 186 (1957)

2082. PHAFF, H. J., and DEMAIN, A. L. *J. biol. Chem.* **218**, 875 (1956)

2083. PHILLIPS, L. L., and CALDWELL, M. L. *J. Amer. chem. Soc.* **73**, 3559 (1951)

2084. PHILPOT, J. ST. L., and STANIER, J. E. *Biochem. J.* **63**, 214 (1956)

2085. PIÉRARD, A., and WIAME, J. M. *Biochim. biophys. Acta* **37**, 490 (1960)

2086. PIERPOINT, W. S., HUGHES, D. E., BADDILEY, J., and MATHIAS, A. P. *Biochem. J.* **61**, 368 (1955)

2087. PIGMAN, W. W. *Advanc. Enzymol.* **4**, 41 (1944)

2088. PIGMAN, W. W. *J. Res. nat. Bur. Stand.* **26**, 197 (1941)

2089. PINCUS, P. *Nature, Lond.* **66**, 187 (1950)

2090. PIZER, L. I., and BALLOU, C. E. *J. Amer. chem. Soc.* **79**, 3612 (1957)

2091. PIZER, L. I., and BALLOU, C. E. *J. biol. Chem.* **234**, 1138 (1959)

2092. PLAGEMANN, P. G. W., GREGORY, K. F., and WRÓBLEWSKI, F. *J. biol. Chem.* **235**, 2282 and 2288 (1960)

2093. PLAGER, J. E., and SAMUELS, L. T. *Arch. Biochem. Biophys.* **42**, 477 (1953)

2094. PLANTA, R. J., and GRUBER, M. *Biochim. biophys. Acta* **53**, 443 (1961)

2095. PLAUT, G. W. E. *J. biol. Chem.* **217**, 235 (1955)

2096. PLAUT, G. W. E., and SUNG, S.-C. *J. biol. Chem.* **207**, 305 (1954)

2097. PLENTL, A. A., and PAGE, I. H. *J. biol. Chem.* **163**, 49 (1946)

2098. POGELL, B. M., and GRYDER, R. M. *J. biol. Chem.* **228**, 701 (1957)

2099. POLANYI, M., and SZABO, A. L. *Trans. Faraday Soc.* **30**, 508 (1934)

2100. POLLISTER, A. W., and POLLISTER, P. F. *Int. Rev. Cytol.* **6**, 85 (1957)

2101. POLLOCK, M. *Brit. J. exp. Path.* **4**, 739 (1950)

2102. POLLOCK, M. R., TORRIANI, A.-M., and TRIDGELL, E. G. *Biochem. J.* **62**, 387 (1956)

2103. POLYANOVSKY, O. L., and KRETOVICH, V. L. *Doklady Akad. Nauk S.S.S.R.* **112**, 1087 (1957)

2104. PONTIS, H., DEGERSTEDT, G., and REICHARD, P. *Biochim. biophys. Acta* **51**, 138 (1961)

2105. PONTREMOLI, S., DE FLORA, A., GRAZI, E., MANGIAROTTI, G., BONSIGNORE, A., and HORECKER, B. L. *J. biol. Chem.* **236**, 2975 (1961)

2106. PORATH, J. *Biochim. biophys. Acta* **22**, 151 (1956)

2107. PORTER, J. W., and LONG, R. W. *J. biol. Chem.* **233**, 20 (1958)

2108. POSTERNAK, T. *J. biol. Chem.* **188**, 317 (1951)

2109. POSTERNAK, T., and ROSSELET, J. P. *Helv. chim. Acta* **37**, 246 (1954)

2110. POSTGATE, J. R. *Biochim. biophys. Acta* **18**, 427 (1955)

2111. POSTGATE, J. R. *J. gen. Microbiol.* **14**, 545 (1956)

2112. POTTER, V. R., in *Methods in Enzymology*, ed. S. P. Colowick and N. O. Kaplan (New York, Academic Press, 1955), Vol. 1, p. 10
2113. POTTER, V. R., and LIEBL, G. J. *Cancer Res.* **5,** 18 (1945)
2114. POTTS, J. T., BERGER, A., COOKE, J., and ANFINSEN, C. B. *J. biol. Chem.* **237,** 1851 (1962)
2115. POWELL, J. F., and HUNTER, J. R. *Biochem. J.* **62,** 381 (1956)
2116. PREISS, J., and HANDLER, P. *J. biol. Chem.* **225,** 759 (1957)
2117. PRESS, E. M., PORTER, R. R., and CEBRA, J. *Biochem. J.* **74,** 501 (1960)
2118. PRICE, J. B., and DIETRICH, L. S. *J. biol. Chem.* **227,** 633 (1957)
2119. PRICE, V. E., and GREENFIELD, R. E. *J. biol. Chem.* **209,** 363 (1954)
2120. PRICER, W. E., and HORECKER, B. L. *J. biol. Chem.* **235,** 1292 (1960)
2121. PUGH, D., LEABACK, D. H., and WALKER, P. G. *Biochem. J.* **65,** 464 (1957)
2122. PULLMAN, M. E., COLOWICK, S. P., and KAPLAN, N. O. *J. biol. Chem.* **194,** 593 (1952)
2123. PULLMAN, M. E., and NAJJAR, V. A. *Science* **119,** 630 (1954)
2124. PULLMAN, M. E., PENEFSKY, H. S., DATTA, A., and RACKER, E. *J. biol. Chem.* **235,** 3322 (1960)
2125. PULLMAN, M. E., SAN PIETRO, A., and COLOWICK, S. P. *J. biol. Chem.* **206,** 129 (1954)
2126. PUMPHREY, A. M., and REDFEARN, E. R. *Biochem. J.* **72,** 2P (1959)
2127. PURVIS, J. L. *Biochim. biophys. Acta* **30,** 440 (1958)
2128. PUTMAN, E. W., LITT, C. F., and HASSID, W. Z. *J. Amer. chem. Soc.* **77,** 4351 (1955)
2129. PUTNAM, F. W., in *The Proteins*, ed. H. Neurath and K. Bailey (New York, Academic Press, 1953), Vol. 1, pp. 807 and 893
2130. PUTNAM, F. W., and NEURATH, H. *J. biol. Chem.* **166,** 603 (1946)
2131. QUASTEL, J. H., and WHEATLEY, A. H. M. *Biochem. J.* **26,** 2169 (1932)
2132. QUASTEL, J. H., and WHEATLEY, A. H. M. *Biochem. J.* **32,** 936 (1938)
2133. QUASTEL, J. H., and WITTY, R. *Nature, Lond.* **167,** 556 (1951)
2134. QUASTEL, J. H., and WOOLDRIDGE, W. R. *Biochem. J.* **22,** 689 (1928)
2135. QUAYLE, J. R., KEECH, D. B. and TAYLOR, G. A., *Biochem. J.* **78,** 225 (1961)
2136. QUAYLE, J. R., and TAYLOR, G. A. *Biochem. J.* **78,** 611 (1961)
2137. RAACKE, I. D., in *Metabolic Pathways*, ed. D. M. Greenberg (New York, Academic Press, 1961), Vol. 2
2138. RABIN, B. R., and CROOK, E. M. *Biochim. biophys. Acta* **19,** 550 (1956)
2139. RABINOWITZ, J. C., and BARKER, H. A. *J. biol. Chem.* **218,** 161 (1956)
2140. RABINOWITZ, J. C., and PRICER, W. E. *J. Amer. chem. Soc.* **78,** 4176 (1956)
2141. RABINOWITZ, J. C., and PRICER, W. E. *J. Amer. chem. Soc.* **78,** 5702 (1956)
2142. RABINOWITZ, J. C., and PRICER, W. E. *J. biol. Chem.* **222,** 537 (1956)
2143. RABINOWITZ, J. C., and PRICER, W. E. *Fed. Proc.* **16,** 236 (1957)
2144. RABINOWITZ, J. C., and PRICER, W. E. *J. biol. Chem.* **229,** 321 (1957)
2145. RABINOWITZ, M. and LIPMANN, F. *J. biol. Chem.* **235,** 1043 (1960)
2146. RACKER, E. *J. biol. Chem.* **167,** 843 (1947)
2147. RACKER, E. *J. biol. Chem.* **177,** 883 (1949)
2148. RACKER, E. *Biochim. biophys. Acta* **4,** 211 (1950)
2149. RACKER, E. *J. biol. Chem.* **184,** 313 (1950)
2150. RACKER, E. *Biochem. biophys. Acta* **9,** 577 (1952)
2151. RACKER, E. *J. biol. Chem.* **196,** 347 (1952)
2152. RACKER, E. *Advanc. Enzymol.* **15,** 141 (1954)

2153. RACKER, E. *J. biol. Chem.* **217,** 855 (1955)

2154. RACKER, E. *J. biol. Chem.* **217,** 867 (1955)

2155. RACKER, E. *Advanc. Enzymol.* **23,** 323 (1961)

2156. RACKER, E., in *The Enzymes*, 2nd edn., ed. P. D. Boyer, H. Lardy and K. Myrbäck (New York, Academic Press, 1961), Vol. 5, p. 397

2157. RACKER, E. *Proc. nat. Acad. Sci. U.S.* **48,** 1659 (1962)

2158. RACKER, E., KLYBAS, V., and SCHRAMM, M. *J. biol. Chem.* **234,** 2510 (1959)

2159. RADEMAKER, W., and SOONS, J. B. J. *Biochim. biophys. Acta* **24,** 451 (1957)

2160. RAFTER, G. W. *J. biol. Chem.* **235,** 2475 (1960)

2161. RAIJMAN, L., GRISOLIA, S., and EDELHOCH, H. *J. biol. Chem.* **235,** 2340 (1960)

2162. RAISTRICK, H. *Proc. roy. Soc.* B, **136,** 481 (1950)

2163. RALL, T. W., and LEHNINGER, A. L. *J. biol. Chem.* **194,** 119 (1952)

2164. RALL, T. W., WOSILAIT, W. D., and SUTHERLAND, E. W. *Biochim. biophys. Acta* **20,** 69 (1956)

2165. RAMAKRISHNAN, C. V., and MARTIN, S. M. *Arch. Biochem. Biophys.* **55,** 403 (1955)

2166. RAMAKRISHNAN, T., and CAMPBELL, J. J. R. *Biochim. biophys. Acta* **17,** 122 (1955)

2167. RAMASARMA, T., and GIRI, K. V. *Arch. Biochem. Biophys.* **62,** 91 (1956)

2168. RAO, D. R., and GREENBERG, D. M. *J. biol. Chem.* **236,** 1758 (1961)

2169. RAO, D. R., and OESPER, P. *Biochem. J.* **81,** 405 (1961)

2170. RAO, M. S. N., and KEGELES, G. *J. Amer. chem. Soc.* **80,** 5724 (1958)

2171. RAO, N. A., CAMA, H. R., KUMAR, S. A., and VAIDYANATHAN, C. S. *J. biol. Chem.* **235,** 3353 (1960)

2172. RAPKINE, L. *C. R. Soc. Biol., Paris* **112,** 790 and 1294 (1933)

2173. RAPKINE, L., RAPKINE, S. M., and TRPINAC, P. *C. R. Acad. Sci., Paris* **209,** 253 (1939)

2174. RAPOPORT, S., and LUEBERING, J. *J. biol. Chem.* **189,** 683 (1951)

2175. RAPOPORT, S., and LUEBERING, J. *J. biol. Chem.* **196,** 583 (1952)

2176. RAPPORT, M. M., MEYER, K., and LINKER, A. *J. Amer. chem. Soc.* **73,** 2416 (1951)

2177. RATNER, S. *Advanc. Enzymol.* **15,** 319 (1954)

2178. RATNER, S., in *Methods in Enzymology*, ed. S. P. Colowick and N. O. Kaplan (New York, Academic Press, 1955), Vol. 2, p. 356

2179. RATNER, S., ANSLOW, W. P., and PETRACK, B. *J. biol. Chem.* **204,** 115 (1953)

2180. RATNER, S., and PETRACK, B. *Arch. Biochem. Biophys.* **65,** 582 (1956)

2181. RATNER, S., and ROCHOVANSKY, O. *Arch. Biochem. Biophys.* **63,** 277 (1956)

2182. RATNER, S., and ROCHOVANSKY, O. *Arch. Biochem. Biophys.* **63,** 296 (1956)

2183. RAVDIN, R. G., and CRANDALL, D. I. *J. biol. Chem.* **189,** 137 (1951)

2183a. RAVEL, J. M., NORTON, S. J., HUMPHREYS, J. S., and SHIVE, W. *J. biol. Chem.* **237,** 2845 (1962)

2184. RAVEL, J. M., GRONA, M. L., HUMPHREYS, J. S., and SHIVE, W. *J. biol. Chem.* **234,** 1452 (1959)

2185. RAVEL, J. M., NORTON, S. J., HUMPHREYS, J. S., and SHIVE, W. *J. biol. Chem.* **237,** 2845 (1962)

2186. RAW, I., and MAHLER, H. R. *J. biol. Chem.* **234,** 1867 (1959)

2187. RAW, I., PETRAGNANI, N., and NOGUEIRA, O. C. *J. biol. Chem.* **235,** 1517 (1960)

2188. RAY, W. J., LATHAM, H. G., KATSOULIS, M., and KOSHLAND, D. E. *J. Amer. chem. Soc.* **82,** 4743 (1960)

2189. RAY, W. J., RUSCICA, J. J., and KOSHLAND, D. E. *J. Amer. chem. Soc.* **82,** 4739 (1960)

2190. RAZZELL, W. E. *J. biol. Chem.* **236,** 3031 (1961)

2191. RAZZELL, W. E., and KHORANA, H. G. *J. biol. Chem.* **234,** 2105 and 2114 (1959)

2192. RAZZELL, W. E., and KHORANA, H. G. *J. biol. Chem.* **236,** 1144 (1961)

2193. RECKNAGEL, R. O. *J. biol. Chem.* **227,** 273 (1957)

2194. REDDI, K. K., and GIRI, K. V. *Enzymologia* **13,** 281 (1949)

2195. REED, L. J., in *The Enzymes*, 2nd edn., ed. P. D. Boyer, H. Lardy and K. Myrbäck (New York, Academic Press, 1960), Vol. 3, p. 195

2196. REED, L. J., DeBUSK, B. G., GUNSALUS, I. C., and HORNBERGER, C. S. *Science* **114,** 93 (1951)

2197. REES, D. A. *Biochem. J.* **80,** 449 (1961)

2198. REES, D. A. *Biochem. J.* **81,** 347 (1961)

2199. REESE, E. T., and MANDELS, M. *Canad. J. Microbiol.* **5,** 173 (1959)

2200. REEVES, R. B., RENNIE, D. W., and PAPPENHEIMER, J. R. *Fed. Proc.* **16,** 693 (1957)

2201. REICHARD, P. *Acta chem. scand.* **11,** 523 (1957)

2202. REICHARD, P. *Advanc. Enzymol.* **21,** 263 (1959)

2203. REICHARD, P., and HANSHOFF, G. *Acta chem. scand.* **10,** 548 (1956)

2204. REIS, J. *Bull. Soc. Chim. biol., Paris* **22,** 36 (1940)

2205. REISSIG, J. L. *J. biol. Chem.* **219,** 753 (1956)

2206. REMMERT, L. F., and COHEN, P. P. *J. biol. Chem.* **181,** 431 (1949)

2207. REMY, C. N., REMY, W. T., and BUCHANAN, J. M. *J. biol. Chem.* **217,** 885 (1955)

2208. REMY, C. N., RICHERT, D. A., DOISY, R. J., WELLS, I. C., and WESTERFELD, W. W. *J. biol. Chem.* **217,** 293 (1955)

2209. RENDI, R., and OCHOA, S. *Science* **133,** 1367 (1961)

2210. RENDINA, G., and COON, M. J. *J. biol. Chem.* **225,** 523 (1957)

2211. RENDINA, G., and SINGER, T. P. *J. biol. Chem.* **234,** 1605 (1959)

2211a. RENSON, J., WEISSBACH, H., and UDENFRIEND, S. *J. biol. Chem.* **237,** 2261 (1962)

2212. *Report of the Commission on Enzymes of the International Union of Biochemistry* (Oxford, Pergamon Press, 1961)

2213. REYNARD, A. M., HASS, L. F., JACOBSEN, D. D., and BOYER, P. D. *J. biol. Chem.* **236,** 2277 (1961)

2214. RICHARDS, F. M., and VITHAYATHIL, P. J. *J. biol. Chem.* **234,** 1459 (1959)

2215. RICHARDS, O. C., and RUTTER, W. J. *J. biol. Chem.* **236,** 3177 and 3185 (1961)

2216. RICHARDSON, K. E., and TOLBERT, N. E. *J. biol. Chem.* **236,** 1280 (1961)

2217. RICHARDSON, K. E., and TOLBERT, N. E. *J. biol. Chem.* **236,** 1285 (1961)

2218. RICHERT, D. A., and WESTERFELD, W. W. *J. biol. Chem.* **203,** 915 (1953)

2219. RICHERT, D. A., and WESTERFELD, W. W. *Proc. Soc. exp. Biol., N.Y.* **76,** 252 (1951)

2220. RIEDER, S. V., and ROSE, I. A. *J. biol. Chem.* **234,** 1007 (1959)

2221. RIKLIS, E., and RITTENBERG, D. *J. biol. Chem.* **236,** 2526 (1961)

2222. RILLING, H. C., and COON, M. J. *J. biol. Chem.* **235,** 3087 (1960)

2223. RIMON, A., and SHAPIRO, B. *Biochem. J.* **71,** 620 (1959)

2224. RINGLER, R. L. *J. biol. Chem.* **236,** 1192 (1961)

2225. RISEBROUGH, R. W., TISSIÈRES, A., and WATSON, J. D. *Proc. nat. Acad. Sci. U.S.* **48,** 430 (1962)

2225a. ROBBINS, E. A., and BOYER, P. D. *J. biol. Chem.* **224,** 121 (1957)

2226. ROBBINS, K. C., BARNETT, E. L., and GRANT, N. H. *J. biol. Chem.* **216,** 27 (1955)

2227. ROBBINS, P. W., and LIPMANN, F. *J. biol. Chem.* **229,** 837 (1957)

2228. ROBBINS, P. W., and LIPMANN, F. *J. biol. Chem.* **233,** 681 (1958)

2229. ROBBINS, P. W., and LIPMANN, F. *J. biol. Chem.* **233,** 686 (1958)

2230. ROBBINS, P. W., TRAUT, R. R., and LIPMANN, F. *Proc. nat. Acad. Sci.,* U.S. **45,** 6 (1959)

2231. ROBERTS, D. W. A. *J. biol. Chem.* **222,** 259 (1956)

2232. ROBERTS, E. *Arch. Biochem. Biophys.* **48,** 395 (1954)

2233. ROBERTS, R. B. *Proc. nat. Acad. Sci. U.S.* **48,** 897 and 1245 (1962)

2234. ROBINSON, W. G., and COON, M. J. *J. biol. Chem.* **225,** 511 (1957)

2235. ROCHE, J., and BAUDOIN, J. *C. R. Soc. Biol., Paris* **137,** 245 (1943)

2236. ROCHE, J., and LACOMBE, G. *Biochim. biophys. Acta* **9,** 687 (1952)

2237. ROCHE, J., LACOMBE, G., and GIRARD, H. *Biochim. biophys. Acta* **6,** 210 (1950)

2238. RODKEY, F. L., and BALL, E. G. *J. biol. Chem.* **182,** 17 (1950)

2239. RODWELL, V. W., TOWNE, J. C., and GRISOLIA, S. *Biochim. biophys. Acta* **20,** 394 (1956)

2240. RODWELL, V. W., TOWNE, J. C., and GRISOLIA, S. *J. biol. Chem.* **228,** 875 (1957)

2241. ROGERS, W. I., and KALNITZKY, G. *Biochim. biophys. Acta* **23,** 525 (1957)

2242. ROHOLT, O. A., and GREENBERG, D. M. *Arch. Biochem. Biophys.* **62,** 454 (1956)

2243. ROMANO, A. H., and NICKERSON, W. J. *J. biol. Chem.* **208,** 409 (1954)

2244. ROODYN, D. B. *Biochem. J.* **64,** 361 (1956)

2245. ROODYN, D. B. *Biochem. J.* **64,** 368 (1956)

2246. ROSE, I. A., GRUNBERG-MANAGO, M., KOREY, S., and OCHOA, S. *J. biol. Chem.* **211,** 737 (1955)

2247. ROSE, I. A., and O'CONNELL, E. L. *J. boil. Chem.* **236,** 3086 (1961)

2248. ROSE, I. A., and RIEDER, S. V. *J. biol. Chem.* **231,** 315 (1958)

2249. ROSE, S. P. R., and HEALD, P. J. *Biochem. J.* **81,** 339 (1961)

2250. ROSENBERG, A. *Ark. Kemi* **17,** 25 and 41 (1960)

2251. ROSENBERG, A. *Biochim. biophys. Acta* **45,** 297 (1960)

2252. ROSENBERG, L. L., and ARNON, D. I. *J. biol. Chem.* **217,** 361 (1955)

2253. ROSSITER, R. J. *J. biol. Chem.* **135,** 431 (1940)

2254. ROTHBERG, S., and STEINBERG, D. *J. Amer. chem. Soc.* **79,** 3274 (1957)

2255. ROTHSCHILD, H. A., and BARRON, E. S. G. *J. biol. Chem.* **209,** 511 (1954)

2256. ROUSH, A. H., and BETZ, R. F. *J. biol. Chem.* **233,** 261 (1958)

2257. ROUSH, A. H., and DOMNAS, A. J. *Science* **124,** 125 (1956)

2258. ROUGHTON, F. J. W. *Disc. Faraday Soc.,* No. 17, 'The Study of Fast Reactions', p. 116 (1954)

2259. ROUGHTON, F. J. W., and CLARK, A. M., in *The Enzymes,* 1st edn., ed. J. B. Sumner and K. Myrbäck (New York, Academic Press, 1951), Vol 1, p. 1250

2260. ROVERY, M., and DESNUELLE, P. *Proceedings of the fifth International Congress of Biochemistry, Moscow,* Symp. No. 4 (Oxford, Pergamon Press, 1963)

2261. ROVERY, M., DESNUELLE, P., and BONJOUR, G. *Biochim. biophys. Acta* **6,** 166 (1950)

2262. ROVERY, M., FABRE, C., and DESNUELLE, P. *Biochim. biophys. Acta* **9,** 702 (1952)

2263. ROVERY, M., GABELOTEAU, C., DE VERNEJOUL, P., GUIDONI, A., and DESNUELLE, P. *Biochim. biophys. Acta* **32,** 256 (1958)

2264. ROVERY, M., POILROUX, M., YOSHIDA, A., and DESNUELLE, P. *Biochim. biophys. Acta* **23,** 608 (1957)

2265. ROVERY, M., YOSHIDA, A., and DESNUELLE, P. *Biochim. biophys. Acta* **20,** 404 (1956)

2266. ROWEN, J. W., and KORNBERG, A. *J. biol. Chem.* **193,** 497 (1951)

2267. ROWSELL, E. V. *Biochem. J.* **64,** 235 (1956)

2268. ROWSELL, E. V. *Biochem. J.* **64,** 246 (1956)

2269. ROY, A. B. *Biochem. J.* **57,** 465 (1954)

2270. ROY, A. B. *Biochim. biophys. Acta* **15,** 300 (1954)

2271. ROY, A. B. *Biochem. J.* **64,** 651 (1956)

2272. ROY, A. B. *Advanc. Enzymol.* **22,** 205 (1960)

2273. ROY, A. B. *Biochem. J.* **74,** 49 (1960)

2274. ROY, D. K., and UNDERKOFLER, L. A. *Cereal Chem.* **28,** 72 (1951)

2275. ROZENFEL'D, E. L., and LUKOMSKAYA, I. S. *Biokhimiya* **21,** 412 (1956)

2276. RUDNEY, H. *J. biol. Chem.* **227,** 363 (1957)

2277. RUDNEY, H., and FERGUSON, J. J. *J. biol. Chem.* **234,** 1076 (1959)

2278. RUSSELL, D. H., THAIN, E. M., and VERNON, C. A. *Proc. chem. Soc.,* p. 255 (1960)

2279. RUTTER, W. J., and LARDY, H. A. *J. biol. Chem.* **233,** 374 (1958)

2280. RUTTER, W. J., RICHARDS, O. C., and WOODFIN, B. M. *J. biol. Chem.* **236,** 3193 (1961)

2281. RYAN, K. J., and ENGEL, L. L. *J. biol. Chem.* **225,** 103 (1957)

2282. RYLE, A. P., and PORTER, R. R. *Biochem. J.* **73,** 75 (1959)

2283. RYLE, A. P., SANGER, F., SMITH, L. F., and KITAI, R. *Biochem. J.* **60,** 541 (1955)

2284. SABLE, H. Z. *Proc. Soc. exp. Biol., N.Y.* **75,** 215 (1950)

2285. SABLE, H. Z., and GUARINO, A. J. *J. biol. Chem.* **196,** 395 (1952)

2286. SADANA, J. C., and McELROY, W. D. *Arch. Biochem. Biophys.* **67,** 16 (1957)

2287. SADANA, J. C., and MOREY, A. V. *Biochim. biophys. Acta* **50,** 153 (1961)

2288. SAGERS, R. D., BECK, J. V., GRUBER, W., and GUNSALUS, I. C. *J. Amer. chem. Soc.* **78,** 694 (1956)

2289. SAITO, Y., HAYAISHI, O., and ROTHBERG, S. *J. biol. Chem.* **229,** 921 (1957)

2290. SAKAGUCHI, K., and MURAO, S. *J. agric. chem. Soc., Japan* **23,** 411 (1950)

2291. SAKAMI, W., and UKSTINS, I. *J. biol. Chem.* **236,** PC50 (1961)

2292. SALLACH, H. J. *J. biol. Chem.* **223,** 1101 (1956)

2293. SALVADOR, R., and BRADY, R. O. *Fed. Proc.* **15,** 345 (1956)

2294. SANADI, D. R., GIBSON, D. M., and AYENGAR, P. *Biochim. biophys. Acta* **14,** 434 (1954)

2295. SANADI, D. R., LITTLEFIELD, J. W., and BOCK, R. M. *J. biol. Chem.* **197,** 851 (1952)

2296. SANGER, F. *Biochem. J.* **39,** 507 (1945)

2297. SANGER, F. *Advanc. Protein Chem.* **7,** 1 (1952)

2298. SANGER, F., and SHAW, D. C. *Nature, Lond.* **187,** 872 (1960)

2299. SANGER, F., and THOMPSON, E. O. P. *Biochem. J.* **53,** 366 (1953)

2300. SANGER, F., and TUPPY, H. *Biochem. J.* **49,** 481 (1951)

2301. SAN PIETRO, A., KAPLAN, N. O., and COLOWICK, S. P. *J. biol. Chem.* **212,** 941 (1955)

2302. SARDA, L., and DESNUELLE, P. *Biochim. biophys. Acta* **30,** 513 (1958)

REFERENCES

2303. SARDA, L., MARCHIS-MOUREN, G., CONSTANTIN, M. J., and DESNUELLE, P. *Biochim. biophys. Acta* **23**, 264 (1957)
2304. SARID, S., BERGER, A., and KATCHALSKI, E. *J. biol. Chem.* **234**, 1740 (1959)
2305. SAROJA, K., VENKATARAMAN, R., and GIRI, K. V. *Biochem. J.* **60**, 399 (1955)
2306. SARTORI, M. F. *Chem. Rev.* **48**, 225 (1951)
2307. SASTRY, L. V. S., and RAMAKRISHNAN, T. *J. Sci. Ind. Res.* **20C**, 277 (1961)
2308. SAUNDERS, B. C. Lect. Roy. Inst. Chem. **1** (1957)
2309. SAUNDERS, B. C. *Some Aspects of the Chemistry and Toxic Action of Organic Compounds containing Phosphorus and Fluorine* (Cambridge University Press, 1957)
2310. SAVAGE, N. *Biochem. J.* **67**, 146 (1957)
2311. SAWIN, P. B., and GLICK, D. *Proc. nat. Acad. Sci. U.S.* **29**, 55 (1943)
2312. SAWYER, C. H. *Science* **101**, 385 (1945)
2313. SAYRE, F. W., JENSEN, D., and GREENBERG, D. M. *J. biol. Chem.* **219**, 111 (1956)
2314. SAZ, H. J., and HILLARY, E. P. *Biochem. J.* **62**, 563 (1956)
2315. SAZ, H. J., and HUBBARD, J. A. *J. biol. Chem.* **225**, 921 (1957)
2316. SCARANO, E. Quoted by H. M. Kalckar, *Biochim. biophys. Acta* **12**, 250 (1953)
2317. SCARANO, E. *J. biol. Chem.* **235**, 706 (1960)
2318. SCARANO, E., BONADUCE, L., and DE PETROCELLIS, B. *J. biol. Chem.* **235**, 3556 (1960)
2319. SCHACHMAN, H. K., ADLER, J., RADDING, C. M., LEHMAN, I. R., and KORNBERG, A. *J. biol. Chem.* **235**, 3242 (1960)
2320. SCHACHMAN, H. K., PARDEE, A. B., and STANIER, R. Y. *Arch. Biochem. Biophys.* **38**, 245 (1952)
2321. SCHACHTER, D., and TAGGART, J. V. *J. biol. Chem.* **208**, 263 (1954)
2322. SCHAFFER, N. K., MAY, S. C., and SUMMERSON, W. H. *J. biol. Chem.* **206**, 201 (1954)
2323. SCHAFFER, N. K., SIMET, L., HARSHMAN, S., ENGLE, R. R., and DRISKO, R. W. *J. biol. Chem.* **225**, 197 (1957)
2324. SCHALES, O., MIMS, V., and SCHALES, S. S. *Arch. Biochem.* **10**, 455 (1946)
2325. SCHALES, O., and SCHALES, S. S. *Arch. Biochem.* **24**, 83 (1949)
2326. SCHAPIRA, G., KRUH, J., DREYFUS, J. C., and SCHAPIRA, F. *J. biol. Chem.* **235**, 1738 (1960)
2327. SCHELLENBERG, K. A., and HELLERMAN, L. *J. biol. Chem.* **231**, 547 (1958)
2328. SCHLAMOWITZ, M. *Fed. Proc.* **16**, 242 (1957)
2329. SCHLAMOWITZ, M., and BODANSKY, O. *J. biol. Chem.* **234**, 1433 (1959)
2330. SCHLESINGER, M. J., and COON, M. J. *J. biol. Chem.* **236**, 2421 (1961)
2331. SCHLOSSMANN, K., BRÜGGEMANN, J., and LYNEN, F. *Biochem. Z.* **336**, 258 (1962)
2332. SCHLOSSMANN, K., and LYNEN, F. *Biochem. Z.* **328**, 591 (1957)
2333. SCHMID, H., and KARRER, P. *Helv. chim. Acta* **32**, 960 (1949)
2334. SCHMID, R., ROBBINS, P. W., and TRAUT, R. R. *Proc. nat. Acad. Sci. U.S.* **45**, 1236 (1959)
2335. SCHMIDT, G. *Z. physiol. Chem.* **208**, 185 (1932)
2336. SCHNEIDER, W. C. *J. Histochem. Cytochem.* **1**, 212 (1953)
2337. SCHNEIDER, W. C., CLAUDE, A., and HOGEBOOM, G. H. *J. biol. Chem.* **172**, 451 (1948)
2338. SCHNUCHEL, G. *Z. physiol. Chem.* **298**, 241 (1954)

2339. SCHNUCHEL, G. *Z. physiol. Chem.* **303,** 91 (1956)

2340. SCHOENHEIMER, R. *The Dynamic State of Body Constituents* (Harvard University Press, 1946)

2341. SCHØNHEYDER, F. *Biochem. J.* **50,** 378 (1952)

2342. SCHRECKER, A. W., and KORNBERG, A. *J. biol. Chem.* **182,** 795 (1950)

2343. SCHUCHER, R., and HOKIN, L. E. *J. biol. Chem.* **210,** 551 (1954)

2344. SCHUEGRAF, A., RATNER, S., and WARNER, R. C. *J. biol. Chem.* **235,** 3597 (1960)

2345. SCHÜTZ, E. *Z. physiol. Chem.* **9,** 577 (1885)

2346. SCHÜTZ, J. *Z. physiol. Chem.* **30,** 1 (1900)

2347. SCHWANDER, H., ZAHLER, P., and NITSCHMANN, H. *Helv. chim. Acta* **35,** 553 (1952)

2348. SCHWARTZ, A., and OSCHMANN, A. *C. R. Soc. Biol., Paris* **92,** 169 (1925)

2349. SCHWEET, R. S., and ALLEN, E. H. *J. biol. Chem.* **223,** 1104 (1958)

2350. SCHWERT, G. W., and KAUFMAN, S. *J. biol. Chem.* **180,** 517 (1949)

2351. SCHWERT, G. W., NEURATH, H., KAUFMAN, S., and SNOKE, J. E. *J. biol. Chem.* **172,** 221 (1948)

2352. SCHWIMMER, S. *Arch. Biochem. Biophys.* **43,** 108 (1953)

2353. SCHWIMMER, S., and BALLS, A. K. *J. biol. Chem.* **179,** 1063 (1949)

2354. SCHWIMMER, S., and PARDEE, A. B. *Advanc. Enzymol.* **14,** 375 (1953)

2355. SCOTT, D. A. *J. biol. Chem.* **142,** 959 (1942)

2356. SCOTT, D. B. M., and COHEN, S. S. *Biochem. J.* **55,** 23 (1953)

2357. SCOTT, D. B. M., and COHEN, S. S. *Biochem. J.* **64,** 686 (1957)

2358. SCOTT, E. M., and JAKOBY, W. B. *J. biol. Chem.* **234,** 932 (1959)

2359. SCRIBA, P., and HOLZER, H. *Biochem. Z.* **334,** 473 (1961)

2360. SEEGMILLER, J. E. *J. biol. Chem.* **201,** 629 (1953)

2361. SEGAL, H. L., and BOYER, P. D. *J. biol. Chem.* **204,** 265 (1953)

2362. SEGAL, H. L., and BRENNER, B. M. *J. biol. Chem.* **235,** 471 (1960)

2363. SEGAL, H. L., KACHMAR, J. F., and BOYER, P. D. *Enzymologia* **15,** 187 (1952)

2364. SEIFTER, S., GALLOP, P. M., KLEIN, L., and MEILMAN, E. *J. biol. Chem.* **234,** 285 (1959)

2365. SEKUZU, I., JURTSHUK, P., and GREEN, D. E. *Biochem. biophys. res. Comm.* **6,** 71 (1961)

2366. SEKUZU, I., TAKEMORI, S., ORII, Y., and OKUNUKI, K. *Biochim. biophys. Acta* **37,** 64 (1960)

2367. SELIGMAN, A. M., and WOLF, G. *J. Amer. chem. Soc.* **73,** 2086 (1951)

2368. SELIM, A. S. M., and GREENBERG, D. M. *J. biol. Chem.* **234,** 1474 (1959)

2369. SELLINGER, O. Z., and MILLER, O. N. *Fed. Proc.* **16,** 245 (1957)

2370. SELLINGER, O. Z., and MILLER, O. N. *J. biol. Chem.* **234,** 1641 (1959)

2371. SELWYN, M. J. Private communication

2372. SEMENZA, G. *Biochim. biophys. Acta* **24,** 401 (1957)

2373. SENTHESHANMUGANATHAN, S. *Biochem. J.* **77,** 619 (1960)

2374. SERIF, G. S., and KIRKWOOD, S. *J. biol. Chem.* **233,** 109 (1958)

2375. SEUBERT, W., and REMBERGER, U. *Biochem. Z.* **334,** 401 (1961)

2376. SHACTER, B., and SHIMKIN, M. B. *J. nat. Cancer Inst.* **9,** 155 (1948)

2377. SHAPIRA, R., and DOHERTY, D. G. *Fed. Proc.* **15,** 352 (1956)

2378. SHAPIRO, B. *Biochem. J.* **53,** 663 (1953)

2379. SHAPIRO, S. K. *Biochim. biophys. Acta* **29,** 405 (1958)

2380. SHAPIRO, S. K., and YPHANTIS, D. A. *Biochim. biophys. Acta* **36,** 241 (1959)

2381. SHAW, D. R. D. *Biochem. J.* **64,** 394 (1956)

2382. SHEPHERD, J. A., and KALNITZKY, G. *J. biol. Chem.* **207,** 605 (1954)

2383. SHEPHERDSON, M., and PARDEE, A. B. *J. biol. Chem.* **235,** 3233 (1960)

2384. SHER, I. H., and MALLETTE, M. F. *Arch. Biochem. Biophys.* **53,** 354 (1954)

2385. SHER, I. H., and MALLETTE, M. F. *Arch. Biochem. Biophys.* **53,** 370 (1954)

2386. SHERRY, S., and TROLL, W. *J. biol. Chem.* **208,** 95 (1954)

2387. SHIELDS, G. S., HILL, R. L., and SMITH, E. L. *J. biol. Chem.* **234,** 1747 (1959)

2388. SHIFRIN, S., and KAPLAN, N. O. *Advanc. Enzymol.* **22,** 337 (1960)

2389. SHIMAZONO, H. *J. Biochem., Tokyo* **42,** 321 (1955)

2390. SHIMAZONO, H., and HAYAISHI, O. *J. biol. Chem.* **227,** 151 (1957)

2391. SHIMAZONO, N., MANO, Y., TANAKA, R., and KAZIRO, Y. *J. Biochem., Tokyo* **46,** 959 (1959)

2392. SHIMURA, K., NAGAYAMA, H., and KIKUCHI, A. *Nature, Lond.* **177,** 935 (1956)

2393. SHUG, A. L., WILSON, P. W., GREEN, D. E., and MAHLER, H. R. *J. Amer. chem. Soc.* **76,** 3355 (1954)

2394. SHUKUYA, R., and SCHWERT, G. W. *J. biol. Chem.* **235,** 1649 and 1653 (1960)

2395. SHUKUYA, R., and SCHWERT, G. W. *J. biol. Chem.* **235,** 1658 (1960)

2396. SHULMAN, S., ALKJAERSIG, N., and SHERRY, S. *J. biol. Chem.* **233,** 91 (1958)

2397. SHUSTER, L., and KAPLAN, N. O. *J. biol. Chem.* **201,** 535 (1953)

2398. SHUSTER, L., and KAPLAN, N. O. *J. biol. Chem.* **215,** 183 (1955)

2399. SIDBURY, J. B., ROSENBERG, L. L., and NAJJAR, V. A. *J. biol. Chem.* **222,** 89 (1956)

2400. SIEBERT, G. *Proceedings of the fifth International Congress of Biochemistry, Moscow*, Symp. No. 2 (Oxford, Pergamon Press, 1963)

2401. SIEBERT, G., CARSIOTIS, M., and PLAUT, G. W. E. *J. biol. Chem.* **226,** 977 (1957)

2402. SIEBERT, G., DUBUC, J., WARNER, R. C., and PLAUT, G. W. E. *J. biol. Chem.* **226,** 965 (1957)

2403. SIEBERT, G., LANG, K., LUCIUS-LANG, S., HERKERT, L., STARK, G., ROSSMÜLLER, G., and JÖCKEL, H. *Z. Physiol. Chem.* **295,** 229 (1953)

2404. SIEBERT, G., and SMELLIE, R. M. S. *Int. Rev. Cytol.* **6,** 383 (1957)

2405. SILVERMAN, M., KERESZTESY, J. C., KOVAL, G. J., and GARDINER, R. C. *J. biol. Chem.* **226,** 83 (1957)

2406. SIMPSON, F. J., and WOOD, W. A. *J. biol. Chem.* **230,** 473 (1958)

2407. SIMPSON, M. V., and VELICK, S. F. *J. biol. Chem.* **208,** 61 (1954)

2408. SINGER, M. F., and FRUTON, J. S. *J. biol. Chem.* **229,** 111 (1957)

2409. SINGER, T. P. *J. biol. Chem.* **174,** 11 (1948)

2410. SINGER, T. P., and HOFSTEE, B. H. J. *Arch. Biochem.* **18,** 229 and 245 (1948)

2411. SINGER, T. P., and KEARNEY, E. B. *Arch. Biochem.* **29,** 190 (1950)

2412. SINGER, T. P., and KEARNEY, E. B. *J. biol. Chem.* **183,** 409 (1950)

2413. SINGER, T. P., KEARNEY, E. B., and BERNATH, P. *J. biol. Chem.* **223,** 599 (1956)

2414. SINGER, T. P., and MASSEY, V. *Record of Chem. Progress* **18,** 201 (1957)

2415. SINGER, T. P., MASSEY, V., and KEARNEY, E. B. *Biochim. biophys. Acta* **19,** 200 (1956)

2416. SINGER, T. P., and PENSKY, J. *Biochim. biophys. Acta* **9,** 316 (1952)

2417. SINGER, T. P., and PENSKY, J. *J. biol. Chem.* **196,** 375 (1952)

2418. SISSAKIAN, N. M. *Advanc. Enzymol.* **20,** 201 (1958)

2419. SISTROM, W. R., and STANIER, R. Y. *J. biol. Chem.* **210,** 821 (1954)

2420. SIU, P. M. L., WOOD, H. G., and STJERNHOLM, R. L. *J. biol. Chem.* **236,** PC21 (1961)

2421. SIVAK, A., and HOFFMANN-OSTENHOF, O. *Biochim. biophys. Acta* **53,** 426 (1961)

2422. SIZER, I. W. *Advanc. Enzymol.* **3,** 35 (1943)

2423. SKÖLD, O. *J. biol. Chem.* **235,** 3273 (1960)

2424. SLATER, E. C. *Biochem. J.* **44,** 305 (1949)

2425. SLATER, E. C. *Disc. Faraday Soc.,* No. 20, 'The Physical Chemistry of Enzymes', p. 231 (1955)

2426. SLATER, E. C. *Disc. Faraday Soc.,* No. 20, 'The Physical Chemistry of Enzymes', p. 308 (1955)

2427. SLATER, E. C. *Advanc. Enzymol.* **20,** 147 (1958)

2428. SLATER, E. C., and BONNER, W. D. *Biochem. J.* **52,** 185 (1952)

2429. SLEIN, M. W. *J. biol. Chem.* **186,** 753 (1950)

2430. SLEIN, M. W. *J. Amer. chem. Soc.* **77,** 1663 (1955)

2431. SLOANE-STANLEY, G. H. *Biochem. J.* **44,** 373 (1949)

2432. SMILEY, J. D., and ASHWELL, G. *J. biol. Chem.* **235,** 1571 (1960)

2433. SMILEY, J. D., and ASHWELL, G. *J. biol. Chem.* **236,** 357 (1961)

2434. SMITH, E. E. B., and MILLS, G. T. *Biochem. J.* **54,** 164 (1953)

2435. SMITH, E. E. B., and MILLS, G. T. *Biochim. biophys. Acta* **18,** 152 (1955)

2436. SMITH, E. L. *J. biol. Chem.* **173,** 571 (1948)

2437. SMITH, E. L. *J. biol. Chem.* **176,** 9 (1948)

2438. SMITH, E. L. *Advanc. Enzymol.* **12,** 191 (1951)

2439. SMITH, E. L., in *The Enzymes,* 1st edn., ed. J. B. Sumner and K. Myrbäck (New York, Academic Press, 1951), Vol. 1, p. 793

2440. SMITH, E. L. *Vitamin B$_{12}$* (London, Methuen, 1960)

2441. SMITH, E. L. *Proc. Nat. Acad. Sci., U.S.* **48,** 677 (1962)

2442. SMITH, E. L., and BERGMANN, M. *J. biol. Chem.* **153,** 627 (1944)

2443. SMITH, E. L., DAVIS, N. C., ADAMS, E., and SPACKMAN, D. H., in *A Symposium on the Mechanism of Enzyme Action,* ed. W. D. McElroy and B. Glass (Baltimore, Johns Hopkins Press, 1954), p. 291

2444. SMITH, E. L., and HILL, R. L., in *The Enzymes,* 2nd edn., ed. P. D. Boyer, H. Lardy and K. Myrbäck (New York, Academic Press, 1960), Vol. 4, p. 37

2445. SMITH, E. L., and KIMMEL, J. R., in *The Enzymes,* 2nd edn., ed. P. D. Boyer, H. Lardy and K. Myrbäck (New York, Academic Press, 1960), Vol. 4, p. 133

2446. SMITH, E. L., KIMMEL, J. R., BROWN, D. M., and THOMPSON, E. O. P. *J. biol. Chem.* **215,** 67 (1955)

2447. SMITH, E. L., and LUMRY, R. *Cold Spring Harbor Symposia on quantitative Biology* **4,** 168 (1949)

2448. SMITH, E. L., and SPACKMAN, D. H. *J. biol. Chem.* **212,** 271 (1955)

2449. SMITH, E. L., and STOCKELL, A. *J. biol. Chem.* **207,** 501 (1954)

2450. SMITH, E. L., STOCKELL, A., and KIMMEL, J. R. *J. biol. Chem.* **207,** 551 (1954)

2451. SMITH, L. *Bact. Rev.* **18,** 106 (1954)

2452. SMITH, L., and STOTZ, E. *J. biol. Chem.* **209,** 819 (1954)

2453. SMITH, M. E., and GREENBERG, D. M. *Nature, Lond.* **177,** 1130 (1956)

874 REFERENCES

2454. SMITH, R. A., and GUNSALUS, I. C. *J. biol. Chem.* **229,** 305 (1957)
2455. SMITH, R. F., and BRIGGS, D. R. *J. phys. Chem.* **54,** 33 (1950)
2456. SMITH, S. W., WEISS, S. B., and KENNEDY, E. P. *J. biol. Chem.* **228,** 915 (1957)
2457. SMITHIES, O. *Advanc. Protein Chem.* **14,** 65 (1959)
2458. SMYTH, D. G., STEIN, W. H., and MOORE, S. *J. biol. Chem.* **238,** 227 (1963)
2459. SMYTHE, C. V., and HALLIDAY, D. *J. biol. Chem.* **144,** 237 (1942)
2460. SNELL, E. E., and BROQUIST, H. P. *Arch. Biochem.* **23,** 326 (1949)
2461. SNOKE, J. E. *J. biol. Chem.* **223,** 271 (1956)
2462. SNOKE, J. E., and BLOCH, K. *J. biol. Chem.* **213,** 825 (1955)
2463. SNOKE, J. E., and NEURATH, H. *Arch. Biochem.* **21,** 351 (1949)
2464. SNOKE, J. E., YANARI, S., and BLOCH, K. *J. biol. Chem.* **201,** 573 (1953)
2465. SNYDER, S. H., SILVA, O. L., and KIES, M. W. *J. biol. Chem.* **236,** 2996 (1961)
2466. SOCQUET, I. M., and LAIDLER, K. J. *Arch. Biochem.* **25,** 171 (1950)
2466a. SOHLER, M. R., SEIBERT, M. A., KREKE, C. W., and COOK, E. S. *J. biol. Chem.* **198,** 281 (1952)
2467. SOLOMON, J. B. *Biochem. J.* **66,** 264 (1957)
2468. SOLOMON, J. B. *Biochem. J.* **70,** 529 (1958)
2469. SOLS, A., and CRANE, R. K. *J. biol. Chem.* **210,** 581 (1954)
2470. SOLS, A., and FUENTE, G. DE LA. *Biochim. biophys. Acta* **24,** 206 (1957)
2471. SOLS, A., FUENTE, G. DE LA, VILLAR-PALASÍ, C., and ASENSIO, C. *Biochim. biophys. Acta* **30,** 92 (1958)
2472. SÖRBO, B. H. *Acta chem. scand.* **7,** 1129 (1953)
2473. SÖRBO, B. H. *Acta chem. scand.* **7,** 1137 (1953)
2474. SÖRBO, B. *Biochim. biophys. Acta* **24,** 324 (1957)
2475. SÖRBO, B., and HEYMAN, T. *Biochim. biophys. Acta* **23,** 624 (1957)
2476. ŠORM, F. *Advanc. Enzymol.* **24,** 415 (1962)
2477. SOURKES, T. L. *Rev. canad. Biol.* **14,** 49 (1955)
2478. SPACKMAN, D. H., SMITH, E. L., and BROWN, D. M. *J. biol. Chem.* **212,** 255 (1955)
2479. SPACKMAN, D. H., STEIN, W. H., and MOORE, S. *J. biol. Chem.* **235,** 648 (1960)
2480. SPAHR, P. F., and HOLLINGWORTH, B. R. *J. biol. Chem.* **236,** 823 (1961)
2481. SPENCER, D. *Austral. J. biol. Sci.* **12,** 181 (1959)
2482. SPENCER, M., FULLER, W., WILKINS, M. H. F., and BROWN, G. L. *Nature, Lond.* **194,** 1014 (1962)
2483. SPEYER, J. F., LENGYEL, P., BASILIO, C., and OCHOA, S. *Proc. nat. Acad. Sci. U.S.* **48,** 441 (1962)
2484. SPIEGELMAN, S., DELORENZO, W. F., and CAMPBELL, A. M. *Proc. nat. Acad. Sci. U.S.* **37,** 513 (1951)
2485. SPOONER, E. T. C., and STOCKER, B. A. D., eds., *Symposium of Bacterial Anatomy* (6th Symposium of the Society for General Microbiology) (Cambridge University Press, 1956)
2486. SPRINSON, D. B., and RITTENBERG, D. *Nature, Lond.* **167,** 484 (1951)
2487. SRERE, P. A. *J. biol. Chem.* **234,** 2544 (1959)
2488. SRERE, P. A. *J. biol. Chem.* **236,** 50 (1961)
2489. SRERE, P. A., COOPER, J. R., KLYBAS. V., and RACKER, E. *Arch. Biochem. Biophys.* **59,** 535 (1955)
2490. SRERE, P. A., and KOSICKI, G. W. *J. biol. Chem.* **236,** 2557 (1961)

2491. SRERE, P. A., KOSICKI, G. W., and LUMRY, R. *Biochim. biophys. Acta* **50,** 184 (1961)

2492. SRERE, P. A., SEUBERT, W., and LYNEN, F. *Biochim. biophys. Acta* **33,** 313 (1959)

2493. SRIBNEY, M., and KENNEDY, E. P. *J. biol. Chem.* **233,** 1315 (1958)

2494. SRI RAM, J., TERMINIELLO, L., BIER, M., and NORD, F. F. *Arch. Biochem. Biophys.* **52,** 464 (1954)

2495. SRINIVASAN, P. R., and SPRINSON, D. B. *J. biol. Chem.* **234,** 716 (1959)

2496. STADTMAN, E. R. *Fed. Proc.* **11,** 291 (1952)

2497. STADTMAN, E. R. *J. biol. Chem.* **196,** 527 (1952)

2498. STADTMAN, E. R., COHEN, G. N., LeBRAS, G., and DE ROBICHON-SZULMAJSTER, H. *J. biol. Chem.* **236,** 2033 (1961)

2499. STADTMAN, T. C. *Biochem. J.* **62,** 614 (1956)

2500. STADTMAN, T. C., CHERKES, A., and ANFINSEN, C. B. *J. biol. Chem.* **206,** 511 (1954)

2501. STADTMAN, T. C., and ELLIOTT, P. *J. biol. Chem.* **228,** 983 (1957)

2502. STAFFORD, H. A., MAGALDI, A., and VENNESLAND, B. *J. biol. Chem.* **207,** 621 (1954)

2503. STAHMANN, M. A., FRUTON, J. S., and BERGMANN, M. *J. biol. Chem.* **164,** 753 (1946)

2504. STANIER, R. Y. *Ann. Rev. Microbiol.* **5,** 35 (1951)

2505. STANIER, R. Y. *Symp. sur le métabolisme microbien* (2nd International Congress of Biochemistry, Paris) (1952), p. 64

2506. STANIER, R. Y., and INGRAHAM, J. L. *J. biol. Chem.* **210,** 799 (1954)

2507. STARK, G. R., STEIN, W. H., and MOORE, S. *J. biol. Chem.* **236,** 436 (1961)

2508. STEARN, A. E. *Advanc. Enzymol.* **9,** 25 (1949)

2509. STEIN, E. A., JUNGE, J. M., and FISCHER, E. H. *J. biol. Chem.* **235,** 371 (1960)

2510. STEIN, S. S., and KOSHLAND, D. E. *Arch. Biochem. Biophys.* **39,** 229 (1952)

2511. STEIN, W. D., and BARNARD, E. A. *J. mol. Biol.* **1,** 350 (1959)

2512. STEIN, W. H., and MOORE, S. *Fifth International Congress of Biochemistry, Moscow.* Symposium No. 4 (Oxford, Pergamon Press, 1963)

2513. STENESH, J. J., and WINNICK, T. *Biochem. J.* **77,** 575 (1960)

2514. STERN, B. K., and VENNESLAND, B. *J. biol. Chem.* **235,** 205 and 209 (1960)

2515. STERN, J. R. *Biochim. biophys. Acta* **26,** 448 (1957)

2516. STERN, J. R., in *The Enzymes,* 2nd edn., ed. P. D. Boyer, H. Lardy and K. Myrbäck (New York, Academic Press, 1961), Vol. 5, p. 511

2517. STERN, J. R., COON, M. J., and DEL CAMPILLO, A. *Nature, Lond.* **171,** 28 (1953)

2518. STERN, J. R., COON, M. J., DEL CAMPILLO, A., and SCHNEIDER, M. C. *J. biol. Chem.* **221,** 15 (1956)

2519. STERN, J. R., and DEL CAMPILLO, A. *J. Amer. chem. Soc.* **77,** 1073 (1955)

2520. STERN, J. R., and DEL CAMPILLO, A. *J. biol. Chem.* **218,** 985 (1956)

2521. STERN, J. R., DEL CAMPILLO, A., and RAW, I. *J. biol. Chem.* **218,** 971 (1956)

2522. STERN, J. R., and DRUMMOND, G. I. *Fed. Proc.* **15,** 363 (1956)

2523. STERN, J. R., DRUMMOND, G. I., COON, M. J., and DEL CAMPILLO, A. *J. biol. Chem.* **235,** 313 (1960)

2524. STERN, J. R., and OCHOA, S. *J. biol. Chem.* **191,** 161 (1951)

2525. STERN, J. R., SHAPIRO, B., STADTMAN, E. R., and OCHOA, S. *J. biol. Chem.* **193,** 703 (1951)

2526. STETTEN, M. R. *J. Amer. chem. Soc.* **81,** 1437 (1959)

2527. STETTEN, M. R., and STETTEN, D. *J. biol. Chem.* **232,** 489 (1958)

2528. STEVENS, A., and HILMOE, R. J. *J. biol. Chem.* **235,** 3016 and 3023 (1960)

2529. STEYN-PARVÉ, E. P. *Biochim. biophys. Acta* **8,** 310 (1952)

2530. STICKLAND, L. H. *Biochem. J.* **44,** 190 (1949)

2531. STICKLAND, R. G. *Biochem. J.* **73,** 646 and 654 (1959)

2532. STICKLAND, R. G. *Biochem. J.* **73,** 660 (1959)

2533. STILL, J. L., BUELL, M. V., KNOX, W. E., and GREEN, D. E. *J. biol. Chem.* **179,** 831 (1949)

2534. STILL, J. L., and SPERLING, E. *J. biol. Chem.* **182,** 585 (1950)

2535. STITCH, S. R., HALKERSTON, I. D. K., and HILLMAN, J. *Biochem. J.* **63,** 705 (1956)

2536. STJERNHOLM, R., and WOOD, H. G. *Proc. nat. Acad. Sci. U.S.* **47,** 289 (1961)

2536a. STOCKELL, A., and SMITH, E. L. *J. biol. Chem.* **227,** 1 (1957)

2537. STOCKEN, L. A., and THOMPSON, R. H. S. *Physiol. Rev.* **29,** 168 (1949)

2538. STODOLA, F. H., KOEPSELL, H. J., and SHARPE, E. S. *J. Amer. chem. Soc.* **74,** 3202 (1952)

2539. STOKSTAD, E. L. R., HOFFMANN, C. E., REGAN, M. A., FORDHAM, D., and JUKES, T. H. *Arch. Biochem.* **20,** 75 (1949)

2540. STOLL, A., and SEEBECK, E. *Advanc. Enzymol.* **11,** 377 (1951)

2541. STOREY, I. D. E., and DUTTON, G. J. *Biochem. J.* **59,** 279 (1955)

2542. STORVICK, W. O., and KING, K. W. *J. biol. Chem.* **235,** 303 (1960)

2543. STRAUB, F. B. *Biochem. J.* **33,** 787 (1939)

2544. STRAUB, F. B. *Biochem. J.* **34,** 483 (1940)

2545. STRAUB, F. B. *Enzymologia* **9,** 143 (1940)

2546. STRAUB, F. B. *Z. physiol. Chem.* **275,** 63 (1942)

2547. STRAUB, F. B., ULLMANN, Á., and ÁCS, G. *Biochim. biophys. Acta* **18,** 439 (1955)

2548. STRAUS, O. H., and GOLDSTEIN, A. *J. gen. Physiol.* **26,** 559 (1943)

2549. STRECKER, H. J. *Arch. Biochem. Biophys.* **46,** 128 (1953)

2550. STRECKER, H. J., and HARARY, I. *J. biol. Chem.* **211,** 263 (1954)

2551. STRECKER, H. J., and KORKES, S. *J. biol. Chem.* **196,** 769 (1952)

2552. STRELITZ, F. *Biochem. J.* **38,** 86 (1944)

2553. STRITTMATTER, C. F., and BALL, E. G. *J. cell. comp. Physiol.* **43,** 57 (1954)

2554. STRITTMATTER, P. *J. biol. Chem.* **236,** 2329 (1961)

2555. STRITTMATTER, P., and BALL, E. G. *J. biol. Chem.* **213,** 445 (1955)

2556. STRITTMATTER, P., and VELICK, S. F. *J. biol. Chem.* **221,** 253 (1956)

2557. STRITTMATTER, P., and VELICK, S. F. *J. biol. Chem.* **228,** 785 (1957)

2558. STROMINGER, J. L. *Biochim. biophys. Acta* **16,** 616 (1955)

2559. STROMINGER, J. L., and MAPSON, L. W. *Biochem. J.* **66,** 567 (1957)

2560. STROMINGER, J. L., MAXWELL, E. S., AXELROD, J., and KALCKAR, H. M. *J. biol. Chem.* **224,** 79 (1957)

2561. STROMINGER, J. L., and SMITH, M. S. *J. biol. Chem.* **234,** 1822 (1959)

2562. STUMPF, P. K., and HORECKER, B. L. *J. biol. Chem.* **218,** 753 (1956)

2562a. STURGE, L. M., and WHITTAKER, V. P. *Biochem. J.* **47,** 518 (1950)

2563. SUGIYAMA, S., YANO, K., and ARIMA, K. *Bull. agr. chem. Soc. Japan* **24,** 243 and 249 (1960)

2564. SUMNER, J. B. *J. biol. Chem.* **69,** 435 (1926)

2565. SUMNER, J. B., in *The Enzymes*, 1st edn., ed. J. B. Sumner and K. Myrbäck (New York, Academic Press, 1951), Vol. 1, p. 873

2566. SUMNER, J. B., CHOU, T. C., and BEVER, A. T. *Arch. Biochem.* **26,** 1 (1950)

2567. SUMNER, J. B., and DOUNCE, A. L. *J. biol. Chem.* **121,** 417 (1937)

2568. SUNDARAJAN, T. A., and SARMA, P. S. *Biochem. J.* **71,** 537 (1959)

2569. SUNDARAM, S., and SARMA, P. S. *Biochem. J.* **77,** 465 (1960)

2570. SUSKIND, S. R. *J. Bacteriol.* **74,** 308 (1957)

2571. SUTHERLAND, E. W., COHN, M., POSTERNAK, T., and CORI, C. F. *J. biol. Chem.* **180,** 1285 (1949)

2572. SUTHERLAND, E. W., POSTERNAK, T., and CORI, C. F. *J. biol. Chem.* **181,** 153 (1949)

2573. SUTHERLAND, E. W., and WOSILAIT, W. D. *J. biol. Chem.* **218,** 459 (1956)

2574. SUTTON, W. B. *J. biol. Chem.* **226,** 395 (1957)

2575. SUZUKI, I., and WERKMAN, C. H. *Biochem. J.* **74,** 359 (1960)

2576. SUZUKI, K., MANO, Y., and SHIMAZONO, N. *J. Biochem., Tokyo* **48,** 313 (1960)

2577. SUZUKI, S., and STROMINGER, J. L. *J. biol. Chem.* **235,** 257, 267 and 274 (1960)

2577a. SUZUKI, I., and WERKMAN, C. H. *Arch. Biochem. Biophys.* **76,** 103 (1958)

2578. SWAIN, C. G., and BROWN, J. F. *J. Amer. chem. Soc.* **74,** 2538 (1952)

2579. SWANSON, M. A. *J. biol. Chem.* **184,** 647 (1950)

2580. SWARTZ, M. N., KAPLAN, N. O., and LAMBORG, M. F. *J. biol. Chem.* **232,** 1051 (1958)

2581. SWEAT, M. L., and LIPSCOMB, M. D. *J. Amer. chem. Soc.* **77,** 5185 (1955)

2582. SWEAT, M. L., SAMUELS, L. T., and LUMRY, R. *J. biol. Chem.* **185,** 75 (1950)

2583. SWELL, L., BYRON, J. E., and TREADWELL, C. R. *J. biol. Chem.* **186,** 543 (1950)

2584. SWELL, L., and TREADWELL, C. R. *J. biol. Chem.* **185,** 349 (1950)

2585. SWENSON, A. D., and BOYER, P. D. *J. Amer. chem. Soc.* **79,** 2174 (1957)

2586. SWICK, R. W. *J. biol. Chem.* **231,** 751 (1958)

2587. SWICK, R. W., and NAKAO, A. *J. biol. Chem.* **206,** 883 (1954)

2588. SWICK, R. W., and WOOD, H. G. *Proc. nat. Acad. Sci. U.S.* **46,** 28 (1960)

2589. SWINGLE, S. M., and TISELIUS, A. *Biochem. J.* **48,** 171 (1951)

2590. SZENT-GYÖRGYI, A. *Biochem. J.* **22,** 1387 (1928)

2591. SZILARD, L. *Proc. nat. Acad. Sci. U.S.* **46,** 277 (1960)

2592. SZÖRÉNYI, E. T., DVORNIKOVA, P. D., and DEGTYAR, P. G. *Doklady Akad. Nauk, S.S.S.R.* **67,** 341 (1949)

2593. TABOR, C. W., TABOR, H., and ROSENTHAL, S. M. *J. biol. Chem.* **208,** 645 (1954)

2594. TABOR, H., and MEHLER, A. H., in *Methods in Enzymology*, ed. S. P. Colowick and N. O. Kaplan (New York, Academic Press, 1955), Vol. 2, p. 228

2595. TABOR, H., MEHLER, A. H., and STADTMAN, E. R. *J. biol. Chem.* **204,** 127 (1953)

2596. TABOR, H., and WYNGARDEN, L. *J. biol. Chem.* **234,** 1830 (1959)

2597. TAGAWA, K., and ARNON, D. I. *Nature, Lond.* **195,** 537 (1962)

2598. TAGAWA, K., and SHIN, M. *J. Biochem., Tokyo* **46,** 865 (1959)

2599. TAGAWA, K., SHIN, M., and OKUNUKI, K. *Nature, Lond.* **183,** 111 (1959)

2600. TAGER, J. M., and RAUTANEN, N. *Biochim. biophys. Acta* **18,** 111 (1955)

2601. TAKAGI, Y., and HORECKER, B. L. *J. biol. Chem.* **225,** 77 (1956)

878   REFERENCES

2602. TAKAHASHI, K. *J. Biochem., Tokyo* **49,** 1 (1961)
2603. TAKAHASHI, N., and EGAMI, F. *Biochem. J.* **80,** 384 (1961)
2604. TAKANAMI, M., and OKAMOTO, T. *Biochi:n. biophys. Acta* **44,** 379 (1960)
2605. TAKEBE, I. *J. Biochem., Tokyo* **50,** 245 (1961)
2606. TALALAY, P., and DOBSON, M. M. *J. biol. Chem.* **205,** 823 (1953)
2607. TALALAY, P., FISHMAN, W. H., and HUGGINS, C. *J. biol. Chem.* **166,** 757 (1946)
2608. TALALAY, P., and MARCUS, P. I. *J. biol. Chem.* **218,** 675 (1956)
2609. TALALAY, P., and WANG, V. S. *Biochim. biophys. Acta* **18,** 300 (1955)
2610. TALLAN, H. H., JONES, M. E., and FRUTON, J. S. *J. biol. Chem.* **194,** 793 (1952)
2611. TANAKA, T., and KNOX, W. E. *J. biol. Chem.* **234,** 1162 (1959)
2612. TANENBAUM, S. W. *Biochim. biophys. Acta* **21,** 335 (1956)
2613. TANENBAUM, S. W., and SHEMIN, D. *Fed. Proc.* **9,** 236 (1950)
2614. TANIGUCHI, S., ASANO, A., IIDA, K., KONO, M., OMACHI, K., and EGAMI, F. *Proc. int. Symp. Enzyme Chem., Tokyo and Kyoto,* **2,** 238 (1958)
2615. TANIGUCHI, S., MITSUI, H., NAKAMURA, K., and EGAMI, F. *Ann. Acad. Sci. fenn.,* Ser. A II, **60,** 200 (1955)
2616. TANG, J., WOLF, S., CAPUTTO, R., and TRUCCO, R. E. *J. biol. Chem.* **234,** 1174 (1959)
2617. TAPPEL, A. L., BOYER, P. D., and LUNDBERG, W. O. *J. biol. Chem.* **199,** 267 (1952)
2618. TARR, H. L. A. *Biochem. J.* **59,** 386 (1955)
2619. TAYLOR, E. S., and GALE, E. F. *Biochem. J.* **39,** 52 (1945)
2620. TAYLOR, J. F., GREEN, A. A., and CORI, G. T. *J. biol. Chem.* **173,** 591 (1948)
2621. TAYLOR, W. H. *Biochem. J.* **71,** 373 and 384 (1959)
2622. TCHEN, T. T. *J. biol. Chem.* **233,** 1100 (1958)
2623. TCHEN, T. T., and BLOCH, K. *J. biol. Chem.* **226,** 921 (1957)
2624. TCHEN, T. T., and VENNESLAND, B. *J. biol. Chem.* **213,** 533 (1955)
2625. THEORELL, H. *Biochem. Z.* **278,** 263 (1935)
2626. THEORELL, H. *Ark. Kemi Min. Geol.* **16A,** No. 2 (1943)
2627. THEORELL, H. *Ark. Kemi Min. Geol.* **16A,** No. 14 (1943)
2628. THEORELL, H., in *The Enzymes,* 1st edn., ed. J. B. Sumner and K. Myrbäck (New York, Academic Press, 1951), Vol. 2, p. 397
2629. THEORELL, H. *Advanc. Enzymol.* **20,** 31 (1958)
2630. THEORELL, H., and ÅKESSON, Å. *J. Amer. chem. Soc.* **63,** 1804 (1941)
2631. THEORELL, H., and ÅKESSON, Å. *J. Amer. chem. Soc.* **63,** 1812 (1941)
2632. THEORELL, H., and ÅKESSON, Å. *Arch. Biochem. Biophys.* **65,** 439 (1956)
2633. THEORELL, H., and BONNICHSEN, R. *Acta chem. scand.* **5,** 1105 (1951)
2634. THEORELL, H., HOLMAN, R. T., and ÅKESSON, Å. *Acta chem. scand.* **1,** 571 (1947)
2635. THEORELL, H., and MCKINLEY MCKEE, J. S. *Acta chem. scand.* **15,** 1797 (1961)
2636. THEORELL, H., and MCKINLEY MCKEE, J. S. *Nature, Lond.* **192,** 4797 (1961)
2637. THEORELL, H., and NYGAARD, A. P. *Acta chem. scand.* **8,** 1649 (1954)
2638. THEORELL, H., NYGAARD, A. P., and BONNICHSEN, R. *Acta chem. scand.* **8,** 1490 (1954)

2638a. THEORELL, H., NYGAARD, A. P., and BONNICHSEN, R. *Acta chem. scand.* **9,** 1148 (1955)

2638b. THEORELL, H., and PAUL, K. G. *Ark. Kemi Min. Geol.* **18A,** No. 12 (1945)

2639. THIERS, R. E., and VALLEE, B. L. *J. biol. Chem.* **226,** 911 (1957)

2640. THOAI, N. V. *Bull. Soc. Chim. biol.* **39,** 197 (1957)

2641. THOMA, J. A., and KOSHLAND, D. E. *J. mol. Biol.* **2,** 169 (1960)

2642. THOMA, R. W., and PETERSON, W. H. *J. biol. Chem.* **210,** 569 (1954)

2643. THOMPSON, E. O. P. *Biochim. biophys. Acta* **10,** 633 (1953)

2644. THOMPSON, E. O. P. *J. biol. Chem.* **208,** 565 (1954)

2645. THOMPSON, R. H. S., in *Symposium on the Biochemical Reactions of Chemical Warfare Agents,* ed. R. T. Williams, Biochem. Soc. Symposia No. 2 (Cambridge University Press, 1948), p. 28

2646. THORN, M. B. *Nature, Lond.* **164,** 27 (1949)

2647. THORN, M. B. *Biochem. J.* **54,** 540 (1953)

2648. THORNE, C. B., in *A Symposium on Amino Acid Metabolism,* ed. W. D. McElroy and B. Glass (Baltimore, Johns Hopkins Press, 1955), p. 41

2649. THORNE, C. B., GÓMEZ, C. G., and HOUSEWRIGHT, R. D. *J. Bact.* **69,** 357 (1955)

2650. THORNE, C. B., and MOLNAR, D. M. *J. Bact.* **70,** 420 (1955)

2651. THORNE, C. J. R. *Biochim. biophys. Acta* **42,** 175 (1960)

2652. THORNE, C. J. R. *Biochem. J,* **76,** 4P (1960)

2653. THURLOW, S. *Biochem. J.* **19,** 175 (1925)

2654. TIETZ, A., and OCHOA, S. *Arch. Biochem. Biophys.* **78,** 477 (1958)

2655. TISELIUS, A., HJERTÉN, S., and LEVIN, Ö. *Arch. Biochem. Biophys.* **65,** 132 (1956)

2656. TISSIÈRES, A. *Biochem. J.* **50,** 279 (1951)

2657. TISSIÈRES, A. *Nature, Lond.* **174,** 183 (1954)

2658. TISSIÈRES, A. *Biochem. J.* **64,** 582 (1956)

2659. TISSIÈRES, A., and BURRIS, R. H. *Biochim. biophys. Acta* **20,** 436 (1956)

2660. TISSIÈRES, A., SCHLESSINGER, D. and GROS, F. *Proc. nat. Acad. Sci. U.S.* **46,** 1450 (1960)

2661. TISSIÈRES, A., and SLATER, E. C. *Nature, Lond.* **176,** 736 (1955)

2662. TISSIÈRES, A., and WATSON, J. D. *Proc. nat. Acad. Sci. U.S.* **48,** 1061 (1962)

2663. TODD, C. M. *Proc. Univ. Otago med. Sch.* **32,** 9 (1954)

2664. TODRICK, A. *Brit. J. Pharmacol.* **9,** 76 (1954)

2665. TOKUYAMA, K. *J. Biochem., Tokyo* **46,** 1379 and 1453 (1959)

2666. TOMKINS, G. M. *J. biol. Chem.* **218,** 437 (1956)

2667. TOMKINS, G. M. *J. biol. Chem.* **225,** 13 (1957)

2668. TOMKINS, G. M., MICHAEL, P. J., and CURRAN, J. F. *Biochim. biophys. Acta* **23,** 655 (1957)

2669. TOOKEY, H. L., and BALLS, A. K. *J. biol. Chem.* **218,** 213 (1956)

2670. TOOKEY, H. L., WILSON, R. G., LOHMAR, R. L., and DUTTON, H. J. *J. biol. Chem.* **230,** 65 (1958)

2671. TOPPER, Y. J. *J. biol. Chem.* **225,** 419 (1957)

2672. TOUSTER, O., REYNOLDS, V. H., and HUTCHESON, R. M. *J. biol. Chem.* **221,** 697 (1956)

2673. TRACEY, M. V. *Biochem. J.* **42,** 281 (1948)

2674. TRACEY, M. V. *Biochem. J.* **61,** 579 (1955)

2674a. TRISTRAM, G. R., in *The Proteins*, ed. H. Neurath and K. Bailey (New York, Academic Press, 1953), Vol. 1, p. 181

2675. TROLL, W., SHERRY, S., and WACHMAN, J. *J. biol. Chem.* **208,** 85 (1954)

2676. TRUBOWITZ, S., FELDMAN, D., MORGENSTERN, S. W., and HUNT, V. M. *Biochem. J.* **80,** 369 (1961)

2677. TRUCCO, R. E., CAPUTTO, R., LELOIR, L. F., and MITTELMAN, N. *Arch. Biochem.* **18,** 137 (1948)

2678. TRUFANOV, A. F., and KIRSANOVA, J. A. *Byull. eksp. Biol. i Med.* **22,** No. 6 (1946)

2679. TSUBOI, K. K., ESTRADA, J., and HUDSON, P. B. *J. biol. Chem.* **231,** 19 (1958)

2680. TSUBOI, K. K., and HUDSON, P. B. *Arch. Biochem. Biophys.* **61,** 197 (1956)

2681. TSUBOI, K. K., and HUDSON, P. B. *J. biol. Chem.* **224,** 879 (1957)

2682. TSUBOI, K. K., PENEFSKY, Z. J., and HUDSON, P. B. *Arch. Biochem. Biophys.* **68,** 54 (1957)

2683. TSUBOI, K. K., WIENER, G., and HUDSON, P. B. *J. biol. Chem.* **224,** 621 (1957)

2684. TSUCHIHASHI, M. *Biochem. Z.* **140,** 63 (1923)

2685. TUBBS, P. K., and GREVILLE, G. D. *Biochim. biophys. Acta* **34,** 290 (1959)

2686. TURBA, F. *Advanc. Enzymol.* **22,** 417 (1960)

2687. TURBA, F., and GUNDLACH, G. *Biochem. Z.* **327,** 186 (1955)

2688. TURNER, D. H., and TURNER, J. F. *Biochem. J.* **74,** 486 (1960)

2689. TURNER, D. H., and TURNER, J. F. *Biochem. J.* **79,** 143 (1961)

2690. TURNER, J. F., and KING, J. E. *Biochem. J.* **79,** 147 (1961)

2691. TUVE, T. W., and ANFINSEN, C. B. *J. biol. Chem.* **235,** 3437 (1960)

2692. UDENFRIEND, S., CLARK, C. T., and TITUS, E. *J. Amer. chem. Soc.* **75,** 501 (1953)

2693. UDENFRIEND, S., and COOPER, J. R. *J. biol. Chem.* **194,** 503 (1952)

2694. UEHARA, K. *J. Chem. Soc. Japan*, Pure Chem. Sect. **73,** 311 (1952)

2695. UMBARGER, H. E. *Cold Spring Harbor Symposia on quantitative Biology* **26,** 301 (1961)

2696. UMBREIT, W. W., BURRIS, R. H., and STAUFFER, J. F. *Manometric Techniques* (Minneapolis, Burgess Publishing Co., 1945)

2697. UMBREIT, W. W., and HENEAGE, P. *J. biol. Chem.* **201,** 15 (1953)

2698. UMBREIT, W. W., O'KANE, D. J., and GUNSALUS, I. C. *J. Bact.* **51,** 576 (1946)

2699. UNDERKOFLER, L. A., and ROY, D. K. *Cereal Chem.* **28,** 18 (1951)

2700. USPENSKAIA, V. D., and GORYACHENKOVA, E. V. *Biokhimiya* **23,** 212 (1958)

2701. UTTER, M. F., and KEECH, D. B. *J. biol. Chem.* **235,** PC17 (1960)

2702. UTTER, M. F., and KURAHASHI, K. *J. biol. Chem.* **207,** 787 (1954)

2703. UZIEL, M., and HANAHAN, D. J. *J. biol. Chem.* **226,** 789 (1957)

2704. VAGELOS, P. R., EARL, J. M., and STADTMAN, E. R. *J. biol. Chem.* **234,** 490 (1959)

2705. VALENTINE, R. C., JACKSON, R. L., and WOLFE, R. S. *Biochem. biophys. res. Comm.* **7,** 453 (1962)

2706. VALENTINE, R. C., and WOLFE, R. S. *J. biol. Chem.* **235,** 1948 (1960)

2707. VALLEE, B. L. *Advanc. Protein Chem.* **10,** 317 (1955)

2708. VALLEE, B. L., in *The Enzymes*, 2nd edn., ed. P. D. Boyer, H. Lardy and K. Myrbäck (New York, Academic Press, 1960), Vol. 3, p. 225

2709. VALLEE, B. L., ADELSTEIN, S. J., and OLSON, J. A. *J. Amer. chem. Soc.* **77,** 5196 (1955)

2710. VALLEE, B. L., ROPLEY, J. A., COOMBS, T. L., and NEURATH, H. *J. biol. Chem.* **235,** 64 (1960)

2711. VALLEE, B. L., STEIN, E. A., SUMERWELL, W. N., and FISCHER, E. H. *J. biol. Chem.* **234,** 2901 (1959)

2712. VALLEE, B. L., and WACKER, W. E. C. *J. Amer. chem. Soc.* **78,** 1771 (1956)

2713. VALLEE, B. L., WILLIAMS, R. J. P., and HOCH, F. L. *J. biol. Chem.* **234,** 2621 (1959)

2714. VAN ASPEREN, K. *J. Ins. Physiol.* **3,** 306 (1959)

2715. VAN ASPEREN, K., and OPPENOORTH, F. J. *Ent. exp. & appl.* **3,** 68 (1960)

2716. VAN EYS, J., and KAPLAN, N. O. *J. Amer. chem. Soc.* **79,** 2782 (1957)

2717. VAN EYS, J., and KAPLAN, N. O. *J. biol. Chem.* **228,** 305 (1957)

2718. VAN GOOR, H. *Enzymologia* **8,** 113 (1940)

2719. VAN HEYNINGEN, R., and PIRIE, A. *Biochem. J.* **53,** 436 (1953)

2720. VAN ORDEN, H. O., and SMITH, E. L. *J. biol. Chem.* **208,** 751 (1954)

2721. VAN SLYKE, D. D., and CULLEN, G. E. *J. biol. Chem.* **19,** 141 (1914)

2722. VAN VUNAKIS, H., and HERRIOTT, R. M., quoted by C. B. Anfinsen and R. R. Redfield, *Advanc. Protein Chem.* **11,** 1 (1956)

2723. VAN VUNAKIS, H., and HERRIOTT, R. M. *Biochim. biophys. Acta* **22,** 537 (1956)

2724. VAN VUNAKIS, H., and HERRIOTT, R. M. *Biochim. biophys. Acta* **23,** 600 (1957)

2725. VEIBEL, S., in *The Enzymes*, 1st edn., ed. J. B. Sumner and K. Myrbäck (New York, Academic Press, 1951) Vol. 1, p. 621

2726. VELICK, S. F., in *A Symposium on the Mechanism of Enzyme Action*, ed. W. D. McElroy and B. Glass (Baltimore, Johns Hopkins Press, 1954), p. 491

2726a. VELICK, S. F. *Biochim. biophys. Acta* **20,** 228 (1956)

2727. VELICK, S. F., and RONZONI, E. *J. biol. Chem.* **173,** 627 (1948)

2728. VELICK, S. F., and STRITTMATTER, P. *J. biol. Chem.* **221,** 265 (1956)

2729. VELICK, S. P., and UDENFRIEND, S. *J. biol. Chem.* **203,** 575 (1953)

2730. VELICK, S. P., and WICKS, L. F. *J. biol. Chem.* **190,** 741 (1951)

2731. VENKATARAMAN, R., and RACKER, E. *J. biol. Chem.* **236,** 1876 and 1883 (1961)

2732. VERNON, L. P. *J. biol. Chem.* **222,** 1035 and 1045 (1956)

2733. VESELL, E. S., and BEARN, A. G. *Ann. N.Y. Acad. Sci.* **75,** 286 (1958)

2734. VILLAR-PALASÍ, C., and LARNER, J. *Arch. Biochem. Biophys.* **86,** 270 (1960)

2735. VILLAVICENCIO, M., and BARRON, E. S. G. *Arch. Biochem. Biophys.* **67,** 121 (1957)

2736. VILLEE, C. A., and SPENCER, J. M. *J. biol. Chem.* **235,** 3615 (1960)

2737. VILLELA, G. G., AFFONSO, O. R., and MITIDIERI, E. *Arch. Biochem. Biophys.* **59,** 532 (1955)

2738. VISWANATHA, T., and LIENER, I. E. *Arch. Biochem. Biophys.* **61,** 410 (1956)

2739. VOGEL, H. J. *Proc. nat. Acad. Sci. U.S.* **39,** 578 (1953)

2740. VOGEL, H. J., in *Symposium on the chemical Basis of Heredity*, ed. W. D. McElroy and B. Glass (Baltimore, Johns Hopkins Press, 1957), p. 276

2741. VOGEL, H. J., and BONNER, D. M. *J. biol. Chem.* **218,** 97 (1956)

2742. VOLK, W. A. *J. biol. Chem.* **235,** 1550 (1960)

2743. WACHSMAN, J. T. *J. biol. Chem.* **223,** 19 (1956)

2744. WADA, H., and SNELL, E. E. *J. biol. Chem.* **236,** 2089 (1961)

2745. WAELSCH, H. *Advanc. Enzymol.* **13,** 237 (1952)

2746. WAGNER, R. P., and MITCHELL, H. K. *Genetics and Metabolism* (New York, John Wiley, 1955)

2747. WAGNER-JAUREGG, T., and MÖLLER, E. F. *Z. physiol. Chem.* **236,** 222 (1935)

2748. WAHBA, A. J., BASILIO, C., SPEYER, J. F., LENGYEL, P., MILLER, R. S., and OCHOA, S. *Proc. nat. Acad. Sci., U.S.* **48,** 1683 (1962)

2749. WAINIO, W. W., EICHEL, B., and GOULD, A. *J. biol. Chem.* **235,** 1521 (1960)

2750. WAKABAYASHI, M., and FISHMAN, W. H. *J. biol. Chem.* **236,** 996 (1961)

2751. WAKIL, S. J. *Biochim. biophys. Acta* **18,** 314 (1955)

2752. WAKIL, S. J. *Biochim. biophys. Acta* **19,** 497 (1956)

2753. WAKIL, S. J. *J. Amer. chem. Soc.* **80,** 6465 (1958)

2754. WAKIL, S. J., and BRESSLER, R. *J. biol. Chem.* **237,** 687 (1962)

2755. WAKIL, S. J., GREEN, D. E., MII, S., and MAHLER, H. R. *J. biol. Chem.* **207,** 631 (1954)

2756. WAKIL, S. J., and HÜBSCHER, G. *J. biol. Chem.* **235,** 1554 (1960)

2757. WAKIL, S. J., and WAITE, M. *Biochem. biophys. res. Comm.* **9,** 18 (1962)

2758. WAKSMAN, S. A., CAREY, C. L., and ALLEN, M. C. *J. Bact.* **28,** 213 (1934)

2759. WALDSCHMIDT-LEITZ, E., and KÖHLER, F. *Biochem. Z.* **258,** 360 (1933)

2760. WALEY, S. G. *Biochim. biophys. Acta* **10,** 27 (1953)

2761. WALEY, S. G., and WATSON, J. *Biochem. J.* **55,** 328 (1953)

2762. WALKER, A. C., and SCHMIDT, C. L. A. *Arch. Biochem.* **5,** 445 (1944)

2763. WALKER, D. A. *Biochem. J.* **74,** 216 (1960)

2764. WALKER, G. C., and NICHOLAS, D. J. D. *Biochim. biophys. Acta* **49,** 350 (1961)

2765. WALKER, G. C., and NICHOLAS, D. J. D. *Biochim. biophys. Acta* **49,** 361 (1961)

2766. WALKER, G. J., and WHELAN, W. J. *Nature, Lond.* **183,** 46 (1959)

2767. WALKER, J. B. *Arch. Biochem. Biophys.* **59,** 233 (1955)

2768. WALKER, J. B. *J. biol. Chem.* **204,** 139 (1953)

2769. WALKER, J. B. *J. biol. Chem.* **218,** 549 (1956)

2770. WALKER, J. B. *J. biol. Chem.* **224,** 57 (1957)

2771. WALKER, J. B. *J. biol. Chem.* **235,** 2357 (1960)

2772. WALL, M. C., and LAIDLER, K. J. *Arch. Biochem. Biophys.* **43,** 299 (1953)

2773. WALLACH, D. P., and GRISOLIA, S. *J. biol. Chem.* **226,** 277 (1957)

2774. WALLENFELS, K., and ARENS, A. *Biochem. Z.* **332,** 247 (1960)

2775. WALLENFELS, K., and BERNT, E. *Angew. Chem.* **64,** 28 (1952)

2776. WALLENFELS, K., and MALHOTRA, O. P., in *The Enzymes,* 2nd edn., ed P. D. Boyer, H. Lardy and K. Myrbäck (New York, Academic Press, 1960), Vol. 4, p. 409

2777. WALLENFELS, K., ZARNITZ, M. L., LAULE, G., BENDER, H., and KESER, M. *Biochem. Z.* **331,** 459 (1959)

2778. WALTI, A. *J. Amer. chem. Soc.* **60,** 493 (1938)

2779. WANG, T. P., and KAPLAN, N. O. *J. biol. Chem.* **206,** 311 (1954)

2780. WANG, T. P., SABLE, H. Z., and LAMPEN, J. O. *J. biol. Chem.* **184,** 17 (1950)

2781. WANG, T. Y., TSOU, C. L., and WANG, Y. L. *Scientia Sinica* **5,** 73 (1956)

2782. WARBURG, O. *Biochem. Z.* **177,** 471 (1926)

2783. WARBURG, O., and CHRISTIAN, W. *Biochem. Z.* **242,** 206 (1931)

2784. WARBURG, O., and CHRISTIAN, W. *Biochem. Z.* **254,** 438 (1932)

2785. WARBURG, O., and CHRISTIAN, W. *Biochem. Z.* **287,** 291 (1936)

2786. WARBURG, O., and CHRISTIAN, W. *Biochem. Z.* **298,** 368 (1938)
2787. WARBURG, O., and CHRISTIAN, W. *Biochem. Z.* **303,** 40 (1939)
2788. WARBURG, O., and CHRISTIAN, W. *Biochem. Z.* **310,** 384 (1941)
2789. WARBURG, O., and CHRISTIAN, W. *Biochem. Z.* **314,** 149 (1943)
2790. WARBURG, O., CHRISTIAN, W., and GRIESE, A. *Biochem. Z.* **282,** 157 (1935)
2791. WARBURG, O., and NEGELEIN, E. *Biochem. Z.* **214,** 64 (1929)
2792. WARREN, L., and BUCHANAN, J. M. *J. biol. Chem.* **229,** 613 (1957)
2793. WARRINGA, M. G. P. J., and GIUDITTA, A. *J. biol. Chem.* **230,** 111 (1958)
2794. WARRINGA, M. G. P. J., SMITH, O. H., GIUDITTA, A., and SINGER, T. P. *J. biol. Chem.* **230,** 97 (1958)
2795. WATANABE, Y., KONISHI, S., and SHIMURA, K. *J. Biochem., Tokyo* **44,** 299 (1957)
2796. WATKINS, W. M., and HASSID, W. Z. *Biochem. biophys. res. Comm.* **5,** 260 (1961)
2797. WATSON, J. D., and CRICK, F. H. C. *Nature, Lond.* **171,** 964 (1953)
2798. WATT, D., and KRAMPITZ, L. O. *Fed. Proc.* **6,** 301 (1947)
2799. WATTIAUX, R., BAUDHUIN, P., BERLEUR, A-M., and DE DUVE, C. *Biochem. J.* **63,** 608 (1956)
2800. WATTIAUX, R., and DE DUVE, C. *Biochem. J.* **63,** 606 (1956)
2801. WAUGH, D. F., BAUGHMAN, D. J., and MILLER, K. D., in *The Enzymes*, 2nd. edn., ed. P. D. Boyer, H. Lardy and K. Myrbäck (New York, Academic Press, 1960), Vol. 4, p. 215
2802. WEAVER, R. H., and HERBST, E. J. *J. biol. Chem.* **231,** 647 (1958)
2803. WEAVER, R. H., and LARDY, H. A. *J. biol. Chem.* **236,** 313 (1961)
2804. WEBB, E. C. *Biochem. J.* **42,** 96 (1948)
2805. WEBB, E. C., in *Symposium on the biochemical Reactions of Chemical Warfare Agents*, ed. R. T. Williams, Biochem. Soc. Symposium No. 2, p. 50 (Cambridge University Press, 1948)
2806. WEBB, E. C., in *Steric Aspects of the Chemistry and Biochemistry of Natural Products*, ed J. K. Grant and W. Klyne, Biochem. Soc. Symposium No. 19, p. 90 (Cambridge University Press, 1960)
2807. WEBB, E. C. *Biochem. J.* (in preparation)
2808. WEBB, E. C. Unpublished observations
2809. WEBB, E. C., and MORROW, P. F. W. *Biochem. J.* **73,** 7 (1959)
2810. WEBSTER, G., and WHITMAN, S. L. *Biochim. biophys. Acta* **61,** 316 (1962)
2811. WEBSTER, G. C. *Biochim. biophys. Acta* **49,** 141 (1961)
2812. WEBSTER, G. C., and VARNER, J. E. *Arch. Biochem. Biophys.* **52,** 22 (1954)
2813. WEBSTER, G. C., and VARNER, J. E. *J. biol. Chem.* **215,** 91 (1955)
2814. WEBSTER, G. R., MARPLES, E. A., and THOMPSON, R. H. S. *Biochem. J.* **65,** 374 (1957)
2815. WEBSTER, L. T., and DAVIE, E. W. *J. biol. Chem.* **236,** 479 (1961)
2816. WEIBULL, C., and TISELIUS, A. *Arkiv. Kemi Min. Geol.* **19A,** No. 19 (1945)
2817. WEICHSELBAUM, T. E. *Amer. J. clin. Path.*, Tech. Sect. **10,** 40 (1946)
2818. WEIL, L., and BUCHERT, A. R. *Arch. Biochem. Biophys.* **34,** 1 (1951)
2819. WEIL, L., BUCHERT, A. R., and MAHER, J. *Arch. Biochem. Biophys.* **40,** 245 (1952)
2820. WEIL, L., JAMES, S., and BUCHERT, A. R. *Arch. Biochem. Biophys.* **46,** 266 (1953)
2821. WEIL-MALHERBE, H. *Biochem. J.* **31,** 2080 (1937)

2822. WEIL-MALHERBE, H. *Biochem. J.* **33**, 1997 (1939)

2823. WEIL-MALHERBE, W., and GREEN, R. H. *Biochem. J.* **61**, 218 (1955)

2824. WEIMBERG, R. *J. biol. Chem.* **234**, 727 (1959)

2825. WEIMBERG, R., and DOUDOROFF, M. *J. biol. Chem.* **217**, 607 (1955)

2826. WEISBLUM, B., BENZER, S., and HOLLEY, R. W. *Proc. nat. Acad. Sci. U.S.* **48**, 1449 (1962)

2827. WEISS, S. B. *Fed. Proc.* **21**, 120 (1962)

2828. WEISS, S. B., KENNEDY, E. P., and KIYASU, J. Y. *J. biol. Chem.* **235**, 40 (1960)

2829. WEISS, S. B., and NAKAMOTO, T. *J. biol. Chem.* **236**, PC18 (1961)

2830. WEISS, S. B., SMITH, S. W., and KENNEDY, E. P. *J. biol. Chem.* **231**, 53 (1958)

2831. WEISSBACH, A., HORECKER, B. L., and HURWITZ, J. *J. biol. Chem.* **218**, 795 (1956)

2832. WEISSBACH, H., LOVENBERG, W., and UDENFRIEND, S. *Biochim. biophys. Acta* **50**, 177 (1961)

2833. WEISSBACH, H., REDFIELD, B. G., and AXELROD, J. *Biochim. biophys. Acta* **54**, 190 (1961)

2834. WEISSBACH, H., REDFIELD, B. G., and UDENFRIEND, S. *J. biol. Chem.* **229**, 953 (1957)

2835. WEISSBACH, H., TOOHEY, J., and BARKER, H. A. *Proc. nat. Acad. Sci. U.S.* **45**, 521 (1959)

2836. WEISSMANN, B. *J. biol. Chem.* **216**, 783 (1955)

2837. WELLNER, D., and MEISTER, A. *J. biol. Chem.* **235**, PC12 (1960)

2838. WELLNER, D., and MEISTER, A. *J. biol. Chem.* **235**, 2013 (1960)

2839. WENNER, C. E., SPIRTES, M. A., and WEINHOUSE, S. *Cancer Res.* **12**, 44 (1952)

2840. WERKHEISER, W. C., and BARTLEY, W. *Biochem. J.* **66**, 79 (1957)

2841. WERLE, E. *Biochem. Z.* **311**, 270 (1942)

2842. WERLE, E., & KOCH, W. *Biochem. Z.* **319**, 305 (1949)

2843. WERLE, E., and KRAUTZUN, H. *Biochem. Z.* **296**, 315 (1938)

2844. WERLE, E., and MENNIKEN, G. *Biochem. Z.* **291**, 325 (1937)

2845. WESTERFELD, W. W., and RICHERT, D. A. *Proc. Soc. exp. Biol., N.Y.* **71**, 181 (1949)

2846. WESTHEAD, E. W., and MALMSTRÖM, B. G. *J. biol. Chem.* **228**, 655 (1957)

2847. WESTLEY, J., and GREEN, J. R. *J. biol. Chem.* **234**, 2325 (1959)

2848. WHARTON, D. C., and GRIFFITHS, D. E. *Arch. Biochem. Biophys.* **96**, 103 (1962)

2849. WHEAT, R. W., and AJL, S. J. *J. biol. Chem.* **217**, 897 (1955)

2850. WHISTLER, R. L., and MASAK, E. *J. Amer. chem. Soc.* **77**, 1241 (1955)

2851. WHITAKER, D. R. *Arch. Biochem. Biophys.* **43**, 253 (1953)

2852. WHITAKER, D. R. *Arch. Biochem. Biophys.* **53**, 439 (1954)

2853. WHITBY, L. G. *Biochem. J.* **57**, 390 (1954)

2854. WHITE, J. W. *Arch. Biochem. Biophys.* **39**, 238 (1952)

2855. WHITELEY, H. R., OSBORN, M. J., and HUENNEKENS, F. M. *J. biol. Chem.* **234**, 1538 (1959)

2856. WHITFELD, P. R., HEPPEL, L. A., and MARKHAM, R. *Biochem. J.* **60**, 15 (1955)

2857. WHITTAKER, V. P., and ADAMS, D. H. *Nature, Lond.* **164**, 315 (1949)

2858. WICKREMASINGHE, R. L., and FRY, B. A. *Biochem. J.* **58**, 268 (1954)

2859. WIDMER, C., and CRANE, F. L. *Biochim. biophys. Acta* **27,** 203 (1958)
2860. WIELAND, O., and SUYTER, M. *Biochem. Z.* **329,** 320 (1957)
2861. WIEME, R. J. *Clin. chim. Acta* **4,** 46 (1959)
2862. WIEST, W. G. *J. biol. Chem.* **234,** 3115 (1959)
2863. WIGGANS, D. S., WINITZ, M., and FRUTON, J. S. *Yale J. Biol. Med.* **27,** 11 (1954)
2864. WIJESUNDERA, S., and WOODS, D. D. *Biochem. J.* **55,** viii (1953)
2865. WILKINSON, G. N. *Biochem. J.* **80,** 324 (1961)
2866. WILKINSON, J. F. *Biochem. J.* **44,** 460 (1949)
2867. WILLIAMS, E. J., SUNG, S.-C., and LASKOWSKI, M. *J. biol. Chem.* **236,** 1130 (1961)
2868. WILLIAMS, F. R., and HAGER, L. P. *J. biol. Chem.* **236,** PC36 (1961)
2869. WILLIAMS, R. J. P. *Biol. Rev.* **28,** 381 (1953)
2870. WILLIAMS, V. R., and MCINTYRE, R. T. *J. biol. Chem.* **217,** 467 (1955)
2871. WILLIAMS, W. J., LITWIN, J., and THORNE, C. B. *J. biol. Chem.* **212,** 427 (1955)
2872. WILLIAMS-ASHMAN, H. G., and BANKS, J. *Arch. Biochim. Biophys.* **50,** 513 (1954)
2873. WILLIAMS-ASHMAN, H. G., and BANKS, J. *J. biol. Chem.* **223,** 509 (1956)
2874. WILLIAMSON, M. B., and PASSMANN, J. M. *J. biol. Chem.* **222,** 151 (1956)
2875. WILLSTÄTTER, R., and KRAUT, H. *Ber. dtsch. chem. Ges.* **56,** 1117 (1923)
2876. WILLSTÄTTER, R., KUHN, R., LIND, O., and MEMMEN, F. *Z. physiol. Chem.* **167,** 303 (1927)
2877. WILSON, D. G., KING, K. W., and BURRIS, R. H. *J. biol. Chem.* **208,** 863 (1954)
2878. WILSON, D. M., and AJL, S. *J. Bact.* **73,** 410 (1957)
2879. WILSON, D. M., and AJL, S. *J. Bact.* **73,** 415 (1957)
2880. WILSON, I. B., in *A Symposium on the Mechanism of Enzyme Action,* ed. W. D. McElroy and B. Glass (Baltimore, Johns Hopkins Press, 1954), p. 642
2881. WILSON, I. B. *Disc. Faraday Soc.,* No. 20, 'The Physical Chemistry of Enzymes', p. 119 (1955)
2882. WILSON, I. B., in *The Enzymes,* 2nd edn., ed. P. D. Boyer, H. Lardy and K. Myrbäck (New York, Academic Press, 1960), Vol. 4, p. 501
2883. WILSON, I. B., and BERGMANN, F. *J. biol. Chem.* **186,** 683 (1950)
2884. WILSON, I. B., BERGMANN, F., and NACHMANSOHN, D. *J. biol. Chem.* **186,** 781 (1950)
2885. WILSON, I. B., and HARRISON, M. A. *J. biol. Chem.* **236,** 2292 (1961)
2886. WILSON, I. B., HATCH, M. A., and GINSBURG, S. *J. biol. Chem.* **235,** 2312 (1960)
2887. WINITZ, M., BLOCH-FRANKENTHAL, L., IZUMIYA, N., BIRNBAUM, S. M., BAKER, C. G., and GREENSTEIN, J. P. *J. Amer. chem. Soc.* **78,** 2423 (1956)
2888. WINKELMAN, J., and ASHWELL, G. *Biochim. biophys. Acta* **52,** 170 (1961)
2889. WINKELMAN, J., and LEHNINGER, A. L. *J. biol. Chem.* **233,** 794 (1958)
2890. WITTENBERG, J., and KORNBERG, A. *J. biol. Chem.* **202,** 431 (1953)
2891. WIXOM, R. L., SHATTON, J. B., and STRASSMAN, M. *J. biol. Chem.* **235,** 128 (1960)
2892. WOJTCZAK, L., and LEHNINGER, A. L. *Biochim. biophys. Acta* **51,** 442 (1961)
2893. WOLD, F., and BALLOU, C. E. *J. biol. Chem.* **227,** 301 (1957)

2894. Wold, F., and Ballou, C. E. *J. biol. Chem.* **227,** 313 (1957)
2895. Wolfe, R. G., and Nielands, J. B. *J. biol. Chem.* **221,** 61 (1956)
2896. Wolff, E. C., Black, S., and Downey, P. F. *J. Amer. chem. Soc.* **78,** 5958 (1956)
2897. Wolff, J. B., Britton, B. B., and Nakada, H. I. *Arch. Biochem. Biophys.* **66,** 333 (1957)
2898. Wolff, J. B., and Kaplan, N. O., in *Methods in Enzymology,* ed. S. P. Colowick and N. O. Kaplan (New York, Academic Press, 1955), Vol. 1, p. 346
2899. Wolff, J. B., and Kaplan, N. O. *J. biol. Chem.* **218,** 849 (1956)
2900. Wolin, M. J., Simpson, F. J., and Wood, W. A. *J. biol. Chem.* **232,** 559 (1958)
2901. Wolochow, H., Putman, E. W., Doudoroff, M., Barker, H. A., and Hassid, W. Z. *J. biol. Chem.* **180,** 1237 (1949)
2902. Wolstenholme, G. E. W., and O'Connor, M., eds. *CIBA Foundation Symposium on the Biosynthesis of Terpenes and Sterols* (London, Churchill, 1959)
2903. Wolstenholme, G. E. W., and O'Connor, C. M., eds. *CIBA Foundation Symposium on Quinones in Electron Transport* (London, Churchill, 1961)
2904. Wong, D. T. O., and Ajl, S. J. *J. Amer. chem. Soc.* **78,** 3230 (1956)
2905. Wong, J. T.-F., and Hanes, C. S. *Canad. J. Biochem. Physiol.* **40,** 763 (1962)
2906. Wong, K. K., Meister, A., and Moldave, K. *Biochim. biophys. Acta* **36,** 531 (1959)
2907. Wong, K. K., and Moldave, K. *J. biol. Chem.* **235,** 694 (1960)
2908. Wood, B. J. B., and Rainbow, C. *Biochem. J.* **78,** 204 (1961)
2909. Wood, H. G., and Stjernholm, R. *Proc. nat. Acad. Sci. U.S.* **47,** 289 (1961)
2910. Wood, W. A., in *Methods in Enzymology,* ed. S. P. Colowick and N. O. Kaplan (New York, Academic Press, 1955), Vol. 2, p. 212
2911. Wood, W. A., and Gunsalus, I. C. *J. biol. Chem.* **181,** 171 (1949)
2912. Wood, W. A., and Gunsalus, I. C. *J. biol. Chem.* **190,** 403 (1951)
2913. Wood, W. A., McDonough, M. J., and Jacobs, L. B. *J. biol. Chem.* **236,** 2190 (1961)
2914. Woolf, B., quoted in *Allgemeine Chemie der Enzyme* by J. B. S. Haldane and K. G. Stern (Dresden and Leipzig, Steinkopff Verlag, 1932), p. 119
2915. Woollen, J. W., Heyworth, R., and Walker, P. G. *Biochem. J.* **78,** 111 (1961)
2916. Wosilait, W. D. *J. biol. Chem.* **235,** 1196 (1960)
2917. Wosilait, W. D., and Nason, A. *J. biol. Chem.* **206,** 255 (1954)
2918. Wosilait, W. D., Nason, A., and Terrell, A. J. *J. biol. Chem.* **206,** 271 (1954)
2919. Wosilait, W. D., and Sutherland, E. W. *J. biol. Chem.* **218,** 469 (1956)
2920. Wright, B. E. *J. biol. Chem.* **219,** 873 (1956)
2921. Wu, F. C., and Laskowski, M. *J. biol. Chem.* **235,** 1680 (1960)
2922. Wyngaarden, J. B., and Ashton, D. M. *J. biol. Chem.* **234,** 1492 (1959)
2923. Wynn, C. H., and Dodgson, K. S. *Biochem. J.* **66,** 44P (1957)
2924. Yakushiji, E., and Okunuki, K. *Proc. imp. Acad. Japan* **16,** 299 (1940)

2925. YAMADA, E. W. *J. biol. Chem.* **236**, 3043 (1961)

2926. YAMADA, E. W., and JAKOBY, W. B. *J. biol. Chem.* **234**, 941 (1959)

2927. YAMADA, E. W., and JAKOBY, W. B. *J. biol. Chem.* **235**, 589 (1960)

2928. YAMADA, H., and YASUNOBU, K. T. *J. biol. Chem.* **237**, 1511 (1962)

2929. YAMADA, H., and YASUNOBU, K. T. *J. biol. Chem.* **237**, 3077 (1962)

2930. YAMAFUJI, K., and ETO, M. *Enzymologia* **16**, 247 (1954)

2931. YAMAFUJI, K., OMURA, H., and MIURA, K. *Enzymologia* **16**, 75 (1953)

2932. YAMAFUJI, K., SHIMAMURA, M., and OMURA, H. *Enzymologia* **17**, 359 (1956)

2933. YAMAMOTO, Y., and BEEVERS, H. *Biochim. biophys. Acta* **48**, 20 (1961)

2934. YAMANAKA, T., KIJIMOTO, S., OKUNUKI, K., and KUSAI, K. *Nature, Lond.* **194**, 759 (1962)

2935. YAMASHINA, I. *Acta chem. scand.* **10**, 739 (1956)

2936. YAMASHINA, I. *Ark. Kemi* **9**, 225 (1956)

2937. YAMASHINA, I. *Biochim. biophys. Acta* **20**, 433 (1956)

2938. YAMAZAKI, I., MASON, H. S., and PIETTE, L. *J. biol. Chem.* **235**, 2444 (1960)

2939. YAMAZOYE, S. *J. Biochem., Tokyo* **23**, 319 (1936)

2940. YANAGITA, T., and FOSTER, J. W. *J. biol. Chem.* **221**, 593 (1956)

2941. YANIV, H., and GILVARG, C. *J. biol. Chem.* **213**, 787 (1955)

2942. YANOFSKY, C. *J. biol. Chem.* **194**, 279 (1952)

2943. YANOFSKY, C. *J. biol. Chem.* **198**, 343 (1952)

2944. YANOFSKY, C. *J. biol. Chem.* **223**, 171 (1956)

2945. YANOFSKY, C., and REISSIG, J. L. *J. biol. Chem.* **202**, 567 (1953)

2946. YATES, R. A., and PARDEE, A. B. *J. biol. Chem.* **227**, 677 (1957)

2947. YEFIMOCHKINA, E. F., and BRAUNSTEIN, A. E. *Arch. Biochem. Biophys.* **83**, 350 (1959)

2948. YONETANI, T. *J. biol. Chem.* **235**, 3138 (1960)

2949. YONETANI, T. *J. biol. Chem.* **236**, 1680 (1961)

2950. YORK, J. L., GROLLMAN, A. P., and BUBLITZ, C. *Biochim. biophys. Acta* **47**, 298 (1961)

2951. YOSHIKAWA, H. *J. Biochem., Tokyo* **38**, 1 (1951)

2952. YOTSUYANAGI, Y. *C. R. Acad. Sci., Paris* **248**, 274 (1959)

2953. YUNIS, A. A., FISCHER, E. H., and KREBS, E. G. *J. biol. Chem.* **235**, 3163 (1960)

2954. YURA, T., and VOGEL, H. J. *J. biol. Chem.* **234**, 335 (1959)

2955. YURA, T., and VOGEL, H. J. *J. biol. Chem.* **234**, 339 (1959)

2956. ZABIN, I., KEPES, A., and MONOD, J. *J. biol. Chem.* **237**, 253 (1962)

2957. ZAKRZEWSKI, S. F., and NICHOL, C. A. *J. biol. Chem.* **235**, 2984 (1960)

2958. ZAMECNIK, P. C., and KELLER, E. B. *J. biol. Chem.* **209**, 337 (1954)

2959. ZATMAN, L. J., KAPLAN, N. O., and COLOWICK, S. P. *J. biol. Chem.* **200**, 197 (1953)

2960. ZATMAN, L. J., KAPLAN, N. O., COLOWICK, S. P., and CIOTTI, M. M. *J. Amer. chem. Soc.* **75**, 3293 (1953)

2961. ZECHMEISTER, L., and ROHDEWALD, M. *Fortschr. Chem. org. Naturst.* **8**, 341 (1951)

2962. ZECHMEISTER, L., and TÓTH, G. *Enzymologia* **7**, 165 (1940)

2963. ZECHMEISTER, L., TÓTH, G., and VAJDA, É. *Enzymologia* **7**, 170 (1939)

2964. ZELITCH, I. *J. biol. Chem.* **201**, 719 (1953)

2965. ZELITCH, I. *J. biol. Chem.* **216**, 553 (1955)

2966. ZELITCH, I. *J. biol. Chem.* **234,** 3077 (1959)

2967. ZELITCH, I., and OCHOA, S. *J. biol. Chem.* **201,** 707 (1953)

2968. ZELLER, E. A., in *The Enzymes*, 1st edn., ed. J. B. Sumner and K. Myrbäck (New York, Academic Press, 1951), Vol. 2 ,p. 536

2969. ZELLER, E. A., BIRKHÄUSER, H., MISLIN, H., and WENK, M. *Helv. chim. Acta* **22,** 1381 (1939)

2970. ZIMMERMAN, S. B., and KORNBERG, A. *J. biol. Chem.* **236,** 1480 (1961)

2971. ZITTLE, C. A., DELLAMONICA, E. S., CUSTER, J. H., and KRIKORIAN, R. *Arch. Biochem. Biophys.* **56,** 469 (1955)

2972. ZITTLE, C. A., and READING, E. H. *J. biol. Chem.* **160,** 519 (1945)

INDEX

Enzymes are indexed under their trivial names in the form 'Trivial name (systematic name) (number), page references'. Where the systematic name comes at a different place in the index, an entry is also made in the form 'Systematic name (number). *See* trivial name', and similar entries are made for alternative or obsolete names.

Aspartate **as** ammonia-carrier, 564, 597–8
— in active centre, 470, 474–5
Aspartate acetyltransferase (acetyl-CoA : L-aspartate N-acetyltransferase) (2.3.1.a)
Aspartate aminotransferase (L-aspartate:2-oxoglutarate aminotransferase) (2.6.1.1), 45, 189, 454, 597, 627, 640, 644
D-aspartate aminotransferase (D-aspartate:2-oxoglutarate aminotransferase) (2.6.1.10), 189
L-aspartate:ammonia ligase (AMP) (6.3.1.1). *See* asparagine synthetase
Aspartate ammonia-lyase (L-aspartate ammonia-lyase) (4.3.1.1), 55, 253, 292–3, 657
Aspartate carbamoyltransferase (carbamoylphosphate:L-aspartate carbamoyltransferase) (2.1.3.2), 455, 506, 509, 609, 799
Aspartate 1-decarboxylase (L-aspartate 1-carboxy-lyase) (4.1.1.11), 647
Aspartate 4-decarboxylase (L-aspartate 4-carboxy-lyase) (4.1.1.12)
Aspartate kinase (ATP:L-aspartate 4-phosphotransferase) (2.7.2.4), 505, 518, 521
D-aspartate oxidase (D-aspartate:O₂ oxidoreductase (deaminating)) (1.4.3.1), 407
D-aspartate:2-oxoglutarate aminotransferase (2.6.1.10). *See* D-aspartate aminotransferase
L-aspartate:2-oxoglutarate aminotransferase (2.6.1.1). *See* aspartate aminotransferase
Aspartate β-semialdehyde, formation of. *See* 1.1.1.3
Aspartate semialdehyde dehydrogenase (L-aspartate-β-semialdehyde:NADP oxidoreductase (phosphorylating)) (1.2.1.11)
Aspartoacylase (N-acylaspartate amidohydrolase) (3.5.1.c)
β-aspartylphosphate, formation of. *See* 1.2.1.11
Aspergillopeptidase A (3.4.4.17), 806
Aspergillus oryzae ribonuclease (ribonucleate 3′-guanylohydrolase) (3.1.4.8), 453
Asymmetric oxidation of citrate, 207
— phosphorylation of glycerol, 206
'Asymmetric synthesis', 205, 666
Asymmetry of active centre, 666
Atlas of crystalline enzymes, 793–808
Atmosphere, primordial, 666
Atomic number of cationic activators, 421
ATP, affinity for magnesium, 440, 442
— as energy store, 620
— as metal-complexing agent, 346, 440

ATP, as phosphate carrier, 189–90, 545–6
— biosynthesis of, 620
— free energy of hydrolysis of, 187, 618
— functions of, 393–6, 398, 486, 490, 618–21
— hydrolysis of. *See* 3.6.1.a, 3–5, 8–9
— in enzyme formation, 478
— in nucleotidyltransferase reactions, 396
— in polypeptide synthesis, 497
— in transmethylation, 402
— phosphorylations by. *See* sub-groups 2.7.1–4
— prevention of mitochondrial swelling by, 619, 631
— reactions involving, colorimetric method for, 25–6
— specificity of kinases for, 215, 394
— structure of, 395
ATP:acetate phosphotransferase (2.7.2.1). *See* acetate kinase
ATP:adenosine 5′-phosphotransferase (2.7.1.20). *See* adenosine kinase
ATP:adenylylsulphate 3′-phosphotransferase (2.7.1.25). *See* adenylylsulphate kinase
ATP:2-amino-2-deoxy-D-glucose phosphotransferase (2.7.1.8). *See* aminodeoxyglucose kinase
ATP:AMP phosphotransferase (2.7.4.3). *See* adenylate kinase
ATP:L-arabinose 1-phosphotransferase (2.7.1.d). *See* arabinokinase
ATP:L-arginine phosphotransferase (2.7.3.3). *See* arginine kinase
ATPase (myosin) (ATP phosphohydrolase) (3.6.1.3), 159, 195, 285–6, 423, 426, 455, 457, 621, 627, 642
— — analysis of, 458
ATPase (ATP phosphohydrolase) (3.6.1.4), 422, 424, 627
ATPase (ATP pyrophosphohydrolase) (3.6.1.8)
ATP:L-aspartate 4-phosphotransferase (2.7.2.4). *See* aspartate kinase
ATP:carbamate phosphotransferase (2.7.2.2). *See* carbamate kinase
ATP:carbamate phosphotransferase (dephosphorylating) (2.7.2.a). *See* carbamate kinase
ATP:choline phosphotransferase (2.7.1.32). *See* choline kinase
ATP citrate lyase (ATP:citrate oxaloacetate-lyase (CoA-acetylating and ATP-dephosphorylating)) (4.1.3.a), 398
ATP:creatine phosphotransferase (2.7.3.2). *See* creatine kinase
ATP:deoxy-CMP phosphotransferase (2.7.4.5). *See* deoxycytidylate kinase
ATP:dephospho-CoA 3′-phosphotransferase (2.7.1.24). *See* dephospho-CoA kinase

'D-enzyme'. *See* 2.4.1.
Δ-isomerases, 197, 295. *See* sub-group 5.3.3
DBC coenzyme, 402–3. *See* coenzyme B$_{12}$
DDT-dehydrochlorinase (1,1,1-trichloro-2,2-bis-(*p*-chlorophenyl)-ethane hydrogenchloride-lyase) (4.5.1.1)
DEAE-cellulose, 44–5, 48, 619, 657
Deamido-NAD:L-glutamine amidoligase (AMP) (6.3.5.1). *See* NAD synthetase
Deamido-NAD pyrophosphorylase (2.7.7.a). *See* nicotinatemononucleotide adenylyltransferase
Deaminases, 194. *See* sub-group 3.5.4
Deamino-NAD, 368
— transhydrogenation with. *See* 1.6.1.1
Death of cells, meaning of, 617–18
Decarboxylases, 195. *See* sub-group 4.1.1
— classification of, 195
— manometric methods for, 22
Decarboxylation, catalysis by metal ions, 425
Deep-freezing of enzymes, 13
Degradation of enzymes, effect on activity, 470–1
'Degree' of rate equations, 98
'Dehydrase', 'dehydratase', 'dehydrogenase', 177
Dehydratases. *See* sub-group 4.2.1
Dehydroascorbate as hydrogen acceptor, 375
Dehydrogenases, 184–5, 203, 265–78, 364, 540–6. *See* group 1
— coenzyme-linked systems, 540–5
— determination by measurement of fluorescence, 21–2
— in cell respiration, 540
— manometric methods for, 22
— specificity of, 203, 209–10, 366–7, 370
— spectrotometric methods for, 20–22
— stereospecificity of, 208–9, 266–9
— Thunberg method for, 22–3
— zinc-containing, 307
Dehydrogenations, mechanism of, 260–78
— typical, 260–1
'Dehydropeptidase II' (3.5.1.b). *See* aminoacylase I
5-dehydroquinate, formation of. *See* 1.1.1.24
5-dehydroquinate dehydratase (5-dehydroquinate hydro-lyase) (4.2.1.10)
5-dehydroshikimate, formation of. *See* 1.1.1.25
— hydration of. *See* 4.2.1.10
Demethylriboflavin, 418–19
Denaturation, heat, fractionation of enzymes by, 36–7

Denaturation of enzymes 12–13, 147–9, 467
— — — at surfaces, 12
— of proteins by chloroform, 48
— — — thermodynamic parameters of, 36–7, 148–9
'Dense bodies' in cytoplasm, 622
Deoxycholate for extraction of enzymes, 34, 386, 549, 635
Deoxycytidylate kinase (ATP:deoxy-CMP phosphotransferase) (2.7.4.5)
Deoxy-CMP deaminase (deoxy-CMP aminohydrolase) (3.5.4.b)
Deoxycorticosterone, hydroxylation of. *See* 1.99.1.10
Deoxy-CTPase (deoxy-CTP nucleotidohydrolase) (3.6.1.b)
2-deoxy-D-glucose as substrate of hexokinase, 216–17
6-deoxy-D-glucose as inhibitor of hexokinase, 358
DeoxyGTPase (deoxy-GTP triphosphohydrolase) (3.1.5.1)
Deoxy-NAD, 368
Deoxyriboaldolase (2-deoxy-D-ribose-5-phosphate acetaldehyde-lyase) (4.1.2.4)
Deoxyribonuclease (deoxyribonucleate oligonucleotidohydrolase) (3.1.4.5), 193, 454, 650, 801
— analysis of, 458
— as reagent for DNA, 624
Deoxyribonuclease II (deoxyribonucleate 3'-nucleotidohydrolase) (3.1.4.6), 193, 627–8, 650
Deoxyribonucleases, occurrence of, 641, 650
Deoxyribonucleic acid (DNA) as template for RNA synthesis, 481, 485–486
— — double-stranded, base-pairing in, 481–3
— — — — structure of, 481–2
— — in protein and enzyme synthesis, 481–6, 632
— — localization in cells, 624, 626, 633, 635
— — replication of, 480–5
2-deoxy-D-ribose 1-phosphate, formation of. *See* 2.4.1.4
2-deoxy-D-ribose 5-phosphate, formation of. *See* 2.7.1.15
Deoxy-TTP:α-D-glucose-1-phosphate thymidylyltransferase (2.7.7.g). *See* glucose-1-phosphate thymidylyltransferase
Deoxy-UMP, formation of. *See* 3.5.4.b
Dephospho-CoA kinase (ATP:dephospho-CoA 3'-phosphotransferase) (2.7.1.24), 190, 604
Dephospho-CoA pyrophosphorylase (2.7.7.3). *See* pantetheinephosphate adenylyltransferase